PSYCHIATRIC DICTIONARY

PSYCHIATRIC DICTIONARY

THIRD EDITION

LELAND E. HINSIE, M.D.
AND
ROBERT JEAN CAMPBELL, M.D.

NEW YORK
OXFORD UNIVERSITY PRESS
1960

PRINTED IN THE UNITED STATES OF AMERICA

PREFACE TO THE FIRST EDITION

AS the title of this Dictionary implies its material has been drawn mainly from the words and concepts current in the field of psychiatry—with definitions and illustrative quotations that aim to give these terms vital, clinical meaning. Though brevity was the ideal, in many instances, where needed, the articles are more or less encyclopedic in character.

The framework of the Dictionary is made up of psychiatric terms, but considerable attention has been devoted to terms in allied fields—clinical neurology, constitutional medicine, genetics and eugenics, mental deficiency, forensic psychiatry, social service, nursing and occupational therapy.

A liberal use of cross-references, including the familiar *q.v.* and *see also,* and double registration of compound expressions under the main idea and under the modifying part, should make the book more serviceable and search for desired information easier and more efficient. For instance, the impulse to buy is registered as *oniomania* and as *buy, impulse to;* excessive hunger is registered as *bulimia* and as *hunger, excessive.* Thus, a technical or scientific term which has escaped one's memory for the moment, may usually be found under its popular English equivalent: *automatic action* is listed as such and as *paraphonic state* and as *action, automatic.*

This Psychiatric Dictionary comprises all important terms and concepts used during the span of time approximately since Hippocrates up to our own days. The terms no longer in use are marked *obs.* (obsolete), while those which are losing currency have been designated as *obst.* (obsolescent). Accordingly, it is possible for the reader to gain an appreciation of the historical development of psychiatric nomenclature and to grasp more clearly the meaning of old and new scientific achievements in the field.

This volume contains approximately 7500 title-entries, including personal names most eminent in the field of psychiatric science. Each entry registers a phonetic transcription of its pronunciation (see p. ix for Key to Pronunciation used in the transliteration) and the philological derivation of the term.

Dr. Leland E. Hinsie is responsible for the definition of terms used in descriptive psychiatry, psycho-analysis, analytical psychology, psycho-biology, forensic psychiatry, mental deficiency, sexology, nursing and social work.

The philological part of the dictionary was done by Dr. Jacob Shatzky. The entire manuscript was prepared for the press by Mr. Judah A. Joffe, to whom the authors and their collaborators are sincerely grateful.

Miss Margaret Neubart did all the secretarial work connected with this volume, and has earned our deepest thanks for her efficiency and capability.

We wish to express our appreciation to the collaborators; to the many authors and publishers who permitted us to quote from their works; and last, but not least, we appreciate with deep gratification the close and cordial co-operation of the staff of the Oxford University Press.

L.E.H.

J.S.

September 1940

PREFACE TO THE THIRD EDITION

IN THE ALMOST TWO DECADES that have passed since publication of the first edition of this Psychiatric Dictionary, the field of psychiatry has seen many changes, modifications, and refinements, in both theory and technique. Time has permitted more clinical testing of psychological hypotheses, and there has been more opportunity to assess the value of the various treatment modalities. Among the significant contributions of this period might be mentioned the growth of psychosomatic medicine and the more widespread acceptance of motivational dynamics in other medical specialties; increasing interest in the genetics of human behavior, in child psychiatry, in the psychology of adolescence, and in geriatric psychiatry; the introduction of the phrenotropic drugs, tranquilizers and energizers; assessment of the role of cultural, social, and interpersonal factors in psychic development; attempts to broaden the applicability of treatment methods by such techniques as group therapy and short-term therapy; and investigation of the neurophysiologic and biochemical substrata of the so-called functional psychoses. In the area of psychoanalysis, these years have witnessed a shift in emphasis from libido psychology to ego psychology, from oedipal conflicts to preoedipal determinants of character structure, and in addition there have been numerous modifications of classical analytic technique. A number of schools of psychoanalysis have seen fit to separate themselves from the orthodox Freudian group, and typically this has led to the development of a new terminology.

The present editor lays no claim to having assimilated these many changes in a way which will satisfy all the various groups. In a field marked by constant revision of hypothetical constructs, no dictionary can ever be complete, and it is hoped that the tolerant reader, recognizing this, will apprise the editor of whatever gaps or defects come to his attention.

While there are certain disadvantages to encyclopedic treatment of some of the terms, this approach has been considered valuable enough to warrant its continuance. Many of the definitions of the first edition have been revised to include generally accepted psychodynamic formulations of common symptoms and syndromes, and many others have been expanded to include more recently accumulated genetic, biochemical, and neurophysiologic data. The first edition and supplement contained over eight thousand listings; approximately thirteen hundred of these have been eliminated, and nearly two thousand new listings have been added.

The editor wishes to express his gratitude to Dr. Leland E. Hinsie, the excellence of whose work with the earlier editions of the Psychiatric Dictionary remained always a challenge and ideal, and whose guidance and encouragement in the preparation of the present edition form the very cornerstone of its existence. The philological portions of the present edition remain essentially the contribution of the late Dr. Jacob Shatzky, whose untimely death prevented his working on this third edition. The editor is also grateful to the collaborators in the earlier editions, whose contributions in most cases have been kept intact, and to the authors and publishers who granted permission for quotation from their works. I wish to express my deepest thanks to Mrs. Julia Reed Kilcolm and to Mr. Robert Riggs for their painstaking secretarial work, and, finally, to the staff of the Oxford University Press for their unstinting help and welcome advice.

R.J.C.

New York
December 1959

KEY TO PRONUNCIATION

ā (bāke), ē (thēme), ī (fīne), ō (slōpe), ū (tūbe)

a (back), e (them), i (fin), o (slop), u (tub)

â—shâre, fâir, beâr

ä—fär, fäther

à—àsk, brànch, bàth

aw—saw, caught, thought

ẽ—(plantar, her, first, motor, purpose; voyeur; folie de persécution)

ô—(ôften, lông, dôg, sôft)

oi—(toil, boy, void)

o͞o—so͞on, move (mo͞ov), rule (ro͞ol)

oo—foot, bush (boosh), wood, would (wood), wool

ou—out, now, bough

b—as in back, bell, cupboard, raspberry

ch—as in church, itch, question (kwes'-chun), nature, virtuous

d—as in do, bidden

f—as in for, effort, phonetic, cough

g—as in go, league, ghastly

gz—as in examine, example

h—as in how, h(a)emophilia, Cajal

hw—as in what, nowhere

j—as in just, judge (juj), gist, gestation

k—as in cake (kāk), tick, eunuch, choir (kwīr)

K—as in Loch Lomond, Bach (bäK)

ks—as in complex, experimental

kw—as in equal, quite, choir (kwīr)

l—as in let, lost, doll, Lloyd

m—as in made, more, immediate, trimmed, dumb, tomb, solemn

n—as in no, never, innumerable, sinned (sind), benign (bē-nīn'), knee

ñ—as in cañon

N—as in F. bon (bôN)

ng—as in sing-song, tongue, language (lang'gwij), slink (slingk), finger (fing'-gẽr), puncture (pungk'chẽr)

p—as in put, place, spot, stop, stopped (stopt)

r—as in red, root, berry, rheumatism, logorrh(o)ea

s—as in say, paste, miss, cent, concept, patience, scissors, sciatica, schizm, psyche

sh—as in shall, fashion, rash, chagrin, machine, brioche, crustacea, pernicious, physician, schist, conscience, nausea, tension, sugar, remission, tissue, intention, differential

t—as in tin, but, mitt, doubt, looked, stripped, thyme, ptotic

th—as in thick, bath, health, litho-

TH—as in their, father, bathe

ü—as in F. menu (mẽ-nü'), G. Wüllner

v—as in vase, reverse, save, of (ov)

w—as in will, question (kwes'chun), suave, choir (kwīr)

y—as in year, million, pinion

z—as in zygote, gauze, raise, Times, positive, possess, scissors (siz'ẽrz), xenophobia

zh—as in seizure, glazier, abrasion, division, measure, garage

'—as in chasm (kàz'm), principle (prin'sip'l)

PSYCHIATRIC DICTIONARY

A

A Rorschach scoring symbol for animal response.

A.A. Abbreviation for (1) *achievement age* (q.v.); (2) *Alcoholics Anonymous* (q.v.).

A$_{obi}$ Rorschach scoring symbol for a response derived from or connected with the body of an animal.

Abadie's sign (à-bà-dēz') (Jean Marie (Charles) Abadie, French ophthalmologist, 1842–1932.) An early sign in tabes in which there is loss of deep pain from pressure on the testes or tendo achillis.

abalienation (ab-ā-lyen-ā'shun) *Obs.* Loss or failing of the senses or mental faculties. It is said that the term was originally employed by Scribonius Largus. (Tuke, D.H. *A Dictionary of Psychological Medicine,* vols. 1–2, Blakiston, Philadelphia, 1892)

abasia (à-bā'zhi-a) Inability to walk. The condition is not uncommon in hysteria. See *astasia-abasia.*

abbess A derisive term for the madam of a brothel. Her male counterpart is called an abbot, while the prostitutes are termed nuns or Sisters of Charity.

abbot See *abbess.*

abderite (ab'de-rīt) *Obs.* Stupid person. Abdera was, 'a town in Thrace, the birthplace of Democritus and several remarkable men; its inhabitants, however, had the character of being more stupid than other people.' (Tuke, D.H. *A Dictionary of Psychological Medicine,* vols. 1–2, Blakiston, Philadelphia, 1892)

A.B.E.P.P. Abbreviation for American Board of Examiners in Professional Psychology.

aberration, mental An obsolescent term referring to any morbid deviation from normal mental activity; when used today the term ordinarily does not relate to deviations in intelligence.

abient See *avoidant.*

abiotrophy (ab-i-ot'rō-fē) Premature loss of vitality of cells or tissues. The longevity of the heart, for instance, may be appreciably shorter than that of other organs of the body, leading to early disturbance in function which upsets homeostasis or organ-equilibrium. Lewis has shown that, in schizophrenia, the heart is hypoplastic and hence functionally inadequate. He believes that the shut-in type of personality, so often found in patients with schizophrenia, is a secondary result of cardiovascular inadequacy.

ablation Removal or interruption of function of a bodily part or organ, especially by surgical means.

ablution From the standpoint of psychiatric nursing ablution is a form of hydrotherapy. 'Have ready a rubber sheet, two bath blankets, towels and basin of water at a temperature of 50° to 60° F. Remove the bedclothes and cover the patient with a bath blanket; slip the rubber sheet covered with a bath blanket under the patient, to protect the bed; remove the gown; expose a part of the body, and apply the water from the hollow of the hand, or by means of a bath mitt; rub vigorously for one or two minutes, applying more water as needed, and dry with a coarse towel. Repeat this procedure until the whole body has been gone over systematically. This treatment is given for insomnia, and will usually bring about quiet, restful sleep.' (Bailey, H. *Nursing Mental Diseases,* 3rd ed., Macmillan, New York, 1935)

ablutomania (ab-lū-tō-mā'ni-à) Morbid impulse to wash or bathe, or incessant preoccupation with thoughts of washing or bathing; seen often in obsessive-compulsive psychoneurosis.

aboiement (à-bwà-mäN') *Obsnt.* Involuntary production of abnormal sounds. It is often observed in schizophrenic patients who not infrequently, in advanced stages, make many animalistic sounds. See *Gilles de la Tourette syndrome.*

abortion, therapeutic Surgical interruption of pregnancy for medical reasons. There are no statutes in the United States which legalize abortion on the basis of serious hereditary disorders, although the procedure in such cases may legally be justified on the basis of unendurable mental strain. Colorado, New Mexico, Maryland, and the District of Columbia have more liberalized statutes than the other states and permit abortion when the mother's health is seriously jeopardized. In New York state, abortion is permitted only as a life-saving measure; within the field of psychiatry, then, the only legally valid indication is the danger of suicide. Current psychiatric opinion in regard to therapeutic abortion tends to the conservative side, since it is well known that a psychosis which develops during or after one pregnancy is not a constant concomitant of all later pregnancies. Further, interruption of pregnancy may be more traumatic to the patient than pregnancy and delivery because of guilt feelings which commonly follow abortion.

aboulia (à-boo'li-à) *Abulia* (q.v.).

above and below When Adler uses this term, he implies the unconscious notion existing in every psyche, male or female, of femaleness as a degradation and maleness as an ideal. In other words, there is the conception of man as *above* and woman as *below,* femininity being a position of inferiority to be avoided while masculinity is a goal of superiority to be striven for.

Abraham, Karl (1877–1925) First psychoanalyst in Germany; manic-depressive psychosis, pregenital stages, character types, symbolism.

Abram man (Possibly connected with Abraham's receiving the beggar Lazarus into his bosom, Luke XVI, 22.) 'Another name for Tom o'Bedlam, so called from the Abraham ward in Bedlam, which had for its inmates begging lunatics, who used to array themselves "with party-colored ribbons, tape in their hats, a foxtail hanging down, a long stick with streamers," and beg alms; but "for all their seeming madness, they had wit enough to steal as they went along." ' (Tuke, D.H. *A Dictionary of Psychological Medicine,* vols. 1–2, Blakiston, Philadelphia, 1892) *Obs.* in the United States.

abreaction The process of bringing to consciousness and, thus, to adequate expression, of material which has been unconscious (usually because of repression). Abreaction refers to the two aspects of a 'complex'—the intellectual representation and the accompanying affect—and includes not only the recollection of forgotten memories and experiences but also their reliving with appropriate emotional display and discharge of affect. The method used to bring the repressed material into consciousness is called *catharsis*

(q.v.); the term abreaction technically refers to the end-result.

The term 'abreaction of emotion' refers to the discharge of emotion in the course of psychotherapy. This process is usually facilitated by the patient's gaining awareness of the causal relationship between the previously undischarged emotion and his symptoms. When such a discharge of emotion occurs during psychotherapy, it is often possible for the patient to see the link between his current irrational behavior and his demands toward his therapist, as well as the forgotten earlier counterpart from which the emotional attitude originated. The patient is thereby enabled to modify his anachronistic, immature, incongruous, and unreal emotional demands in favor of more adequate and appropriate behavior.

abreaction, motor The living-out of an unconscious impulse through muscular or motor expression is called *motor abreaction.*

While writing on *The Psycho-Analysis of Wit and the Comical,* Ferenczi relates a joke associated with the condensation of the two words *familiar* and *millionaire* into *famillionaire.* He then says that 'the laughter, as he [Freud] shows by numerous examples, springs from the fact that the intellectual effort that we would normally have had to exert to associate the idea of the family with that of the millionaire, and which—by following the speaker— we have already set in motion, has as a result of the condensation suddenly become superfluous, so that the nervous tension that was already stored up for thinking purposes and which we have thus economized is abreacted involuntarily as a motor innervation of the muscles of laughter—is discharged in laughter.' (Ferenczi, S. *Further Contributions to the Theory and Technique of Psycho-Analysis,* tr. by Suttie, J.I., Leonard and Virginia Woolf and The Institute of Psychoanalysis, London, 1926)

abscess, brain Abscess of the brain (purulent encephalitis, encephalopyosis) is an inflammatory condition due to the invasion of pyogenic micro-organisms resulting in a circumscribed collection of pus in any part of the brain.

absence Freud uses *absence* to indicate the loss of consciousness in the hysterical attack. It 'is derived from the fleeting but unmistakable loss of consciousness which can be observed at the climax of every intensive (also auto-erotic) sexual gratification.' (Freud, S. *Collected Papers,* vol. 2, tr. by Riviere, J., Leonard and Virginia Woolf and The Institute of Psychoanalysis, London, 1924–25) The term is also used to refer to an attack of petit mal.

absent-mindedness A tendency to be occupied with one's own thoughts to such degree that only inadequate attention is given to events which occur in external reality; consequently, memory may seem to be faulty, especially for routine and relatively insignificant happenings. Absent-mindedness, then, is habitual inattention, but without the implication of severe pathology such as is associated with autism and withdrawal.

absorption Engrossment with one object or idea with inattention to others.

abstinence 'The act or practice of voluntarily refraining from the use of something or from some action.' (The Century Dictionary) One of the important parts of the definition is the voluntary nature of abstinence. The term is used extensively in psychoanalysis, particularly with a sexual connotation. According to psychoanalysis, abstinence may be voluntary or involuntary. More frequently it is involuntary, being influenced largely by repressed complexes, such as a deeply rooted sense of guilt. While the fear of actual dangers (infection, legal forces, pregnancy) may be an impelling reason for abstinence, it is more than likely that forces within the personality contribute largely to it.

The term abstinence is also used in a non-sexual sense in the case of alcoholism and addictions, to refer to refraining from the addicting drug.

abstraction 'The drawing out or isolation of a content (e.g. a meaning or general character, etc.) from a connection, containing other elements, whose combination as a totality is something unique or individual, and therefore inaccessible to comparison.' (Jung, C.G. *Psychological Types,* Harcourt, Brace, 1923.) Abstraction is an activity which belongs to psychological functions in general, and Jung differentiates between abstracting thinking, abstracting feeling, abstracting sensation, and abstracting intuition. 'Abstracting-thinking brings into relief a content that is distinguished from other irrelevant

elements by its intellectual, logical qualities. Abstracting-feeling does the same with a content characterized by feeling; similarly with sensation and intuition.' (ibid.)

absurdity In psychoanalysis the word absurdity possesses a special meaning. Anything that is contradictory or incoherent or meaningless in a train of thought or a constellation of ideas is described as absurd.The absurdities are only apparent, not real. 'I will begin with a few examples in which the absurdity of the dream-content is apparent only, disappearing when the dream is more thoroughly examined.' (Freud, S. *The Interpretation of Dreams,* 3rd ed., tr. by Brill, A.A., Macmillan, New York, 1933)

abulia (à-bū′li-à) Absence of will-power or wish-power; the term implies that the individual has a desire to do something but the desire is without power or energy. Abulia itself is rarè and with few exceptions occurs only in the schizophrenias. The more frequent disturbance in the will is a reduction or impairment (hypobulia) rather than a complete absence. Bleuler included abulia and hypobulia among the fundamental symptoms of the schizophrenias.

Social abulia means inactivity, focal or diffuse, of an individual toward the environment, due to inability to settle on a plan of action. There may be a desire to contact the environment, but the desire has no power of action.

abulic-akinetic syndrome See *syndrome, akinetic-abulic.*

acalculia (à-kal-kū′li-à) Inability to perform simple arithmetic operations.

acanthesthesia (à-kan-thes-thē′zhi-à) A type of paresthesia in which the patient experiences a sensation of pinpricks.

acarophobia (à-kar-o-fō′bi-à) A morbid dread of mites. The meaning of the term has been extended to include a wide variety of small things, animate (e.g. worms) or inanimate (e.g. pins, needles). The fear may be associated with the idea that insects or worms are crawling beneath the skin, a thought not uncommon in patients suffering from alcoholism or drug addiction. It is perhaps also associated with Lilliputian ideas.

acatalepsia (à-kat-à-lep′si-à) Impairment

of the reasoning faculty; abnormal inability to comprehend.

acatalepsy (à-kat′à-lep-sē) *Obs.* Formerly used synonymously with *dementia*.

acatamathesia (à-kat-à-mà-thē′zhi-à, -zi-à) *Obs.* Inability to understand language. (*Dictionary of Philosophy and Psychology*, ed. by Baldwin, J.M., Macmillan, New York, 1928) This is the perceptive (sensory) aspect of *aphasia*. See also *speech disorders*.

acataphasia (ā-kat-à-fā′zhi-à) A form of disordered speech in which 'the patients either do not find the expression appropriate to their thoughts, but only produce something with a similar sound ("displacement paralogia"), or they let their speech fall into quite another channel ("derailment paralogia"). A patient said he was "wholly without head on the date" for "he did not know the date"; another complained he "lived under protected police" instead of "under the protection of police." ' (Kraepelin, E. *Dementia Praecox and Paraphrenia,* tr. by Barclay, R.M., Livingstone, Edinburgh, 1919) See also *speech disorders*.

acathexis (à-kà-thek′sis) Certain things, objective or subjective, hold no feelings or emotions for an individual; they are not infused with emotions; they are not charged or cathected. This idea has received special consideration in the field of psychoanalysis, with reference to the attachment of affects to ideas or thoughts. Some patients have an unusual capacity for separating affect from an idea that is highly significant to them. The affect may be transferred to an indifferent or inconsequential idea or it may attach itself to some unconscious material. Thus, one may express an idea or a series of ideas that seem to have no meaning or feeling for him. At times an entire complex may be utterly devoid of affect when it comes into consciousness.

acathisia (à-kath-i′zi-à) Also termed acathisia paraesthetica, acathisia psychasthenica, acathisia spastica. Inability to sit down because of the intense anxiety provoked by the thought of doing so. In acathisia spastica, the thought or act of sitting provokes hysterical convulsions.

accessory Additional, contributory, or secondary as opposed to fundamental or primary. In psychiatry, the term is chiefly used in reference to the symptomatology of the schizophrenias, whose symptoms were divided by Bleuler into (1) fundamental or primary symptoms and (2) accessory or secondary symptoms.

accidental In psychoanalysis, accidental refers to that which is adventitious or of external origin, in contradistinction to that which is endowed or of inherent origin. Accidental experiences are of two kinds: dispositional, when they occur early in life and strongly influence character development; and definitive, when they occur later and act as precipitating or provocative agents.

accident, cerebrovascular Apoplexy; stroke. Cerebrovascular accidents include those conditions in which gross cerebral damage, hemorrhage, or softening follow a group of acute vascular disorders—cerebral thrombosis (82%), cerebral hemorrhage (15%), and cerebral embolism (3%).

Cerebral thrombosis is commonly a manifestation of cerebral arteriosclerosis and occurs in that age group, although children with an acute infectious disease and young syphilitic adults may also develop cerebral thrombosis.

Often the patient awakens in the morning completely paralyzed on one side of the body, monoplegic or aphasic. Not infrequently, however, thrombosis occurs in the daytime, especially when the patient is inactive, but also during exertion. Most cases recover with gradual recession of the pathologic change.

Cerebral hemorrhage may occur suddenly, without warning, as a true 'stroke.' It occurs most commonly as a result of arteriosclerosis or hypertension, in the middle and older age groups.

Children and young adults with congenital abnormalities of the cerebral vasculature, such as aneurysms, may likewise be afflicted. Since hypertension of the essential type is so frequently familial, death from cerebral hemorrhage correspondingly runs in families. The exciting causes are such acts as straining at stool, coughing, retching, coitus, violent emotion, or heavy eating, all of which elevate the blood pressure. Thus, hemorrhage frequently occurs in the daytime during periods of activity, although many cases occur at night during periods of insomnia. Unconsciousness occurs suddenly and the patient topples over or falls to the ground. Coma may gradually deepen and the patient die in a few hours. Far more common is a coma of several days' duration during which the patient may rouse a little and then lapse back into deep coma. Some patients gradually recover consciousness and survive the attack.

Cerebral embolism creates the same clinical picture as cerebral thrombosis; but emboli are usually multiple and the syndrome may be more bizarre. The commonest causes of emboli are: (1) diseases of the heart—as with auricular fibrillation and coronary occlusion with mural thrombi, which may break off and become embolic to the brain; or as in bacterial endocarditis, with valvular vegetations, which may become dislodged and flow to the brain; (2) pulmonary diseases, with septic emboli lodging in a cerebral vessel, damaging the wall of the vessel, causing one or more brain abscesses and sometimes meningitis. Cerebral embolism comes on suddenly, without warning, and severe general symptoms appear as in hemorrhages. There may be convulsions and coma. Death may occur in a few hours when the embolus has lodged in vital areas. The embolism may produce only softening, but most frequently hemorrhage also. It is the most frequent cause of sudden hemiplegia in childhood.

accident, intentional Huddleson stresses the consideration that accidents may be psychologically determined. 'If an outraged employee with no other means of retaliation is so preoccupied, worried, or angry that he "accidentally" thrusts his hand between gears and thus gains many weeks of compensation and care in lieu of employment and chagrin following the threat of imminent discharge, sociologic sympathy with his predicament ought not to obscure a psychologic estimate of his injury as virtually self-inflicted.' (Huddleson, J.H. *Accidents, Neuroses and Compensation,* Williams & Wilkins, Baltimore, 1932)

accident-proneness See *proneness, accident.*

accident, purposeful See *proneness, accident.*

accommodation 1. Adjustment, especially of the eye for various distances. Absolute accommodation is the accommodation of either eye separately; binocular accommodation is like accommodation in both eyes in co-ordination with convergence (the accommodation reflex). Accommo-

dation occurs on shift of far to near vision, which is followed by thickening of the lens, convergence of the eyes, and constriction of the pupils. The most widely accepted theory of the mechanism of accommodation is that of Helmholtz: contraction of the ciliary muscle reduces the tension of the zonular muscle, thus permitting the elastic capsule of the lens to shape the lens and to increase its convexity. Convergence is produced by the action of both internal rectus muscles (innervated by N. III); pupillary constriction is produced by the action of the sphincter muscle of the iris (innervated by the short ciliary nerves, the parasympathetic outflow from the Edinger-Westphal nucleus to the ciliary ganglion).

2. Nerve accommodation is the rise in threshold during the passage of a constant, direct electric current because of which only the make and break of the current stimulates the nerve.

3. Social accommodation refers to the functional changes in habits and customs occurring in persons and groups in response to other persons and groups and in response to the common environment. Such accommodation is typically made for the sake of social harmony. The concept of accommodation is used in analyzing attitudes in situations of superordination and subordination, as those of slavery, caste, class, status, and leadership. The social heritage, culture, and social organization are accommodations which are transmitted from generation to generation.

acculturation Originally, a term of social anthropology: the transfer of one ethnical group's culture to another. By extension, the implanting in children of the customs, beliefs, and ideals held to be important by adults of the culture group: a process of cultural indoctrination of children. Modern educators seem to emphasize the concept of cultural indoctrination which, under a more innocent term, is called acculturation. Nevertheless, a great deal of such indoctrination is carried out by educators without a formal plan, as an unconscious attempt at disseminating their own beliefs. (Sladen, F.J. *Psychiatry and the War,* Thomas, Springfield, Ill., 1943)

accuracy compulsion A term used in Rorschach interpretation to refer to the tendency of the subject to be overly accurate in his responses to the cards; he makes many corrections and indicates dissatisfaction with his responses, but is unable to improve them.

acedia (à-sē'di-à) *Obsnt.* A rarely used term for a syndrome characterized by carelessness, listlessness, apathy, and melancholia.

acenesthesia (à-sen-es-thē'zhi-à) Absence of the feeling of physical existence, a common symptom in many psychiatric states.

acerophobia (à-sēr-ō-fō'bi-à) Fear of sourness.

acetylcholine (à-sēt-il-kōl'ēn) A reversible acetic acid ester of choline, $CH_3 \cdot CO \cdot O \cdot CH_2 \cdot N(CH_3)_3 \cdot OH$. It is generally believed that acetylcholine, which is normally present in many parts of the body, is the sole mediator at autonomic synapses and in the transmission of the nerve impulse from motor nerve to skeletal muscle. It has been suggested that acetylcholine is also the sole mediator for central synaptic transmission, although there is no direct evidence for this. More recent work suggests that other substances (viz. serotonin and norepinephrine) are more likely the central synaptic neurohumors. For the theory of mechanism of action of acetylcholine in nerve impulse transmission, see *process, elementary.*

achievement age (A.A.) The term denotes the relationship between the chronological age and the age of achievement as established by standard achievement tests. The latter comprise a series of educational tests as distinguished from intelligence tests. Achievement age is synonymous with educational age and one speaks of educational or achievement quotient. When the latter is divided by the mental age (I.Q.) the result is expressed as accomplishment quotient (A.Q.).

Achilles reflex Ankle jerk. Tapping the tendo achillis results in plantar flexion at the ankle due to contraction of the soleus and gastrocnemius muscles; the tibial nerve is both afferent and efferent for this reflex, and its center is S 1–2.

achluophobia (à-klū-ō-fō'bi-à) Fear of darkness.

achromatic color response A Rorschach scoring term for a response of black, gray, white, or mention of lack of color; also designated C'.

achromatic response A Rorschach scoring term for a response of texture or of anything which is described as achromatic.

achromatopsia (à-krō-mà-top'si-à) Total color blindness.

acme In psychoanalysis the term means the highest point of pleasure in sexual intercourse.

acmesthesia (ak-mes-thē'zhi-à) Perception of sharp points by touch rather than by pain; acuesthesia.

acolasia (à-ko-lā'zi-à) *Obs.* Morbid intemperance or lust.

aconuresis (à-kon-ū-rē'sis) See *enuresis.*

acoria (à-kō-'ri-à) 'With Hippocrates it meant moderation in eating; but in Aretaeus it is used in regard to drink in the sense of insatiable desire. Bulimia.' (Tuke, D.H. *A Dictionary of Psychological Medicine,* vols. 1–2, Blakiston, Philadelphia, 1892)

acousma (à-kōōz'mà) See *akoasm.*

acousticophobia (à-kōōs-ti-kō-fō'bi-à) Fear of sounds.

acrai (ä'krī) An Arabian term, obsolete, at least in the United States, 'apparently synonymous with nymphomania and satyriasis.' (Tuke, D.H. *A Dictionary of Psychological Medicine,* vols. 1–2, Blakiston, Philadelphia, 1892)

acrasia, acrasy (à-krā'zi-à, ak'rà-sē) Morbid intemperance in anything; at one time it was synonymous with *acratia,* debility, impotence, inefficiency.

acro- (ak'rō) combining form meaning pertaining to *extremity* or *tip,* from Gr. *ákros,* highest, topmost.

acrocinesia, acrocinesis (-si-nē'si-à, -nē'sis) Excessive movements, as those, for example, observed in the manic phase of manic-depressive psychosis.

acrocyanosis (-sī-à-nō'sis) Blueness of the extremities, extending usually to the wrists and ankles, is commonly observed among psychiatric patients, particularly among the group affected by schizophrenia. The cause is not known, though it is believed that the vascular system may be largely responsible for the discoloration. The thought is expressed in constitutional medicine that in individuals with an asthenic habitus the venous bed preponderates over the arterial. The inequality and its consequences are cited as partially responsible for the blueness of the extremities.

acrodynia (-din'i-à) Vegetative neurosis; trophodermatoneurosis; pink disease; erythroedema polyneuritis. A disorder of the vegetative nervous system occurring in children between the ages of 4 months and 7 years and consisting of myelin degeneration in the peripheral nerves and chromatolysis of the anterior horn cells. The disease is most common in Australia and North America and occurs typically between the fall and early spring. Some believe the disorder is infective in origin, others regard it as a deficiency disease. Symptoms include irritability, photophobia, excessive sweating, an irritating and erythematous rash with slight swelling on the hands and feet, and symptoms of polyneuritis. The disease usually lasts for 3 to 12 months. Treatment is symptomatic.

acroesthesia (-es-thē'zhi-à) Increased sensitivity to pain in the extremities.

acrohypothermy (-hī'pō-thēr-mē) Abnormal coldness of the extremities commonly observed in psychiatric patients. It is especially noticeable in patients with schizophrenia, in whom it is commonly associated with acrocyanosis. The cause of either is not known, although it has been suggested that the conditions are associated with the vascular apparatus.

acromania (-mā'ni-à) *Obs.* Chronic, incurable insanity.

acromegaly, acromegalia (-meg'à-lē, -mēgā'li-à) Hyperpituitarism produced usually by an acidophilic adenoma of the anterior lobe (epithelial portion) of the hypophysis; acromegaly is sometimes seen in individuals with no adenoma whose hypophysis shows an increase in number of eosinophilic cells in an otherwise normal gland. The disorder was first clearly defined by Pierre Marie in 1886 and hence is sometimes called 'Marie's disease.' Acromegaly occurs in adults after the epiphysial lines have closed; acidophilic adenomas arising prior to closure of the epiphysial lines in adolescence produces gigantism. Acromegaly consists of a localized increase in size of various structures (head, hands, feet, lips, jaw) resulting in a peculiar bodily configuration seen in no other disorder. Associated with this is profuse, offensive perspiration; bitemporal or frontal headache, excessive growth of hair, impotence, sterility, increase in basal metabolic rate, and glycosuria are also seen frequently. Bitemporal hemianopia develops with progression of the disorder.

Schizophrenic and manic-depressive psychoses are said to be rare in acromegaly, although it is quite regularly accompanied by striking alterations of personality: impulsiveness (*c.* 90% of cases), moodiness and mood swings (60%), anger outbursts (50%), and often periodic or constant somnolence.

acromicria (-mik'ri-à) Term used in constitutional medicine, especially by Kretschmer, and Pende, for the physical condition characterized by selective smallness and shortness of one or more extremities.

acrophobia Fear of high places.

ACT Atropine coma therapy. See *therapy, atropine coma.*

ACTH Adrenocorticotropic hormone; one of the anterior pituitary hormones. See *syndrome, general adaptation.*

act-habit This term, used in both general psychiatry and, but more specifically, the field of child study and child psychiatry, refers to the importance of differing cultural aspects of the environment in providing and determining special developmental aspects of the child's personality.

J.McV. Hunt (*Personality and the Behavior Disorders,* vol. 2, Ronald Press, New York, 1944) states: 'The contrast between Tennessee hill-country families described by Claudia Lewis (1943) and those of metropolitan areas is not limited to the contrast between the infant who is nursed for months and the infant who is fed by the bottle method on a rigid schedule. Toilet training is different when there are no toilets. The hill-country child accompanies his mother on every sort of activity, shopping, to funerals, and even births, at the age of two to four, while metropolitan children are usually limited to a relatively restricted area, and generally accompany mothers only to places like the grocery store and the parks.'

Similarly such environmental attitudes as 'minimal attention' handling of infants, 'scientific' upbringing of children, 'oversolicitousness,' 'over-warmth,' and 'over-attention' may all result in chronic and repetitive activities on the part of the child which make for habituation and personality-rooted character traits.

acting out, neurotic The partial discharge of instinctual tension that is achieved by responding to the present situation as if it were the situation that originally gave rise to the instinctual demand. Acting out is a displacement of behavioral response from one situation to another; not every displacement, however, results in acting out. As so defined, acting out includes the phenomenon of transference. The term transference is employed if the attitude or behavior is in response to certain definite persons; the mechanism is called acting out if something has to be done indiscriminately. Acting out is more than a mere feeling or thought, a mere mimic expression, or a mere single movement— it is a real acting. 'It is an acting which unconsciously relieves inner tension and brings a partial discharge to warded-off impulses (no matter whether these impulses express directly instinctual demands, or are reactions to original instinctual demands, e.g. guilt feelings); the present situation, somehow associatively connected with the repressed content, is used as an occasion for the discharge of repressed energies; the cathexis is displaced from the repressed memories to the present "derivative," and this displacement makes the discharge possible.' (Fenichel. 'Neurotic Acting Out,' *Psychoanalytic Review 32,* 197, 1945) Fenichel says further: 'It is true that there are also symptoms which involve a certain acting; but these symptoms could also be called "acting out." In general, compulsive acts, e.g., are not included in the conception of "acting out," because they are limited in their extent, and because they are experienced as strange and not as ego-syntonic. If certain rituals are rationalized to such an extent that the subject identifies himself with them, they certainly can be included in the conception of "acting out." '

In psychoanalysis, the patient may act out memories, instead of recalling them. An unmarried female patient, for example, imagined herself pregnant from a much older man during the course of her analysis. It later became apparent that the patient was acting out her infantile incestuous desires for her father, desires which, in the beginning, she was unable to verbalize under analysis.

But acting out does not occur only in psychoanalysis. The character structure of an individual, for example, is a chronic and habitual pattern of reaction which develops as the result of conflict between instinctual demands and the frustrating outer world. Although the individual's behavior pattern originates in the family situation, he preserves this pattern throughout his life as his typical method of reacting to any frustration. This displacement also constitutes acting out.

action, automatic In discussing *suggested action,* P. Janet writes: 'these characteristics of the performance of suggested actions have often received specific names. Delboeuf proposed to speak of the state in which they were performed as a "paraphonic state." I myself have generally used the expression "automatic" actions or beliefs. In my more recent writings, I have tried to show the place occupied by automatic actions among the degrees of the activation of tendencies. These tendencies, these dispositions to the performance of an aggregate of co-ordinated movements, may remain in "latent condition," or may be "activated" more or less completely by passing through the stages of "erection," "desire," and "effort," in order to reach at length the stage of "completed action," or the stage of "triumph." ' (Janet, P. *Psychological Healing,* vols. 1–2, tr. by Paul, E. and C., Macmillan, New York, 1925)

action, chance See *chance-action.*

action, deferred This expression carries special meaning in psychoanalysis. Thus, when discussing the primal scene (in the case of the Wolf-man), Freud says that the patient observed his parents in the act of sexual intercourse, when the patient was 1½ years old. The impressions, however, were not understood by the child at the time; at a later period, though, certain experiences occurred that caused revival of the primal experience and gave significance to it. There was deferred action. Freud believes that *deferred action* often takes place with regard to castration threats.

action, faulty See *act, symptomatic.*

action, ludic See *activity, ludic.*

action, psychomotor Action resulting directly from an idea or perception.

action, social 'The term "social action" in its broadest sense implies any concerted movement by organized groups toward the achievement of desired objectives. It is thus opposed to or contrasted with individual action.' (Fitch, J.A., in *Social Work Year Book 1939*, edited by Kurtz, R.H., Russell Sage Foundation, New York)

action, subconscious See *activity, ludic.*

action, symbolic Symbolic actions are performed unconsciously and automatically. They are considered entirely accidental by the person doing them. Depending on their mechanism they are simple or complex and manifest themselves in such unconscious mannerisms as playing with a moustache, jingling coins in a pocket, arranging or disarranging clothes. These acts conceal definite meaning, yet when questioned about them, people usually say they were just playing. An example of a more complex symbolic action is the following cited by Brill: 'A man consulted me once, and brought along a big heavy overcoat. When he left my office, he forgot to take it and I called him back. Upon returning, it occurred to him to inquire about something else he was anxious to know. When he was done, he left, again forgetting to take his coat, and when I called him back for the second time, he exclaimed: "Damn my father-in-law, I have to carry this coat to his office." ' (Brill, A.A. *Basic Principles of Psychoanalysis,* Doubleday, New York, 1949)

active In psychoanalysis the term active bears special significance from the standpoint of sex. Active refers to masculine qualities, while passive is associated with effeminacy. Moreover, the term active is defined from the point of view of the goal, not from that of the impulse or instinct. The latter is always active.

The expression active is also used to describe a state of the analyst while he is analyzing. He is active when he endeavors to influence the patient to produce material for analysis.

activities, graded In occupational therapy, those occupations and handicrafts which have been classified according to the degree of mental and physical effort required for accomplishment. By means of this classification it is possible to increase the complexity of the work as the capacity of the patient increases.

activity In occupational therapy, any occupation or interest wherein participation requires exertion of energy.

activity, concealed antisocial The antisocial nature of certain types of behavior is sometimes concealed by the fact of its arising out of socially approved motivation. Kardiner refers to this as *concealed antisocial activity.* For example, he writes: 'competitiveness must be regarded in our society as a normal manifestation of self-assertion, when it is governed by the super-ego system. But there are neurotic and criminal forms of self-assertion. A neurotic self-assertion is an attempt to deny by force a deep feeling of inferiority or insecurity. There are some types of self-assertion that are injurious in intent, but that escape being criminal by a technicality. A good trader may misrepresent by omission, but not by commission. If he misrepresents by omitting damaging details, he is merely a sharp trader and is both condemned and applauded; if he deliberately misrepresents, he is lying and is therefore only condemned. It is by this route that much concealed antisocial activity passes for normal.' (Kardiner, A. *The Psychological Frontiers of Society,* Columbia University Press, New York, 1945)

activity, dream The *dream-activity* that gains most attention today, from the standpoint of a practical, working hypothesis, is best described by Freud. He believes that sleep involves more than a mere shutting off of psychic activity from the external world. During sleep the material of the unconscious is activated in ways that are different from those manifested during the waking stage. The unconscious becomes relatively autonomous, producing activity that accords with the laws of the unconscious. It utilizes primitive machinery in giving expression to unfulfilled and repressed tendencies. The dream is a primitive method of psychic activity, exhibiting such phenomena as condensation, displacement, symbolization, etc. When such phenomena are encountered in dreams, they are called dream-activities.

activity, group In occupational therapy an activity in which several patients participate. Its chief value is its socializing effect upon the mentally ill patients who are asocial.

activity, immobilizing Slavson suggests

this term in relation to activity group psychotherapy as a form of *libido-binding* activities. By this he means activities that tie one down to a specific interest or occupation: to attain this he has devised a special environment for group psychotherapy, which is in contrast to *stimulating* or libido-activating activities. (Slavson, S.R. *An Introduction to Group Therapy,* The Commonwealth Fund, Oxford University Press, New York, 1943) See *psychotherapy, group.*

activity, libido-binding See *activity, immobilizing.*

activity, ludic Automatic action is as a rule insufficient, in that it 'cannot produce the appropriate outward effects, since there is a more or less complete suppression of those perfectionments of the action which would render it psychologically real. This is the stage of "quasi-action" (Baldwin), or of "ludic action." If the insufficiency relates especially to the outward characteristics of the action, to its objective consequences, we have to do with "play" properly so called. If, on the other hand, the insufficiency relates especially to the subjective modifications of the individual, to the adaptations of his own personality to the action, then we have to do with "automatic action." When the alterations of individual sentiment are pushed to an extreme, and when automatic actions are performed by one who does not remember what he has done and is unaware of what he is doing at the time, we term such actions "subconscious actions." ' (Janet, P. *Psychological Healing,* vols. 1–2, tr. by Paul, E. and C., Macmillan, New York, 1925)

It has been established that higher animals have a quantity of energy left after performing all the movements required by their physiological life-processes. This excess energy must be expended (without purpose) in some way, most usually in play-activity, called *ludic activity.*

activity, socializing In therapy groups, this term denotes the activity that brings an individual into interaction with other members of the group.

activity, stimulating The opposite of immobilizing activity. See *activity, immobilizing.*

act, purposeless See *act, symptomatic.*

act, reflex While discussing *The Psychology of the Dream Processes,* Freud em-

phasizes that 'all our psychic activities proceed from (inner or outer) stimuli and terminate in innervations.' There is a sensory and a motor end to the psychic apparatus. See *system.* He adds that 'the psychic apparatus must be constructed like a reflex apparatus. The reflex act remains the type of every psychic activity as well.' (Freud, S. *The Interpretation of Dreams,* 3rd ed., tr. by Brill, A.A., Macmillan, New York, 1933)

act, symptomatic The expression *symptomatic act* gains distinction particularly in psychoanalysis. A symptomatic act, like a symbol, is said to be representative of some unconscious component. According to Freud, symptomatic acts must fulfill three conditions: (1) they must fall within normal limits, that is, they must not be morbid acts; (2) they must be temporary manifestations, subject to easy correction; and (3) if unrecognized by the individual committing them, when his attention is called to them, he should not understand the motivation, but ascribe it to inattention or accident.

Symptomatic acts constitute some of the peculiarities of everyday life. They are expressed as mannerisms, slips of the tongue (*lapsus linguae*) or of memory (*lapsus memoriae*) or of the pen (*lapsus calami*), misprints, fake visual recognition, mislaying of objects, etc.

actual neurosis See *neurosis, actual.*

act, unintentional See *act, symptomatic.*

acuesthesia (à-kū-es-thē′zhi-à) See *acmesthesia.*

aculalia (à-kū-lā′li-à) Nonsensical or jargon speech, such as is seen with Wernicke's type of aphasia associated with lesions of the left angular gyrus (and usually also the base of the first and second temporal convolutions) in right-handed persons. The affected subject shows marked intellectual impairment, an inability to comprehend spoken or written language, and although the patient can speak he is likely to talk nonsense. This corresponds to Head's 'syntactical aphasia.'

-acusia (-à-kū′z[h]i-à) Combining form meaning hearing.

acute affective reflex Kretschmer's term for the earliest indications of emotional discharge (usually, tremors) in response to great stress.

acute brain disorders The various psychiatric syndromes due to temporary, reversible, diffuse impairment of brain tissue function. These disorders are part of the group formerly designated 'organic psychoses'; the term acute, as used in the revised nomenclature, refers primarily to the reversibility of the process, and an acute brain disorder is one from which the patient will ordinarily recover.

adaptability, cultural This term, according to Freud, indicates man's personal capacity, under the influence of the erotic, to transform the egoistic impulses into social drives.

adaptability, heterogeneous See *adaptability, homogeneous.*

adaptability, homogeneous The capacity to adapt that is uniformly possessed by all members of the species, such as the adaptation to intensity of light entering the eye by means of the pupillary reflex. Homogeneous adaptability is differentiated from heterogeneous adaptability, which refers to genetic variability within the species or within a population (i.e. differences between individuals) in the capacity to adapt.

adaptation Act of fitting or conforming one thing to another. The term implies that advantageous change takes place. In psychiatry it usually refers to the changes which an individual experiences, either as regards himself or as regards his relationship with his environment; usually a change in the one affects the other. When the changes are favorable to all concerned, the individual is said to be adapted. Psychiatrists use the term to mean a rearrangement of the mental attitude. The result of the act of adaptation is called adjustment.

In occupational therapy this term means modification or alteration of an occupation to suit the specific need or disability of a patient.

In neurophysiology, adaptation refers to the diminished rate of discharge shown by an end-organ subjected over a period of time to a constant stimulus. Adaptation in this sense is comparable to the term tolerance when the latter is used in reference to a drug.

adaptation, alloplastic See *psychodynamics, adaptational.*

adaptation, autoplastic See *psychodynamics, adaptational.*

adaptation, ontogenetic See *psychodynamics, adaptational.*

adaptation syndrome See *syndrome, general adaptation.*

adaptedness The state which results from appropriate adjustments to conditions, as distinguished from adaptation, which strictly speaking refers only to the process whereby the adjustments are brought about. In common usage, the term adaptation has both meanings.

adaptiveness, social When used in the sphere of mental deficiency, this expression has distinctive meaning. Tredgold says: 'From the point of view of mental deficiency, the most important group is that concerned with social adaptation, and in view of the ambiguity and various meanings attached to the term "intelligence," it might perhaps be advisable to apply the term "common sense" to the quality which is characteristic of this group. In any case, whether we call it social adaptiveness, social intelligence, common sense, *nous,* or the more popular "gumption," the ability is clearly a composite one and made up of many different processes, such as comprehension, discrimination, reasoning, prevision and planning.' (Tredgold, A.F. *A Text-Book of Mental Deficiency,* 6th ed., Wood, Baltimore, 1937)

He further writes: 'It is seen . . . that the psychological basis of mental deficiency consists essentially in the imperfect, and often irregular, development of that group of intellectual factors of mind which combine to form what we may designate *social adaptiveness.*' (ibid.)

addephagia Variant of *adephagia.* (q.v.). See also *bulimia.*

addiction Strong dependence, both physiological and emotional, upon alcohol or some other drug. True addiction is characterized by the appearance of a typical abstinence syndrome of organic origin when the drug is withdrawn. It appears that in the addicted individual the presence in the body of the addicting drug is necessary to maintain normal cellular functions, and when the drug is withdrawn distortion of physiological processes ensues.

The majority of addicting drugs fall into one of four categories: (1) morphine and its transformation products (e.g. codeine, heroin, dilaudid); (2) synthetic analgesics (meperidine series, methadone series, morphinan series, dithienyl-butenes and dithienyl-butanes); (3) sedatives and hypnotics (barbiturates, paraldehyde, chloral hydrate, alcohol); (4) miscellaneous drugs such as marihuana, cocaine, mescaline, amphetamine.

The term addiction is to be differentiated from habituation, which refers to a psychic craving manifested when a drug is withdrawn which has been used over a prolonged period of time; and from tolerance, which refers to increasing resistance to the usual effects of a drug.

addiction, cyclic A syndrome originally described by Wulff which occurs most commonly in women and consists of periods of depression, feelings of ugliness, and overeating or overdrinking alternating with periods of normal or elated mood, feelings of beauty, and ascetic behavior. These patients show a preoedipal mother conflict with unconscious hatred of the mother and of femininity. Their urge to eat is an attempt to incorporate something to counteract femininity—milk, penis, child and/or narcissistic supplies which soothe anxieties. Although described as a psychoneurosis by Wulff, cases of cyclic addiction are often found to fall nosologically within the schizophrenic group.

addiction, enema The frequent and habitual taking of enemas to gratify deep, hidden, unconscious character needs, but usually rationalized 'for health,' especially as an antidote against illusional 'autointoxication.' The illusion of having been poisoned by 'something taken in' has usually been displaced from its true hidden source onto the relatively innocent and innocuous food introject. The enema then functions as an easily available riddance and purification mechanism.

A 50-year-old white man complained of fatigue, headache, 'slow digestion,' and accompanying 'toxemia.' He felt his sluggishness was due to a 'toxic' condition and poor bowel function. Frequently he not only would force himself to vomit (purge from above) but was also addicted to the enema habit (purge from below) for purposes of relieving his 'autointoxication.' (Weiss, E., and English, O.S. *Psychosomatic Medicine*, 2nd ed., Saunders, Philadelphia and London, 1949)

addiction, polysurgical A phenomenon not infrequently met with in psychiatric pa-

tients who are addicted to surgical operations: they solicit or, through multiple symptoms, manage to have many operations though as a rule 'the necessity for an operation seems more psychological than physical.' (Menninger, K.A. *Man against Himself*, Harcourt, Brace, New York, 1938)

addict, object A term used to describe the behavior of certain schizophrenic patients who, to prove that they maintain some contact with the objective world, seek out and cling to objects and ideas and on the basis of this develop obsessions, monomania, elaborate inventions, etc.

additive W A Rorschach scoring term for a response in which the subject reports details but finally combines these into a whole response.

ademonia (à-dē-mō'ni-à) *Obs.* 'Restless thought, great mental distress or anxiety . . . Occasionally used as a synonym for melancholy.' (Tuke, D.H. *A Dictionary of Psychological Medicine*, vols. 1–2, Blakiston, Philadelphia, 1892)

ademosyne (à-dē-mos'i-nē, -moz'i-nē) *Obs.* Formerly synonymous with nostalgia.

adenoid See *type, adenoid.*

adenoma, basophil(e) (bā'sō-fil ad-ē-nō'mà) Basophil adenoma or Cushing's syndrome is a condition due to tumor of the anterior lobe of the pituitary gland, characterized by a pluriglandular symptom complex. The symptoms are adiposity of the body and face but sparing the limbs, amenorrhea and hypertrichosis in women, acrocyanosis with cutis marmorata, hypertension, purple striae distensae, at times polycythemia and peculiar softening of bones, and frequently hyperglycemia.

Young adults are more commonly affected and duration of life is about five years following appearance of symptoms.

adephagia (à-dē-fā'ji-à) *Obs.* A morbidly voracious appetite, synonymous with *bulimia.*

adiadochokinesis (à-dī-ad-ō-kō-ki-nē'sis) Loss of power to perform rapid alternating movements. This symptom is indicative of disorder of the cerebellum or its tracts.

adient Positively oriented or moving-toward. The adient drive or behavior or response is a situation which results in behavior acting toward the stimulus, increasing and perpetuating its action; it is the opposite of the avoidant drive.

adiposogenital dystrophia (ad-i-pō-sō-jen'i-tal dis-tro'fi-à) See *Frohlich's syndrome* and *Laurence-Moon-Biedl syndrome.*

adjustment reaction In the 1952 revision of psychiatric nomenclature, this term is used to refer to certain *transient situational personality disorders* (q.v.) occurring in various periods of life.

adjustment, social Adaptation of the person to his social environment, in the field of social problems referring 'to the relations of the person to his family, community, political state or economic order in reference to some assumed standard or norm.' (Young, K. *Encyclopaedia of the Social Sciences,* vol. 1, Macmillan, New York, 1930, p. 438) Adjustment may take place by adapting one's self to the environment or by changing the environment.

Adler, Alfred (1870–1937) Austrian psychiatrist, founder of the school of Individual Psychology.

admission, first An individual admitted for the first time to an institution of a given class (i.e. hospitals for mental disease) is called a first admission.

Example. The following table shows the number of first admissions to the New York civil State hospitals during the year ended June 30, 1938, classified according to sex and type of mental disorder.

Mental Disorders	Number		
	Males	Females	Total
General paresis...............	688	215	903
With other syphilis of central nervous system............	115	56	171
With epidemic encephalitis....	43	31	74
With other infectious diseases..	43	30	73
Alcoholic.....................	679	152	831
Due to drugs or other exogenous poisons...............	7	24	31
Traumatic....................	136	23	159
With cerebral arteriosclerosis..	1255	1162	2417
With other disturbances of circulation....................	39	44	83
With convulsive disorders.....	116	96	212
Senile	515	722	1237
Involutional	174	523	697
Due to other metabolic, etc., diseases	18	43	61
Due to new growth..........	20	21	41
With organic changes of nervous system	51	31	82
Psychoneuroses	177	233	410
Manic-depressive	315	606	921
Dementia praecox	1665	1481	3146
Paranoia and paranoid conditions	51	76	127
With psychopathic personality.	188	97	285
With mental deficiency.......	141	141	282
Undiagnosed	35	32	67
Without psychosis	162	54	216
Primary behavior disorders....	75	34	109
Total	6708	5927	12,635

adolescence The state or period of growth from puberty to maturity. In normal subjects its beginning is marked by the appearance of secondary sexual characteristics, commonly at about age 12; its termination is at about age 20. Adolescence is the period in which sexual maturity is achieved in that for the first time both the sexual and reproductive instincts attain full maturity and unite into a single striving; it can further be considered the age of final establishment of a dominant positive ego identity, the age in which 'tu-ism' replaces narcissism, the age in which sexual development dovetails into the development of object relationships leading to the mature, adult stage of impersonal object love (alloerotism) and unhampered orgastic heterosexuality.

Adrenalin A proprietary brand of *epinephrine* (q.v.)

adrenergic A term used for all nerves which release sympathin at their terminals; viz. the postganglionic sympathetic fibers, excluding those to the sweat glands and certain blood vessels. It is believed that central sympathetic nervous system fibers may also be adrenergic.

adrenochrome See *psychotomimetic.*

adrenocorticotropic hormone ACTH; one of the anterior pituitary hormones. See *syndrome, general adaptation.*

adult, feebleminded A feebleminded person over the age of sixteen. (Tredgold, A.F. *A Text-Book of Mental Deficiency,* 6th ed., Wood, Baltimore, 1937) The English legal definition of an adult feebleminded person is as follows: 'Persons in whose case there exists mental defectiveness which, though not amounting to imbecility, is yet so pronounced that they require care, supervision, and control for their own protection or for the protection of others.'

adultomorph (à-dul'tō-morf) A term suggested by Dr. L. Kubie to designate those psychoanalysts who, according to him, audaciously interpret in public the phantasies ascribed to infants and analyze them in terms of adult verbal logic. Sladen identifies this group with the so-called anthropomorph of the last century and expresses an adverse opinion of them. Many other authors, nevertheless, give considerable credit to this adultomorph group and accept their theories as important basic principles in the science of modern infantile psychiatry. (Sladen, F.J. *Psychiatry and the War.* Thomas, Springfield, Ill., 1943) See also *anthropomorph.*

adultomorphism Interpretation of the behavior of children in terms of adult behavior.

advantage by illness See *illness, advantage by.*

adventurousness The condition characterizing the child in the preschool period in which there is an urge to rough-and-tumble freedom and curiosity. This involves the need of using the larger muscles rather than the smaller ones. Activities such as climbing, running, tricycle riding, ball playing, the use of big toys, the need to touch and handle everything within reach, and wandering away in search of new adventures characterize this period. The short span of attention required produces a rapid shifting from one activity to another. See *wanderlust.*

Adx A Rorschach scoring symbol for a response of a part or a detail of an animal where most subjects would see the whole animal; also known as an oligophrenic response.

adynamia (ad-i-nā′mi-à) Weakness; asthenia; a common symptom among psychiatric patients.

aedoeomania (ē-dē-ō-mā′ni-à) *Obs.* Nymphomania.

aelurophobia (ā-lūr-ō-fō′bi-à) *Ailurophobia* (q.v.)

aero- (ā-ĕr-ō-) combining form meaning *air,* from Greek, *aĕr,* air.

aero-acrophobia (-ak-rō-fō′bi-à) Fear of open, high spaces: the morbid dread of being at a great height such as occurs when one is in an airplane. This malady should not be confused with air-sickness, which is a disturbance of vertigo-type.

aëroasthenia (-as-thē′ni-à) See *aëroneurosis.*

aëroneurosis (-nū-rō′sis) A form of psychoneurosis, perhaps an actual neurosis, said to occur among aviators; the symptoms are anxiety, restlessness, and varying physical phenomena.

aërophagia (-fā′ji-à) The swallowing of air is of psychological importance particularly in those patients who have a so-called complex about being pregnant. In the belief, generally unconscious, that

pregnancy is the result of oral activity (eating), the individual may swallow great amounts of air and therefore feel, though she does not relate the two, that she is pregnant. Sometimes the abdominal enlargement is misleading. Often associated with the vicarious pregnancy is the fear of it, giving rise to an inordinate release of air from the body. The condition may be observed in men who have a marked feminine component. Psychic bisexuality is not at all rare.

aërophobia Morbid dread of air is a relatively rare symptom in psychiatric disorders, although the fear of air in motion (drafts) is not uncommon among those who in general are regarded as average or normal. Sometimes the condition is so pronounced in normal individuals that some doubt may arise regarding the normality of the person expressing the dread. In many instances the fear is related to allegedly deleterious air-borne influences and seems to be allied in principle to the demoniacal ideas of past generations and of primitive peoples. Aërophobia may be related also to functions of one's own body, in that there is fear of one's body odors (from sweat glands and from the gastro-intestinal tract). Fear of the latter may mean to the patient that his body is deteriorating or that the bad air may harm or kill others. The idea of death, to oneself or to another, is often a central theme in aërophobia. In the paranoid form of schizophrenia, persecutors try to harm or kill the patient, or simply to annoy him, by creating bad air about him. Since members of the same sex persecute him and since the bad air is often associated with flatus from the lower intestines, the question of aërophobia as a symbolic expression of anal homosexuality may be raised.

aerumna (ē-room′nà) *Obs.* Melancholia associated with a physical ailment.

aeschromythesis (es-krō-mi-thē′sis) *Obs.* 'A term used by Hippocrates for the obscene language uttered by the delirious or maniacal, especially in puerperal mania.' (Tuke, D.H. *A Dictionary of Psychological Medicine,* vols. 1–2, Blakiston, Philadelphia, 1892)

affect (ă′fekt) The feeling-tone accompaniment of an idea or mental representation. The affects are the most direct psychic derivatives of the instincts and are psychic representatives of the various bodily changes by means of which instincts manifest themselves. The affects regularly attach themselves to ideas and other psychic formations to which they did not originally belong, and as a result their origin and meaning remain hidden from consciousness. The affect itself may thus be conscious although it is typically displaced onto an idea to which it did not originally belong, and the original idea is unconscious. If an affect is completely suppressed, it may appear not as an emotion but rather as physical changes of innervations, such as perspiration, tachycardia, paresthesia, etc. In other cases, especially in catatonic and manic states, the affects may appear without disguise.

The term affect is also used, more loosely, as a class name for feeling, emotion, or mood.

In Burrow's phylobiology: symbolically biased feeling that contrasts with the organism's primary total feeling—the distorted composite resulting when the organism's total pattern of motivation is overtly intercepted and superseded by the symbolic or partitive pattern of behavior. Affect always implies the partitive (personal, projective, symbolic) type of attention that results from the artificial linkage of feeling and symbol. This (affect-symbol) linkage represents a principle of motivation that is now rooted in the behavior of man as a neuro-social mechanism. Synonyms: image-feeling, projective feeling, partitive reaction. (Burrow, T. *The Biology of Human Conflict,* Macmillan, New York, 1937, pp. 165–6)

affectability *Obs.* The state of being able to express emotion or feeling. The expression is seldom employed in psychiatry, although inquiry is frequently made into the emotional susceptibility of the individual.

affectate *Obs.* In psychiatry a rarely used term meaning to arouse feeling or emotion. Its use as an adjective is likewise unusual among psychiatrists.

affectation Artificiality of manner or behavior. Affectation is a form of simulation in that there is a crudely disguised effort to act as someone else, usually for purposes of gaining esteem.

affect-block See *block, affect.*

affect, charge of '. . . that part of the instinct which has become detached from the idea, and finds proportionate expression, according to its quantity, in processes which become observable to perception as affects.' (Freud, S. *Collected Papers,* vol. 4, Leonard and Virginia Woolf and The Institute of Psychoanalysis, London, 1925) See *cathexis.*

affect, detached This is a term used by Freud to explain the psychological theory of obsessions and phobias. An idea which is unbearable to the ego may have its associated affect separated from it, and this affect persists in the psychical sphere. The unbearable idea is thus weakened and remains present in consciousness, detached from all associations. Its affect, now freed from the unbearable idea, attaches itself to other ideas, which are not in themselves unbearable, but which through this 'false connection' grow to be obsessions. The detachment of its affect from an unbearable idea is undertaken as a defense against this idea.

'In all the cases I have analyzed it was in the sexual life that a painful affect— of precisely the same quality as that attaching to the obsession—had originated.' (Freud, S. *Collected Papers,* vol. 1, tr. by Riviere, J., Leonard and Virginia Woolf and The Institute of Psychoanalysis, London, 1924–25)

affect, discharge of This term, employed by Freud, indicates an energetic reaction to an affective experience. This energetic reaction includes the whole range of voluntary and involuntary reflexes, by which, according to experience, the emotions— from weeping up to a clear act of revenge —are habitually worked off.

'If this reaction occurs with sufficient intensity a great part of the affect disappears; common speech bears witness to these facts of everyday observation in the expressions "to cry oneself out," "to storm oneself out." ' (Freud, S. *Collected Papers,* vol. 1, tr. by Riviere, J., Leonard and Virginia Woolf and The Institute of Psychoanalysis, London, 1924–25)

affect, dislocated See *affect, transposition of.*

affect, displacement of See *affect, transposition of.*

affected, germinally This genetic term (equivalent to the German *keimkrank*) qualifies an individual (1) as being heterozygous for some *recessive* morbid character and thus carrying the predisposition for this trait in its genotype without manifesting it phenotypically, or (2) as a homozygote for any kind of hereditary character with *inhibited* manifestation.

affect-energy The energy that comes from the excitement which may be engendered by applying a psychic stimulus to the whole human organism, with all its individual systems. Also called *affective energy.*

affect-hunger See *hunger, affect.*

affect, inversion of When affects are transformed into their opposites, Freud speaks of the *inversion or reversal of affect.* 'If I am conversing with a person to whom I must show consideration while I should like to address him as an enemy, it is almost more important that I should conceal the expression of my affect from him than that I should modify the verbal expression of my thoughts.' (Freud, S. *The Interpretation of Dreams,* 3rd ed., tr. by Brill, A.A., Macmillan, New York, 1933). It is also known as *counter-affect.*

affectio hypochondriaca (àf-fek'tē-ō hē-pō-kôn-drē'à-kà) *Obs.* Hypochondriasis.

affection A general term, implying feeling and emotion, as distinguished from cognition and volition. Baldwin (*Dictionary of Philosophy and Psychology,* vols. 1–2, Macmillan, New York, 1928, p. 23) defines it as 'any states of pronounced feeling. In English usage, the term applies both to the more permanent sentiments (Ger. *Gefühle*), and to passing emotional states (Ger. *Affekte*). The best writers distinguish it from passion, as having less vehemence, and as less distinctly, if at all connected with a sensuous basis.'

affection, masked By this term Stekel describes the kind actions and tender behavior adopted by certain individuals in order to disguise their real inner sentiment of hatred for the person toward whom they act so kindly. It is as if they wore a mask of love to cover the real face of hate. This is clearly illustrated in the following example: A seventeen-year-old patient intensely hated his father, who gave all his attention and preference to the patient's younger brother. Hate against father, brother, indeed his whole family, was a very definite and strong sentiment in this patient, yet he began to act with great kindness and solicitude toward them. He assumed every disguise of tenderness

and by turns 'played the role of the good, the virtuous, the well-behaved and contented lad, hoping he would be able to supplant his brother. He wore the mask of affection, never betraying by so much as a gesture that he detested his brother and the rest of the family.' (Stekel, W. *The Interpretation of Dreams,* Liveright, New York, 1943) See also *reaction-formation.*

affection, partial Suggested by Hirschfeld as synonym for *fetishism* (q.v.).

affective Pertaining to affect.

affective-cathexis (-kà-thek'sis) See *cathexis.*

affective reactions In the 1952 revision of psychiatric nomenclature, this group includes those psychoses which are characterized by a primary, severe disorder of mood and secondary disturbances in thinking and behavior which are in consonance with the affect, viz. manic-depressive psychosis in its various forms and psychotic depressive reaction. Involutional depressive psychoses are kept apart in the 1952 nomenclature, although other systems have included 'involutional melancholia' within the affective psychoses.

affective-sensation See *feeling-sensation.*

affectivity Affectivity is the susceptibility to affective stimuli. Bleuler says that 'every psychism can be divided into two parts, an intellectual and an affective.' He then adds that 'under the term affectivity we comprise the affects, the emotions and the feelings of pleasure and pain.' (Bleuler, E. *Textbook of Psychiatry,* tr. by Brill, A.A., Macmillan, New York, 1930)

affectivity, disturbances of One of Bleuler's fundamental symptoms of the schizophrenias. Typical disturbances include indifference, blunted affect, and shallowness, flatness, and constriction of the affects. Early in the course of the disorder there may be oversensitivity, overlability or sanguineness. Mood is often inconsistent or exaggerated, with a lack of adaptability and of capacity for appropriate modulation of mood-tone. Parathymia, paramimia, disharmony of mood, dissociation of affect and intellect, and contradictoriness of emotional expression are also among the schizophrenic disturbances of affectivity.

affectomotor Characterized by intense

mental excitement and muscular movements. The term conveys the idea that there is inordinate emotional and motor activity. The combination, seldom seen alone, but usually found in conjunction with other symptoms, is common to many psychiatric states, though it has been used to refer to the manic phase of manic-depressive psychosis, much in the same way that the expression 'affective psychosis' has been employed. Both 'affectomotor' and 'affective psychosis' are loose terms when used to designate a specific syndrome.

affect, organ localization of An affect, especially anxiety, can be felt in any organ of the body, but particularly in the organs that are directly supplied by the autonomic nervous system, such as the heart, lungs, stomach, intestines, etc.

affecto-symbolic Burrow's term for the type of behavior that is distorted by emotional bias, associated with the undue attachment of man's feeling processes to symbolic constructs. Contrasted with organismic, orthopathic. Synonym: partitive.

affect-phantasy This expression is used by Jung to denote phantasies that are strongly imbued with feelings. While discussing *participation mystique,* he refers to a primitive tribe to whom a native word means both God and the sun. The belief is held by the tribe that, 'when the sun is up there [high in the heavens], that is not God, but when it rises, that is God (or then it is God).' Jung says that 'it is immaterial to the primitive mind which of these two versions is correct. Sunrise and its feeling of relapse are for him the same divine experience, just as night and its anxiety are one and the same. Naturally his affect is more important to him than physics; therefore he registers his affect-phantasies.' (Jung, C.G. *Contributions to Analytical Psychology,* tr. by Baynes, H.G. and C.F., Kegan Paul, Trench, Trubner, London, 1928)

affect, retention of See *affect, strangulated.*

affect, strangulated *Strangulated affect* is a term used by Freud to indicate the effect upon an affect when it is repressed together with its attached mental content, and thus not permitted free conscious expression. It remains in the unconscious and together with its psychic component produces morbid symptoms.

affect-tonus (-tō′nus) A normal state of stimulation of the affect on a continuously even level, analogous to the normal, stabile, basic muscular and nervous tonus. The 'emotional reactions' represent qualitative and quantitative changes of this basic, normal current.

affect, transformation of Affects may be disposed of in several ways: they may be frankly expressed; they may be 'reduced to zero'; they may be transformed into their opposites. When the affects are expressed through some vicarious agency, they are said to be transformed.

affect, transformation of in dreams In psychoanalytic interpretation it is often found that the feelings that one may really have masquerade in dreams as their exact opposites. The emotion of joy turns up as sorrow. Love is found disguised as the feeling of hatred. Sobs are discovered to be concealed by laughter. This process, usually referred to as the *transformation of an affect (feeling) into its opposite,* is one of the many processes by which the dream obscures its true meaning. If the psychic material out of which the dream is constructed contains an affect that has been repressed, this affect can gain representation in the dream by inversion into an opposite affect.

affect, transposition of Displacement of the affective component of an unconscious idea onto an unrelated and harmless idea, seen typically in obsessive-compulsive and depressive patients.

affectus animi (af-fek′toos ā′nē-mē) (L. 'disposition of mind') *Obs.* A general term for any type of mental disorder.

affinal (a-fī′nal) Related by marriage.

affinity A marriage-partner's relationship contracted with the other partner's (blood-)kindred, by the act of marrying. See *kinship.*

affusion This is a form of hydrotherapy. 'The patient sits or stands in a bathtub. A sheet is placed around the body under the arms, and water at a temperature of 50° to 60° F. is poured from a pitcher from fifteen to twenty seconds. The patient is then rubbed with coarse towels until reaction is obtained.' (Bailey, H. *Nursing Mental Diseases,* 3rd ed., Macmillan, New York, 1935)

after-expulsion Freud uses the term *after-expulsion* synonymously with secondary repression—which is commonly known simply as repression. See *repression*.

after-sensation Continuation of sense impression after stimulation of the sense organ has ceased; after-image.

agapism The doctrine exalting the value of love, especially in its general, nonsexual sense.

agastroneuria (à-gas-trō-nū′ri-à) Neurasthenia of the stomach.

AGCT Army General Classification Test of intelligence, used during World War II and after. It is designed for use with literate adults.

âge critique (äzh krē-tēk′) (F. 'critical age') The menopausal or climacteric period.

âge de retour (äzh dē rē-tōōr′, F. 'age of return') The period of old age or senility, when vital powers begin to be or are diminished.

agenesis, agenisia (à-jen′e-sis, aj-ē-nē′si-à) See *aplasia*.

agenetic Showing defective, or absence of, development of some part or parts of the body.

agent, catalytic In group psychotherapy, a patient who activates catharsis in other patients.

agent provocateur (à-zhäN′ prô-vô-kà-tēr′) (F. 'instigating agent') While writing on *The Etiology of Hysteria*, Freud said that 'you know that in the opinion of the influential school of Charcot heredity alone is to be recognized as the real cause of hysteria, whilst all other harmful influences of the most varying kind and intensity only play the part of exciting causes, or "agents provocateurs."' (Freud, S. *Collected Papers*, vol. 1, tr. by Riviere, J., Leonard and Virginia Woolf and The Institute of Psychoanalysis, London, 1924–25). The term is synonymous with *precipitating cause*.

agerasia (aj-ē-rā′si-à) A youthful appearance in an old person.

ager naturae (à′ger nä-tōō′rī) (L. 'the field of nature') The uterus.

ageusia, ageustia (à-gū′si-à, à-gūs′ti-à) Absence or impairment of the sense of taste; it may be due to disorder in the gustatory apparatus (i.e. the taste buds). It is not uncommon in psychiatric conditions, particularly in depressions; patients frequently refer to the fact that foodstuffs are tasteless. Among depressed patients of the manic-depressive type, the complaint is frequent that there is an absence or deficiency of all somatic sensations, 'as if the entire body were dead,' the sensation of taste included. It appears that ageusia may be emotionally caused. Ageusia is observed also in many other psychiatric syndromes, for example, those characterized by depersonalization, notably hysteria and the schizophrenias.

agglutinations, image Kretschmer says that in dreams and twilight states mental activity appears in the form of sensory images. He says: 'What was thought of during the day in words, at night passes before us in dreams, in a visible series of images. These images sometimes maintain a scenic arrangement, but, with deeper clouding of consciousness, they fall to pieces into fragments of pictures which apparently go on without rules or regulations, and, under the influence of affects, again conglomerate into peculiar image groups, the *image agglutinations*. The faces of several persons, several objects of similar emotional value, in the dreams are seen as one, and are conglomerated into unity; this we call, with Freud, "*condensation*."' (Kretschmer, E. *Hysteria*, tr. by Boltz, O., Nervous & Mental Disease Publishing Company, New York and Washington, 1926)

aggregation Summation; integration; synthesis. Bernard has subdivided evolution into five periods, each of which is a result of aggregation such as occurred when unicellular organisms first colonized to produce multicellular organisms (physical aggregation). In the fifth period, in which man emerges, the aggregation is psychical, occurring through the instinct of gregariousness and leading to the emergence of a 'super-mind.'

aggression, aggressiveness, aggressivity In psychiatry *aggression* is usually defined in connection with its emotional association. In the instinctual psychology of Freud it is postulated that an instinct may undergo four possible vicissitudes: it may revert to its opposite; it may be introjected; it may be repressed; it may be sublimated. These are, as Freud calls them, 'modes of defense against the instincts.' Aggression is sadism; it is one of the primary instincts. When aggression is turned inwardly upon the subject himself it is called masochism.

McDougall believes that sadism and masochism are separate instincts. The one he calls the instinct of self-assertion and the other that of submission.

Aggression signifies action carried out in a forceful way. Freud speaks of an aggressive impulse or instinctual quality, which achieves its highest degree of expression in the form of the death impulse. According to this concept, the self-destructive tendency is innate in every individual; the destructive impulse may be turned away from the individual, as a means of defending one's ego.

Aggressive impulses are biologically determined and, when sublimated, serve to foster progressive and constructive forms of adaptation. The latter is particularly true when the aggressive quality is combined with the tender component, called in general the libidinous impulse.

'If in this instinct we recognize the impulse to self-destruction of our hypothesis, then we can regard that impulse as the manifestation of a *death instinct,* which can never be absent in any vital process. And now the instincts, in which we believe, separate themselves into two groups; the erotic instincts, which are always trying to collect living substance together into ever larger unities, and the death instincts which act against that tendency, and try to bring living matter back into an inorganic condition.' (Freud, S. *New Introductory Lectures on Psycho-Analysis,* tr. by Sprott, W.J.H., Norton, New York, 1933)

Freud says that 'we maintain the hypothesis of a special instinct of aggression and destructiveness in man. . . .' (ibid.)

aggressive instinct See *instinct, death.*

agitation A tension state in which anxiety is manifested in the psychomotor area with hyperactivity (such as handwringing or pacing) and general perturbation.

agitolalia (aj-i-tō-lā′li-à) Agitophasia.

agitophasia (aj-i-tō-fā′zhi-à) Cluttered speech due to excessive rapidity under stress of excitement.

agnosia (ag-nō′si-à) Loss of ability to comprehend the meaning or to recognize the importance of various types of stimulation. The term agnosia is usually confined to loss of recognition of symbols in the non-language field, for auditory and visual agnosias in the language field are essentially aphasias. The most common

agnosias are: astereognosis (tactile agnosia; loss of power to perceive the shape and nature of an object and inability to identify it by superficial contact alone); anosognosia (ignorance of the existence of disease, especially hemiplegia or depersonalization in regard to paralyzed parts of the body); autotopagnosia or somatotopagnosia (impairment in ability to identify or orient the body or the relation of its individual parts); ideational or sensory apraxia is also essentially an agnosia.

In psychiatry, agnosia refers to the loss or disuse of knowledge of objects, when the knowledge appears to have been altered by emotional circumstances. In some schizophrenics, for example, the desire not to know their families produces a special kind of agnosia in that they will maintain that they have no knowledge whatsoever of the parents or siblings who stand before them. Such agnosia is seen also in hysterics, in depressed patients, and in epileptics, and it can be reproduced under hypnosis.

agnosia, social Wilhelm Reich's term for the inability of the psychopath to achieve satisfaction in living.

agnosia, tactile Inability to recognize objects, such as paper, glass, soap, cotton, metals, etc. by touching them.

agnosia, visual-spatial A syndrome described by Paterson and Zangwill consisting of failure to analyze spatial relationships and inability to perform simple constructional tasks under visual control. This syndrome is usually associated with lesions of the posterior portions (occipito-parietal) of the right cerebral hemisphere in right-handed patients.

agoraphobia (ag-ō-rà-fō′bi-à) The dread of open spaces is more common in the psychoneurotic than in other psychiatric syndromes. The patient becomes panic-stricken, sometimes at the thought of, but more often at the impending visit to an open space. As a reaction against such an eventuality he generally remains indoors and prefers to be at home, near the mother or someone possessing a kind, helpful, guiding influence. The symptom has been traced to the childhood bonds obtaining in the mother-sibling relationship.

agrammaphasia (à-gram-à-fā′zhi-à) Ungrammatical, incoherent speech.

agrammatism (à-gram'à-tiz'm) Ungrammatical speech; a form of *aphasia* (q.v.) in which the individual forms his words into a sentence without regard for grammatical rules of declension, conjugation, comparison of adjectives and adverbs, auxiliary verbs, prepositions, conjunctions, articles, etc. With some authors the term is synonymous with *syntactic aphasia* (q.v.). See also *speech disorders*.

agraphia (à-graf'i-à) Loss of the power, or the inability, to communicate (ideas) in *writing,* and thus a subdivision of *aphasia* (q.v.). This is the motor (or expressive) aspect of the ailment of which the sensory (or perceptive) counterpart is *alexia* (q.v.). The inability may involve individual letters, or syllables or words or phrases, as in varieties of aphasia, and is usually attributed to cerebral disorders.

When *agraphia* is not a physiological ailment, but due to psychic or emotional factors and is merely voluntary, it is the graphic counterpart of *mutism* (q.v.). A patient who acknowledged organic ability to write was entirely unable to write a letter or a word, lest, as she thought, it would result in serious harm; she possessed excellent intelligence and manual dexterity. Patients with involutional melancholia are often inhibited emotionally from writing, but the inhibition in this respect is only representative of more or less categorical inhibition. See also *speech disorders*.

agraphia, acquired 'Loss of a previous ability to write resulting from brain injury or brain disease.' (Orton, S.T. *Reading, Writing and Speech Problems in Children,* Norton, New York, 1937)

agraphia, congenital Orton defines congenital or developmental agraphia as 'unusual difficulty in learning to write which is out of harmony with the other intellectual accomplishments and manual skills of the individual.' (Orton, S.T. *Reading, Writing and Speech Problems in Children,* Norton, New York, 1937)

agriothymia (ag-ri-ō-thim'i-à) *Obs.* Insane ferocity. 'Maniacal furor'; at one time synonymous with 'homicidal insanity.' (Tuke, D.H. *A Dictionary of Psychological Medicine,* vols. 1–2, Blakiston, Philadelphia, 1892)

agriothymia ambitiosa (àm-bē-tē-ō'za) The desire to destroy nations.

agriothymia hydrophobica (hē-drô-fō'bē-kà) Irresistible impulse to bite.

agriothymia religiosa (re-lē-gē-ō'zà) 'The irrepressible desire to uproot and destroy other religions and those cultivating them —Mohammedism.' (Tuke, D.H. *A Dictionary of Psychological Medicine,* vols. 1–2, Blakiston, Philadelphia, 1892)

agromania (ag-rō-mā'ni-à) Morbid impulse to live in the open country or in solitude, not infrequently a symptom of schizophrenia.

agrypnia (à-grip'ni-à) *Obs.* Insomnia.

agrypnia excitata (eks-kē-tä'tà) Insomnia associated with mental excitement and listlessness as to surroundings.

agrypnia pertaesa (per-tī'zà) Insomnia due to physical disorder.

agrypnia senilis (se-nē'lēs) Sleeplessness of old age.

agrypnocoma (à-grip-nō-kō'mà) Coma vigil.

agrypnotic (ag-rip-not'ik) Inducing wakefulness; somnifugous; relating to or characterized by insomnia.

ague, leaping (ā'gū) Dancing mania. See *choreomania.*

agyiophobia (à-ji-yō-fō'bi-à) Fear of street; approximately equivalent to *agoraphobia* (q.v.).

aha, ah-hah A term used to refer to a type of experience in which there is sudden insight into or solution of a problem; at a particular moment, the features of the problem suddenly fit together in a unitary pattern.

ahypnia (ā-hip'ni-à) Insomnia.

aichmophobia (āk-mō-fō'bi-à) The fear of pointed objects is not uncommon in many psychiatric syndromes, gaining particular prominence in the compulsive-obsessive psychoneurotic patient. The dread is usually associated with the thought of using the pointed instrument (generally a knife) as an offensive weapon against someone, though it is recognized that there is no patent reason for doing so. The phobia, like most phobias, stems from early parental relationships and is therefore more vividly expressed in the patient's original home, though the fear may extend later to those who represent the members of his former home. The symptom commonly leads to peculiar eating habits, such as eating alone and without silverware, or to the selection of occupations in which dangerous implements or their psychical equivalents (symbols) are not likely to be encountered. Sometimes the most diverse objects, without any reasonable similarity to dangerous instruments, may be feared, causing the patient to remain secluded at home in a relatively bare room. The patient may not feed himself and may go without food unless fed by another, who is not allowed to use a pointed article in the process of feeding. It appears that oral factors and the killing impulse are commonly associated. These patients are severely sadistic in many other forms of activity. They destroy anything resembling harmony in the family and later spread their intense animosity to people in general. Their unbridled sarcasm is but one manifestation of the oral expression of sadism.

aidoiomania (ī-dō-yō-mā′ni-à) Erotomania.

ailment, functional A mild transitory episodic symptom, usually the result of disturbed physiological functioning (pathophysiology). Such disturbed functionings are the visceral components of emotion, or the visceral expression of emotion or emotional conflicts. (Sharpe, E.F., *Collected Papers on Psycho-analysis*. The Hogarth Press, and The Institute of Psychoanalysis, London, 1950) See *neurosis, vegetative*.

ailurophobia (ī-lū-rō-fō′bi-à) Fear of cats. The term is synonymous with galeophobia and gatophobia. The fear of cats has the same psychical significance as the fear of animals in general. It is a fear of being injured by them; usually, upon careful inquiry, it is found that there is dread of injury to a particular part of the body, namely, the genital area or its psychical equivalent. The fear is thought to be related to the conscious fear of, coupled with an equally strong unconscious desire, for sexual congress. Since the fear arises in early childhood, in individuals whose social and extra-familial contacts are markedly restricted, it appears to have parental relationships. The fear is commonly associated also with castration.

aim The expression *aim* is commonly used in psychoanalysis. 'Freud draws a distinction between the sexual object, the source of attraction, and the sexual aim,

the activity in which the impulse manifests itself; the difference between these is evident when one dissociates such an impulse as the masochistic one—i.e., the desire to obtain enjoyment through experiencing submission or pain—from its objective, which may be either a male or female person.' (Jones, E. *Papers on Psycho-Analysis,* 4th ed., Wood, Baltimore, 1938). In general it may be considered that *aim* refers to a tendency, an impulse, a wish. The tendency of the affects is to seek discharge of their tensions or wishes.

'What distinguishes the instincts from one another and furnishes them with specific attributes is their relation to their somatic *sources* and to their *aims*. The source of the instinct is an exciting process in an organ, and the immediate aim of the impulse lies in the release of this organ stimulus.' (Freud, S. *The Basic Writings of Sigmund Freud,* tr. by Brill, A.A., Random House, New York, 1938)

The modes of pleasure during the so-termed infancy period, that is, up to the latency period, chiefly center around the several erotogenic zones (oral, anal, dermal, muscular, etc.). During the latency period much of the energy and pleasure formerly identified with these zones is deflected into sublimations. The relinquishment of energy from the pre-genital areas is called '*aim*-inhibited.' At puberty there is reanimation to a greater or lesser extent of the aim-inhibited tendencies and their somatic manifestations.

aim-inhibited See *aim*.

aim-transference The transfer of an individual's objectives from one life situation to another. The development of aim-transference is encouraged particularly in short-term psychotherapy, when conditions do not permit the development and subsequent solution of the transference neurosis, as defined by psychoanalysts. Aim-transference is illustrated by the case of an 18-year-old schizophrenic male whose mother allowed him no independence. She had dressed and fed the patient throughout his life. The patient himself desired to be independent and in fact wanted to become strong and dominant, like his father. These aims were encouraged in therapy and by the strong male personality of the psychiatrist, who arranged special situations that enabled the patient to become the active leader of a small group. This transfer of early aims to the therapeutic situation constitutes the aim-transference. In the situation described, aim-transference was reinforced by aim-experience, when the therapist maneuvered the environment so that the patient was able to achieve his goals.

akataphasia (à-kat-à-fā′zhi-à) See *acataphasia.*

akatizia (à-ka-tē′zhe-à) Motor restlessness and, specifically, a feeling of muscular quivering; one of the possible complications of treatment with the phenothiazines. Often, the symptom is of such intensity that it becomes 'impossible for the patients to sit still day or night, and which is described by them as more difficult to endure than any of the symptoms for which they had been originally treated. Acquaintance with this symptom of akatizia, which often persists for a considerable time after the drug has been withdrawn, is important because it is sometimes mistaken for an agitated depression and wrongly treated with ECT.' (Kalinowsky, L. *American Journal of Psychiatry, 115:* 294–198, 1958)

Akerfeldt test See *ceruloplasmin.*

akinesia algera (à-kē-nā′sē-à al′ge-rà) This is an expression used by Moebius to designate a clinical syndrome characterized by general painfulness associated with any kind of movements. Moebius restricted the use of the term to those conditions arising on a psychogenic basis; to him it was a manifestation of hysteria.

akinesis, akinesia (ak-i-nē′sis, ak-i-nē′si-à) The absence or diminution of voluntary motion may be occasioned by organic or by psychical factors, or by both. Reduction of voluntary physical activity is very common in psychiatric disorders and ranges in intensity from moderate inactivity to almost complete immobility. As a rule, reduction in mental activity is paralleled by reduction in physical motility. For example, in the stupor phase of the manic-depressive syndrome, there is almost complete physical and mental immobility. There may be a similar psychosomatic reduction in the stupor of the catatonic form of schizophrenia. Occasionally, however, akinesis may be concomitant with a profusion of ideas, as is not uncommonly the case in involutional melancholia.

Akinesis may be circumscribed in the sense that a patient may become immobile in a given setting or while under the influence of a given trend of thought. The schizophrenic patient, for instance, who suddenly becomes immobile when he has the thought that by so doing he also immobilizes all action in the universe serves to exemplify a special kind of selective akinesis. The psychoneurotic patient, whose obsession is to experience death, may lie down as immobile as possible. The idiopathic epileptic individual, in a twilight state, assumes the role of God and stands majestically in the all-powerful pose. From the psychical point of view, most instances of akinesis represent symbolic posturing.

akinetic-abulic syndrome See *syndrome, akinetic-abulic.*

akinetic epilepsy A type of petit mal epilepsy. See *epilepsy.*

akoasm (ak′ō-az'm) White says that an akoasm is an elementary auditory hallucination. 'Such would be simple sounds, as buzzing, crackling, ringing, and the like. The more complicated hallucinations which are conceived by the patient to be "voices"—verbal auditory hallucinations —are known as *phonemes.*' (White, W.A. *Outlines of Psychiatry,* 12th ed., Nervous & Mental Disease Publishing Company, Washington, D.C., 1929)

akoluthia (à-ko-lū′thi-à) Semon's term for a phase of engraphy corresponding to what others have termed 'primary memory' or 'memory in the making.'
'The fact is, we cannot observe mental events in the happening; what we really do is to observe them in retrospect. And yet it is not the kind of retrospect that is usually associated with past events of some time ago; it is more the observing of a point of time intermediate between the present and the past. . . . What we are observing in this case is not the present, nor is it such a past as involves the functioning of memory . . ." (Nicole, J.E. *Psychopathology,* 4th ed. Bailliere, Tindall & Cox, 1947.)

alalia (à-lā′li-à) Speechlessness; loss of ability to talk. It was used in the eighteenth and late into the nineteenth century for what is now generally denoted by *aphasia.* In 1757 alalia was still hardly distinguished from aphonia, as may be gathered from Delius's *De Alalia et Aphonia* (Nova Acta naturae curiosorum, T.VII, Obs. XVIII, Norimb., 1757). At present the *-lalia* frequently used in compositions like *echolalia, bradylalia,* etc., connotes *talking* rather than '*speaking—saying,*' i.e. the exercise of the power of talking as contrasted with the faculty for significant or meaningful speech. See *speech disorders.*

alarm reaction See *reaction, alarm.*

Albright's disease. A syndrome consisting of multiple pseudocysts in the skeleton, segmental pigment disorders of the skin and pubertas praecox; the disease is due to hypothalamic-hypophysial dysfunction.

alcohol-antabuse reaction See *antabuse.*

alcoholic psychoses See *alcoholism.*

Alcoholics Anonymous (A.A.) An organization formed in 1935 by an Akron physician and a New York broker, both former alcoholics, for the purpose of rehabilitating chronic alcoholics. Since its founding, Alcoholics Anonymous has expanded into an international movement. Its principles include: (1) a belief in God or natural law; (2) frank self-appraisal; (3) a willingness to admit and correct wrongs done to others; (4) a trust in mankind, and (5) dedication to the rescue of those who sincerely desire to conquer alcoholism by making them members of the organization as successful abstainers.

alcoholism Alcohol poisoning; the effects of excess intake of alcohol. Various groups are ordinarily considered to fall within the category 'alcoholic psychoses'; in the 1952 revision of psychiatric nomenclature, some of these are classified as acute or chronic brain disorders, while chronic alcoholism is classified as addiction. More detailed description of the various entities will be found in separate listings, as indicated.

The so-called alcoholic psychoses, or forms of reaction to alcohol, are:

1. acute intoxication (see *intoxication, alcoholic*).

2. pathologic intoxication, or mania à potu (see *intoxication, alcoholic*).

3. chronic alcoholism (see *alcoholism, chronic*).

4. *delirium tremens* (q.v.).

5. alcoholic hallucinosis, acute and chronic (see *hallucinosis, alcoholic*).

6. *Korsakoff psychosis* (q.v.).

7. alcoholic dementia (see *dementia, alcoholic*).

8. alcoholic pseudoparesis (see *pseudoparesis, alcoholic*).

9. alcoholic epilepsy (see *epilepsy, alcoholic*).

10. *Wernicke's encephalopathy* (q.v.).

alcoholism, chronic Addiction to alcohol; in the 1952 revised nomenclature of psychiatric disorders, this is considered as one of the sociopathic personality disturbances. A patient is considered to suffer from chronic alcoholism if (1) his use of alcohol is of such extent as to interfere with successful physical, personality, and/ or social functioning and (2) he is either unable to recognize the deleterious effects of his habit or, recognizing them, he is nonetheless unable to curtail his alcohol consumption and continues in an almost compulsive way to drink heavily. This definition thus differentiates the chronic alcoholic from the excessive or 'problem' drinker, who may use alcohol to excess and while under its influence behave pathologically, but who is able to control his drinking once he becomes aware of the possible disastrous effects of his habit.

It has been estimated that there are approximately four and a half million chronic alcoholics in the United States; that the incidence of chronic alcoholism of all degrees is 4390 per 100,000; that the incidence of chronic alcoholism with complications is 1097 per 100,000. While it has been said that 85 per cent of all chronic alcoholics are male, it is generally agreed that the female is beginning to account for a greater percentage of chronic alcoholism than formerly. About 80 per cent of patients fall within the 35 to 50 years age group; those who appear superficially to be chronic alcoholics at an earlier age are likely to be in the psychopathic or schizophrenic groups, and those who are older more commonly have involutional reactions.

Although the psychodynamics of alcoholism are only poorly understood, it is believed that most chronic alcoholics are characterized by a (? constitutional) increase in orality and that the attitudes of their parents are typically such as to frustrate these oral needs. Resultant disappointment and rage must be turned away from those on whom the individual is dependent, leading to tense depression, guilt, and masochism, with a turning to alcohol which (1) physiologically reduces the strength of the drives, particularly the aggressive drives; (2) minimizes the effects of stress; and (3) affords a symbolic substitute for the desired gratification, thus giving a temporary pleasure and elation and allowing a retreat to the original infantile megalomania. Eventually, a pattern is established: frustration brings anxiety and rage, alcohol brings relief, but this is only temporary and does not bring a solution and more alcohol is required, leading to secondary frustration, to anxiety and rage, to more alcohol, etc.

More recently, Williams has postulated that chronic alcoholism is a genetotrophic disease; this may be a more accurate description of what has been described as the constitutional increase in orality. See *disease, genetotrophic.*

alcoholomania (al-ko-hôl-ō-mā'ni-à) *Rare.* A morbid craving for alcoholic beverages.

alcoholophilia (-fil'i-à) *Rare.* Morbid craving for alcohol.

alector (à-lek'tĕr) *Obs.* 'One who is unable to sleep.' (Tuke, D.H. *A Dictionary of Psychological Medicine,* vols. 1–2, Blakiston, Philadelphia, 1892)

Alexander, Franz Hungarian psychoanalyst; trained with Sachs and Abraham in Berlin; in 1929 appointed the first (and to date the only) Professor of Psychoanalysis at the University of Chicago; chief contributions have been in the area of brief analytic therapy and psychosomatic medicine.

Alexanderism This is an older expression, derived from the name of Alexander the Great, defined by D.H. Tuke as 'the insanity of conquest, the irrepressible desire to destroy or exterminate nations.' It was also known as *agriothymia ambitiosa.* (Tuke, D.H. *A Dictionary of Psychological Medicine,* vols. 1–2, Blakiston, Philadelphia, 1892)

alexia (à-lek'si-à) Loss of the power to grasp the meaning of written or printed words; word-blindness; visual aphasia. See *lobe, occipital; reading, disabilities of; speech, disorders of.*

alexia, acquired 'Loss of a previous skill in reading which follows disease or damage to certain parts of the brain.' (Orton, S.T. *Reading, Writing and Speech Problems in Children,* Norton, New York, 1937)

alexia, congenital (cf. *agraphia, congenital*) Orton defines congenital or developmental alexia as 'inability to learn to read with the rapidity and skill which would be expected from the individual's mental age and achievements in other subjects.' (Orton, S.T. *Reading, Writing and Speech Problems in Children,* Norton, New York, 1937)

algedonic (al-jē-don'ik) Characterized by or relating to pleasure and pain, or the agreeable and the disagreeable.

-algesia (-al-jē'zi-à) Combining element meaning pain, from Gr. *álgēsis,* sense of pain.

algesimeter (al-je-sim'ē-tĕr) Same as *algometer* (q.v.).

algolagnia (al-gō-lag'ni-à) Schrenck-Notzing coined the term algolagnia to cover both sadism and masochism. Sadism thus came to be known as active algolagnia, while masochism was called passive algolagnia. (*Zeitschrift für Hypnotismus,* vol. IX, pt. 2, 1899)

algometer (al-gom'ē-tĕr) An instrument which purports to measure sensitiveness to pain in terms of amount of pressure exerted upon the skin by a blunt instrument. It is sometimes called *algesimeter.*

algophily (al-gof'i-lē) *Rare.* A term coined by Féré (*L'Instinct Sexuel,* p. 138), synonymous with masochism.

algophobia (al-gō-fō'bi-à) Morbid fear of pain.

algopsychalia (al-gō-sī-kā'li-à) See *psychalgia.*

alienatio mentis (à-lē-ā-nä'tē-ō men'tēs) (L. 'alienation of the mind') Insanity.

alienation 1. A general term, now largely restricted to forensic psychiatry, indicating mental or psychiatric illness or insanity; when used in this way, alienation is ordinarily qualified by the adjective, mental. 2. The repression, inhibition, blocking, or dissociation of one's own feelings so that they no longer seem effective, familiar, or convincing to the patient. Such alienation of one's own feelings is characteristic of obsessive-compulsive psychoneurosis. It may also be seen in the schizophrenias, but in the latter certain organs, body areas, or even the whole body are often perceived as if they did not belong to the person or as if they were different from the usual. The result is estrangement and depersonalization.

alienist Just as the term alienation in a psychiatric sense has been gradually restricted to the field of medical jurisprudence, so also the expression alienist refers to the specialist in psychiatry from the standpoint of law. It seems, however, that the designation is being used less and less; indeed, some already regard the term as obsolete.

alienus (à-lē-ā'noos) *Obs.* Delirious, maniacal.

allachesthesia (à-làk-es-thē'zhi-à) Referral of a tactile sensation to a point remote from the point of stimulation; allesthesia.

allegorization In 1898 Neisser used this expression to denote the formation of new words or sentences, that is, neologisms, so extensively found in patients with schizophrenia. He spoke of the 'allegorization of a whole process.' The term *condensation* is synonymous with *allegorization* in the sense of Neisser.

allele (a-lēl'), **allelomorph** (a-lē'lō--morf) In genetics these interchangeable terms mean either of two genes which go to different mature germ cells: each gene is an *allele* of, or is *allelic* to, the other.

The two conditions of a character which are developed by allelic genes are usually called 'alleles' too. Brown and blue eyes in man are alleles of each other, as is red and white color in snapdragons. The separation of such allelic genes to different cells is explained by the fact that they occupy the same locus in their respective chromosomes and come together side by side, when the *homologous* chromosomes unite to form a pair (see *homologue*). Obviously alleles must arise by unlike mutations of originally homologous genes located at the same position in a chromosome pair.

Three or more genes occupying the same locus in homologous chromosomes in a species are called *multiple alleles.* The best known instance of multiple alleles in man is the blood groups.

allelic, allelomorphic Pertaining to or having the nature of an *allele* or *allelomorph.*

allesthesia (al-es-thē'si-à) See *allachesthesia.*

allo- (al'ō-) A combining form, meaning different, other.

alloch(e)iria (al-ō-kī'ri-à) A condition, apparently of neural origin, in which the location of touch or pain sensations is transferred to a corresponding place on the part of the body opposite to that stimulated.

allocortex (al-ō-kor'teks) Rhinencephalon; a part of the olfactory and allied systems of the cerebral cortex. The term is used primarily in speaking of the cytoarchitecture, or microscopic structure, of the cortex, in which case the allocortex is contrasted to the isocortex (or neocortex).

alloerotic (al-ō-e-rot'ik) Of or pertaining to the extension of erotism or libido upon other individuals.

alloerotism, alloeroticism The term alloerotism is used principally in psychoanalysis. It expresses the direction of flow of libido away from the subject and toward objects. When the main volume of libido converges upon the individual himself the expression autoerotism is used. The phase of alloerotism sets in at the phallic stage, at which time libido begins to be externalized. The parents are the first principal objects toward whom the libido is directed, but during the latency period the various manifestations of it undergo important modifications; part of the libido is taken up in the further organization of character traits, another portion may contribute to the field of sublimation, while still another division enters into the construction of identifications with others. The objectivation of libido takes the name alloerotism and is the equivalent of Jung's extraversion, save that Jung denies the more or less exclusively sexual connotation of the process.

Jones defines alloerotism as 'erotism in connection with the idea of another human being.' (Jones, E. *Papers on Psycho-Analysis,* 4th ed., Wood, Baltimore, 1938)

'The development of sexuality may be conceived, broadly, as follows: the first stage is autoerotic, although alloerotic stimuli are also present (suckling at the mother's breast, caressing of the infant, etc.'). (Stekel, W. *Bi-Sexual Love,* tr. by van Teslaar, J.S., Badger, Boston, 1922)

allolalia (al-ō-lā'li-à) Any unusual or abnormal state of speech or utterance.

allophasis (al-of'à-zis) *Obs.* Incoherent speech.

alloplasty (al'ō-plas-tē) There is considerable mobility of the libido from one division of the psyche to another, eventuating in a final arrangement. The process of molding psychic structures within the individual is called autoplasty.

At a later period, beginning especially at the latency phase, libido takes an outward course, away from the self and toward other people and things. This objectivation of libido necessitates adapting it to the environment; the process is termed alloplasty.

'Catalepsy and mimicry therefore would be regressions to a much earlier primitive method of adaptation of the organism, an autoplastic adaptation (adaptation by means of alteration in the organism itself), while flight and defense aim at an alteration in the environment (alloplastic adaptation).' (Ferenczi, S. *Further Contributions to the Theory and Technique of Psycho-Analysis*, tr. by Suttie, J.I., Leonard and Virginia Woolf and The Institute of Psychoanalysis, London, 1926)

allopsyche (al-ō-sī′kē) The mind or psyche of another.

all-or-none The principle that, regardless of the intensity of the stimulus, a single neuron reacts either with maximal intensity or not at all.

allotriogeusia (a-lot-ri-ō-gū′si-à) Perversion of the sense of taste.

allotriogeustia (a-lot-ri-ō-gūs′ti-à) 1. Perversion of the sense of taste. 2. Abnormal appetite.

allotriophagy (a-lot-ri-of′a-jē) Morbid impulse to eat unnatural foodstuffs.

allotropy (a-lot′rō-pē) Adolf Meyer's term for *allopsyche*.

alogia (à-lō′ji-à) Speechlessness usually due to intellectual deficiency or confusion. See *speech disorders*.

alogous (al′ō-gus) *Obs*. Unreasonable, irrational.

alpha-arc A term suggested by Frost to refer to the sequence of a stimulus leading to motor behavior via a simple sensorimotor path. Beta-arc refers to arousal of higher cortical paths by the functioning of an alpha-arc (thus leading to a 'sensation' rather than simple 'awareness'), and not by an outside stimulus directly. The term alpha-arc is approximately equivalent to 'immediate response' in Watson's behavioristic psychology, while the term beta-arc is roughly equivalent to Watson's 'delayed response' or 'implicit behavior.'

alphabet and symbols Words spoken or read are but symbols of mental activities. The alphabet originally consisted of symbols for objects or ideas; the addition of graphic tokens for individual vowels and consonants was a much later development. In the Hebrew alphabet, for instance, which is a direct descendant of the first known alphabet, the Phoenician, the *alef* represents graphically an ox, and the *beth* a house. The Chinese ideographs and the hieroglyphics of the ancient Egyptians also are pictographs, or symbolic representations of definite objects. (Brill, A.A. *Basic Principles of Psychoanalysis,* Doubleday, New York, 1949)

alpha rhythm, alpha wave See *electroencephalogram*.

alter-egoism An altruistic feeling for only those individuals who are in the same situation as oneself.

alternative, third A choice outside the two presenting themselves for the choosing. 'One educational method of value in psychotherapy is of introducing the concept of the third alternative. Many patients think of a problem in terms of two alternatives only, and when both alternatives are blocked by external or internal difficulties, they see no way out . . .' By introducing a 'third alternative,' or possibility, the impasse can be broken and new attempts at adjustment can be made. (Levine, M. *Psychotherapy in Medical Practice*, Macmillan, New York, 1943)

altrigenderism (al-tri-jen′dĕr-iz'm) The state of being of or attracted to the other gender. Beginning in the late infantile period the child takes an interest, to a greater or lesser extent, in members of the other *gender,* i.e. of the opposite sex. This term *altrigenderism* is suggested for these natural, wholesome activities between members of the two genders. When the interests become amorous, though not overtly sexual, *heteroerotism* is the proper term. When the sexual element (without sexual congress) enters into these relations, the condition is called *heterosexuality,* while *heterogenitality* as a term is limited to sexual intercourse.

altruism A term coined by the French philosopher, Auguste Comte (1798–1857), who maintained that the chief problem of existence is 'vivre pour autrui' (to live for the sake of others). In psychiatric literature altruism and morality seem to be closely related, if not identical. Bleuler equates altruism with ethics. Freud says that 'a child is absolutely egotistical; he feels his wants acutely, and strives remorselessly to satisfy them.' He adds that 'morality, of course, does not develop simultaneously in all its departments, and furthermore, the duration of the amoral period of childhood differs in different individuals.' (Freud, S. *The Basic Writings of Sigmund Freud,* tr. by Brill, A.A., Random House, New York, 1938)

Bleuler says: 'The ethical impulses are of particular importance for every being living in society. They preserve the community, and hence they often conflict with the interests of the individuals. . . .' (Bleuler, E. *Textbook of Psychiatry,* tr. by Brill, A.A., Macmillan, New York, 1930)

'Freud says that the development from egotism to altruism is brought about through the formation of libidinal ties which inevitably limit narcism. This, according to him, is the only basis for the development of community interest.' (Healy, W., Bronner, A.F., and Bowers, A.M. *The Structure and Meaning of Psychoanalysis,* Knopf, New York, 1930)

alucinatio (à-lōō-kē-nä'tē-ō) Hallucination.

alusia (à-lū'si-à) *Obs.* Insanity; hallucination.

alusia hypochondriaca (hē-pô-kôn-drē'à-kà) Hypochondriasis.

alysm (al'iz'm) Restlessness exhibited by a sick person.

alysmus (al-iz'mus) 'A term for the mental anxiety and mournfulness of spirits generally accompanying disease.' (Tuke, D.H. *A Dictionary of Psychological Medicine,* vols. 1–2, Blakiston, Philadelphia, 1892)

alysosis (à-li-sō'sis) Boredom, sometimes appearing as a central phenomenon in the simple form of schizophrenia. It is also known as *otiumosis.* (Bergler, E. *Psychiatric Quarterly 19,* 38, 1945)

Alzheimer's disease (Alois Alzheimer, German neurologist, 1864–1915) Presenile dementia; a progressive dementia with apraxia and speech disturbances. Symptoms include memory loss, loss of interest, and carelessness which progress until disorientation, epileptiform attacks and, finally, spastic contractures are evident. Family history often reveals some degree of hereditary tainting.

The disease occurs more often in women than in men (in a ratio of 2½ to 1) and begins insidiously between the ages of 40 and 60 (average age at onset, 55 years). At first, there is loss of interest, difficulty in concentration, increased muscle tone, and difficulty in walking; later, suspiciousness and ideas of reference appear. Eventually there is complete disorientation for time, place, and person, and there is marked emotional and intellectual regression. Speech deteriorates progressively from paraphasic talkativeness to isolated words and phrases (logoclonia).

The pathology consists of generalized brain atrophy, most marked in the frontal lobes; microscopically, neurofibrillary tangles are seen to replace the nerve cells and are typically arranged in the form of whorls or baskets. Senile argentophile plaques are also present.

Alzheimer's disease may last anywhere from several months to over 10 years, but the average duration of life once symptoms are discovered is 6½ years. There is no known treatment.

amathophobia (à-math-ō-fō'bi-à) Fear of dust.

amaurosis (am-aw-rō'sis) Complete blindness.

amaurotic family idiocy This is a neurological disease, known also as Tay-Sachs's disease, characterized by progressive degeneration of cerebral neurones, and resulting in blindness, muscular enfeeblement and wasting, and intellectual deficiency.

Emphasis has been placed on the role of heredity. Sjögren believes it is the result of specific changes in the genes, transmitted as a Mendelian recessive.

Four forms are recognized: (1) *infantile form,* originally found mainly among Polish Jews, the symptomatology appearing as early as the third month; (2) *late infantile form,* appearing between the second and fifth years; (3) *juvenile form,* appearing in older children between the sixth and twelfth years was described by Spielmeyer. It resembles the infantile type, shows gradual mental impairment and terminates in blindness and death within two years. Although optic atrophy occurs, there are no changes in the macula lutea; (4) *adult form,* occurring after puberty, though usually not beyond the third decade. Some writers refer to the infantile form only as Tay-Sachs's disease, to the late infantile form as Bielschowsky's disease, to the juvenile form as Vogt-Spielmeyer's disease, and to the adult or tardive form as Kuf's disease.

amaxophobia (à-mak-sō-fō′bi-à) Fear of being in a vehicle.

ambi- Combining form meaning *both.*

ambilevous (am-bi-le′vus) 'Poor in manual dexterity with both hands; "doubly left-handed." ' (Orton, S.T. *Reading, Writing and Speech Problems in Children,* Norton, New York, 1937)

ambisexuality Ferenczi proposed that, from the standpoint of the psyche, the term ambisexuality be used instead of bisexuality. In their earliest manifestations emotions should not be regarded as masculine or feminine; rather they are qualities that have the capacity for association with either masculinity or effeminacy or with both.

ambitendency Although some authors use the term ambitendency in the same sense that they use ambivalency, others seem to imply that an ambitendency is ambivalency in action. Bleuler equates ambivalence of the will with ambitendency.

'Along with this ambivalency there is an *ambitendency* which sets free with every tendency a counter-tendency. With this basal supposition it can be understood why the fluctuation of the manic-depressive is a fluctuation between conditions which are diametrically opposed.' (Jelliffe, S.E. and White, W.A. *Diseases of the Nervous System,* 6th ed., Lea & Febiger, Philadelphia, 1935)

ambition Psychodynamically, ambition represents a fight against *shame* (q.v.) by proving that there is no need to be ashamed any more.

ambition, negative Reik's term used to describe the behavior of the masochistic individual who evades every possibility of achieving his goal: he seems to follow the line of greatest resistance against himself, instead of that of greatest advantage for himself. The negative ambition is a grim reversal of an originally strong and positive ambition, in such a way that every opportunity is missed, every chance of success is turned into failure, every competition is avoided. The individual is 'so excellent a loser that it is to be suspected that he is not a good loser at all.' (Reik, T. *Masochism in Modern Man,* Farrar and Rinehart, New York, 1941)

ambit, partial Burrow's term for the sphere of the organism's partial, false, conditioned mergents. It represents a system of reflexly conditioned habituations which unites or separates clusters of individuals on a partitive or symbolic basis. Contrasted with total ambit.

ambit, total Burrow's term for the sphere of the organism's total or true mergents. It embodies such reaction-patterns as are expressive of an inherent principle of phylo-organismic equilibrium. Contrasted with partial ambit.

ambivalence (am-biv′à-lens), **ambivalency** Bipolarity; the co-existence of antithetic emotions, attitudes, ideas, or wishes toward a given object or situation. The term was coined by Bleuler, who differentiated between affective or emotional ambivalence, intellectual ambivalence, and ambivalence of the will. In current usage, the term ambivalence without further qualification ordinarily refers to affective ambivalence.

Ambivalence is characteristic of the unconscious and of children. Its overt appearance in the adult implies the presence of definite pathology, such as obsessive-compulsive psychoneurosis, manic-depressive psychosis, or schizophrenia.

Ambivalence is one of the fundamental symptoms of schizophrenia (Bleuler), and here it may appear in any one or more of its three forms. In affective ambivalence, the very same concept is accompanied simultaneously by pleasant and unpleasant feelings; thus a patient suffers the most intense anxiety that 'they' will shoot her and yet constantly begs the doctor to shoot her. Another patient professes great love for her nurse and seems, in fact, to be very positively disposed toward the nurse, but in almost the same breath she asks how she can kill her. In ambivalence of the will, the desire to do a certain thing is accompanied by a desire not to do that thing. Thus a patient wants to eat and does not want to eat; or he demands work only to become furious when something is given him to do. In ambivalence of the intellect, an idea appears simultaneously with the counter-idea. One schizophrenic patient, for example, complained that he had no face and yet asked for a razor to shave the beard off his face; another answered, 'Definitely not' when asked directly if he heard voices and when then asked what they said replied, 'Oh, all sorts of things.' Ambivalence of the will and intellect are often at the basis of what is considered to be obsessive doubting in schizophrenic patients.

Affective ambivalence was noted by Abraham to be characteristic also of manic-depressive psychosis, and he described these patients as having a 'constitutional ambivalence of the object cathexis.' Among the psychoneuroses, the obsessive-compulsive group most characteristically shows ambivalence of severe degree. The ambivalence seen in the schizophrenias is often distinguishable from that seen in the manic-depressive and in the obsessive-compulsive groups in that schizophrenic ambivalence tends to be of severer degree, more widespread throughout all the object relationships of the patient, more overtly expressed, and often fully conscious to the patient.

Ambivalence persists normally to some degree throughout life, but even in late childhood it is markedly reduced in comparison to the age period of 2 to 5 years, and in the adult it typically appears in one part in consciousness while the antithetic feeling or idea or goal remains unconscious. Ambivalence first makes its appearance in the oral sadistic stage, when introjection and incorporation are the important methods of forming object relationships. The object relationships of this stage represent the earliest and most extreme form of ambivalence, from which are later derived love and hate.

ambivalent Relating to the co-existence of antithetic emotions.

ambiversion This psychiatric term designates the balance of the two traits, introversion and extraversion. The two main temperamental or personality organizations denoting the person's general attitude to the environment, namely, introversion and extraversion, are present at birth and believed to be constitutional. When, in certain individuals, extraversion and introversion are combined in about equal amounts their personality organization is more properly to be called ambiversion. (Hinsie, L.E. *Understandable Psychiatry,* Macmillan, New York, 1948)

amblynoia simplex et catatonica (am-blē-noi′à) Evenson's term for dementia praecox (the schizophrenias).

amblyopia (am-blē-ō′pē-à) Dimness or partial loss of vision without discoverable lesion in eye structures or optic nerve; often, it appears to develop as a result of intoxication with drugs, including tobacco.

ambulatory insulin treatment See *treatment, ambulatory insulin.*

amelectic (am-ē-lek′tik) *Rare.* Indifferent, careless, apathetic.

ameleia (am-ēl′ē-yà) Indifference.

amenomania (à-men-ō-mā′ni-a) A term introduced by B. Rush to denote a form of monomania, which apparently was the equivalent of what modern psychiatrists call the manic phase of manic-depressive psychosis.

ament (ā′ment) One afflicted with mental deficiency.

ament, facile See *deficiency, mental.*

amentia (à-men′shi-à) Subnormal development of the mind, with particular reference to intellectual capacities. A.F. Tredgold defined amentia as 'a state of restricted potentiality for, or arrest of, cerebral development, in consequence of which the person affected is incapable at maturity of so adapting himself to his environment or to the requirements of the community as to maintain existence independently of external support.' Its synonyms are: feeblemindedness, mental deficiency, intellectual inadequacy, hypophrenia, oligophrenia and oligergasia.

Amentia implies intellectual incapacity prevalent from birth or from the early months of life. Dementia has a wider meaning, being used to designate disorder in the intellectual, ideational, and emotional spheres. When the term dementia is used, there is ordinarily the implication that the individual at one time possessed healthy and relatively intact mental faculties, from which he subsequently regressed. Amentia, however, carries the inference that the intellectual defects have been in evidence since birth or a short time thereafter. The term amentia is more widely used in England than in the United States.

Some authorities use the term amentia as a diagnosis for acute hallucinatory confusion with a toxic-infective-exhaustive etiology. Such use of the word, originating in the Viennese school, has not been generally accepted in the United States.

Tredgold classified the amentias as follows:

A. *Primary or congenital amentia,* based

on numerical deficiency, irregular arrangement, and imperfect development of cortical neurones
1. simple 2. microcephalic 3. mongolian
B. *Secondary or aquired amentia,* based on arrested development of cortical neurones
  I. due to gross cerebral lesions
    4. syphilitic 5. amaurotic 6. hydrocephalic 7. porencephalic 8. sclerotic 9. paralytic 10. other toxic, inflammatory, and vascular
  II. due to defective cerebral nutrition
    11. epileptic 12. cretinous 13. nutritional 14. isolationary or sense deprivative

amentia, acquired Tredgold uses the expression *acquired amentia* (i.e. mental deficiency, oligophrenia) to refer to amentia that is environmentally determined. The expression is now generally replaced by the term *secondary amentia.*

amentia, congenital See *amentia, primary.*

amentia, degree of In England, where 'the legal concept of mental deficiency is that of social incapacity' (Tredgold), three terms are used to designate the degree of mental deficiency: *idiocy, imbecility,* and *feeble-mindedness.* Each of these three grades is subdivided again into *high-, medium-,* and *low-grade.*

In England idiots are defined as 'persons in whose case there exists mental defectiveness of such a degree that they are unable to guard themselves against common physical dangers.' Individuals with an intelligence quotient (I.Q.) of less than 25 are idiots.

Imbeciles are defined as 'persons in whose case there exists mental defectiveness, which, though not amounting to idiocy, is yet so pronounced that they are incapable of managing themselves or their affairs, or, in the case of children, of being taught to do so.' An imbecile possesses an I.Q. of between 25 and 50.

The feeble-minded are legally defined in England as 'persons in whose case there exists mental defectiveness which, though not amounting to imbecility, is yet so pronounced that they require care, supervision, and control for their own protection or for the protection of others, or, in the case of children, so that they appear to be permanently incapable by reason of such defectiveness of receiving proper benefit from the instruction in ordinary schools.'

The general range from the standpoint of I.Q. is from 50 to 90. In America the term *moron* corresponds closely to the English *feeble-minded,* though the I.Q. is usually stated to range from 50 to 75. (Tredgold, A.F. *A Text-Book of Mental Deficiency,* 6th ed., Wood, Baltimore, 1937)

amentia, deprivative When amentia (mental deficiency) 'is due to the lack, or insufficiency, of some constituent of the environment which is necessary for complete development' of the brain, the expression *deprivative amentia* is used. Tredgold, from whom the quotation is taken, says that among the several deprivative factors three are well recognized. First, the involvement of the endocrine glands, particularly the thyroid, associated with cretinism; second, 'some cases of amentia are associated with a marked degree of malnutrition. The cause of this is unknown; it may be some general or special disorder of metabolism; but for the time being such cases, which are uncommon, may be termed *nutritional amentia.*' Third, 'the growth of the brain and mind may be interfered with by a lack of sensory stimuli. It seems clear that afferent impressions impinging upon the cerebral cortex through the avenues of special sense not only play an important part in the development of neuroblasts into neurones, but that they are also very largely the basis of mind, since they constitute the experience indispensable for feeling and thought. A defect or insufficiency of such impressions produces the clinical variety known as *amentia due to sense deprivation or isolation amentia.*' (Tredgold, A.F. *A Text-Book of Mental Deficiency,* 6th ed., Wood, Baltimore, 1937)

amentia, developmental This is an expression used by some authorities to denote mental deficiency that appears to be occasioned in part by germinal and in part by environmental factors. Tredgold feels that 'the essential cause is germinal and there is no adequate reason against including them [such cases] in the primary form' of amentia. (Tredgold, A.F. *A Text-Book of Mental Deficiency,* 6th ed., Wood, Baltimore, 1937)

amentia, eclampsic (ek-lamp'sik) Craig and Beaton say that the term ' "eclampsic" amentia was formerly applied to cases which manifested epileptiform convulsions for a short period only in early infancy, but it is now commonly agreed that no true clinical distinction can be drawn between these and the epileptic group.' (Craig, M., and Beaton, T. *Psychological Medicine,* 4th ed., Churchill, London, 1926)

amentia, ethnic classification of The ethnic classification suggested in 1866 by J. Langdon Down, according to which he differentiated four groups—namely, Mongolian, Ethiopian, Caucasian, and American Indian—has long been abandoned, save that the term *Mongolian type* has been retained.

amentia, exhaustive See *amentia; delirium, collapse.*

amentia, hydrocephalic (hī-drō-sē-fal′ik) Mental deficiency associated with hydrocephalus, that is, excessive cerebro-spinal fluid within the ventricles (internal hydrocephalus) or in the subarachnoid space (external hydrocephalus).

amentia, infective When mental deficiency is determined by arrest of development due to some form of cerebral infection, the expression infective amentia is used. Three forms are usually recognized: meningitic, encephalitic, and hydrocephalic. The term infective is generally synonymous with inflammatory. In present-day nomenclature, such cases would be classified as chronic brain syndrome associated with intracranial infection, with mental deficiency.

amentia, inflammatory See *amentia, infective.*

amentia, isolation See *amentia, deprivative.*

amentia, microcephalic (mī-krō-sē-fal′ik) Mental deficiency associated with microcephaly; ordinarily the greatest circumference of the skull is 17 inches; yet the general configuration of the skull has to be considered when the question of microcephaly is raised; the majority of aments with microcephaly are either idiots or imbeciles.

amentia, mongolian See *mongolism.*

amentia, nevoid (nē′void) Mental deficiency associated with a venous angioma.

amentia, phenylpyruvic (fē-nil-pī-rōō′vik) Mental deficiency (usually idiocy) associated with abnormal quantities of phenylpyruvic acid in the urine. See *phenylketonuria.*

amentia, primary When mental deficiency exists at birth and is 'due to inheritance and to some intrinsic peculiarity of the germ cell, it is called *primary amentia.*' (Tredgold, A.F. *A Text-Book of Mental Deficiency,* 6th ed., Wood, Baltimore, 1937). It used to be known as congenital amentia.

amentia, sclerotic (skle-rot′ik) Mental deficiency associated with cerebral sclerosis or overgrowth of neuroglial tissue.

amentia, secondary When 'there is no abnormal inheritance and no germ peculiarity, but the full development of the brain has been prevented by adverse factors of the environment,' the resulting mental deficiency is called secondary amentia; it corresponds with the older expression acquired amentia. (Tredgold, A.F. *A Text-Book of Mental Deficiency,* 6th ed., Wood, Baltimore, 1937)

amentia, sub-cultural Tredgold says that 'from the psychological aspect, many defectives appear to differ quantitatively rather than qualitatively from their non-defective fellows; indeed, they are often regarded as merely the tail end of a normal variation, and have been termed *subcultural* defectives by Dr. Lewis.'

amentia, syphilitic When mental deficiency is directly associated with syphilis, the condition is known as syphilitic amentia.

amentia, traumatic Mental deficiency connected with cerebral injury.

amimia (à-mim′i-à) A disorder of language, characterized by the inability to use gestures appropriately to conform with the idea to be expressed. The individual may also be unable to imitate or reproduce by motion the facial expressions and gestures of others. He may likewise make the inappropriate or wrong gestures in endeavoring to convey his thoughts or feelings, e.g. shaking his head sidewise when saying yes, and nodding his head in disapproval. This is the motor (or expressive) aspect of amimia. Its counterpart is sensory (or perceptive) amimia when the patient does not understand or assigns a wrong meaning to another's gesture, taking that a sidewise shake of the head means consent, and the other person's nod means disapproval.

The condition is believed to be the result of a neural disorder. It is not observed in the so-called psychogenic disabilities. On the contrary, the capacity to gesticulate and mimic is ordinarily highly developed in psychogenic conditions. See also *speech disorders*.

amine oxidase *Monoamine oxidase* (q.v.).

amnemonic (am-nē-mon'ik) Relating to loss of memory.

amnesia (am-nē'zhi-à) The inability to recall past experiences is widespread among psychiatric disorders. Often the onset is acute, following a psychical or physical trauma severe to the individual. It may develop subacutely (as sometimes occurs in idiopathic epilepsy) or chronically (as in dementia praecox).

When the loss of memory is associated with physical injury, in an individual who prior to the injury had not exhibited any essential psychopathology, the extent of the amnesia in time is generally limited to the more recent and immediate experiences relating to the injury; furthermore, the amnesia is ordinarily complete for all experiences covering the time in question.

When the loss of memory is identified with psychical trauma (loss of a loved one), while the amnesia may include loss of memory for all experiences, generally it is restricted to a loss of memory of experiences directly and remotely connected with the cause of the amnesia. Sometimes, as in states of extreme stupor (manic-depressive) all past experiences are unavailable for recollection.

When the origin of amnesia appears to be essentially endogenous, that is, derived from the unconscious mind of the individual, it may show a peculiarly selective quality. A hysterical mother was unable to recall any part of her life with her husband or child, although her memory was excellent for other experiences extending over the period of time corresponding to her selective or systematized amnesia.

The terms retroactive or retrograde amnesia are used to designate loss of memory for events prior to the onset of the trauma. The patient, while unable to recall those experiences, may still possess good memory for experiences more recent than the trauma itself.

amnesia, anterograde See *amnesia, retrograde*.

amnesia, autohypnotic While discussing the question of forgetting, Jung says that 'normal forgetting is by far the most frequent process, while repression is an artificial loss of memory, an autohypnotic amnesia.' (Jung, C.G. *Contributions to Analytical Psychology,* tr. by Baynes, H.G. and C.F., Kegan Paul, Trench, Trubner & Company, London, 1928)

amnesia, catathymic (kat-à-thī'mik) When amnesia is circumscribed and is limited to a given experience or memory, it is called *catathymic amnesia*. A patient with clear memory for all other events had no memory for circumstances connected with her pregnancy.

'Thus an hysteric suddenly forgot everything that related to her physician, *Janet*, and mistook him for a new assistant physician.' (Bleuler, E. *Textbook of Psychiatry,* tr. by Brill, A.A., Macmillan, New York, 1930)

amnesia, circumscribed See *amnesia, retrograde*.

amnesia, continuous Anterograde amnesia. 'In *continuous or anterograde* amnesia the subject forgets every experience nearly as fast as it happens.' (Prince, M. *The Unconscious,* Macmillan, New York, 1916)

amnesia, episodic M. Prince says that 'in the first two types [episodic and epochal] the experiences which are forgotten may have occurred during the previous normal condition. In the episodic the particular episode which is forgotten may have been, strangely enough, one which from the very important part it played in the life of the subject and its peculiar impressiveness and significance we should expect would be necessarily remembered, especially as memory in other respects is normal.' (*The Unconscious,* Macmillan, New York, 1916)

amnesia, epochal M. Prince writes that 'in the epochal type of amnesia a person, perhaps after a shock, suddenly loses all memory for lost *epochs;* it may be for days and even for years of his preceding life. In the classical case of Mr. Hanna, studied by Boris Sidis, the amnesia was for his whole previous life, so that the subject was like a new-born child.' (Prince, M. *The Unconscious,* Macmillan, New York, 1916)

amnesia, feigned 'Amnesia is more frequently alleged [i.e. feigned] than any other mental anomaly. It is obviously a convenient defense, and it is a simple matter for a person accused of a serious crime to assert that he has no memory whatever concerning it. The first thing to decide in such a case is the presence or absence of those disorders which experience suggests may be associated with some degree of amnesia: alcoholism, epilepsy, hysteria, melancholia, mania, confusional insanity, dementia praecox, dementia paralytica, senile dementia, and amentia.' (East, W.N. *An Introduction to Forensic Psychiatry in the Criminal Courts,* Wood, Baltimore, 1927, p. 354)

amnesia, hysterical Loss of memory concerning a particular period of past life or certain situations associated with great fear or shameful humiliation. There is a peculiarly selective or systematized quality to this variety of amnesia.

amnesia, infantile Amnesia for the period of infancy and early childhood, i.e. from birth to the end of the fifth year of life. Memory for this period of our lives is practically nil and even those few isolated fragments which some people believe they can remember 'as clearly as though it were yesterday' are seldom wholly accurate.

The infant's mind contains much material which, innocent though it may be in the infancy period, is unacceptable to adult standards. The expression of this material is vigorously discouraged and sometimes even brings on punishment, and this acquaints the child with the fact of its unacceptability to adults. Through the mental mechanisms of suppression and repression the unacceptable forbidden material becomes buried in the unconscious, together with all material in association with it. Infantile mental processes involve potential trends and wishes which are denied gratification because of unacceptability according to adult standards.

Jones writes: 'Early training largely consists in weaning the child from these desires and directing his mind towards other interests; the chief of these processes Freud terms "sublimation." The primitive trends themselves . . . have to be suppressed, and the mental processes representing them are repressed and become unconscious. This, however, is not effected without a certain cost to the individual and amongst other penalties paid is the amnesia for infantile mental life.' (Jones, E.J. *Papers on Psycho-Analysis,* Williams and Wilkins, Baltimore, 1949)

amnesia, negativistic A condition in which the delusion is held that memory and orientation are lost.

amnesia, post-hypnotic Loss of memory for events transpiring during the hypnotic stage.

'But if we avoid using any kind of suggestion, then, in some cases, chiefly in the deepest hypnosis, memory of even the hypnotic proceedings cannot be recalled after awakening.' (Moll, A. *Hypnotism,* tr. by Hopkirk, F., Scribner's, New York, 1909)

amnesia, retrograde Amnesia means loss of memory. Generally the beginning of the loss of memory is moderately well delimited; the same may be said about the termination. One then speaks of circumscribed amnesia. When the amnesia extends backward, so to speak, to include material antedating the onset of amnesia proper, it is called retrograde amnesia. When the amnesia encompasses material subsequent to the onset of amnesia it is termed anterograde amnesia.

amnesia visualis verbalis (vis-ū-à'lis ver-bàl'is) Witmer's term (1907) for a type of *reading disability* (q.v.).

amnestia (am-nest'i-à) *Obs.* Older term for *amnesia* (q.v.).

amnestic aphasia See *aphasia, amnestic.*

amnestic apraxia See *apraxia, amnestic.*

amniotic (am-ni-ot'ik) Equivalent of *intra-uterine.*

amok See *amuck.*

amoker One who runs amok.

amoralia (à-mō-ral'i-à) *Obs.* Moral imbecility.

amor lesbicus (à'môr les'bi-koos) Sapphism.

amphierotism (am-fi-er'ō-tiz'm) A term coined by Ferenczi to indicate the condition in which an individual is able to conceive of himself as a male or female or both simultaneously.

amphigenesis (am-fi-jen'ē-sis) Amphigenesis is a form of sexual inversion in which an individual, predominantly homosexual, is able also to have sexual relations with members of the opposite sex. Thus one speaks of amphigenic inversion in contradistinction to absolute inversion, in which sexuality is restricted to the members of the same sex only.

amphimixis (am-fi-mik'sis) 1. A term used to indicate the fact that both parents contribute to the inheritance of their offspring. 2. Ferenczi's term for the union and integration of the component instincts (oral, anal, and urethral) into the genital function. The genitals attain their specific importance only when the earlier phases have been more or less surmounted and the genitals become the leading sexual zone and the central organ for discharging the entire libido. After puberty, the residues of the earlier developmental phases find expression in preparatory activities (forepleasure) and serve merely to stimulate the genital strivings.

amuck Bleuler says that 'on the basis of two clear-cut cases *Kraepelin* would like to class with epilepsy the *running amok* of the Malays, in which the patients run through the streets with drawn daggers, cut people down at random until they collapse, or, which is more frequent, are shot down or made harmless in some other way.' (Bleuler, E. *Textbook of Psychiatry,* tr. by Brill, A.A., Macmillan, New York, 1930)

amusia (à-mū'zi-à) Musical inability, whether for perception or (re)-production of musical (or vocal) sounds.

amychophobia (à-mi-kō-fō'bi-à) Morbid fear of being scratched.

amygdala (à-mig'dà-là), **amygdaloid nucleus** A part of the basal ganglion complex; the amygdala is a small, discrete, nuclear mass situated on the roof of the temporal horn of the lateral ventricle at the inferior end of the caudate nucleus. It projects directly to the hypothalamus, and interruption of these connections gives rise to sham rage. See *rhinencephalon.*

amygdaloidectomy (a-mig-dà-loid-ek'tō-mē) Ablation of the amygdaloid nucleus; this psychosurgical procedure has been used particularly in hallucinating patients, in the belief that the amygdaloid nucleus is a mechanism for transforming thought processes into temporally patterned motor movements. either of the vocal musculature as in subjective auditory experiences, or of the still vaguer projections or representations experienced through vision, smell, taste, or touch.

amyostasia (à-mi-ō-sta'zhē-à) Muscle tremor.

amyosthenia (à-mi-os-thē'nī-à) See *aphoria.*

amyotony (à-mī-ot'ō-nē) See *aphoria.*

amytal interview (am'i-tal) See *narcotherapy.*

An Rorschach scoring symbol for anatomy response.

anabolic (an-à-bol'ik) Pertaining to or characterized by anabolism. In constitutional medicine the term is more specific, applying to the theories of Pende, who believes 'that it is becoming more and more possible to place the entire analysis and interpretation of human individuality upon the fundamental principle of rhythm and anabolic-catabolic balance of material metabolism.' (Pende, N. *Constitutional Inadequacies,* tr. by Naccarati, S., Lea & Febiger, Philadelphia, 1928)

'It is upon this orientation of the metabolism of matter and energy, which varies with the individual not only in the organism considered as a whole, but also in the separate organs and tissues, that both the functional orientation of the organism in its entirety and of its organs and tissues, as well as the psychic orientation and character depend.' (ibid.)

The anabolic biotype is the fundamental underlying biotype to which the more superficial characterizations of the types called *megalosplanchnic, brachymorphic* and *parasympathicotonic* (q.v.) are related. See *type, pyknic; pyknic.*

anabolism Biochemical changes by which food is converted into living materials within a cell or the combination of cells forming an organism.

anaclinic (an-à-klin'ik) See *anaclitic.*

anaclisis (à-nàk'li-sis) A reclining. The infant is dependent upon its mother or a substitute for its well-being and sustenance. Such dependence is called anaclitic. Some individuals continue throughout life to depend upon others for physical and emotional support. The term is used in psychiatry almost exclusively from the emotional point of view. Individuals who lean emotionally on others are anaclitic. The term would be applied, for instance, to the passive, effeminate husband whose feelings, actions and thoughts are largely regulated by a dominant wife.

'These attachments are likely in the beginning to be strongly anaclitic in nature; the child will turn first to those who assist it in its helplessness and gratify its self-preservative needs.' (Healy, W., Bronner, A.F., and Bowers, A.M. *The Struc-*

ture and Meaning of Psychoanalysis, Knopf, New York, 1930)

According to Jones, anaclisis is the process of the sexual drive becoming attached to and exploiting various nonsexual self-preservative trends such as eating and defecation.

anaclitic, anaclinic (an-à-klit'ik, -klin'ik) Relating to or characterized by anaclisis or dependence upon another or others; characterized by dependence of libido on another instinct, e.g. hunger.

'If we could speak of "object choice" in this early stage of infancy, we would say that the first object choice is an anaclitic one, in which the individual leans on another object for gratification of hunger, bodily needs, for protection, and the like.' (Nunberg, H. *Principles of Psychoanalysis,* International Universities Press, 1955)

anaesthesia See *anesthesia.*

anagogy, anagoge (an-a-gō'jē) The term anagogy, but more frequently its adjective anagogic, is used in psychoanalytic psychiatry to indicate psychic material that is expressive of ideals. Silberer believes that dreams are susceptible of two different interpretations. One of the interpretations is that usually ascribed by psychoanalysts, namely, infantile sexual interpretation. The other is related to the spiritual, idealistic, non-sexual forces of the unconscious; hence, the expression anagogic interpretation. The latter is of the kind stressed by Jung in his understanding of deeply lying forces in the unconscious.

'The other, the more important interpretation, which he (Silberer) calls the *anagogic* interpretation, reveals the more serious and often profound thoughts which the dream-work has used as its material.' (Freud, S. *The Interpretation of Dreams,* 3rd ed., tr. by Brill, A.A., Macmillan, New York, 1933)

analeptic (an-à-lep'tik) A stimulating or restorative drug, such as caffeine or amphetamine.

anal-erotic Relating to libidinal phenomena of the anal zone.

anal-erotism According to psychoanalytic formulations, during the infancy period, libido spreads diffusely over the body, but certain areas, known as erotogenic zones, take up a large quantity of libido. Three such zones merit special consideration: the oral, anal, and genital. The earliest

concentration of libido is in the oral zone; with further development most of the oral libido shifts to the anal region, which in turn gives up a fair portion of its libido to the third or genital area.

The localization of libido in the anal zone is known as anal erotism. According to psychoanalysts this phase of libidinal organization assumes great importance, not only during the phase of so-called infantile sexuality, but throughout the rest of life. The libido which is originally connected with the anal zone subsequently goes over into other services. Part of it, for instance, becomes attached to the habits and disciplines identified with anal training (regularity of stool, etc.); hence, regularity of action later becomes incorporated in the personality without conscious recognition of its original manifestation. Regularity, punctuality and allied character traits are therefore also called anal-erotic. Another part of anal libido shifts over to the genital zone, or, as it is called during the infancy period, the phallic zone. A third part remains in more or less original form, in the anal zone.

Psychoanalysts place great stress not only on the function of the anal structure but also on the results (feces) of anal activity. 'Thus the interest in feces is carried on partly as interest in money, partly as a wish for a child, in which latter an anal-erotic and a genital impulse ("penis-envy") coincide.' (Freud, S. *Collected Papers*, vol. 2, tr. by Riviere, J., Leonard and Virginia Woolf and the Institute of Psychoanalysis, London, 1924–5, p. 169)

analfabetia partialis (à-nal-fa-bet'i-à pàrtē-à'lis) Wolff's term (1916) for a type of *reading disability* (q.v.).

analgesia, analgia (an-al-jē'si-à, à-nal'ji-à) Loss of the sense of pain. Analgesia may be of somatic or of psychic origin. It possesses psychiatric significance particularly in conversion hysteria, although the term is not as often seen today as it was in former years. Analgesia may be experimentally induced by hypnosis. Diminution of the sense of pain is not uncommon in advanced states of schizophrenia; its meaning in the latter condition is undetermined.

Older forms of the word are analgia and analgesthesia.

Analgesia refers to the absence of pain sensation brought about by some endogenous cause. Absence of pain sensation may also be induced by an exogenous agent, usually called an anodyne.

'Nothing is more common than hysterical anaesthesia or analgesia.' (Freud, S.)

anality A general term referring to the anal components of sexuality, to manifestations of instinctual conflict centering about the anal stage of sexual development, to manifestations of anal erogeneity which indicate fixation at the anal stage of development. Anality is prominent in obsessive-compulsive neurosis, hypochondriasis, and masochism. See *anal erotism*.

analogue, libido This is an expression introduced by Jung (analytical psychology) to refer to 'the symbol which converts energy.' He adds that 'by this I define a representation that is suited to express the libido equivalent, by virtue of which the libido is led over into a form different from the original one. Mythology offers innumerable images of this sort, ranging from sacred objects like *churingas,* fetishes, etc., up to figures of gods. The rites with which the sacred objects are surrounded often disclose very plainly their character as transformers of energy. Thus, for example, the primitive rubs his *churinga* rhythmically and thereby takes into himself the magic power of the fetish, at the same time imparting a fresh "charge" to the fetish.' (Jung, C.G. *Contributions to Analytical Psychology,* tr. by Baynes, H.G. and C.F., Kegan Paul, Trench, Trubner, London, 1928)

anal-sadism See *sadism, anal.*

anal-sadistic Relating to anal-sadism or the aggressive instinctual quality identified with the anal region and its functions.

anal triad See *triad, anal.*

analysand (à-nal′i-zand) The one who is being analyzed.

analysis A word of widespread use in psychiatry and psychoanalysis: (1) alone in the more specific sense of psychoanalysis; (2) in combination with various modifying adjectives or phrases; (3) in its root, to form other derivative words.

analysis, active A method of dream interpretation used in a technique in which the analyst does not confine himself to the mere passive elucidation of the patient's free associations but intervenes directly and actively, making revelations and giving advice suggested to him mainly by the manifest content of the dream. This method, introduced by Stekel, is also called 'active analytical psychotherapy.' It constitutes a departure from the passive method of free association, and it is, indeed, 'an interpretation which lays more stress upon the manifest content of the dream' than on any other factor. Critics of this method emphasize the fact that it constitutes an 'intuitive' technique and that this 'intuitive power' cannot be taught to other analysts. Stekel admits that the 'imaginative insight into the workings of the dreamer's mind' is an essential factor. In the active analytical method the psychiatrist is concerned with 'interpretation that he has enucleated as much as possible from the symbolical wrappings without any aid from the patient.' Referring to this method, Gutheil is of the opinion that dream interpretations 'will not become a teachable and learnable science until one's technique of interpretation has grown independent of associations and other remarks of the patient, except for the trifling items of information about persons and things. In that event the interpretation will certainly become less copious, but more trustworthy.' (Gutheil, E.A. *The Language of the Dream,* Macmillan, New York, 1939.) In such circumstances, of course, the interpretation of dreams will rather depend on the interpreter's perspicacity and intuition, as the two qualities essential in the technique of active analysis. (Stekel, W. *The Interpretation of Dreams,* Liveright, New York, 1943)

analysis, anamnestic (an-am-nes′tik) Investigations of the mental history of an individual, partly derived from the subject himself, partly from his associates, constitute what is called anamnestic or mental analysis. The expression is used by Jung to distinguish his methods from those of Freud. Jung says: 'The third method of anamnestic analysis is of greater importance, both as a method of investigation and of therapeutics. It practically consists in a careful anamnesis, or reconstruction of the historical development of a neurosis.' (Jung, C.G. *Contributions to Analytical Psychology,* tr. by Baynes, H.G. and C.F., Kegan Paul, Trench, Trubner, London, 1928)

Strictly speaking, all mental analyses are anamnestic; they are simply given other names to indicate special points of view.

analysis, character Psychoanalysts believe that the main volume of personality characteristics is the consequence of the libidinal organization of the first four or five years of life. Instinctual qualities first infuse the soma, that is, the erotogenic zones; a certain quantity of the instincts remains attached to those zones, while the rest becomes attached to the psychical representations of the zones and to other mental processes. The principal dynamisms involved are reaction-formation, symbolization, sublimation, and identification. The degree and nature of these dynamisms comprise the index for normal or abnormal. Psychoanalysts do not attempt to define normality. Abraham implies a definition when he speaks of 'a relative success in overcoming the more primitive types of mental structure.' (Abraham, K. *Selected Papers,* tr. by Bryan, D. and Strachey, A., Leonard and Virginia Woolf and The Institute of Psychoanalysis, London, 1927)

Certain individuals develop character traits or personalities that exhibit wide variations from the average of well-adjusted people, but they do not show symptom-formations characteristic of the well-defined psychiatric classifications. The personality traits themselves constitute the equivalent of a neurosis; thus, one speaks of a character neurosis. The psychoanalyst analyzes character traits, not only morbid symbolic representations such as compulsions, obsessions, phobias, delusions, or hallucinations. See *defense, character.*

Character analyses are undertaken also by specialists in other psychological disciplines. Jung, Adler, Meyer, Stekel, and others analyze from their particular points of view.

analysis, child The term is used chiefly in psychoanalysis, though in a generic sense it may be applied to mental analysis from any point of view. In the field of psychoanalysis it had its start in Freud's *Analysis of a Phobia in a Five-Year-Old Boy.* It is used simply to distinguish adult analysis from child analysis. Comparatively very little work has been done to date in child analysis. Melanie Klein led the way; she has been followed in this field by several others.

'Analyses of children yield very interesting results. Possibly, in the future, they will grow in importance. As far as theoretical findings are concerned, there can be no doubt as to the value of these analyses.' (Freud, S. *The Problem of Lay-Analyses* Brentano, New York, 1927)

'Although we have had as yet only a few years' experience in this work, the results, so far, have been most promising and instructive.' (Jones, E. *Papers on Psycho-Analysis,* 4th ed., Wood, Baltimore, 1938)

The technique carried out in children is quite different in many respects from that carried out in adults. For example, Anna Freud says of the analyst that 'he must analyze and he must educate, must in one breath permit and forbid, loosen and hold in check again.' Melanie Klein has done extensive experimental work under the heading of play technique.

analysis, content Interpretation of a subject's production on the basis of what is said, rather than on the basis of how it is said. The interpretation of symbols in a patient's dream, for example, is content analysis. Lindner advocated the use of content analysis as a supplemental technique to the more formal analytical procedures in interpretation of the Rorschach test. He isolated 43 responses which were said to be characteristic of specific diagnostic groupings and/or to indicate essential motivants and dynamisms.

analysis, direct Direct analysis, or direct analytic therapy (as Federn termed it), is a method advocated by Rosen for treatment of schizophrenics. The method consists essentially of the therapist's entering into the patient's delusional reality and making direct interpretations of the patient's unconscious based upon the therapist's guess as to what the important and significant psychodynamics might be. The unparalleled success claimed originally for the technique has not been substantiated or verified by independent investigators.

analysis, distributive This is an expression used in objective psychobiology. The analysis of information gained about the patient 'is distributed by the physician along the various lines which are indicated by the patient's complaints and symptoms, by the problems which the physician himself can recognize, by the patient's imaginations concerning the present and the past as well as by actual situations, attitude to the future and outstanding features of his personality.' (Diethelm, O. *Treatment in Psychiatry,* Macmillan, New York, 1936)

analysis, ego In the early years of psychoanalysis, attention was paid largely to the understanding of the components of the unconscious. Later, the elements of the conscious sphere and, still later, those of the environment became the objects of investigation. In psychotherapeutic practice the course of action is reversed, in that the analysis proceeds from environmental to ego to id factors. The analysis of ego components (ego-ideal, ego proper, superego) is called ego analysis. In a transference neurosis the greater volume of analysis refers to the relationship between the ego and the id; in a narcissistic neurosis between the ego and the superego; and in the psychosis between the ego and reality.

analysis, existential See *existentialism.*

analysis, fractional A technique employed by Alexander as one of his brief therapy methods. In fractional analysis, psychotherapy is suspended for calculated intervals, while the patient works through insights already attained and prepares himself for gaining more.

analysis, group Analytic group psychotherapy. See *psychotherapy, group.*

In Burrow's phyloanalysis, the term refers to the investigation of the impairment of co-ordinate group function.

analysis, minor This term describes a psychotherapeutic method in which the analysis of psychic material is rather minor: it attempts neither an exhaustive study of (as does Freudian analysis in general) nor deeper delving into the subconscious conflicts of the individual, but confines itself only to the elucidation of the salient details considered of primary importance in relation to the neurosis and the individual's personality conflict. In minor analysis the method employed is, of course, of shorter duration than in the so-called orthodox, or Freudian, psychoanalysis, with the analyst's intuition and perspicacity playing a leading role in this technique. Through the interpretation of the most conspicuous of the psychic materials the analyst arrives at conclusions, makes revelations, and gives suggestions with the aim of enabling the patient to gain a quick insight into his troubles. (Stekel, W. *The Interpretation of Dreams,* Liveright, New York, 1943)

analysis, orthodox The strictly Freudian analysis, better known as psychoanalysis, and constituting the science of the function of the unconscious. It uses primarily the technique of free association, interpretation of dreams, and elucidation of everyday mistakes in order to unmask the patient's unconscious motivations. The psychic material obtained in this manner is then made available to the patient, in order to prompt the emotional acceptance rather than the intellectual knowledge of his conflicts. It must be emphasized that the patient gains very little from the intellectual knowledge of his conflicts; what really counts and helps is the release of tension through emotional acceptance. 'It is not so important that the patient knows as that he *feels* the forgotten wish or experience.' Psychoanalytical education is conducted in various centers and institutes and is based on the training of students in Freudian theories and techniques, with a prerequisite that every student undergo a complete analysis himself, which is called 'didactic analysis.'

analysis, passive Stekel uses this expression to describe the feature of Freudian psychoanalysis which calls upon the psychiatrist to wait patiently for the production of free associations by the individual and subsequently to interpret them without active intervention. Departing from this technique, Stekel has introduced his own method of active psychoanalytical therapy, in which the analyst arrives at conclusions without the help of the patient's associations, simply by resorting to the study of the manifest content of dreams. Stekel asserts that if 'we follow the plan of waiting for free associations, the patient will take advantage of our inactivity in order to circumvent us.' In a general sense, Stekel and his disciples employ the term passive analysis as synonymous with Freudian *orthodox psychoanalysis.* See *analysis, orthodox.* (Stekel, W. *The Interpretation of Dreams,* Liveright, New York, 1943)

analysis, Schicksal Szondian depth analysis, an eclectic system that borrows heavily from Freudian and Jungian psychology and further emphasizes the 'familial unconscious,' or hereditary tendencies. See *test, Szondi.*

analysis, self The analysis of oneself, that is, of one's psychic components. According to the most acceptable doctrines today, self-analysis cannot be expected to be successful save in the understanding of the most superficial aspects of oneself. It has psychotherapeutic value only in this meager way and is regarded by psychiatrists as merely an adjunctive procedure.

analysis, structural A type of psychotherapy described by E. Berne (*American Journal of Psychotherapy 11,* 293–309, 1957), based on the belief that psychiatric disorders arise from pathological relationships between the various ego states: exteropsychic (Parent), neopsychic (Adult) and archaeopsychic (Child). Structural analysis aims at strengthening the boundaries between these states so that the Adult can become the effective executive of a healthy way of living.

analysis, training See *analysis, tuitional; analysis, orthodox.*

analysis, tuitional A term used by Ferenczi to refer to character analysis carried out for purposes of training the individual in the concepts and problems of psychoanalysis (Freudian) through personal analysis of the individual. The analysand is in the position of a student who pays tuition for his instruction.

analysis, vector Alexander's term for the process of determining the degree of participation of the organism's basic tendencies—reception, elimination, and retention—in the genesis and development of neurosis.

analyst One who analyzes, that is, resolves a whole into its parts. In psychiatry today there are four main classes of analysts of the psyche, according to the schools they represent. While the term psychoanalyst has its generic meaning, it is understood today to refer to those who adhere to the formulations of the psychoanalysis of Freud. Analysts who follow Jung's concepts are called analytical psychologists; those who use the concepts of Meyer are psychobiologists; those following Adler are individual psychologists.

analyst, lay See *psychiatrist.*

analytical Relating to analysis or to the resolution of something into its parts.

analytic group psychotherapy See *psychotherapy, group.*

analytic psychology Jung's system of psychology, which, compared with Freudian psychoanalysis, minimizes the role of sexuality in emotional disorders. Jung regards the mind as something much more than the result of past experiences; for him it also is a preparation for the future, with aims and goals which it tries to realize within itself. The reminiscences of personal experience become unconscious and then join with fundamental ideas and trends of all mankind ('collective unconscious') which act as the background of all human thought and emotion. Jung stresses a mystical, religious factor in the unconscious.

anamnesia (an-am-nē′zhi-à) *Rare.* This term refers to the recollection of phenomena which immediately precede an illness.

anamnesis (an-am-nē′sis) The term literally means recollection. In medicine it commonly refers to the historical account of a patient's illness antedating the period of illness. It is distinguished from catamnesis, which refers to the history of the individual following an illness.

'Before a psychobiologist begins actual treatment he makes an extensive survey of the patient's life. . . . A good anamnesis contains the observable facts.' (Hinsie, L.E. *Concepts and Problems of Psychotherapy,* Columbia University Press, New York, 1937)

anamnesis, associative A type of psychiatric history-taking developed by Deutsch which attempts to elicit the causal relationship between the patient's somatic symptoms and his psychic structure. Of consequence in the anamnesis are not only the factual details but how they are said and when they are said in the interview. The patient is stimulated to give information by having him describe his organic complaints without making him aware of a psychological background. He is allowed to give a detailed account of his complaints and his ideas about the illness. Then he stops and waits to be questioned by the interviewer. When it is clear that the patient will not continue spontaneously, the examiner repeats one of the points of the patient's last sentence in interrogative form, using the same words the patient used insofar as possible. The patient then gives new information about his symptoms and is stimulated to further associations. Reference to individuals in his environment, present or past, then appear. The person who appears first in the case history is usually the relevant person from a psychosomatic point of view. Somatic and emotional symptoms with reference to this person are used as word stimuli for further associations. Then the patient himself usually correlates his organic illness with his emotional life. During the associative anamnesis, the examiner is on the lookout for three essential points in establishing the psychosomatic unity of the patient's complaints: the old conflict, the recent conflict, and the time factors involved. The associative anamnesis is used to greatest advantage with psychosomatic disorders. The anamnesis is taken in one sitting, which lasts from one to two hours. (*Psychoanalytic Quarterly 8,* 353, 1939)

anancasm (à-nang'kaz'm) A psychiatric term for any form of repetitious, recurrent, orderly, stereotyped behavior or thinking which if left unperformed will lead to an increase in anxiety and tension. Though including obsessive and compulsive traits, the term does not apply to repeated fulfillment of recurrent physiologically determined needs such as sleep and sex. Dr. Helen G. Richter believes that phobias are also anancasms, because they may drive the individual to seek protection through compulsions or obsessions. ('Some Observations on Anancasm,' *American Journal of Psychiatry 96,* 1459–67, 1939–40)

anancastia (à-nang-kas'ti-à) E. Kahn's term for the compulsive, obsessive type of personality.

anandria (an-an'dri-à) Absence of masculinity.

anaphase (an'à-fāz) The biological term *anaphase* signifies the third stage of the division of a cell by mitosis, characterized by polar migration of the chromosomes.

anaphia (an-à'fi-à) Absence of sense of touch; commonly used to refer to a relative rather than an absolute loss of tactile sensibility.

anaphrodisia (an-af-rō-diz'i-à) Absence of sexual feeling.

anaphylaxis, psychic (an-à-fi-lak'sis) A psychiatric term used analogously to its medical prototype when it denotes 'the state of unusual or exaggerated susceptibility to a foreign protein which sometimes follows a primary injection of such protein' (Dorland's *Medical Dictionary*):

i.e. reactivation of earlier symptoms by an event similar to the one that initially produced the symptoms. As in physical anaphylaxis, the initial event may be called the sensitizing agent, the later event the activating agent. A patient with severe asthma demonstrated psychic anaphylaxis; through psychoanalysis his symptoms were discovered to be derived from an early childhood experience of near-drowning. The asthma itself was an anxiety equivalent related to his fear of loss of love and his mother's scream for help. The sensitizing agent in this case was the early trauma of near-drowning; the activating agent was his fear of loss of love when his wife threatened to leave him. It is noteworthy that in psychic anaphylaxis, at least, the reaction is specific and is a response to the sensitizing agent rather than to the activating agent.

anarthria (an-är'thri-à) Complete inarticulateness. In 1867 Leyden proposed this term of *aphasia* (q.v.). See also *speech disorders.*

anasarca hystericum (à-nà-sär'kà hē-ster'ē-koom) A transient swelling, generally of the abdominal parietes, in a hysterical person; phantom tumor.

anathymiasis (à-na-thim-ī'à-sis) *Obs.* An old term for hysterical flatus or 'the vapors,' used by the old Greek philosophers to describe the soul; an exhalation.

anaudia (an-aw'di-à) Aphonia.

androgyneity (an-drō-ji-nē'i-tē) Bipolar potentiality in sex, until the individual, in certain primitive societies, is turned into one of definte sex upon the performance of a rigidly prescribed ritual. Androgyn(eit)y is an anthropological term referring to this ritual and does not in any way connote the biological facts of hermaphroditism—the actual manifestation of the characters of both sexes in a single individual. [In Yiddish an *andrigines* means a namby-pamby creature, neither fish nor flesh.] (*Psychoanalytic Review 16,* 280, 1929)

androgynism, psychic (an-droj'i-niz'm) Bisexuality in the mental sphere. Dualism produced by the co-existence of masculine and feminine traits.

androgynous, androgynal, androgynoid, androgynic (an-droj'i-nus, -nal, -in-oid, -drō-jin'ik) Exhibiting the state or condition of, or the resemblance to a combination of male and female characteristics in one individual. Sometimes, used in a more specialized sense, indicating, in contrast to *gynandrous,* the predominance of *masculine* features in a hermaphrodite with certain female characteristics.

andromania (an-drō-mā′ni-à) Synonym of *nymphomania* (q.v.).

andromonoecism (an-drō-mō-nē′siz′m) See *hermaphroditism.*

androphobia Morbid fear of men.

androphonia *Obs.* An old term for homicide.

androphonomania *Obs.* Homicidal insanity.

anemia, cerebral An inexact, descriptive term for reduced blood flow to the brain. The diminished blood supply may be in the brain as a whole (generalized cerebral anemia) or it may be limited to one or more specific areas of the brain (local cerebral anemia). Generalized cerebral anemia may be acute, as in cardiac failure or in psychological or physiological shock, or it may be chronic, as in pernicious anemia, leukemia, other blood dyscrasias, repeated blood loss, cerebral arteriosclerosis, cachexia, etc. Symptoms of acute cerebral anemia include: roaring in the ears, spots before the eyes, swaying, weakness, apathy, somnolence, unconsciousness, profuse sweating, and cold, pale skin. Symptoms of chronic cerebral anemia include: headaches, feeling of pressure in the head, roaring in the ears, dizziness, insomnia, or drowsiness, and in many cases progression to an organic reaction with memory disturbances, delusions, and hallucinations.

Local cerebral anemia is seen in cerebral arteriosclerosis, intracranial tumor, vasospasm, hypertensive encephalopathy, etc. Symptoms include fleeting pareses, transient aphasias, temporary sensory disturbances, hemianopsia and focal convulsive twitches.

anemophobia (an-ē-mō-fō′bi-a) Fear of wind.

aneos (a′nē-os) 'Struck with the loss of voice and reason.' (Motherby, G. *A New Medical Dictionary,* 5th ed., for J. Johnson, St. Paul's Church-Yard, etc., London, 1801)

anergasia (an-ēr-gas′i-à) Diminution of functional activity. When a clinical psychiatric syndrome is associated with structural pathology of the brain, it is classified by Adolf Meyer as an anergasia. The organic psychoses are called anergastic reaction-types.

anergia, anergy (an-ēr′ji-à, an′ēr-jē) Lack of energy; passivity.

anerotism (an-er′ō-tiz′m) See *negativism, sexual.*

anesthesia, anaethesia (an-es-thē′zhi-à) Absence of sensation. Any organ of the body, including the skin, may suffer loss of sensibility; anesthesia may be occasioned by organic or by psychic causes.

Psychic anesthesia is not uncommon in hysterical individuals. It is said that its purpose is to cover up (or shut out for the patient) the sexual significance of the area on which the patient's attention is, in spite of this, focused more than ever.

anesthesia, glove A disorder in the sensory field in which the patient has no sense of feeling in an area roughly corresponding to that covered by a glove; this anesthesia is believed to be psychogenic.

anesthesia, sexual Sexual anesthesia is synonymous with *frigidity* (q.v.).

anesthesia, spiritual The total loss of moral sensibility, which Stekel characterizes as the cocaine of the soul ('das seelische Kokain'): practically a flight into moral irresponsibility. Certain neurotic patients use this mental mechanism in order to avoid making painful decisions. For instance, a man has a magnanimous and loving wife and also a mistress without whom he cannot live; he constantly avoids taking any step either toward divorce or toward abandoning his mistress, building in himself a spiritual insensibility. (Stekel, W. *The Interpretation of Dreams,* Liveright, New York, 1943)

anethopath (à-neth′ō-path) An ethically or morally uninhibited person.

anethopathy (an-ē-thop′à-thē) Also, less properly, *anetopathy* (an-ē-top′à-thē). The absence of moral inhibitions; unethicalness; Karpman's term for primary, essential, genuine, idiopathic, or constitutional psychopathy (*psychopathic personality*) (q.v.). (Karpman, B. 'Psychopathy as a Form of Social Parasitism,' *Journal of Clinical Psychopathoiogy 10,* 160–94, 1949.) In his article 'The Problem of Psychopathies' (*Psychiatric Quarterly 3,* 495, 1929) Karpman states that psychopathy is a very specific mental disease. He emphasizes that this is the group from which the so-called habitual criminals come. (In such cases, usually no deep-seated psychic motivations can be elicited, and patients appear to be 'psychopath fast'—no matter what is done for them in terms of psychotherapy, their patterns of reaction continue unchanged.) The conspicuous trait in their mental makeup is complete egocentricity, which is also reflected in their narcissistic sexual behavior.

aneuthanasia (an-ū-thà-nā'zi-à) Painful death.

anginophobia (an-jī-nō-fō'bi-à) Fear of choking.

angiogram (an'jē-ō-gram) An X-ray of the blood vessels of an area following injection of an artery supplying the area with a suitable contrast medium (usually Diodrast®). In neurology, internal carotid angiography is used to study the arterial vessels of the cerebral hemispheres; vertebral angiography (arteriography) is used to study the circulation of the posterior fossa and the posterior portions of the cerebral hemispheres. Angiography is useful in demonstrating intracranial aneurysms, vascular malformations, and tumors.

angioneurotic edema See *edema, angioneurotic.*

anhedonia (an-hē-dō'ni-à) Absence of pleasure in acts that are normally pleasurable. It is seen often in schizophrenic patients and may be one of the earliest signs in the pseudoneurotic variety described by Hoch and Polatin.

anhidrosis (an-hi-drō'sis) Deficiency or absence of perspiration.

aniconia (à-ne-kō'ni-à) Absence of mental imagery.

anilingus (ā-ni-ling'gus) One who practices application of the mouth to the anus. The concept is important because of the number of patients with strong so-called anal fixations. Thus, a compulsive-obsessive psychoneurotic individual, vividly obsessed with many anal manifestations, had an unconquerable fear that he would perform the act.

anima (àn'i-mà) In current psychiatry the term *anima* is almost invariably associated with the analytical psychology of Jung. Jung distinguishes between the anima (soul) and the psyche. 'By the psyche I understand the totality of all the psychic processes, both conscious as well as unconscious; whereas by *soul* I understand a definitely demarcated function-complex that is best characterized as a "personality." ' (Jung, C.G. *Psychological Types,* tr. by Baynes, H.G., Harcourt, Brace, New York, 1923). He postulates an inner and an outer personality. 'I term the outer attitude, or outer character, the *persona,* the inner attitude I term the *anima or soul.'*

Jung makes a further distinction when he maintains that 'a very feminine woman has a masculine soul,' that is, an *animus,* 'and a very manly man a feminine soul or an *anima.'* (ibid.)

animastic (an-i-mas'tik) Of or pertaining to the soul; psychic.

animatism (an'i-mà-tiz'm) The ascription of psychic qualities to inanimate as well as animate objects is called animatism. The condition is vividly exemplified, for example, in schizophrenic subjects, who often personify the whole of the inanimate world, as if the latter possessed the same mental qualities as human beings do.

'What led to the formulation of these names [i.e. animism and animatism] is the insight into the very remarkable conceptions of nature and the world of those primitive races known to us from history and from our own times. These races populate the world with a multitude of spiritual beings which are benevolent or malevolent to them, and attribute the causation of natural processes to these spirits and demons; they also consider that not only animals and plants, but inanimate things as well are animated by them.' (Freud, S. *The Basic Writings of Sigmund Freud,* tr. by Brill, A.A., Random House, New York, 1938)

animi agitatio (à'nē-mē à-gē-tä'tē-ō) Mental agitation.

animism (an'i-miz'm) From the psychiatric point of view animism refers to the theory that all things in nature, both animate and inanimate, contain the so-called spirit or soul.

'Animism in the narrower sense is the theory of psychic concepts, and in the wider sense, of spiritual beings in general.' (Freud, S. *The Basic Writings of Sigmund Freud,* tr. by Brill, A.A., Random House, New York, 1938). See *animatism.*

animus See *anima.*

anisocoria (an-ī-sō-kō'ri-à) Inequality of the pupils in size.

ankle-jerk Achilles reflex.

anlage (än'là-gĕ) A particular genetic factor predisposing to a given trait or the entire *genotypical* structure of an individual. The term is an abbreviation of *Er-banlage* or *hereditary predisposition*, and this is the sense in which it is actually used in American genetics (see *predisposition*).

annihilation, Milligan method See *Milligan annihilation method*.

annulment A mental mechanism by which the patient annuls, i.e. renders 'nonexistent,' certain specific events or ideas which are painful or disagreeable to him. In certain respects, this mechanism resembles repression, but it is basically of an entirely different nature. 'The fundamental difference lies in the fact that in annulment painful experiences are shifted into daydreams, while in repression painful experiences may be eliminated from consciousness and pushed into the unconscious, after which they may reappear in dreams or symptoms.'

Annulment can be compared with hysterical amnesia, with the following differences: (1) in annulment specific events or specific ideas are rendered 'nonexistent'; (2) the patient's amnesia is not general, but concerns individual factors; and (3) the knowledge of these facts at no time leaves the realm of the patient's consciousness. 'The patient behaves as if the event in question never existed.' (Stekel, W. *Compulsion and Doubt,* Liveright, New York, 1949)

annulment, marriage See *marriage, psychiatric aspects of*.

annulus fibrosus (an'ū-lus fi-brō'sus) See *disk, herniated lumbar intervertebral*.

anoesia (an-ō-ē'zhi-à) *Obs.* Mental deficiency.

anoesis (-ē'sis) Absence of cognition or knowledge; a state of sheer feeling, having no reference to objects; non-cognitive consciousness.

anoia (à-noi'à) This term was defined by C.A. Mercier as 'that defect of conduct and mind that begins at the top, in the highest level [of mental activity], and may remain limited to a mere shaving off of that level, as in the case of a clever lunatic, or may extend downward to any

depth until at last it touches the bottom in coma. Whether it invades a person who has reached the full stature of conduct and mind, and takes some of it away, or whether it is congenitally absent and has never been attained, makes no difference to the form of the insanity. It is still anoia.' (Mercier, C.A. *A Text-Book of Insanity,* George Allen and Unwin, London, 1914)

anomalous Relating to deviations from the average, but excluding the deviations due to disease processes.

anomaly A deviation from the average. In medicine anomalies are distinguished from disease processes, although the clinical signs and symptoms may be similar in both. For example, an underdeveloped heart may be anomalous; it may be too small, organically and functionally, for the body in which it is located. The anomaly may be relative or absolute.

The personality of an individual may be anomalous. The so-called 'character neuroses' are of that order, in that the personalities are in the periphery of the normal or average personality circle. Schizoidism and cycloidism are also regarded as anomalies.

anomaly, constitutional See *inadequacy, constitutional*.

anomia (an-ō'mi-à) Benjamin Rush used this term to mean congenital defect of the moral sense. In neurology, anomia is a type of aphasia with a disturbed capacity to name objects.

anorexia (an-ō-rek'si-à) Loss of appetite.

anorexia, elective Conscious restriction of the quantity of food eaten to the extent of incurring a morbid reaction to foodstuffs. (Déjérine and Gauckler)

anorexia, mental Déjérine and Gauckler say: 'It sometimes happens that a physician has patients—they are more apt to be women—whose appearance is truly shocking. Their eyes are brilliant. Their cheeks are hollow, and their cheek bones seem to protrude through the skin. Their withered breasts hang from the wales of their chest. Every rib stands out. Their shoulder-blades appear to be loosened from their frame. Every vertebra shows through the skin. The abdominal wall sinks in below the floating ribs and forms a hollow like a basin. Their thighs and the calves of their legs are reduced to a skeleton. One would say it was the picture of an immured nun, such as the old masters have portrayed.' (Déjérine, J. and Gauckler, E. *The Psychoneuroses and Their Treatment by Psychotherapy*, 2nd ed., tr. by Jelliffe, S.E., Lippincott, Philadelphia & London, 1915). The authors describe patients who have no organic basis for their trouble, and then say that 'these patients are what are known as mental anorexics, who without having any physical lesions, but by the association of various troubles, all having a psychic origin, have lost a quarter, a third, and sometimes a half of their weight.'

anorexia nervosa (när-vō′sa) A psychiatric syndrome first described by Sir William Gull (1868) as apepsia hysterica; Gull proposed the term anorexia nervosa in 1874. The chief symptoms are inability to eat, weight loss, and amenorrhea. There is usually an accompanying mood change of depression and often also complaints referable to the lower gastrointestinal tract, the most common of which is constipation. It is worthy of emphasis that although the clinical picture is termed anorexia, there need not be a true loss of appetite; the important feature is that, for some reason, food is not taken in. Patients offer various rationalizations for this, ranging from disgust reactions to specific foods to fear of choking on food and to fear of vomiting after eating.

Anorexia nervosa occurs typically in females between the ages of 12 and 21; it has been reported also, however, in older women and in men (in which case impotence rather than amenorrhea seems to be a cardinal feature). Anorexia nervosa is not a specific disorder and there is no neurosis or psychosis which is specific to this syndrome. Many authors stress the frequent occurrence of schizophrenia in such cases; others have grouped it with the obsessive-compulsive or hysterical disorders.

Differentiation should be made between anorexia nervosa, as described above, and pituitary cachexia (Simmond's disease). The latter tends to occur in middle age, is usually precipitated by physical illness, and weight loss occurs later in the course of the illness. In Simmond's disease, amenorrhea is seen only in approximately 50 per cent of cases, despite such other indications of endocrine dysfunction as premature aging, wrinkling of the skin, deciduation of pubic and axillary hair,

loss of sexual desire, and atrophy of the sexual organs. Lassitude and weakness are conspicuous in Simmond's disease but are surprisingly infrequent in anorexia nervosa despite severe weight loss. The 17-ketosteroids are reduced in Simmond's disease but normal in anorexia nervosa.

anorexia, primary mental See *anorexia, secondary mental.*

anorexia, secondary mental Déjérine and Gauckler describe as secondary mental anorexia those cases where the taking of food has been restricted with the idea of relieving some former digestive trouble. 'We shall give the name primary mental anorexia to those cases in which originally, and often voluntarily, the amount of food taken by the individual had, for some cause or other, been diminished. The common characteristic of all these patients is that, when their affection has reached a certain stage, they get to the point where *if they should want to eat they would not be able to,* for they no longer have any feeling of hunger.' (Déjérine, J. and Gauckler, E. *The Psychoneuroses and Their Treatment by Psychotherapy*, 2nd ed., tr. by Jelliffe, S.E., Lippincott, Philadelphia and London, 1915)

anorexia, social This is an expression used by Déjérine and Gauckler to refer to the anorexia 'of poor people, who are obliged by the necessities of life to deprive themselves [of food] to such a degree that, when the illness or lack of employment which has caused these privations has disappeared, they find it impossible to take food again.' (Déjérine, J. and Gauckler, E. *The Psychoneuroses and Their Treatment by Psychotherapy*, 2nd ed., tr. by Jelliffe, S.E., Lippincott, Philadelphia and London, 1915)

anorgasmy (à-nor′gaz-mē) Lack of sexual pleasure.

anosmia (an-oz′mi-à) Absence of sense of smell.

anosognosia (à-nos-ō-gnō′zhi-à) Unawareness of physical illness.

anosphresia (an-os-phrē′si-à) *Anosmia* (q.v.).

ANS *Autonomic nervous system* (q.v.).

answers, syndrome of approximate An individual's tendency to answer questions with relevance to the general topic, but with glaring disregard of details—the so-called 'syndrome of approximate answers,' also known in psychiatric literature as the *Ganser syndrome* (q.v.), the condition having been first described by Ganser.

For instance, when shown a 25-cent piece the patient calls it a dollar or a dime. He writes three when asked to write two, raises the left arm when asked to raise the right, calls a match a cigarette; a comb is a brush or something to use for the hair. This syndrome usually occurs in persons facing criminal responsibility and is an attempt to avoid trial and punishment. (Hinsie, L.E. *Understandable Psychiatry,* Macmillan, New York, 1948)

Antabuse A drug used in the treatment of chronic alcoholism; known also as disulfiram and tetraethylthiuram disulfide. It appears that Antabuse interferes with the enzyme systems which normally break down alcohol in the organism. As a result, when alcohol is ingested by an individual with an adequate blood level of Antabuse, there occurs within a few minutes a characteristic response, the alcohol-Antabuse reaction. This consists of flushing, injection of the conjunctivae, sweating, a sensation of warmth, and tachycardia; in 20 to 30 minutes, additional symptoms may appear—headache, dizziness, chest pain, palpitation, dyspnea, pallor, and nausea. With more severe reactions, vomiting, hypotension, vasomotor collapse, and sometimes convulsions may occur. Chronic alcoholics who sincerely wish to stop drinking are kept on a maintenance dose of Antabuse as an aid to control while other more specific therapeutic measures are utilized. Antabuse treatment is a form of deconditioning and as such it is to be considered adjunctive therapy; used alone, it is ineffectual in curing alcoholism.

anthropo- (an'thrō-pō-) Combining form meaning *man, human being.*

anthropocentrism (an-thrō-pō-sen'triz'm) The doctrine or belief that man is the center of the universe to which all else has reference.

anthropology (-pol'ō-jē) The science of man or mankind in the widest sense; the history of human society. This term designates the extensive branch of natural science which studies the developmental aspects of man as a species, using archaeology as one of its main methods.

Although anthropological research covers the history of human society regardless of time and space, it is primarily related to early times and primitive people, as it deals not only with the question of the earliest appearance of man and his rise from lower forms, but also with all the problems concerning the differential development of human races, languages, and cultural forms. The individual person has little, if any, significance in these studies and is bound to disappear in the cultural or racial groups to which he belongs, since there exists no record of individual activity for prehistoric times.

Anthropology is usually subdivided into: (1) zoological anthropology, investigating the evolutionary conditions of humanity; (2) descriptive anthropology or ethnology, describing the division of mankind into races and studying the origin, distribution, and relations of these racial groups; (3) general anthropology, dealing with the evolution of mankind as a human society.

The last division is anthropology proper and, according to Franz Boas (*General Anthropology,* Heath, Boston, 1938), includes the following three main problems: (1) the reconstruction of human history; (2) the determination of types of historical phenomena and their sequences; and (3) the dynamics of change.

anthropology, psychological That branch of anthropology which deals with the psychology of different civilizations and cultures and which studies especially folklore, the myths, and other expressions of the mentality of the people. Through comparisons the psychological investigations throw light on many observations made in children or in mentally sick persons in our culture. See *ethnology.* (Hinsie, L.E. *Understandable Psychiatry,* Macmillan, New York, 1948)

anthropometry (-pom'ē-trē) The scientific method pre-eminently applied in the field of *anthropology* (q.v.), which uses the measurement of the human body for the description of the typical anatomical variability of a population. In anthropology, more attention must be given to the bony structure than to any other part of the body, since a comparison between present and past conditions can be based only on comparisons of skeletons.

The size of the body is measured by stature, by weight, and sometimes by volume. The length of the limbs is measured on the skeleton by the length of the long bones; on the living, by the determination with the greatest possible accuracy of the corresponding lengths. The head measures most commonly used on the living are length of head, measured from the glabella to the most distant point of the occiput; the greatest transversal diameter of the head; and the greatest width of the face measured between the zygomatic arches. 'These are preferred on the living, because they can be taken with the greatest accuracy, since the points from which the measurements have to be taken are well defined and the soft parts covering these regions are rather thin.' (Boas, F. *General Anthropology*, D.C. Heath, Boston, 1938)

anthropomorph (an'thrō-pō-morf) An expression used by some authors to designate a member of the group of psychologists and philosophers who in the past century studied the mental activity of animals and interpreted them in terms of human adult logic. (Sladen, F.J. *Psychiatry and the War*, Thomas, Springfield, Ill., 1943)

anthroponomy (-pon'o-mē) Hunter's term for his behavioristic psychology.

anthropophobia (an-thrō-po-fō'bi-à) Fear of man in general.

anthropos (an'thrō-pos) Primal man; one of Jung's archetypes. See *archetype; archetype, mother.*

anthroposcopy (an-thrō-pos'kō-pē) This obsolescent term is used in reference to various debatable procedures of character-reading from the features or other parts of the human body.

anthrotype (an'thrō-tīp) This term is used in some systems of constitutional medicine, to classify various constellations of all the morphological, physiological, immunological, and psychological characteristics making up the human individual. It is usually interpreted in terms as general as those of biotypology, that is, in the sense of including the entire phenotypical make-up of human organisms. Consequently, biotypology and the study of anthrotypes are practically identical, although the etymological derivation of 'anthrotype' indicates that the application of this concept is limited to human beings, as, in practice, the meaning of 'biotype' is also similarly limited (see *biotypology*).

anti-cathexis (an-ti-kà-thek'sis) When an emotional charge (cathexis), associated with a given impulse, is shifted to an impulse of an opposite character, the term anti-cathexis is used. For example, the unconscious hate may appear as conscious love.

'Like all other defense dynamisms, reaction-formation is only significant for pathogenesis when the anti-cathexis or counter-investment made by the Ego takes an exaggerated form.' (Healy, W., Bronner, A.F., and Bowers, A.M. *The Structure and Meaning of Psychoanalysis,* Knopf, New York, 1930)

Anti-cathexis is synonymous with *counter-investment.*

anticipation The act of dealing with, doing, foreseeing, or experiencing beforehand. Anticipation of the future is characteristic of the ego and is necessary for judgment and planning of suitable later action. Anticipation is dependent upon reality testing, by trying in an active manner and in small dosage what might happen to one passively and in unknown dosage. With the development of speech, name symbols can be substituted for things, and thus anticipation can take place in the imagination in the model world of words. This affords the possibility of judging reality and is an important factor in development of the ability to tolerate tensions.

anticipatory maturation See *maturation, anticipatory, principle of.*

antifetishism (an-ti-fē'tish-iz'm) Magnus Hirschfeld uses this term to refer to the condition in which homosexual individuals develop certain aversions as a protection against the recognition of homosexuality in themselves.

'One man dislikes women with large feet, another is repelled by women with hair on their bodies. Such a woman causes him to have a distinct nausea. . . . His search is endless because he is truly, though secretly, attracted by the male. His sexual goal is man.' (Stekel, W. *Bi-Sexual Love,* tr. by van Teslaar, J.S., Badger, Boston, 1922)

anti-instinctual force See *anti-cathexis; counter-cathexis.*

antikinesis (-ki-nē'sis) This term is not in use today. The physiologist Bethe proposed 'that only such terms shall be employed as shall serve to indicate the immediate dependence of the volitional no less than the reflex movement upon the functional capacity of the central nervous system. With this end in view Bethe has suggested that all forms of nervous response should be designated as *antikineses*, while those recurring regularly and in a definite manner in response to stimulation shall be called *reflexes*, whereas all the volitional responses in which there is a variable factor due to the greater complexity and elaboration in the physiological mechanism shall be classed together as *antiklises*.' (Paton, S. *Psychiatry*, Lippincott, Philadelphia and London, 1905)

antiklisis (an-ti-klī'sis) See *antikinesis*.

anti-nodal behavior See *behavior, nodal*.

antisocial The term *antisocial*, meaning against the social order, is commonly used in psychiatry. It is represented by the extension of the sadistic impulse or instinct upon some part of the environment. Antisocial tendencies may and usually do appear to a greater or lesser degree in all psychiatric states. In point of performing an act of antisocial behavior, special significance is gained by the diagnostic group termed *psychopathic personality* (q.v.).

antisocial activity, concealed See *activity, concealed antisocial*.

antisocial reaction The 1952 revision of psychiatric nomenclature uses this term to refer to many cases previously classified as constitutional psychopathic state or psychopathic personality (q.v.). The antisocial reaction includes those individuals who are always in trouble, profiting neither from experience nor punishment, and maintaining no real loyalties to any person or group. They lack a sense of responsibility and judgment is defective.

antithesis, neurotic Opposition, contrast. Adler uses this term to indicate that the neurotic individual measures a thing, a force, or an event, by an opposite which is fitted to it.

Adler states: 'Among these I have regularly found the following: (1) Above-beneath, (2) masculine-feminine. One furthermore always finds an arrangement of memories, feelings and actions according to this type of *antithesis* in the sense the patient takes them (not always in the generally accepted sense), i.e., inferior—beneath, feminine; powerful—above, masculine.' (Adler, A. *The Neurotic Consti-*

tution, tr. by Glueck, B. and Lind, J.E., Moffat, Yard, New York, 1917)

antlophobia (ant-lō-fō'bi-à) Fear of floods.

anus Termination of the alimentary canal. Both the proximal (oral) and the distal (anal) ends of the gastrointestinal tract achieve high distinction in the field of psychiatry. Many psychotic patients center much of their attention on the anal region and activities associated with it. They often transfer much of their thoughts and feelings to the anal zone, conceiving the zone in the light of personal objects; that is, they personalize the region. A schizophrenic patient believed that he ruled the world through his anus; he also thought that feces were the people of the world to whom he gave birth.

Other patients are less overt in their anal interests. The psychoneurotic individual disguises his anal tendencies through the use of symbolic expressions. He develops, for instance, an intense dread of subways, cellars, and other subterranean structures.

According to psychoanalysis early infantile interests in the anal region are gradually sublimated, taking the form of character traits, professional leanings, etc. It is said, for example, that the triad of personality traits, orderliness, parsimony and stubbornness, are derivatives of early anal impulses.

Psychoanalytic literature abounds in material relating to psycho-anal relationships.

'Brill and Federn have commented on the relation between anal-erotic sensations and the earliest impulses of sadism. . . .' (Jones, E. *Papers on Psycho-Analysis*, 4th ed., Wood, Baltimore, 1938)

'Among civilized people, also, it may be added, the final and invincible seat of modesty is sometimes not around the pubes, but the anus. . . .' (Ellis, H. *Studies in the Psychology of Sex*, 3rd ed., vol. 1, Davis, Philadelphia, 1919)

anus feminarum amatarum lambere (à'nōos fe-mē-nà'room à-mà-ta'room làm-bā're) Among the many expressions of sexual perversions, the impulse to apply the lips to the anal zone is occasionally encountered.

anxietas (àngk-sē'e-tàs) A nervous condition of unrest; anxiety.

anxietas praesenilis (prī-se-nē'lis) Farrar describes three main forms of involutional melancholia. First, melancholia vera, characterized essentially by a clinical syndrome resembling manic-depressive psychosis; second, anxietas praesenilis, in which there is extreme anxiety with feelings of unreality; third, depressio apathetica, the central symptom of which is apathy.

anxietas tibiarum (tē-bē-ä'room) A nervous agitation, continually impelling the patient to change the position of his legs.

anxiety An affect which differs from other affects in its specific unpleasurable character. Anxiety consists of a somatic, physiological side (disturbed breathing, increased heart activity, vasomotor changes, musculoskeletal disturbances such as trembling or paralysis, increased sweating, etc.) and of a psychological side (perceptions of specific unpleasurable feelings and sensations, apprehension, etc.). Anxiety is to be differentiated from fear; the latter is a reaction to a real or threatened danger, while anxiety is more typically a reaction to an unreal or imagined danger.

Freud's earlier view was that anxiety arises by transformation of libido which cannot otherwise be discharged. He later abandoned this view and came to believe that anxiety arises automatically whenever the psyche is overwhelmed by an influx of stimuli too great to be mastered or discharged. Such 'automatic anxiety' may arise in response to stimuli either of external or of internal origin, but most frequently they arise from the id, that is, from the drives ('id anxiety'). When anxiety develops automatically according to this pattern, the situation is called a traumatic one. Automatic anxiety is characteristic of infancy, when the ego is weak and immature, and of so-called 'actual' anxiety neurosis of adult life.

There is a second type of anxiety, characteristic of the psychoneuroses, which Freud called 'signal anxiety.' In the course of development, the child learns to anticipate the advent of a traumatic situation and reacts to this possibility with anxiety before the situation becomes traumatic. The unpleasure arising from this threat of a danger situation automatically sets into operation the pleasure principle. The latter acts by enabling the ego to check or inhibit whatever id impulses might be giving rise to the danger situation. There is a series of typical danger situations which occur in sequence in the child's life; these persist to some degree throughout life in the unconscious, and it is one or another of these dangers which the psychoneurotic patient unconsciously fears. The first of these dangers, characteristic of ego development up to about 1½ years, is separation (known also as loss of the love object, and as primal anxiety); the second, seen at 1 to 2 years, is loss of love; the third, seen at 2½ to 3 years, is castration or other genital injury; and the fourth, which is seen after the age of 5 or 6 years, when the superego has been formed, is guilt (disapproval and punishment by the superego).

'We understand from our discussion of anxiety that when the ego opposes the emergence of an id impulse it does so because it judges that the emergence of that impulse will create a danger situation. The ego then produces anxiety as a signal of danger, wins the help of the pleasure principle in this way, and is able to offer successful opposition to the emergence of the dangerous impulses. In psychoanalytical terminology we speak of such opposition as the *defense* or as the defensive operation of the ego.' (Brenner, C. *An Elementary Textbook of Psychoanalysis,* International Universities Press, 1955.)

'Anxiety is a biological reaction of the ego with the aim of self-preservation. In infancy, the ego and the id are scarcely differentiated, and it is almost impossible to determine whether a reaction belongs to the id or to the ego. It is thus irrelevant whether the anxiety of the infant (and actual anxiety) is psychic or not. According to Freud's formulation, psychic processes are somatic processes which are originally unconscious. It is only in the course of development that id reactions (which are unconscious) are taken over by the ego and thus gain access to the perceptive and motor end of the psychic apparatus. In other words, when the ego is differentiated from the id, the affect of anxiety reaches the system Cs. of the ego and is experienced there and expressed by the psychic complex "anxiety." ' (Nunberg, H. *Principles of Psychoanalysis,* International Universities Press, 1955)

anxiety, anal castration Fenichel writes: 'A special characteristic of how regression operates may be seen when it fails in its defensive purpose. We see then that the shift of the instinctual center of gravity to the anal field did not enable the patient to avoid castration anxiety: he develops what might be called "anal castration anxiety." ' (Fenichel, O. *Outline of Clinical Psychoanalysis,* tr. by Lewin, B.D. and Zilboorg, G., The Psychoanalytic Quarterly Press and Norton, New York, 1934)

anxiety, annulment of A psychoanalytic term used to stress the necessity for distinguishing between the relief (or annulment) of the therapist's anxiety and the therapeutic resolution (or annulment) of the patient's anxiety. The analyst's unresolved character-rooted anxiety may demand constant evidence of symptomatic improvement or cure from the patient. If the therapist is constantly reassured and pleased at every symptomatic improvement in his patient only to be discouraged, downcast, and alarmed at intermittent unhappiness in the patient, then the therapist's anxiety is a constant obstacle to the central work of the psychoanalytic procedure. The patient's cure depends on the annulment of his own anxiety through the specific process of bringing the previously repressed and denied infantile and primitive instinctual urges from the realm of the unconscious into the realm of the conscious (mind), where they can be tolerated, modified, and accepted. This shift of unconscious material into the conscious can be accomplished by the patient only when he is helped by the therapist to become aware of his defensive resistances, which are deeply rooted in his character and which tend to reject and deny in consciousness these very infantile and primitive trends and urges.

This resolution of the patient's unconscious ego defenses or resistance is crucial in the therapeutic psychoanalytic annulment of anxiety. E.F. Sharpe (*Collected Papers on Psycho-analysis,* The Hogarth Press and The Institute of Psychoanalysis, London, 1950) states: 'The only thing that truly delivers us from anxiety is the bringing to light of our infantile fears and hatreds. We are psychically safe when we are safe from them, and, through analysis, that means when the ego can deal with them, instead of the super-ego.'

anxiety-attack, equivalent of This is a term employed by Freud to indicate that the physical symptoms often associated with manifest anxiety may alone constitute the anxiety-attack just as the anxiety

itself can. These *equivalents* (physical symptoms) take on a variety of forms; for example, attacks of sudden diarrhea or attacks of sweating, often nocturnal.

anxiety, automatic See *anxiety.*

anxiety, basic Horney's term for a feeling of loneliness and helplessness toward a potentially hostile world. This concept is more comprehensive than Freud's 'real' anxiety. (Horney, K. *The Neurotic Personality of Our Time,* Norton, New York, 1937)

anxiety, castration The castration complex has multiple representations and ramifications. The term, however, according to Freud should be reserved 'for the occasion when the idea of such deprivations comes to be associated with the loss of the male organ.'

The castration complex has its foundation laid down in the pregenital stage of development. Alexander, for example, refers to the many deprivations and losses suffered by the infant from the time of birth. He says that the child loses its mother's body and its fetal membrane at birth. A pleasure-giving organ is replaced by a painful condition. The next important loss is the pleasure-giving nipple (Staercke's oral primal castration); then the pleasure-giving stool is lost (Freud's anal primal castration); finally, there is fear of the loss of the penis.

Alexander says: 'The expectation of castration is only one manifestation of an expectation of a general narcistic wound. It is the deposit of an ontogenetic experience—that every pleasure has its outcome in loss, in pain.'

'The handing over of feces for the sake of (out of love for) someone else becomes a prototype of castration; it is the first occasion upon which an individual gives up a piece of his own body (it is as such that feces are invariably treated by children) in order to gain the favor of some person whom he loves.' (Freud, S. *Collected Papers,* vol. 3, p. 562, tr. by Strachey, A. and J., Leonard and Virginia Woolf and The Institute of Psychoanalysis, London, 1925)

These early losses, first expressed organically, are indelibly imprinted upon the psyche and appear later in the form of character traits, depending upon the way they were solved or resolved in the early years.

anxiety, conscious and unconscious A psychoanalytic term which stresses the power that unconscious anxiety maintains in causing symptomatic traits, attitudes, and actions. Unconscious anxiety, i.e. anxiety of which the individual is unaware, results in compulsive and impulsive behavior which is then secondarily rationalized to conform with conscious realistic motives. In this way unconscious anxiety functions in the unconscious as a well-spring for character-rooted symptomatic trends toward action. In other words, unconscious anxiety is not felt in consciousness as anxiety per se, but rather as a tense urge toward action, and its presence in the unconscious is inferred from this conscious urge. On the other hand, conscious anxiety is apprehended in consciousness as such by the individual, and motivates voluntary actions striving toward the relief of the unpleasant sensations of conscious anxiety.

E.F. Sharpe (*Collected Papers on Psycho-analysis,* The Hogarth Press and The Institute of Psychoanalysis, London, 1950) states: 'Conscious anxiety is a half-way house to the understanding and resolution of it [i.e. unconscious anxiety], but unconscious anxiety [in the psychoanalyst himself] can drive the [psychoanalytic] technician to premature interpretation, and to inability to keep the patient's pace; it can make him delay when he should speak, and speak when he should be silent.'

anxiety, death A form of depression in which fear of death, poverty, etc. is the most prominent complaint.

anxiety, depressive The specific anxiety observed in a person afflicted with depression. '. . . the preservation of the good internalized objects with whom the ego is identified as a whole. In the latter case—which is the case of the depressive—the anxiety and feelings of suffering are of a much more complex nature. The anxiety lest the good objects and, with them, the ego should be destroyed, or that they are in a state of disintegration, is interwoven with continuous and desperate efforts to save the good objects both internalized and external.' (Klein, M. *Contributions to Psycho-analysis* 1921–1945), The Hogarth Press, London, 1948)

anxiety, discharge of A psychoanalytic term referring to the process by which unconscious anxiety (tension) is chronically, repetitively, and more or less constantly nullified through action and deed in the integral activity of everyday life. The reality activities of everyday life thus have a specific phantasy or symbol component for the individual, and these activities are utilized for the gratification of unconscious drives and urges. If this gratification did not occur more or less constantly and repetitively, these urges would succumb to repression and thus form the nidus for symptomatic anxiety and symptom formation. The trend toward the excessive utilization of this method of nullifying anxiety in contrast to such other common methods as the suppression of feeling or the guarding over thinking has been called 'the flight into reality.'

Sexual activity, with orgastic discharge, is a specific activity frequently employed as a method of discharging anxiety of unconscious origin. E.F. Sharpe (*Collected Papers on Psycho-analysis,* The Hogarth Press and The Institute of Psychoanalysis, London, 1950) states: 'On my drawing attention to a well-marked reparation system in the analysis of a normal person, I was appealed to by the patient in these words: "But for a long time I was unable to do any kindness for anybody. That was surely wrong. Are you suggesting now that it is wrong to think of and do things for others?" An answer here is imperative. One says: "We are not dealing with a question of right and wrong. We want to know why you were unable to do kindnesses formerly and why now you are driven to do them, and especially why you are unhappy and anxious if your plans are thwarted. You are being driven not by 'right' and 'wrong,' but by fears and anxieties." '

anxiety, dramatization of A psychoanalytic phrase referring to the tendency of many patients to act out their unconscious conflicts in the presence of and for the benefit of the analyst with whom they are working. The acting out with dramatic emphasis directed at the figure of the analyst occurs within the context of what is called the transference situation. At the time of the acting out or dramatization of the unconscious conflict, the patient is unaware of its logical, true—but unconscious—meaning and significance. Repetitive dramatizations emanating from the same conflict sources of anxiety frequently occur in the same analysis.

E.F. Sharpe (*Collected Papers on Psycho-analysis*, The Hogarth Press and The Institute of Psychoanalysis, London, 1950) states: 'That re-enacting means that the psyche is forever trying the same way to overcome an unconscious problem connected with an event. What we need to find out in order that this futile repetition may be resolved are (1) the buried memories and (2) the unconscious factors.'

anxiety, ego A psychoanalytic term referring to the threat of internal dangers to the ego in contrast to fear, which refers to the threat of external dangers to the ego. The internal dangers are twofold. First, the stress of more or less powerful instinctual urges that press discharge or gratification onto the ego. These are sources of danger as they meet with internal and external prohibitions relating to reality consequences attendant upon the gratification of these instinctual urges. The second great internal threat to the ego, productive of ego anxiety, emanates from the warning intimidations that stem from those internalized moral forces in the human personality which have come to be called 'conscience' (or superego).

The power of the instinct is always met by a punishing threat of approximately equal power. The twofold combination of aroused instinct and conscience-producing gratification of instinct results in the inner drive of anxiety that motivates every type of ego defense.

E.F. Sharpe (*Collected Papers on Psycho-analysis*, The Hogarth Press and The Institute of Psychoanalysis, London, 1950) states: 'The inner drive of anxiety compels the world-conqueror to externalize his problems into terms of his country, with which he identifies himself . . . By fair means or foul, by violence or unscrupulousness, all who oppose his country, i.e. himself, must be removed. Only in his supremacy is he safe . . .

'In resolving an anxiety state, we have to subject the unconscious factors to reality. We have to bring into consciousness the feared unconscious impulse. We have to show how for that wish the unconscious super-ego [i.e. conscience] has provided a dreadful punishment of exactly the same nature as the wish.'

anxiety, erotized A paradoxical reaction to anxiety in which, instead of flight from the source of anxiety, the tendency is to head directly toward the source and enjoy it. 'We have called this reaction, where fear of danger is replaced by love of danger, eroticized anxiety.' (Laforgue, R. *The Relativity of Reality*, Nervous and Mental Disease Monographs No. 66, New York, 1940)

anxiety, examination It is the opinion of Freud that the anxiety attendant upon examinations is intensified by experiences of the past, usually unconscious, which had to do with 'the punishments we suffered as children for misdeeds we had committed—memories which were revived in us on the *dies irae, dies illa* of the grueling examination at the two critical junctures in our careers as students.' (Freud, S. *The Interpretation of Dreams*, 3rd ed., tr. by Brill, A.A., Macmillan, New York, 1933)

anxiety, free-floating Freud says: 'Anxious expectation is the nuclear symptom of this neurosis [i.e. anxiety-neurosis]; it clearly reveals, too, something of the theory of it. We may perhaps say that there is here a *quantum of anxiety in a free-floating condition,* which in any state of expectation controls the selection of ideas, and is ever ready to attach itself to any suitable ideational content.' (Freud, S. *Collected Papers*, vol. 1, tr. by Riviere, J., Leonard and Virginia Woolf and The Institute of Psychoanalysis, London, 1924–25)

anxiety-hysteria This is a primitive reaction type and the most frequent neurosis of childhood. The main symptom is a specific fear, which has usually arisen from the binding of primary diffuse anxiety to a specific content. The thing that is feared may be feared because it represents a temptation (especially a situation which would ordinarily call forth an aggressive or a sexual response), or it may be feared because it represents the punishment for the forbidden impulse either directly or indirectly through symbolism, or it may be feared because of a combination of these factors. Further, the phobia may be a fear that the anxiety will return; this is seen in some agoraphobics whose initial attacks occurred in the street. The phobia may not represent castration and punishment directly, but may be concerned mainly with a fear of loss of love.

The defense in anxiety-hysteria is (1) through anxiety itself, which gives warning to the ego so that the situation can be avoided; (2) repression of the impulse by development of substitutes for the real fear; (3) by projection of an internal instinctual danger onto an external perceptional danger (this is the most frequent type of displacement in anxiety hysteria); (4) by regression to childhood in order to ward off the wishes of the genital Oedipal complex.

The two most famous cases of phobia in psychoanalytic literature are those of little Hans (Freud 1902) and the wolf man (Freud 1918).

anxiety, ictal See *emotions, ictal.*

anxiety, id See *anxiety.*

anxiety, instinctual A term used by Freud interchangeably with the term 'neurotic anxiety.' In discussing the meaning and significance of anxiety, Freud distinguishes between true anxiety and neurotic anxiety: true anxiety is anxiety in regard to a known real danger threatening from some external object; neurotic anxiety is anxiety in regard to an unknown danger. Upon investigation, this latter danger is found to be an instinctual danger. Accordingly, the term instinctual anxiety is used to refer to neurotic anxiety. But there are some cases in which neurotic anxiety is intermingled with true anxiety. In these cases the danger is known and real, 'but the anxiety in regard to it is disproportionately great, greater than in our judgment it ought to be.'

In general, anxiety originates as the reaction to helplessness in a traumatic situation. Later on, as the ego develops, it either anticipates that a situation of helplessness will occur, or it is reminded by the present situation of a previous traumatic experience. The situation that causes this anticipation or reminder is called the danger-situation, and the ego now reacts with anxiety, 'a call for help' in the danger-situation. Thus, anxiety has become an expectation of trauma. Through experiencing this anxiety, or call for help, in a danger-situation, the ego is able to attempt to protect itself against, or even master, the threatening situation.

Now, instinctual anxiety is intimately related to anxiety in regard to a real danger. In the case of instinctual anxiety, the ego is anticipating a trauma arising from an instinctual danger. Whether the danger is instinctual or arises in external reality, however, the ego will protect itself in the same way—by means of the anxiety signal. Moreover, instinctual de-

mands often become dangerous only because their gratification would bring about an external danger: therefore an internal danger is tantamount to an external danger.

In its attempt to protect itself against instinctual danger, the ego, 'in consequence of an imperfection of the psychic apparatus,' often finds that it cannot master its instinctual anxiety. As a result its defensive activity eventuates in neurosis. Analysis brings this unknown instinctual danger into consciousness and, in this way, the neurotic or instinctual anxiety becomes a real anxiety, anxiety over a known danger. (Freud, S. *The Problem of Anxiety,* Norton, New York, 1936)

anxiety-neurosis In 1894, Freud detached the particular syndrome of anxiety-neurosis from neurasthenia and described the clinical characteristics of anxiety-neurosis as: general irritability, anxious expectation and pangs of conscience, the anxiety-attack, and phobias. In anxious expectation there is a quantum of anxiety in a free-floating condition which is ever ready to attach itself to any suitable ideational content. Thus common physiological dangers, such as snakes or vermin, are exaggeratedly feared; and the affect of anxiety is also commonly attached to locomotion, as in agoraphobia. But this is not a true hysterical channeling, for it does not originate in a repressed idea. The anxiety attack includes cardiac disturbances, respiratory disturbances, sweating, tremor and shuddering, ravenous hunger often with giddiness, diarrhea, vertigo, congestion and vasomotor neurasthenia, paresthesiae, awakening in fright (the pavor nocturnus of adults), urinary frequency, seminal emissions, blurring of vision, tinnitus, general fatiguability, etc.; in other words, the somatic symptoms may involve any or all of the bodily systems.

Anxiety-neurosis is very uncommon in pure form. Freud considered that the etiology of the anxiety-neurosis was a current or contemporary one, in which forced abstinence, frustrated sexual excitement, incomplete or interrupted coitus, sexual efforts which exceed the psychical capacity, etc. all unite in disturbing the equilibrium of psychical and somatic functions in sexual activity, and in hindering the psychical co-operation necessary to relieve the nervous economy from sexual tension. He found that it appeared in females in the following cases: as virginal anxiety or anxiety in adolescents, provoked by their first meeting with the sexual problem; as anxiety in women whose husbands suffer from ejaculatio praecox or from impaired potency; and as anxiety in women whose husbands practice coitus interruptus or reservatus; as anxiety in widows and voluntarily abstinent persons, when it is often combined with obsessional ideas; as anxiety in the climacteric during the last great increase in sexual need. Anxiety-neurosis appears in men in the following cases: the voluntarily abstinent, in prolonged sexual frustration as in a long courtship without intercourse, in men who practice coitus interruptus, and in aging men.

Freud considered the basis of anxiety-neurosis to be a deflection of somatic sexual excitation from the psychical field, and the symptoms to be substitutes for the specific activity which should follow upon sexual excitation, should such activity be allowed. Neurasthenia, on the other hand, he considered to result from a deflection of methods of sexual gratification from more to less satisfactory means. Anxiety-neurosis would thus be the somatic counterpart of hysteria; the excitation is from the soma and chemically mediated, and it cannot be mastered by the psyche and so is deflected into somatic channels. In hysteria, the excitation results from intrapsychic (rather than somatic) conflict which cannot be mastered and so is deflected into somatic channels.

anxiety, neurotic Freud distinguishes between objective anxiety and neurotic anxiety. He says that the latter is encountered in three forms. 'Firstly, we have free-floating, general apprehensiveness, ready to attach itself for the time being to any new possibility that may arise in the form of what we call expectant dread, as happens, for instance, in the typical anxiety-neurosis. Secondly, we find it firmly attached to certain ideas, in what are known as *phobias,* in which we can still recognize a connection with external danger, but cannot help regarding the anxiety felt toward it as enormously exaggerated. Thirdly and finally, we have anxiety as it occurs in hysteria and in other severe neuroses; this anxiety either accompanies symptoms or manifests itself independently, whether as an attack or as a condition which persists for some time, but al-

ways without having any visible justification in an external danger.' (Freud, S. *New Introductory Lectures on Psycho-Analysis,* tr. by Sprott, W.J.H., Norton, New York, 1933)

anxiety-object The displacement of anxiety to an object that is a symbolic representation of the individual who originally caused the anxiety. For example, a child fears a horse. The horse elicits marked anxiety in the child because the horse is a symbolic representation of the father who was the original focus for anxiety.

anxiety, objective See *anxiety-preparedness.*

anxiety, oral A psychoanalytic term denoting the infantile anxiety occurring at the primary or oral stage of libidinal (personality) development. (See *libido, displaceability of* and *phase, oral incorporative*) It is assumed that such massive expressions of infantile rage and fear are associated with or stem from phantasy images, within the infant, of an immense internal object in countless small pieces. This image, theoretically an analytic reconstruction, has its origin in the ideas of swallowing, incorporating, and chewing up a dangerous or loved object, i.e. the parent, a body organ, or part thereof.

E.F. Sharpe (*Collected Papers on Psycho-analysis,* The Hogarth Press and The Institute of Psychoanalysis, London, 1950) states: 'There must be some correlation between the excessive anxiety in oral stages, which is associated with the phantasy of a huge image in pieces inside; and the fact that at this time there is as little coordination of the bodily as of the psychical ego.'

anxiety, organic The anxiety that is associated with organic pain and that can be markedly attenuated in the dream state by the process of denial, transformation, and displacement; these mechanisms represent attempts at cure through wish-fulfillment.

anxiety, phobic Anxiety associated with a phobia.

anxiety-preparedness This is a Freudian concept. Freud distinguishes between objective anxiety and neurotic anxiety. He describes the former as 'an intelligible reaction to danger—that is, to anticipated injury from without—and the latter altogether puzzling and, as it were, purposeless. In our analysis of objective anxiety we explained it as a condition of increased sensory attention and motor tension, which we called *"anxiety-preparedness."* Out of this the anxiety-reaction arises.' (Freud, S. *New Introductory Lectures on Psycho-Analysis,* tr. by Sprott, W.J.H., Norton, New York, 1933)

anxiety, primal See *anxiety.*

anxiety, psychogenic Anxiety states conditioned by mental causes, such as phobias, obsessions, doubts, indecisions, etc.

anxiety-reaction According to the 1952 revision of psychiatric nomenclature, this is the acceptable term for conditions formerly diagnosed anxiety state, or anxiety-neurosis. See *anxiety-neurosis.*

anxiety, real Anxiety produced by actual danger in the external world of reality. Freud calls it *Realangst* (real anxiety).

anxiety, resolution of A specific psycho-analytic term referring to the therapeutic process through which the unconscious roots of anxiety are brought into consciousness and there mastered, in contrast to other autotherapeutic or psychotherapeutic methods by which conscious or unconscious anxiety is alleviated or prophylactically forefended. The key to the resolution of anxiety is the recovery, in consciousness, by the patient, of repressed, albeit 'forgotten' infantile, instinctual, conflict-ridden experiences, which have been mastered or overcome, and which remain fixation and regression focal points in the pseudo-adult character. Full ego maturity, in the neurotic, cannot be achieved except through this arduous path. All the forces of defense and resistance combine and conspire to defeat this process.

E.F. Sharpe (*Collected Papers on Psycho-analysis,* The Hogarth Press and The Institute of Psychoanalysis, London, 1950) states: 'The work consists of getting behind the scenes that *are* being staged, to those which preceded them. I mean there is a repetition of certain scenes in a drama as though they were the whole story. We have to get the earlier ones to understand the enacted ones and it is against the earlier ones that all the defenses are directed.'

anxiety, separation The reaction seen in a child who is isolated or separated from its mother, consisting usually of tearfulness, irritability, and other signs of distress. This is considered by most to be an indication that the child is attempting to adjust to the changes imposed upon him and, therefore, presumptive evidence of good emotional reactivity. Although these symptoms of protest may culminate in an acute physical upset and in temporary or even prolonged refusal to adjust, the separation symptoms are not in themselves thought to be evidence of personality defect or unbearable trauma. For a discussion of more pathologic reactions to separation, see *depression, anaclitic.*

anxiety, signal See *anxiety.*

anxiety, signal of This psychiatric term denotes the use of anxiety by the ego as a signal that an increase in unpleasure is impending. According to Freud, anxiety is a state of unpleasure in which there is an increase of excitation or tensions produced by stimuli from the external world or from instinctual demands. It originates in the infant in situations of helplessness in which the infant is flooded with excitations it cannot discharge. Later on, as the ego develops, it anticipates that a situation of helplessness will occur or it is reminded by the present situation of a previous traumatic experience. The situation that is the cause of this anticipation is called the danger-situation, and the ego will now react with anxiety, 'a call for help,' in the danger-situation. Thus anxiety has become an expectation of trauma. Through experiencing this anxiety or call for help in a danger-situation, the ego is able to attempt to protect itself against or master the threatening situation. For 'the ego pursues pleasure and seeks to avoid unpleasure.'

In this way the ego has acquired control over the affect of anxiety and itself reproduces it as a signal that a state of unpleasure, a danger, from within or without, is expected and foreseen. Thus the overwhelming anxiety that originally would have developed can be avoided, because, having been forewarned, the ego takes steps to protect itself. (Freud, S. *An Outline of Psychoanalysis,* Norton, New York, 1949)

anxiety, simple MacCurdy's term for a type of depression in which fears of sexual assault and bodily harm are prominent.

anxiety-state, pre-release This term refers to the anxiety phenomena which some individuals, inmates of penal institutions, develop through fear of being set free and having to face the world again. (Seliger,

R.V., et al. *Contemporary Criminal Hygiene,* Oakridge Press, Baltimore, 1946)

anxiety, superego Anxiety caused by the unconscious functioning of the superego, which itself can become a source of continual danger.

anxiety, true See *anxiety, basic.*

anxiety, urethral Tension, anxiety, fear, and inhibition associated with urination.

anxiety, virginal Ferenczi says: 'Virginal anxiety is one of the best known forms of anxiety-neurosis described by Freud. It arises from the fact that the unprepared psyche cannot associate itself with the libido on the occasion of the first sexual experiences.' (Ferenczi, S. *Further Contributions to the Theory and Technique of Psycho-Analysis,* tr. by Suttie, J., Leonard and Virginia Woolf and The Institute of Psychoanalysis, London, 1926)

anypnia (à-nip'ni-à) *Obs.* An older term for sleeplessness.

aochlesia (ā-ō-klē'si-à) *Obs.* An older term for catalepsy.

apandria (à-pan'dri-à) Aversion to men.

apanthropia, apanthropy (ap-an-thrō'pi-à, à-pan'thrō-pē) *Obs.* Aversion to man, to human society.

apastia (à-pas'ti-à) Abstinence from food as a symptom of a psychiatric disorder.

apathetic (ap-à-thet'ik) Without feeling; listless; hebetudinous.

apathy Want of feeling. The term refers to absence of feeling from the psychical, not from the somatic or physical point of view. It means absence of affect. It is observed in vivid form as a symptom in deep, stuporous states of depression and in certain schizophrenic syndromes.

'Pathological states show exaggerations or mixtures of normal moods, or apparent complete absence of affect (apathy).' (Henderson, D.K. and Gillespie, R.D. *A Text-Book of Psychiatry,* 4th ed., Oxford University Press, London, 1936)

'Nevertheless there are many cases of *schizophrenia* which for years show no impulses or affects.' (Bleuler, E. *Textbook of Psychiatry,* tr. by Brill, A.A., Macmillan, New York, 1930)

apathy, disorganization A synonymous expression for despair, one of the two great manifestations of chronic demoralization, the other manifestation being discourage-ment. Disorganization apathy constitutes a problem of morale.

When one recalls that the inculcation of mass despair or disorganization apathy played a successful role in the German psychiatric strategy in the early days of World War II, one immediately realizes the importance of such a technique. 'The person in despair is reduced to a vestigial state of humanness. What goes on in the mind is almost entirely accidental and goes on to no particular purpose.' The behavior of individuals under such a state is purposeless and merely seems to follow a course that leads nowhere. (Sladen, F.J. *Psychiatry and the War,* Thomas, Springfield, Ill., 1943)

apathy, emotional Hebetude.

apathy, euphoric This is an expression used by C.G. Jung, who says that 'we notice the same in the euphoric apathy of dementia praecox.' (*The Psychology of Dementia Praecox*). He refers to happy indifference, analogous to the 'belle indifférence' of the hysterical subject.

apeirophobia (à-pī-rō-fō'bi-à) Fear of infinity.

apepsia hysterica (à-pep'sē-à hēs-ter'ē-kà) *Anorexia nervosa* (q.v.).

aphalgesia (af-al-jē'si-à) E. Tanzi writes that 'a peculiar and not very common manifestation of hysteria is that anomalous condition of sensibility which Pitres has termed *aphalgesia.* It consists in pain, which is caused, either in a particular region or in any part of the body, by contact with some special substance, such as copper, tin, silver or gold. To these may be added juice of lemons, peach-skins, and many other things which produce feelings of repugnance in some patients, even with their eyes closed (idiosyncrasies).' (Tanzi, E. *A Text-Book of Mental Diseases,* tr. by Robertson, W. and Mackenzie, T.C., Rebman, New York, 1909)

aphanisis (à-fan'i-sis) Aphanisis, a term proposed by Jones, refers to extinction of sexuality. He says that 'the concept "castration" should be reserved, as Freud pointed out, for the penis alone, and should not be confounded with that of "extinction of sexuality" for which the term "aphanisis" is proposed. Privation in respect to sexual wishes evokes with the child the fear of aphanisis, i.e., is equivalent to the dread of frustration.' (Jones, E.

Papers on Psycho-Analysis, 4th ed., Wood, Baltimore, 1938)

aphasia (à-fā′zhi-à) A general term for all disturbances of language due to brain lesions but not a result of faulty innervation of the speech muscles, involvement of the organs of articulation, or general mental or intellectual deficiency. The word, language, as used in this definition, refers not only to the expression or communication of thought by word, writing, and gesture, but also to the reception and interpretation of such acts when carried out by others and also to the retention, recall, and visualization of the symbols involved. Thus aphasia would technically include the agnosias and the apraxias.

Head has aptly termed the present state of opinion on the aphasias as 'chaos.' There are many systems of classification, some primarily anatomical (e.g. Bastian, Broadbent, Wernicke), others primarily functional or physiologic (e.g. Jackson, Marie, Goldstein, Head). Anatomical classifications have subdivided the aphasias into the motor type, with lesions in the lower precentral region, and the sensory type, with lesions in the superior temporal, the angular, or the supramarginal gyri. The sensory type is further divided into the cortical, subcortical, and transcortical groups.

Head classified the aphasias as follows:

A. Verbal aphasia—disability in the formulation of words.

B. Syntactical aphasia—inability to arrange words in proper sequence.

C. Nominal aphasia—defective use of words, inability to name objects.

D. Semantic aphasia—inability to recognize the full significance of words.

Following Weisenburg, the following classification has been suggested:

A. Expressive aphasia—apraxia; an inability to execute purposive movements or complex acts in the absence of paralysis of the motor apparatus for carrying out such acts; this group includes oral expressive aphasia or aphemia (comparable to Broca's motor aphasia and Head's verbal aphasia), and usually follows lesions in the lower motor area; also included are agraphia, acalculia, paragraphia or jargon writing, asymbolia, and amimia.

B. Receptive aphasia or agnosia—visual receptive aphasia or visual sensory aphasia or visual agnosia, including alexia (word blindness); auditory receptive aphasia, including word deafness, agrammatism, paraphasia, jargon aphasia.

C. Expressive-receptive aphasia, including total or global aphasia.

D. Amnesic aphasia—comparable to Head's nominal aphasia.

Brain suggests the following classification:

A. Pure word-deafness and word-blindness. In pure (subcortical) word-deafness, the patient distinguishes words from other sounds but does not understand them; the lesion is believed to be in the subcortical white matter beneath the left first temporal convolution. In pure or subcortical word-blindness (visual aphasia), the patient can visualize colors but cannot recognize words, letters, or colors; the lesion is in the lingual gyrus.

B. Visual asymbolia (cortical word-blindness). A combination of visual aphasia with agraphia due to a lesion of the left angular gyrus.

C. Central aphasia (syntactical aphasia). Difficulty in understanding spoken speech is associated with gross disorder of thought and expression, due to a lesion in the left temporo-parietal region; included are such forms as paragrammatism, paraphasia, jargon aphasia, and total aphasia.

D. Nominal aphasia (amnestic aphasia). The patient has difficulty in comprehending spoken and written language due to failure to recognize the meaning of words; the lesion here is usually between the angular gyrus and the first temporal gyrus on the left side.

E. Expressive aphasia (cortical motor aphasia, verbal aphasia). The patient may be completely speechless or he may be reduced to constant repetition of the same word or phrase; the lesion is usually in the third frontal convolution (Broca's area) and the lower part of the precentral convolution.

F. Pure word-dumbness (subcortical motor aphasia). Uttered speech is disturbed as in expressive aphasia, but inner speech is intact, comprehension is unimpaired and writing is normal. The lesion is thought to lie in the white matter in Broca's area.

G. Agraphia, acalculia, amusia. In idiokinetic agraphia, the patient may be able to copy but is unable to write spontaneously; the lesion is in the left angular gyrus. Agraphia may also be produced by a lesion in the second frontal convolution.

In acalculia, there is a defect in the use of mathematical symbols; this usually occurs as a part of aphasia of the expressive type. (Cf. Brain, W.R. *Diseases of the Nervous System,* 4th ed., Oxford University Press, 1951)

aphasia, amnestic Nominal aphasia; a difficulty in finding the right name for an object, even though the subject usually insists that he knows what the object is. In its mildest form, nominal or amnestic aphasia is a common disturbance and is seen following anxiety, fatigue, intoxication, or senility. When due to a focal cerebral lesion, amnestic aphasia usually indicates a lesion between the angular gyrus and the posterior part of the first temporal gyrus on the left side.

aphasia, auditory Word-deafness. 'In pure or subcortical word-deafness the patient distinguishes words from other sounds but does not understand them, so that his own language sounds to him like a foreign tongue. Sometimes he recognizes the meaning of an individual word, but not of a whole sentence. Owing to this defect he cannot repeat words or write to dictation, but there is no other change in speaking, reading or spontaneous writing. . . . The lesion is thought to be in the subcortical white matter beneath the posterior part of the left first temporal convolution.' (Brain, W.R. *Diseases of the Nervous System,* 4th ed., Oxford University Press, 1951)

aphasia, central Syntactical aphasia. 'In central aphasia, the difficulty in understanding spoken speech is associated with gross disorder of thought and expression. Spoken speech is fluent, in marked contrast to the speech of the patient with expressive aphasia, but it is disordered by verbal and grammatical confusions—paragrammatism—difficulty in evoking words as names for objects, actions, and qualities, and the utterance of non-existent or incorrect words—paraphasia (the syntactical aphasia of Head). The comprehension of spoken speech is impaired, but reading is less affected, and the patient can usually understand what he reads silently, though if he reads aloud he may be confused by the inaccuracies in his verbal expression of what he sees. Writing is usually less affected than articulate speech. Defective comprehension of spoken speech prevents the patient from noticing his own errors in speaking, and in severe cases he pours forth a stream of unintelligible jargon (jargon aphasia). The lesion responsible for central aphasia is situated in the left temporo-parietal region.' (Brain, W.R. *Diseases of the Nervous System,* 4th ed., Oxford University Press, 1951)

aphasia, congenital A more or less general term used in the fields of neurology and neuropsychiatry. It refers to the inborn or constitutionally determined clinical symptomatic appearance of varied types of verbal or symbol-handling difficulty. The specific disability may appear in the fields of speaking, reading, writing, spelling, arithmetic, and even musical appreciation. The reading disability (dyslexia, i.e. congenital word-blindness) has received the most intensive study.

Specific reading, writing, and spelling difficulty is often found connected with a tendency to reverse letters and words in reading and writing. This condition has been named *strephosymbolia.*

'Congenital word-deafness, a rare form of congenital aphasia, is characterized by the inability of otherwise intelligent children to comprehend the meaning of words heard. Deafness, in the ordinary sense, is not present.'

Certain forms of congenital aphasia, like stuttering, seem connected with the whole question of *handedness, eyedness, footedness, laterality,* or the predominance, physiologically, of one cerebral hemisphere over the other in motor function. (Hunt, J.McV. *Personality and the Behavior Disorders,* vol. 2, Ronald, New York, 1944)

aphasia, expressive See *aphasia, motor.*

aphasia, global Total aphasia, which results from massive destruction of the fronto-temporal region of the left hemisphere.

aphasia, jargon A type of central or syntactical aphasia in which the patient pours forth a stream of unintelligible jargon. See *aphasia, central.*

aphasia, motor Expressive aphasia; verbal aphasia; word-dumbness. 'In this form of aphasia the expressive aspect of speech suffers severely. In severe cases the patient may be completely speechless or able to say only "yes" or "no," and even these words may be inappropriately used and cannot be repeated to order. He may be limited to the same phrase constantly repeated—a recurring utterance. Emotional speech suffers less than "propositional," and an otherwise almost speechless individual may be able to swear or utter other emotional ejaculations. . . . When the patient cannot think of the right word himself he will recognize it when it is offered to him.' (Brain, W.R. *Diseases of the Nervous System*, 4th ed., Oxford University Press, 1951.) The lesion responsible for motor aphasia is usually in the posterior part of the third frontal convolution (Broca's area) and the lower part of the precentral convolution.

Brain also differentiates a type of aphasia called pure word-dumbness or subcortical motor aphasia in which uttered speech is disturbed in the same way as above but in which there are no associated disturbances in inner speech, comprehension, or writing. The lesion here is thought to be deep in the white matter in Broca's area.

aphasia, nominal See *aphasia, amnestic.*

aphasia, semantic The inability to grasp the meaning of words or speech. The patient may be able to utter words but does not understand their significance. He perceives the words, but does not apperceive them.

aphasia, sensory Receptive aphasia; inability to perceive speech by the senses, regardless of the retention of the power of using speech, which is usually meaningless and confined to parrot-like utterances. Sensory aphasia may combine visual aphasia and auditory aphasia.

aphasia, syntactical See *aphasia, central.*

aphasia, total Global aphasia; a combination of motor and sensory aphasia. See *aphasia, global.*

aphasia, verbal See *aphasia, motor.*

aphasia, visual Word-blindness. In pure (subcortical) form, the patient can visualize colors but cannot recognize words, letters, or colors; he can write spontaneously but cannot copy. The lesion is in the lingual gyrus.

Visual aphasia is more often combined with agraphia; this is known as visual asymbolia or cortical word-blindness and is produced by a lesion of the left angular gyrus. Inability to read is termed alexia.

aphelxia (af-elk'si-à) See *ecphronia.*

aphemia (à-fē'mi-à) Speechlessness; loss of power of speech. An earlier term for the disorder known as *aphasia* (q.v.).

aphemia hysterica (hēs-te'rē-kà) Inability to speak, due to hysteria.

aphemia pathematica (pà-thā-mà'tē-kà) Loss of speech due to fright.

aphemia plastica (plàs'tē-kà) Voluntary *mutism* (q.v.).

aphemia spasmodica (spàz-mô'dē-kà) Spasmodic speechlessness.

aphephobia (af-ē-fō'bi-à) Haptephobia; haphephobia; fear of being touched.

aphilanthropia (à-fi-lan-thrō'pi-à) Asociability. An old term, coined by Wedelius.

aphonia, aphony (à-fō'ni-à, af'ō-nē) Voicelessness; dumbness. Aphony may be due to organic or psychic causes, though the term is generally used today with organic etiology in mind. Aphony conveys the idea that the patient is unable to use his voice owing to structural or organic changes.

'Loss of speech is, therefore, the loss of power to propositionize.' (Head, H. *Aphasia and Kindred Disorders of Speech*, University Press, Cambridge (England), 1926) See also *catalepsy; speech disorders.*

aphonia, hysterical Inability to speak, appearing as a symptom in and of hysteria. Hysteria is a neurosis and is a consequence of a conflict in the unconscious part of the psyche. When the mental struggle, unacceptable to the conscious mind, gains expression by means of physical symptoms, the condition is known as conversion hysteria, provided the conversion phenomena occur in a hysterical individual. Thus, aphonia appearing as the physical symptom through which an emotional conflict is gaining expression is called hysterical aphonia. An emotional conflict has simply been converted into a physical symptom. The symptom has an entirely emotional causation, not an organic one.

aphoria (à-fō'ri-à) In the chapter devoted to treatment by rest, P. Janet speaks of 'the incapacity for being trained (in the athletic sense), or "aphoria," as Deschamps terms it. The subjects are absolutely incapable of being trained as we can train one who is in good health or one who is convalescent from illness. There may not seem to be much amiss with them; but they [neurotics] are constitutionally incapable of increasing their stores of energy by regular exercise, as really healthy people can do. If the patient takes five or ten years in learning how to walk for five minutes longer, can we call that training? The same fundamental disorder is responsible for the amyosthenia, or diminution of motor activity, and for the amyotony, or decline in automatic muscular tone.' (Janet, P. *Psychological Healing*, vols. 1–2, tr. by Paul, E. and C., Macmillan, New York, 1925)

aphraenous (à-frē′nus) An older term for *insane.*

aphrasia (à-frā′zhi-à) Inability to utter or understand words connected in the form of phrases. A subdivision of *aphasia* (q.v.) which involves only the order of words in the phrase and goes a stage beyond individual words: the patient's power (1) *expressive* (motor), i.e. to utter, or (2) *perceptive* (sensory), i.e. to understand *single words* may be unimpaired, whereas *groups* of words forming phrases may baffle him completely as far as using or understanding them is concerned. See also *speech disorders.*

aphrasia paranoica (par-à-nō′i-kà) See *paranoia.* An old expression referring to the clinical syndrome characterized by stupor followed by talkativeness.

aphrenia (à-frē′ni-à) Dementia. At one time aphrenia was used synonymously with apoplexy, but that usage is now obsolete. The expression has been handed down to refer to the loss or dysfunction of the conscious mind, in contrast to the unconscious mind. With that meaning in view, older authorities used the term in a generic sense to indicate that the conscious mind was not functioning at all or was functioning in a morbid way. Hence, unconsciousness in the sense of unawareness was called aphrenia. So, too, unawareness or inattention to oneself and to one's environment, common in advanced states of schizophrenia, was referred to as aphrenia. It is a well-established fact that patients, to whom the term dementia is applied, may have a very rich and active mind, though the mind may have little or no natural relationships with the objective world.

Strictly speaking, therefore, aphrenia or dementia is possible only in acephalism.

aphrodisia (af-rō-diz′i-à) the state of sexual excitation.

aphrodisiac Characterized by sexual exci-

tation; also, any agent (e.g. odor) that stimulates sexual activity.

'In close relation to stuff-fetishism cases must be considered in which beasts exercise an aphrodisiacal influence over human beings. One feels tempted to call it *Zoophilia Erotica.*' (Krafft-Ebing, R. v. *Psychopathia Sexualis,* Samuel Login, New York, 1908)

aphrodisia phrenitica (frā-nē′tē-kà) An older term for a psychiatric state due, as was thought, to sexual causes.

aphrodisiomania (af-rō-diz-i-ō-mā′ni-à) The state of excessive sexual excitement; morbid desire for venery; erotomania.

aphronesia (àf-rō-nē′zi-à) *Obs.* Dementia.

aphthongia (àf-thông′ē-à, àf-thông′jē-à) A form of motor aphasia characterized by spasm of the speech muscles.

apiphobia (à-pi-fō′bi-à) Morbid dread of bees.

aplasia (à-plā′zhi-à) Aplasia refers to complete or partial failure of tissue to grow or develop. When tissue ceases at some stage to develop form and structure that is appropriate for the age of the organism, it is said to be aplastic. As a generality, aplasia means arrested development. It is to be distinguished from atrophy, which refers to the loss or diminution of structure which once had normal or average development.

Aplasia is synonymous with agenesis; when tissue growth is partial, the term hypoplasia is used; when it is above average, one speaks of hyperplasia.

Speaking of aplasias of the cerebellum, Jelliffe and White say: 'These are congenital and represent a vast array of different conditions; total lack of cerebellum, absence of the lateral (in old sense) lobes, absence of vermis, unilateral loss, irregular defects, and general congenital smallness of the cerebellum and cerebrum.' (Jelliffe, S.E. and White, W.A. *Diseases of the Nervous System,* 6th ed., Lea & Febiger, Philadelphia, 1935)

aplastic (ā-plas′tik) Without power to grow toward normal, healthy tissue.

aplestia (àp-les′ti-à) Greediness.

apocarteresis (ap-ō-kär-tē-rē′sis) Suicide by hunger or starvation.

apocleisis (ap-ō-klē′sis) Aversion to, or absence of desire for, food.

apomathema (ap-ō-math'ē-mȧ) *Obs.* Loss of memory.

apoplectic See *habitus apoplecticus.*

apoplexia cataleptica (ap-ō-plek'si-ȧ kat-ȧ-lep'ti-kȧ) *Obs.* Catalepsy.

apoplexy The term has had different implications at different times. In the early use of the word it referred to a clinical state of mental and physical disability induced presumably by some external force. In early Greek medicine (Galen) the body and the mind were one. At another time apoplexy was synonymous with catalepsy. (Tuke, D.H. *A Dictionary of Psychological Medicine,* vols. 1–2, Blakiston, Philadelphia, 1892)

As used today, the term is associated with the symptoms due to acute vascular lesion of the brain, the principal causes of which are arteriosclerosis and syphilis. 'The favorable site, then, is in the central or basal ganglia, with predominant involvement of the internal and external capsules, thalamus, and striate body.' (Wechsler, I.S. *Textbook of Clinical Neurology,* 4th ed., Saunders, Philadelphia, 1939, p. 349). The arteries usually involved are the lenticulo-striate and lenticulo-optic. See *accident, cerebrovascular.*

apopnixis (ȧ-pop-nik'sis) Globus hystericus (Moschion).

apositia (ap-ō-sish'i-ȧ) Hippocrates used this term to mean a loathing of food.

apostle of the idiots The title generally applied to Édouard Séguin (1812–80), a French psychiatrist whose life-work was the care and welfare of the mentally deficient.

apparatus, autonomic From the standpoint of Kempf 'the autonomic apparatus is constituted of all the vital organs, including the ductless secretory glands, unstriped muscles and the ganglionic nervous systems that have to do with the *assimilation, conservation, distribution* and *expenditure* of energy-giving metabolic products and the *elimination* of the waste products. This includes the entire digestive, circulatory, respiratory and urinary systems, sex organs, glands of internal secretion, glands of external secretion and the autonomic nervous system.' (Kempf, E.J. *Psychopathology,* Mosby, St. Louis, 1921)

apparatus, autonomic affective This is an expression used by Kempf, who says that 'the various systems of the body, if grouped according to their functions, form two great divisions, the *autonomic apparatus* and its *projicient apparatus.* The sensory streams flowing from the periphery of different segments of the autonomic apparatus constitute the affective cravings or feelings, and the sensory streams flowing from the projicient apparatus, as it is compelled to work by the affective stream, constitutes the kinesthetic stream.' Kempf further writes: 'Since all of the autonomic apparatus is more or less active all the time, the stream of cravings flowing from its tensions is more or less active; that is, all of our wishing functions whether we are conscious of them or not are more or less active all the time. Each moment's behavior is the resultant of the manner in which the cravings, re-enforcing or inhibiting one another, converge upon the striped muscle; hence, upon the sequence of acts or stream of activity, and the content of consciousness.

'The innumerable compensatory strivings of the autonomic apparatus that become conditioned to attain social esteem as well as segmental gratification become integrated into a *unity* or *ego* which is opposed by the segments which tend to compel actions that may jeopardize the *ego.* In this manner the conflict between the *ego* and the not quite socially justifiable or utterly unjustifiable cravings becomes established and is incessantly waged even in the normal. *In the psychoses the conflict is far more severe than normal, due to the vigor of the segment or the weakness of the ego.*' (Kempf, E.J. *Psychopathology,* Mosby, St. Louis, 1921)

apparatus, lie detector See *detector, lie.*

apparatus, mental A more or less colloquial term for mental structure.

apparatus, projicient (prō-jish'ent) Kempf says that 'the striped muscle apparatus and the cerebrospinal nervous system proper constitute the *projicient apparatus* which has been developed by the autonomic apparatus in order to master the environment.' (Kempf, E.J. *Psychopathology,* Mosby, St. Louis, 1921)

apparition 'Delusion of a dreadful dream' (Scott) : a visual hallucination. The term is not in common usage in psychiatry. In former years it referred to visual hallucinations, particularly of false visual impressions appearing in delirious states.

Since an apparition implies the false interpretation of a real, external object, it is incorrect to speak of it as a hallucination; it is an illusion, resulting from the visual distortion of an object and the interpretation of the object in terms of the (usually unconscious and morbid) impulses of the individual. In alcoholic delirium, for instance, an object (any piece of furniture in the room) may be regarded as a person who is about to kill the patient. The delusion of impending death or assault is represented by visual distortion. In the delirium of the senile individual, the visual illusion may be interpreted in terms of a pleasant experience of the past.

apperception Conscious realization, i.e. when the individual is aware of the content of his mind.

That part of the content of the mind of which he is unaware or upon which he is not focusing his attention is subsumed under the heading imperception or agnosia. Apperception implies clear and correct recognition of things in the mind. When a mental image is clearly perceived, but is falsely interpreted or understood, one speaks of abnormal apperception.

Leibnitz, who first used the term, said: 'It is well to make a distinction between perception, which is the inner state of the monad, representing external things, and apperception, which is consciousness, or the reflexive knowledge of this interior state, which is not given to all souls, nor always to the same soul.' (*Nature and Grace*, trans. by N. Porter)

It is said that 'his (Leibnitz's) actual meaning is practically coincident with that of attention in modern psychology.' (Baldwin, J.M. *Dictionary of Philosophy and Psychology*, vols. 1–2, Macmillan, New York, 1928)

From the standpoint of analytical psychology (Jung), apperception 'is a psychic process by which a new content is articulated to similar already-existing contents in such a way as to be understood, apprehended or clear. We discriminate *active* from *passive* apperception; the former is a process by which the subject, by himself, from his own motives, consciously and attentively apprehends a new content and assimilates it to another content standing in readiness; the latter is a process in which a new content from without (through the senses) or from within

(from the unconscious) presses through into consciousness, and, to a certain extent, compels attention and apprehension upon itself. In the former case, the accent of activity lies with the ego; in the latter with the obtruding new content.' (Jung, C.G. *Psychological Types*, tr. by Baynes, H.G., Harcourt, Brace, New York & London, 1923)

apperception, scheme of By this term Adler indicates that the individual perceives what he wishes to perceive, and selects from his whole experience what is useful in view of his directive fiction, forgetting or rejecting the rest of reality.

apperceptions, Gestalt See *intelligence*.

appersonification, appersonation Appersonification is the act of embodiment or impersonation of another. From the psychiatric point of view it generally implies a form of unconscious identification with another in part or in whole. While the phenomenon occurs in many psychiatric conditions, it is very overtly expressed in patients with schizophrenia. A patient is thoroughly convinced that he is Christ; another says that he is the person who died in the next bed; a third affirms that she has the cancer her husband had.

appetite, depraved *Obs.* Pica.

appetitus caninus (ăp-pe-tē′toos kă-nē′noos) (L. 'doglike appetite') *Obs.* Bulimia.

apprehensio (ăp-pre-hen′sē-ō) P. Zacchias used this term for catalepsy.

apprehension Royce defines the term as '(1) The intellectual act or process by which a relatively simple object is understood, grasped, or brought before the mind. (2) A relatively simple or elementary intellectual act itself (without regard to its object), as opposed to a complex act, such as judgment, or a more finished sort of knowledge, such as comprehension.' (Baldwin, J.M. *Dictionary of Philosophy and Psychology*, vols. 1–2, Macmillan, New York, 1928, p. 62)

If the object is not understood correctly, the expression misapprehension is used. Apprehension is 'merely a simple cognition.' (ibid.) In his *Critique of Pure Reason*, Kant regards apprehension as a synthetic act, in which a perceived object is described in terms of time and space.

The history of the word apprehension shows that it has been used synonymously with a variety of words: intellectuality, cognition, perception, conception, retention, attention, memory, imagination, emotion, etc. In psychiatry such synonymous use has been abandoned.

There is a tendency today to disregard also another meaning of the term, viz. a mental concept from which one judges what may happen in the future. The inclusion of a prophetic implication is now less frequently associated with the word, when used by psychiatrists. When it is used in this sense, it is almost invariably connected with the feeling of fear, anxiety, or dread. States of so-called apprehension are common in psychiatric practice and are generally identified with fear of impending danger. There is a tendency, however, to use more circumscribed expressions, such as anxiety, in place of such a general term as apprehension.

apprehension, irresistible Kraepelin's diagnostic term for what is now termed the compulsive-obsessive form of psychoneurosis.

apprehensiveness The faculty of apprehending, of seizing quickly with the mind. Just as the term apprehension, as used in psychiatry, is gradually narrowing to the field of intelligence and is losing its association with the emotional life of the individual, so too, apprehensiveness is undergoing a similar restriction of meaning. Indeed, the term is not used as commonly as it used to be. It is too loose and general, ranging in meaning from an ill-defined intellectual process to an equally ill-defined emotional quality. The newer emotional psychology has served to be more definitive in the use of expressions formerly very general.

Psychiatrists seldom use the term today to refer to the act of ready and quick apprehension. But the tendency to use the adjective apprehensive to imply anticipation of evil or harm is common.

approach, environmental From the standpoint of the psychiatric social worker 'the *personal approach* is through the interview as it is employed to explore emotional reactions, interpret conflicts, suggest new points of view and stimulate interest in new lines of action. The *environmental approach* covers essentially manipulation of the material situations presented by physical illness, financial difficulty, employment, neighborhood conditions, etc.; this manipulation of the environment is

exercised to relieve undue external pressure and call forth new and better attitudes in the client toward his responsibilities so that ultimately he may carry them unassisted.' (*Proceedings of the American Association of Hospital Social Workers,* 1926) See *treatment, psychiatric social.*

apraxia (à-prak'si-à) A disorder of voluntary movement in which the patient is more or less completely incapacitated to carry out purposeful movements, in spite of the absence of paralysis or other motor or sensory impairment.

apraxia, akinetic A condition in which the ability to carry out spontaneous movements is lost.

apraxia, amnestic Inability to carry out a movement on command, owing to inability to remember a command—though there is the ability to perform that movement.

apraxia, ideational Sensory apraxia. The patient does not know the use of objects; he may fumble with a toothbrush, pen or cigarette, but will not know what to do with them.

apraxia, motor Along with ability to understand and name objects, the inability to carry out the purposive movement with them.

apraxia, sensory See *apraxia, ideational.*

aprosexia (ap-rō-sek'si-à) Inability to maintain attention. The condition is common among organic states that affect the brain and amid psychiatric conditions in which (1) there are present overwhelming emotions that constantly interfere with thought processes; (2) ideas are sparse, as in states of pronounced depression; (3) ideas are so abundant that the patient cannot fix attention upon external objects, as in productive mania; (4) fixed ideas of the patient compel his constant attention. The patient may show excellent attentive capacity when his special interests are involved, that is, aprosexia may be selective for certain matters.

apsithyria, apsithuria (ap-si-thī'ri-à, -thū'ri-à) *Obs.* Aphonia.

apsychia (ap-sik'i-à, à-sī'ki-à) *Obs.* Loss of consciousness.

apsychosis (à-sī-kō'sis) This infrequently used term is defined by F.M. Barnes, Jr. as 'absence of function.' He explains that 'in this condition thought processes may be said to be entirely absent, as, for example, in certain cases of stupor'; he adds: 'the term *psychosis* is here used in the limited psychologic sense meaning any thought process, either normal or abnormal and not in the psychiatric clinical sense of insanity or mental disorder.' (Barnes, F.M. *An Introduction to the Study of Mental Disorders,* 2nd ed., Mosby, St. Louis, 1923)

Barnes speaks of *hyperpsychosis* (exaggeration of function), *hypopsychosis* (diminution of function), and *parapsychosis* (perversion of function).

aptitude In occupational therapy, the ability and natural skill of a patient in certain lines of endeavor. Information on this point is of great importance in prescribing a suitable occupation for a patient.

A.Q. Abbreviation for *accomplishment quotient.*

aquaphobia (ak-wà-fō'bi-à) A special morbid fear of water, i.e. of going (for bathing or swimming purposes) into a *body* of water where one may drown. Of somewhat questionable impeccability in composition, this psychiatric term is undeniably serviceable as a label for this particular fear, because the well-known word *hydrophobia* (literally its equivalent, with the Greek *hýdōr,* water, in lieu of Latin *aqua* as the first half) has acquired an entirely different and narrowly restricted meaning in the English language. (Law, S. *Therapy through Interview,* McGraw-Hill, New York, 1948)

arachnephobia (ä-rak-nē-fō'bi-à) Fear of spiders.

arachnoid (a-räk'noid) See *meninges.*

arachnoiditis See *pseudotumor cerebri.*

arc de cercle (ärk dē ser'kl', F., arc or segment of a circle) A pathological posture characterized by pronounced bending of the body, anteriorly or posteriorly.

The condition, usually appearing as opisthotonos, may be induced by organic or psychical causes. It is sometimes observed as a symptom of hysteria.

'Possibly the well-known *arc de cercle* of major hysterical attacks is nothing but an energetic disavowal of this kind [viz. antagonistic inversion of the innervation], by antagonistic innervation of the position suitable for sexual intercourse.' (Freud, S. *Collected Papers,* vol. 2, tr. by Riviere, J., Leonard and Virginia Woolf and the Institute of Psychoanalysis, London, 1924–25) The arc described by Freud in this instance has its convexity in a backward direction (emprosthotonos).

In describing a phase of so-called hystero-epilepsy, one author says: 'a period of disordered movements commences, which generally begins with the phenomenon called a "segment of a circle" (l'arc de cercle), very analogous to that observed in some tetanic patients; the body rests on the feet and occiput only; the trunk is raised, and according to the expression of the patients forms a kind of "bridge" on the bed; most frequently this segment of the circle consists in opisthotonos, more rarely pleurosthotonos, sometimes also in emprosthotonos.' (Tuke, D.H. *A Dictionary of Psychological Medicine,* vols. 1–2, Blakiston, Philadelphia, 1892)

archaeology The science of antiquities. This term denotes the science which studies the history, use, and meaning of prehistoric objects in different countries, in order to throw light on the remote past of mankind (see *anthropology*).

'Under unusually favorable conditions *archaeological* data give us information on the gradual changes of material culture and allow also inferences regarding a few aspects of the inner life of the people.' (Boas, F. *General Anthropology,* Heath, Boston, 1938)

archaic The psyche appears to have its own ancestral past just as the soma possesses its historical background. It seems that, from the psychical point of view also, ontogeny repeats phylogeny. Thought and language in their development progress from feeling, concreteness, and perception to reasoning, differentiation, and abstraction. Psychiatrists recognize psychical material (primordial images) which is representative of the distant past of humanity or which is expressed in the framework of primitive mentality. Concepts may be modern, yet they may be expressed in accordance with the laws of primitive mentality. The latter is common in the psychoneuroses, while in the psychoses, particularly schizophrenia, both the psychical contents and their vehicle of expression may closely resemble those of a much earlier stage of mental development.

archaism From the standpoint of analytical psychology (Jung), archaism means 'the *ancient* character of psychic contents and functions. By this I do not mean archaistic, i.e., imitated antiquity, as exhibited for instance in later Roman sculpture or the nineteenth century "Gothic," but qualities which have the character of *survival*. All those psychological traits can be so described which essentially correspond with the qualities of primitive mentality. It is clear that archaism primarily clings to the phantasies of the unconscious, i.e., to such products of unconscious phantasy-activity as reach consciousness. The quality of the image is archaic when it possesses unmistakable mythological parallels.' (Jung, C.G. *Psychological Types*, tr. by Baynes, H.G., Harcourt, Brace, New York and London, 1923)

A mental image derived from the deepest layers of the mind, is said by Hall to be a 'relic of the most central experiences of many generations, a fleeting fancy, all that survives of ages of toil and blood, a feeling that only peeps out for a moment in infancy, the far-off dying echo of what was once the voice of a great multitude. Yet these psychophones, whatever they are, are wax to receive and marble to retain.' (Hall, G.S. *Adolescence,* vol. 2, Appleton, New York, 1908, pp. 64–5)

archeopsychism (ar-kē-ō-sĭ′kiz'm) See *archaism.*

archetype (är′kē-tīp) 'In the theory of C.J. Jung, an inherited idea or mode of thought, derived from the experience of the race, and present in the unconscious of the individual, controlling his ways of perceiving the world.' (*Webster's New International Dictionary,* 2nd ed., Merriam, Springfield, Mass., 1948.) An understanding of Jung's concept of these archetypes, especially with regard to his application of them in therapy, is basic for an understanding of Jung's system of psychology.

The unconscious part of the mind is separated by Jung into two subdivisions, termed by him the *personal* unconscious and the *collective* unconscious. (1) The *personal* unconscious lies directly beneath consciousness and contains psychic material that is not in consciousness, yet is subject to conscious recall. Because it has to do with the person's life-experience this material can be made conscious, at least theoretically, since we are dealing with the actual person whom it concerns. Thus the term personal unconscious is particularly apt. (2) Constituting by far the largest area of the mind, and situated beneath the personal unconscious, is the *collective* unconscious. The material contained in this area is *not* derived from the life-experience of the person, but from the life-experience of the person's progenitors, *all of them,* and, therefore, of the entire human race. The whole history of human psychic functioning, the collective experience of humanity, is the inheritance of each individual psyche. The record of this history and experience contains ideas, modes of thought, patterns of reaction that are fundamental and typical in all humanity: the archetypes are their representations in the collective unconscious.

'The form of these archetypes is perhaps comparable to the axial system of a crystal, which predetermines as it were the crystalline formation in the saturated solution, without itself possessing a material existence. This existence first manifests itself in the way the ions and then the molecules arrange themselves . . . The axial system determines, accordingly, merely the stereometric structure, not, however, the concrete form of the individual crystal . . . and just so the archetype possesses . . . an invariable core of meaning that determines its manner of appearing always only in principle, never concretely.' (Jung, C.J. *Die psychologischen Aspekte des Mutter-Archetypus,* Eranos-Jahrbuch, 1938, Rhein-Verlag, Zürich, 1939)

Jung believed that the collective unconscious represented the wisdom of the ages and, in consequence, contained tendencies superior to the individual's. This conception 'had a significant influence on his therapeutic approach. A part of the process of self-development consisted in bringing a person into contact with his collective unconscious. This was done to a great extent through the interpretation of dreams. Jung saw the dream as having meanings on several levels. There was the personal meaning relating to the immediate life of the patient. If one pushed associations beyond that, one finally reached the collective unconscious meaning. Thus a dream about the father would finally come to a conception of all fatherhood, the father archetype. At this level supposedly the knowledge acquired by mankind through the centuries becomes available to the patient.' (Thompson, C. *Psychoanalysis: Evolution and Development,* Hermitage House, New York, 1950)

'In the language of the unconscious, which is a picture-language, the archetypes appear in personified or symbolized picture form. Their number is relatively limited, for it corresponds to the "possibilities of typical fundamental experiences," such as human beings have had since the beginning of time. Their significance for us lies precisely in that "primal experience" which they represent and mediate. The motives of the archetypal images are the same in all cultures. We find them repeated in all mythologies, fairy tales, religious traditions, and mysteries. What else is the myth of the night sea-voyage, of the wandering hero, or of the sea monster than our timeless knowledge, transformed into a picture of the sun's setting and rebirth? Prometheus, the stealer of fire, Hercules, the slayer of dragons, the numerous myths of creation, the fall from Paradise, the sacrificial mysteries, the virgin birth, the treacherous betrayal of the hero, the dismembering of Osiris, and many other myths and tales portray psychic processes in symbolic-imaginary form. Likewise the forms of the snake, the fish, the sphinx, the helpful animals, the World Tree, the Great Mother, and otherwise the enchanted prince, the *puer aeternus,* the Magi, the Wise Man, Paradise, etc., stand for certain figures and contents of the collective unconscious. The sum of the archetypes signifies thus for Jung the sum of all the latent potentialities of the human psyche—an enormous, inexhaustible store of ancient knowledge concerning the most profound relations between God, man, and the cosmos.' (Jacobi, J. *The Psychology of C.G. Jung,* Kegan Paul, Trench, Trubner, London, 1942)

archetype, mother Jung's term denoting a specific archetype, the archetype 'Mother.' An archetype is an inherited idea, mode of thought, or pattern of reaction derived from the experience of the race. It is present in the unconscious part of the mind and is universally more or less the same in content in all individuals. An understanding of Jung's concept of archetypes is fundamental for an understanding of his system of psychology. See *archetype*.

Jung's method of treatment in psychiatry involves a procedure which he termed *individuation.* 'The process of individuation is an intense analytical effort which concentrates, with strictest integrity and under the direction of consciousness, upon the internal psychological process, eases the tension in the pairs of opposites by means of highest activation of the contents of the unconscious, acquires a working knowledge of their structure, and leads through all the distresses of a psyche that has lost its equilibrium, hacking through layer upon layer, to that center which is the source and ultimate ground of our psychic existence—to the inner core, the Self.' (Jacobi, J. *The Psychology of C.G. Jung,* Kegan Paul, Trench, Trubner, London, 1942)

Jacobi states further that 'the course of individuation has been roughly plotted and exhibits a certain formal regularity. Its sign posts and milestones are various archetypal symbols, whose form and manifestation vary according to the individual. To describe the archetypal symbols of the individuation process in all the manifold forms in which they appear would require a thorough knowledge and consideration of the different mythologies and of symbolic accounts of human history.' (ibid.) There exist, however, certain archetypes that seem to be universally identified with and characteristic of the four principal stages of the individuation process. They are, in chronological order: (1) the archetype of the shadow; (2) the archetype of the soul-image; (3) the archetype (in men) of the old wise man or of the Magna Mater (in women); (4) the archetype of the self.

'The archetype "Mother" is pre-existent and superordinate to every form of manifestation of the "motherly." It is a constant core of meaning, which can take on all the aspects and symbols of the "motherly." The primordial image of the mother and the characteristics of the "Great Mother" with all paradoxical traits are the same in the soul of present-day man as in mythological times.' (ibid.) See *Magna Mater.*

arc, psychic reflex While discussing hysteria Ferenczi refers to 'topographical regression to a depth in the psychic apparatus at which states of excitation are no longer disposed of by means of a mental cathexis—even if only hallucinatorily—but simply by a motor discharge.' He says that 'chronologically this region of the mind corresponds to a very primitive onto- and phylogenetic stage of development, in which adaptation was not yet achieved by a modification of the outer world, but by modifications of the individual's own body.' (Ferenczi, S. *Further Contributions to the Theory and Technique of Psycho-Analysis,* tr. by Suttie, J., Leonard and Virginia Woolf and The Institute of Psychoanalysis, London, 1926). It is the autoplastic stage described by Freud.

'We should have to conceive the psychic processes here as simplified in *form* to the level of a physiological reflex.' (ibid.)

area, delinquency A neighborhood or community with a disproportionately high rate of juvenile delinquents. It is typically an area adjacent to the central business district or a major industrial development and 'characterized by physical deterioration, decreasing population, high rates of dependency, high percentages of foreign-born and Negro population, high rates of adult offenders and marked deterioration of the traditional institutions and neighborhood organization.' (Shaw, C.R. and McKay, H.D. *Social Factors in Juvenile Delinquency,* National Commission on Law Observance and Enforcement, Government Printing Office, Washington, D.C., 1931)

area striata (â′rē-à strē-ā′ta) See *lobe, occipital.*

Argyll Robertson pupil (Argyll Robertson, Scottish physician, 1837–1909) A pupil, usually myotic, which responds to accommodation but does not respond to light and reacts slowly to mydriatics. It is usually found in patients with neurosyphilis, although it may appear in other conditions (traumatic brain injury, brain tumor, infectious diseases of the brain, multiple sclerosis, etc.).

Ariëns Kappers (ä′ri-ens käp′ērs) **Cornelius Ubbo,** (1877–   ) Dutch neuropathologist.

aristogenic (a-ris-tō-jen′ik) Best-endowed eugenically. A term describing the individuals whose parenthood is to be encouraged through *positive* eugenic measures. See *eugenics.*

arithmomania (à-rith-mō-mā′ni-à) A morbid impulse to count. The condition may be observed in a variety of psychiatric disorders, though it achieves special distinction among psychoneurotic individuals, particularly those with a compulsive-obsessive syndrome. Thus, a patient had to count more or less incessantly from one to thirty-three and then back to one. If he

did not count backward, he would experience an attack of anxiety.

'Case 6. Obsession of arithmomania. A woman became obliged to count the boards in the floor, the steps in the staircase, etc. —acts which she performed in a state of ridiculous distress.

Reinstatement. She had begun the counting in order to turn her mind from obsessive ideas of temptation. She had succeeded in so doing, but the impulse to count had replaced the original obsession.' (Freud, S. *Collected Papers,* vol. 1, tr. by Riviere, J., Leonard and Virginia Woolf and the Institute of Psychoanalysis, London, 1924–25)

arousal Cortical vigilance, or readiness, or tone, which is presumed to be in response to sensory stimulation (? via the reticular activating system). See *formation, reticular.*

arrangement, neurotic This term is applied to describe the construction and marshaling of erroneous ideas on the part of a neurotic patient in order to justify his neurosis with apparently logical reasons, by rearranging the events of his life to suit his neurosis. These patients have an ingenious way of accounting for their failures; for instance, a man asserted that he had a 'historic mission' to accomplish in life, yet did nothing in that direction and justified his hidden inferiority by saying to himself: 'If you had sound nerves, if you did not suffer from night terrors, you would have gone far.' This type of neurotic arrangement does not confine itself to the simple construction of erroneous ideas but may also be present in the somatic sphere: the patient magnifies an existing organ inferiority or creates one if it does not exist. (Stekel, W. *The Interpretation of Dreams,* Liveright, New York, 1943)

arreptio (a-rep′shō) *Obs.* Insanity.

arrhostia (a-rōs′ti-à) *Obs.* Imbecillitas.

ars amandi (ärs′ à-màn′dē) A poetical expression for sexual potency, coined in connection with a famous work of erotic poetry, *De Arte Amatoria* in three books, by the Roman poet Publius Ovidius Naso (43 B.C.–17 A.D.).

arsphenamine hemorrhagic encephalitis (ärs-fen′à-mēn hem-o-raj′ik en-sef-à-lī′tis) A toxic and probably idiosyncratic reaction (hence more correctly termed an encephalopathy) to the intravenous administration of arsphenamine. This is a rare complication and usually occurs one to two days after injection. Vomiting and headache are rapidly followed by restlessness and delirium, passing into coma with stertorous respiration and often generalized convulsions. In fatal cases, there is edema of the brain, capillary engorgement, and perivascular hemorrhage, and also nonhemorrhagic perivascular areas of necrosis and demyelination.

art The study of artistic productions has thrown much light upon questions of psychology and psychopathology. Like dreams and phantasies, art is regarded as representing factors or themes of the psyche. From the psychiatric standpoint art is analyzed in much the same way that dreams and phantasies are. Freud applies his methods of investigation also to the problem of artistic creativeness, its nature and sources. He says: 'the artist is originally a man who turns from reality because he cannot come to terms with the demand for the renunciation of instinctual satisfaction as it is first made, and who then in phantasy-life allows full play to his erotic and ambitious wishes.' (Freud, S. *Collected Papers,* vol. 4, tr. by Riviere, J., Leonard and Virginia Woolf and the Institute of Psychoanalysis, London, 1924–25). Many other psychoanalysts discuss the origin of interest in painting, modeling and scupture. J.W. Brown ('Psycho-Analysis and Design in the Plastic Arts,' *International Journal of Psychoanalysis,* 1929) calls attention to the prevalence of the castration theme. Others have described motives that stem from the oral and anal stages of libidinal development. Brown concludes that art represents 'primarily an attempt to call forth feelings which satisfy certain unconscious wishes connected with the idea of potency as a negation of the idea of castration.'

Jung says: 'Art, like every other human activity, proceeds from psychic motives. . . .' Speaking of poetic art, he quotes Gerhart Hauptmann, to wit: 'Poetry means the distant echo of the primitive word behind our veil of words.' Jung expresses a similar idea when he asks 'to what primordial image of the collective unconscious can we trace the image we see developed in the work of art?' He adds that 'the shaping of the primordial image is, as it were, a translation into the language of the present which makes it pos-

sible for every man to find again the deepest springs of life which would otherwise be closed to him.' (Jung, C.G. *Contributions to Analytical Psychology,* tr. by Baynes, H.G. and C.F., Kegan Paul, Trench, Trubner, London, 1923)

arterenol (ar-te-rē'nol) Norepinephrine; see *epinephrine.*

arteriogram *Angiogram* (q.v.).

arteriosclerosis, cerebral (är-tē-ri-ō-sklē-rō'sis, ser'ē-bral) Hardening of the arteries of the brain. Cerebral arteriosclerosis is a nosologic entity included in the *Standard Classified Nomenclature of Disease,* 1935. It may or may not be associated with mental changes, depending upon the extent of the process and the consequent interference with nourishment of the cerebral areas involved.

The onset of mental and physical symptoms may be sudden or insidious. When the blood vessel bursts, sending a volume of blood into neighboring tissues, symptoms develop promptly and vary with the extent of the hemorrhage and the particular area in which the hemorrhage occurs. The symptom common to the acute form is stupor or coma with hemiplegia or paralysis.

Owing to the gradual narrowing of the caliber of the artery, a progressively diminishing quantity of blood reaches its destination, producing anemia of the given parts. The anemia, together with changes in the constituents of the blood, gives rise to alterations in the anatomy and physiology of the structures affected. Symptoms common to the chronic form, in the early stages, are headache, dizziness, noises in the ears, lack of power of concentration, insomnia, and memory defect. As the arteriosclerotic process progresses, the patient becomes more irritable, the memory more noticeably impaired, and transient symptoms of temporary occlusion of a vessel appear, such as a fleeting aphasia, twitchings, sudden attacks of vertigo, and slight paresis.

As the progress of the disease advances, the memory defect, especially for recent events, becomes very marked. The patient may show some disorientation and delusions, especially of jealousy and infidelity, and hallucinations may appear. Gradually, all the faculties become impaired, sustained mental operations are impossible, confusion is marked and memory even of remote events becomes defective. The patient misidentifies people and cannot recall the names of or recognize the members of his family. He becomes careless about his person and may wet and soil himself. Ethical and moral values are impaired, the patient manifesting odd behavior and conduct disorders, and often sexual perversions.

The brain shows disseminated areas of softening.

arthralgia hysterica (är-thrăl′gē-á hĕs-te′rē-kà) Hysterical joint-pain; arthropathia hysterica.

arthritism (är′thri-tiz′m) See *diathesis, arthritic*.

arthritism, infantile In constitutional medicine this refers to the arthritic diathesis or arthritism which manifests itself in young children. See *diathesis, arthritic*.

arthro-, arthr- (är′thrō-, är′thr-) Combining form meaning *joint, articulation*.

arthropathy (är-throp′á-thē) Also known as Charcot joint, occurring in tabes; affection of a joint, consisting of edema and effusions within the joints, associated usually with painless swellings; proliferation and destruction of the cartilages, capsule and bony surfaces of the joint may occur with the formation of new bone, fragments of which may be free within the joint.

articulation, disorders of See *speech disorders*.

artificialism Piaget's term for the child's tendency to believe that natural phenomena are caused by some human agency.

artificial neurosis See *neurosis, experimental*.

asaphia (ä-saf′i-à, à-saf-ī′á) *Obs.* Indistinctness of voice.

asapholalia (à-sà-fō-lä′lē-à) Indistinct or mumbling speech.

asceticism See *character, ascetic*.

Aschaffenburg, Gustav (à-shäf′en-boork) (1866–) German psychiatrist.

Aschner ocular phenomenon (Bernhardt Aschner, Viennese physician, 1863–) Pressure exerted over the eyeball produces a slowing of the pulse; also known as the oculocardiac reflex.

Aschner treatment of schizophrenia A method of 'constitutional' therapy employed by the Viennese physician Bernhardt Aschner (b. 1863) in the treatment

of schizophrenia; the method includes the use of cold baths, sweats, drastic purgatives, emmenagogues, emetics, blisters, and periodic blood-letting.

asemasia (as-ē-mā′zhi-à) A synonym of *asemia* (q.v.), though of much more restricted currency.

asemia (à-sē′mi-à) A generic term for loss of power that the individual once possessed to make or understand any sign or token of communication.

As in all speech disorders the perceptive and the expressive (or sensory and motor) aspects may manifest themselves singly or both combined, when the disability may be called total. The subdivisions of asemia are: amimia, alexia, agraphia. It includes the trainman's or switchman's inability to grasp the meaning of signs by semaphore or colored lights, the bellboy's irresponsiveness to the various buzzes or bell-combinations, the telegrapher's inability to convey or 'read' messages on the ticker, the student's blindness to letters, figures, and mathematical signs and symbols, the pianist's blank stare at a page of formerly familiar music, though he may still be able to play the piece from memory, the soldier's 'disregard' of bugle calls, etc.

Sometimes the inability is psychically determined. In such cases, careful checking reveals that the loss is but another manifestation of a more fundamental disorder, for instance, a full-blown Oedipus complex with denial of the parents and everything associated with them, language included. See also *speech disorders*.

asexuality Magnus Hirschfeld defines asexuality as the absence of sexual desire or feeling, due, he believes, to the 'loss of sexual glands.' The loss of sexual interests may also be observed in many psychiatric conditions in which no pathology of the sexual apparatus may be demonstrated. As extreme examples, mention may be made of patients in a deep depression and those schizophrenic patients who show deeply regressive phenomena.

'as if' This term, borrowed from the philosopher Vaihinger, is used by Adler to indicate the fictitious and imaginary goal of complete superiority obtained by many individuals.

Adler states, 'That this fiction of a goal of superiority so ridiculous from the viewpoint of reality, has become the principal conditioning factor of our life as hitherto known . . . this goal introduces into our life a hostile and fighting tendency . . . whoever takes this goal of godlikeness seriously or literally, will soon be compelled to flee from real life and compromise, by seeking a life within life; if fortunate,—in art, but more generally,—in pietism, neurosis or crime.' (Adler, A. *The Practice and Theory of Individual Psychology,* tr. by Radin, P., Kegan Paul, Trench, Trubner, London, 1924) 'As if' also is used to refer to a personality type seen typically in schizophrenics before or between acute episodes. See *personality, as if.*

asitia (à-sish′i-à) Anorexia.

asocial Not social. Many psychiatric patients, who find it impossible to live out their impulses in a social setting, withdraw their interests from the environment and transfer their psychic energies to clinical syndromes that have no relationship to reality as the latter actually exists. Such patients are said to be asocial. Thus, the schizophrenic individual who regresses to a deeply narcissistic level of adaptation serves as a classical example of an asocial being.

aspermia, psychogenic (a-sper′mi-a) See *impotence, psychic.*

assimilation This term is given special meaning in analytical psychology (Jung). It is defined as 'the absorption or joining up of a new conscious content to already prepared subjective material, whereby the similarity of the new content with the waiting subjective material is specially emphasized, even to the prejudice of the independent quality of the new content. Fundamentally, assimilation is a process of apperception . . . which, however, is distinguished from pure apperception by this element of adjustment to the subjective material.' (Jung, C.G. *Psychological Types,* tr. by Baynes, H.G., Harcourt, Brace, New York and London, 1923)

Jung maintains that *dissimilation* 'represents the adjustment of subject to object, and a consequent estrangement of the subject from himself in favour of the object, whether it be an external object or a "psychological" or inner object, as for instance an idea.' (ibid.)

assimilation, social Social assimilation is 'a name given to the process or processes by which peoples of diverse social origins and different cultural heritages, occupying a common territory, achieve a cultural solidarity.' (Park, R.E. *Encyclopaedia of the Social Sciences,* vol. 2, Macmillan, New York, 1930, p. 281)

Assimilation was early defined as 'the growing alike (of persons) in character, thoughts and institutions' (Simons, *American Journal of Sociology*), but later as a result of the Americanization Studies recognition was given to the element of diversity in the process of the interpenetration and the fusion of the experiences, memories, and attitudes of persons and groups by which they are incorporated into a common cultural life.

Assimilation is generally considered in terms of the fusion of immigrants or of members of a minority group into the national culture, but it applies equally to the nature and degree of participation of a newcomer in a group, institution, or neighborhood.

association Relationship. In psychiatry, association refers particularly to the relationship between the conscious and the unconscious, ideas in the former being connected to the latter.

Associations may be free or induced. When an individual without prompting is allowed to raise and to expand upon an idea or ideas, the process is known as 'free' association. This is one of the methods used by psychoanalysts in tracing the origin and development of ideas or groups of ideas.

Induced associations involve the giving of stimulus words; 'the experimenter calls out a word to the test-person, and the test-person immediately replies with the next association that comes into his mind.' (Jung, C.G.)

Originally the test was employed as a means by which complexes were revealed. It is still used by some for that purpose. As a rule, however, for practical, therapeutic purposes, the free association method is used, not alone for uncovering complexes, but principally for gaining information on the organization and development of the contents of the mind. Dreams of the 'test-person' constitute the best means for the method of so-called free association.

Freud 'maintains that, when a subject is asked to make free associations from a given theme to which he is attending, and wholly to suspend the active-selective criticism that under such circumstances is instinctively exercised towards the incoming thoughts, the associations must be directly or indirectly related, in a causative manner to the initial theme.' (Jones, E. *Papers on Psycho-Analysis,* 4th ed., Wood, Baltimore, 1938)

Jung uses the term association-method to mean the procedure; the tests are called association-experiments.

association, clang When psychic associations are the result of sounds or clangs, they are called clang associations. Clang association is commonly observed in the manic phase of manic-depressive psychosis, and in the schizophrenias.

association-disturbances See *associations, disturbances of.*

association, evidential By this term Stekel denotes the quality that free association has of proving the hidden conflict of the patient. In other words, free association is able to bring forward the psychic material which reveals to the patient the real identity of the factors responsible for his ailment. Despite this quality of association, Stekel thinks that it is not necessarily indispensable for the task of uncovering hidden conflicts, and he holds that 'the death symbolism of the dream would still be unknown, if we had always scrupulously waited for the dreamer's evidential associations.' (Stekel, W. *The Interpretation of Dreams,* Liveright, New York, 1943)

association-experiment See *association.*

association, false Stekel's term for the dreamer's various identifications simultaneously with several persons who, nevertheless, represent the same love-object, these associations (given by the dreamer) being only partly valid, inasmuch as they correspond to incomplete situations. In a way, false associations may be considered as evasions.

They are not, however, completely false but only half-true, because they correspond to two different situations reported by the patient as being only one.

This type of association may lead the analyst to details concerning one of the persons with whom the dreamer identifies his love-object, when in reality this association pertains to another person, also a partial substitute for the real love-object. (Stekel, W. *The Interpretation of Dreams,* Liveright, New York, 1943)

association, free The trends of thought or chains of ideas which spontaneously arise when restraint and censorship upon logical thinking are removed and the individual orally reports everything that passes through his mind. This fundamental technique of modern psychoanalysis assumes that when relieved of the necessity of logical thinking and reporting verbally everything going through his mind, the individual will bring forward basic psychic material and thus make it available to analytical interpretation. 'Mistakes of everyday life, and dreams in which the partial liberation from fetters of logic and repression is already achieved, constitute a particularly interesting material in this respect.' This method was originally introduced by Freud after he had been disillusioned with the results of hypnosis. In trying to overcome the post-hypnotic amnesia, Freud found out that, when urged to make an effort, the hypnotized individual was able to recall almost everything that had been said to him, although he could not remember anything that had happened during the hypnotic trance.

Freud applied the same technique to patients he could not hypnotize. He 'urged them to tell him everything that came to their minds, to leave out nothing, regardless of whether they considered it relevant or not. He persuaded them to give up all conscious reflection, abandon themselves to calm concentration, follow their spontaneous mental occurrences, and impart everything to him. In this way he finally obtained those free associations which lead to the origin of the symptoms. As he developed this method, he found that it was not as simple as he had thought, that these so-called free associations were really not free, but were determined by unconscious material which had to be analyzed and interpreted. He, therefore, designated this new technique psycho-analysis.'

The combined work of repressive influences of the ego prevents the unconscious material from entering into the field of consciousness. Such material can be obtained only through the technique of free association. In other words, free association overcomes, or sidetracks, the repressive forces and makes it possible for the psychic unconscious material to come forward into consciousness. In this manner the psychiatrist is able to reach the inner layers of the mental life of the patient, interpret them, and finally bring them into the range of the patient's insight. The methodological principle of free association is a common basis for the classical Freudian analysis and the Jungian type of analysis. (Freud, S. *The Basic Writings of Sigmund Freud,* tr. by Brill, A.A., Random House, New York, 1938; Schilder, P. *Psychotherapy,* Norton, New York, 1938)

association, induced See *association.*

association-method See *association.*

association, psychosis of A form of psychosis in which certain of the mental symptoms of one patient (the principal) appear in similar or identical form in one or more other people (the associates) who are closely associated with the first. This association is typically intrafamilial, as in two siblings, or in parent and child, or in husband and wife; but it has also been reported among pairs of patients on a psychiatric ward and in pairs of friends who have been in intimate social contact over a period of time. When the number of people involved is two, the condition is sometimes called *folie à deux* (q.v.); there may be three (*folie à trois*), four (*folie à quatre*) or many (*folie à beaucoup*) involved. Other names by which the condition has been known are: infectious insanity (Ideler, 1838); psychic infection (Hoffbauer, 1846); familial mental infection (Séguin, 1879); reciprocal insanity (Parsons, 1883); collective insanity (Ireland, 1886); double insanity (Tuke, 1887); influenced psychosis (Gordon, 1925); mystic paranoia (Pike, 1933).

Most writers agree that psychosis of association is limited to paranoid and depressive forms of psychosis, and in the case reports in the literature even purely depressive forms are a relative rarity. Four types of psychosis of association are recognized: (1) imposed (described by Laseque and Falret, 1877), in which the associate accepts the delusions of the principal with little elaboration, and separation of the patients typically results in disappearance of the delusions in the associate; (2) simultaneous (described by Regis, 1880), in which there is simultaneous appearance of identical symptoms in more than one subject, and these symptoms are typically depression and/or persecutory ideas; (3) communicated (described by Marandon de Montyel, 1881), in which the associate takes over the delusions of the principal and works them into his own system, often with elaboration, and these delusions are usually maintained even after separation of the two; and (4) induced (described by Lehmann, 1885), wherein a second receptive patient adds the principal's delusions to his own symptoms.

associations, contiguity of This term is used by Freud to indicate 'that an internal connection which is still undisclosed will announce its presence by means of a temporal proximity of associations; just as in writing, if "a" and "b" are put side by side, it means that the syllable "ab" is to be formed out of them.' (Freud, S. *Collected Papers,* vol. 3, tr. by Strachey, A. and J., Leonard and Virginia Woolf and The Institute of Psychoanalysis, London, 1925)

As an example, Freud refers to the case of Dora (*Analysis of a Case of Hysteria*) in which Dora recognizes that Frau K. would always fall ill whenever Herr K. returned from one of his long journeys, to be able to escape the conjugal duties which she so much detested. At this point Dora referred to her own alternations between good and bad health during the first years of her girlhood. Freud then suspected that her states of health depended upon something else, in the same way as Frau K.'s.

associations, disturbances of One of Bleuler's fundamental symptoms of the schizophrenias. The associations are the innumerable related threads which guide thinking, and in the schizophrenias the associations are interrupted and lose their contiguity. As a result, thinking becomes haphazard, seemingly purposeless, illogical, confused, incorrect, abrupt, and bizarre. Among the many possible association-disturbances are clang associations, indirect associations, stereotypy in speech, dearth of ideas to the point of monoideism, 'thought-deprivation' (blocking), 'naming' (echopraxia) or 'touching,' pressure of thoughts, inappropriate application of clichés, Klebedenken, impoverishment of thought, replacement of thinking proper by a senseless compulsion to associate.

associations, indirect One of the disturbances of associations seen often in the schizophrenias. With indirect associations, *A* may be connected to *B* and *B* may be connected to *C,* but the connecting link *B* is unexpressed so that the listener finds the statement incomprehensive, illogical, or bizarre.

association-test See *association.*

associative thinking See *thinking, associative.*

assurance Some psychiatrists speak of assurance as a method of psychotherapy; it appears, however, that it has never gained the position of a method as such, but it is a form of conviction by which the psychiatrist aspires to convince the patient of the psychiatrist's way of thinking. When the patient can be made to identify himself with the physician, so that the two think and feel alike about some troublesome problem, it is said that the physician assures the patient. The repetition of assurance is called reassurance. Both seem to be a 'cover-up method' of psychotherapy, in that they serve to convince the conscious ego of its superiority over the given symptoms. See *psychotherapy.*

astasia (à-stā′zhi-à) The inability to stand, when there is no organic reason for the disability. See *astasia-abasia.*

astasia-abasia Astasia combined with abasia. Inability to walk or stand in the absence of recognizable organic disorder. Although astasia-abasia is not confined to any single psychiatric group, it is probably most common in conversion hysteria.

astereognosis (às-ter-ē-og-nō′sis) Loss of power to perceive the shape and nature of an object and inability to identify it by superficial contact alone, in the absence of any demonstrable sensory defect; sometimes called tactile agnosia, although in astereognosis there is a defect in the higher correlation of proprioceptive sensations as well. Some use astereognosis for minor defects in which the patient cannot recognize form, and tactile agnosia for more profound defects in which there is inability to identify objects. Astereognosis follows lesions of the parietal lobe, especially in the posterior portions.

asthenia (as-thē′ni-à) Want or loss of strength, debility, diminution of the vital forces. In the field of constitutional medicine it does not imply the specific meaning conveyed by the adjective *asthenic* (q.v.).

asthenia, mental Church and Peterson say: *'the capacity for mental work is abridged,* just as the muscular power is reduced. . . . This *mental asthenia* also shows itself in the reduction of the mental concentration necessary for fixing and maintaining attention. Neurasthenics cannot keep their minds on the printed page nor follow a line of thought for any great length of time.' (Church, A. and Peterson, F. *Nervous and Mental Diseases,* 8th ed., Saunders, Philadelphia and London, 1916)

asthenia, neurocirculatory A clinical syndrome, also called effort syndrome, characterized by palpitation, shortness of breath, labored breathing, subjective complaints of effort and discomfort, all following slight exertion; other symptoms may be dizziness, tremulousness, sweating, insomnia. Neurocirculatory asthenia is not a condition marked by anatomic lesions.

asthenic (as-then′ik) See *type, asthenic.*

asthenology (as-thē-nol′ō-jē) The doctrine of diseases or anomalies, structural or functional, associated with weakness or debility. In psychiatry the term has special, though not exclusive, reference to matters pertaining to constitutional medicine, including such concepts as constitutional inadequacies, early structural or functional wearing out of organs or systems of organs, imbalance of organic systems, etc. For example, it is believed that among certain psychiatric patients, particularly the schizophrenic, the cardiovascular system retains puerile structure and function, as a consequence of which adult parts of the body have to get along with puerile parts. Such anomalies often lead to debility of a greater or lesser order. Asthenology includes studies of such disability or debility.

asthenophobia (as-thē-nō-fō′bi-à) Fear of weakness.

asthenopia (as-thē-nō′pi-à) Weakness of vision or sight.

asthma, sexual The asthmatic condition induced by the act of coitus.

astraphobia, astrapophobia (as-tra-fō′bi-à, -pō-fō′bi-à) Morbid fear of thunder and lightning is usually a symptom of a psychoneurosis, produced 'in order to prevent the anxiety from breaking out. The phobia is thrown up before the anxiety like a frontier fortress.' (Freud, S. *The Interpretation of Dreams,* 3rd ed., tr. by Brill, A.A., Macmillan, 1933) Freud says that 'a word, as the point of junction of a number of ideas, possesses, as it were, a predestined ambiguity, and the neuroses (obsessions, phobias) take advantage of the opportunities for condensation and disguise afforded by words quite as eagerly as do dreams.' (ibid., p. 325)

astrocyte (as'trō-sīt) See *neuroglia*.

astrology The study of planets particularly in their influence on the destiny of the universe including human beings, their actions, personality, body, and health. The medicine of the Middle Ages was strikingly dominated by demonology, witchcraft, sorcery, and astrology, and statements which assumed that there existed no infirmity or disease not due to the influence of some planet or planets were not uncommon. Saturn was assumed to govern the spleen; Jupiter ruled over the lungs, liver, and semen; Mars controlled the kidneys; Venus, the uterus, breasts, and genitals of the female; Mercury stood for the mental processes; and the Sun ruled the brain and the nerves, the right half of the body, and the left eye of the woman. Paracelsus expanded this school of medical thought considerably: among other things he believed that with a magnet he was able to shift the diseases of the body into the earth. (Hinsie, L.E. *Understandable Psychiatry,* Macmillan, New York, 1948)

astyphia (à-stif'i-à) Sexual impotence.

astysia (à-stis'i-à) Sexual impotence.

asyllabia (à-si-lā'bi-à) A form of aphasia (agraphia or alexia); inability to combine individual letters (or sounds) into syllables. See also *speech disorders*.

asylum An old term defined as a 'place safe from violence or pillage. The ancients set apart certain places of refuge where the vilest criminals were protected, and the name later on got to be applied specially to an institution which afforded a place of refuge or safety for the infirm or unsound of mind.' (Tuke, D.H. *A Dictionary of Psychological Medicine,* vols. 1–2, Blakiston, Philadelphia, 1892)

asylum, insane *Obs.* Psychiatric hospital or institution.

asymbolia (as-im-bō'li-à) Inability to make or understand symbols or signs.

A term proposed by F.C. Finkelburg in 1870 for what is now denoted by the more generally accepted term *asemia* (q.v.) suggested by Steinthal. Kussmaul argued that asymbolia is less comprehensive, because back of *symbol* stands an *idea* and thus it is narrower than *sign* or *token*, which frequently has merely a *feeling* back of it. See also *speech disorders*.

asymbolia, visual See *aphasia, visual*.

asymmetry Absence of symmetry or congruence between two or more parts of a whole. Generally the term is used in medicine to designate anatomical disharmony of homologous parts.

Psychiatric patients may believe that their bodies are entirely asymmetrical, in spite of normal asymmetry. One patient asserted that the right side of his body was absent; he called the right side the masculine side; the delusion was equated with castration. Another patient—and this is not uncommon—believed that the anatomy and physiology of his right side were masculine while those of his left were feminine. In this instance the delusion of asymmetry was based on the delusion of bisexuality.

asymmetry, mental The disparity in form and the unbalanced relationship between two opposite mental processes. In this regard, one may assert that a very frequent symptom in compulsion neurosis is the patient's tendency to compare various parts of his body with one another: some patients spend hours in front of a mirror comparing the two sides of their faces and even may often assert that they are of different form (asymmetric). This is but an expression of their mental disparity and unbalance and their conclusions are drawn merely with reference to their own egos. The patient compares not only different parts of his own body but also 'compares himself with his father, with his brothers and sisters, and with other people.' He compares also various achievements in his life, especially homosexual and heterosexual trends. (Stekel, W. *Compulsion and Doubt,* Liveright, New York, 1949)

asymptotic See *wish-fulfillment, asymptotic*.

asyndesis (às-in-dē'sis) A language disorder seen most commonly in the schizophrenias and to a lesser extent in other organic brain syndromes in which there is juxtaposition of elements without adequate linkage between them. Images and meanings which are connected in the mind of the patient are superimposed on each other in a sentence without explanation as to what the connecting links are; to the listener, the language then seems disjointed and disconnected. 'One of our patients, for example, when asked what caused the wind to blow, said it was "due to velocity, due to loss of air, evaporation of water . . . the contact of trees, of air in the trees." ' (Cameron, N., in Kasanin, J.S. (ed.). *Language and Thought in Schizophrenia,* University of California Press, Berkeley, 1944)

asynergia (ås-i-nĕr′ji-à) See *ataxia.*

asynergia of Babinski, major Inco-ordination in standing and walking as a result of involvement of the cerebellum.

asynergia of Babinski, minor As a consequence of involvement of the cerebellum, there results a decomposition of movements giving rise to a 'breaking up' of simple acts; when the patient attempts to carry out such acts as kneeling on a chair, elevating the leg while in a supine position, sitting up from a recumbent position, etc. the movements are disjointed and awkward.

asynesia (ås-in-ē′shi-à) Profound mental dullness; stupidity.

asynesis (à-sin′ē-sis) *Obs.* Aphasia.

asynetous (à-sin′ē-tus) *Obs.* Stupid, foolish.

At Rorschach scoring symbol for anatomy response.

ataraxy (a′tar-ak-sē) Absence of anxiety or confusion; untroubled calmness. The ataractic drugs are commonly called tranquillizers.

atavism (at′à-viz'm) When mental or physical traits, dormant for one or more generations, reappear in the offspring, the condition is known as atavism. The term is commonly used in biology and less frequently in psychiatry. There are no clear-cut examples of atavism, strictly speaking, in psychology or psychiatry, although it is not unlikely that the many components of the sphere of the unconscious that constitute the 'collective' unconscious of Jung may be regarded as atavistic, particularly when they are expressed overtly in the daily life of the individual (as in schizophrenia).

ataxia (à-tak′si-à) Absence or lack of order. In this general sense it may refer to the absence of order of any bodily function or system, physical or mental. It is most commonly used in the field of neurology to designate a loss of power of muscular co-ordination. The condition may be due to disorder in the brain or spinal cord. There is a form called autonomic or vasomotor ataxia, resulting from imbalance of the sympathetic and parasympathetic nervous systems.

The term ataxia is used also in conjunction with certain psychic functions. Stransky coined the expression intrapsychic ataxia, regarding it, as Urstein did, as a cardinal symptom of schizophrenia; it refers to lack of co-ordination between thoughts and feelings. A schizophrenic patient may laugh heartily, while he believes that his body is being cut into millions of pieces. Intrapsychic ataxia is most vividly expressed in schizophrenia; it is not uncommon in hysteria; it may appear in other psychiatric and non-psychiatric states.

ataxia, Friedreich's A familial, hereditary, and slowly progressive disorder consisting of degeneration of the posterior columns and the spinocerebellar tracts of the spinal cord, mainly in its lower portion, and of the pyramidal tracts. Onset is between 5 and 15 years of age, with ataxia, loss of deep reflexes, nystagmus, dysarthria, intention tremor, and, because of early degeneration of the pyramidal tracts, development of pes cavus. The Babinski and Romberg are usually positive and there is often a mild dementia. Death usually occurs within 20 years from first appearance of symptoms.

ataxia, intrapsychic Stransky introduced this term in an effort to describe the condition of the emotions in schizophrenia. He stressed the thought that patients with that disorder seemed not to show destruction of the feelings, but rather a separation of them from other mental phenomena; he spoke of *ataxic feelings.*

Kraepelin says that Stransky's concept is 'not without justification.' He adds that he is 'inclined to assume that this confusion in the emotional life is caused essentially by the weakening of the higher permanent feelings, whose task it is on the one hand to check sudden oscillations of feeling, on the other hand to give to our inward states permanently equable tension and temperature, and so to become security for the agreement of our emotional relations with the outer world.' (Kraepelin, E. *Dementia Praecox and Paraphrenia,* tr. by Barclay, R., Livingstone, Edinburgh, 1919)

ataxia, locomotor See *tabes.*

ataxia, Marie's hereditary cerebellar (Pierre Marie, French physician, 1853–1940) A familial, hereditary disorder consisting of cerebellar and pyramidal tract degeneration and, in some cases, optic atrophy. Onset is during or after adolescence. Symptoms include ataxia, nystagmus, dysarthria, and intention tremor; in contrast to Friedreich's ataxia, reflexes are normal, pes cavus is not seen, and the Babinski and Romberg reflexes are negative. It would appear that this is a mixed group rather than a pure clinical or pathological entity.

ataxia, mental This expression is the equivalent of intrapsychic ataxia. 'In dementia praecox there is marked ataxia between the emotions and the intellectual and volitional powers of the mind. The dementia praecox patient may be depressed and have apparent reason to be so, yet his conduct at the time of apparent depression is in absolute opposition to the content of his consciousness. He cries when he should laugh, and vice versa.' (Bowers, P.E. *Manual of Psychiatry,* Saunders, Philadelphia, 1924)

ataxia spirituum (à-tàk′sē-à spē-rē′too-oom) *Obs.* Nervous diathesis.

ataxophemia (à-tak-sō-fē′mi-à) Impaired co-ordination of words; incoherence.

atelia (à-tē′li-à) The doctrine of incomplete development.

ateliosis (à-tē-li-ō′sis) A form of dwarfism. The term means incomplete development of the mind or body or both. While usually synonymous with infantilism, it is broad enough to include incomplete development or arrest at any stage of growth. In general it may be said that development may be arrested in one or both of the two major systems, the psyche or the soma (the physique). Usually defects in one system are associated with defects in the other. More specifically arrested development may appear preponderantly in the field of experience, emotions, intelligence, organic physiology, and anatomy.

From a strictly psychiatric point of view, psychogenic mental disorders may be a reflection of arrested development or fixation of feelings and interests at one of the earlier stages of growth. For instance, schizophrenia may be a form of psychic infantilism or puerilism or puberism. Feeble-mindedness may represent in-

complete development of intellectual faculties, while microsomia (small physique) refers to generalized arrest of perhaps all the tissues of the body.

atephobia (ā-tē-fō′bi-à) Fear of ruin.

ater succus (ä′ter sook′koos) (L. 'black juice or sap.') *Obs.* Melancholia.

athetosis (ath-ē-tō′sis) Irregular, slow, objectively purposeless movement with some apparent pattern, occurring mainly in the toes and fingers, in the form of extension and flexion and spreading of the digits.

Athetosis results from a lesion in the extrapyramidal pathways, usually the corpus striatum, or from other lesions which interrupt the circuit of the suppressor reactions between cortical areas 4s and 4.

athletic See *type, athletic.*

athymia (à-thim′i-à, -thī′mi-à) Hippocratic term for melancholia.

atomism (at′um-iz′m) See *psychology, atomistic.*

atom, social 'The social atom consists of the psychological relations of one individual to those other individuals to whom he is attracted or repelled, and their relation to him. It is the smallest social structure in a community. Developing from the time of birth, it first contains mother and child. As time goes on, the child adds from the persons who come into his orbit such persons as are unpleasant or pleasant to him, and, vice versa, those to whom he is unpleasant or pleasant. Persons who do not leave any impression, positive or negative, remain outside of the social atom as mere acquaintances. The feeling which correlates two or more individuals is called tele. The social atom is, therefore, a compound of the tele relationships of an individual. As positively or negatively charged persons may leave the individual's social atom and others may enter it, the social atom has a more or less ever-changing constellation.' (Moreno, J.L. *Who Shall Survive?* Nervous & Mental Disease Publishing Company, Washington, D.C., 1934)

atonic (à-ton′ik) Relating to or characterized by antonia, i.e. by lack of tone or vital energy. It refers to the whole body, to a particular system of the body or to single organs, especially to contractile organs.

In the system of constitutional types described by Pende the term is used in a more specialized sense to indicate a sub-group of the *megalosplanchnic hyper-vegetative* (q.v.) constitution and also a sub-group of the *microsplanchnic hypo-vegetative* (q.v.) constitution. 'We can understand the importance of our division of the great megalosplanchnic group into two sub-groups, one of which we designate as the atonic and flaccid, and the other as the hypertonic and hypersthenic. The first includes individuals morphologically hypoevolute in almost all their organs, with a dominant parasympathicotonia and a torpid orientation of the animal nervous system and psyche; with slow metabolism; and with lymphatic plethora, a deficiency in the development of the arterial portion of the heart as compared with the venous, and of the blood as compared with the lymph.' (Pende, N. *Constitutional Inadequacies,* tr. by Naccarati, S., Lea & Febiger, Philadelphia, 1928)

Similarly there is a distinction between the atonic and hyposthenic sub-group and the hypersthenic and hypertonic sub-group of the microsplanchnic hypovegetative constitution. In the former sub-group we have the slender type with small skeleton and muscles and also with hypoevolutism of the cardiovascular system and the endocrine glands.

The concept of an *atonic constitution* is further used in the system of Rostan, in which it refers to a type characterized by atonia of all systems, corresponding to the *lymphatic* (q.v.) type of classical antiquity and also in the system of Stiler, in which it is identical with the *ptotic habitus* (q.v.).

atony, atonicity, atonia (at′ō-nē, à-tō-nis′i-tē, à-tō′ni-à) The tonus or state of tonicity of body tissues is normally described in terms of the tonicity of the neuro-muscular apparatus. All tissues of the body are normally under a given physiological tension. 'Tonus may be defined as a condition of contraction or of tension which exists independently of voluntary innervation.' (Howell, W.H.) Among the many investigators who have offered opinions on tonus from the psychosomatic point of view, the suggestion is common that the tonus of the body is often modified by the state of mind. In referring to what he calls the *neutralization* theory, Kempf says that 'the different segments of the autonomic apparatus are stimu-

lated to assume different types of postural tensions and activities, which give rise to an affective nervous stream, which, in turn, co-ordinates the projicient apparatus and compels it to act so as to expose the receptors of the organism so that they will acquire certain types of stimuli and avoid others.' (Kempf, E.J. *Psychopathology,* Mosby, St. Louis, 1921) Kempf then speaks of counter-stimulation and neutralization as being associated with the physiology of the *wish.*

It is presumed also that the psyche has its own tonus, conceived as mental pressure. When the mental pressure is below average, the term atony is used. Thus, depressed patients often claim that the mind is dead, that ideas and emotions have gone from them, that there is no psychic initiative or drive. The musculature as a whole usually participates in this expression of atonicity.

atrabiliary, atrabilious (at-rà-bil′i-er-ē; -bil′yus) An old term meaning depressed or melancholic.

atra bilis (ät′rà bē′lēs) (L. 'black bile') A term used by ancients for black bile, the supposed cause of melancholia.

atrophy, optic (at′rō-fē) A degenerative process involving the optic nerve fibers. The condition is primary or secondary. Primary optic atrophy may occur in tabes, multiple sclerosis, or may be due to poisons such as methyl alcohol, tryparsamide, lead, atoxyl, quinine, carbon bisulphide, and nitrobenzol. Occasionally, the condition may occur following severe hemorrhage and in malaria. Ophthalmoscopically, the disk is grayish white in color, with some 'cupping,' the margins being sharply outlined.

Secondary optic atrophy may occur as a result of optic neuritis and choked disk. Here the fundus, disk, and vessels usually manifest residual signs of the previous condition.

Tumors of the pituitary gland, of the optic chiasm, and in some cases of the frontal lobe frequently give rise to optic atrophy—usually unilateral for a time.

atrophy, peroneal muscular Charcot-Marie-Tooth's disease; neural progressive muscular atrophy. A hereditary disorder, transmitted as a Mendelian dominant, more often affecting males, beginning between the ages of 5 and 10 years, with wasting of the small muscles in the peripheral limbs secondary to degeneration of the peripheral nerves and spinal cord. The muscular wasting results in a steppage gait, 'fat bottle' calf when the lower part of the calf is wasted, and 'inverted champagne bottle' limb when the lower third of the thigh is wasted. The disease runs a slow course and may become arrested at any stage; it does not shorten life, and there are no associated intellectual changes.

atrophy, progressive muscular See *sclerosis, amyotrophic lateral.*

attachment, liquidation of P. Janet uses this term to mean freedom from painful situations. 'In this connexion, our first aim must be to put an end to the unceasing efforts occasioned by "attachments." We must "disattach" the patients, we must unravel, as far as may be, the complicated situations in which they find themselves, and in which they have become enmeshed. In some cases of a comparatively simple type, we must ourselves perform actions which will modify the environing conditions, and will achieve a solution for the patient. We must take responsibilities, formulate decisions, make the requisite efforts, and vicariously solve the patient's problem.' (Janet, P. *Psychological Healing,* vols. 1–2, tr. by Paul, E. and C., Macmillan, New York, 1925)

attack, first An illness occurring for the first time, whether or not it results in hospitalization, is a first attack.

Example: A group of 155 first admissions with manic-depressive psychoses had had an average of 1.5 attacks. A group of 175 patients with schizophrenia had had an average of only 1.1 attacks prior to admission to the hospital.

attack, psychomotor A term sometimes used interchangeably with the term *psychic equivalent* of epilepsy. See *equivalent, epileptic.*

attention Attention may be defined as the application of energy in the sphere of consciousness by the individual aware of the application of the energy. One should not speak of attention when the mind functions without the overt knowledge of the subject.

Maher regards attention as the application of intellectual energy. Regarding attention in the patient with manic-depressive psychosis MacCurdy says: 'In this psychosis we saw that attention may be

directed to a conscious perception which is a suitable vehicle for expression of a co-conscious idea-function. All attention may be of this nature and inevitably dependent on the dominance in the co-conscious of some group of idea-functions.' (MacCurdy, J.T. *The Psychology of Emotion,* Harcourt, Brace, New York, 1925)

In Burrow's phylobiology: partitive attention, (1) because it selects a part-element or item of an object which thereafter constitutes the sign or symbol of it, and (2) because the process of attention is then invariably involved in secondary, extraneous affect-elements which tend either to re-route man's basic feeling or to partition it off from the organism's primary empathic channels of activation. See also *affect; partitive; social image.* Contrasted with cotention. Synonyms: symbolic attention, projective attention. (Burrow, T. *The Structure of Insanity,* Kegan Paul, Trench, Trubner, London, 1932, pp. 27, 80)

attention, blocking of See *blocking.*

attention, deterioration of Bleuler lists this as one of the fundamental symptoms of the schizophrenias, where often there is seen an impairment in the ability to heed, observe, and concentrate on external reality. This fundamental symptom appears to be related to deterioration of affectivity (another fundamental symptom) and the patient's disinterest in many things about him. The impairment of attention is inconstant and shifting, for attention may appear normal when it is directed to something the patient wants to do. Inability to concentrate is seen also in other psychiatric disorders, but in this latter case it is almost always secondary, i.e. a result of emotional pressure, while in the schizophrenias it appears to be primary.

attention-getting A technique used by the individual to gain attention and recognition when the ego is starved for them, as observed most often in a child who feels unloved. At first the child will attempt to do whatever he feels the parents like and will gain their attention. If this is not successful, the child will develop temper-tantrums or other behavior disorders, preferring a display of displeasure or even a harsh disciplinary measure to no attention at all. See *processes, unconscious.*

attention, vigility of 'The *vigility* of the attention is a term used by some clinicians to indicate the fact that the direction of the stream of energy is dirigible' (i.e. controllable). (Paton, S. *Psychiatry*, Lippincott, Philadelphia and London, 1905)

attitude Jung defines *attitude* as 'a readiness of the psyche to act or react in a certain direction. . . . To have a certain attitude means to be ready for something definite, even though this definite something is unconscious, since having an attitude is synonymous with an *a priori* direction toward a definite thing, whether this be present in consciousness or not.' (Jung, C.G. *Psychological Types*, tr. by Baynes, H.G., Harcourt, Brace, New York and London, 1923)

attitude, captative In the early ego development 'things of the external world it conceives of only from its own viewpoint and in their relation to itself. We agree with Pichon in qualifying as "captative" this attitude of the ego.' (Laforgue, R. *The Relativity of Reality*, Nervous and Mental Disease Monographs No. 66, New York, 1940)

attitude, catatonoid A type of behavior that resembles catatonia. According to Fenichel, it may be found in individuals who 'are on the verge of becoming psychotic.' Apparently, this phrase refers to a certain lack of the expected emotional response in personal or social situations: instead, there is found a stereotyped response, which never varies from situation to situation. For example, if the same vacant smile adorns an individual's countenance when he hears his friend's story of a recent personal tragedy or is told an uproarious anecdote, the individual demonstrates a catatonoid attitude. These stereotyped responses on the part of 'schizoid characters,' which occur when the individual becomes psychotic, would be easily recognized as catatonic symptoms. (Fenichel, O. *The Psychoanalytic Theory of Neurosis,* Norton, New York, 1945)

attitude, collective This is an expression used by Jung (Analytical Psychology) to refer to the *attitude* (q.v.) which is peculiar 'not to one individual, but to many, at the same time, i.e., either to a society, a people, or to mankind in general.' (Jung, C.G. *Psychological Types,* tr. by Baynes,

H.G., Harcourt, Brace, New York and London, 1923)

attitude, fear An expression used by Kanner to designate a fear reaction observed in some children 'who are literally *always afraid of everything*. It is not, one object or situation or a limited number of them that is feared.' (Kanner, L. *Child Psychiatry,* Thomas, Springfield, Ill., 1935)

attitude, inner Soul, according to Jung's point of view.

attitude, masculine, in female neurotics. See *masculine attitude in female neurotics.*

attitude, mummy Henderson and Gillespie use this expression to denote the inactive, immobilized patient in the state of catatonic stupor.

'Then a state of dull stupor develops, with mutism, refusal of food, and with such a diminution of all activities that the patient may sit idly in one position, with the hands stretched out on the knees, and the head bowed between the shoulders, the whole aspect being that of a mummy.' (Henderson, D.K. and Gillespie, R.D. *A Text-Book of Psychiatry,* 4th ed., Oxford University Press, London, 1936)

attitude, preadaptive The initial reaction to a stimulus or experience, before the subject has become accustomed to it. P. Steckler (*Archives of Neurology and Psychiatry 80,* 625–628, 1958) notes that the preadaptive attitude of schizophrenics to hallucinations or feelings of estrangement is of a fairly consistent pattern: anxiety, fear, search for reassurance, doubts as to sanity, search for a rational explanation and, finally, autonomic and muscular system reactions.

attitude, social An attitude is a tendency to act. It is defined more precisely by W.I. Thomas and F. Znaniecki, who first introduced the term, as 'a process of individual consciousness which determines real or possible activity of the individual in the social world.' (*The Polish Peasant in Europe and America,* 1920; 1927). These authors point out that 'the attitude is the individual counterpart of social value; activity, in whatever form, is the bond between them.' (ibid) According to H. Blumer, however, they failed precisely to define the specific differentiation and interrelation between attitude and value. (Critical appraisal of W.I. Thomas and F. Znaniecki, *The Polish Peasant in Europe and America*)

Attempts have been made to measure attitudes but these have been subject to the criticism that they measure opinions rather than attitudes.

attitudes passionelles (à-ti-tüd pa-syō-nel′) See *hysteria.*

attitude therapy See *therapy, attitude.*

attitude-tic See *tic, attitude.*

attitude-type See *function-type.*

attonity (at-on′i-tē) Attonity is a clinical state of stupor with complete or almost complete immobility. Bleuler believes that the condition occurs most frequently in the catatonic form of schizophrenia, though it is also observed in states of depression; it is then known as melancholia attonita. Other authorities consider that the latter designation refers also to the catatonic type of schizophrenia.

audiogenic seizure (aw-di-ō-jen′ik) See *seizure, audiogenic.*

audition, thought G.W. Jacoby writes of 'thought audition in which everything the patient thinks or speaks is announced or repeated by the voices' (hallucinatory). (Jacoby, G.W. *The Unsound Mind and the Law,* Funk & Wagnalls, New York and London, 1918)

auditory nerve See *nerve, acoustic.*

aulophobia (aw-lō-fō′bi-à) Fear of seeing, handling, or playing a flute or similar wind instrument, which can serve as a phallic symbol.

aura (aw′rà) A premonitory symptom to warn the individual of some approaching physical or mental disorder. It is a symptom of a special nature in that it is not regarded as an essential part of the disease or disorder, because it disappears or loses its force after it has performed its function of warning.

The term is usually restricted to certain symptoms that appear in genuine epilepsy before the major symptoms set in. Bleuler says: 'the attack is often preceded by prodromata which last a few hours, more rarely days; most frequently they are represented by "moods," but also by any illfeeling, more rarely hallucinations and twilight states. In most instances these prodromata disappear in a trice with the attack.' (Bleuler, E. *Textbook of Psychiatry,* tr. by Brill, A.A., Macmillan, New York, 1930)

In the grand mal type of epilepsy, an aura precedes loss of consciousness in about 60 per cent of cases (the others are known as the 'thunderclap' variety). The aura localizes the epileptogenic focus in the brain and thus appears in many forms, depending upon the specific location of the lesion: (1) psychic aurae—complex mental states such as feeling of unreality, or feeling of familiarity and déjà vu and déjà fait, disembodied feeling, intense but inexplicable fear; (2) sensory aurae—olfactory and gustatory hallucinations, visual hallucinations with complex scenes or simple flashes of light or balls of fire, auditory hallucinations of words, phrases, or merely crude sounds, and various paresthesiae; (3) visceral aurae—vertigo, epigastric discomfort; (4) motor aurae—as in cursive epilepsy.

aura cursoria (ou′rà koor-sô′rē-à) This is a condition, usually associated with epilepsy, occurring immediately before an epileptic seizure and characterized by an aimless running around.

aurae, auditory (aw′rē) A form of epilepsy described as sensory seizures in which buzzing noises may occur suddenly, last a short period of time, and then disappear without the patient's having a grand mal attack. This would indicate a focus in the temporal lobe. In grand mal attacks, the patient occasionally may have an auditory aura just prior to the grand mal seizures, as a warning that a convulsive seizure is about to occur.

aurae, visual A form of epilepsy described as sensory seizures in which flashes of light may occur suddenly, last a short period of time, and then disappear without the patient's having a grand mal attack. This would indicate a focus in the temporooccipital area. In grand mal attacks, the patient occasionally may have a visual aura just before the grand mal seizure, as a warning that a convulsive attack is about to occur.

auroraphobia (aw-rō-rà-fō′bi-à) Fear of northern lights.

autarchy (aw′tär-kē) This term, meaning supreme, autocratic power, absolute sovereignty, is used in psychiatry in reference to the early infantile period, when no demands are made on the child and, insofar as possible, his instinctual demands are satisfied immediately. During this period the child is indeed absolute ruler—his slightest cry brings instinctual gratification, there is no need to deny himself pleasure, and there need be no deferral of pleasure.

autemesia (awt-ē-mē′zi-à) So-called idiopathic vomiting. Certain psychiatric patients are able to vomit at will.

authoritarianism (aw-thor-i-tâ′ri-an-iz′m) P. Janet writes that 'we are apt to think that the habit of domination, and a passion for command, are appropriate to persons of energetic temperament, to those whose will is active and powerful. We therefore feel surprised to find that authoritarianism is one of the symptoms of psychological depression. But the feeling that there is something paradoxical here can be dispelled by drawing a distinction between the genuine domination exercised by the strong, and the authoritarianism of the weak, which is but a parody of true domination.' (Janet, P. *Psychological Healing,* vols. 1–2, tr. by Paul, E. and C., Macmillan, New York, 1925)

authoritative imperative See *imperative, authoritative.*

authority, irrational Power or command over others that, contrary to reason and logic, is based on neurotic craving for power and has no justification in competence; authority imposed on others through sheer will power, without their consent. Fromm distinguishes this from rational authority, which is based on genuine ability and competence and is exemplified by the teacher imparting knowledge to a pupil. The person who recurs to irrational authority for security may find power by being a *magic helper* (q.v.) or from various forms of intimidation; he may also find that power through identification with the authoritarian force, be it a person, a group, or an idea. Hence, Fromm considers Freud's superego as a manifestation of authoritarian power.

The classical legend based on a vivid account by Pliny the Elder (*Historia Naturalis, XXXV,* 10, 36, §85) which gave rise to a widespread saying is a striking illustration of the gulf between rational and irrational authority. The great Greek painter Apelles (fl. 330 B.C.), valuing the opinion of the common folk, was in the habit of showing a new canvas in his (porch) studio and, hiding behind a painting, would listen to their observations. A passing shoemaker found fault with one sandal-loop being smaller than the other. The artist redrew it later in the day. The next morning the same shoemaker, emboldened by the artist's compliance, began to jeer about the leg. Emerging from his hiding place, Apelles squelched the glib critic with the crushing: 'A cobbler should not judge above the sandal.' ('Shoe-maker, stick to your last.')

authypnobatesis (awth-hip-nō-bà-tē′sis) *Obs.* Spontaneous somnambulism.

autism (aw′tiz′m) A form of thinking, more or less genuinely of a subjective character; if objective material enters, it is given subjective meaning and emphasis. Autism generally carries with it the thought that the material is derived from the individual himself, appearing in the nature of daydreams, phantasies, delusions, hallucinations, etc. The content of thought, in other words, is largely endogenous. In classical instances of autistic thinking, such as occurs in schizophrenia, the unconscious sphere makes the largest contribution to autism.

Autism is a form of narcissism, yet a narcissist is not restricted in the content of the conscious mind to subjective material; he is one who interprets material largely in terms of himself.

Autism, dereism, and introversion are closely allied to one another. Some authorities speak of the autistic temperament, meaning by it 'the bashful, retiring type that shrinks from all contact with life. The subject is "shut-in," inaccessible and introverted, a day-dreamer.' (Bridges, J.W. *An Outline of Abnormal Psychology,* 2nd ed., Adams & Company, Columbus, 1921)

Autism, when it is a pervasive and generalized dereistic life-approach, is one of the fundamental symptoms of the schizophrenias (Bleuler).

autism, early infantile Kanner uses this term in reference to children whose extreme withdrawal, self-absorbed inaccessibility, and inability to form the usual relations to people are noticeable from the beginning of life. Such children manifest an excessive aloneness and an anxious, obsessive desire for preservation of the *status quo.* Language difficulties are common and include mutism, the use of verbal negation as a magical protection against unpleasant occurrences, literalness, inability to accept synonyms or different connotations of the same preposition, and an echolalic type repetition of whole phrases. Pronominal reversals, the child's referring to itself as you and to the person spoken to as I, are typical and almost pathognomonic. Seemingly nonsensical, silly, incoherent, or irrelevant utterances are frequent and actually represent private and self-contained metaphoric transfers. Thus one child called every basket a home bakery. Originally the family's term for the bread basket, this was generalized by the child to include any basket. The voice of such a child lacks emotional tone and expressiveness and seems to be foreign to the personality itself. (Kanner, L. 'Irrelevant and Metaphorical Language in Early Infantile Autism,' *American Journal of Psychiatry 103*, 242, 1946.) It is likely that many, if not all, such cases represent childhood schizophrenia.

autistic (aw-tis'tik) Relating to mentation that is more or less subjective.

autistic psychosis See *psychosis, symbiotic infantile.*

auto-analysis See *analysis, self.*

autocastration, anticipatory A symbolic self-castration appearing as either a symptom or a personality trait, to forestall castration which under the circumstances is unconsciously perceived by the patient as an unavoidable threat. This anticipatory autocastration may be the unconscious reason for 'feminine' behavior in boys: if the boy 'castrates himself' by acting like a girl, he can no longer be threatened with actual castration.

Fenichel explains this behavior as a manifestation of primitive thinking. If the threatened individual punishes himself, he will be protected by the threatening force, which is the father or super-ego in unconscious terms. This thinking is clearly seen in prayer or in sacrifices to the gods, where the individual ingratiates himself with the gods by a self-inflicted lesser or symbolic punishment and thus wards off a more severe punishment.

Actual autocastration, however, takes place in some cases and apparently a 'passive-submissive merging' with the omnipotent person is obtained thereby: by abandoning all activity, the individual shares the omnipotence. By these means religious fanatics endeavor to obtain a union with God. (Fenichel, O. *The Psycho-*

analytic Theory of Neurosis, Norton, New York, 1945)

autocentric (aw-tō-sen'trik) Self-centered. 'In its most fundamental sense, conversion is a natural, normal, universal, and necessary process at the stage [i.e. adolescence] when life pivots over from an autocentric to an heterocentric basis.' (Hall, G.S. *Adolescence,* vol. 2, Appleton, New York, 1908, p. 301)

autochiria (aw-tō-kī'ri-à) *Obs.* Suicide.

autochthonous (aw-tok'thō-nus) Aboriginal to the site of appearance, brought about by the independent activity of the structure in which the activity appears.

autochthony The state of originating in an organ itself, independent of any essential influences outside of the organ in question. Many organs of the body act in part in virtue of forces inherent in the organs and in part because of forces or factors coming from distant sources. The heart, for instance, continues to beat for a time after it has been removed from the body. It is then said to function autochthonously. The same principle of independent action may be applied to the psyche, in the sense that the psyche can and does originate many of the forces found in it. The expression *psychogenic* carries this implication, for it means 'born in the psyche.' It is believed, for example, that dreams are products of the psyche; they are autochthonous to the psyche; they are psychogenic.

autoctonia (aw-tok-tō'ni-à) *Obs.* Suicide.

auto-echolalia (aw-tō-ek-ō-lā'li-à) Stransky coined the expression auto-echolalia to denote that type of stereotypy in which the patient repeats over and over again some word or phrase of his own. The condition is most commonly observed in the patient with the catatonic form of schizophrenia. This term is synonymous with verbigeration.

auto-echopraxia (-prak'si-à) This is a term introduced by Stransky to refer to the form of stereotypy in which the patient, usually with schizophrenia, constantly repeats an action which he had formerly experienced. The patient echoes, so to speak, his own motions. When he echoes that of another person, one speaks of echopraxia. Kraepelin says that 'the patients stand or kneel for hours, days, or still longer, on the same spot, lie in the most uncomfortable positions in bed, fold their hands spasmodically, even till pressure-sores appear, take up the position of fencing.' (Kraepelin, E. *Dementia Praecox and Paraphremia*, tr. by Barclay, R.M., Livingstone, Edinburgh, 1919)

autoerotism, autoeroticism Havelock Ellis invented the term 'auto-erotism' to mean 'the phenomena of spontaneous sexual emotion generated in the absence of an external stimulus proceeding, directly or indirectly, from another person.' (Ellis, H. *Studies in the Psychology of Sex*, vol. 1, 3rd ed., Davis, Philadelphia, 1919, p. 161)

Common usage has made autoerotism synonymous with masturbation. The latter, however, is a special subdivision of autoerotism. The term onanism has likewise been diverted to mean masturbation or autoerotism, though, as Ellis says, 'Onan's device was not auto-erotic, but was an early example of withdrawal before emission, or *coitus interruptus*.' (ibid., p. 163)

According to Freud autoerotism is primordial; it is not something that has to develop in the sense that the ego has to develop. It is 'an early state of the libido.'

Jones defines autoerotism as 'self-generated erotism, gratified in relation to the person alone.' (Jones, E. *Papers on Psycho-Analysis*, 4th ed., Wood, Baltimore, 1938) According to him autoerotism is contrasted with alloerotism, which implies association with another.

'Her desire in it (Oedipus complex) to possess a penis of her own saves her threatened libido by deflecting it into the safer auto-erotic direction. . . .' (Jones, E., ibid.)

Healy, Bronner, and Bowers describe autoerotism as 'a phase in which the libido is directed along one main channel, namely, toward the individual's own body at the time when there is no sensing of "I" or "it." Autoerotism is the utilization of local erotic excitability without any accompanying libidinal relation to the self or outer world, neither of which is as yet distinguished as such.' (Healy, W., Bronner, A.F., Bowers, A.M. *The Structure and Meaning of Psychoanalysis*, Knopf, New York, 1930)

According to Abraham, the autoerotic stage first becomes manifest during the oral sucking period. It is the opinion of some (Rickman) that autoerotism is dis-

tinguished from narcissism in that the former is objectless, while in narcissism the 'I' is recognizable. When the infant takes his own body as the love object, the condition is known as narcissism.

autoerotism, secondary This is an expression suggested by Sadger to refer to that form of self-pleasure indirectly connected with the erogenous zones. For example, the pleasure associated, not with the act of urination, but with the urine itself, is called secondary autoerotism. A patient in the manic phase of manic-depressive psychosis drank her own urine.

autofellatio (-fel-lä'tē-ō) Autofellatio is the practice of putting the male genital organ in one's own mouth. Bragman describes a man who, while sitting on the edge of a chair, lowered his head between his thighs. He added, 'experiencing an erection in this attitude, he placed his penis in his mouth until an ejaculation occurred.' (*Medical Journal and Record*, CXXVI, p. 488, 1927)

'While he occasionally practices self-irrumation (self-fellatio) to relieve sexual tension which has already been aroused, he more often employs it to stimulate sexual excitement in himself.' (Kahn, E. and Lion, E.G. *American Journal of Psychiatry*, 95, p. 132, 1935)

'. . . a considerable portion of the population does record attempts at self-fellation, at least in early adolescence. Only two or three males in a thousand are able to achieve the objective, but there are three or four histories of males who had depended upon self-fellation as a masturbatory technique for some appreciable period of time—in the case of one thirty-year-old male, for most of his life.' (Kinsey, A.C., et al. *Sexual Behavior in the Human Male*, Saunders, Philadelphia, 1948)

autofetishism Hirschfeld's term for the state of loving a material object (e.g. article of clothing) of one's own possession. The object acts as a sexual excitant.

autoflagellation Hirschfeld's term for the act of whipping oneself as a sexual excitant.

autogeny, autogenic (aw-toj'en-ē, -to-jēn'ik) See *endogenous; endogeny*.

autognosis (aw-tog-nō'sis) Knowledge of oneself.

auto-hypnosis (-hip-nō'sis) Auto-hypnosis

is self-hypnosis. In one of Freud's early communications (on the *Psychical Mechanism of Hysterical Phenomena*, 1893), he emphasized the need on the part of the patient not only to remember the painful experience, but to live out its affect at the same time. He called this abreaction. Some patients are able to abreact on occasion when under the influence of auto-hypnosis.

auto-infection, mental With this term Kornfeld in 1897 denoted a psychotic state in which the person believes himself wronged and brings every misfortune and unpleasant event into relation with his delusion. (Kornfeld, H. *On Mental Auto-Infection. Journal of Mental Science 43,* 96, 1897)

autointoxication An obsolescent term denoting toxicity allegedly due to the absorption of the waste products of metabolism or of the products of intestinal decomposition.

auto-libido See *libido*.

automagnetization Baragnon's term for autosuggestion.

automasochism (aw-tō-maz'ok-iz'm) A term used by Hirschfeld synonymously with Freud's conception of *masochism*.

automatic seizures A type of psychomotor epilepsy. See *epilepsy*.

automatism (aw-tom'à-tiz'm) A condition in which activity is carried out without conscious knowledge on the part of the subject. Automatic actions and speech are seen in clear form in the catatonic form of schizophrenia, in which incessant repetition may prevail without the patient's awareness. Automatisms are common also in other clinical states, particularly in those associated with a fugue.

'Automatic actions are not directly noticed by the patient himself; he neither feels that he wishes to accomplish the action, nor that he executes it. If the action lasts for some time, he takes notice of it like a third person, by observing and listening.' (Bleuler, E. *Textbook of Psychiatry,* tr. by Brill, A.A. Macmillan, New York, 1930) See *obedience, automatic*.

automatism, ambulatory A rhythmic form of automatic activity.

automatism, ambulatory comitial (kō-mish'al) A term devised by D.H. Tuke to denote automatic acts often observed in epileptic patients.

automatism, command When an individual strictly obeys a command, without the exercise of any critical judgment, he is said to show command automatism. The condition may be induced through hypnosis. It is not uncommon during the stage of hypersuggestibility in the catatonic form of schizophrenia; the patient may 'automatically' follow orders that lead to dangerous results.

'As an outward contrast to negativism there is sometimes found in our patients an automatic obedience to given commands. . . .' (Bleuler, E. *Textbook of Psychiatry,* tr. by Brill, A.A., Macmillan, New York, 1930)

automatism, post-ictal See *epilepsy*.

automatism, primary ictal A type of psychomotor epilepsy. See *epilepsy*.

automatization (aw-tōm-à-ti-zā'shun) While discussing the probable fundamental reason for the development of a neurosis, Waelder defines a neurosis as 'the automatization of anxiety reaction,' the individuals 'remaining perpetually infantile in an important part of their being.' A neurotic subject is therefore regarded as an automaton, acting at the mercy of his infantile impulses. The schizophrenic patient, whose life is built around concepts of infancy, succumbs completely to the deeply lying forces of his unconscious. The compulsive neurotic must give automatic obedience to his symptoms.

automonosexualism The term, coined by Rohleder, is synonymous with narcissism. It is not in common usage.

automysophobia (aw-tō-mī-sō-fō'bi-à) Morbid dread that the person himself is filthy or smells bad—not infrequently a symptom of psychoneurosis.

autonomasia (-nō-mā'zhi-à) A variety of amnesic aphasia, characterized by 'the impossibility or the difficulty of recalling substantives.' (Tanzi, E. *A Text-Book of Mental Diseases,* tr. by Robertson, W.F. and Mackenzie, T.C., Rebman, New York, 1909)

autonomic-affective law See law, *autonomic-affective*.

autonomic nervous system Vegetative nervous system. 'The autonomic nervous system consists of a series of cerebrospinal nuclei and nerves with widely distributed ganglia and plexuses which subserve the vegetative functions of the body. In its peripheral ramifications the system is characterized by a series of synaptic junctions which are situated outside the central nervous system. From anatomic and physiologic points of view there are two primary divisions, (1) the parasympathetic, or craniosacral, and (2) the sympathetic, orthosympathetic or thoracicolumbar. This subdivision is based upon the point of outflow from the central nervous system, the distribution of peripheral ganglia, the general antagonism in physiologic effects on visceral tissues most of which receive innervation from both divisions, and the response to pharmacologic agents. Each peripheral division of the autonomic nervous system is characterized by a two-neuron chain and consists of two histologic elements, the preganglionic neuron which terminates in a peripheral ganglion, whence the postganglionic neuron, or neuron of the second order, carries impulses to their destinations on the viscera. No impulse goes directly to an organ of termination. Anatomically the two divisions are designated the craniosacral and the thoracicolumbar portions, or outflows, but clinically the favored terms are either parasympathetic and sympathetic systems or parasympathetic and sympathetic divisions.' (De-Jong, R.N. *The Neurologic Examination*, Hoeber, 1950)

The autonomic nervous system is under control of higher centers, the most important of which is the hypothalamus. The hypothalamus appears to be the chief subcortical center for the regulation of both sympathetic and parasympathetic activities and for the integration of these. The anterior and medial nuclei of the hypothalamus are chiefly concerned with parasympathetic functions, while the lateral and posterior hypothalamic nuclei are chiefly concerned with sympathetic regulation.

autonomy (aw-ton'ō-mē) One of the essential features of the living organism by which it differs from any other object in nature. By this is meant that the organism does not represent merely an inactive element but is, to a large extent, a self-governing entity. The biological process, therefore, is not entirely a resultant of external forces, but is in part governed by specific biological forces which are endogenous. The organism possesses a certain degree of freedom in the sense of

Spinoza: it acts according to its own inherent nature, which is based on intrinsic forces, and not under the compulsion of outside influences. (Angyal, A. *Foundations for a Science of Personality*, The Commonwealth Fund, Oxford University Press, New York, 1941)

autonomy-heteronomy (-het-ēr-on'ō-mē) The autonomy of the organism is not absolute: the self-determination is restricted by outside influences which are heteronomous with relation to the organism. Every organismic process is always a resultant of two components, autonomy and heteronomy (endogenous and exogenous factors). In living beings of different species we find marked variations in the importance of autonomous and heteronomous determinants in their lives. Autonomy essentially means self-government; heteronomy means government from the outside. The expression autonomy-heteronomy is also used on the symbolic level, for instance, in relation to self-awareness. There is no absolute separation between the biological subject and the environment and, therefore, there is no sharp boundary between the experience of the self and the outside world. There are only degrees of ego proximity and ego distance. The degrees of ego proximity and ego distance are the symbolic expressions of the gradient of autonomy-heteronomy. (Angyal, A. *Foundations for a Science of Personality*, The Commonwealth Fund, Oxford University Press, New York, 1941)

autonyctobatesis (aw-tō-nik-tō-bà-tē'sis) *Obs.* Somnambulism.

autopathic (aw-tō-pa'thik) A term used by Burrow to signify feeling that has been distorted by self-consciousness and bias. Contrasted with orthopathic.

autopathy (aw-top'à-thē) Disease or disorder without apparent cause.

autophagy (aw-tof'à-jē) Biting or eating one's own flesh.

autophilia (aw-tō-fil'i-à) Self-love; narcissism.

autophobia (-fō'bi-à) Morbid fear of being alone; fear of self.

autophonia (-fō'ni-à) *Obs.* Suicide.

autophonomania (-fō-nō-mā'ni-à) *Obs.* Suicidal insanity.

autoplasty (aw'tō-plas-tē) The process of

forming libidinized structures in the psyche. See *alloplasty*.

autopsyche (aw-tō-sī'kē) The mind of one's self.

autopsychosis, moral (-sī-kō'sis) *Obs.* Wernicke's term for 'moral insanity,' i.e. psychopathic behavior traits, based on schizophrenia.

auto-sadism (-sad'iz'm) Garma says: 'suicide is an action originating in intensive auto-sadism. The ego attacks itself.' (*Imago, XXIII,* p. 65)

Auto-sadism is synonymous with *masochism*. 'The first stage of sadism is thus aggression linked with activity against an outside object. The second stage, which may appear as a form of defense, consists of a turning against the subject which is identical with a change of object (auto-sadism). If the object is entirely absorbed by the ego, then the sadism is transformed into secondary masochism, which then grafts itself upon the primary masochism preceding the sadism, and strengthens it.' (Nunberg, H. *Principles of Psychoanalysis,* International Universities Press, 1955)

autoscopy (aw-tos'kō-pē) The term used by Schilder to describe the psychological process in which the individual doubles his body-image and projects it to the outside world. This second, or duplicate, image can be modified according to the needs of his subconscious wishes, as clearly illustrated in the case of the patient, leading a very unhappy life, who saw herself dressed in medieval costume, far removed from the present. Such duplications are not rare in psychopathology and are by no means confined to the corporal image only; indeed, we often find duplications of experience in contrast to what actually took place or happened to the normal individual in whom total experience is summed up in a unified meaning. Through the phenomena of autoscopy, the patient duplicates and projects bodily defects without losing the consciousness of his own defects. Ordinarily, in the projected duplicate image, the physical defect is magnified. A patient of Schilder's 'had a crippled arm and saw persons opposite him not merely with a crippled arm, but also with a crippled leg.' This seems to follow the same pattern as the psychological process of the normal individual who tends to exaggerate the magnitude or scope of things important to him. (Schil-

der, P. *Mind, Perception and Thought,* Columbia University Press, New York, 1942)

autosome (aw'tō-sōm) Ordinary chromosome which has no relation to sex and is distinguishable from the heterosome or sex chromosome. See *sex determination*.

auto-somnambulism Somnambulism occasioned by 'self-hypnosis.' 'Or let us take those cases of auto-somnambulism which have so frequently obtained for their subjects the fame of being divinely inspired.' (Moll, A. *Hypnotism,* tr. by Hopkirk, F., Scribner's, New York, 1909)

auto-suggestibility The state of influencing oneself; self-suggestibility.

auto-suggestion When suggestion comes from the individual himself it is called auto-suggestion, in contradistinction to heterosuggestion or that which emanates from another.

'Everyone is susceptible to suggestions which are produced in himself. This tendency is termed auto-suggestion.' (Diethelm, O. *Treatment in Psychiatry,* Macmillan, New York, 1936)

'We also speak of *autosuggestion,* but this is merely a name for the effects of affectivity upon one's own logic and bodily functions.' (Bleuler, E. *Textbook of Psychiatry,* tr. by Brill, A.A., Macmillan, New York, 1930)

Regarding hysterical blindness, Freud says: 'the idea of blindness does not arise from the suggestion of the hypnotist, but spontaneously, so to speak, through auto-suggestion.' (Freud, S. *Collected Papers,* vol. 2, tr. by Riviere, J., Leonard and Virginia Woolf and The Institute of Psychoanalysis, London, 1924–25)

Auto-suggestion is synonymous with self-suggestion.

autosymbolism Silberer's term for hallucinations which represent, in symbolic form, what is thought or felt at a given instant. Autosymbolism is a phenomenon of the hypnagogic state, when neither full sleep nor full waking is predominant. It consists, essentially, of translation of thoughts into pictures and to this extent is identical with dream formation, differing from the latter only in that the other factors in dream-work are absent.

autosynnoia (aw-tō-sin-oi'à) *Obs.* Complete or almost complete self-centeredness.

autotomia (-tō'mi-à) In zoology this term refers to the severance of a part of the body; according to Ferenczi, this phenomenon appears to have its analogue in human activity. Some patients mutilate or cut off parts of the body that offend them. 'A similar tendency for freeing oneself from a part of the body which causes pain is demonstrated in the normal "scratch-reflex," where the desire to scratch away the stimulated part is clearly indicated, in the tendencies to self-mutilation in catatonia and in the like tendencies symbolically represented in the automatic actions of many tic patients. . . .' (Ferenczi, S. *Further Contributions to the Theory and Technique of Psychoanalysis*, London, 1926.)

autotopagnosia (aw-tō-top-ag-nō'si-à) Inability to identify or orient the body or the relation of its individual parts; i.e. a defect in appreciation of the body scheme. This type of agnosia occurs in lesions of the thalamoparietal pathways or of the cortex in the region of the angular gyrus. The patient with such a lesion behaves as if he had no arm or leg on that side, even though he may feel stimuli on that side if his attention is called to the limb.

avalanche, law of See *law of avalanche; conduction, avalanche.*

Avellis' syndrome (George Avellis, German laryngologist, 1864–1916) A bulbar syndrome due to involvement of the vagus nerve and the bulbar portion of the spinal accessory nerve. Symptoms are: homolateral paralysis of the soft palate, pharynx, and larynx, and contralateral dissociate hemianesthesia, with loss of pain and temperature but not of touch and pressure.

average, arithmetic The mean; the sum of all items in a group divided by the number of items in the group. Example: the average age of four children aged 7, 10, 12, and 15 years, is the sum of their ages (44) divided by the number of children (4), which is 11 years.

aversion, partial *Antifetishism* (Magnus Hirschfeld) (q.v.).

avoidant Negatively oriented or moving away from; an avoidant drive or behavior or response is a situation which results in behavior drawing away from the stimulus. Withdrawal behavior and defense reactions are types of avoidant behavior. Also known as abient behavior.

aypnia (a-ip'ni-à) Insomnia, sleeplessness.

B

babbling A form of speech preceding articulate speech, characterized by sound combinations devoid of meaning.

Babinski-Nageotte's syndrome (Joseph François Felix Babinski, Paris physician, 1857–1932, and Jean Nageotte, Paris histologist, 1866–) A bulbar syndrome produced by scattered lesions of the glossopharyngeal, vagus, spinal accessory (bulbar portion), and trigeminal nerves. Symptoms are: homolateral paralysis of the tongue, pharynx, and larynx; homolateral loss of taste in posterior tongue; homolateral Horner's syndrome; homolateral loss of pain and temperature sense in the face; homolateral asynergia and ataxia with a tendency to fall to the side of the lesion; contralateral hemiplegia, and contralateral dissociate hemianesthesia with loss of pain and temperature sense but preservation of touch and pressure.

Babinski's reflex Described by Joseph Babinski (1857–1932), a French neuropathologist, in 1898 and 1903, as extension of the toes instead of flexion when stimulating the sole of the foot. It 'consists in the comparatively slow dorsal extension of the great toe when the plantar reflex is tested and at the same time there is a slight spreading apart of the toes.' (Jelliffe, S.E. and White, W.A. *Diseases of the Nervous System,* 6th ed., Lea & Febiger, Philadelphia, 1935) The same phenomenon (great toe extension) may be produced by other tests—see *Oppenheim, Gordon, Chaddock.*

baby talk A form of speech characterized by defective articulation of certain consonants; it is rapidly outgrown unless adults in the environment contribute to its maintenance by using it themselves in conversing with the child. In severe behavior disorders and schizophrenia, the patient may revert to this type of speech development.

bacillophobia (bà-sil′ō-fō′bi-à) Morbid fear of bacilli or of microörganisms in general.

backwardness Tredgold says: 'Backward differ from dull children in the fact that their educational retardation is not usually due to intrinsic, but to extrinsic causes. When these causes can be removed the arrears are usually made up, although in some cases this may not entirely take place. They compose about one-third of all retarded children. The causes of extrinsic backwardness are numerous, but they may be grouped under the heading of (1) environmental or social; (2) physical.' (Tredgold, A.F. *A Text-book of Mental Deficiency,* 6th ed., Wood, Baltimore, 1937)

bad object See *object, bad.*

bad self See *self, bad.*

Baillarger, Jules (1809–90) (bà-yär-zhā′) French psychiatrist; investigated manic-depressive insanity as *folie á double forme* (1853–54) and *cretinism* (1873).

balance, group The result of grouping patients in accordance with clinical and personal criteria, in order to prevent intensification of a specific problem or set of problems.

balbutiate (bal-bū′shi-āt) *Rare.* To stammer.

ballistophobia (ba-lis-tō-fō′bi-à) Abnormal fear of missiles.

balneology (bal-nē-ol′ō-jē) Study of waters used in baths.

balneum (bal′nē-um, L. pron. bàl′ne-oom) Bath.

balneum arenae (bàl-ne-oom à-rā′nī) Sand bath.

balneum calidum (kà′lē-doom) Hot bath.

balneum frigidum (frē′gē-doom) Cold bath.

balneum tepidum (te′pē-doom) Warm bath.

Baló's disease Concentric demyelination. See *sclerosis, diffuse.*

baragnosis (bar-ag-nō′sis) Absence of ability to recognize weight of objects, generally tested by placing objects in the hand.

barognosis (bar-og-nō′sis) The sense of weight-differences, usually by lifting objects in the hand.

barophobia (bar-ō-fō′bi-à) Fear of gravity.

barrier, incest During the stage of infantile sexuality the child expresses sexual interests in the parents, usually in the parent of the opposite sex. During the latency period the erotic impulses are deflected from their sexual aims. The many forms of desexualized expressions, erected during the latency period, constitute the incest-barrier.

'But in relation to these objects [parents] it is confronted [at puberty] by the obstacle of the incest-barrier that has in the meanwhile been erected.' (Freud, S. *Collected Papers,* vol. 4, tr. by Riviere, J., Leonard and Virginia Woolf and The Institute of Psychoanalysis, London, 1924–25)

barrier, schizophrenic Schizophrenic patients show a barrier between the conscious and unconscious levels of their minds. This becomes especially manifest in their drawings, which are very often broken into two segments by an arbitrary line or barricade. The schizophrenic's mental splitting between the conscious and unconscious is shown by the contents of the two portions of the picture, which are devoid of any continuity in line or in ideation. (Baynes, H.G. *Mythology of the Soul,* Williams and Wilkins, Baltimore, 1940)

baryglossia (bar-i-glos′i-à) *Obs.* Thick, heavy speech, usually implying a disorder of the tongue.

barylalia (-lā′li-à) An indistinct and thick speech, observed principally in patients with an organic lesion, often in the central nervous system (Broca's area). It is common in advanced states of general paresis.

baryphonia (-fō′ni-à) A heavy quality of voice; generally deep and hoarse.

barythymia (-thī′mi-à) *Rare.* Depression of emotions. It is usual in depressive states and is generally accompanied by difficulty in thinking and acting.

basal ganglia Masses of gray matter lying deep within each cerebral hemisphere. The basal ganglia are composed of: (1) corpus striatum, including (a) pallidum (globus pallidus), (b) neostriatum (putamen and caudate nucleus) and (c) amygdala and claustrum; and (2) the internal capsule. The lenticular nucleus is used to refer to the outer putamen and the globus pallidus. The corpus striatum is an important unit of the *extrapyramidal system* (q.v.). The neostriatum receives

fibers from the thalamus and the cortex (frontal cortex and pyramidal tract) and sends efferents mainly to the pallidum. The pallidum sends efferents to the thalamus, hypothalamus, subthalamus, substantia nigra, midbrain, pons, and medulla.

Lesions in the corpus striatum may cause various symptoms, including muscular rigidity, involuntary movements (e.g. tremor, chorea, athetosis), and hypotonia. Lesions of the globus pallidus or substantia nigra are most commonly associated with muscular rigidity and tremor, as in Parkinsonism.

The internal capsule is a band of white fiber tracts separating the lenticular nucleus from the caudate and thalamus. It contains all the fibers which ascend to and descend from the cortex: pyramidal tract, thalamocortical fibers, optic radiation from the lateral geniculate body, auditory radiation from the medial geniculate body, fronto- and temporo-pontine tracts, fibers of the corpus striatum, and the corticothalamic tracts. Lesions in the internal capsule, common in cerebrovascular accidents, result in contralateral spastic hemiplegia.

Basedow's disease Hyperthyroidism or overactivity of the thyroid gland. Karl A. von Basedow, German physician (1799–1854), described the disease exophthalmic goiter in 1840. It is characterized by enlargement of the thyroid gland, protrusion of the eyeballs, rapid heart action, fine muscular tremors, and so-called general nervousness. It is as commonly called Grave's disease and less frequently Begbie's, Marsh's, Parry's, Parsons', or Flajani's disease.

basiphobia (bà-si-fō′bi-à) Morbid fear of walking. In the absence of sound reasons, fear of walking is morbid. It is common in the psychoneuroses, less so in the psychoses. Generally it is related to the individual's fear of collapse and death, rather than to fear of objects while walking. It has close kinship with fear of fainting and psychogenetically is associated with fear of death. Like other morbid fears it stems from the sphere of the unconscious. See *abasia.*

basistasiphobia (bà-si-stas-i-fō′bi-à) See *stasibasiphobia.*

basophobia (bà-sō-fō′bi-à) Basiphobia.

basostasophobia (bā-sō-stas-ō-fō′bi-à) *Stasibasiphobia* (q.v.).

Bastian's law (Henry Charlton Bastian, English neurologist, 1837–1915) In severe crush or complete interruption of the spinal cord, there results a total and permanent loss of reflexes with flaccid paralysis; death ensues within a few days or weeks.

bath, Brand See *bath, cold.*

bath, cold I.J. Sands says: 'Cold baths, usually referred to as the Brand baths, are occasionally employed in states of high temperature and deliria caused by it. The temperature is usually from 70° to 85° F. The patient is covered with a sheet and the body immersed in a cold tub. Friction of the body is immediately instituted and continued as long as the patient is in the tub. The patient should not be permitted to remain longer than fifteen minutes in the cold bath. He should then be removed and covered with dry, warm blankets.' (Sands, I.J. *Nervous and Mental Diseases for Nurses*, 3rd ed., Saunders, Philadelphia and London, 1937)

bath, cold foot H. Bailey says: 'The feet are placed in a tub of water 50° to 60° F. and vigorously rubbed and dried with coarse towels.' (Bailey, H. *Nursing Mental Diseases*, 3rd ed., Macmillan, New York, 1935)

bath, continuous I.J. Sands says: 'The *continuous bath* is a valuable therapeutic agent in the management of the very excited, delirious, and exhausted patients. The tub is arranged for a continuous inflow and outflow of water at a constant temperature of approximately 98° F. The patient is permitted to lie comfortably in a canvas suspended in the tub, and the body immersed in water. . . . He may be kept in the tub from four to twenty-four hours, or even longer.' (Sands, I.J. *Nervous and Mental Diseases for Nurses,* 3rd ed., Saunders, Philadelphia and London, 1937)

bath, drip A form of hydrotherapy. Standing in a tub filled with just enough water at a temperature of 105° F. to cover the ankles, the patient is soaked with cool water applied to the torso; this is followed by vigorous friction.

bath, hot air As a rule, a hot air bath is given in a cabinet heated by electric light bulbs. It is said that when a tonic effect

is desired the temperature of the air surrounding the body should range from 110° to 120° F. For eliminative purposes the temperature is maintained around 160° F.

bathophobia (bath-ō-fō′bi-à) Morbid dread of depths. The term commonly refers to fear of height, that is, fear of losing control of oneself while in a high place; it is a fear of falling from the height and of thus being killed. The fear is common among normal individuals, who, however, are able to control the impulse without much anxiety. It is morbid when the anxiety is intense and lasting and leads to measures to avoid high places. Common to many psychiatric conditions, it gains particular prominence among psychoneurotic subjects. It is symbolic of an unconscious impulse, the nature of which is unknown to the individual ruled by the fear.

bath, prolonged warm 'The tub is filled two-thirds with water at 90° to 100° F. The patient should recline and be encouraged to relax. The treatment may continue for twenty minutes. When ready to be taken out, a cold spray or sponge may be given, after which the patient is rubbed dry, gowned, wrapped in a blanket, placed in bed and given a warm drink.' (Bailey, H. *Nursing Mental Diseases,* 3rd ed., Macmillan, New York, 1935)

bath, sitz The sitz bath is 'given locally to the pelvis, in a tub of special construction. Depending upon the action desired these may be hot, cold, neutral, or prolonged. A blanket is placed about the patient and pinned at the back of the neck. [The patient] is then seated in the tub, and the feet placed in a foot bath at a temperature of 105° to 110° F. The upper edge of the blanket is brought up around the shoulders and over the edge of the tub, and the lower edge covers the foot bath.' (Bailey, H. *Nursing Mental Diseases,* 3rd ed., Macmillan, New York, 1935)

bath, whirlpool K.M. Steele says: 'This is a local bath given in a small tub for either arm or leg. There is a mixer to provide both hot and cold water and to make it possible to control the temperature. The temperature of the whirlpool bath ranges from 104° to 120° F. Air under pressure enters the tub under the surface of the water. Whirlpool baths are given for from

15 to 45 minutes.' (Steele, K.M. *Psychiatric Nursing,* Davis, Philadelphia, 1937)

bathyesthesia (ba-thi-es-thē′z[h]i-à) Deep sensibility; sensibility of the parts of the body beneath the surface. 'Here deep pressure pain, muscle and joint sense and bony sensibility are to be tested. Deep pressure with the thumb and fingers, or a special instrument (baresthesiometer) is used. The pressure should be sufficient to cause pain.' (Jelliffe, S.E. and White, W.A. *Diseases of the Nervous System,* 6th ed., Lea & Febiger, Philadelphia, 1935)

batophobia (ba-tō-fō′bi-à) Fear of (being on or passing) high objects or buildings.

batrachophobia (bat-rà-kō-fō′bi-à) Fear of frogs.

battarismus (bat-ar-iz′mus) Stammering; stuttering; hesitating speech.

battle fatigue See *shell-shock.*

Bayle's disease Antoine Bayle, French physician (1799–1858), first described it in 1822. *Obs.* Commonly known as general paralysis or paresis; dementia paralytica.

bdelygmia (dē-lig′mi-à) A Hippocratic term referring to a morbid loathing of food.

Beard, George Miller (1840–83) American psychiatrist; introduced the term *neurasthenia* in a paper, 'Neurasthenia or Nervous Exhaustion.' *Boston Medical and Surgical Journal, LXXX,* 217–21, 1869.

Bechtereff-Mendel reflex V.M. Bechtereff, Russian neurologist (1857–1927); Kurt Mendel, German physician (1874–   ). Also known as the cuboidodigital or dorsocuboidal reflex; by striking the outer part of the dorsum of the foot, there results normally a dorsal flexion of the toes; in abnormal conditions such as pyramidal tract disease, there is plantar flexion.

Bedlam The name of the Priory of St. Mary of Bethlehem, founded in London in 1247, turned into a mental hospital in 1402 and incorporated in 1547 as the Hospital of St. Mary of Bethlehem. The proper name of this first English 'lunatic asylum' became a common appellation for 'lunatic asylum' in general and, still later, synonymous with states of frenzy, excitement, wild tumult, pandemonium.

bedlamism *Rare.* A word or act which is characteristic of psychosis or of psychotic individuals; a trait of psychosis.

bedlamite *Obs.* Psychotic individual.

Beevor's sign (Charles Edward Beevor, British neurologist, 1854–1908) Upward excursion of the umbilicus, observed when the lower half of the abdominal muscles are paralyzed.

beggar, emotional A term describing that type of individual who is always 'holding his mental palm out to people, yet always expecting it to be slapped down. . .' The emotional beggar has been unable to detach himself from his parents (usually the parent of the opposite sex). 'He cannot get away from the desire to possess and be possessed' by the parent and 'is always seeking more,' no matter how close to the parent he has managed to attach himself emotionally. This impulse usually begins in infancy, the person never having been weaned physically or emotionally. 'His general reaction to people is a suckling one.' He flies into a tantrum if his desires are not fulfilled, and learns how to wheedle people into affectionate displays. His 'affection-begging is not much different with men than it is with women. All people are potential mothers to him.' (Hinsie, L.E. *Understandable Psychiatry,* Macmillan, New York, 1948)

behavior The manner in which anything acts or operates. With regard to the human being the term usually refers to the action of the individual as a unit. He may be, and ordinarily is, acting in response to some given organ or impulse, but it is his general reaction that gives rise to the concept *behavior.* Each component of the body has its own special ways of reacting; when the action of individual parts is meant, terms such as physiology and pathology are used. A hungry man seeks food; the seeking constitutes behavior. Food gets into his stomach; the stomach acts and reacts, that is, it exhibits physiology or pathology.

Healy, Bronner, and Bowers define behavior as 'the sum total of responses to stimuli, internal and external.' (Healy, W., Bronner, A.F., Bowers, A.M. *The Structure and Meaning of Psychoanalysis,* Knopf, New York, 1930)

To the special school of psychology called behaviorism the expression means that all human action, normal or abnormal, can be understood in terms of the reflex arc, reflex action, and conditioned reflexes.

behavioral reaction See *personality disorder.*

behavior, catastrophic A term introduced by Kurt Goldstein in 1939 to describe a certain type of behavior disorder that seemed more or less characteristic, or specific, for patients suffering from those disturbances of language and thought that had been grouped under the general diagnostic term *aphasia.* This symptomatic behavior takes the form of an inability to carry on a simple course of action once it is interrupted. The patients 'become agitated and fearful and more than usually inept when presented with once simple tasks that they can no longer do.' Goldstein interprets such traits of behavior as characteristic of a trend toward fanatical orderliness and the reaction of disinterest and aversion as defensive methods of avoiding 'catastrophic' embarrassment. It would seem that the catastrophic reaction stems from the personality (or psychological) response to the organic brain injury that underlies so many aphasia cases. (Hunt, J.McV. *Personality and the Behavior Disorders,* vol. 2, Ronald, New York, 1944)

behavior, chaotic An extreme disorderliness in organizing one's humdrum affairs, with respect to the time to be made available for different needs, the necessary money for various expenditures, or the disposition of personal effects—all suggesting or betokening a straying from mental health. On the other hand, the normal individual's ordinary personal needs, his various social situations, and the many other problems of day-to-day living are managed in a fairly systematic way. Fenichel states that chaotic behavior appears usually as a character trait of hysterical individuals. He explains that chaotic behavior 'represents a striving to get rid of traumatic impressions by actively repeating them.' (Fenichel, O. *The Psychoanalytic Theory of Neurosis,* Norton, New York, 1945)

behavior, collective The behavior which results when every individual in a group, an assemblage or a public 'is moved to think and act under the influence of a mood or a state of mind, in which each shares and to which each contributes.' (Park, R.E. *Collective Behavior; Encyclopaedia of the Social Sciences,* vol. 3, Macmillan, New York, p. 631)

In the broadest sense all group behavior is collective behavior. In the narrow sense collective behavior is applied not so much to customary and conventional behavior as to the emergence of new forms of behavior under conditions of inter-stimulation wherein 'individuals reflect one another's states of feeling and in so doing intensify this feeling.' (Blumer, H.E., in Park, R.E. *Principles of Sociology,* Barnes & Noble, New York, 1939)

Elementary forms of collective behavior are to be observed in the street crowd, the acting crowd, the expressive crowd, the mob, the gang, the panic, the riot, the stampede, and the mutiny; intermediate forms in mass behavior, the public, public opinion, the party, and crusades; and more highly organized forms in propaganda, advertising, religious movements, nationalistic movements, fashion, reform, and revolution.

behavior, criminotic Terms such as criminotic, criminotic behavior, criminosis have been introduced into psychiatric literature by Arthur N. Foxe. The word criminosis is coined on the pattern of neurosis and psychosis in regard to form, but differs in meaning in that it does not specifically connote mental illness. The criminotic is not necessarily mentally or emotionally ill, but the term criminosis would imply or describe his condition. And the term criminotic behavior would refer to the crime-committing activities of that person, as constituting the evidences of criminality or *criminosis* (q.v.).

behavior disorders This term refers to a group of psychiatric disorders in children and adolescents which are not secondary to somatic diseases or defects or to convulsive disorders and which are not part of a well-defined psychosis or psychoneurosis. The primary behavior disorders are considered to be reactions to an unfavorable environment; they appear as problems of personality development, as persisting undesirable traits or unfavorable habits (the so-called habit disorders, including nail-biting, thumb-sucking, enuresis, masturbation, temper tantrums, etc.), as delinquency or conduct disorders (truancy, fighting and quarreling, disobedience, untruthfulness, stealing, forgery, setting fires, destruction of property, use of alcohol, use of drugs, cruelty, sex offenses, vagrancy, etc.), as certain neurotic traits (such as tics and habit spasms, sleep-walking, overactivity and fears), and as problems of school and general educational or vocational difficulties. In the past, children with such disorders were referred to as 'problem children.'

behaviorism A term coined by J.B. Watson in 1913 'Psychology as the Behaviorist Views It,' *Psychological Review XX;* also *Behaviorism—An Introduction to Comparative Psychology,* Holt, New York, 1914) to indicate that all habits may be explained in terms of conditioned glandular and motor reaction.

'Behaviorism, on the contrary, holds that the subject matter of human psychology is the *behavior or activities of the human being.* Behaviorism claims that "consciousness" is neither a definable nor a usable concept; that it is merely another word for the "soul" of more ancient times.' (Watson, J.B. *Behaviorism,* The People's Institute, New York, 1924)

behavior-language This term means that the actions of the child, before he learns to speak, constitute a real language or means of expression. The crying, fretting, anxiety, quiescence, satiety, smiling, and self-activity are the words of a language the infant uses before acquiring the capacity of producing articulate sounds. (Sladen, F.J. *Psychiatry and the War,* Thomas, Springfield, Ill., 1943) See *jargon, organ.*

behavior, multidetermined A psychiatric term for a concept of special use and importance in the understanding of psychiatric etiology and causation and psychiatric prophylaxis or prevention. Human behavior, healthy or disordered, can be conceived of as being carried out at four fundamental levels: (a) the eugenical; (b) the physiological; (c) the psychological, and (d) the environmental. Multitudinous factors stemming from past experience, on the one hand, and the current, present environmental situation on the other constantly interact and interreact to determine the current behavior at the present cross-sectional level.

A.T. Mathers expressed himself in 1931 as follows (quoted by J.McV. Hunt): 'The causes [of human behavior] are multiform and variable, vague and subtle, rooted widely and deeply in the very fundamentals of life and society.' In the field of prevention, this important concept of the multidetermined origin of human be-

havior is the basis for the 'all out,' 'gun shot,' 'total push,' eclectic methods of approach toward psychiatric treatment and prevention. (Hunt, J.McV. *Personality and the Behavior Disorders,* vol. 2, Ronald, New York, 1944)

behavior, nodal In group therapy, the peak of hyper-aggressivity and hilarity on the part of children. This high peak is always followed by a period of quietude, which is the *anti-nodal phase.* This alternation of the quiet and action occurs in cycles. The frequency of this manifestation decreases as therapy progresses.

belle indifference See *hysteria.*

Bell's mania (Luther V. Bell, 1806–62, American physician) A term used by Luther Bell in 1849 for what is now designated as acute manic excitement.

Bell's palsy See *nerve, facial.*

belonephobia (bel-ō-nē-fō'bi-à) Fear of needles.

Bender, Lauretta (1897–) American neuropsychiatrist; Visual Motor Gestalt test; child psychiatry, especially schizophrenia and brain damage.

bends, the *Caisson disease* (q.v.).

Benedikt's syndrome (Moritz Benedikt, Austrian physician, 1835–1920) The symptoms following a lesion of the red nucleus in the midbrain which involves the oculomotor fibers passing through the midbrain: homolateral oculomotor paralysis, contralateral hyperkinesis.

benign (bē-nīn') The term is used in psychiatry to be the equivalent of recovery. It does not refer to the intensity of the clinical syndrome. A benign psychosis may be extremely intense, as the benign stupor state, from which the patient generally recovers or experiences appreciable amelioration.

Benommenheit (be-nom'en-hīt) Literally, a benumbing; Bleuler's term for one of the acute syndromes of the schizophrenias in which there is a slowing of all psychic processes but no dejection of mood or self-depreciatory ideas. Patients with Benommenheit are unable to deal with any relatively complicated or unusual situation; they make many mistakes and show marked apraxia and impaired comprehension. This syndrome may persist for long periods, even decades, but it is not otherwise indicative of a poor prognosis.

berdache (ber-dash′) Transvestite.

Berger rhythm, Berger wave See *electro-encephalogram.*

Bernheim (bârn-hâN′), **Hippolyte-Marie** (1840–1919) French psychotherapist; hypnotism and suggestibility.

Berz, Josef (1866–　　) (bârts′) Austrian psychiatrist; schizophrenia.

bestiality Any type of human behavior which resembles that of beasts; in general, it relates to sex, specifically to sexual congress between humans and animals.

beta-arc See *alpha-arc.*

bewildered A term often used to describe the lost, dazed, perplexed, puzzled patient who appears to be confused but shows a sort of numb apathy about his confusion. Bewilderment is often associated with conscious ambivalence, with dereistic or autistic thinking, with preoccupation, and with vacuity or sterility of thinking.

Bianchi, Leonardo (1848–1927) (bē-äng′-kē) Italian psychiatrist and neurologist.

biblioclast (bib′li-ō-klast) One who destroys or mutilates books.

'Among biblioclasts some act in groups, *cornering* copies of a rare book and making a *"pool"* of any volumes which are not immaculate; from among these they complete or perfect as many copies as possible, and destroy the remainder. . . .' (Jackson, H. *The Anatomy of Bibliomania,* Scribner's, New York, 1932)

biblioklept (-klept) One who steals books.

bibliokleptomania (-klep-tō-mā′ni-à) Morbid tendency to steal books.

bibliomania (-mā′ni-à) Book-madness; an intense desire to collect and possess books, especially rare and curious ones.

bibliophobia (-fō′bi-à) A morbid dread or hatred of books.

bibliotherapy (-ther′à-pē) The term denotes the utilization of reading as an adjunct to psychotherapy. Books may be recommended to patients for the following reasons: (1) to help the patient understand better his own psychological and physiological reactions to frustration; (2) to remedy insufficient or erroneous knowledge; (3) to facilitate communication between patient and therapist by helping the patient understand the terminology of therapy; (4) to stimulate the patient to discuss and verbalize certain problems by helping to remove the fear, shame, or guilt related to those problems; (5) to stimulate the patient to think constructively between interviews; (6) to reinforce accepted social and cultural patterns and thereby inhibit certain infantile patterns of behavior; (7) to stimulate the patient's imagination and give him vicarious satisfactions which reality cannot afford without danger; (8) to enlarge the patient's sphere of interest; (9) as an adjunct to a program of vocational rehabilitation. The reading matter recommended must, of course, be selected individually for the specific patient, depending on the goals of therapy, the intellectual capacities of the patient, and his stage of achievement in therapy.

Bichat, law of (Marie François Xavier Bichat, French anatomist, 1771–1802) According to Bichat there are two great body systems, called by him the vegetative and the animal. The former provides for assimilation and augmentation of mass, while the latter provides for the transformation of energy, 'that is, for the relations with the environment.' The two systems 'are in inverse ratio of development in ontogenetic evolution—the greater the development of the vegetative system, the less developed is the system of relation.' (Pende, N. *Constitutional Inadequacies,* tr. by Naccarati, S., Lea & Febiger, Philadelphia, 1928)

Biedl-Moon-Laurence syndrome See *Laurence-Moon-Biedl syndrome.*

Bielschowsky's disease (Max Bielschowsky, German neuropathologist, 1869–1940) See *amaurotic family idiocy.*

Binet-Simon tests See *tests, Binet-Simon.*

Binswanger, Otto (1852–1929) (bēn′-swäng-gēr) German neurologist and psychiatrist.

bioanalysis (bī-ō-à-nal′i-sis) '. . . The question presents itself to me whether the term psychoanalysis is really broad enough and whether another more comprehensive and more all-inclusive term, such as *bio-analysis* or *psychobioanalysis* should not be substituted for it, especially if we would include the analysis of the somatic symptoms of the psychoneuroses, psychoses, and other psychic states as well as the multiform conduct of man at every stage of evolution and development.' (Solomon, M. 'Plea for Broader Standpoint in Psychoanalysis,' *Psychoanalytic Review 2,* 66, 1915)

biodynamics (bī-ō-dī-nam'iks) Masserman's system of psychoanalytic psychiatry; '. . . biodynamics derives some of its essential dynamic orientations from analysis, and serves no greater practical function than to generalize fundamental analytic concepts and to demonstrate their theoretical, experimental and clinical applicability to a wide range of phenomena in animal and human behavior.' (Masserman, J.H. *The Practice of Dynamic Psychiatry,* Saunders, Philadelphia, 1955.) The four principles of biodynamics—motivation, milieu, adaptation and conflict—are stated as follows: (1) all organisms are actuated by their physiologic needs; (2) every organism reacts to its own interpretations of its milieu in terms of its individual needs, special capacities, and unique experiences; (3) whenever an organism's goal-directed activities are frustrated by external obstacles, the organism either changes its techniques to reach that same goal or changes its goal; (4) when two or more urgent motivations conflict so that the adaptive patterns attendant to each are mutually exclusive, the organism experiences anxiety and its somatic and muscular behavior becomes either ambivalent, poorly adaptive, and ineffectively substitutive (neurotic), or progressively more disorganized, regressive, and bizarrely symbolic (psychotic).

biogenetic law of Haeckel See *law, Haeckel's biogenetic.*

biometry (bī-om'e-trē) Biometry means the measurement of life. Specifically, it refers to the calculation of the probable duration of life. It includes the study of all the factors, endogenous and exogenous, that enter into the determination of the duration of life. Just to mention a few of the determinants in the schizophrenic individual, possessing an asthenic habitus: hypoevolutism of the cardio-arterial system, blood, muscular and ligamentous systems; hypoadrenalism; hypogenitalism; drop heart; pulmonary tuberculosis. Each of these factors and many others (occupation, sanitation, climate, etc.) contribute to the problems of biometry.

bionegativity (bī-ō-neg-à-tiv'i-tē) A personality constellation in which one or more part processes disturb the total function of the organism. In an entirely healthy organism the various part processes are integrated in such a way that they subserve and promote the total function of the organism, while in an abnormal condition the integration is impaired and one or more part functions impede or disturb instead of promote the total function. Instead of being viewed as an abnormality such an impairment is, therefore, conceived as an integrational state, a specific relation between part and whole, and is called bionegativity.

biophilia (bī-ō-fil'i-à) Instinct of self-preservation.

biosphere (bī'ō-sfēr) The realm or sphere of life in which the total biological process takes place. The biosphere includes both the individual and his environment not as interacting parts or constituents that have an independent existence, but as aspects of a single reality which can be mentally separated only by abstraction. The limits of life extend as far as the organism is able to exert an influence on the events outside of him. (Biosphere corresponds to the German term *Lebenskreis.*) Angyal, A. *Foundations for a Science of Personality,* The Commonwealth Fund, Oxford University Press, New York, 1941)

biostatistics (-stà-tis'tiks) Vital statistics. Biostatistics is the numerical representation of conditions associated with life.

biothanatos (-than'à-tos) An old term, used by Forestus, in reference to 'one who dies a violent death, either by his own hand or otherwise. A synonym of suicide.' (Tuke, D.H. *A Dictionary of Psychological Medicine,* vols. 1–2, Blakiston, Philadelphia, 1892)

biotype This genetic term comprises all individuals who equal each other *genotypically,* whether or not their *phenotypical* appearance may show any obvious resemblance. The phenotypical features of two individuals belonging to the same biotype may be dissimilar to a considerable extent, since every hereditary predisposition has a certain amount of variability of manifestation.

biotypogram In Pende's system of constitutional medicine, a variety of constitutional formulae as they are to be recorded in the individual's *'book of health'* for the purpose of a 'diagrammatic representation' describing the various types in all their somatic and psychological aspects.

The reclamation of poor constitutions in the interest of individual as well as nation is the objective of Pende's suggestion to institute the method of biotypograms in all progressive countries.

'Modern analysis of the individual biotype cannot be made today by any other method than the clinical, that is, the *correlational*. It must be dominated by the principles of correlations between the morphological, the humoral and the psychological side of the individuality.' (Pende, N. *Constitutional Inadequacies*, tr. by Naccarati, S., Lea & Febiger, Philadelphia, 1928)

biotypology (bī-ō-tī-pol'ō-jē) The systematic study or doctrine of biotypes. In this sense it no longer corresponds to the original biological meaning of biotype. Although the genetic concept of biotype applies to individuals equaling each other *genotypically,* it has been taken in the field of constitutional studies, especially by the Italian school, to indicate the phenotypical constellation of all characteristics making up the 'somatic-psychic individuality' of a human individual, including the morphological, physiological and psychological aspects of the given type.

bipolarity (bī-pō-lar'i-tē) *Ambivalence* (q.v.).

Birnbaum, Karl (1878–   ) (bērn'-boum) German psychiatrist; forensic psychiatry.

birth, anal In psychoanalytic theory this term refers to the sexual phantasies or dreams directly connected with anal erotism when these phantasies or dreams are expressed in the symbolic form of a wish to be reborn through the anus. In this respect, Freud gave the following dream as example: 'Spending the summer beside Lake _____ she flings herself into the dark waters at the place where the pale moon is mirrored.' Freud defined this dream as an expression of anal birth. The interpretation of the dream reveals that 'she flings herself into the water' means 'she comes out of the water,' that is to say, 'that she is born.' The moon represents an anal symbol derived from the French language in which the 'derrière' (the 'behind') is vulgarly spoken of as 'la lune' (the moon).

birth control Prevention of conception for the purpose of limiting the number of offspring, particularly among those who are termed *cacogenic* (q.v.). 'Planned parenthood' is a better term than 'birth control' to characterize the eugenic objectives. In many instances what is sought is not a reduction in the size of families, but the proper 'spacing' of children, so that they will come when the mother, the home, and the family budget are best prepared for their advent into the world. 'Children, like any guest in a home, it is felt, should arrive only when they are welcome.' (Scheinfeld, A. *You and Heredity*, Book of the Month Club, New York, 1939)

Various contraceptive measures have been medically devised for the practice of birth control. Within the special program of 'negative' eugenic measures proposed for the application to those hopelessly insane and mentally defective individuals who are considered unfit to have *any* children, the most drastic form of birth control is sterilization.

birth, multiple In biology and vital statistics the term applies to all instances in which women produce more than one child at the same birth. The tendency to multiple births seems to run in certain families, although it has not yet been proved that it is based on a specific hereditary factor.

Twins come about once in every 90 births in most of the American and European countries. The proportion of fraternal to identical twins is approximately 3 : 1 (see *twin*).

Triplets occur once in about 8,000 births. They also may be identical or 'unmatched' multiples, that is, developed either from one egg or from three separate eggs. The third possibility is that only two members of a set of triplets are identical, developed from one egg, and the third is a fraternal, developed from a different egg.

Quadruplets are reported by Scheinfeld to occur once in about 700,000 births, with only a few sets surviving. Here the following combinations are possible: (1) All four identicals; (2) three identicals and one fraternal; (3) two identicals and two fraternals; and (4) most rarely, all four fraternals.

The birth of five human beings at one time is believed to have happened not more than sixty times in the last five hundred years. In all cases, however, these *quintuplets* are said to have perished soon after birth, with the only exception of the famous *Dionne* quintuplets who were born in Canada in May, 1934 (the attending obstetrician was Dr. Allan Dafoe) and are now generally classified as *identical* multiples.

birth trauma See *trauma, birth.*

bisexuality The presence of the qualities of both sexes in the same individual. The term is synonymous with hermaphroditism, though the latter term appears to have gained almost exclusive reference to the organic manifestations of the condition. The term intersex, introduced by Goldschmidt, is used 'to designate hermaphrodites as individuals who started out either male or female from a genetic standpoint but who after a certain period completed their sexual development in the opposite direction. In the intersex there is first a female phase and later a male phase, or vice versa, and in the second phase a typical mixture of both sexes exists.' (Young, H.H. *Genital Abnormalities, Hermaphroditism and Related Adrenal Diseases,* Williams & Wilkins, Baltimore, 1937)

In the classical sense a bisexual or hermaproditic individual is one 'who has the gonads and external genitalia of both sexes and is capable of living as either a man or a woman.' (ibid)

Bisexuality manifests itself also in the psyche. Indeed, it is of great importance to the mental make-up of an individual. While writing about an infantile neurosis Freud says that 'it would seem palpably obvious that the repression and the formation of the neurosis must have originated out of the conflict between masculine and feminine tendencies, that is, out of bisexuality.' (Freud, S. *The Basic Writings of Sigmund Freud,* tr. by Brill, A.A., Random House, New York, 1938)

'But, since the nature of the human being unites masculine and feminine elements, a man can live the feminine in himself, and a woman the masculine in herself.' (Jung, C.G. *Contributions to Analytical Psychology,* tr. by Baynes, H.G. and C.F., Kegan Paul, Trench, Trubner, London, 1928)

'Psycho-analysis has proven that all homosexuals, without exception, show heterosexual tendencies in early life. There is no exception to this rule. *There are no monosexual persons!*' (Stekel, W. *Bi-*

Sexual Love, tr. by van Teslaar, J.S., Badger, Boston, 1922)

bivalence (bī-vā′lens, biv′à-lens) Some authors use the terms bivalence and ambivalence interchangeable. See *ambivalence.*

bizarreness Striking incongruity or eccentricity; discordant, disharmonious, contradictory behavior such as is seen most commonly in schizophrenic patients.

black-out A term denoting the loss of consciousness produced by anemia of the brain. When the loss of consciousness is only partial and of lesser importance, the term applied is *gray-out.* This condition is often observed in pilots of high-speed airplanes.

bladder, automatic The filling and spontaneous evacuation of the urinary bladder occurring in cases of transsection of the spinal cord.

blaesus (blē′sus) *Obs.* General paralysis.

Blandford, George Fielding (1829–1911) British psychiatrist.

-blast, blasto- (blas′tō-) A combining form meaning *sprout, shoot, germ, embryonic,* from Gr. *blastós,* sprout, shoot, twig.

blast concussion See *neurosis, postconcussion.*

blastomere (blas′tō-mēr) Cell(s) formed by the first cell divisions of a fertilized egg undergoing the process of *cleavage* (q.v.).

blastopore (blas′tō-pōr) See *gastrulation.*

blastula (blas′chū-là) In this embryological stage of a human organism, there is continued cell division beyond the 32-cell stage and the appearance of an enlarging central cavity, the blastocele, in the fertilized egg undergoing the segmenting process of *cleavage* (q.v.).

At first the blastula is a hollow sphere whose wall is a single layer of morphologically and functionally identical cells, the primitive *ectoderm* (q.v.). Only in the later stages of this *monodermic* blastula condition one finds those larger cells at the pole opposite that of the location of the polar bodies, which foreshadow the future *entoderm* (q.v.).

blepharospasm (blef′à-rō-spaz′m) The spasmoid closing of the orbicular muscle of the eyelid. It is not infrequently observed in psychiatric patients, in whom a relatively large quantum of emotions is referred to the external ocular apparatus.

In extreme instances, as in catatonic states, the lids may be held tightly approximated in the effort to shut off all light stimuli coming from the environment.

Bleuler, Eugen (1857–1939) (bloi'lĕr) Swiss psychiatrist, dementia praecox. In 1911, Bleuler suggested the term 'schizophrenia' to replace dementia praecox. His monumental treatise, *Dementia Praecox or the Group of Schizophrenias,* differentiated between the fundamental and the accessory symptoms of schizophrenia, and it remains today the authoritative source book on the development and manifestations of schizophrenic symptoms.

blindism This term refers to undesirable mannerisms and habitual movements seen in blind patients, and particularly in children, such as repeated rubbing of the eyes, shaking and rolling the body, poking at the eyes or ears, shaking the hands when excited and, if there is some vision, fanning the fingers in front of the eyes. Usually the blindism is given up as the child grows older.

blindness, circumferential See *field defect.*

blindness, cortical psychic A condition usually due to bilateral occipital lobe lesions producing a loss of topographical orientation, of optic memory image, and of spatial orientation.

blindness, emotional A term used by L.E. Hinsie to designate *hysterical blindness.*

blindness, hysterical Blindness arising from mental causes in a hysterical individual. In principle it bears out the popular belief that we see what we want to see and are blind to the things we do not want to see. Hysterical blindness is of the same order. A young woman, inordinately fond of her father, tried frantically to drive him out of her mind. Realizing the unnaturalness of her love for him, she became blind, owing to her strong sense of guilt and because she could no longer look upon her father.

blindness, mind This term implies a condition in which objects and space dimensions are seen by the eye but are not properly recognized by the mind. It is synonymous with psychic blindness. The outstanding clinical picture in these cases is characterized by the fact that the patient has an erroneous idea of the size of objects and the three dimensions of space. Sometimes the individual sees objects as flat, and when the condition improves stereoscopic vision is recovered. In a case described by Willbrandt, objects appeared to the patient as being smaller than she had previously seen them before the onset of mind blindness. Generally speaking, it seems that uncertainties concerning human relations constitute the basic element responsible for the loss of the sense of the third dimension, the changes in size, and the seemingly greater distance of objects. In relation to this former misconception, Schilder describes the case of a patient, who, during analytical treatment, had the impression of seeing the analyst seated in a chair very far away. In anxiety cases the distance between the individual and the beloved person is the only space that seems real to the patient. Accordingly, when the beloved person is away, or out of sight, the space seems to become immense. 'In some phobias connected with walking the patients occasionally dream that their feet do not touch the ground.' This, according to the psycho-analytical interpretation of Schilder, symbolizes the distance of their genitals from mother. (Schilder, P. *Mind, Perception and Thought,* Columbia University Press, New York, 1942)

blinking Quick, involuntary, apparently purposeless and repetitious movement of the eyelids (alone or associated with similar movements involving other groups of muscles and belonging to the category of tics or habit spasms) observed in nervous children.

block, affect Inability to discharge emotions adequately or appropriately, seen typically in obsessive-compulsives, who often appear cold, unfeeling, and emotionally stiff and overcontrolled. Freud termed this 'isolation of affect.' 'In such cases a fantasy connected with a wish or a crucial memory from the past may have ready access to consciousness, but the emotion, usually a painful one, which should be connected with it does not become conscious. Moreover, such patients usually manage to keep from feeling too much emotion of any sort. . . . However, in some unfortunate individuals it goes so far that in the end the individual has hardly any awareness of emotions of any kind and seems like a caricature of that equanimity which ancient philosophers put forward as an ideal.' (Brenner, C. *An Elementary Textbook of Psychoanaly-*

sis, International Universities Press, New York, 1955)

blocking Sudden cessation in the train of thought or in the midst of a sentence. The patient is unable to explain the reason for the sudden stoppage, which may occur in the absence of intellectual defect or sensorial disorder. 'Often thinking stops in the middle of a thought; or in the attempt to pass to another idea, it may suddenly cease altogether, at least as far as it is a conscious process (blocking). Instead of continuing the thought, new ideas crop up which neither the patient nor the observer can bring into any connection with the previous stream of thought.' (Bleuler, E. *Dementia Praecox or the Group of Schizophrenias,* International Universities Press, New York, 1950) Blocking is also known as 'thought-deprivation.' It is usually experienced by the patient as unpleasant. Bleuler considered a positive response by a patient to the question of whether or not he had ever experienced thought-deprivation pathognomonic of schizophrenic association-disorder. See *obstruction.*

blocking, counter-impulse in The opposite of the impulse that is blocked. Kraepelin particularly stressed that counterdrives may cause blocking. Bleuler points out that '. . . the denial of any impulse is so very often associated with a counter-impulse that, in stressing the counter-impulse, we only emphasize a different aspect of the same process, but we do not gain a new perspective.' (Bleuler, E. *Dementia Praecox or the Group of Schizophrenias,* International Universities Press, New York, 1950) One schizophrenic patient demonstrated blocking whenever he was asked about his father. Further investigation indicated that the patient had marked ambivalence toward his father, and questioning him touched upon his hatred for the father and at the same time upon his love for the father. Here the impulse appeared to be canceled out, as it were, by the counter-impulse, and blocking resulted.

block, partial genetic See *disease, genetotrophic.*

boarding-out system See *system, boarding-out.*

bodies, geniculate See *geniculate bodies.*

body build, index of A standard devised by Eysenck in his studies on the relationship between somato-type and psychosis. The I.B. consists of a measurement of stature and transverse chest diameter;

$$\text{I.B.} = \frac{\text{stature} \times 100}{\text{transverse chest diameter} \times 6.}$$

body cell See *cell, body.*

body-image See *image, body.*

body-language A term used by L.E. Hinsie to characterize the expression of feelings or thoughts by means of bodily movements. See *language, primitive psychosomatic.*

body-memory A memory retained by the body as opposed to a mind-memory which is retained by the mind. The theory of body-memories holds that the body remembers and repeats. This is noted particularly during psychoanalytical treatment. Although frequently the treatment cannot recover memories from the early years of life, the patient behaves like an infant: he exhibits tantrums, grimaces, or peevishness; cries for attention or yells and screams; flails his limbs when not getting what he wants, and he may assume the posture of an infant. In this way the patient speaks a body-language. His behavior 'looks like a throwback to infancy and the appearance is frequently supported by what the patient says.' These infantile activities are explained by the theory that the body remembers and repeats. Indeed 'some patients say that they do not think, their bodies do.' (Hinsie, L.E. *Understandable Psychiatry,* Macmillan, New York, 1948.) See also *engram.*

body-mindedness The term body-mindedness is used by L.E. Hinsie interchangeably with the term *psychosomatism* (q.v.).

body of Luys (Jules Bernard Luys, French physician, 1828–1898) See *subthalamus.*

body, polar In sexual reproduction, the female germ cells or oögonia divide into two unequal daughter cells, the smaller of which is called the first or second polar body, according to whether it is produced by the first or second meiotic division. Only the larger cells or oöcytes have a reproductive function, while the polar bodies gradually disintegrate and disappear. See *egg.*

body-protest See *protest, body.*

body-scheme See *ego, body.*

bogeyman A spirit or goblin who will punish the child for misdoings or for 'being naughty.' The childhood fear of the bogeyman has its precise psychoanalytic interpretation, as a result of what is called 'internalized parental prohibitions.' The growing child soon discovers that there are many things he might receive pleasure from which are prohibited by his parents. Through the double fear of punishment and losing his parents' affection he begins to follow out these prohibitions even when his parents are not on hand. As a result a part of the child's mind is continually on guard so that he may not behave in such a way that the parents' disapproval will be aroused. These 'internalized parental prohibitions' are forerunners of the superego. One way in which the child handles these terrible threats of punishment is to project them onto persons in the external world. Thus the bogeyman is in reality what Fenichel calls an 'externalized pre-super-ego.' And the fear of this terrifying being is in reality the terror of punishment arising from 'internalized parental prohibitions.' (Fenichel, O. *The Psychoanalytic Theory of Neurosis,* Norton, New York, 1945)

Bonhoeffer, Karl (1868–1939) (bôn'hĕf-ĕr) German psychiatrist and neurologist; alcoholism; forensic psychiatry.

Bonnier's syndrome (Pierre Bonnier, French physician, 1861–1918) Symptoms resulting from a lesion involving the acoustic, glossopharyngeal, and vagus nerves: paroxysmal vertigo (Ménière's disease), contralateral hemiplegia, aphonia, dysphagia, and loss of gag reflex.

boundary, ego A concept introduced by Federn to refer to 'the peripheral sense organ of the ego.' The ego boundary discriminates what is real from what is unreal. Because the boundary is flexible and dynamic, it will vary in accordance with different ego states. There are two main ego boundaries, the inner and the outer. The inner ego boundary is the boundary toward the repressed unconscious. This is strengthened by countercathexes (anticathexes) and thus is able to prevent the entrance of repressed material. Its flexibility is demonstrable in hypnagogic states and in normal falling asleep, where the ego and its boundaries lose cathexis and unegotized material enters. The external or outer ego boundary is the boundary toward stimuli of the external world. The external ego boundary includes the sense organs but it is more than mere summation of these, for the sense of reality of an object comes not alone by stimulation of a sense organ but further requires that the non-ego material impinges upon a well-cathected external ego boundary. If the boundary loses cathexis these perceptions, no matter how vivid, will have a strange, unfamiliar, or even unreal quality.

bouquet de malades (boo-kā' dĕ mà-làd') The distinctive odor said to be characteristic of psychiatric patients.

Bourneville's disease (Désiré-Magloire Bourneville, Paris neurologist, 1840–1909) Tuberous sclerosis.

Bovarism (From the title character in the novel *Madame Bovary,* by Gustave Flaubert) Confusion of daydreaming with the facts of the perceptual world; failure to differentiate between phantasy and reality.

bovina fames (bô-vē'nà fà'mes) (L. 'ox-like hunger') Bulimia.

boxer's traumatic encephalopathy (en-sef-à-lop'à-thē) See *dementia, boxer's.*

brachuna (brà-kū'nà) Acrai; nymphomania and/or satyriasis.

brachy- (brak'ē-) Combining form meaning (abnormally) short.

brachycephaly, brachycephalism (-sef'à-lē, -liz'm) A skull with shortened antero-posterior diameter. See *index, cephalic.*

brachylineal (-lin'ē-al) Brachymorphic.

brachymorphic (-mor'fik) Relating to or characterized by brachymorphy. In the systems of constitutional types of the Italian school, this is equivalent to the *megalosplanchnic* type of Viola, although in analogy to eumorphic and normosplanchnic, the difference in the etymology of brachymorphic and megalosplanchnic indicates a difference of the criteria used for assessing the type, namely, general structure in contrast to visceral size and its effect. It has been affirmed, however, that there is a complete correspondence between the incidence of these general and external morphological criteria on the one hand, and those of the internal anatomy and its results on the other.

Generally speaking, the *brachymorphic type* is built along lines that are shorter and broader than the normal figure, and corresponds roughly to the *pyknic* type.

brachymorphy (-mor'fē) Shortness of stature. See *brachymorphic*.

brachyskelic (-skel'ik) Characterized by an excessive shortness of the legs. See *pyknic*.

brachytypical (-tip'i-kal) Synonymous with *brevilineal* (q.v.) and *brachymorphic* (q.v.).

brady- (brad'ē-) Combining form meaning slow, from Gr. *bradýs*.

bradyarthria (-är'thri-à) Slowness of speech. It implies that its cause is organic and is due to some disorder in the central or peripheral apparatus connected with speech. See *bradylogia,* the implication of which is psychical.

bradyglossia (-glos'i-à) Slowness of speech or bradyglossia carries with it the idea that the slowness is the result of difficulties in the movements of the tongue. The original cause may be distant from the tongue.

bradykinesis, bradykinesia (-ki-nē'sis, -si-à) Slow or retarded movement; it may be organically or psychically determined. It is common in depressive states and is often observed in schizophrenia.

bradylalia (-lā'li-à) Abnormal slowness of speech, or bradyarthria. It may, like bradylexia, be occasioned by organic or psychological pathology or both. It is not uncommon in the symptomatology of depressed states.

bradylexia (-lek'si-à) Abnormal slowness in reading, which may be organically or psychologically (emotionally) determined or both. It is observed that, in the depressed patient, for instance, slowness in reading is but one of the many phenomena of mental retardation. Bradylexia may or may not be associated with intellectual incapacity as such.

bradylogia (-lō'ji-à) Slowness of speech may be representative of physical or psychical causes. When it occurs, for example, in general paresis, it is usually, though not always, the consequence of organic lesions. When it is observed in depressive states (e.g. the depressive phase of manic-depressive psychosis), it is believed to be a reflection of psychic (emotional) inhibition.

bradyphasia (brad-i-fā'zhi-à) Slowness of speech.

bradyphrasia (-frā'zhi-à) Bianchi defines this as 'slowness of thought.'

bradyphrenia (-frē'ni-à) A general term for sluggish mentality. It is used by some as the equivalent of feeblemindedness, by others as the equivalent of psychomotor retardation.

Bradyphrenia may be symptomatic of any acquired disorder that interrupts the functioning of intelligence.

Bradyphrenia is focal when there is retardation in the presence only of disagreeable or painful ideas; it is diffuse when it is vague and unvarying irrespective of the topic in mind.

Slowness in thinking is often associated with states of intense emotion, as in severe anxieties and depressions; in the latter there may be a marked paucity or such a profusion of ideas as to lead to great difficulty in concentrated thinking. Bradyphrenia, like intellectual retardation, may be initial, that is, slowness in starting, or consistent, that is, slowness in continuing.

bradypragia (-prā'ji-à) Unusually slow action. The expression is more frequently employed in reference to physical than to psychical matters. When, for instance, the thyroid gland is underactive, the physiology of the body in general is diminished. Some authorities apply the word also to slow mentation, although bradyphrenia is the term relating directly to the mind.

bradytrophism (-trō'fiz'm) This term was introduced in constitutional medicine by Bouchard to designate a syndrome which is caused by a slowing down of the nutritive movement. The condition may be generalized or localized, and is characteristic of such diseases as gout, diabetes, asthma, various chronic or recurrent rheumatisms, and various forms of lithiasis and of pruritic and chronic or recurrent desquamative dermatosis.

General bradytrophism results in products of imperfect metabolism and chronic autotoxemia. *Local* bradytrophism is best understood as a nutritive torpor of the organs which leads to the accumulation of lymph and waste material in their interstitium and gradually produces fatty infiltration, sclerosis, and early aging of the organs.

braid-cutting A perversion, relatively rare nowadays, consisting of the cutting of the hair from the victim. This perversion is a form of sadism combined with a fetish-istic preference for hair. It expresses the idea, 'I am the castrator, not the castrated one,' and often also the complementary idea, 'I am only a pseudo-castrator, not a real castrator.' The knowledge that the hair will grow back is an important part of the reassurance which the patient gains from the perverse act in that it proves to him that castration need not be final.

braidism (brād'iz'm) The theory of hypnosis named after James Braid, English surgeon (1795–1861), who published in 1843, *Neurypnology, or, the Rationale of Nervous Sleep, considered in relation with animal magnetism.*

brain The part of the nervous system confined in the skull; it includes the cerebrum, mid-brain, cerebellum, pons, and medulla.

brain disorder A term used to refer to any psychiatric syndrome caused by impairment of brain tissue function; this group corresponds in general to that formerly called the 'organic psychoses' or the 'organic reaction types.' The brain disorders are termed acute or chronic depending upon their reversibility; those which are ordinarily temporary and reversible are called acute, while those from which full recovery is not anticipated are called chronic.

brain-stem This term refers to the *pons* (q.v.) and the *medulla oblongata* (q.v.).

brain tumor See *tumor, intracranial.*

brain, visceral See *rhinencephalon.*

brain-washing See *deprivation, sensory; menticide.*

breakdown, nervous A sudden onset of severe painful emotions such as anxiety, tension, or feeling of guilt, etc. which may also be accompanied by various physical symptoms such as headaches, dizziness, tremors, fainting spells, nausea, vomiting, diarrhea, etc., all without a real physical basis. With people who have gone along at a certain level of adaptation to their environment and handled their problems of ordinary living fairly well without suffering too much distress in the various situations in which they find themselves, this adjustment is utterly disrupted and a nervous breakdown occurs. These breakdowns may afflict already neurotic as well as normal people and among their manifold causes may be in-

volved such things as physiological stress, certain particularly disturbing experiences, physical illness, fatigue, and many other factors. (Fenichel, O. *The Psychoanalytic Theory of Neurosis,* Norton, New York, 1945)

Breuer, Joseph (1841–1925) (broi'ēr) Viennese neurologist; published (1895) with Freud, *Studien über Hysterie.*

brevilineal (brev-i-lin'ē-al) In constitutional medicine, this term refers to one of the two constitutional types distinguished by Manouvrier on the basis of the configuration of the body as a whole. In contradistinction to the longilineal type, it designates the type built along lines that are shorter and broader than the average figure.

Persons of this type correspond roughly to the *pyknic* type of Kretschmer, the *brachymorphic* type of Pende, and to their equivalents in other systems.

bribe Bribing is a common concept in psychoanalysis. It is closely identified with, if it is not actually, compromising. The symptoms of a neurosis are regarded as symbolic representations of repressed impulses. At first the ego rejects the symptoms; later it becomes reconciled with them, for it recognizes in them a certain protection to the security of the ego. The symptoms are accepted by the ego in the nature of a bribe, but the acceptance carries certain favorable elements. For instance, there is the so-called secondary gain from suffering. The repressed impulse is released in the guise of symptoms; the patient does not recognize the released impulse in its new manner of expression. Moreover, in order to placate the *super-ego* or inner conscience, the ego bribes it by suffering. 'Thus, forbidden pleasure gratification, by being presented to the Ego as a punishment, is made acceptable. At the same time, the Super-Ego itself, which recognizes the latent meaning of the symptom in spite of disguise, is "bribed with suffering." ' (Healy, W., Bronner, A.F., and Bowers, A.M. *The Structure and Meaning of Psychoanalysis,* Knopf, New York, 1930)

Briggs' law See *law, Briggs'.*

Brigham, Amariah (1798–1849) American psychiatrist; founded *American Journal of Insanity* (1844), now the *American Journal of Psychiatry;* 'moral treatment.'

Brill, A.A. (1874–1948) First American psychoanalyst; translated Freud's works into English.

Briquet, Paul (1796–1881) (brē-kā′) French psychiatrist; author of a monumental treatise on hysteria (1859).

Broca's speech area (Paul Broca, Parisian anthropologist and surgeon, 1824–1880) The motor speech area; areas 44 and 45 of Brodmann; the inferior end of the motor area in the third left frontal convolution. Lesions here in a right-handed subject result in motor aphasia; in pure motor aphasia, the patient is able to write or otherwise indicate his desires, but articulate speech either is impossible or is restricted to a few ill-pronounced expletives.

bromidrosiphobia (brō-mi-drō-si-fō′bi-à) Morbid dread of the alleged offensive odors of the body.

bromidrosis (-drō′sis) Perspiration with foul odor.

brontophobia (bron-tō-fō′bi-à) Fear of thunder. When it assumes morbid proportions it is usually encountered among psychoneurotic patients. It is related in part to the dread of allegedly demonical phenomena of nature, akin to personalization of such phenomena by primitive man. In psychopathology the dread of natural phenomena is often associated with that of real persons, such as a father or someone occupying a paternal role.

brooding Anxious or moody pondering, usually about very abstract matters. Brooding is seen frequently in obsessive-compulsive neurotics as a thinking compulsion, a need to worry very much about apparently insignificant things. This is a form of displacement onto a small detail and represents an attempt to avoid objectionable impulses or affects by escaping from the world of emotions into a world of intellectual concepts and words; this is also termed 'intellectualization.'

Brudzinski sign See *sign, Brudzinski.*

Bruns, Ludwig (1858–1916) (broons′) German psychiatrist and neuropathologist.

bruxism (bruk′siz'm) Gnashing or grinding of the teeth, which occurs typically at night, during sleep. It is said to be especially common in alcoholics and to indicate repressed aggressivity or hostility.

bruxomania (bruk-sō-mā′ni-à) A neurotic state associated with a grinding, pounding, or setting of the teeth apart from the normal activity of mastication. There results a loosening of the teeth and a bleeding of the gums.

B.S.T. Brief stimulus therapy. See *therapy, brief stimulus.*

buffoonery-psychosis See *psychosis, buffoonery.*

bufotenin (bu-fō′te-nin) Dimethyl-serotonin. An analogue of serotonin which, unlike serotonin itself, is psychotomimetic in the cat, monkey, and man and produces effects similar to those seen following lysergic acid or mescaline administration. It has been suggested that conversion of serotonin into bufotenin rather than breakdown by monoamine oxidase into 5-hydroxyindole acetic acid may be of significance in the etiology of endogenous psychoses.

bug, cocaine One of the more common unpleasant tactual paresthesiae which occurs during withdrawal of cocaine in a cocaine addict. Also known as formication. The patient typically interprets the sensation as an itching, biting, crawling, or sticking due to an insect.

bugger Colloquial for a homosexualist.

bulbar Referring to the bulb (medulla oblongata).

bulbocapnine (bul-bō-kap′nin) One of the drugs used relatively early in the many experiments of H.H. DeJong on experimental production of catatonia.

bulbotegmental reticular formation (bul-bō-teg-men′tal) See *formation, reticular.*

bulimia, bulimy (bū-lim′i-à, bū′li-mē) Insatiable hunger.

Bumke, Oswald (1877–   ) (boom′kē) German psychiatrist and neurologist.

Buscaino, Vito Maria (1887–   ) (boos-kà-ē′nô) Italian neurologist.

by-idea While discussing speech disorders in dreams, Kraepelin said: 'The common feature in all these observations (dream paraphasias) is the displacement of the basic thought by the entrance of a by-association, for an essential link of the chain of ideas. The derailment of speech or of thought to a by-association is due, in my opinion, to lack of distinctness in the ideas.' He also said: 'The by-idea causing the displacement of thought was distinctly a narrower and more comprehensive idea which suppressed the more general and more shadowy one.' He referred to this condition as *metaphoric paralogia*. (Kraepelin, E. *Dementia Praecox and Paraphrenia*, tr. by Barclay, R.M., Livingstone, Edinburgh, 1919)

C

C Rorschach scoring symbol for color response.

C′ See *achromatic color response.*

C$_n$ A Rorschach scoring symbol for color-naming.

cacergasia (kas-ĕr-gas′i-à) *Obs.* Deficient mentality.

cachexia (kà-kek′si-à) Malnourishment proceeding to wasting of body tissues, seen usually as part of a chronic disease process. See *cachexia, hypophysial; anorexia nervosa.*

cachexia, hypophysial (hī-pō-fiz′i-al) A condition due to necrosis or other destruction of the anterior lobe of the pituitary gland, occurring most commonly in women. Characteristic symptoms are: marked asthenia, great loss of weight with extreme emaciation, chilliness, slow pulse, anemia, low basal metabolic rate, loss of hair, amenorrhea or impotence, somnolence, apathy, poor memory, and occasionally hallucinations and delirium. Also known as Simmonds's disease (Morris Simmonds, a Hamburg pathologist [1855–1925]). See *anorexia nervosa.*

cachinnation (kak-i-nā′shun) Inordinate laughter without apparent cause; it is common in the hebephrenic form of schizophrenia.

caco- (kak′ō-) Combining form meaning bad, vitiated, distorted, from Gr. *kakós,* bad, evil.

cacodaemonomania (-dē-mon-ō-mā′ni-à) A condition in which the patient believes himself to be, or to be inhabited by, or possessed of, a devil or some evil spirit; it is not uncommonly a symptom of the hebephrenic form of schizophrenia.

cacogenic (-jen′ik) The term (the opposite of *aristogenic* or *eugenic,* q.v.) means 'giving rise to a deteriorated race' and refers to deteriorating agencies in heredity. A. Myerson cites a case of artificial insemination in a woman with a prominent family history of otosclerosis and paranoid mental disease. The woman herself was delusional and was not fully desirous of impregnation. The procedure in this case would be termed cacogenic insemination.

cacogeusia (-gū′si-à) A bad taste; a frequent complaint in idiopathic epilepsy.

cacopathia (-path′i-à) A Hippocratic designation for a severe mental disorder.

cacosomnia (-som′ni-à) *Obs.* Sleeplessness.

cacothymia (-thim′i-à, -thī′mi-à) *Obs.* 'Any mental affection with depravation of the morals.' (Tuke, D.H. *A Dictionary of Psychological Medicine,* vols. 1–2, Blakiston, Philadelphia, 1892)

cadiva insania (kà-dē′và in-sà′nē-à) (L. 'falling or epileptic insanity') *Obs.* Epilepsy.

caduca passio (kà-dōō′kà pàs′sē-ō) (L. 'falling disease') *Obs.* Epilepsy, 'the falling sickness.'

caducus morbus (kà-dōō′koos môr′boos) (L. 'falling sickness.') *Obs.* Epilepsy.

cainophobia (kī-nō-fō′bi-à) See *kainotophobia; neophobia.*

cainotophobia (kī-nō′tō-fō-bi-à) See *kainotophobia; neophobia.*

Cairns' stupor Akinetic or diencephalic stupor: stupor, rigidity, postural catatonia, absence of spontaneous movement and emotion.

caisson disease See *disease, caisson.*

calcarine area See *lobe, occipital.*

calf-love The fleeting mild infatuation of a susceptible teen-ager with a member of the opposite sex, abruptly ending only to be followed by a fresh adventure with another object of affection. The term probably originated in the seemingly inexplicable antics of a calf ceaselessly transferring its attentions and attachments to various members of a herd or group of cattle. See also *puppy-love.*

callipedia (kal-i-pē′di-à) The desire to give birth to a beautiful child. Some people believe that if a gravid woman concentrates her attention upon a beautiful child, or the picture or thought of one, she will give birth to its equal. The idea is associated with the magic of thought and with other primitive concepts concerning reproduction.

callomania (kal-ō-mā′ni-à) 'A synonym of the monomania of beauty and grace.' (Tuke, D.H. *A Dictionary of Psychologi-*

cal Medicine, vols. 1–2, Blakiston, Philadelphia, 1892)

calorie, psychic In psychiatric literature this term is used to describe a transference relationship. Without the psychic calories (i.e. sustenance) obtainable through the analyst's person, those patients who are too dependent on the analytic relationship cannot achieve a realization of their own self. (Baynes, H.G. *Mythology of the Soul,* Williams and Wilkins, Baltimore, 1940)

camisole A canvas shirt with very long sleeves, used to restrain a violently psychotic person; the shirt is put on and securely laced, and then the patient's arms are folded and the ends of the sleeves are fastened behind the back; sometimes simply a square of canvas fastened behind with a buckle, binding the arms to the sides of the body.

camouflage, neurotic A term for neurotic endeavor to disguise. 'It represents an attempt to reconcile two psychic processes which tend to go in opposite directions. The patient wishes to be obedient to the compulsion imposed by the neurosis, but at the same time he feels impelled to heed the psychic necessity of making his behavior conform to the requirements of his social milieu. . . I venture to assert that social camouflage constitutes a typical feature in the behavior of all psychoneurotics at a certain stage of development of their neurosis.' (Reik, T. 'Neurotic Camouflage and Thought-Rehearsal,' *American Imago 2,* 86, 1941.) The neurotic camouflage is particularly evident in the obsessive-compulsive patient, whose need to conform often drives him to obsessional rehearsal. See *rehearsal, obsessional.*

camptocormia (kamp-tō-kawr′mi-à) A bending of the trunk of the body, usually anteriorly; during World War I the symptom was often encountered as a form of traumatic neurosis; the condition was given the name camptocormia by Souques in 1915.

canalization (kà-nal-i-zā′shun) Act of directing into channels. Janet says that mental energy 'may assume either of two forms. It may be latent energy; energy in reserve, or capitalized energy, if the phrase be permitted. In that case, the energy is inconspicuous, and we do not know clearly in which psychological phenomena

it plays a part.' The second form of energy he calls *kinetic,* adding that 'the energy is kinetic when the tendency has been awakened, and is undergoing more or less complete activation.' (Janet, P. *Psychological Healing,* vols. 1–2, tr. by Paul, E. and C., Macmillan, New York, 1925)

Janet then speaks of the discharge of energy. 'The tendency may lose its charge, may "discharge" itself in various ways. One method of discharge is by the production of many vigorous, rapid, and long-continued movements; but it would seem that this form of discharge is a slow one, especially in the case of strongly charged tendencies. It may be canalized by a tendency which has a higher tension; nothing can discharge a tension more effectively than a high-tension action effected at its expense. It is probable, as we are coming more and more to see, that the more highly a tension is charged, the more essential it is that it shall be counterposed by a high-grade tendency in order to effect canalization.' (ibid.)

cancer, fear of The fear of cancer occurs quite frequently, especially in older individuals, but sometimes it is seen as a phobia in younger patients too. A patient with a cancer phobia is often not afraid of cancer, but of unconscious ideas which he is unable to face. For instance, one patient began to fear that he was about to develop a cancer in his nose. He thought that this would come from friction, because he had rubbed and pressed his nose for many years: he feared that his nose would become diseased and he would lose it. Later on he was able to see the connection that he did not mean his nose, but really meant his penis, and that the fear of cancer actually was but a disguised fear of castration, which had been displaced into a fear of cancer. (Hinsie, L.E. *Understandable Psychiatry,* Macmillan, New York, 1948.) See *displacement.*

canchasmus (kang-kaz′mus) *Obs.* Inordinate laughter sometimes observed in hysterical and schizophrenic patients.

canina appetentia (kà-nē′nà àp-pe-ten′-tī-à) (L. 'dog-appetite') *Obs.* Bulimia.

cannibalistic The noun cannibal is seldom used in psychiatric practice, though the adjective is often used. Certain patients, who are described as having cannibalistic impulses, speak of eating human flesh. The oral, sadistic component is particularly vivid among these individuals and they incorporate many psychic drives (anal, Oedipal, homoerotic, pregnancy, etc.) in the oral zone. The cannibalistic complex may be literally expressed by advanced schizophrenic patients; it is sometimes spoken of by psychoneurotic patients; with the latter the thought is usually thickly veiled, highly disguised. Cannibalistic phenomena are said to be reflections of pronounced regression.

Cannon hypothalamic theory of emotion Cannon and Bard offered a more modern version of Head's thalamic theory: afferent impulses from peripheral receptors may evoke patterned efferent 'emotional' responses directly through reflex pathways at the thalamic level, and/or indirectly through arousal of 'conditioned responses' at the cortical level, which in turn release diencephalically integrated patterns of emotional response from cortical inhibition. At the same time, upward discharges from the activated diencephalon reach the cortex, thus adding a patterned 'quale' to the sensory experience and transforming the 'object-simply-apprehended' to the 'object-emotionally-felt.'

Capgras See *syndrome, Capgras'*.

capsule, internal See *basal ganglia*.

captation (kap-tā′shun) An old term used by Descourtis to denote the first stage in hypnosis.

captivation Max Hirsch's term for the state of light hypnosis; Hirschlaff called the state one of pseudo-hypnosis.

caput obstipum (kà′put ob′sti-pum) See *torticollis*.

carbon dioxide inhalation See *therapy, carbon dioxide inhalation*.

cardiazol (kär′di-à-zōl) Metrazol.

cardiopathia adolescentium (kär-dē-ô-pà′thē-à à-dô-les-ken′tē-oom) Individuals with an asthenic type of body build, the asthenic habitus first described by Stiller, often possess anomalies of the heart that represent immaturity. For example, the heart frequently assumes a vertical position; it is often below average in size, though it may be small only in comparison with the size of the body as a whole; the condition called drop heart may also be present. De Giovanni and Benecke have demonstrated that the right side of the

heart may predominate over the left, a condition characteristic during childhood, but anomalous when continued into adulthood.

The cardiovascular apparatus has centered much attention on the schizophrenic patient with the asthenic habitus. It is believed that the patient's illness may be a reflection of general physical and physical immaturity.

cardio-renal disease, psychosis with This is a nosologic entity included in the 1935 edition of the Standard Nomenclature. In the 1952 revision of psychiatric nomenclature, this entity would be classified as acute (or chronic) brain syndrome associated with circulatory disturbance. This diagnosis is made on those patients with heart disease, especially in the stages of decompensation, who show psychotic symptoms. These symptoms usually take the form of deliria or temporary periods of confusion, often worse at night. Memory may be impaired and concentration may be defective; at times, fearful hallucinations may occur.

carebaria (kar-ē-bà-ri′à) Unpleasant head sensations, such as pressure or heaviness in the head.

carnivorous Though in zoölogy it applies to animals (carnivora) adapted to flesh-eating, in constitutional medicine the term refers to a type described by Bryant and corresponds roughly to Kretschmer's *asthenic* (q.v.).

carotodynia (kà-rot-ō-dī′ni-à, -din′i-à) Pain in the malar (cheek) region, in the back of the neck, and about the eyes due to pressure on the common carotid artery.

carphology (kär-fol′ō-jē) Aimless picking or plucking (Galen's term). It is not uncommon among those with a senile psychiatric disorder, although it may be a symptom in any patient in a delirious state. The patient picks aimlessly, usually at his clothes or bed coverings.

carrier See *taint-carrier; trait-carrier*.

carus catalepsia (kà′roos kat-a-lep′si-à) Catalepsy.

carus lethargus (lā-thär′goos) Lethargy.

case, index (Genetics) The case in a family or group which is the subject of investigation.

case work, social 'Social case work is one of the major divisions of social work along with social group work and community organization or social welfare planning.' '. . . its concern is with social relationships and its disciplines directed toward the release of individual capacities and the relieving of environmental pressures. There have not been any notable changes in the accepted definitions since the well-known one by Mary Richmond in 1922. . . . "Social adjustments, consciously effected, individual by individual, between man and his social environment." Seven years later, the report of the Milford Conference . . . showed that more stress was being laid on the client's own purposes, and that the "distinguishing concern of social case work is the capacity of the individual to organize his own normal social activities in any given environment." ' (Hamilton, G. in *Social Work Year Book 1939,* edited by Kurtz, R.H., Russell Sage Foundation, New York)

caste A caste is composed of 'persons who can live with, eat with, and marry only individuals of the same group.' (Sighele, S. *Psychologie des Sectes.*) Under the caste system, accordingly, a person cannot rise from a lower to a higher caste. 'It is in India that the caste has had its completest development.' (Kroeber, A.L. *Encyclopaedia of the Social Sciences,* vol. 3, Macmillan, New York, 1931, p. 255). Other illustrations of caste are the Eta of Japan and the Negro in the United States, particularly in the Southern states.

castrate Castrated person; eunuch. Although practically this term denotes a man deprived of manhood through loss of the testicles, and is thus in a sense identical with *eunuch,* the original meaning of the term naturally applies to individuals of either sex whose gonads were removed, that is, the ovaries in the female and the testes in the male. See *castration; eunuchism; eunuch.*

castration In its original and broadest biological sense, this term simply means the surgical operation of removing the sex organs' (gonads) which are essential to reproduction as well as to the development of the secondary sex characters, that is, the ovaries in the female or the testes in the male. The operative removal of the ovaries is usually called *ovariotomy* or *oöphorectomy.*

Castrating operations are now performed in both sexes for medical reasons only. Castration as a eugenic policy, as previously executed in sex-offenders especially, is no longer practiced in civilized countries. For eugenic purposes, *sterilization* by *vastectomy* or *salpingectomy* is now preferred, as these sterilizing operations affect only the capacity for reproduction but not the secondary sex characters.

When performed or occurring *after* puberty, castration has in neither sex such drastic effects upon the sex balance as are observed following surgical removal or another serious derangement of the sex organs in early life, when the secondary sex characters of the organism have not yet developed. Castration *before* puberty results in *eunuchoidism* or *eunuchism*—the development of the secondary sexual characteristics of the opposite sex. *Eunuchoid women* are recognizable by male body proportions, deep voice, and hairiness of body and face, and *eunuchoid men* by large hips, narrow sloping shoulders, absence of beard and body hair, high-pitched voice, etc.

In psychological medicine castration implies the penis alone.

The theme of castration is a pivotal point in psychoanalysis. Although issues that lead up to the castration complex from the point of view of the phallus are revealed in the pregenital organization of libido, the theme acquires specific impetus during the stage of phallic primacy. Psychoanalysts are in agreement that the castration complex is universal, appearing in normal and abnormal individuals. It is intimately bound up with the Oedipus situation. The manner in which the castration complex is handled determines in a large measure the fate of the Oedipus complex.

The theme is so complicated that one can mention here only a few of its central issues. During the late infancy period, an unusually large volume of libido converges upon the genital area, giving rise to what is called the phallic stage. Freud believes that the child possesses vague memories of fears, resident in the primitive division of the unconscious. These fears are activated during the stage of phallic primacy; as Freud says, 'the child constructs this danger for itself out of the slightest hints, which will never be wanting.'

It is said that children of either sex first come to believe that everyone is born with a penis. When the male child finds out that there are some people (girls) who have no penis, he becomes intensely alarmed, because he is now faced with proof to support his phantasy that he might lose his own organ. He had lost other valuable possessions. During the oral stage the nipple was taken from him; during the anal stage he lost the feces, to which he had attached so much importance. Owing to these previous experiences and their many representations, the thought of something disastrous befalling his penis gains in intensity. The boy believes that the girl once had such an organ as his, but it was taken away from her. At about this time he begins to feel that if he continues to show sexual interest in his mother, his penis will be removed. The Oedipus situation becomes acute with such a dread and is amplified with the many sexual and non-sexual threats that come from both parents.

In the normal individual the castration complex and its many associations, principally the Oedipal, give way in a large measure to the reaction-formations, sublimations, substitutions, extra-parental identifications, etc. that characterize the so-called latency period. During the latency period the threat of castration, especially that from the father, causes the son to identify himself with his father, thus setting up within himself the latter's prohibitions. The castration complex is in this way internalized, 'covered up'; it is also free from external authority, until it is re-animated at puberty.

The castration complex in the girl is not as clearly defined as it is in the boy. 'Nevertheless,' Freud says, 'we know that the female child is extremely sensitive about the lack of a sex organ equal to that of the male child. Accordingly, the girl comes to consider herself inferior to the boy, developing a condition of "penis envy" from which may be traced a whole chain of reactions characteristic of the female.' (Freud, S. *Collected Papers*, vol. 2, tr. by Riviere, J., Leonard and Virginia Woolf and The Institute of Psychoanalysis, London, 1924–25) The girl feels that she has been injured in her infancy and she generally blames her mother for it. Thus the castration phantasy plays an important role in the development and termination of the Electra complex or, as it is also known, of the female Oedipus complex.

castrophrenia (kas-tro-frē'ni-à) See *noöklopia.*

catabolic (kat-à-bol'ik) Pertaining to, or characterized by, *catabolism* (q.v.). In constitutional medicine the term applies to the *anabolic-catabolic balance,* which, according to the theories of Pende, is the most fundamental criterion in describing or typing human beings (see *anabolic*).

On the basis of this concept, the *catabolic biotype* constitutes the fundamental underlying type to which the more superficial characterizations of the types called *microsplanchnic, dolichomorphic,* and *sympathicotonic* (qq.v.), among others, apply.

catabolism (kà-tab'ō-liz'm) In physiology and general medicine, this means *destructive metabolism* (q.v.), or a downward series of changes by which complex bodies are broken down into simpler forms. In certain cases, of course, catabolism can be constructive, especially in botany.

catabythismomania (kat-à-bith-iz-mō-mā'-ni-à) *Obs.* Morbid impulse to commit suicide by drowning.

catabythismus Suicide by drowning.

cataclonia (kat-à-klō'ni-à) Cataclonus.

cataclonus (-klō'nus) This term denotes more or less rhythmic convulsive movements best understood today in terms of psychogenesis; when convulsive-like movements are said to be psychically determined, the expression *cataclonus* is used.

'The authors [Meige and Feindel] state that there are also attitude-tics, that [are] no longer the lightning-like clonic convulsions but tonic rigidity in particular attitudes of the head of a limb. There is no doubt that these cases are transitional between cataclonic and cataclonic innervation.' (Ferenczi, S. *Further Contributions to the Theory and Technique of Psycho-Analysis,* tr. by Suttie, J.I., Leonard and Virginia Woolf and The Institute of Psychoanalysis, London, 1926)

catagelophobia (kat-à-jel-ō-fō'bi-à) Fear of ridicule.

catalentia (-lent'i-à) *Obs.* A. Paracelsian term for epilepsy.

catalepsia cerea (-lep'si-à kā're-à) *Obs.* Catalepsy.

catalepsy (kat'à-lep-sē) Inordinate maintenance of postures or physical attitudes. The term is usually synonymous with flexibilitas cerea. 'The muscular system may be in a condition of *waxy flexibility,* permitting of the molding of the limbs into any position where they remain indefinitely—*catalepsy.*' (Jelliffe, S.E. and White, W.A. *Diseases of the Nervous System,* 6th ed., Lea & Febiger, Philadelphia, 1935, p. 1031) Catalepsy is regarded as a high degree of suggestibility and is not infrequently associated with other forms of suggestibility, such as echopraxia, echolalia, command automatism, etc.

'The patients make no movements of their own volition; but, if they are placed in no matter how uncomfortable an attitude they maintain it for a very long time.' (Bleuler, E. *Textbook of Psychiatry,* tr. by Brill, A.A., Macmillan, New York, 1930)

Wax-like postures may also appear with rigid rather than flexible musculature, so-called rigid catalepsy.

Cataleptic states may appear in a wide variety of clinical syndromes, but are most common in schizophrenia and hysteria. It may be psychically induced through hypnotism. 'Cerebellar patients, also, and certain types of cases with fronto-cerebellar pathway disturbances show what is known at *cataleptic rigidity* in this (erect) position.' (Jelliffe, S.E. and White, W.A. *Diseases of the Nervous System,* 6th ed., Lea & Febiger, Philadelphia, 1935, p. 79)

catalepsy In the 17th century catalepsy was 'also called *catoche, catochus, congelatio;* and by Hippocrates, *aphonia;* by Antigenes, *anaudia;* by Coelius Aurelianus, *apprehensio, opressio;* and also by some *apoplexia cataleptica, detentio; encatalepsis; prehensio, comprehensio, deprehensio.*' (Motherby, G. *A New Medical Dictionary,* 5th ed., for J. Johnson, St. Paul's Church-Yard, etc., London, 1801)

catalepsy, accessory *Obs.* 'Catalepsy originated by or associated with hysteria, epilepsy, tetanus, mania, and other nervous affections.' (Tuke, D.H. *A Dictionary of Psychological Medicine,* vols. 1–2, Blakiston, Philadelphia, 1892)

catalepsy, artificial Catalepsy occurring during induced hynosis.

catalepsy, epidemic When cataleptic states affect many individuals as a consequence of imitation, the malady is called epidemic catalepsy.

catalepsy, rigid See *catalepsy.*

catalexia (kat-à-lek′si-à) A type of reading disability characterized by a tendency to reread words and phrases.

catalysator, catalyzator (kat′à-li-zā-tĕr) An external stimulus that serves to loosen inhibitions; a catalyzer.

catamite (kat′à-mīt) *Rare.* A boy who submits to pederasty.

catamnesis (kat-am-nē′sis) The medical history of a patient following a given illness is called the catamnesis. It constitutes the so-called 'follow-up' history. Others use it for the history of the patient and his illness following the initial examination.

cataphasia (kat-à-fā′zhi-à) The repetition of words or phrases, seen in pronounced form in the catatonic form of schizophrenia; see *stereotypy.*

cataphora (kà-taf′ō-rà) A form of coma which may be interrupted by transitory states of partial consciousness; coma somnolentium.

cataplectic attack (kat-à-plek′tik) See *cataplexy.*

cataplexy (kat′à-plek-sē) Temporary 'paralysis' or immobilization. 'Cataplexy denotes paroxysmal attacks of loss of muscle tone (often without loss of consciousness), so that the patient sinks to the ground. It is usually associated with narcoleptic attacks (paroxysms of sleep).' (Henderson, D.K. and Gillespie, R.D. *A Text-Book of Psychiatry,* 4th ed., Oxford University Press, London, 1936)

cataptosis (kat-ap-tō′sis) Galen's term for an epileptic or apoplectic seizure.

catastrophe See *theory, catastrophe; behavior, catastrophic.*

catathymia (kat-à-thī′mi-à, -thim′i-à) The existence in the unconscious of a complex. It is assumed that the complex is sufficiently charged with affects to produce effects in consciousness. The effects of an affectively accentuated complex are designated as catathymic by H.W. Maier.

catatonia, katatonia (kat-à-tō′ni-à) A lowering of tension. From the clinical point of view many different syndromes have been called catatonia. Modern descriptions of the clinical condition were first given by Kahlbaum in 1874 (Die Katatonie) and the general concepts laid down by him have prevailed, save for minor changes. Kahlbaum regarded catatonia as a nosologic entity, but since the later works of Kraepelin it has been looked upon as a subdivision of schizophrenia. It is true that catatonic or rather cataleptoid syndromes are not infrequently a part of other diagnostic groups (e.g. hysteria and manic-depressive psychosis), but the tendency is to restrict the term catatonia to the schizophrenic group. Cataleptoid states may also be observed in association with organic pathology, such as is found, for example, in lethargic encephalitis.

The clinical syndrome called *catatonia* is characterized as a rule by (1) stupor, associated with either marked rigidity or flexibility of the musculature or (2) overactivity in conjunction with various manifestations of stereotypy.

catatonia, depressive Synonymous with, but rarely used today for, catatonic stupor. See *schizophrenia, catatonic.*

catatonia, manic Synonymous with *excitement, catatonic;* it is rarely used today. See *schizophrenia, catatonic.*

catatonia mitis (mē'tēs) Some catatonic patients run a mild and relatively short course of catatonia, exhibiting stupor and immobility as the principal symptoms. The condition is known as *catatonia mitis.*

When the catatonic syndrome is more extensive, resembling that described under the heading *schizophrenia, catatonic,* the expression catatonia protracta is sometimes used.

catatonia protracta (prō-trak'tà) See *catatonia mitis.*

catatonic schizophrenia (kat-à-ton'ik skiz-ō-frē'ni-à) See *schizophrenia, catatonic.*

catatony (kà-tat'ō-nē) A rarely used Anglicized form for catatonia.

catharsis (kà-thär'sis) In psychiatry the term was first used by Freud to designate a type of psychotherapy. He tried through the methods of 'free-association' and hypnosis to bring so-called traumatic experiences and their affective associations into consciousness. Psychiatric symptoms or symbols are looked upon as disguised representations of forgotten and repressed ideas or experiences. When the latter are brought back into the sphere of consciousness and lived out fully (in a therapeutic sense), the method is called catharsis. *Abreaction* and *catharsis* are often used synonymously.

catharsis, activity In psychotherapy, especially in activity group psychotherapy, a catharsis in which the patients convey their unconscious preoccupations and conscious intent through *action* rather than through language.

catharsis, community A term used to designate 'the purification, i.e. the freeing a community's population of guilt-feelings.' 'Sociodrama deals with problems which . . . can neither be clarified nor treated in a secret chamber and by the seclusion of two. . . It needs, therefore, a milieu which differs entirely from the psychoanalytical situation, a forum in which the group can be treated with the same earnestness as the individual in a consultation room. The *ideal* form for this is the drama that all can share in . . . and the effect is a *community catharsis.*' (Moreno, J.L. 'The Concept of Sociodrama,' *Sociometry VI,* 4, 446–7, Nov. 1947)

catharsis, emotional A name given by Freud to the process of cure by which 'pent up emotions could be drained from their unnatural incorporation in organs of the body.' At the close of the nineteenth century Freud was the first to see the connection between the body symptoms of a hysterical patient and the emotional shocks in his early life. In dissecting the mental life and history of the patient he was able to expose the emotions, which had sprung from past experiences, and to relate them to the patient's symptoms. (Hinsie, L.E. *Understandable Psychiatry,* Macmillan, New York, 1948) See *abreaction.*

catharsis, psychodramatic See *psychodrama.*

cathect, cathecticize (kà-thekt', kà-thek'-ti-sīz) To charge with, to infuse with psychic energy. Ideas and impulses are charged with energy, particularly those ideas that are significant to the feeling life of an individual. Thus, the concept love or hate is said to be cathected. Speaking of phantasy-formation, Freud says: 'They draw near to consciousness and remain undisturbed so long as they do not become strongly cathected. . . .' (Freud, S. *The Basic Writings of Sigmund Freud,* tr. by Brill, A.A., Random House, New York, 1938)

cathexis (kà-thek'sis) Concentration of psychic energy upon a given object. Jones defines it as 'charge of energy; investment (of an idea) with feeling and significance.' It is believed, for instance, that 'anxiety arises in relation to over-development of a libidinal cathexis.' (Jones, E. *Papers on Psycho-Analysis,* 4th ed., Wood, Baltimore, 1938) From the standpoint of instinctual qualities the charge of energy may be either libidinal or sadistic. 'Here the sadistic phase sets in late, and so neither the oral nor the clitoris stage receives any strong sadistic cathexis.' (ibid.)

From the standpoint of general location of cathexis psychoanalysts refer to (1) ego-cathexis; when the psychic energy is attached to the conscious division of the ego. Hence, the expressions ego-libido or narcissism arise. Some use the term *self-libido* or *auto-libido* in contradistinction to *object-libido.* (2) Phantasy-cathexis; when psychic energy is attached to wish-formations or phantasies or to their original sources in the unconscious, the expression phantasy-cathexis is used. Both ego-cathexis and phantasy-cathexis are associated with primary narcissism. (3) Object-cathexis; the expression is employed to refer to psychic energy that is attached to some object outside of the individual himself or to its representation in the mind of the individual. Object-cathexis is less stable or fixed than the other forms, because it is associated with manifestations of secondary narcissism, which, in turn, are less durable than those of the primary kind.

When there is an overcharge of psychic energy in an object, the term *hyper-cathexis* is used; when an undercharge *hypocathexis.*

It appears that the term *mental tension* is synonymous with *cathexis.*

Other words are often prefixed to the term cathexis: (1) to signify the quality of the charge—adjectives, as in affective-cathexis, libidinal-cathexis, erotic-cathexis, instinctual cathexis; nouns, as in word-cathexis, thought-cathexis, thing-cathexis, or: (2) to express the degree of cathexis, as in hypercathexis, hypocathexis, acathexis.

catochus (kat′ō-kus) D.H. Tuke says: 'This is an old term for catalepsy, but it has been more especially applied to that phase of ecstacy or trance in which the patient is conscious, but cannot move or speak. Under this head would be comprised those cases in which persons have been laid out as dead and even buried, without being able to arouse themselves or show signs of life.' (Tuke, D.H. *A Dictionary of Psychological Medicine,* vols. 1–2, Blakiston, Philadelphia, 1892)

caudate nucleus (kaw-′dāt) See *basal ganglia.*

causalgia (kaw-sal′jē-à) Sensation of burning pain in the distribution of a peripheral nerve, associated with glossy skin devoid of hair or wrinkles. Other associated changes include swelling, redness, sweating, and curling of the nails. Causalgia is usually due to irritation of a nerve by injury; the median or sciatic nerves are the most commonly involved.

C.C.C. Citrated calcium carbamide; recommended in the treatment of chronic alcoholism as superior to Antabuse (disulfiram) because it is said to have no undesirable side-effects and more rapid action.

cell In biology, the term denotes those minute structural units of protoplasmic nature which determine the different organic qualities of plant and animal bodies. Cells are ubiquitous and represent the fundamental elements of all organisms. They are so small—ranging ordinarily from 0.01 to 0.1 mm. in diameter—that there may be billions of them in a cubic inch of tissue.

Each cell consists of a denser protoplasmic body, the *nucleus,* which exerts a governing influence over all cellular activities, and the surrounding *cytoplasm.* All development from seed or egg involves cells, and each phase of hereditary transmission is guided and affected by cellular elements.

In embryonic development a great deal depends on how the cells are placed in relation to one another. All other cellular activities are governed by the rule that no cell works by itself in a multicellular animal, but every cell is influenced by others around it or even at a distance from it. (Shull, A.F. *Heredity,* 3rd ed., McGraw-Hill, New York and London, 1938) Dissolved substances pass through any of the ordinary envelopes around cells, although in certain tissues there are protoplasmic bridges from cell to cell. Only the vegetative cells of plants are usually surrounded by a rather rigid wall of cellulose, while most animal cells lack such a pronounced wall.

In the many-celled animals there are two genetically different classes of cells, the *somatic* or *body* cells, which are directly responsible for the actual manifestation of inherited characters but have nothing to do with their transmission, except in primitive types of reproduction; and the *germ* cells, which perform the transmission from generation to generation in the higher forms of reproduction. In animals, the somatic cells produce germ cells only very rarely, while the germ cells give rise in every generation to both somatic and germ cells, thus constituting a reserve out of which the genetic continuity of the germ cells and the repetition of the production of bodies in each generation are maintained. (Shull, ibid.)

The process of cell division is initiated and controlled largely by the nucleus and is commonly called *mitosis*.

cell, body The biological term body cell refers to that type of somatic cell which forms the somatoplasm of higher animals and does not produce germ cells. According to Weismann's germ plasm theory, the body cells have nothing to do with the hereditary transmission of inherited characters, but are responsible only for their phenotypical manifestations, at least in the higher forms of reproduction. See *plasm, germ; somatoplasm.*

cell, germ According to Weismann's *germ plasm* theory, which is essential for the understanding of hereditary mechanisms in human beings, there are two fundamentally different types of cells in multicellular animal bodies, the *germ cells* and the *somatic* or *body cells*. Even if this sharp distinction does not hold true in plants and lower animals, the concept of a distinct germ plasm is of great value in the field of human genetics. It is to be assumed that in the higher forms of reproduction only the germ cells give rise both to germ cells and body cells, while the function of the body cells is confined to the actual manifestation of hereditary characters.

cell, padded A room used for isolation of acutely disturbed patients who are potentially destructive to themselves or others. The room usually has a large mattress on the floor and padding on the walls. Often restraints are applied to the patient within the room. Modern psychiatry utilizes sedation and individual attention to the patient's needs rather than the padded cell.

cell, Purkinje (Johannes Evangelista Purkinje, Bohemian physiologist, 1787–1869) See *cerebellum.*

celom (sē′lom) In the tridermic stage of embryological development, the split-like cavity formed by the lateral plates of the middle germ layer or *mesoderm* (q.v.).

cene-, coene- (sē′ne) From Gr. *koinós,* common or general.

cenesthesia (-es-thē′z(h)i-à) It is believed that certain sensations created by the activities of internal organs are registered in the unconscious part of the psyche, that is, without the conscious recognition of the individual.

'In the study of the vegetative neurotonus and its relation to psychic character, great importance attaches to the inquiry into the sympathetic, that is, the internal sensitivity—all that array of subconscious afferent impulses which arrive at the brain from all the various organs of vegetative life and are synthesized in the general feeling of well-being or of malaise; or they may appear in consciousness as impulses and instincts.' (Pende, N. *Constitutional Inadequacies,* tr. by Naccarati, S., Lea & Febiger, Philadelphia, 1928)

Many of the mental constituents to which Kempf gives the name *autonomic affective craving* are regarded as cenesthetic.

The prefix *cen,* meaning *common,* refers to the general sense of bodily existence; the latter is a resulting of multiple stimuli coming from various parts of the body.

cenesthesic (-es-thē′sik) Relating to mental constituents caused by stimuli from organs other than the one in which the constituent appears.

cenesthopathic (-es-thō-path′ik) Relating to the general feeling of illness, not specifically referring to any location in the body.

cenesthopathy (-es-thop′à-thē) The feeling or sense of general physical ill-being. The feeling ordinarily is not referable to any special part of the body, but is more in the nature of a general feeling of illness, and is commonly expressed in psychiatric patients. Many authorities, particularly those in psychoanalysis, hold that cenesthopathic states are also produced by psychical activities. It is believed that body function may be appreciably altered as a consequence of psychogenic factors. Some forms of hypochondriasis are explained on that basis. Anxiety hysteria, in which state the body as a whole participates in the feeling of imminent collapse, is regarded as a form of cenesthopathy derived from the psyche.

cenophobia (-ō-fō′bi-à) See *kenophobia*.

cenotrope, coenotrope (-ō-trōp) Instinct; behavior characteristic of all members of a group having the same biological and experimental background.

censor The word *censor* was far more popular during the earlier years of psychoanalysis than it has been within recent times. It used to be interpreted too concretely, as an agent that critically investigated all unconscious material seeking external expression. The agent supposedly resided in that region of the mind called the preconscious.

The expression has been supplanted by censorship, a term that carries with it the connotation of agency rather than a specific agent. See *censorship*.

censor, endopsychic (en-dō-sī′kik) See *censorship*.

censorship As instinctual qualities progress from their original source, the id, out into reality they must gain the approval to pass from one region to another. In the normal adult they first meet the superego, which is the embodiment of the disciplines incorporated in the mind of the individual during the infancy and perhaps the early childhood period. The instinctive impulse may be allowed to pass on without any modification or it may have to submit to certain alterations. That is, the superego has censorship functions. Impulses from the id are often turned back without the individual recognizing that the impulse was on its way to the conscious level. Or the impulse may be so disguised or modified that its original quality becomes unrecognizable.

When the instinctual quality has been allowed to traverse the sphere of control of the superego, it enters the realm called the preconscious, where it again submits to examination. The preconscious also possesses the function of censorship.

Finally, when the instinctual quality reaches the field of consciousness, usually with ideas and experiences that it has gained en route, it is subjected to the close scrutiny of two censoring influences, the ego and the ego-ideal, the latter representing the forces of reality, while the ego acts as an intermediate agency between the forces from without and those from within.

Each of these censoring agencies is but a link in a chain, that is, they form a continuum. Before the instinctual quality in final form reaches the realm of consciousness, all the censoring agencies become aware of its expected presence.

'But we shall do well not to regard this complication as a difficulty, but to assume that to every transition from one system to that immediately above it (that is, every advance to a higher stage of mental organization) there corresponds a new censorship.' (Freud, S. *Collected Papers*, vol. 4, tr. by Riviere, J., Leonard and Virginia Woolf, London, 1925)

'The characteristic function of consciousness is the exercise of this censoring influence. . . . It is probable that between preconscious and conscious processes a censorship action is also interposed, of the same kind as that between unconscious and preconscious processes.' (Jones, E. *Papers on Psycho-Analysis*, 4th ed., Wood, Baltimore, 1938)

Speaking of the phenomena of dream-distortion and of censorship, Freud says: 'We should then assume that in every human being there exist, as the primary cause of dream-formation, two psychic forces (tendencies or systems), one of which forms the wish expressed by the dream, while the other exercises a censorship over this dream-wish, thereby enforcing on it a distortion.' (Freud, S. *The Interpretation of Dreams*, 3rd ed., tr. by Brill, A.A., Macmillan, New York, 1933)

censorship, dream Dreams are highly disguised representations of unconscious impulses. They are under the constant rule of censoring influences. 'The stricter the domination of the censorship, the more thorough becomes the disguise, and, often enough, the more ingenious the means employed to put the reader on the track of the actual meaning.' (Freud, S. *The Interpretation of Dreams*, 3rd ed., tr. by Brill, A.A., Macmillan, New York, 1933)

center, physical (sī′ki-kal) This is an older concept, intended to convey the idea that the mind and intelligence were localized as centers in the brain.

center, psychomotor The part of the cerebral cortex around the central fissure, embracing the centers of voluntary muscular movement; psychocortical center.

central constant See *constant, central*.

central excitatory state See *summation*.

centrencephalic system See *system, centrencephalic*.

centrifugal (sen-trif'ū-gal) Radiating or flying off from a center. See *centripetal*.

centripetal (sen-trip'e-tal) Directed toward the center. In psychiatry the term implies a moving toward the psyche. It is said, for example, that the psychoanalysis of Freud is essentially a centripetal psychology. 'For Freud the aims of empirical science, with its centripetal bias towards a minute and detailed analysis of observable facts, were absolute; whereas for Jung a purely objective psychology was not enough, in that it entirely omitted the undeniable reality and power of the idea.' (Baynes, H.G. Translator's Preface to Jung's *Psychological Types,* Harcourt, Brace, New York and London, 1923)

The expression implies that the basic functions of the mind serve the individual himself. Experiences seek the psyche for the value they can give to the psyche.

The opposite of centripetal forces (of the mind) are centrifugal ones. Jung is today the outstanding upholder of the centrifugal point of view, the principal representation of which is his *collective unconscious*. Baynes says: 'To Jung the psyche is a world which contains all the elements of the greater world, with the same destructive and constructive forces —a pluralistic universe in which the individual either fulfils or neglects his essential role of creator.' (ibid.)

centrolobar sclerosis (sen-trō-lō'bar sklerō'sis) See *sclerosis, diffuse*.

centrosome (sen'trō-sōm) Central body. This biological term refers to a central cytoplasmic particle which is thought to be important in the mechanism of cell division. See *cytoplasm*.

cephalalgia (sef-al-al'ji-à) Headache.

cephalalgia, histaminic (his-ta-min'ik) See *histamine*.

cephalogenesis (sef-al-ō-jen'e-sis) In embryological development, the stage which follows *notogenesis* (q.v.) and is associated with the origin of the primordia of the head.

This stage is initiated by the appearance of the *neural plate*, the primordium of the nervous system, and the formation of the head-fold which delimits the head end of the embryo from the extra-embryonic blastoderm. The neural plate forms the floor of the *neural groove*, which is bounded along both borders by a *neural fold* developing subsequently into the *neural tube,* lined with neural ectoderm, from an overlying epidermal ectoderm. The cephalic portion of a neural tube produces three dilatations which later become forebrain, midbrain, and hindbrain, the primordia of the future cerebrum, cerebellum, and pons and medulla oblongata. The later steps in cephalogenesis lead to the formation of the face and the head as well as of the eyes and the ears.

ceraunophobia (sē-raw-nō-fō'bi-à) See *keraunophobia*.

cerchnus (sērk'nus) *Obs.* Hoarseness.

cerea flexibilitas (ka'rē-à flek-sē-bē'lē-tàs) See *catalepsy*.

cerebellum (sēr-e-bel'loom) A large, oval structure with a laminated appearance which lies in the posterior fossa of the skull behind the pons and medulla oblongata. It is joined to the brain-stem by three peduncles, the superior, middle, and inferior, and appears grossly to be divided into two lateral lobes (the cerebellar hemispheres) and an unpaired median lobe (the vermis). Morphologically, however, 'the cerebellum has two primary divisions: (1) the flocculonodular lobe, the most primitive part, with connexions which are entirely vestibular, and (2) the corpus cerebelli, itself divided into (i) a palaeocerebellar division, receiving vestibular and spinocerebellar fibres, and composed anteriorly of lingula, centralis, and culmen, and posteriorly of pyramis, uvula, and paraflocculi, and (ii) a neocerebellar division, constituting the greater part of the corpus cerebelli, with connexions mainly corticopontine.

'The cerebellum consists mainly of white matter which is covered with a thin layer of grey matter, the cerebellar cortex, and contains several grey masses, the nuclei. These are divided into lateral nuclei, the nuclei dentatus and emboliformis, and middle and roof nuclei, the nuclei globosus and fastigii.

'Microscopically the cortex consists of three principal layers of cells, the molecular layer, which lies most superficially, the granular layer, which is the deepest, and the layer of Purkinje cells, which lies between the two.' (Brain, W.R. *Diseases of the Nervous System,* Oxford University Press, London, 1951)

'. . . the neocerebellum is essentially a reinforcing and co-ordinating organ which plays an important part in graduating and harmonizing muscular contraction, both in voluntary movement and in the maintenance of posture.

'The anterior lobe and the roof nuclei are concerned with the regulation of stretch reflexes and the anti-gravity posture. The flocculonodular lobe is an important equilibratory centre and lesions of this region cause swaying, staggering, and titubation. The neocerebellum regulates voluntary movement.' (ibid.) Thus the cerebellum maintains orientation in space and it brakes volitional movements, especially those requiring checking or halting, and the fine movements of the hands.

Lesions of the cerebellum may produce the following symptoms: dysmetria, intention tremor, inability to perform alternating movements (dysdiadochokinesia), ataxia, decomposition of movement, rebound, nystagmus, vertigo, dysarthria, plurosthotonus, hypotonia, skew deviation of the eyes, and cerebellar 'fits.' To a considerable extent, however, other parts of the nervous system are able to compensate for loss of cerebellar function.

cerebral embolism (ser'e-bral em'bō-liz'm) See *accident, cerebrovascular.*

cerebral hemorrhage (hem'or-raj) See *accident, cerebrovascular.*

cerebral palsy *Little's disease* (q.v.).

cerebral peduncle (ped'ung-k'l) See *midbrain.*

cerebral syphilis (sif'i-lis) See *syphilis, cerebral.*

cerebral thrombosis (throm-bō'sis) See *accident, cerebrovascular.*

cerebrasthenia (ser-ē-bras-thē'ni-à) *Obs.* Neurasthenia relating to the head.

cerebration (-brā'shun) Lewes used this term for 'cerebral actions consecutive on a perception'; today it generally means any kind of conscious thinking.

cerebration, unconscious *Obs.* Mental activity occurring without conscious direction. Hamilton referred to it as *latent thought.*

cerebria (ser-ē'bri-à) A term used by Pinel for mental derangement in general.

cerebria acuta (ke-rē'brē-à a-kōō'tà) (L. 'acute mental derangement') Pinel's term for mania.

cerebria chronica (krô'nē-kà) (L. 'chronic mental derangement') *Obs.* Imbecility.

cerebria partialis (pär-tē-ä'lēs) (L. 'par-tial mental derangement') *Obs.* Monomania.

cerebria sympathetica (sēm-pà-thä'tē-kà) (L. 'sympathetic mental derangement') *Obs.* Hypochondriasis or hysteria.

cerebro-psychosis (ser-ē-brō-sī-kō'sis) This is an old term and concept referring to 'those forms of mental disturbance which result from disease of the psychic centres, such as mania and general paralysis. Also used in a generic sense for all mental affections.' (Tuke, D.H. *A Dictionary of Psychological Medicine,* vols. 1–2, Blakiston, Philadelphia, 1892)

cerebrotonia (-tō'ni-à) A personality type, described by Sheldon, which is associated with the ectomorphic body build and is characterized by restraint, inhibition, alertness, and a predominantly intellectual approach to reality.

ceremonial, compulsive A term used to describe the ritualistic behavior that is characteristic of the compulsion-neurotic. As in all neurotic symptoms, the compulsive ceremonials defend against certain unconscious instinctual demands which are threatening to the ego. According to Freud, this ritualistic behavior demonstrates the use of two types of defense mechanisms in particular: 'undoing' and 'isolation.' Undoing 'is a kind of negative magic which by means of a motor symbolism would "blow away," as it were, not the consequences of an event (an impression, an experience), but the event itself.' Through motor means, that is, by a gesture or act which is symbolic and is repeated countless times, the patient tries to undo an undesirable or traumatic experience. For example, a patient with a washing compulsion is undoing a previous dirtying action (either real or imaginary). The dirtying action is usually masturbation, which by anal regression (characteristic of the compulsion-neurotic) is conceived of as dirty. The instinctual impulse to defend oneself against is masturbation.

Isolation 'consists in the interposition (after an unpleasant experience, as also after some act of the subject's own which is of significance in the sense of his neurosis) of a refractory period in which nothing more is allowed to happen, no perception registered, and no action performed.' In this way both the emotional meaning of the experience and its associations for the patient can be repressed. The compulsion-neurotic usually conceals his emotions and acts as a cold abstract thinker. Through order, routine, system he tries to isolate his experiences and rid them of their emotional concomitants. In analysis he finds it extremely difficult to associate or to experience any emotional reactions no matter how exciting his ideas may be.

According to Freud, the mechanism of isolation originates in the taboo of touching. Touching, or physical contact, 'is the most immediate aim of aggression no less than of tender object-cathexes.' That is, all forbidden impulses, such as masturbation or Oedipal feelings, presuppose contact with an object. To avoid contact, then, is basic for warding off forbidden impulses. Thus the mechanism of isolation fundamentally abolishes the possibility of touching, since it prevents a particular thought from coming into contact with other thoughts.

This mechanism of isolation is seen most vividly in compulsive ceremonials which center around the taboo of touching. Many compulsion-neurotics have routines concerning which objects should not be touched and which should, and, in the latter case, in which order the objects should be touched. These rituals frequently concern routines to be followed in washing or bathing, but they may involve any ordinary daily activity such as crossing thresholds, handling doorknobs, etc. (Freud, S. *The Problem of Anxiety*, Norton, New York, 1936)

ceremonial, defensive A more or less elaborate pattern of actions unconsciously devised by a person as a defense against anxiety and compulsively executed by him whenever this anxiety threatens.

In discussing the symptomatology of the chronic phase of the traumatic syndrome (as occurring in soldiers in consequence of traumatic combat experience), Kardiner and Spiegel state: 'A large group of patients have symptoms that are chiefly unconscious defense reactions against the original trauma.' For example, '. . . the symptom may be a more complete elaboration of a defensive reaction that was not carried out on the original traumatic occasion.' (Kardiner, A., and Spiegel, H. *War Stress and Neurotic Illness*, Hoeber, New York, 1947) Whatever actions might be gone through in this elaboration of the incompleted defensive reaction would constitute a defensive ceremonial. For example, during World War

I a soldier was needlessly overcome during an enemy poison-gas attack. It so happened that as he was hurriedly donning his gas mask upon seeing gas shells exploding near by, the mask was accidentally pulled from his hand in the sudden turmoil of the attack. The panic attendant upon being absolutely without protection in the face of what he believed to be certain annihilation constituted an intensely severe trauma. Falling to the ground, he tried frantically and hopelessly to escape the approaching gas by burrowing his face into the earth. Fright overwhelmed him and he lost consciousness. The soldier recovered from the gassing, and the frightening aspects of the event underwent repression. For some years thereafter it was observed, as a symptom of an ensuing traumatic neurosis, that he would go through the motions of putting on an imaginary gas mask, *this time completing the procedure.*

A 'defense ceremonial has the nature of a compulsory act which the patient carries out without knowing exactly why, but which relieves him of anxiety.' It is '. . . usually carried out with no more control of the will than is shown in the ordinary compulsive ritual. . . The ceremonial which the patient unconsciously devises takes form some years after the original traumatic event.' (ibid.)

certification From the psychiatric point of view, this commonly refers to the court procedure by which a mental patient is committed to a hospital or institution.

certify Formally to declare a person insane.

ceruloplasmin (ser-ū-lō-plas′min) An alpha globulin which contains almost all the copper in blood serum. Among other substrates, ceruloplasmin acts on serotonin and norepinephrine (which have been suggested by some to be the central neurohumors for the parasympathetic and sympathetic nervous systems, respectively). Ceruloplasmin tends to be elevated in many chronic diseases; it tends not to be elevated in chronic schizophrenia, although it is often elevated in acute schizophrenia. The reasons for such elevation are unknown, but it has been suggested that in schizophrenia an abnormal ceruloplasmin (? taraxein) is formed through a metabolic error and that the abnormal ceruloplasmin fails to neutralize certain naturally occurring, noxious metabolites such as adrenoxine and adrenolutin. Others have hypothesized that ceruloplasmin is elevated in acute schizophrenia to compensate for taraxein, a substance closely related to ceruloplasmin and reported to have been found in schizophrenic serum. Taraxein may produce schizophrenic symptoms by lowering the resistance of the blood-brain barrier to various potentially toxic substances which are then able to attack certain portions of the brain (especially the septal region or the limbic lobe). According to this hypothesis, the taraxein and/or the toxic substances may arise as a result of genetically determined metabolic error.

Related to the increase of ceruloplasmin in schizophrenia are: (1) the more rapid oxidation of adrenalin by schizophrenic serum, and (2) the Akerfeldt test, i.e. the more rapid oxidation of N-N-dimethyl-paraphenyline diamine by schizophrenic serum.

Vitamin C antagonizes ceruloplasmin, and some workers disavow both of the above hypotheses, claiming that the more rapid oxidations and the relative increase in ceruloplasmin that have been observed reflect only a vitamin C deficiency induced by dietary inadequacies in long-term hospitals.

c.e.s. Central excitatory state. See *summation.*

CF Rorschach scoring symbol for a response determined by color and form, with color dominant.

chaero-, chairo-, chero- (kī-ro-) From Gr. *chaírein,* to rejoice.

chalasis (kal'à-sis) Inhibition of resting posture. Hines, in her studies on the maturation of excitability in the precentral gyrus, describes chalastic foci which cause inhibition of resting posture.

chance-action An action that is executed by mere chance and has no conscious aim or purpose, but nevertheless subserves the execution of an unconscious intention. Under this heading Freud distinguishes three separate categories: (a) habitual actions such as fingering one's hair; (b) actions which are usual under certain circumstances, such as doodling, coin-jingling, etc.; and (c) isolated chance actions. One example of the last variety might be the loss of a wedding ring on the honeymoon, indicating an unconscious wish to dissolve the marriage. Another might be the leaving of personal articles such as gloves, a cigarette lighter, etc. in the psychotherapist's office, indicating the patient's difficulty in tearing himself away.

Freud separates these 'symptomatic' or 'chance' actions from those carried out erroneously. In the latter we have to do with an action that has a conscious intention but is carried out erroneously, this erroneous execution reflecting the person's unconscious intention. Manifestly, the line of demarcation between these two categories is not definite.

change of sex, magic Psychiatric patients often express delusions regarding the alleged transformation of their sex. Their thoughts are frequently similar to those of primitive peoples. 'In accordance with this it is from the great biological turning points, i.e., puberty and death, that the formation of magic thoughts takes place. Puberty especially, which by primitive man everywhere was regarded as a fundamental segment of life, was surrounded by the strangest rites and usages; in many tribes the so-called ceremonies of initiation of the youths is the central mystery of their existence (Frazer). The belief prevailed everywhere that the child does not reach manhoood spontaneously but he must be made a man by magic ceremonies.' (Storch, A. *The Primitive Archaic Forms in Schizophrenia,* tr. by Willard, C., Nervous and Mental Disease Publishing Company, New York and Washington, 1924)

change, social Social change is defined by McIver as 'the changing ways in which human beings relate themselves to one another.' (*Society, Its Structure and Changes,* Smith, New York, 1931)

Changes in culture or the social heritage take place through invention, that is, through any new element in culture. (Ogburn, W.F. *Encyclopaedia of the Social Sciences,* vol. 3, Macmillan, New York, 1931, p. 331) Major social changes have resulted from technological inventions as the bow and arrow, writing, printing, the steam engine, etc. Social changes taking place in modern society give rise to many problems of personal and social adjustments.

changing, compulsive A symptom found in some compulsion-neurotics, expressing itself in a tendency to change continuously. This changing apparently has no limitations and may involve anything anywhere: personal habits, dress, work, social relations, opinions, etc.

The neurotic afflicted with this compulsion has the need to have 'the world . . . obey . . . [his] . . . compulsive system.' The changing is an effort 'to bring the world into accord with . . . [the patient's] . . . system.' Apparently through compulsive changing the patient can avoid the reality that the world does not obey his compulsive system. (Fenichel, O. *The Psychoanalytic Theory of Neurosis,* Norton, New York, 1945)

character As used by psychiatrists today, the term is more or less synonymous with *personality*. It is made up of patterns of behavior, characteristic for the given individual, expressed as physical and mental activities. The character of an individual is the resultant of forces emanating from the inner life of the person and from the environment. It is the agency through which inner personal and outer environmental forces are brought together, critically evaluated, and acted upon. It may be said to correspond in structure and function to what is generally described as the ego, namely, to the constituents of the conscious part of the psyche. See *personality; defense, character.*

character, anal One of the most important concepts connected with psychoanalysis concerns the origin and development of character traits or personality. The formation of character traits is explained on the basis of instinctual psychology. Instinctual qualities, arising from the id, are first attached to the soma, that is, to physical parts. With development of the psyche part of the instinctual qualities go over to it as energizing agents of psychical components. The three most important somatic zones in the life of the infant are the oral, anal, and phallic. Through experience and habit-training the activities of these zones come to occupy an important role in the mind of the child, that is, the activities are deeply imprinted upon the psyche. They become mental characteristics.

The anal character is made up of three cardinal traits. The first is orderliness (reliability, conscientiousness, punctuality, etc.), the second is parsimony, which may be expressed as avarice, while the third is obstinacy and its closely allied traits (defiance, vindictiveness, irascibility, etc.).

character, ascetic A mode of life characterized by rigor, self-denial, and mortifi-

cation of the flesh. Asceticism is seen typically as a phase in puberty, where it indicates a fear of sexuality and a simultaneous defense against sexuality. Asceticism is also seen as an extreme type of masochistic character disorder, where almost all activity is forbidden because it represents intolerable instinctual demands. In such cases, the very act of mortifying may become a distorted expression of the blocked sexuality and produce masochistic pleasure. An example of this is the eccentric who devotes his life to the combating of some particular evil which unconsciously represents his own instinctual demands.

character, daemonic Masochism represents the existence of an impulse that has self-destruction as its aim; it is older than sadism and is of a repetitive-compulsive character. 'There are people who, all their lives, repeat, to their own detriment, the same reactions, without any correction, or who seem to be dogged by a relentless ill-fortune, though a closer investigation shows that they are unwittingly bringing this ill-fortune upon themselves. Thus we explain what is called a "daemonic" character as being due to the repetition-compulsion.' (Freud, S. *New Introductory Lectures on Psychoanalysis,* tr. by Sprott, W.J.H., Norton, New York, 1933)

character, epileptic Some epileptologists have described a special array of character traits which they consider constitute the epileptic character. The basic traits are built around extremely developed ambivalence. The patients vividly exhibit antithetic qualities; they love and hate intensely; they are piously religious at one time and utterly sacrilegious at another; they are remarkably meticulous, and presently they are careless; they alternate between high morality and the performance of all kinds of sexual perversions, between generosity and penuriousness, between insolence and obsequiousness, etc.

character, exploitative Fromm's term for a new presentation of the character pattern described by Abraham as *oral aggressive* (see *defense, character*), in agreement with the so-called cultural school of psychoanalysis, which has made its own classification of character types. Instead of viewing character structure as the result of libido sublimation or reaction formation, this school sees the character types as basic attitudes in the process of socialization and coping with each particular life situation. Accordingly, Fromm believes that such a person develops in a frustrating atmosphere and hence comes to feel that one can have only what one takes and that the only source of security lies in exploiting others. When threatened with danger, the exploitative character tries to manipulate the situation by flattery, cajolery, aggression, or any other means.

character, genital The expression *genital character* is a psychoanalytic concept. It is believed that character traits are the outcome of the fate of libidinal cathexes with reference to the three principal erogenous zones—the oral, anal, and genital. Through reaction-formation and gradual sublimation libidinal investments in each of these zones are progressively transferred to the disciplines imposed upon the child by the parents. For example, cleanliness and regularity of anal habits are later represented as cleanliness and regularity with regard to non-anal activities. The original habits developed around the pregenital (oral, anal) levels must undergo appreciable modification to meet the requirements for later social adaptation. For instance, the sucking and biting of the early oral stage must give way to higher expression of oral activities —good table manners, oral cleanliness (physical and verbal), independence from the mother, etc.

The habits of the two earlier, pregenital zones coalesce, so to speak, and form what is generally known as personality. With the introduction of the third, that is, the genital zone, as an area of intense interest to the child some of the personality traits of the pregenital levels are put into the service of the genital zone; a part of the traits which have been de-oralized and de-analized is attached to objects in the environment in the form of favorable social relations.

With the advent of genital primacy the Oedipus situation is well under way. The genital character is the resultant of those character traits (handed down from the pregenital levels) which serve the interest of genitality and of the traits that issue from the Oedipus complex. During the pregenital stages the management of instinctual energies was largely of an auto-erotic and narcissistic character; now, since the object of the genital impulses is outside of the individual, the instincts strive toward alloerotic (homosexual and heterosexual) expression.

In the normal individual the final formation of the genital character is relatively unnarcissistic and unambivalent. 'Generally speaking, we may say that when the child has been able to subdue his Oedipus complex with all its constituents, he has made the most important step toward overcoming his original narcism, and his hostile tendencies; and at the same time he has broken the power of the pleasure principle to dominate the conduct of his life.' (Abraham, K. *Selected Papers,* tr. by Bryan, D. and Strachey, A., Leonard and Virginia Woolf, London, 1927)

Both primary and secondary forms of identification play an eminent role in the formation of character traits at the genital level.

character, hysterical It is a common observation among psychiatrists that the individual presenting a hysterical syndrome usually has what is called a hysterical character, described separately from the syndrome itself. Among the character traits are mentioned egoism, vanity, unbridled display of affects, exhibitionism, dramatization, sometimes a sacrificial and altruistic attitude, etc.

'In certain relations Ziehen is right when he says that hysteriacs rarely show objective interests. This is especially the case among women, but the hysteriac has still a greater need for a *personal* relationship than the normal woman.' (Bleuler, E. *Textbook of Psychiatry,* tr. by Brill, A.A., Macmillan, New York, 1930)

character, neurotic See *neurosis, character.*

character, oral Abraham says: 'The first, and therefore perhaps the most important step the individual makes toward maintaining a normal attitude in his final social and sexual relationships consists in dealing successfully with his oral erotism.' (Abraham, K. *Selected Papers,* tr. by Bryan, D. and Strachey, A., Leonard and Virginia Woolf, London, 1927) According to him there are two principal ways of expressing oral activity: (1) sucking and (2) biting, from each of which arise definite types of personality.

If the infant suffered no difficulties or privations during the sucking period, if the sucking phase was largely pleasurable, it is believed that the pleasure is carried over as a character trait, leading to the optimistic type of individual, the one who always believes that he will succeed in any undertaking. Moreover, the individual may exhibit carefree indifference and perhaps inactivity. The mother's breast will 'flow for them eternally.' Because the infant was treated so generously, identification with the mother gives rise to generosity as an important trait in the child.

If, on the other hand, the infant failed to achieve gratification during the sucking period, it develops a pessimistic attitude. In later life the child is apprehensive and demanding; it is never satisfied and comes to believe it never will be.

The second or biting stage is said also to lead to the development of character traits: to a tendency to hate and to destroy. 'This fundamental difference extends to the smallest details of a person's behavior.' (Abraham, K., ibid.)

character, paranoiac By this expression psychiatrists refer to the character traits of the individual prior to the time that he develops the full-fledged paranoiac syndrome. The projection mechanism is foremost, in that the individual constantly blames the environment for his difficulties. Moreover, he generally has greatest trouble in getting along with members of his own sex. The paranoiac usually superimposes his false claims upon some real circumstances in the environment, thus giving some degree of plausibility to his delusional formations.

The *paranoid character* possesses the same fundamental traits, but to a more marked degree. Furthermore, it is usually easy to detect the delusional basis for his trouble.

character, paranoid See *character, paranoiac.*

character, receptive A type described by Fromm; such an individual is passive, dependent, clinging, and compliant. This type is similar to the passive-oral or passive-dependent types of other writers.

character, reformation of A psychoanalytic term referring to a form of defense that occurs in everyday life and also frequently as a way-station in the course of the psychoanalytic procedure. In this form of defense the patient leans over backward in the proverbial 'reformed rake' fashion. By his meticulosity and carefully guarded behavior, he denies the presence of the 'old' recently uncovered 'bad' traits and 'bad' instinctual desires.

He is constantly preoccupied with 'selling' the picture of himself, as a reformed character, to himself, the analyst, and the world. The process of reaction-formation, i.e. leaning over backward against certain instinctual trends and developing the overlay of 'just the opposite' superficial traits, is nuclear in the 'character reformation' process as used in this sense.

E.F. Sharpe (*Collected Papers on Psycho-analysis,* The Hogarth Press and The Institute of Psychoanalysis, London, 1950) states: 'We have to demonstrate that the same impulses are discernible in the reformation as before it, that obedience has in it the same factors as disobedience—that black is white and white black . . . that anxiety is being allayed by this system of goodness and obedience.'

character structure See *structure, character; defense, character.*

character-traits According to Adler, such character-traits as timidity, shyness, fear of strangers, hyper-sensitiveness, prudishness, avarice, envy, etc. in the neurotic permit an inference as to the nature of the abnormal attitude.

He states: 'All [character-traits], in the last analysis, are to be traced back to the exaggerated and false evaluations of masculine and feminine features.' (Adler, A. *The Practice and Theory of Individual Psychology,* tr. by Radin, P., Kegan Paul, Trench, Trubner, London, 1924)

character, unit See *unit-character.*

character, urethral A character type, mentioned briefly by Freud and Ferenczi and belonging to the classificatory group which stresses the libido origin of character structure (see *defense, character*). The urethral character commonly gives a history of bed-wetting beyond the usual age. The behavioral characteristics of this type depend on reaction formation in relation to the specific fear of urethral eroticism, which is shame. Burning ambition, a need to boast of achievement, and great impatience are typical of this character type.

Charcot, Jean-Martin (1825–93) (shàr-kō′) French neurologist and psychiatrist; localization of function in cerebral disease; hysteria; hypnosis; the first modern physician to make a serious attempt to treat emotional disorders on an individual psychotherapeutic basis.

Charcot-Marie-Tooth's disease (Jean-

Marie Charcot; Pierre Marie, French physician, 1853–1940; and Howard Henry Tooth, English physician, 1856–1926) See *atrophy, peroneal muscular.*

Charcot's syndrome Multiple sclerosis.

Charcot triad See *sclerosis, multiple.*

charge, mental Cathexis.

charm Light hypnosis; hypotaxis.

chart, life See *biographic sketch.*

chasmus hystericus (kàz'moos hēs-te'rē-koos) Persistent yawning, usually on a hysterical basis.

chastity, conjugal The state of husband and wife living in celibacy.

cheimaphobia (kī-mà-fō'bi-à) Fear of cold.

cheiro- See *chiro-.*

chemopallidectomy (kē-mō-pal-i-dek'tō-mē) Injection of small amounts of alcohol into the globus pallidus, used in the therapy of basal ganglia hyperkinetic disorders.

chemo-psychiatry A psychiatric term intended to designate the application and effect of chemical substances in psychiatry.

cher- See *chaer-.*

cheromania (kē-rō-mā'ni-à) *Obs.* Morbid impulse to gaiety. The elated syndrome of manic-depressive psychosis.

cherophobia Morbid aversion to gaiety.

Cheyne-Stokes psychosis See *psychosis, Cheyne-Stokes.*

childbirth, envy of According to some authorities the boy has an envy of the girl's ability to bear children, which in its intensity matches the girl's envy of the boy's penis. Fenichel does not believe this to be the case. He points out that both boys and girls may have a 'passionate wish to give birth to babies, a wish that is doomed to frustration.' On the other hand, however, little boys 'can actually get pleasure from their penis.' This is clearly not the case in the girl's side of the situation, i.e. since little girls can in no possible way bear children any better than can little boys. (Fenichel, O. *The Psychoanalytic Theory of Neurosis*, Norton, New York, 1945)

child, bright A generic term originating in the desire to establish categories in the large group of children with superior intellectual abilities. Clinical observation and intelligence testing are the two main avenues of approach for establishing these categories. In its specific meaning, the term 'the bright child' has become a tool in the technical equipment of those dealing, in the main, with the problems and concepts of child guidance. In general, children of superior ability have been divided into four groups: (a) the bright child; (b) the superior child; (c) the gifted child; (d) the prodigy.

(a) The special ability of the *bright child* can best be ascertained by intelligence tests. A bright child, as contrasted with the dull or subnormal child, is one who possesses average qualifications, when judged by the mental level of our civilization. The brightness of the child consists specifically in his ability to perceive, grasp, and absorb communicated knowledge more quickly than is usual with his own age group. Bright children assimilate more easily and may offer more original products in creative work.

(b) *Superior children* are more than bright. They have extraordinary capabilities, usually being endowed with some particular superiority in their special field.

(c) *Gifted children* are those with a specific talent against a background of bright, average, or dull abilities. Gifted children are usually one-sided, or have a tendency to overdevelop in the direction of their ability only.

(d) The *prodigy* (among superior children) is rare, and is a child who from the earliest stage of his life shows an unusual and practically untrained capability in one or more fields. Most frequently such children are seen on the concert stage, but some attract attention in the fine arts, literature, and science. (Harms, E. *Handbook of Child Guidance*, Child Care Publications, New York, 1947)

child, gifted See *child, bright.*

child guidance Used especially in the psychiatric, sociological, and psychological study and treatment of the developing child, this psychiatric term intends to emphasize preventive or prophylactic measures directed toward the goal of minimizing the chances of mental and emotional disorders developing in adult life. These measures are focused mainly upon the familial, educational, and social environmental milieu of the developing child.

Child guidance strives to influence the child's developmental familial and social milieu mainly through education, support, insight, and understanding, directed at both the child's immediate family and such influential parent surrogate figures as the doctor, the minister, the nurse, and the teacher. A major portion of this preventive program is directed toward alleviating the neurotic anxiety of parents and parent surrogates as it is acted out in their close relationship with the child, and easing the anxiety of the child, who is inevitably, albeit unconsciously, affected in the process.

childhood The period of life from birth to puberty.

childhood, land of In speaking of the practical application of his theory of analytical psychology, Jung used this expression to describe 'that time in which the rational consciousness of the present was not yet separated from the "historical soul," the collective unconscious, and thus not only into that land where the complexes of childhood have their origin but into a prehistorical one that was the cradle of us all. The individual's separation from the "land of childhood" is unavoidable, although it leads to such a removal from that twilit psyche of primordial time that a loss of the natural instincts thereby occurs.' (Jacobi, J. *The Psychology of C.G. Jung,* Kegan Paul, Trench, Trubner, London, 1942) 'The consequence of this is want of instinct and therefore disorientation in general human situations. The separation has, however, also the result that the "land of childhood" remains definitely infantile and so becomes a constant source of childish inclinations and impulses. Naturally these intruders are highly unwelcome to consciousness, which therefore represses them. This repression merely increases the separation from the source and intensifies the want of instinct to the point of sterile rationalism. Consciousness therefore either is overwhelmed with infantility or must constantly defend itself against it in vain. The one-sidedly rational attitude of consciousness must, in spite of its undeniable successes, be regarded as unadapted and contrary to the demands of life. Life is dried up and longs to return to its source. The source, however, can only be found in the "land of childhood," where one, as formerly, can receive directions from the unconscious. Not only he is childish, though, who remains a child too long but also he who parts himself from his

childhood and supposes it has therewith ceased to exist. For he does not know that everything pertaining to the psyche has a double face. The one looks forward, the other back. It is ambiguous and therefore symbolic, like all living reality. . . In consciousness we stand upon a peak and childishly imagine that the road leads on to greater heights beyond the peak. That is the chimerical rainbow-bridge. In order to gain the next peak one goes nevertheless—one must go, if one will reach it—down into the land where the roads first begin to branch.' (Jung, C.G. *The Integration of the Personality,* Farrar and Rinehart, New York, 1939)

child, intelligent See *child, bright.*

child-penis-feces See *concept, feces-child-penis.*

child, problem A child whose behavior presents deviations from the norm, such as would warrant investigation and treatment by methods of clinical guidance, child psychiatry, etc. The deviations are manifested primarily in the adaptation to the social group, but may be related to habit training or neurotic traits which make social adaptation difficult. Wile considers the term problem child a misnomer and expresses the opinion that it should be abolished, because, 'the majority of problems are not inherent in children, but are created by situations. Truancy is not inherent in youth, but created by mandatory education laws and other factors. It is quite apparent that to speak of a child as a problem child is to hold him responsible for the existence of difficulties.' (*American Journal of Orthopsychiatry,* vol. 1, 255, 1930–31)

child prodigy See *child, bright.*

child, superior See *child, bright.*

chionophobia (kī-ō-nō-fō'bi-à) Fear of snow.

chiro- From Gr. *cheír,* hand.

chiromania (kī-rō-mā'ni-à) An old term and concept which implied causal relationship between masturbation and psychiatric states; morbid impulse to masturbate.

choc fortuit (shawk' fawr-twē') (F. 'accidental shock') In 1887 Binet coined this expression to denote an accidental shock to the psyche. The shock or psychic trauma is usually of a sexual character and is influential in modifying to a greater or lesser degree the subsequent adjustment of the individual.

choice, object In psychoanalysis the term refers to the object (usually a person) upon which psychic energy is centered.

'First there existed an object-choice, the libido had attached itself to a certain person.' (Freud, S. *Collected Papers*, vol. 4, tr. by Riviere, J., Leonard and Virginia Woolf and The Institute of Psychoanalysis, London, 1924–25)

choice, of neurosis See *compliance, somatic.*

choleric See *type, choleric.*

cholinergic (kō-lin-er′jik) A term used for all nerves which release acetylcholine at their terminals, viz. all postganglionic parasympathetic nerves, all autonomic preganglionic fibers whether parasympathetic or sympathetic, and postganglionic sympathetic nerves to sweat glands and certain blood vessels, and the somatic nerves to skeletal muscles.

cholinesterase (kō-lin-es′ter-ās) See *process, elementary; acetylcholine.*

chorea (kō-rē′à) A disorder characterized by irregular, spasmodic, involuntary movements of the limbs or facial muscles. Without a modifying word it usually means Sydenham's chorea or St. Vitus' dance.

chorea (Sydenham's), acute (Thomas Sydenham, English physician, 1624–1689). This condition includes acute and chronic mental disturbances associated with Sydenham's chorea. The latter is an infectious disease related to tonsillitis, rheumatism, and endocarditis and characterized by spontaneous, irregular, spasmodic, involuntary, and objectively purposeless movements of the various muscle groups. Restlessness, irritability, and insomnia occur. Memory disturbances, hallucinations, delirium, depression, or mania may be observed. The condition represents a toxic-infectious psychosis.

chorea demonomania (dē-mun-ō-mā′ni-à) Choromania.

chorea, epidemic During the Middle Ages convulsive dances, called epidemic chorea, spread among the population like an epidemic.

chorea, Huntington's (G. Huntington, American neurologist, 1850–1916) Chronic degenerative hereditary chorea. A rare, hereditary and familial affection of the nervous system, occurring in adults from 30 to 50 years of age, and characterized by a chronic, progressive chorea, associated with mental deterioration which finally terminates in dementia.

The symptoms include choreic movements which gradually become widespread and violent; facial grimacing; bizarre, dancing, jerking gait; speech impairment; smacking of the tongue and lips, etc.

Mental symptoms include, in the early stages, impairment of memory; poor attention; irritability; at times, apathy and suicidal tendencies. The mental deterioration progresses gradually until total dementia occurs. There are usually no delusions or hallucinations.

chorea, hysterical When choreiform movements constitute the outstanding symptoms of hysteria, the condition is known as hysterical or mimetic chorea.

chorea insaniens (kō-rā′à ēn-sä′nē-ens) (L. 'raving chorea') Chorea with delirium. See *chorea, maniacal.*

chorea magna (mȧg′nȧ) (L. 'great chorea') A term infrequently used today for 'severe associated contractions of a choreic character, but which do not seem to be a special disease, but rather a form of hysteria or some epidemic psychosis, or it may be malingering.' (Tuke, D.H. *A Dictionary of Psychological Medicine*, vols. 1–2, Blakiston, Philadelphia, 1892)

chorea major (mä′yôr) (L. 'major or greater chorea') An older term, synonymous with chorea magna.

chorea, maniacal 'A name given to those cases of chorea in which the mental disturbance is very great. It occurs chiefly in females, at or soon after puberty, or during pregnancy. The mental disturbance may precede or accompany the chorea, which may remain slight, while the mental symptoms assume an intense form. There are delusions with wild, violent, and aimless excitement, accompanied by garrulity, rarely partaking, however, of the incoherent type of acute mania; food has to be administered by force. . . . The excitement subsides after a short period, and leaves dullness and apathy, taciturnity, and sometimes persistent hallucinations. The mental condition may slowly improve, but occasionally persists for weeks or months after the cessation of the chorea.' (Tuke, D.H. *A Dictionary* *of Psychological Medicine,* vols. 1–2, Blakiston, Philadelphia, 1892)

chorea, mental An old term for a manic condition with inco-ordination of ideas.

chorea, methodical A form of chorea in which the movements take place at definite intervals.

chorea, mimetic See *chorea, hysterical.*

chorea nutans (nōō′tàns) A hysterical symptom characterized by rhythmical nodding; also called *chorea oscillatoria,* though the latter term refers to rhythmical hysterical movements seen in any part of the body.

chorea oscillatoria (os-kil-à-tō′ri-à) See *chorea nutans.*

chorea, psychogenic The frequent involuntary repetition of the same movement met with in children, and often mistaken for Sydenham's chorea. It is really a habit tic or spasm, in the nature of a compulsion.

chorea, rhythmic Methodical chorea.

chorea rotatoria (kō-rā′à rō-tà-tō′rē-à) A form of chorea characterized by rotation or oscillation of the head, trunk, or limbs, many times a minute.

chorea saltatoria (sàl-tà-tō′rē-à) A form of chorea in which the patient involuntarily jumps rhythmically or irregularly.

chorea, tetanoid (kō-rē-à, tet′à-noid) See *degeneration, hepatolenticular.*

choreiform (kō-rē′i-form) Resembling chorea, choreoid.

choreo-athetosis (kō-rē-ō-a-the-tō′sis) A combination of the clinical features of *chorea* (q.v.) and *athetosis* (q.v.). Both chorea and athetosis physiologically present features which are the opposite of the symptoms of Parkinsonism, and it has therefore been suggested that while Parkinsonism represents a loss of function of the corpus striatum, chorea and athetosis are due to a disorganization of its activity and are due to lesions involving especially the caudate nucleus and the putamen. 'We do not at present know what determines the difference between chorea, athetosis, and torsion-spasm. That these disorders are closely allied is indicated by their possession of common physiological features, and by the occurrence of intermediate forms. Their differences may depend upon whether the striatal lesion is diffuse or focal, and whether or not other structures are also involved.' (Brain, W.R. *Diseases of the Nervous System,* 4th ed., Oxford University Press, 1951.)

choreomania (kō-rē-ō-mā′ni-à) Dancing mania; epidemic chorea. At different times in different countries epidemics of frenzied dancing have taken place. During the fourteenth and fifteenth centuries such epidemics were prominent in western Germany, where they were known as *Tanzwut;* later they were called *chorea Germanorum* to distinguish the condition from *chorea Anglorum* or the form of chorea first described by Sydenham.

chrematophobia (krē-mà-tō-fċ′bi-à) Fear of money.

Christotherapy Marcus Gregory, in his *Psychotherapy, Scientific and Religious* (1939) thus calls the psychotherapeutic methods used by Christ.

chromatic In genetics the term relates to the protoplasmic cell substance called *chromatin* which stains the nuclear network and constitutes the morphological basis of heredity.

chromatid (krō′mà-tid) In genetics the term is used with reference to the chromosomes which originate in the nucleus of a cell during the meiotic process of cell division (see *chromosome*).

According to Sinnott and Dunn: 'In the prophase of the first division the two members of each elongated pair approach each other side by side and become so closely associated that they sometimes seem to have fused into a single *bivalent* chromosome. During synapsis, or previously, each member of the bivalent pair splits longitudinally into two exactly equal daughter chromosomes or chromatids, so that for a time a *tetrad* is formed consisting of four chromatids.' (Sinnott, E.W. and Dunn, L.D. *Principles of Genetics,* 3rd ed., McGraw-Hill, New York and London, 1939)

chromatin (krō′mà-tin) Stainable tissue. *Biol.* This collective biological term refers to a reticulum of protein substances in the nucleus of a cell, which are readily stainable and render the nucleus conspicuous in dyed tissues. Although this chromatin network may include more minute granules suspended upon an axis of *linin,* it is considered by Sinnott and Dunn as consisting of only a single substance which 'differs in its appearance and staining reactions at different times and under different conditions.' (Sinnott, E.W. and Dunn, L.D. *Principles of Genetics,* 3rd ed., McGraw-Hill, New York and London, 1939)

All present evidence indicates that the nuclear chromatin elements represent the actual seat of the hereditary characters (see *nucleus*).

chromatophobia (krō-mȧ-tō-fō'bi-ȧ) Morbid dread of certain color or colors.

chromesthesia (krō-mes-thē'zhi-ȧ) A form of synesthesia in which colors are seen in association with other forms of sensation, and especially in association with sounds (colored hearing).

chromidrosis (krō-mi-drō'sis) Colored perspiration.

chromomere (krō'mō-mēr) This genetic term denotes those minute nodules in the chromosomes of a cell nucleus which form a chain of chromatic bodies, particularly in the early stages of mitosis, and are strung like beads on a fine thread. They show persistent differences in size and distribution and presumably have also different chemical compositions. There are sound reasons for believing that many chromomeric nodules are too small to be visible.

Some biologists have been tempted to identify the chromomeres with the *genes.* Much evidence is against this theory, however, especially Bridge's discovery of still smaller elements of morphological structure in the crossbands of the salivary gland cells of Drosophila. It is most likely that even these particles are *not* ultimate and cannot be identified with the genes (see *chromosome*).

chromophobia (krō-mō-fō'bi-ȧ) Fear of color(s).

chromosomal, chromosomic, chromosomatic (krō-mō-sō'mal, -som'ik, -sō-mat'ik) The adjectives not only refer to the minute chromosome particles themselves into which the scattered chromatin of a cell nucleus separates at the beginning of cell division, but are also used to characterize that part of the mechanism of heredity which is based on the activities of the chromosomes.

chromosome (krō'mō-sōm) This is a biological term relating to the minute chromatic particles—in the nuclei of dividing cells—which are now regarded as the essential carriers of the Mendelian gene units. On account of a biochemical affin-

ity for certain dyes, Waldeyer introduced the term *chromosome* for these 'color bodies.'

Thanks to the spectacular experimental studies of modern genetics it has been possible not only to identify the characteristic behavior of the chromosomes in cell division with the fundamental mechanisms of *heredity,* but also to determine many details of the biochemical chromosome structure as well as the very specific arrangement of the *gene units* on the chromosome and their relative positions (see *cell division*).

It is believed that there is a pair of *homologous* chromosomes in every cell of an organism. 'Particle by particle, from one end of the chromosome to the other, the same order of sizes is followed in one chromosome of every cell. The same arrangement of particles is found, with minor modifications, in every individual of the same species. When the chromosomes are doubled, each nodule which the chromosomes contain is duplicated. The value of this duplication, part by part, in maintaining a combination of living structures which is successful—which had to be successful in order to survive—can hardly be overestimated.' (Shull, A.F. *Heredity,* 3rd ed., McGraw-Hill, New York and London, 1938)

chromosome, sex See *sex-chromosome.*

chronaxia, chronaxy (kron-ak'si-ȧ, krō'-nak-sē) The shortest duration which a current of a certain defined strength takes to flow through a nerve in order to produce a muscular contraction.

chronic brain syndrome See *brain disorder; nomenclature, 1952 revision.*

chronophobia (kron-ō-fō'bi-ȧ) A neurotic fear of time. This is the most common psychiatric disorder in prison inmates, and sooner or later almost all prisoners suffer chronophobia to some degree: it occurs in every potential neurotic who goes to prison. The duration and immensity of time are terrifying to the patient, and the passage of time throws him into a panic. The frequency of chronophobia in prisoners has led to the condition's being called prison neurosis.

Chronophobia appears suddenly, without warning, at the time the inmate comes to grips with his sentence. The introductory phase of imprisonment is ordinarily marked by hopes and plans for a new trial or the like, by uncertainty, and by a studied indifference or carefree attitude. After the novelty of prison has worn off, and the real length of the sentence is felt, chronophobia sets in. The prisoner goes into a panic, usually while in his cell, and fears his enclosure and restraint, but this apparent claustrophobia arises from fear of time, as represented by the prison. After the first attack, more or less constant anxiety, restlessness, insomnia, dissatisfaction with life, numerous hypochondriacal complaints, and progressive inability to adjust himself to his surroundings appear. The intensity of the crisis usually passes within a few weeks or months, though mild relapses may occur. But the prisoner becomes essentially a phlegmatic, indifferent automaton who serves the rest of his sentence by the clock and lives wholly in the present, one day at a time.

A 23-year-old forger was sentenced to prison for three years and had his first attack of panic in his cell while writing home to his parents. After the acute panic subsided, he developed hypochondriacal complaints which persisted through the remainder of his sentence. Upon discharge, symptoms disappeared completely. Three months after discharge the patient was sentenced again for a ten-year term. All of the previous symptoms reappeared within two months and persisted until the end of the new term.

In the mouths of speakers from the population groups that furnish the highest percentage of chronophobia patients ('exchange students' in mental institutions from jails and penitentiaries) the phrase 'doing time' is the usual widespread colloquial *terminus technicus* for serving a sentence in jail. There is hardly any wonder that with the words 'doing time' firmly lodged in his consciousness the new prisoner—if a potential neurotic—is a marked and easy victim for this variety of ailment, from the early days after the door has been locked behind him in the cell.

chronotaraxis (kron-ō-târ-ak′sis) Confusion for time, as for date, season of year, time of day, and overestimation or underestimation of duration of time; this symptom has been reported as occurring as a result of bilateral lesions of the dorsomedial and anterior thalamic nuclei.

chthonic (thon′ik) Relating to the depths of the earth. Jung likens the psyche to the earth. Speaking of psychic archetypes, he says that 'they are essentially the chthonic portion of the mind—if we may use this expression—that portion through which the mind is linked to nature, or in which, at least, its relatedness to the earth and the universe seems most comprehensible.' (Jung, C.G. *Contributions to Analytical Psychology,* tr. by Baynes, H.G. and C.F., Kegan Paul, Trench, Trubner, London, 1928)

cibophobia (sib-ō-fō′bi-à) Fear of food. Sitophobia.

ciliospinal reflex (sil-i-ō-spī′nal) A superficial reflex; scratching or pinching of the skin on the side of the neck produces dilatation of the pupil; strong light and accommodation must be avoided in this test.

cipher method A method in secret writing. While writing on the question of dream interpretation Freud refers to the 'cipher method,' which 'treats the dream as a kind of secret code in which every sign is translated into another sign of known meaning, according to an established key.' (Freud, S. *The Interpretation of Dreams,* 3rd ed., tr. by Brill, A.A., Macmillan, New York, 1933) The method is said by psychiatrists to possess no scientific value.

circle, closed See *theory, immanence.*

circle, Papez' See *emotion, Papez' theory of.*

circular In psychiatry the term is used in characterizing manic-depressive psychosis, because the psychosis is sometimes characterized by cycles of mania and depression.

circumscription, monosymptomatic (mon-ō-simp-tō-mat′ik) When a patient has but a single symptom psychiatrists speak of monosymptomatic circumscription. A patient, apparently well adjusted in all other situations, developed intense anxiety whenever he encountered a particular individual.

circumstantiality A disorder of associations seen in schizophrenic patients in which too many associated ideas come to consciousness because of too little selective suppression. Many things which are implicit in ordinary conversation are explicitly communicated and, typically, to an absurd and bizarre degree. One of Bleuler's patients, for example, wrote the following in a letter to his mother: 'I am writing on paper. The pen I use for it is from a factory called Perry & Co., the factory is in England. I am assuming that. After the name Perry Co. the city of London is scratched in; but not the country. The city of London is in England. That I know from school.' Some patients who are aware of their circumstantiality will describe an accompanying subjective experience that the central idea has not been communicated until all of its facets have been considered in detail. This same sort of uncertainty and doubt about adequacy of communication may be seen in obsessional disorders where it usually appears as overmeticulousness, precision, or ostentatious honesty.

cistern puncture See *puncture, cistern.*

cisvestite (sis-ves'tīt) One who keeps to wearing clothes within the conventions of one's sex.

cisvestitism (sis-ves'ti-tiz'm) Dressing in the clothes of one's own sex, but in clothes inappropriate to one's station in life. When an adult dresses as a child, or a child as an adult, or a citizen as an army officer—such acts are called cisvestitism. See *transvestitism.*

cittosis (si-tō'sis) Pica.

claim, neurotic Horney's term for the belief held by certain patients (whom Freud called 'the exceptions') that they are in some way superior and that others should fulfill their wishes and needs.

clasp-knife phenomenon See *rigidity, decerebrate.*

class 'The community of those who as a group have the same lot in life, or the same "life-chance," as determined typically by material possessions, rank or station and cultural factors.' (Weber, M. *Wirtschaft und Gesellschaft,* Tübingen, 1922)

'Any portion of a community which is marked off from the rest, not by limitations arising out of language, locality, function or specialization, but primarily by a sense of social distance [which] involves also as a rule objective differences, income levels, occupational distinctions and so forth, within a society.' (McIver, R.M. *Society, Its Structure and Changes,* Smith, New York, 1931)

'Classes in modern societies may be described as groups of individuals who, through common descent, similarity of occupation, wealth and education, have come to have a similar mode of life, a similar stock of ideas, feelings, attitudes and forms of behavior and who, on any or all of these grounds, meet one another on equal terms, and regard themselves, although with varying degrees of explicitness, as belonging to one group.' (Ginsberg, M. 'Class Consciousness,' *Encyclopaedia of the Social Sciences,* vol. 3, Macmillan, New York, 1930, p. 536)

classification, mechanistic The reference herein is to the classification suggested by Kempf, who speaks of 'mechanistic classification of neuroses and psychoses produced by distortion of the autonomic-affective functions.' He states that 'it seems, therefore, much more practical to use a system of classifying psychopaths according to the nature of their autonomic-affective difficulties and their attitudes towards them, because this keeps the dynamic factors directly in psychiatric attention and permits of revision as the cases change.' (Kempf, E.J. *Psychopathology,* Mosby, St. Louis, 1921)

Kempf designates all psychiatric conditions as neuroses, which may be benign or pernicious. There is a further subdivision into: (1) suppression, (2) repression, (3) compensation, (4) regression, and (5) dissociation neuroses.

classification of disordered behavior (Rado) See *disordered behavior, classification of.*

classification of post-traumatic and post-encephalitic syndromes See *post-traumatic and post-encephalitic syndromes, classification of.*

classification of psychiatric disorders See *nomenclature, 1952 revision.*

claudication, cerebral intermittent (klaw-di-kā'shun) A vasomotor phenomenon in which a transient spasm and closure of the lumen of an artery occurs, temporarily depriving a part of the brain of its blood supply, producing a transitory hemiplegia. This condition is usually observed in the course of cerebral arteriosclerosis.

claudication, mental A transitory spasm of the blood vessels of the brain. Some authors hold that mental claudication may be responsible for the sudden fleeting episodes of mental confusion.

claustrophilia (klaws-trō-fil'i-à) A pathological desire to be confined and enclosed within a small space—the exact opposite of *claustrophobia.* Claustrophilia is a manifestation of a strong tendency to withdraw in a somatic way and is seen in many catatonic episodes. It has been suggested that certain criminals have adopted a psychopathic reaction pattern, thus inviting incarceration, which represents a protected withdrawal from unbearable environmental tension. In these cases claustrophilia is interpreted psychoanalytically as an escape from the world and a tendency to return to the womb. A disposition to claustrophilia is often seen in asthmatics, who symptomatically withdraw into their own respiratory cavities. Such patients show a predilection for introversion and isolation, often with a strong need for solitude and silence.

claustrophobia (-fō'bi-à) Fear of being locked or shut in, fear of enclosed places. This is a common psychiatric symptom, notably among psychoneurotic patients. The fear is said to be related to the older and deeper phantasy of rebirth. It is usually accompanied by anxiety phenomena (feelings of compression, suffocation, increased heart beat, severe panic, etc.). It is believed that the fear is the antithesis of the unconscious wish.

claustrophoboid (-fō'boid) Dr. Bertram D. Lewin's term for one afflicted with claustrophobia (*Psychoanalytic Quarterly 4, 227, 1935.*) As the suffix *-oid* has an established meaning in psychiatric literature, the question arises whether the form *claustrophobiac* would not be more properly used.

claustrum (klaws'trum) See *basal ganglia*.

clavus (klā'vus) A common symptom in psychiatry, from which point of view it refers to a severe pain in the head, sharply defined and usually described by the patient as a sensation produced by a nail being driven into the head. It is usually regarded as a conversion symptom and often appears in discussions on hysteria.

clavus hystericus (klä'voos hē-ster'ē-koos) See *clavus*.

cleavage In the developmental process of any organism originating by sexual reproduction, this term denotes the stage in the embryological development of a fertilized egg, which follows fertilization and, in fact, is initiated by it. Reproduction occurring without prior fertilization is known as *parthenogenesis* (q.v.).

The mode of cleavage is conditioned by the character of the egg; it is of the mio-

lecithal type (with little yolk) in the case of the human egg.

The character of the egg with respect to yolk-content imposes a particular type of cleavage, influencing the whole series of subsequent stages in the earlier development. Miolecithal eggs segment totally and produce *blastomeres* as the result of segmentation, which are equal in size. This type of cleavage is known as *holoblastic equal* segmentation or, as is true in the case of human cleavage with blastomeres of almost, but not quite, equal size, as *adequal holoblastic* segmentation.

Up to and including the 32-cell stage, the product of the cleavage of the miolecithal egg is a solid sphere of cells, called a *morula*. Subsequently a central cavity appears and the segmenting egg becomes a *blastula*. See *reproduction*.

Clérambault-Kandinsky complex See *complex, Clérambault-Kandinsky*.

client Psychiatric social workers' term for a patient.

client-centered therapy See *therapy, client-centered*.

climacophobia (klī-mak-ō-fō'bi-à) Fear of stairs.

climacteric (klī-mak-ter'ik) Of or pertaining to the so-called involutional period of life, characterized in the woman by the cessation of the menses and less definitely characterized in men.

climacterium (-tē'ri-um) In medicine the word today refers to the menopausal period of life. As such it applies to women, denoting the time at which they cease to menstruate. When applied to men, the term is not so well defined physiologically, though it has reference in general to changes in the sexual life of the individual.

The *climacterium* is often associated with pronounced physical and psychical changes. Because of the prevalence of depressions, the mental diseases occurring at the *climacterium* are called involutional melancholia. *Involutional* in this instance is synonymous with *climacteric*.

climacterium, male An ill-defined syndrome in males, in middle life, and thought of as analogous to the menopause in females. The major symptoms are usually nocturnal frequency, fatigue, indecision, flushes, decreased sexual desire, and decreased erective and intromissive potency. Various other symptoms may be present also. It is a moot question whether this syndrome constitutes a separate and distinct clinical entity, or whether it is not a symptomatic manifestation of a psychoneurotic breakdown in middle life, revolving, in the main, around psychogenic impotence and anxiety. In a very small percentage of cases, a true organic, or gonadal, endocrine etiology, secondary to testicular atrophy and degeneration, has been diagnostically validated by means of the therapeutic test with androgens and gonadotrophic assays of the urine. Heller and Meyer state: 'Whereas, in the female, the menopause is an invariable and physiologic accompaniment of the aging process, in the male, the climacteric is an infrequent and pathologic accompaniment of that same process.' (Weiss, E., and English, O.S. *Psychosomatic Medicine*, 2nd ed., Saunders Company, Philadelphia and London, 1949)

climacterium virile (klē-màk-tā'rē-oom vē-rē'le) A term introduced by Kurt Mendel in 1910 to designate the period of life when procreative power ceases in the male sex. As a rule the climacterium in males is reached between the ages of 50 and 65. There is a psychiatric state, known as involutional melancholia, taking its name from the period (climacterium, involutional) at which it occurs.

clinical psychologist See *psychologist, clinical.*

clithrophobia (klith-rō-fō'bi-à) *Obs.* Claustrophobia.

clitoris (kli'tō-ris) A female organ, the analogue of the penis. It is about an inch and a half in length and is composed of two corpora cavernosa capped by a glans. It is part of the external genitalia.

Its psychical importance is emphasized particularly in psychoanalysis. It enters into the formation of the castration complex, has relationship with the Oedipal situation, and is one of the erogenous zones.

According to psychoanalysis, the first genital belief of the child is that everyone possesses a penis. The little girl regards her clitoris as an undeveloped penis. Deutsch stresses that in the beginning of the phallic stage the clitoris possesses for the girl the same pleasure-giving capacities as the penis has for the boy. There is clitoral primacy just as there is phallic primacy.

clitoromania (kli-tor-ō-mā'ni-à) Nymphomania.

cloaca (klō-ā'kà) The cloaca is an embryological organization of the rectum and urogenital sinus. In the embryo the rectum and the urethra have a common opening. Later when the anal membrane ruptures, the rectum acquires its own orifice.

In psychoanalysis emphasis is placed upon the child's cloaca phantasy, the so-called 'cloaca theory,' that babies are expelled by way of the anal aperture. At the time that children develop this concept their interests are largely coprophilic; hence, there is nothing illogical to them in the belief that babies follow the same anatomical course as feces. Nor do children at this early age know that only females bear children; they believe both sexes can perform that function.

It is believed that to the child's imagination the abdomen is merely a receptacle where food goes and feces come out. The knowledge that the baby grows in the body of the parent is associated with the idea of eating and of expulsion. Hence *baby* and *feces* are equated. Jones has collected a number of words the etymology of which showed the association between babies, feces, and odors.

The cloacal theory is clearly demonstrable in many patients with schizophrenia. The male patient, for instance, may believe that he has but a single opening at the pelvis through which he gives birth to children.

clone, clon (klōn, klon) A group of organisms which have originated from a single individual by asexual reproduction. Since all these organisms must be endowed with the same hereditary equipment, it may generally be assumed that differences in their phenotypical appearance are due to modifying conditions of their environment. See *paravariation.*

clonus (klō'nus) Muscular spasm, with alternating rigidity and slackness. 'Continuous oscillatory movements, usually of the foot or lower leg, produced on sudden passive bending of a joint. The muscles, which are thus stretched, contract; this stretches the muscles on the opposite side, which contract in turn, and so the process goes on indefinitely. It bespeaks a loss of voluntary control, which is usually the result of disease in the central nervous system, but may be a purely neurotic phenomenon.' (MacCurdy, J.T. *The Psychology of Emotion,* Harcourt, Brace, New York, 1925)

clonus, ankle A clonic rhythmical tremor of the foot elicited by placing the leg in semiflexion, holding the leg with one hand, grasping the foot with the other and briskly dorsiflexing the foot one or more times.

clonus, patellar (på-tel'ĕr) Patellar clonus is elicited by extending the leg, grasping the patella (knee cap) between index finger and thumb, and briskly pushing the cap down one or several times.

closing-in The term for a symptom of constructive apraxia in which the patient tends to close-in on the model when performing constructive tasks. For example, when attempting to copy from a model, the patient moves toward the model; or, in setting-up exercises, he will bring his hands ever closer to those of the demonstrator. The symptom, which becomes worse with an increase in the difficulty of the task, may be the result of a fear of empty space, but more likely it represents an attempt to perform better when there is a disturbance in the ability to make an abstract copy from a concrete model. (*Journal of Nervous and Mental Disease 88,* 1, 1938)

closure, law of and life-course An individual's course of life is based on a general law of Gestalt dynamics, the *law of closure.* This means that every uncompleted whole tends to a kind of continuation which is in accordance with the inherent system of that given whole. In the early phase of life only a few initial lines of the life patterns are apparent, and the continuation patterns may take many different directions. The more the pattern nears completion, the less variation in the pattern continuation is possible. (Angyal, A. *Foundations for a Science of Personality,* The Commonwealth Fund, Oxford University Press, New York, 1941)

clouded states, epileptic See *epileptic clouded states.*

cloudiness See *sensorium.*

clouding (of consciousness) A condition, seen most commonly in the acute and chronic brain disorders (the organic reaction types), in which there is impairment of orientation, perception, and attention.

Clouston, Sir Thomas Smith (1840–1915) British psychiatrist and neurologist.

clownism A popular term denoting clownish, grotesque attitudes assumed by certain psychiatric patients; seen especially in the so-called Faxenpsychosis and buffoonery psychosis and, to a lesser extent, in Ganser state.

clumsiness, arranged An unconsciously prepared inaptitude through which the neurotic individual prevents himself from properly performing certain acts which he secretly fears. In a general sense, arranged clumsiness is an escape mechanism by means of which the performance of certain acts is avoided by the individual through the pretence of lack of skill. In a more specific way, this expression is used in relation to the unconsciously prearranged inability to find the vaginal entrance in an attempt to perform coitus, and to other inadequacies in the performance of sexual acts. When the male individual is unable to consummate the sexual act, one may say that the female involved often represents, directly or indirectly, a taboo symbol. (Stekel, W. *Compulsion and Doubt,* Liveright, New York, 1949)

cluttering Rapid, confused and jumbled speech, commonly associated with motor awkwardness and personality and behavior changes (e.g. behavior is erratic, disorganized, impulsive, untidy). Other language disorders such as delay in beginning to speak, reading disability, and spelling disability are common. Family history frequently reveals clutterers in the same family and the condition is often mistaken for stammering. Like stammering, it is more common in boys, but cluttering tends to persist throughout life and the cluttered speech is characteristic. It is hurried, even precipitate (tachylalia), and confused.

'The child starts a sentence in several different ways before he can proceed. Finally, having gotten started, he continues to mix his words and thoughts so that he ends up with a different idea from the one with which he started. Words, phrases, and even short sentences are repeated while the speaker gropes for the proper ones. . . . The position of words is confused, some being inserted too early, others too late. . . . The clutterer has great difficulty in finding the right words, and he may, consequently, get panicky while talking. Hoarseness and stammering episodes are frequent.' (Bakwin, H. and Bakwin, R.M. *Clinical Management of Behavior Disorders in Children,* Saunders, Philadelphia, 1953.)

'Probably the most famous clutterer

was the Reverend W.A. Spooner, Warden of New College, Oxford, whose word confusions have come to be known as spoonerisms. Typical examples include "The two great English poets, Kelly and Sheets" (for "Shelley and Keats") and "The Lord is a shoving leopard" (for "loving shepherd").' (ibid.)

Cluttering is also sometimes called agitolalia.

cocainism (kō-kān′iz′m, -kā′in-iz′m) The state of being afflicted with the signs and symptoms of cocaine poisoning.

cocainomania (-ō-mā′ni-à) Morbid craving for cocaine.

coccygodynia (kok-sig-ō-din′i-à) Pain at the tip of the coccyx.

cochlear nerve (kok′lē-ēr) See *nerve, acoustic.*

cocomania (kō-kō-mā′ni-à) An old term for cocainism; cocomania was first described by A. Erlenmeyer in 1886.

co-conscious, co-consciousness This concept was extensively studied by Morton Prince. It includes 'conscious states that we are not aware of, simply because [they are] not in the focus of attention but in the fringe of the content of consciousness. The term would also include pathologically split-off and independently acting co-conscious ideas or systems of ideas such as occur in hysteria, reaching their apogee in conscious personalities and in automatic writings.' (Prince, M. *The Unconscious,* Macmillan, New York, 1916)

In psychoanalysis the term preconscious is in general equivalent to co-conscious. 'We were accustomed to think that every latent idea was so because it was weak and that it grew conscious as soon as it became strong. We have now gained the conviction that there are some latent ideas which do not penetrate into consciousness, however strong they may have become. Therefore we may call the latent ideas of the first type *preconscious,* while we reserve the term *unconscious* (proper) for the latter type which we came to study in the neuroses.' (Freud, S. *Collected Papers,* vol. 4, tr. by Riviere, J., Leonard and Virginia Woolf, London, 1925)

Co-conscious, preceded by *the,* is often used as a noun.

coefficient, correlation See *correlation.*

coefficient of reality See *reality, coefficient of.*

coefficient, regression See *correlation.*

coelom (sē′lom) Celom.

coene See *cene-.*

cognition, paranormal Obtaining knowledge by means outside of the normal processes of perceiving and thinking, as in extra-sensory perception. See *perception, extra-sensory.*

cohabitation See *coitus.*

coitophobia (kō-i-tō-fō′bi-à) Fear of the sexual act.

coitus, coition (kō′i-tus, kō-ish′un) Sexual intercourse per vaginam between male and female. Psycho-dynamic accompaniments of the act have been a topic of extensive discussion in psychoanalysis. Coitus is a central theme around which are constructed, directly or indirectly, many of the formulations of Freud, since coitus is one of the final aims of the individual.

In medicine *coitus, copulation, cohabitation* and *sexual intercourse* are used synonymously, though the words have a widely different meaning in their original setting.

coitus a tergo (à ter′gō) See *pederasty; coitus more ferarum.*

coitus, external Perineal coitus.

coitus, incomplete *Coitus interruptus* (q.v.).

coitus inter femora (kô′ē-toos ēn′ter fem′ô-rà) Sexual relations by the insertion of the penis between the thighs of the partner.

coitus interruptus (ēn-ter-roop′toos) Cessation of sexual intercourse before emission; synonymous with *onanism.* (Popular usage, however, has equated onanism with masturbation.)

coitus more ferarum (mō′re fe-rä′room) (L. 'sexual intercourse in the manner of [wild] beasts') The carrying out of the act of heterosexual intercourse in the 'natural' position of lower animals, that is, from the rear, and usually with the female on hands and knees. The penis is inserted into the vagina; when it is inserted into the rectum, the act is called anal intercourse. This latter practice is called *pederasty* (q.v.) when the partner is a boy, and *sodomy* (q.v.) when the sexual relation is with an animal through the vagina.

Coitus more ferarum is not sodomy, but

is thought of as primitive. The axis of the vagina, in this position, is in direct correspondence with the axis of the penis in erection. This might indicate the primitive biological congruity of this position. Certain elements of tenderness, which are dominant in the so-called 'normal,' or face-to-face, position, are, however, excluded in this approach. R. Sterba (*Introduction to the Psycho-analytic Theory of the Libido,* Nervous and Mental Disease Monographs No. 68, New York, 1942) states: 'Pleasure satisfaction in the anal sadistic zone, or the buttocks, is indicated by the preference of many people for coitus more ferarum, or "a tergo" (from the rear).'

coitus oralis (ō-rä′lēs) Fellatio.

coitus per anum (per ä′noom) Synonym of *pederasty* (q.v.).

coitus, perineal (kō′i-tus, per-i-nē′al) External coitus; Lacassagne coined the expression for the act of rubbing the penis against the perineal region.

coitus, psychic Ellis writes: 'Brooding on sexual images, which the theologians called *delectatio morosa,* may lead to spontaneous orgasm in either sex, even in perfectly normal persons. Hammond described as a not uncommon form of "psychic coitus," a condition in which the simple act of imagination alone, in the presence of the desired object, suffices to produce orgasm.' (Ellis, H. *Studies in the Psychology of Sex,* 3rd ed., vol. 1, Davis, Philadelphia, 1919)

coitus reservatus (kô′ē-toos re-zer-wä′toos) Sexual intercourse in which the male partner delays or withholds his orgasm until the female partner has hers, or indefinitely as a means of birth control.

colic, hysterical Hysterical pain felt in the abdominal region.

collaboration As used by Sullivan, a type of interpersonal relationship in which there is not only co-operation but also sensitivity to the needs of the other person.

collateral This term describes an individual related by blood to a series of siblings, but not descended from the same line of immediate ancestors. A first cousin is the most closely related instance of a collateral.

The term also means 'indirect' when applied to this line of descent of an individual or to the form of inheritance of a Mendelian factor as characteristic of *recessiveness* (q.v.), that is, the transmission of a trait to the descendants of the siblings of a trait-carrier.

collection The impulse to collect is given much prominence in psychoanalysis. It is intimately associated with the instinctual life of the individual and as such has many meanings. It is related, for example, to object-love. 'To objects we have grown to like through use, or because of their esthetic value, we obviously have a personal relationship which is quite analogous to sexual attraction. There are many different degrees of this kind of object-love. Many persons have almost no needs in this respect, while others are completely under the domination of their passion for certain objects. . . . A passion for collection is frequently a direct surrogate for a sexual desire; and in that case a delicate symbolism is often concealed behind the choice of objects collected.' (Abraham, K. *Selected Papers,* tr. by Bryan, D. and Strachey, A., Leonard and Virginia Woolf and The Institute for Psychoanalysis, London, 1927)

It is the belief of psychoanalysts that the desire to possess and control is a reflection also of early oral and anal conditions. In the oral stage the motive is to gain, in the anal it is to hold. 'The possessiveness of anal love shows itself clearly in the collector; the objects collected are associated symbolically with excrement.' (Healy, W., Bronner, A.F., and Bowers, A.M. *The Structure and Meaning of Psychoanalysis,* Knopf, New York, 1930)

'That the collecting mania is a reaction to an unconscious need, to an inner feeling of voidness concerning some particular craving, is best seen in the collections made by the insane.' (Brill, A.A. *Fundamental Conceptions of Psychoanalysis,* Allen & Unwin, London, 1921)

'All collectors are anal-erotics, and the objects collected are nearly always typical copro-symbols; thus, money, coins (apart from current ones), stamps, eggs, butterflies—these two being associated with the idea of babies—books, and even worthless things like pens, old newspapers, etc.' (Jones, E. *Papers on Psycho-Analysis,* 4th ed., Wood, Baltimore, 1938)

collective This term gains significance in psychiatry by virtue of the meaning given to it by Jung. 'All those psychic contents I term collective which are peculiar not to one individual, but to many, at the same time, i.e., either to a society, a people, or to mankind in general. Such contents are the "mystical collective ideas" ("representations collectives") of the primitive described by Levy-Bruhl; they include also the *general concepts* of right, the State, religion, science, etc., current among civilized men. . . . The antithesis of *collective* is *individual*.' (Jung, C.G. *Contributions to Analytical Psychology*, tr. by Baynes, H.G. and C.F., Kegan Paul, Trench, Trubner, London, 1928)

Jung refers to two divisions of the unconscious, the *personal* and the *collective*. The former 'embraces all the acquisitions of the personal existence—hence the forgotten, the repressed, the subliminally perceived, thought and felt. But, in addition to these personal unconscious contents, there exist other contents which do not originate in personal acquisitions but in the inherited possibility of psychic functioning in general, viz. in the inherited brain-structure. These are the mythological associations—those motives and images which can spring anew in every age and clime, without historical tradition or migration. I term these contents the *collective unconscious*.' (ibid.)

collective life handicap See *handicap, collective life*.

colloidal gold reaction See *Lange's colloidal gold reaction*.

colloidoclastic diathesis (kol-oi-dō-klas'tik dī-a'the-sis) See *diathesis, colloidoclastic*.

colony, Gheel See *Gheel*.

coma The profoundest degree of stupor in which all consciousness is lost and there is no voluntary activity of any kind. Among the various conditions which may produce coma the most common are: encephalitis, cerebral hemorrhage, cerebral thrombosis, cerebral embolism, subarachnoid hemorrhage, intracranial tumor, head injury, post-epileptic coma, diabetic coma, hypoglycemic coma, hypertensive encephalopathy, uremic coma, acute alcoholism, intoxication with opiates or other sedatives, hypothalamic lesions, congestive attacks of general paralysis, hysterical trance, and catatonic stupor.

coma somnolentium (kō'ma sōm-nō-len'tē-oom) (L. 'coma of the somnolent') Cataphora.

coma-vigil Coma in which the eyes remain open. Coma-vigil occurs in certain acute brain syndromes associated with systemic infection (the infective-exhaustive psychoses, also known as acute toxic encephalopathy, acute toxic encephalitis, or acute serous encephalitis).

combat exhaustion Same as *combat fatigue*. See *shellshock*.

combination In genetics, this term refers to the hereditary variations which represent the effect of *hybridization* and which occur in crossbred products originating from the union between two individuals with unlike hereditary equipment. The formation of new hereditary combinations which account for the majority of genetic differences among animals and plants and also explain why hybrids do not breed true, takes place in accordance with the *Mendelian law,* which governs the reassortment of the different genetic factors involved in a given cross (see *variation*).

combined degeneration of the spinal cord See *sclerosis, posterolateral*.

cometophobia (kom-e-tō-fō'bi-à) Fear of comets.

comfort-dream See *dream, convenience*.

comic Freud says: 'The comic is content with only two persons, one who finds the comical, and one in whom it is found. The third person to whom the comical may be imparted reinforces the comic process, but adds nothing new to it.' He adds that, because of the many difficulties in understanding the comic, 'we may therefore expect that we shall learn nothing about the nature of the comic other than that which we have already become aware of in wit.' (Freud, S. *The Basic Writings of Sigmund Freud,* tr. by Brill, A.A., Random House, New York, 1938)

command, posthypnotic See *suggestion, posthypnotic*.

commission, lunacy See *lunacy commission*.

commitment See *certification*.

communication Transmission of emotions, attitudes, ideas, and acts from cne person to another. Through communication 'habits of doing, thinking, and feeling (are transmitted) from the older to the younger. . . . Society . . . may fairly be said to exist *in* transmission, *in* communication.' (Dewey, J. *Democracy and Education,* Macmillan, New York, 1916)

The distinction is made between the *primary* techniques of communication common to all men, as language, gesture, the imitation of overt behavior and social suggestion, and the *secondary* techniques which facilitate communication, as writing, symbolic systems including stop-and-go lights, bugle-calls and other signals, and physical conditions allowing for communication, including the railroad, the steamship, the telegraph, the telephone, the motion picture, the radio, and the airplane. (Sapir, E. 'Communication,' *Encyclopaedia of the Social Sciences,* vol. 4, Macmillan, New York, 1931, pp. 78–80.)

communication, privileged Information which a patient discloses to his physician while the latter is attending him in a professional capacity; such information is termed privileged because in some states and according to ethical precepts of the medical profession the physician is not allowed to divulge such information without the patient's consent. This is, in other words, the patient's privilege of silence in regard to confidential matters on the part of his physician.

communion, magical According to psychoanalytic theory, in unconscious thinking, 'by incorporating objects one becomes united with them.' That is, to eat something or be eaten by someone is an unconscious way of achieving union with that object. In countless experiences of everyday living one shares ideas, emotions, activities with others. Some of these experiences of sharing with others present as their unconscious significance, psychoanalytically, the type of mystical or magical union described above. This magical communion of 'becoming the same substance' takes place when the same food is jointly eaten or the respective bloods of the individuals involved are mixed. The latter type of communion is seen in many tribal rites of friendship, and, symbolically, in our custom of handshaking. The magical union mediated through food is seen not only in the old idea that friendship and hospitality are associated with breaking bread together, but also and particularly in the well-known religious rites of the Eucharist, the bread and wine (distributed to the parishioners) symbolizing, as in the Last Supper,

Christ's body and blood. (Fenichel, O. *The Psychoanalytic Theory of Neurosis,* Norton, New York, 1945)

community 'A group (of persons) occupying a territorial area (and) sharing a whole set of interests wide enough and complete enough to include their lives.' (McIver, R.M. *Society, Its Structure and Changes,* Smith, New York, 1931) Comprised under the term community are not only hamlets, villages, towns, cities, and local areas within the city, but also metropolitan regions, states, nations, and the world. In the literature two different aspects of the community are stressed (1) as structure in terms of an 'aggregation of individuals residing in a specified area or locality, characterized by greater or lesser mutual interdependence and maintaining primary institutions, such as the church and the school, and (2) in terms of consensus, socialization and solidarity.' (Linderman, E.C. 'Community as Process,' *Encyclopaedia of the Social Sciences,* vol. 4, Macmillan, New York, 1931, pp. 102–5.)

community-feeling The sense of relationship between the individual and the community. Adler states that out of community-feelings 'are developed tenderness, love of neighbour, friendship and love, the desire for power unfolding itself in a veiled manner and seeking secretly to push its way along the path of group consciousness.' (Adler, A. *The Practice and Theory of Individual Psychology,* tr. by Radin, P., Kegan Paul, Trench, Trubner, London, 1924)

community, therapeutic A psychiatric or mental hospital which emphasizes the importance of socioenvironmental and interpersonal influences in the therapy, management, resocialization and rehabilitation of the long-term patient. Self-control, dignity, and trust are employed rather than excessive imposed controls, restrictions, regimentation, and meaningless rituals. 'It seeks continually to solve its problems in terms of interpersonal relations, by helping the patient to identify himself with a social group and through identification modify his social attitudes and behavior because of his growing awareness of his role in relationship to other people.' (Wilmer, H.A. 'Toward a Definition of the Community.' *Am. J. Psychiat. 114,* 824–33, 1958)

companion, imaginary It has often been

observed that a child will create an imaginary companion for himself and will endow this product of phantasy with the qualities of reality. The imaginary companion will have a name, a definite appearance and personality—even an imaginary family created for it, and so on.

Imaginary companions are created mostly by only children, or by children whose siblings are much older, or who for any reason are without real playmates. The imaginary companion thus fulfills the child's need for intimate companionship and friendship and serves an important function in his emotional life. For the imaginary companion is freely taken into confidences from which parents are distinctly barred and becomes 'someone to tell its troubles to' and 'to share its secret pleasures with.' In general, the imaginary companion is so created by the child that it has everything the child desires but lacks. The play *Harvey* presents an amusing and not dissimilar instance of this imagery, a huge white rabbit created as an imaginary companion. Though it is an animal and the imaginary creation of an adult, its origin and function are much the same as those of the imaginary companions of children.

compartmentalization Isolation; keeping separate parts of one's personality which should be kept together.

compensation From the standpoint of analytical psychology Jung defines *compensation* 'as a general functional adjustment, an inherent self-regulation of the psychic apparatus. In this sense, I regard the activity of the unconscious as a compensation to the onesidedness of the general attitude produced by the function of consciousness.' He adds that 'in the normal condition the compensation is unconscious, i.e., it performs an unconscious regulation of conscious activity. In the neurotic state the unconscious appears in such strong contrast to the conscious that compensation is disturbed. The aim of analytical therapy, therefore, is to make the unconscious contents conscious in order that compensation may be reestablished.' (Jung, C.G. *Psychological Types,* tr. by Baynes, H.G., Harcourt, Brace, New York and London, 1923)

compensation, autonomic From the standpoint of Kempf's psychopathology *'compensation* is one of the most fundamental attributes of living tissue and occurs particularly where there exists some sort of painful irritation or the tendency of the autonomic-affective apparatus to be forced into the *fear state*. The cause of the fear state may be due to pain from the disease or injury of some organ (as the heart, lung, kidney, skeleton, skin) or the potential danger of injury, failure, persecution, prosecution, loss of social esteem or property, etc. . . . If the cause of *fear* is a segmental compulsion within ourselves an attempt to *eliminate* it, or, if regarded as a social inferiority, an attempt to *compensate* by some estimable work is reflexly initiated.' (Kempf, E.J. *Psychopathology,* Mosby, St. Louis, 1921)

compensation-ideal This term is used by Adler to indicate a substitution in dream or phantasy of some superior image for an inferior one.

Adler says: 'Napoleon, Jesus, Jeanne d'Arc, the Virgin, as well as the Kaiser, father, uncle, mother, brother, etc. are frequent *compensation-ideals* of the intensified lust for superiority and represent at the same time, the directive and emotionally-steeped preparations of the psychic life of the neurotic.' (Adler, A. *The Neurotic Constitution,* tr. by Glueck, B. and Lind, J.E., Moffat, Yard, New York, 1917)

compensation-neurosis See *neurosis, compensation.*

competence, mental See *incompetence.*

competition The struggle for existence and for a livelihood. Competition may be either unconscious or conscious; as it becomes self-conscious it tends to pass over into social conflict. 'Competition is a term . . . which associates the fact of a struggle with the function of order. . . . It is by competition . . . that the fittest survive: individuals, instruments and institutions of different capacities are given places in a going society; and an industrial system . . . is adapted to new conditions. Competition is at once a process of selection, an economic organization and an agency of social development.' (Hamilton, Walton, 'Competition,' *Encyclopaedia of the Social Sciences,* vol. 4, Macmillan, New York, 1931, pp. 141–2)

complacency, principle of W.B. Cannon formulated the thesis that 'instincts' and 'drives' are in a sense attempts on the part of the organism to maintain its optimal body economy (homeostasis). R.B.

Raup called it the principle of complacency, thereby indicating that every organism is a physiological system which tends to preserve its stationary condition or to restore the stationary condition as soon as it is disturbed by any variation occurring within or outside the organism. In a sense all needs and desires are behavior patterns, such as withdrawal, or attack, or flight, in direct or indirect consequence of this general tendency to keep a physiological condition constant.

complex A group of repressed ideas interlinked into a complex whole, which besets the individual, impelling him to think, feel, and perhaps act after a habitual pattern. Jung, who introduced the term *complex* to psychiatry, describes it as the grouping 'of physic elements about emotionally-toned contents.' He adds that it 'consists of a nuclear element and a great number of secondarily constellated associations.' Apparently the contents of a complex may be in consciousness or in the unconscious. It is believed that the nuclear component is always in the unconscious. Jones defines a complex as 'a group of emotionally invested ideas partially or entirely repressed.' (Jones, E. *Papers on Psycho-Analysis,* 4th ed., Wood, Baltimore, 1938)

In general it may be said that fundamental psychic conflicts, usually those derived during the stages of infantile sexuality, may give rise to a complex. Thus, one speaks of the Oedipus, Electra, and castration complexes.

MacCurdy defines a complex as 'a group of ideas constellated by an instinctive process. The ideas are linked together, because they form a chain in some potential instinctive reaction. A complex is always unconscious, or at least, owes its importance to elements in it which remain unconscious.' (MacCurdy, John T. *The Psychology of Emotion,* Harcourt, Brace, New York, 1925)

complex, active castration The ideas centered around the fear of losing the penis and the emotions linked with these ideas. The passive castration complex is the idea that the penis has already been lost and/or the wish to lose the penis.

complex, anti-Oedipus The attitude taken by an individual in order to overcome the Oedipus conflict.

complex, apprentice The time in a boy's life when he aims to be like his father

and will act as a pupil or apprentice: in psychoanalytic terms, will have a penis like his father. To achieve this, he is submissive, passive, with the idea or phantasy that by this method, in the future, he will be prepared to be masculine and active like his father. 'Apprentice complex' is the name given to this facet of the emotional relationship with the father.

Sometimes this attitude toward the father and father figures in the individual's environment is exaggerated and persists as the individual matures. According to Fenichel, such is the case in 'pregenitally oriented compulsive characters' and in some homosexuals. In these individuals there are 'mobilized (the aforementioned) pregenital passive aims toward the father . . . connected with the penis.' (Fenichel, O. *The Psychoanalytic Theory of Neurosis,* Norton, New York, 1945)

complex, Atreus See *complex, Medea.*

complex, authority A group of emotionally invested ideas centering around the concept of authority. These emotions are entirely or partly repressed together with the original ideas concerning authority to which they are attached. If a person's earliest experiences with authority have been sufficiently painful, it is likely that both the experiences and the associated affects have undergone repression. The material thus repressed constitutes a complex and is termed an authority complex. The person will always react to authority just as he did originally, although he will not be aware of this fact. Unconsciously overdetermined reactions to authority either in the direction of rebellion against it or in submission to it are common in neurotic patients.

complex, autonomous This concept, employed by Jung (analytical psychology) 'is used to distinguish all those psychic formations which at first are developed quite unconsciously, and only from the moment when they attain threshold-value are able to break through into consciousness. The association which they then make with consciousness has not the importance of an assimilation, but rather of a perception; which means to say, that the autonomous complex, although certainly perceived, cannot be subjected to conscious control, whether in the form of inhibition or of voluntary reproduction. The autonomy of the complex reveals itself in the fact that it appears or vanishes when and in such guise as accords with its own intrinsic tendency; it is independent of the option of consciousness.' (Jung, C.G. *Contributions to Analytical Psychology*, tr. by Baynes, H.G. and C.F., Kegan Paul, Trench, Trubner, London, 1928)

complex, brother See *complex, Cain.*

complex, Cain An expression synonymous with *brother complex;* rivalry, competition, aggression, or destructive impulses directed against a brother.

'We are right in suspecting here also a pathological *brother complex* (Cain complex) based on envy.' (Gutheil, Emil A. *The Language of the Dream,* Macmillan, New York, 1939)

complex, chronological See *complex, subject.*

complex, Clérambault-Kandinsky (klā′-räN-bô kän-dēn′skē) (Gatian G. de Clérambault, 1872–1934, French psychiatrist.) A psychotic syndrome which may be associated with any clinical picture in which the patient feels that his mind is controlled by another person or by an outside power.

complex, Clytemnestra This refers to the wife who kills her husband so that she may possess one of his male relatives.

complex, creative Constructive complex. The creative complex is autonomous. 'Practical analysis of artists invariably shows not only the strength of the creative impulse springing from the unconscious, but also its splenetic and arbitrary character.' (Jung, C.G. *Contributions to Analytical Psychology,* tr. by Baynes, H.G. and C.F., Kegan Paul, Trench, Trubner, London, 1928)

complex, dart and dome The spike and wave type of electroencephalographic tracing seen in petit mal epilepsy. See *epilepsy.*

complex, Demosthenes The neurotic need to achieve mastery over inferiority feelings through words and language in the process of speaking.

complex, Diana The wish of a female to be a male.

complex, ego This term has a special meaning in analytical psychology. Jung defines a complex as a grouping 'of psychic elements about emotionally-toned contents.' When the emotionally toned contents are associated with the ego, Jung speaks of an ego-complex. (Jung, C.G.

Contributions to Analytical Psychology, tr. by Baynes, H.G. and C.F., Kegan Paul, Trench, Trubner, London, 1928)

complex, Electra (Electra, the daughter of Agamemnon, King of Mycenae, induced her brother Orestes, just returned after long years of self-exile, to wreak on their mother Clytemnestra and her former paramour, and new husband, the effeminate Aegisthus, vengeance for having together butchered Agamemnon in his bathtub. The dark broodings over the dismal fate of her beloved hero-father possessed the wedlock-scorning Electra till death, a tragic image immortalized for posterity by the great Greek dramatists Aeschylus, Sophocles, and Euripides.) Since the early formulations of Freud the Electra complex, as a doctrine, has held a position of importance in psychiatry equal to that of the Oedipus complex. It is the analogue of the latter and refers to the relationship of father and daughter. Since the principles involved in both are so nearly alike, it is customary today to refer to both as the Oedipus complex. Some authors, however, call the Electra complex the female Oedipus complex.

complex, emotional See *memory, automatic,* for viewpoint of Morton Prince.

complex, Eshmun Castration complex. 'Here apparently Eshmun, the beautiful youth, castrates himself to escape the incestuous situation, and thereafter his activities become associated with a more neutral or perhaps feminine type of function. . . .' (Lewis, N.D.C., 'The Psychology of the Castration Reaction,' *Psychoanalytic Review 15:* 174, 1928)

complex, femininity Psychoanalysts believe that, in the infantile life of the boy, there is a phase equivalent to the 'penis' phase in the little girl. Girls believe that they once possessed a phallus just like the one that boys have, but through some misdeed on their part it was taken from them. The male child develops the same fear of frustration (castration phantasy), which Klein calls a *femininity complex.* In essence it is the inferiority complex of Adler. The boy thinks that the mother is the castrator. In order to save his phallus from the fate suffered by girls he identifies himself with his mother and wishes for a vagina and breasts. There is thus 'vaginal envy' in boys as there is 'penis envy' in girls. At the same time there is a dread on his part against the feminine role which castration would bring about. The dread may appear as its opposite, aggression. 'A tendency to excess in the direction of aggression which very frequently occurs has its source in the femininity-complex.' (Klein, M. *The Psycho-Analysis of Children*, tr. by Strachey, A., Norton, New York, 1932)

complex, flatus The infant's interest in the production of intestinal gas.

complex, function This term, used principally by Jung, denotes the purpose or function of a psychic structure. 'Thus, the persona is a function-complex which has come into existence for reasons of adaptation or necessary convenience, but by no means is it identical with individuality. The function-complex of the persona is exclusively concerned with the relation to the object.' (Jung, C.G. *Psychological Types*, tr. by Baynes, H.G., Harcourt, Brace, New York and London, 1923)

complex, grandfather The concept *grandfather complex* is often referred to by psychoanalysts. For example, Jones says: 'A deeper reason for this association [between grandson and grandfather] is as follows: With very many children there is a lively desire to become the parents of their own parents, and they may even entertain the fantastic belief that just in proportion as they grow bigger, so will their parents grow smaller, till in time the present position of affairs will be completely reversed. This curious construction of the imagination, which is probably one of the sources of the belief in re-incarnation, is evidently closely connected with incestuous wishes, since it is an exaggerated form of the commoner desire to be one's own father.' (Jones, E. *Papers on Psycho-Analysis*, 4th ed., Wood, Baltimore, 1938)

complex, Griselda (Griselda, or Griselidis, was a paragon of womanly purity, virtue, and endless patience, widely celebrated in medieval romances.) The name given by Putnam to the father's complex in regard to his daughter. In the father-daughter complex, or the Griselda complex as Putnam called it, the father unconsciously grudges giving up his daughter to another man, not wishing to part with her himself. According to Jones, parental complexes are ultimately derived from infantile ones of the Oedipus type, the father's complex in regard to his daughter being a later development and

manifestation of his own original Oedipus complex for his mother. Contemplation of the marriage of his daughter—the future mother—reactivates the older Oedipal yearning for his own mother. The father's reluctance to give up his daughter to another man is often thinly disguised under the pretext of altruistic solicitude for the daughter's welfare. (Jones, E. *Hamlet and Oedipus*, Norton, New York, 1949)

complex, heir of the Oedipus See *heir of the Oedipus complex*.

complex, Heracles The hatred of a father for his children.

complex, incest See *incest*.

complex, inferiority See *inferiority; inferiority, feeling of*.

complex, Jocasta The term proposed by Raymond de Saussure (*Internationale Zeitschrift für Psychoanalyse VI*, No. 2, 118–22, 1920) for the morbid attachment of a mother for her own son—from the marriage of Jocasta to her son Oedipus (see *Oedipus complex*). The Jocasta complex represents a type of perverted mother love and has 'various degrees of intensity—from the maternal instinct slightly deformed to a frank sexual attachment in which both physical and psychic satisfaction is found.'

complex, masculinity Rebellion against castration in the girl, leading to masculine attitudes and behavior. This term is used by Freudian psychoanalysts in much the same way that Adler uses masculine attitude in female neurotics. See *attitude, masculine*.

complex, Medea The hatred and/or homicidal wishes of the mother toward her child. The death-wishes against the offspring are usually motivated unconsciously by a desire for revenge against the father. Fritz Wittels has used the term in a more limited way to indicate a mother's death-wish against her daughter. Strictly speaking, this is not correct, for the Medea of Euripides had only sons. The term Atreus complex has been suggested for a father's death-wishes against his offspring. The Medea complex is probably the clue to an explanation of the baseless accusation of ritual murder practiced by the Jews on Christian children. The accusation likely represents a projection of the accuser's death-wishes against his own children. The Medea complex may lead to dyspareunia, prevention and interruption of pregnancy, failure of breast feeding, and other sources of marital discord. (Stern, E.S. 'The Medea Complex,' *Journal of Mental Science,* 321, 1948)

complex, not-knowing The phrase *not-knowing* is sometimes referred to as a complex. A child's inferiority may be considerably re-enforced when he is led to believe that there are many things about which he should not know. When, for instance, adults carry on conversations with an air of secrecy and mystery, the child's curiosity impulse is aroused, but because it cannot know what the adults are talking about it develops a 'not-knowing' complex, the influences of which may modify the child's later personality growth to a great extent.

complex, nuclear In psychoanalysis, synonymous with Oedipus complex.

complex, obscenity-purity T. Schroeder says: 'I have found that the zeal of the Puritan or religious denunciation of any particular manifestation of sex, is an exact measure of the intensity of its lure for such a person.' (*Encyclopaedia Sexualis.*) Schroeder quotes from W.A. White: 'The man who expresses abhorrence for a certain act is much nearer the possibility of such an act himself than is he who can view it undisturbed and with a judicial attitude of mind; he therefore must summon all his reserves to escape it.' (*Mechanism of Character Formation,* Macmillan, New York, 1916)

complex, Oedipus According to Greek mythology, Oedipus was a son of Laius, King of Thebes, and Jocasta, his wife. The King learned from an oracle that he was fated to be killed by his son. When a boy was born, the King gave him (with a spike driven through his feet) to a shepherd to leave him on Mt. Kithaeron to die. However, the compassionate shepherd gave the infant to the childless King of Corinth, Polybus. When Oedipus reached the age of puberty and an oracle told him that he would kill his father and form an incestuous union with his mother, he decided not to return to Corinth to his alleged father. In his journey he met Laius, whom he slew in a quarrel. When Oedipus arrived at Thebes the Sphinx presented a riddle for solution. Oedipus solved the riddle and the Thebans in gratitude gave him Jocasta as wife. When finally he discovered the

relationship between him and his wife he blinded himself, while Jocasta hanged herself. Oedipus wandered away, accompanied by his daughter, Antigone, being finally destroyed by the avenging deities, the Eumenides. The principles of the Oedipus situation are regarded by psychoanalysts as characteristic of all individuals. Every child must pass through what is called the Oedipus situation or family romance. During the phase of late infancy, the child shifts a quantum of energy into sexual interests in the parents. Normally the boy becomes chiefly attached to his mother, the girl to her father. The solution of the struggle determines the character of the child's later reactions. During the latency period the Oedipus complex is normally relinquished in favor of extraparental activities and interests. With the advent of puberty the original, infantile Oedipus situation is again aroused, and is normally dissolved by the centering of interests in others.

However, the average psychiatric patient never successfully manages his Oedipus complex. Schizophrenia serves as an excellent example. A schizophrenic patient believed implicitly that he was not the child of his parents, that his mother was his wife and that his brothers and sisters were his children; he maintained that his father did not exist. The same patient also insisted that he was blind; on other occasions he spoke of having been castrated. The schizophrenic patient relives the Sophoclean tragedy often with minute precision, even to the point of claiming royal birth.

The same theme is common to psychoneurotic patients, but it is often highly symbolized as a fear, a compulsion, or a conversion phenomenon.

Freud is responsible for the introduction of the Oedipus concept into psychiatry. 'One says rightly that the Oedipus complex is the nuclear concept of the neuroses, that it represents the essential part in the content of the neuroses. It is the culminating point of infantile sexuality, which through its after-effects decisively influences the sexuality of the adult.' (Freud, S. *Three Contributions to the Theory of Sex,* 4th ed., tr. by Brill, A.A., Nervous and Mental Disease Publishing Company, New York and Washington, 1930)

complex, Oedipus, passing of The fate of the Oedipus complex is not yet clearly understood. Freud says: 'Normally an Oedipus complex should be abandoned or thoroughly changed simultaneously with the termination of early sexual life.' He adds: 'This transformation is not thorough enough; therefore, during the period of puberty the Oedipus complex may be revived, in which case it is liable to induce dire results.' In the same communication (*The Problem of Lay Analyses*) he asserts that 'at puberty, the impulses and object-relations of a child's early years become reanimated and amongst them the emotional ties of the Oedipus complex.' The passing of the complex is considered by many psychoanalysts as finally accomplished during the first half of the adolescent period with the energy formerly given to the complex now distributed upon objects apparently unrelated to the parents. In psychiatric conditions, however, there is never a complete dissolution; indeed, it is usually very incomplete.

According to Freud the immediate determinant (in the boy) for the dissolution of the Oedipus complex is the castration complex which 'literally smashes to pieces the Oedipus complex.' (*The Passing of the Oedipus Complex*) It is also called *dissolution of Oedipus complex.*

complex, Orestes (Orestes, the son of the Mycenaean King Agamemnon, who killed his own mother Clytemnestra and her paramour Aegisthus for murdering her husband Agamemnon.) The psychiatric term proposed for a son's killing, or desire to kill, his own mother. Frederick Wertham believes this is a universal complex, like the Oedipus complex. The majority of psychoanalysts disagree with this view and feel, instead, that when it occurs the Orestes complex is an outgrowth of the Oedipus complex and is a reaction by the male child to rejection or frustration by the Oedipal love-object, the mother. But whether universal or not, the Orestes complex does not invalidate the Oedipus complex. (*Psychoanalytic Quarterly 12*, 582–3, 1943)

complex, parental See *complex, Oedipus.*

complex, passive castration See *complex, active castration.*

complex, perceptual It is one of the characteristics of the mentality of primitive peoples and of schizophrenic patients that they think in terms of percepts or images. 'The distortions and condensations of schizophrenics can be explained in an analogous manner. Their root is in the mode of thinking in perceptual complexes, which, in schizophrenics, has to a greater or lesser extent supplanted logical and rational thinking.' (Storch, A. *The Primitive Archaic Forms in Schizophrenia,* tr. by Willard, C., Nervous & Mental Disease Publishing Company, New York and Washington, 1924)

complex, Phaedra This refers to the mother who is in love with her son.

complex, power 'The total complex of all those ideas and strivings whose tendency it is to range the ego above other influences, thus subordinating all such influences to the ego, quite irrespective of whether they have their source in men and objective conditions, or spring from one's own subjective impulses, feelings, and thoughts.' (Jung, C.G. *Psychological Types,* tr. by Baynes, H.G., Harcourt, Brace, New York and London, 1923)

complex, quality Discussing the nature of schizophrenic thinking, Storch says: 'Separate concurrent ideas are collected together as a whole to form a single complex. Instead of a content of consciousness composed of separate parts organized in a definite structure, we find in the mind of the patient absolutely undifferentiated, diffuse, total expressions, resembling emotions rather than ideas, often only vague fragments of ideas, echoes, or mere reverberations of some content or another not in itself present in consciousness at all. Thus we discover a peculiar characteristic of the schizophrenic which is likewise a characteristic for the perception of objects both in primitives and in certain animal groups. We will refer again to these structural characteristics of the so-called "quality complexes." ' (Storch, A. *The Primitive Archaic Forms in Schizophrenia,* tr. by Willard, C., Nervous & Mental Disease Publishing Company, New York and Washington, 1924)

complex, self-reference While discussing the processes involved in the forgetting of names, Freud says that the memory loss protects the individual against some unpleasant narcissistic trauma; if the name were recalled it would bring to consciousness the unpleasant affect associated with it. Freud calls the condition a self-reference complex.

complex, small penis While speaking on

the dread of castration, Jones says: 'This whole group of ideas is strongest in men with a "small penis" complex, often accompanied by impotence, and it is with them that one gets the clearest insight into the genesis. What such a man is really ashamed of is not that his penis is "small," but the reason *why* it is "small." ' (Jones, E. *Papers on Psycho-Analysis,* 4th ed., Wood, Baltimore, 1938)

complex, spike and wave The dart and dome type of electroencephalographic tracing seen in petit mal epilepsy. See *epilepsy.*

complex, subject This is an expression used by Morton Prince as one of the subdivisions of *systematized complexes.* A systematized complex, made up of 'subjects or departments of human experience,' is a subject-complex.

A systematized complex that embraces 'the experiences of certain epochs of our lives rather than the subject material included in them' is called a *chronological-complex* or *chronological system.*

A systematized complex constituting 'certain dispositions toward views of life which represent natural inclinations, desires, and modes of activity, which for one reason or another, we tend to suppress or are unable to give full play to, is called a *disposition* or *mood* system.' (Prince, M. *The Unconscious,* Macmillan, New York, 1916)

complex, symptom Syndrome. 'Syndromes are complexes of symptoms that belong together genetically.' (Bleuler, E. *Textbook of Psychiatry,* tr. by Brill, A.A., Macmillan, New York, 1930)

complex, systematized Morton Prince says: 'In contrast with the limited group of fixed ideas, organized with one or more emotions (i.e., instincts) I have been describing, are the large *systems* of complexes or associated experiences which become organized and fairly distinctly differentiated in the course of the development of everyone's personality. In many, at least, of these systems there will be found a predominant emotion and certain instinctive tendencies, and a predominant feeling tone—of pleasure or pain, of exaltation or depression, etc. It is quite possible that careful investigation would disclose that it is this conflicting affective force which is responsible for the differentiation of one system from another with

opposing affects and tendencies. . . . Among such systems may here be mentioned those which are related to certain *subjects* or departments of human experience, or are related to *time,* or to certain dispositions of *moods* of the individual. The first may be called *subject* systems, the second *chronological* systems, and the last *mood* systems.' (Prince, M. *The Unconscious,* Macmillan, New York, 1916)

compliance, somatic The degree to which the individual's organic structure coincides with his psychological mechanisms in the symptomatic expression of his pathological defenses. In conversion symptoms, for instance, the entire cathexis of the objectionable impulses is condensed onto a definite physical function. The ability of the affected function to adsorb this cathexis is its somatic compliance. The function may be chosen because the organ in question presents a locus minoris resistentiae (see *inferiority, organ*), or because the erogeneity of the afflicted part corresponds to the unconscious phantasies seeking expression (as in the case of a person with oral fixations who, when symptoms are developed, will show primarily oral symptoms), or because of the situation in which the decisive repression occurred (the organ or function under highest tension at the decisive moment is likely to become the seat of disturbance), or because of the organ's ability to symbolize the unconscious drive in question (thus convex organs such as the hand, nose, and breasts may symbolize the penis and represent masculine wishes).

component-instinct A component-instinct is also called a part-instinct. It is not the instinct alone, but it is the instinct and the agent that convey it.

'It appeared that normality developed as the result of repression of certain component-instincts and components of the infantile disposition, and of a subordination of the remainder under the primacy of the genital zone in the service of the reproductive function. . . .' (Freud, S. *Collected Papers,* vol. 1, tr. by Riviere, J., Leonard and Virginia Woolf and The Institute of Psychoanalysis, London, 1924–25)

Freud says that '. . . we see a large number of component instincts, arising from various regions of the body, which strive for satisfaction more or less independently of one another, and find this satisfaction in something that may be called *"organ-pleasure."* ' (Freud, S. *New Introductory Lectures on Psycho-Analysis,* tr. by Sprott, W.J.H., Norton, New York, 1933)

See *impulse, component,* with which component-instinct is synonymous.

composition See *dream, agreement in.*

compos mentis (kom'pos men'tis) L. 'sound of mind.'

compression In *The Interpretation of Dreams,* Freud uses this term interchangeably with *condensation.*

compression, cerebral This term is used to refer to any degree of head injury (concussion, brain contusion, or cerebral laceration) which is followed by intracranial hemorrhage. The latter may be subdural (which is twice as common) or extradural. Acute subdural hemorrhage is usually the result of severe cerebral laceration; extradural hemorrhage is usually due to laceration of the middle meningeal artery by fractured bone, and in this case the posterior branches of the artery are more frequently involved than the anterior.

compromise-distortion In contradistinction to *compromise-formation* as occurring in normal and neurotic development, Freud uses the term *compromise-distortion* to describe an analogous process in a psychosis. Owing to a compromise between the resistance of the ego and the strength of the idea under repression the return of the repressed becomes distorted into a delusion or a hallucination. 'A circumstance quite peculiar to paranoia . . . is that the repressed reproaches return as thoughts spoken aloud. They must thereby suffer a two-fold distortion, first, through a censorship, which leads to their substitution by other associated ideas or to a disguise by indefinite kinds of expressions, and secondly, through their relation to current experiences which are merely analogous to the original.' (Freud, S. *Collected Papers,* vol. 1, tr. by Riviere, J., Leonard and Virginia Woolf and The Institute of Psychoanalysis, London, 1924–25)

compromise-formation A term widely used in psychoanalysis. It is a substitutive idea or act representing a repressed complex. Freud holds that as a consequence of the ego's contacts with reality three typical danger situations arise, each derived from the stage of infantile sexuality. They are (1) danger of the loss of love;

(2) danger of castration; and (3) danger of loss of superego approval. Normally these fears are left behind, but the neurotic individual acts as if the dangers continue to be real. 'As a result both normal and neurotic development is largely a compromise between Ego fears, denials and defenses, and Id strivings.' (Healy, W., Bronner, A.F., and Bowers, A.M. *The Structure and Meaning of Psychoanalysis,* Knopf, New York, 1930) Compromise may be expressed in a variety of ways.

'Of especial interest is the fact that the repressed conflict, which was responsible for the forgetting, betrayed itself in the replacement-memory, which was, as is always the case, a compromise-formation.' (Jones, E. *Papers on Psycho-Analysis,* 4th ed., Wood, Baltimore, 1938)

All psychogenic symptoms are compromises, for they arise on the basis of repressed material and thus serve to give release to the pressure or tension resident in the repressed complex.

'It is in the nature, moreover, of the obsessional neurosis—as of all similar affections—that its manifestations (symptoms, including also the obsessive acts) fulfil the condition of a compromise between the opposing forces of the mind.' (Freud, S. *Collected Papers,* vol. 2, tr. by Riviere, J., Leonard and Virginia Woolf and The Institute of Psychoanalysis, London, 1924–25)

compulsion Action due to irresistible impulse. As a morbid phenomenon it is an act contrary to the conscious will of the subject at the time the act is performed. When an individual carries out an act of which he is not conscious or aware, such as may occur during certain epileptic states or during a period of hysterical amnesia, the action is not known as a compulsion, for the action does not have simultaneous opposition from the subject. Nor is the term *compulsion* used in psychiatry to denote morbid action that has the approval and encouragement of the subject. This delimitation of the meaning of the term expresses the general opinion of psychiatrists today.

Compulsions are usually the result of obsessions. They are obsessions in action. From the nosologic point of view the terms *compulsion* and *obsession* are generally combined as follows: compulsive-obsessive (syndrome). See *obsession.*

compulsion, external The process of bringing up a child, no matter how liberal parents are, plants problems in the youngster's mind and provokes in him a number of manifestations of defiance and rebellion against the limitations imposed upon his drive to obtain pleasure. These reactions of defiance are called external compulsions. A cultural rule, such as that of being clean and tidy, prevents the child from deriving pleasure through the satisfaction of his organic compulsion to urinate and defecate on his own terms, and at his own time. The child may then react against the cultural rule with defiance and rebellion. These outside cultural rules to which the child reacts with manifestations of defiance are called external compulsions, and constitute ways of achieving pleasure in the child's subconscious mind. (Stekel, W. *Compulsion and Doubt,* Liveright, New York, 1949)

compulsion, internal (organ) The psychiatric term for the child's primitive urge to obtain pleasure through the satisfaction of his organic functions: the satisfaction of physical urges causes pleasure as for example in urination and defecation. And still, the child may occasionally tend to resist this organ compulsion: 'One may find the first reactions of resistance to organ compulsions in the attempt of a child to suppress the urge to urinate or defecate, in order to obtain pleasure on his own terms, as it were, and at his own time. If a cultural compulsion, such as that of being clean and tidy, undertakes to subdue the organ compulsion, it may cause defiance reactions, because it encroaches upon some of the child's primitive instincts.' (Stekel, W. *Compulsion and Doubt,* Liveright, New York, 1949)

compulsion, masked A mental mechanism by which the neurotic individual hides his real obsessive idea behind a compulsion. This compulsion acts only as a disguise (= mask) for the obsessive idea. Such is the case of the patient who has the compulsion of constantly complaining of pain when, in reality, what he is trying to do is to avoid the knowledge of the real cause of his trouble, which is produced by the existence of obsessive ideas. The patient complains of pain instead of obsessions because in this way he can continue with these same obsessions. 'It is diagnostically important that the usual sedatives are always ineffective in these cases or, if forced upon the patient, may lead to narcoto-

mania.' (Stekel, W. *Compulsion and Doubt,* Liveright, New York, 1949)

compulsion, repetition See *repetition-compulsion.*

compulsion, thinking See *brooding.*

compulsive-obsessive psychoneurosis See *obsessive-compulsive psychoneurosis.*

compulsive personality See *personality trait disturbance; defense, character.*

conarium (kō-nā'ri-um) The point of contact of mind and body in Cartesian philosophy. The basic tenet of this philosophy was that the human mind is a thinking substance in intimate association with the body. The Cartesian conarium was renamed the *id* by Freud, who regarded it as the place in which the instincts in both their organic and their psychic manifestations are localized and from which they spread to diverse sections of the body and the mind. The Cartesian philosophy is to a large extent dualistic, but holds that mind and body are in intimate contact with each other. Freud's *id,* however, is not perceived from a dualistic point of view. (Hinsie, L.E. *Understandable Psychiatry,* Macmillan, New York, 1948)

conation (kō-nā'shun) Striving, inclination, tendency to do actively or purposively. Many psychologists distinguish between three categories of mental functioning: the cognitive (perceptual or intellectual), the emotional, and the conative. Conation includes instincts, drives, wishes, cravings, etc.

concentric demyelination (dē-mī-ē-li-nā'shun) Baló's disease. See *sclerosis, diffuse.*

concept, feces-child-penis According to psychoanalysis, many factors connected with the anal stage have significant bearing upon the Oedipus and castration complexes. As Freud says: 'The handing over of feces for the sake of (out of love for) someone else becomes a prototype of castration; it is the first occasion upon which an individual gives up a piece of his own body (it is as such that feces are invariably treated by children) in order to gain the favor of some person whom he loves. So that a person's love for his own penis, which is in other respects narcissistic, is not without an element of anal-erotism.' The same reasoning applies to the concept of child. Hence, feces, child and penis are equated. (Freud, S. *Collected Papers,* vol.

3, tr. by Strachey, A. and J., Leonard and Virginia Woolf and The Institute for Psychoanalysis, London, 1925)

conception In biology, the process by which a female's egg or eggs are fertilized and thus enabled to form an embryo.

conception-hallucination. See *hallucination of perception.*

conceptive *Biol.* Capable of conceiving, that is, of being fertilized and forming an embryo.

concretism In analytical psychology concretism is defined as 'a definite peculiarity of *thought* and *feeling* which represents the antithesis of abstraction. The actual meaning of concrete is "grown together." A concretely-thought concept is one that has grown together or coalesced with other concepts. Such a concept is not abstract, not isolated, and independently thought, but always impure and related. It is not a differentiated concept, but is still embedded in the sense-conveyed material of perception. Concretistic thinking moves among exclusively concrete concepts and views; it is constantly related to sensation.' (Jung, C.G. *Psychological Types,* tr. by Baynes, H.G., Harcourt, Brace, New York and London, 1923)

concretization (kon-krē-ti-zā'shun) *Concretism* (q.v.).

concussion Trotter defines concussion as a condition of widespread paralysis of brain function, due to a blow on the head, with a strong tendency to spontaneous recovery, and not necessarily associated with gross organic brain damage. Experimental evidence suggests that this functional disturbance is due to a direct physical injury to the neuron which is reversible, the rate of recovery being proportional to the severity of the injury.

concussion, blast See *neurosis, postconcussion.*

condemnation With Freud the term means 'rejection based on judgment.' In his communication *Repression,* he discusses the fate of libido. He says that one cannot flee from internal stimuli; 'with an instinct, flight is of no avail, for the ego cannot escape from itself. Later on, rejection based on judgment (*condemnation*) will be found to be a good weapon against the impulse.' (Freud, S. *Collected Papers,* vol. 4, tr. by Riviere, J., Leonard and Virginia Woolf and The Institute of Psychoanalysis, London, 1924–25)

condensation In psychiatry one of the meanings of condensation refers to the process by which an idea is made to contain all the emotion associated with a group of ideas. A single word or phrase may be over-cathected or over-charged with emotion when it stands for something else of a much larger order. Thus, a schizophrenic patient became enraged when the word *bill* was mentioned or occurred to him. The word was associated, not to his conscious knowledge (until it was analyzed), with a friend, Bill, with whom the patient had had many experiences that later constituted a vigorous complex. The patient condensed his feelings for his friend into the word *bill* and subsequently into words rhyming with *bill.*

This process of emotional condensation is characteristic of almost all dreams. As Jones expresses it, a person in a dream 'may be constituted by the fusion of the memories of several different actual persons.' (Jones, E. *Papers on Psycho-Analysis,* 4th ed., Wood, Baltimore, 1938)

A second meaning of condensation is a corollary of the first. Many ideas or allied experiences may be compressed into a single thought or word. Thus, the word *theatre* may summarize a host of ideas. A phobia is never an entity; it is representative of a chain of circumstances; it is a symbol that expresses a number of experiences.

'The incompleteness of ideas facilitates the formation of *condensations* which are consequently unusually frequent in schizophrenia. Various lovers, various places of residence are no longer kept apart, sometimes one lover and one place are the representatives of the entire total conception. . . .' (Bleuler, E. *Textbook of Psychiatry,* tr. by Brill, A.A., Macmillan, New York, 1930)

condensation, dream The role of condensation in dream-work is as important as in other forms of psychical activity. 'The first thing that becomes clear to the investigator when he compares the dream-content with the dream-thoughts is that a tremendous *work of condensation* has been accomplished. The dream is meagre, paltry, and laconic in comparison with the range and copiousness of the dream-thoughts. The dream, when written down, fills half a page; the analysis, which contains the dream-thoughts, requires six, eight, twelve times as much space.' (Freud, S. *The Interpretation of Dreams,* 3rd ed., tr. by Brill, A.A., Macmillan, New York, 1933) See *condensation.*

conditionalism This term was introduced by Jung, who maintained that 'under conditions of such and such a kind, such and such dreams can occur.' (Jung, C.G. *Seminar on Children's Dreams,* 1938–9, privately printed.) But the concept and method of conditionalism comes from the physiologist and philosopher Max Verworn (Göttingen, 1863–1921), who defines it as 'a state or process . . . unambiguously determined by the totality of its conditions. From this follows: (1) The same states or processes are always the expression of the same conditions; different conditions are expressed in different states and processes. (2) A state or process is identical with the totality of its conditions. From this follows: A state or condition is scientifically completely known when the totality of its conditions is determined.' (*Kausale und Konditionale Weltanschauung,* 3rd ed., 1928) 'The decisive factor is thus always the situation in question with its contemporary, momentary conditions. The same problem, the same cause may have, according to the total context, a correspondingly different significance; from the viewpoint of conditionalism they can have many meanings, not just always the same one without regard to the situation and the variability of their forms of appearance. Conditionalism is an expanded form of causality, it is a manifold interpretation of causal relations. . .' (Jacobi, J. *The Psychology of C.G. Jung,* Kegan Paul, Trench, Trubner, London, 1942) Conditionalism thus endeavors 'to conceive strict causality by means of interplay of conditions, to enlarge the simple significance of the relation between cause and effect by means of the manifold significance of the relations between effects. Causality in the general sense is not thereby destroyed, but only accommodated to the many-sided living material.' (Jung, C.G. *Seminar on Children's Dreams*)

condition, hysteriform See *hysteriform.*

condition, paranoid See *paranoid.*

conduct 1. According to Healy, Bronner, and Bowers 'that behavior of the individual which has more or less definite implications.' (Healy, W., Bronner, A.F., and Bowers, A.M. *The Structure and Meaning of Psychoanalysis,* Knopf, New York, 1930) Bridges speaks of acquired and inherited behavior. As a rule the word *conduct* refers to the action or behavior of the total individual rather than to parts of him (such as movement of an extremity as an isolated act). *Conduct* implies psychic as well as somatic activity.

2. Self-conscious behavior (Park, R.E. and Burgess, E.W. *Introduction to the Science of Sociology,* University of Chicago Press, Chicago, 1924) The standards of conduct for the person are set by his social environment.

conduct-disorder See *behavior disorders.*

conduction, avalanche Spread of nerve impulse to many more neurons so that an effect disproportionate to the initial stimulus is produced. See *law of avalanche.*

confabulation In psychiatry, the act of replacing memory loss by phantasy or by reality that is not true for the occasion. The term implies also lack of insight, in the sense that the subject fully believes his answers to be correct. Confabulation is not uncommon in organic brain diseases in which intellectual impairment is a prominent feature. For example, the patient with a Korsakoff syndrome often fills in the memory gaps with incorrect details. A patient, bedridden in the hospital for months, said that he had just returned from a European journey and gave many details of the trip, believing thoroughly in his account.

Confabulation is to be differentiated from *pseudologia fantastica* (q.v.), which occurs mainly in the 'psychopathic' group and in other conditions in which acting-out is prominent. In pseudologia fantastica, the phantasy is believed only momentarily and will quickly be dropped if patient is confronted with contradictory evidence. The confabulator, in contrast, will stick steadfastly to his story.

confabulation, opportune While discussing Korsakoff's psychosis, W.A. White says: 'The characteristic symptom [i.e. memory defect] is associated with the amnesia and consists of a peculiar *falsification of memory.* The gaps in memory are filled by all sorts of *fabrications* which are narrated in great detail and with perfect appearance of lucidity—*opportune confabulation.*' (White, W.A. *Outlines of*

Psychiatry, 12th ed., Nervous & Mental Disease Publishing Company, Washington, D.C., 1929)

confabulation, suggestion White says: 'In many cases [of Korsakoff's psychosis] the fabrications can be suggested by leading questions and the patient may be led to make almost any statement, no matter how contradictory—*suggestion confabulation.*' (White, W.A. *Outlines of Psychiatry,* 12th ed., Nervous & Mental Disease Publishing Company, Washington, D.C., 1929)

confession-dream See *dream, confession.*

confidence, level of A quantitative expression of the degree of reliability of an inference; a 5 per cent level of confidence, for example, is a statement that the particular inference would be wrong 5 per cent of the time. Thus the per cent specified is seen to be negatively related to the degree of confidence involved, and a small per cent denotes a high degree of confidence or a low degree of uncertainty.

configuration Gestalt. See *psychology, Gestalt.*

conflict The concept is used extensively in psychiatry, gaining its most exhaustive psychodynamic meaning from the field of psychoanalysis. When an instinct leaves its original source, the id, and goes in the direction of the environment, it encounters the critical scrutiny of several different forces, each of which demands that the instinct conform to certain requirements before it can take the next step forward. The instinct does not want to undergo any modifications; it does not want to suffer any restrictions. It opposes and demands of the successive forces it encounters, namely, the superego, ego, ego-ideal and reality. Consequently there is a *conflict* leading to one of many results, such as repression, symbolization, etc.

'From the very beginning our view was that men fall ill owing to the conflict between the demands of their instincts and the internal resistance which is set up against them.' (Freud, S. *New Introductory Lectures on Psycho-Analysis,* tr. by Sprott, W.J.H., Norton, New York, 1933)

'A solution of the conflict between the repressing and repressed forces may be reached, however, whereby the energy of the latter is diverted to other aims, in much the same way as a conservation and transformation of energy takes place in

the physical world.' (Jones, E. *Papers on Psycho-Analysis,* 4th ed., Wood, Baltimore, 1938)

'He (Freud) showed that such conflicts are not always, or commonly, fought out to a decisive issue; but that rather one of the contending forces, some specialized instinctive urge toward some special goal, is apt to be suppressed or repressed, but not thereby deprived of its power.' (McDougall, W. *Outline of Abnormal Psychology,* Scribner's, New York, 1926)

conflict, actual 'A conflict precipitating the crisis. It occurs when the struggle begins between the conscious and unconscious forces. This must be differentiated from *root conflict* which represents the early source of the struggle, which has been dormant in the unconscious since childhood and repressed.' (London, L.S. *Libido and Delusion,* Mental Therapy Publications, 2nd ed. enlgd., Washington, D.C., 1946)

conflict, experimental This psychiatric term denotes an artificial situation created through hypnotic suggestion in order to demonstrate to the patient his inner attitude toward the real conflict. Accordingly one may refer to it as 'an experimental neurosis' deliberately induced by the hypnotist so as to direct his patient toward awareness of the true motivations of his real neuroses. (Wolberg, L.R. *Hypnoanalysis,* Grune and Stratton, New York, 1945)

conflict, inner Social workers use the term to mean 'a distinct conflict within the personality between two or more opposing impulses or desires which tend to irresolution, tension, or neurotic behavior.' (Hamilton, G. *A Medical Social Terminology,* Presbyterian Hospital, New York, 1930)

conflict, race 'Race conflicts like wars are fundamentally the struggles of racial groups for status.' (Park, R.E. and Burgess, E.W. *Introduction to the Science of Sociology,* University of Chicago Press, Chicago, 1921)

'The major contemporary arenas of race conflict are now the Pacific regions where the white and yellow races are struggling for supremacy; the United States with its Negro problem; and the Indies and Africa.' (Kohn, H. 'Race Conflict,' *Encyclopaedia of the Social Sciences,* vol. 13, Macmillan, New York, 1934, p. 38)

conflict, root In psychiatry, a term that refers to the earliest source of the patient's struggle, lying at the root of the conflict. 'There was no doubt that the roots of masturbation and other sexual traumas occurred earlier in his life, but they were too deeply submerged and could not be brought to the conscious level. . . His actual conflict began when he was rejected as a suitor. His root conflict was only disclosed by hearsay, the story of his reactions when his mother gave her affections to his younger sister of whom he was jealous. This fact could not be brought out either in the analysis or hypnosis. It was assumed that it occurred before three years of age.' (London, L.S. *Libido and Delusion*, Mental Therapy Publications, 2nd ed. enlgd., Washington, D.C., 1946)

conflict, social Conflict is 'conscious competition, and competitors become self-conscious rivals, opponents or rivals.' (Lasswell, H.D. 'Conflict, Social,' *Encyclopaedia of the Social Sciences*, vol. 4, Macmillan, New York, 1931, p. 194)

Conflict is typically for status, whether between persons, groups, or nations. Simmel, who emphasizes the function of conflict in socialization, differentiates the types of conflict as war, feud and faction, litigation, and the conflict of impersonal ideas. (Simmel, G. 'The Sociology of Conflict,' *American Journal of Sociology* IX, 1903–1904)

Conflict between the standards of conduct of social groups, e.g. the family and the gang, may find expression in mental conflict in the individual. Problems of cultural conflict arise with movement of persons from the country to the city, with migration to a new country, and with contacts with the standards of a different social class.

confluence Used in individual psychology (Adler) to refer to the flowing together of several instincts into a single object.

conformity, automaton The course of blindly adopting the pattern of culture of one's environment and bowing submissively to its dictates: the individual accepts the way to live, to feel, and to think as implicitly or explicitly recommended by the group. The effects of culture on personality have been greatly emphasized by Fromm. Man has today become aware of himself as a separate entity. The growing realization of his separateness gives him a sense of isolation and a longing to return to the earlier feeling of solidarity with others. So he uses certain irrational methods of relating back to the group. These are termed mechanisms of escape and include sadomasochism, destructiveness, and automaton conformity.

confusion In psychiatry this generally means a state of disordered orientation. It represents a disturbance of consciousness in the sense that awareness of time, place, or person is unclear. Confusion may be occasioned by organic or psychic causes.

confusion, primary W.A. White says: 'It must not be forgotten that certain other psychoses, particularly dementia praecox and manic-depressive psychosis, may originate under the same conditions which lead to the development of the infection-exhaustion psychoses, and further, that aside from the condition of confusion described (*primary confusion*), states of infection and exhaustion may complicate any psychosis, producing a confusion engrafted on the original disorder (*secondary confusion*).' (White, W.A. *Outlines of Psychiatry*, 12th ed., Nervous & Mental Disease Publishing Company, Washington, D.C., 1929)

confusion, secondary See *confusion, primary.*

congelatio (kôn-ge-lä′tē-ō) *Obs.* Rigid state of the body in catalepsy; same as *gelatio*. See *catalepsy.*

congenital Existing or possessed since birth; in biology applied to an attribute, or anomaly, possessed and manifested by an individual since *birth*. Opposed to *hereditary.*

connotation The significance of a word as it applies to a whole class rather than to a specific or concrete embodiment of the word. Thus, the connotative meaning of the word *chair* would include all the qualities essential to any chair and would be most closely indicated by the phrase *chair in general as a physical entity.* This is to be distinguished from denotation, or denotative meaning, which (in this case) would refer to certain chairs or to a specific chair.

It has been noted that schizophrenics typically demonstrate a reduction in their connotation ability and are able to define words only as they apply to specific objects and not in their general sense as representative of a group or class. As a result, there is relative overemphasis on denotation and thinking comes to be pathologically concretized. (See *concretism*.) This would also appear to be an important factor in the schizophrenic's overliteralness and inability to use metaphor.

Conolly, John (born between 1794 and 1796; died 1866) British psychiatrist; psychotherapy.

conquassationes animi (kôn-kwȧs-sȧ-tē-ō′nes ȧ′nē-mē) (L. 'severe shakings of the soul') *Obs.* Mental derangement.

consanguinity In contradistinction to *affinity* or the relation by marriage, *consanguinity* means relation by blood or descent from a common ancestor within the same family stock. See *kinship*.

conscience Those psychical organizations that stand in opposition to the expression of instinctual actions. Conscience relates to the moral and esthetic and ethical attitudes of the individual. When the parental attitudes, prohibitions, and commands take up their position in the unconscious to form the superego, it is the superego that is conscience. Later in development, when the individual begins to emulate others outside the family circle and develops an ego-ideal, he acquires another conscience. There is, however, a continuity between the two.

The function of conscience is to warn the ego to avoid the pains of intense guilt feelings. 'Conscience becomes pathological when it (a) functions in too rigid or too automatic a manner, so that realistic judgment about the actual outcome of intended actions is disturbed ("archaic superego") or (b) when the breakdown toward "panic" occurs and a greater or lesser sense of complete annihilation is experienced instead of a warning signal, which is the case in severe depressions.' (Fenichel, O. *The Psychoanalytic Theory of Neurosis,* Norton, New York, 1945)

conscience, double This term indicates a dissociation and splitting of consciousness leading to the production of abnormal states of consciousness; a fundamental manifestation of hysteria.

conscience, health While speaking of the sense of guilt R.H. Jokl asserts that 'observation teaches us the unconscious sense of guilt does not simply sustain the neurosis, but may also come into consciousness as a "health-conscience"—, and be in

this form directed against the illness. Preconsciously or consciously it invests real objects with a special moral sensitiveness and repudiates the symptom itself, while supporting such attitudes of the ego as are healthy.' (*International Journal of Psycho-Analysis VIII:* 479, 1927)

conscience, inner A term used by L.E. Hinsie to designate the superego. (Hinsie, L.E. *Understandable Psychiatry,* Macmillan, New York, 1948)

conscience-instinct See *instinct, conscience.*

conscience, outer A term used by L.E. Hinsie to designate the ego-ideal. The ego-ideal is a mental organization formed by the child's teachers, playmates, and other associates. This organization constitutes a conscious standard guiding the individual. Through the formation of the ego-ideal or outer conscience some of the individual's mental energy is diverted from the parents to others. (Hinsie, L.E. *Understandable Psychiatry,* Macmillan, New York, 1948)

conscience, primitive A type of superego derived from man's archaic past.

conscious In psychiatry *conscious* is used: (1) (less frequently) as an adjective descriptive of a function of consciousness or of the conscious realm as a perceptive faculty. As such, it is synonymous with: aware; having knowledge of; present in the field (or realm) of consciousness. (2) (usually) as a noun, to denote a particular division of the psyche. In such use it is practically synonymous with *consciousness,* and is invariably preceded by the definite article: *the conscious,* as is generally the case with *the preconscious, the unconscious, the collective unconscious.*

'The conscious is that part of mental life, proportionately infinitesimal, of which the individual is aware at any given time. Though consciousness is a continuum during normal waking life, its content is extremely transitory, constantly changing.' (Healy, W., Bronner, A.F., and Bowers, A.M. *The Structure and Meaning of Psychoanalysis,* Knopf, New York, 1930)

'It is possible to say, however, that anything psychical will take on the aspect of consciousness if it comes into association with the ego.' (Jung, C.G. *Contributions to Analytical Psychology,* tr. by Baynes, H.G. and C.F., Kegan Paul, Trench, Trubner, London, 1928. To Jung the ego is 'the perceptive self.'

'We can go further and in support of an unconscious mental state allege that only a small content is embraced by consciousness at any given moment, so that the greater part of what we call conscious knowledge must in any case exist for very considerable periods of time in a condition of latency, that is to say, of unconsciousness, of not being apprehended by the mind.' (Freud, S. *Collected Papers,* vol. 4, tr. by Riviere, J., Leonard and Virginia Woolf and The Institute of Psychoanalysis, London, 1924–25)

Kempf's definition of consciousness is as follows: 'The phenomena of consciousness of self or of the environment is the result of all the [autonomic] segments reacting together more or less vigorously, as a *unity*, to the sensational activity of any one or several of its parts.' (Kempf, E.J. *Psychopathology,* Mosby, St. Louis, 1921)

consciousness See *conscious.*

consciousness, clouding of See *sensorium.*

consciousness, disintegration of Jung says: 'The vast majority of mental diseases, in so far as they are not of a definitely organic nature, are due to a disintegration of consciousness caused by an irresistible inundation of unconscious contents.' (Jung, C.G. *Contributions to Analytical Psychology,* tr. by Baynes, H.G. and C.F., Kegan Paul, Trench, Trubner, London, 1928.) This means that material from the unconscious more or less gradually causes the disruption and disintegration of the contents of consciousness.

consciousness, double; dual See *personality, alternating.*

consciousness, dream See *ego, dream.*

consciousness, location of Freud believes 'that consciousness occurs actually *in the locality* of the memory-trace.' (Freud, S. *The Interpretation of Dreams* (3rd ed.), tr. by Brill, A.A., Macmillan, 1933.) He makes the statement with some reservation. For the location of the memory-trace, see *system.* Consciousness is situated in what Freud calls the *P-system* (q.v.).

consciousness, splitting of When a set of experiences, a mental constellation exist, as for instance, in hysteria, essentially alone in consciousness, without associations with other components of consciousness, it is said that there is a splitting of consciousness. See *hysteria, defense.*

consciousness, subliminal See *tendency, subliminal.*

consensual light reflex When light enters the pupil of one eye only, the iris of the other eye contracts; the phenomenon is known as the consensual light reflex.

consensus Agreement reached by the resolution of conflict. (Kallen, H. 'Consensus,' *Encyclopaedia of the Social Sciences,* vol. 4, Macmillan, New York, 1931, pp. 225–6) Four types of group agreement have been differentiated: by authority, by compromise, by majority determination, and by integration. (McIver, R.M. *Society, Its Structure and Changes,* Smith, New York, 1931)

conservation M. Prince says: 'We have a feeling, a perhaps justifiable belief, that a desired piece of knowledge is not lost, that it is back somewhere in our minds, but we cannot get at it. If, sooner or later, under one circumstance or another, with or without the aid of some kind of stimulus, we can recall the desired knowledge we say it was preserved (or conserved). If we continue, under all circumstances and at all moments, to be unable to recall it we say it is lost, that our memory of it is not conserved. So the notion of conservation of knowledge being something apart from recollection enters even into popular language.' (Prince, M. *The Unconscious,* Macmillan, New York, 1916)

constant, central Burrow's term for the primary principle governing the organism's total action pattern. Essentially homeostatic, this principle, on the basis of phyloörganismic behavior, relates the organism of man-as-a-species to its environment. Contrasted with extrinsic constant. Synonym: intrinsic constant. (Burrow, T. *The Biology of Human Conflict,* Macmillan, New York, 1937, pp. 341–3)

constant, extrinsic Burrow's term for the secondary, symbolic principle in organism-environment relationship. It refers to the partial reaction-patterns mediated through the cortex and conforms symbolically to the consistency of phenomena throughout the external world. The organism's extrinsic constant regulates the secondary, partial system of word-conditioned reflexes, and is subordinate to the organism's primary principle or central constant. Contrasted with intrinsic constant. (Burrow, T. *The Biology of Human Conflict,* Macmillan, New York, 1937, pp. 341-3)

constant, intrinsic See *constant, central.*

constellation In psychiatry a *constellation* is made up of groups of allied thoughts, centering around a nuclear idea. Jung says: 'The nuclear element has a constellating power corresponding to its energic value. From this power there follows a specific constellation of the psychic contents; and thus is developed the complex, which is a constellation of psychic contents dynamically conditioned by the energic value.' (Jung, C.G. *Contributions to Analytical Psychology,* tr. by Baynes, H.G. and C.F., Kegan Paul, Trench, Trubner, London, 1928)

constellation, emotional This expression is used as an 'astronomical metaphor' for the affective system formed by all the persons to whom the individual is strongly attached and by whom he is chiefly influenced. In the Freudian doctrine, the center of this constellation is, in a general sense, the mother or the father of the individual. Stekel speaks of 'infantile constellation' in reference to the hatred of the child toward the father. This, in fact, constitutes one of the manifestations of the Oedipus complex. (Stekel, W. *The Interpretation of Dreams,* Liveright, New York, 1943)

constellation, infantile See *constellation, emotional.*

consternatio (kon-ster-nä′tē-ō) (L. confusion, consternation) *Obs.* Night terrors in children.

constipation, neuropathic Déjérine and Gauckler use the word neuropathic in the sense of mental. They say that 'nearly all the nervous constipations' are due to what they call education, that is, through faulty 'psychic impressions.' It is the type of education by which some 'form a habit of having a movement by artificial means only, such as enemata, or inserting suppositories into the rectum, etc. In these cases artificial defecation is often practiced without the slightest preliminary attempt to have a normal passage.

'Certain individuals reach the point of no longer experiencing the slightest need of defecation. It is an absent idea.' (Déjérine, J. and Gauckler, E. *The Psy-*

choneuroses and Their Treatment by Psychotherapy, 2nd ed., tr. by Jelliffe, S.E., Lippincott, Philadelphia and London, 1915)

constitution Few expressions in contemporary medical literature are applied with so little unanimity and exactness as is the term *constitution.* Its identification with the phenotype, body build, or genotype of an individual is almost as common as its usage—with or without the epithet 'hereditary'—for denoting the general biological make-up or the particular genetic structure of an organism. Many authors still use the term 'constitutional' in connection with diseases which are caused 'internally' or affect, as do gout or diabetes, the whole organism. Another school describes the constitution in terms of the different types of physique and seeks in them the primary etiologic basis of variations in clinical pathology.

This inaccuracy in terminology and conception is understandable when one considers that the knowledge of constitution is almost as old as medicine itself, and that all definitions of constitution incorporate the special ideas of both the time and the branch of medicine in which they have been formulated. From Hippocrates to the present there have been systems of constitutional types and diseases, which changed in content and could be more finely subdivided when further knowledge was added. Up to the nineteenth century, all diseases not localized in the pathology of a single organ were constitutional. When the knowledge of pathogenesis advanced, the number of these so-called 'constitutional' diseases was correspondingly reduced.

Following the discovery of the physiological and chemical cell processes in the bacteriological era, constitutional research was almost forgotten and had to retreat to the classification of different physical types. Although these studies were to some extent successful, especially in psychiatry and under the influence of Kretschmer's systematic work, there were many disappointments in other fields of medicine so long as the study of constitution was confined to purely anthropological investigation of the individual and the concept of constitution was not founded on accurate genetic principles. The classification of constitutional disease groups as clinical entities was bound to remain useless, because there is no disease which is purely constitutional, and there is no constitutional system which is alone the pathogenetic basis for a specific pathology.

According to the principles of modern physiological genetics the furthest one can go is to distinguish between predominantly hereditary and predominantly peristatic diseases (see *peristasis*). Consequently, the concepts of heredity and constitution have become practically inseparable, although it is clear that the constitution is not to be identified with either the genotypical structure or the phenotypical make-up of a person. While the phenotype is the *changeable* picture of the manifest appearance of an organism and is always modified by its external life-situation, constitution represents a *relatively constant* state of the person and classifies this person according to his biological values. It is therefore best understood as an auxiliary concept of medical classification and general pathology.

Consequently, as constitution is only a part of the person, although an important one, and is always bound to the person, one may say that there is about the same relationship between a person and his constitution as between the United States and its Constitution. A nation's life and activities are governed by its Constitution, but the Constitution is not the State.

With reference to this fundamental conception of modern human genetics the following definition of constitution may be preferred as at the same time precise and comprehensive:

'Constitution is the relatively constant physiological composition and biological make-up of the human organism by which its resistances are governed.'

More complex definitions are found in different schools of constitutional medicine. Draper defines constitution as 'that aggregate of herediterial characters, influenced more or less by environment, which determine the individual's reaction, successful or unsuccessful, to the stress of environment.' (Draper, G. *Disease and the Man*, Macmillan, New York, 1930)

Pende conceives of the constitution as 'the morphological, physiological and psychological resultant (variable in each individual) of the properties of all the cellular and humoral elements of the body, and of the combination of these in a special cellular state having a balance and functional output of its own, a given capacity for adaption and a mode of reaction to its environmental stimuli.' This resultant is believed to be 'determined primarily by the laws of heredity and secondarily by the disturbing influences exercised by the environment upon the individual's hereditary plan of organization.' (Pende, N. *Constitutional Inadequacies*, tr. by Naccarati, S., Lea & Febiger, Philadelphia, 1928)

The concept of Kretschmer who defined constitution as 'the totality of all individual peculiarities which are referable to heredity, i.e., which have a genetic basis' seems oversimplified to an extent similar to that of Johannsen, who described it as 'the totality of all the morphological, functional and evolutionary elements of an organism which are inherited or inheritable.'

In interpreting the physical and mental resistance of an individual in the dynamic terms of the capacity of producing *compensatory reactions* to pathogenic influences, Lewis conceives of the constitution as 'the expression of the integration of formative elements comprising the inherited organic units, cosmic elements, subhuman living environment, psychological influences, including those more or less rigid patterns determined by tradition, social ideas, moulding childhood experiences, and the influence of contact-persons in the human environment.' (Lewis, N.D.C. *Constitutional Factors in Dementia Praecox*, Monograph No. 35 of the Nervous & Mental Disease Publishing Company, New York, 1923) As this synthetic conception seeks to unite the morphological, physiological, and psychological aspects of the individual, it certainly constitutes a promising working hypothesis for approaching the field of constitutional medicine from all possible angles.

constitutional In modern medicine it has become necessary to define the term *constitutional* in accordance with the principles of physiological genetics and to relate its meaning exclusively to those elements in the biological make-up of an individual organism which are inherent in its given constitution, that is, in the relatively constant physiological composition and biological make-up of the human organism by which its resistances are governed.

If the concept of *constitution* is thus to have its own precise meaning which neither coincides with the genotype or the phenotype of an individual nor disagrees with the other definitions of the biological structure and development of a human being, as they appear in the light of modern physiological genetics, it is based on the distinction of three different factors determining the final nature of an individual; namely, the inherited elements which make up the *genotype* and are again transmissible, the *peristatic* conditions of the environment, and the *dispositional response* of the individual organism. A change in any of these factors is bound to modify the phenotypical appearance of the organism, although the genotypical structure is of primary importance to the prospective biological development in that it expresses the actual equipment of the individual as a classified member of a particular species or group, and demarcates the limits and qualities of all future reactions of the given organism to its individual life situation.

The modifications of these reactive abilities depend on the dispositional determinants as well as on the degree of the individually developed physical and mental resistance which finds its expression in constitution and character. What the *character* is in the province of mental development, the *constitution* is in the physical field. Together they make up what finally appears as the individual personality and as a biological entity, although this unit always consists of two characteristic components which are determined in themselves by the given hereditary elements of the individual, as they become the subjects of various modifications through exposure to special life situations.

constitutional mania See *disposition, constitutional mania.*

constitutional type See *type, constitutional.*

constitution, carcinomatous (kär-si-nom′-à-tus, nō′mà-tus) Introduced by Beneke, this term denotes a constitutional type believed to be predisposed to carcinoma by a particular physique, practically identical with the *neoplastic diathesis.*

constitution, emotional A term that defines one of the etiologic theories of conversion hysteria. In the opinion of Déjérine, who advances this theory, 'an emotional constitution is marked by functional over-

reaction to emotional stimuli in an organ or a group of organs, the mental representation of the function being dissociated from the field of consciousness.' (Strecker, E.A. *Fundamentals of Psychiatry*, Lippincott, New York, 1942; 4th ed. 1947)

constitution, epileptic psychopathic E. Bleuler (*Textbook of Psychiatry*, Macmillan, New York, 1930) says: 'Specific psychic peculiarities are connected with epilepsy, which as a rule increase with the duration of the disease. According to the degree, one speaks of an epileptic character, epileptic psychopathic constitution, and, in severe cases, of epileptic dementia.' See *epilepsy; personality, epileptic.*

constitution, hydropic (hī-drop′ik) This constitutional anomaly is a form of *exudative diathesis* in children, which is characterized by thermic unbalance, instability of body weight, a tendency to edema and the accumulation of water and salt in the tissues, and a marked instability of the combining property of water in the tissues themselves. These features are often supplemented by the development of certain nervous disorders, especially in the sphere of the vegetative nervous system.

constitution, hyperadrenal (hī-per-ad-rē′nal) This term denotes a type associated with oversecretion of the adrenal gland (medullary portion?). The type's physical characteristics are an apoplectic habitus with muscular overdevelopment and hypertonia, marked muscular strength, hypertonic peripheral arteries with a blood pressure above the average, hypertrichosis, hyperglycemia, and hypercholesterinemia. The psychological features are said to be characterized by euphoria and great moral and intellectual energy.

'In the female there is general tonic adiposity with wealth of hair of masculine type and premature sexual development with a tendency to dissociation of sexual characteristics and to a masculine character, which when present to a marked degree constitutes the condition of *precocious matronism.*' (Pende, N. *Constitutional Inadequacies*, tr. by Naccarati, S., Lea & Febiger, Philadelphia, 1928)

constitution, hyperpituitary (-pi-tū′i-ter-ē) This term denotes a type characterized by oversecretion of the pituitary gland occurring after or toward the end of the period of normal growth, as compared with such oversecretion occurring earlier in life and producing *gigantism.*

The general constitutional aspects of this *hyperpituitary* type correspond to Kretschmer's *athletic* type with *dysplastic* features and mainly consist of strong long bones, massive face, hands, and feet, thick oily skin, scanty scalp with seborrhea, large external genitalia, a tendency to tachycardia, hypertension, and arteriosclerosis, increased basal metabolism, and a restless mental attitude with reason prevailing over passion.

constitution, hyperthymic (-thī′mik) In the system of constitutional types described by Pende and Berman, this term denotes a type associated with overdevelopment of the thymus gland and its persistence into adulthood.

In infancy, this constitutional type is represented by the angelic type, with pretty and well-proportioned features, transparent skin, silky hair, delicate body proportions, exceptional grace of motion and an alert mind. These children seem to be models of beauty, but they are unfit for the struggle with life and fall easy victims to tuberculosis, meningitis, and other infections.

After puberty, all hyperthymic constitutions are distinguished by a strong tendency to inversion of physical and mental sex characteristics, hypoplastic hearts and arteries, insufficient muscular strength, and a tendency to sudden circulatory unbalance which often leads to sudden death or a rupture of the hypoplastic arteries. While the *male* hyperthymic is characterized by elegant feminine body outlines, long thorax, rounded pelvis, soft skin and milky color, the *female* type shows delicate skin and nails, little hair, deficient mammary development, delayed menstruation and, in some cases, a certain persistent adiposity and juvenility.

On the psychic side, there is a certain moral irresponsibility, with definite tendencies to homosexuality or masochism, impulsiveness, incapability for adaptation to the difficulties of social life, and a tendency to crime and suicide.

constitution, hyperthyroid (-thī′roid) This constitutional type is associated with excessive secretion of the thyroid gland and is said to be characterized by youthfulness, well-developed sexual characteristics, well-formed nails and teeth, large brilliant and sometimes rather prominent eyes, hyperpigmentation of the skin, slightly enlarged thyroid, swiftness of all functional reactions, marked irritability of the sympathetic nervous system, and general hyperemotivity and instability. The physical and psychological aspects of this type correspond to those of the *asthenic.*

constitution, hypoadrenal (hī-pō-ad-rē′- nal) The constitutional type associated with a deficient secretion of the adrenal gland (medullary portion?) and described by Pende as characterized by a hypoplastic trunk, slender bones, habitual leanness, marked developmental deficiency of both skeletal and smooth muscles, an accentuated universal lymphatism with or without hyperplasia of the thymus, marked arterial hypotention, lymphocytosis, and a hypotrophic skin with increased pigmentation, especially on the exposed parts of the body, and often an abundance of pigmented moles. 'Psychologically there is a tendency to melancholia, while the intelligence is normal or supernormal.' (Pende, N. *Constitutional Inadequacies,* tr. by Naccarati, S., Lea & Febiger, Philadelphia, 1928)

constitution, hypopancreatic (-pan krē-a′- tik) See *constitution, hypoparathyroid.*

constitution, hypoparathyroid (-par-à- thī′roid) This constitutional type is distinguished by deficient secretion of the parathyroid glands and is said by Pende to be characterized by hyperkinesis and hyperreflexia of the striated as well as the smooth muscles, sensory hyperexcitability, fragility of the incisors, a tendency to rickets in infancy, and anomalies of the calcium metabolism. There is also a frequent association of this type with the *hypopancreatic* constitution, which results from a diminished tolerance for carbohydrates and constitutes a transition to true diabetes.

constitution, hypopituitary (-pi-tū′i-ter-ē) In the system of constitutional types described by Pende this term refers to a type associated with deficient secretion of the pituitary gland. The general constitutional aspects of this type correspond to the *hypoplastic* group in Kretschmer's system, although age and sex considerably modify them.

The *infant* type is characterized: (a) in *both sexes,* by defective stature and growth, increased adiposity, small head short bones, irregular dentition, thin lips, poorly spaced eyes with scanty eyebrows, small hands, and circular mouth; (b) in the *male,* by small external genitals and, sometimes, by cryptorchism; and (c) in the *female,* by a feminine appearance even in early childhood.

The *adult* (adolescent) type is characterized: (a) in the *male,* by delicate facial features, smooth bony contours, silky hair, large pelvis, feminine distribution of fat and pubic hair, hairless trunk and extremities, small hands, and defective sex activity; (b) in the *female,* by small breasts, frigidity, and the tendency to sterility and masculinism; and (c) in *both sexes,* by muscular asthenia, vagotonia, low blood pressure, slow pulse, increased carbohydrate tolerance, polyuria, and general mental torpor.

constitution, hypothyroid (-thī'roid) In constitutional medicine, this term refers to a type with a deficient secretion of the thyroid gland. While the body build of this type generally corresponds to that of a *pyknic* or *megalosplanchnic* individual, its further characteristics mainly consist of generalized adiposity with special fatty deposits on face and neck, large head, thick neck, short and stubby hands, small and expressionless eyes, short and thick nose, round face with poorly marked features, poor pigmentation of the skin, premature baldness, dystrophic teeth and nails, torpid vasomotor reactions, normal sex development, acrocyanosis, habitual hypoglycemia with great carbohydrate tolerance, diminished basal metabolism, and a torpid and apathetic mental attitude.

constitution, paranoid (par'a-noid) See *character, paranoiac.*

constitution, personality Psychiatrists generally use the expression *personality constitution* when they refer to the organization of the personality as it exists prior to the development of a psychiatric condition. Several forms of personality constitution have been described, among which may be mentioned the schizoid (schizothymic), cycloid (cyclothymic), epileptoid, and hysteroid.

From the standpoint of Jung there are two general reaction types, the introverted and the extraverted, each of which is subdivided into four functional types, namely, thinking, feeling, sensation, and intuition.

Psychoanalysts describe types of personality in terms of their relationship with the major influences of infantile components. Among the personality or character forms, according to psychoanalysis, are the anal, oral, and genital characters.

constitution, post-traumatic The clinical syndromes, subsumed under this heading, vary from individual to individual; the symptomatology is often a mixture of both neurotic and psychotic phenomena. Friedmann's complex is one of the most common syndromes; it is said to be due to cerebral vasomotor disturbance and is characterized by headache, dizziness, insomnia, easy fatigue, irritability, and other character changes.

In 1904 Adolf Meyer described five types:

'a: Types with mere facilitation of reaction to alcohol, grippe, etc.

b: Types with vaso-motor neurosis.

c: Types with explosive diathesis.

d: Types with hysteroid or epileptoid episodes with or without convulsions (such as most reflex-psychoses).

e: Types of paranoiac development.' (Meyer, A. *American Journal of Insanity* LX, 439, 1904)

constitution, psychic It is generally agreed among psychiatrists that the psyche has its own special laws of growth and development, analogous to those of physical structures. The psyche has its own embryology, microscopic and gross anatomy, physiology, and pathology.

Jung lays great stress upon the collective unconscious. He says that 'man is born with a complicated psychic precondition, that is anything but a *tabula rasa.* Even the boldest phantasies fall within limits determined by psychic inheritance, and through the veil of even the wildest phantasy there shimmer those dominants which have been inherent in the human psyche from the very beginning.' (Jung, C.G. *Contributions to Analytical Psychology,* tr. by Baynes, H.G. and C.F., Kegan Paul, Trench, Trubner, London, 1928) The fundamental elements are the inherited 'roots of the mind.' To Jung there are also such subdivisions of the unconscious mind as the *anima, animus,* the *personal unconscious,* etc. Likewise consciousness has its special structures and functions. There is, for example, the *persona* and the *ego.*

Freud likewise emphasizes phylogenetic psychic elements. He believes that ontogeny epitomizes phylogeny in the mental sphere, just as definitely as it does in the physical. The unconscious of the infant contains the *id* and its many elements. Later it also contains the *superego* and forgotten memories. The principal structure of the conscious is the Ego and that subdivision of it called the *ego-ideal.*

The structures of the psyche have their more or less well-defined functions. When psychiatrists use the expression *constitutional* they generally refer to the original structure and function laid down in the individual as distinguished from acquired modifications.

constitution, psychopathic (sī-kō-path′ik) This expression denotes 'many anomalies of character which because normal or usual to the individual cannot be said to properly constitute a psychosis, but because they lead to a rather inefficient type of adjustment of the individual to his environment, and because persons exhibiting these peculiarities often become actively disordered, may be considered as borderland conditions.' (White, W.A. *Outlines of Psychiatry,* 12th ed., Nervous & Mental Disease Publishing Company, Washington, D.C., 1929)

Included in the group of such borderland conditions are cranks, ill-balanced, eccentric individuals, pathological liars, swindlers, those who manifest what is called *psychopathic depression* and *psychopathic elation,* etc.

constitution, sexual In psychoanalysis, this refers to the hereditary tendencies that account for the various erogenous zones being charged with different amounts of cathexis or different degrees of ability for discharge. Little is known about such constitutional factors.

constitution, traumatic A mental and nervous disorder following head injuries, which is characterized by such symptoms as headache, fatigability, irritability, emotional instability, and sometimes severe and serious dispositional changes. This condition is included, by most authors, among the *traumatic psychoses* (q.v.). (Strecker, E.A. *Fundamentals of Psychiatry,* Lippincott, 1942; 4th ed. 1947)

constraint of movement See *constraint of thought.*

constraint of thought This phrase is used by Kraepelin to describe the idea, expressed especially by patients with schizo-

phrenia, that the patients' thoughts are under the influence of other people.

'They never tire of describing this constraint of theirs in ever varying ways. The patient's *thoughts are influenced,* inspired, pressed on him; he must receive them like a telephone; they are forced on him by hypnotism and suggestion, act on him "by suggestion."' (Kraepelin, E. *Dementia Praecox and Paraphrenia,* tr. by Barclay, R.M., Livingstone, Edinburgh, 1919)

When the same idea of constraint prevails as regards the patient's movements, one speaks of *constraint of movement.*

It is to be noted that psychiatric usage differentiates between constraint and *constriction* (q.v.).

constriction When applied to thinking or movement, this term implies a reduction in range or variability. Constriction is associated with diminished spontaneity. It is to be noted that psychiatric usage differentiates between constriction and *constraint* (q.v.).

constructive Jung says that 'this concept is used by me in an equivalent sense to *synthetic,* almost in fact as an illustration of the latter concept. Constructive means "building up." I employ "constructive" and "synthetic" in describing a method that is opposed to the reductive. The constructive method is concerned with the elaboration of unconscious products (dreams, phantasies, etc.). It takes the unconscious product as a basis or starting point, as a *symbolical* expression, which, stretching on ahead, as it were, represents a coming phase of psychological development.' (Jung, C.G. *Psychological Types,* tr. by Baynes, H.G., Harcourt, Brace, New York and London, 1923)

contamination In a psychiatric sense the term *contamination* refers to an error of speech characterized by amalgamating a part of one word with that of another (Freud). Bleuler gives as an example the neologism 'gruesor,' derived from gruesome and sorrowful. Apparently the result of contamination is a neologism. Freud states that contamination is the first step in the process of condensation.

In Rorschach interpretation, contamination is a pathological response, pathognomonic of schizophrenia, characterized by the following: 'First, the patient is unaware of what he is doing; second, the resulting response is perceptually unintelligible; third, at least two different percepts overlap so that the same area is covered by different percepts simultaneously; and fourth, the patient is unable to disjoin the condensed percepts at will and with clarity.' (Piotrowski, Z.A., *Perceptanalysis,* Macmillan, New York, 1957.)

contemplatio (kôn-tem-plä′tē-ō) Ecstasy.

content, dream See *dream-content.*

contentious Some patients, particularly those with a manic syndrome and those in the early stages of a paranoid reaction, feel that they and others are being treated unfairly; they see slights when none is present or intended, as a result of which they incessantly quarrel about discriminations.

'The fighting maniacs stand between those who feel in the right and forever appeal to the law, on the one hand, and the paranoid litigants, on the other.' (Bleuler, E. *Textbook of Psychiatry,* tr. by Brill, A.A., Macmillan, New York, 1930)

content, latent This concept, particularly emphasized and developed by Freud, refers to the consideration that the bulk of psychiatric phenomena is made up of symbolic expressions. Phobias, compulsive-obsessive symptoms, delusions, hallucinations, conversion symptoms, dreams, etc., in themselves, do not reveal the nature of the disorder. They constitute what is called the *manifest content.* The real meaning of the symptoms or symbols is concealed, that is, latent. Thus, a patient must always perform an act a certain number of times; if he does not obey the compulsion something dreadful will happen to someone. That is the manifest content. Analysis reveals that the repetition compulsion is associated with his mother and that she is the one who will suffer death, if he does not repeat the compulsion. The underlying components constitute the latent content.

content, manifest See *content, latent.*

content, perception This is a psychoanalytic expression. Freud says that in early infancy consciousness is 'only a sense-organ for perceptions,' but with further development it 'becomes also a sense-organ for a part of our thought-processes. There are now, as it were, two sensory surfaces, one turned toward perception and the other toward the preconscious thought-processes.' (Freud, S. *The Inter-*

pretation of Dreams, 3rd ed., tr. by Brill, A.A., Macmillan, 1933) The elements of perception constitute a perception-content. For example, dream-content is usually perception-content.

continuity, social Social continuity 'implies the existence of a body of tradition which is transmitted from the older to the younger generations.' (Park, R.E. and Burgess, E. W. *Iintroduction to the Science of Sociology,* University of Chicago Press, Chicago, 1931)

'This concept is used to indicate that existing culture forms are outgrowths or modifications of antecedent forms.' (Willey, M. 'Continuity, Social,' *Encyclopaedia of the Social Sciences,* vol. 4, Macmillan, New York, 1931, p. 315) The chief agencies of social continuity are the family, the play group, the church, the school, and all other instrumentalities of communication.

contraception The act of interfering with the female's natural capacity, or process, of conception.

contraceptive Aiming at or producing contraception; preventing conception or impregnation.

contraction, habit See *tic.*

contracture, hysterical Contraction of a muscle or muscle group due to a hysterical condition.

contrary sexual An invert.

contrasexual Jacobi's term for the 'repressed side' in Jung's theory of analytical psychology. Jung maintains that there is a male and a female side to everyone, the side which is not dominant being repressed; i.e. in the male the female side is repressed and vice versa. 'The second stage of the individuation process [self-realization through Jungian analysis] is characterized by the meeting with the figure of the *"soul-image,"* named by Jung the *anima* in the man, the *animus* in the woman. The archetypal figure of the soul-image stands for the respective contrasexual portion of the psyche, showing partly how our personal relation thereto is constituted, partly the precipitate of all human experience pertaining to the opposite sex. In other words, it is the image of the other sex that we carry in us, both as individuals and as representatives of a species. "Jeder Mann trägt seine Eva in sich" (Every man carries his

Eve in himself), affirms a popular saying. According to psychic law . . . everything latent, unexperienced, undifferentiated in the psyche, everything that lies in the unconscious and therefore the man's "Eve" and the woman's "Adam" as well, is always projected. In consequence one experiences the elements of the opposite sex that are present in one's own psyche no otherwise than, for example, one experiences his shadow—*in the other person.* One chooses another, one binds one's self to another, who represents the qualities of one's own soul.

'The soul-image is a "more or less firmly constituted functional complex, and the inability to distinguish one's self from it leads to such phenomena as those of the moody man, dominated by feminine drives, ruled by his emotions, or of the rationalizing, animus-obsessed woman who always knows better and reacts in a masculine way, not instinctively." (Wolff, T. *Einführung in die Grundlagen der Komplexen Psychologie,* p. 112) 'One has then the impression that another, a strange person, has "taken possession" of the individual, "a different spirit has got into him," etc., as proverbial speech so profoundly expresses it. Or we see the man who blindly falls victim to a certain type of woman—how often one sees precisely highly cultivated intellectuals abandon themselves helplessly to hussies because their feminine, emotional side is wholly undifferentiated!—or the woman who, apparently incomprehensibly, falls for an adventurer or swindler and cannot get loose from him. The character of our soul-image, the anima or animus of our dreams, is the natural measure of our internal psychological situation. It deserves very special consideration in the way of self-knowledge.' (Jacobi, J. *The Psychology of C.G. Jung,* Kegan Paul, Trench, Trubner, London, 1942)

contrectation Tumescence or the swelling of the penis; erection. Moll uses the term also in a more general sense, namely, as the 'instinct to approach, touch, and kiss another person, usually of the opposite sex,' i.e. the acts of pleasure, such as handling, that lead to genital excitation.

control In clinical psychiatry, control usually refers to conscious limitation of impulses, wishes, tendencies, etc., that is, to suppression of instincts and affects.

In experimental psychiatry, control re-

fers to regulation of all known variables in the experimental situation except the variable which is under investigation. This is an attempt to insure that whatever effects are produced will be a function of the experimental variable and not due to extraneous factors. In assessing the value of a particular drug in the treatment of depression, for instance, a 'control group' may be formed of patients matched in age, clinical condition, and treatment conditions to the 'experimental group,' the only difference being that the control group does not receive the drug while the experimental group does. In such an experiment, a *placebo* (q.v.) may be used in place of the drug under investigation to mimic more closely all the extraneous factors which may influence the response of the experimental group to the experimental drug.

control, birth See *birth-control.*

control, co-twin A method used in biogenetics in which one member of an identical twinship is trained, treated, etc. while the other is not.

control, social The influence upon the behavior of a person exerted by other persons, particularly as members of a social group or of a society. 'In its wider sense the term social control describes any influence exerted by society upon the individual.' (Everett, H. 'Control, Social,' *Encyclopaedia of the Social Sciences,* vol. 4, Macmillan, New York, 1931 p. 344)

Spontaneous forms of social control arising in the mutual responsiveness of members of the group are to be seen 'in the crowd, in ceremony, prestige, and taboo; its more explicit expression, in gossip, rumor, news and public opinion; its more formal organization, in law, dogma, and in religious and political institutions.' (Park, R.E. and Burgess, E.W. *Introduction to the Science of Sociology,* University of Chicago Press, Chicago, 1921)

The formal control of society over its members exemplified by law and by institutions derives its effectiveness in large part from their conformity to the folkways, the mores, and public opinion.

contusion, brain A diffuse disturbance of the brain, secondary to head trauma, with edema and multiple intracerebral hemorrhages, most commonly at the poles of the hemispheres. Typically, cerebrospinal fluid pressure is raised and this plays an important part in the production of symptoms (coma, stupor, drowsiness, or confusion). A late result of the edema of the brain may be localized, severe demyelination. Although a patient may recover rapidly and completely from cerebral contusion, persistent disabling symptoms are extremely common. The three cardinal late symptoms are headache, dizziness, and mental disturbances (typically, a mild dementia, with inability to concentrate, memory impairment, and anxiety).

conventions, social 'Conventions are rules or standards of conduct or behavior prescribing what is to be done or not to be done by the members of a given group or community. . . . They are generally held to be less binding and authoritative than moral precepts and legal rules and are often criticized in the light of moral ideals.' (Ginsberg, M., 'Conventions, Social,' *Encyclopaedia of the Social Sciences,* vol. 4, Macmillan, New York, 1931, pp. 351–2)

convergence See *accommodation.*

conversion The term, taken from psychoanalysis, means in psychiatry the symbolic representation of a psychical conflict in terms of motor or sensory manifestations. The symbolization is the means by which repressed instinctual tendencies gain external expression; usually, as for instance in hysteria, the symbolization also contains the defense set up against the instinctual impulses.

Psychoanalysts have studied conversion particularly in patients with hysteria. They are patients whose sexuality is usually of the so-called infantile type, meaning among other things an incomplete resolution of the Oedipus complex. The female hysterical patient cannot emancipate herself, her instinctual impulses, from early parental inclinations, especially with reference to genitality. Unconsciously she longs to possess her father; unconsciously also there is much aversion to the possession. When the conflict becomes too acute and vigorous, it finally breaks through the repressing forces of the psyche, but it does not enter consciousness directly. That would be too intolerable and painful to the ego. The conflicting elements achieve external expression by appearing as motor or sensory symptoms. A woman complained of a right-sided paralysis, identical with a real paralysis shown by her mother.

She had always wanted to be like her mother, for it would put her in the same relation with her father that her mother was in. The primary wish was to have the father. As a consequence of her psychically induced paralysis, she not only possessed him, but she also suffered, because of the psychic fulfillment of the impulse.

Ferenczi says that the hysterical individual with conversion symptoms 'represents by means of motor and sensory symptoms both the desires that are unable to become conscious as well as the defense set up against them.' (Ferenczi, S. *Further Contributions to the Theory and Technique of Psycho-Analysis,* tr. by Suttie, J., Leonard and Virginia Woolf and The Institute of Psychoanalysis, London, 1926) It is believed that conversion represents the autoplastic fixation, in the sense that no effort is made by the individual to adapt himself to reality by modification of the external world; rather the adaptation is attempted through modification of his own body.

Conversion phenomena are particularly common also in other diagnostic groups. Indeed, there is perhaps no psychiatric disorder in which they may not appear.

In their most extensive and complete manifestation, conversion phenomena are common in schizophrenia. The schizophrenic individual may 'translate' almost all of his psychic material in terms of physical functioning. He may and often does completely forsake reality as it exists, incorporating into his physique the whole of reality as he conceives it. He becomes the cosmos.

Hypochondriasis is a form of psychic conversion. Certain individuals possess a unique knack of shifting mental conflicts to organic areas.

The conflict in conversion hysteria is said to be genital, stemming from the stage 'when complete primacy of the genital zone had already been reached.' Conversion hysteria genitalizes those parts of the body at which the symptoms are manifested. But a conversion phenomenon may reflect from any one of the psychic levels.

conversion hysteria See *conversion; hysteria.*

conversion-reaction See *conversion; hysteria.*

convulsion An involuntary, violent muscular contraction.

convulsion, clonic Convulsion characterized by alternate contraction and relaxation of muscular tissue.

convulsion, hysterical Convulsion-like seizures in hysteria.

convulsion, static This expression sometimes refers to special forms of motor aurae of epilepsy. The phenomena may consist, for example, of backward, forward, or rotatory movements.

convulsion, tonic Sustained contraction of a muscle.

co-operation Co-operation in human society 'may be defined as a form of interaction of two or more persons directed toward some goal, the result of whose common action, mutual helpfulness, will benefit them.' (Young, K. *An Introductory Sociology,* American Book Company, New York, 1934)

Two chief forms of co-operation should be distinguished: *economic* co-operation, in which individuals act together to obtain the advantages of combined effort, and *societal* co-operation, which results from mutual identification and social solidarity. In addition there is 'competitive co-operation in which the incidental results of activity unintentionally react to the benefit of others.' (Reuter, E.B. and Hart, C.W. *Introduction to Sociology,* McGraw-Hill, New York, 1933)

co-operation, antagonistic Alexander uses this term to describe the organizational nature of our present-day society. He says that in our free and competitive society we are at one and the same time both friends and rivals: we live in an 'antagonistic co-operation' with our fellowmen. This life pattern can lead to fears and hostility, frustrations and thwarted hopes, exaggerated ambitions and discouragement, all of which can cause disturbed human relations and can lead to mental and nervous symptoms. (Alexander, F., and French, T.M. *Studies in Psychosomatic Medicine,* Ronald Press, New York, 1948)

copro- (kop'rō-) Combining form meaning feces, filth, from Gr. *kópros,* dung, ordure, filth.

coprolagnia (-lag'ni-à) Sexual pleasure from handling feces. See *anal erotism; anal sadism.*

coprolalia (-lāl'i-à) Literally, fecal speech; hence, the involuntary utterance of vulgar or obscene words, seen in some schizophrenics who play with words as though they were feces. See *coprophrasia.*

coprophagy (kop-rof'à-jē) The ingestion of feces.

coprophemia (kop-rō-fē'mi-à) Obscene speech. E. Jones speaks of the curious perversion of coprophemia in which 'the sexual act consists solely of uttering indecent words to women.' (*International Journal of Psychoanalysis I,* 258, 1920)

coprophilia (-fil'i-à) Inordinate attention given to rectal excreta. This is given special psychodynamic consideration in psychoanalysis. According to psychoanalysis, anal erotism possesses two chief aspects, the first concerned with the retention and expulsion of fecal material, and the second with pleasure in the product itself. During the stage of sphincter-training the aim is twofold—to perform regularly and not to soil. The discipline associated with so-called anal training is later carried over in the form of character traits, while a certain quantum of libido remains fixed in its original form. A third possibility exists, namely, that the interest in the product is later transferred to other objects which to the individual bear fecal resemblance, although he may not be consciously aware of the resemblance. Thus Ferenczi traces the development from feces through its various forms of symbolizations, namely, mud pies, sand, pebbles, marbles, buttons, jewels, coins, currency, securities, etc. Hence, ownership of valuables is traced chiefly, but not exclusively, to early anal interests; that is, it is a coprophilic interest.

Many patients literally exhibit coprophilia. A patient hoarded his feces as earlier he had hoarded his money. Another patient 'decorated' himself, as he put it, with feces. A third said she loved her feces 'as if it were her child.' A fourth could experience sexual potency only when thinking of feces.

Coprophilic interests may be sublimated in such forms as painting, sculpturing, cooking, and the like.

coprophobia (-fō'bi-à) Fear of rectal excreta, a not uncommon symptom in the compulsive-obsessive form of psychoneurosis. Usually, however, it is not expressed literally, but as fear of dirt or of contamination (e.g. fear of an infectious disease). A patient expressed it by dreading to touch anything lest he acquire an ailment. The symptom is regarded by psychoanalysts as a form of defense against its opposite, namely, coprophilia. It is called a reaction-formation or a reversal-formation and represents the antithesis of the unconscious impulse. It is a derivative of the anal stage of libidinal development.

coprophrasia (-frä'zhi-à) Bianchi says: 'If the interjection is an obscene or offensive word, as when the patient in talking with the friend who has come to visit him hisses in his face the word *"merde"* (feces) or *"cochon"* (pig) (cases of Charcot and others), or another word very frequent in the low speech of certain Southern countries, the automatism is stronger, and it goes under the name of *coprolalia*, or, better, *coprophrasia*.' (Bianchi, L. *A Text-Book of Psychiatry*, tr. by MacDonald, J.H. Baillière, Tindall & Cox, London, 1906)

copulatio analis (kô-poo-lä'tē-ō à-nä'lis) (L. 'anal coitus') Pederasty.

copulation See *coitus*.

Cornell, William Mason (1802–95) American psychiatrist; mental hygiene.

corpora quadrigemina (kor'por-a kwa-dri-gem'in-à) Four raised eminences, arranged in pairs, on the dorsal surface (tectum) of the midbrain. The two superior colliculi and the two inferior colliculi make up the four corpora. The superior colliculi are optic reflex centers and receive fibers from the lateral geniculate body via the superior quadrigeminal brachium. The more prominent inferior colliculi are associated with the auditory system and are the termination of the lateral lemniscus. The inferior colliculi project to the medial geniculate body via the inferior quadrigeminal brachium.

corpus callosum (kor'poos ka-lō'soom) A broad, white fiber-tract which connects the cerebral hemispheres and forms the roof of the lateral and 3rd ventricles. Most of its fibers arise in various parts of one hemisphere and terminate in the symmetrical area of the opposite hemisphere.

corpus striatum (kor'poos strē-ä'toom) See *basal ganglia*.

corrective emotional experience See *experience, corrective emotional*.

correlation Mutual relation. (A) Tendency to concomitant change in two variables. (1) If the change, whether positive or negative, in one is accompanied by a like (i.e. in the same direction) change in the other variable, the correlation is positive with a maximum coefficient of $+1$. (2) If an increase in one corresponds to a decrease in the other (or, vice versa, a decrease in one corresponds to an increase in the other) the correlation is negative, with a maximum coefficient -1. (3) If there is no change in the second variable, the correlation is 0.

Example. Correlation between weight and length of male infants at birth $= +$ 0.644. Correlation between respiration rate and height $= -0.144$. Correlation between oral temperature and height $= 0$.

Information taken from Pearl, Raymond, *Medical Biometry and Statistics*, 1st ed., Saunders, Philadelphia, 1923, p. 310.

(B) The principle of correlation is frequently useful as evidence of heredity when other signs fail. It indicates 'a connection between two properties of the individuals of a population such that, as one of the properties varies, the other tends to vary.' (Shull, A.F. *Heredity*, 3rd ed., McGraw-Hill, New York and London, 1938) If as one property increases the other tends to increase, the correlation is *positive*. If as the one property increases the other tends to decrease, the correlation is *negative*. Positive correlations mean that the two qualities have part of their physiological bases in common, and the physiological bases are frequently genetic.

The most commonly used measure of correlation is Pearson's coefficient of correlation, while the best method describing an individual in terms of the degree to which he possesses the factors that vary *independently* of one another is constituted by the analysis of a person according to 'independent variables' as devised by Spearman, Cohen, and others (see *type*).

With factors which are related, the change which takes place in one factor for a unit change in the other can be computed; this statistic is known as the 'regression coefficient.' Computation of this latter allows the value of one factor to be estimated when the value of the other factor is known. Even when the correlation is very high, however, the error of this estimate may be large.

To be noted in any consideration of correlation is the fact that evidence of association is not necessarily evidence of causation, and the possible influence of other factors common to the ones for which correlation is discovered must always be remembered in interpreting correlation coefficients.

correlative Pertaining to the values of a reciprocal relation between biological phenomena as indicated by the method of correlation.

cortex, cerebral (kor'teks, ser'e-bral) The most anterior portion of the telencephalon; the cerebral cortex is made up of the two cerebral hemispheres, each of which is subdivided into the frontal lobe, parietal lobe, occipital lobe, temporal lobe, and insula. Strictly speaking, the rhinencephalon is not considered part of the cerebral cortex, although by implication the rhinencephalon is included where the term cerebral cortex (or cerebrum) is used.

For a more detailed description of function, see under the various divisions of the cortex—e.g. *lobe, frontal.* See also *isocortex.*

cortex, motor See *motor cortex.*

cortex, olfactory (ol-fak'tō-rē) See *rhinencephalon.*

cortex, visual See *lobe, occipital.*

corvus (kawr'voos) Fellator.

cosmic Relating to the universe.

cosmic identification See *identification, cosmic.*

cosmos Concepts relating to the cosmos assume great significance in psychiatry. Many psychiatric patients, notably those with schizophrenia, often give direct and vivid expression to the concept of identification with the universe. Thus, a hebephrenic patient says that he is the universe, that there is no distinction between him and the entire cosmos. The degree of cosmic identification may be complete. The patient may say he is all of nature.

'The thing aimed at by the [schizophrenic] patient in reconstructing his ego is mainly the attainment of greatness and likeness to God, in short, unity with the cosmos.' (Storch, A. *The Primitive Archaic Forms in Schizophrenia,* tr. by Willard, C., Nervous & Mental Disease Publishing Company, New York and Washington, 1924)

Cotard's syndrome (Jules Cotard, French neurologist, 1840–87) A psychotic state

characterized by anxious depression, suicidal tendencies, and ideas of negation. The patient feels he no longer has a body.

cotention Burrow's coinage for the type of attention concomitant to a specific distribution of internally perceptible tensional patterns. It marks the organism's total tensional reaction to environmental situations. In the cotentive reaction the organism's generalized tensional patterns are sensed as contrasted with the more definitely localized tensions characteristic of the symbolic segment. The reaction of cotention appears to be coterminous with the arrest or reduction of the eye-movements concomitant to habitual mental or symbolic attention. To this extent cotention precludes the usual play of wishful phantasies with their affects and strivings as well as the partitive reaction of competitiveness and concern unconsciously adhering to man's traditional social imagery. Contrasted with *attention,* in which a part-function of the organism focuses upon selective objects of the environment and is adapted to them through symbolic or projective processes. (Burrow, T. *The Structure of Insanity,* Kegan Paul, Trench, Trubner, London, 1932, p. 24; *The Biology of Human Conflict,* Macmillan, New York, 1937, p. 215)

co-therapy See *psychotherapy, multiple.*

co-twin control See *control, co-twin.*

cough, convulsive, of puberty This is a condition characterized by paroxysms of coughing, lasting about a minute, and due, it is believed, to mental causes, presumably hysteroid in character. A. Clark described a paroxysm as consisting in one patient 'of a succession of loud, dry, clanging, convulsive coughs, varying in intensity and duration, broken into irregular bars or phrases, and resembling at one time the barking, and at another the howling, of a dog.' (Tuke, D.H. *A Dictionary of Psychological Medicine,* vols. 1–2, Blakiston, Philadelphia, 1892)

counter-affect See *affect, inversion of.*

counter-cathexis (-ká-thek'sis) Anticathexis.

counter-compulsion A compulsion secondarily developed to fight the original compulsion, when the patient finds himself deprived of the means to continue the performance of such original compulsion. The patient supplants the original compulsion with the new one in order to continue his compulsive behavior. In the opinion of Stekel, 'every compulsion causes a counter-compulsion in the same way that every pressure causes a counter-pressure.' The compulsion to keep silent is in opposition to the compulsion to talk. (Stekel, W. *Compulsion and Doubt,* Liveright, New York, 1949)

counter-ego The unconscious part of the self which acts antagonistically toward the ego proper or consciousness. In Stekel's opinion, this mental mechanism may be compared to a chess game in which the players are, on one side, the ego proper (consciousness) and, on the other, the counter-ego (unconsciousness or quasi-personification of the id). This mechanism seems to be 'essential to the mental equilibrium, to the balance of the mind.' It constitutes a result of the law of mental bipolarity necessary in maintaining a proper distribution of mental energy. Such a distribution does not exist in the neurotic individual who is the victim of bipolar affective tension between the ego and its inner subconscious antagonistic part—the counter-ego (Stekel, W. *The Interpretation of Dreams,* Liveright, New York, 1943)

counter-formula A new formula often resorted to by a compulsive patient under certain (insurmountable) circumstances and constituting the *exact opposite* of his hitherto established *tenet.* A tenet characteristic of the compulsive patient might be: 'If I do not perform this action my father will die.' Very often, however, it is impossible to carry out the particular action. When such an impossibility is encountered, the patient goes through a series of compulsions and obsessions until he eventually finds a solution, by amending his formula in the following manner: 'My father will die if I *do* perform this action.' The final version is called the counter-formula. (Stekel, W. *Compulsion and Doubt,* Liveright, New York, 1949)

counter-identification A form of counter-transference in which the analyst identifies with the patient.

counter-impulse See *blocking, counter-impulse in.*

counter-investment When an intensely painful idea is repressed, the ego must constantly expend much energy in keeping the idea repressed. The complex struggles to

get back into consciousness. The ego may compromise by allowing the idea connected with the affect (but not the affect itself) to return to consciousness; in so doing, however, the idea must be joined with affect that is not painful, that is, there must be a counter-investment of the idea. For example, a patient, dreading that he would kill his father, repressed the affect and replaced it with that of love.

Counter-investment is synonymous with anticathexis.

counterphobia A term denoting actual preference for or seeking of the very situation which the phobic person is, or was, afraid of. Probably the basic component of the pleasure derived from the counterphobia is the gratification which the individual takes in the fact that indulging in the particular pleasure is now possible without anxiety. The counterphobic attitude is similar to the mechanism (seen normally in childhood and frequently in cases of traumatic neurosis) of striving to master excess anxiety through repeated coping with danger. Such repetition makes possible the transformation of passivity into activity; and it may also indicate libidinization of the anxiety or a flight into reality.

counter-transference Annie Reich (*International Journal of Psychoanalysis 32:* 1–7, 1951) defines counter-transference as the effects on his understanding or technique of the analyst's unconscious needs and conflicts. The patient's personality, or the material he produces, or the analytic situation as such represents an object from the analyst's past, onto which past feelings and wishes are projected. A broader definition would include not only situations in which the patient serves as a real object onto whom something is transferred, but also those where the patient serves merely as a tool to gratify some need of the analyst, such as alleviation of anxiety or mastery of guilt feelings. Counter-transference is a necessary part of psychoanalytic therapy, for it is within the framework of counter-transference that the analyst's unconscious perception and understanding of his patient's productions come about, typically by means of partial and short-lived identifications with the patient at which points the analyst gains insight and comprehension of the patient's previously incomprehensible and confusing productions. But the analyst must be able to give up this identification and swing back into his objective role, thus preserving the neutrality of his reactions to the patient's emotions which makes the patient's transference possible.

Ideally, the analyst's unconscious mechanisms will be sublimated successfully into the qualities necessary for the practice of psychoanalytic technique. If this has not occurred, however, there may appear various undesirable counter-transference manifestations. These may be acute, temporary, and short-lived, and such manifestations are often based on identification with the patient or on reactions to the specific content of the patient's productions. As an example of the former, Reich cites the case of the analyst who was in pain and taking analgesics. His patient began to make aggressive demands for attention which irked the analyst because he was himself in a situation which would justify similar demands, but he was forced to control himself. As an instance of reaction to specific content, Reich describes the analyst who became sleepy and found it hard to concentrate or remember when his patient produced material which he perceived as relating to the primal scene; in the therapeutic situation, he reacted with the same defenses which he had himself used as a child when exposed to the primal scene.

More serious, however, are long-lasting, frequently recurring, or even permanent manifestations of counter-transference; these are usually based on deeply ingrained personality disturbances. Thus passive masochistic wishes in the analyst may make it impossible for him to analyze resistances in the patient; instead, he accepts them at face value and lets the patient accuse and mistreat him. Or unconscious aggression may make the analyst overconciliatory, hesitant, and unable to be firm. Unconscious guilt feelings may lead to boredom or therapeutic overeagerness. A not uncommon type of counter-transference is based on a paranoid attitude in the analyst so that he unearths in the patient what he wants not to see in himself, even if such content exists in only a small degree in the patient. A need to show that he is unafraid of the unconscious and its manifestations may produce a compulsion in the analyst to understand the unconscious intellectually, but such isolation renders him unable to understand defense mechanisms. If the analyst doubts the veracity of unconscious expressions, he may be afraid to make any interpretations, or he may overcompensate by making too early and too deep interpretations whenever any small bit of unconscious material is recognized. When analysis represents mainly a source of narcissistic gratification for the analyst, he will see himself as a magic healer who restores potency and heals castrations; this will lead to therapeutic overambitiousness, overestimation of patients, and hostility toward patients who do not improve. A pedagogic attitude in the analyst results in reassurance therapy rather than analytic therapy, for in essence he is saying to the patient: 'You see, the world is not as bad as you think, and I do not mistreat you as you were mistreated in childhood.'

counter-volition Many people are familiar with the experience of having a dream in which they find themselves absolutely unable to carry out some act or other, however hard they may try. One wishes to shout, but no sound emerges; to run, but no movement results; and so on. In explanation of this interesting dream phenomenon Freud postulated the concept of counter-volition. According to this concept the sensation of inhibited movement which accompanies inability to perform some act in a dream is caused by a conflict between a will (to act) being opposed by a counter-will (not to act). It is to this mechanism that the expression, counter-volition, refers. In a larger sense, however, counter-volition is the mechanism by which Freud seeks to explain *all* instances of inability to do something in a dream and not just those that have to do with movement and the sensation of inhibition thereof. Inability to do a thing may appear simply as part of the dream content. For example, in a dream a young man may wish to visit his sweetheart, but is unable to find her house, although he had been there many times previously. Inability to do something is certainly present in this dream, yet any sensation of inhibited movement is absent.

Concerning this aspect of dreams, Freud writes: 'The inability to do something in the dream is the *expression of a contradiction*. . . .' and: 'In other dreams in which the inability to do something occurs, not merely as a situation, but also as a sensation, the same contradiction is more emphatically expressed by the sensation of inhibited movement, or a will to which a counterwill is opposed.' (Freud, S. *The Interpretation of Dreams,* 3rd ed., tr. by Brill, A.A., Macmillan, New York, 1933) Contradiction, then, would seem to be the essence of counter-volition. For whether by means of movement inhibition or by a purely situational element in the dream content, one volition stands contradicted by another and the objective of the contradicted volition *is not achieved.*

counterwill, hysterical An impulse or a wish, unconsciously determined, which expresses the opposite of a conscious wish.

'A child who is very ill at last falls asleep, and its mother tries her utmost to keep quiet and not to wake it; but just in consequence of this resolution (hysterical counterwill) she makes a clucking noise with her tongue.' (Freud, S. *Collected Papers,* vol. 1, tr. by Riviere, J., Leonard and Virginia Woolf and The Institute of Psychoanalysis, London, 1924–25)

counting, compulsive See *arithmomania.*

coupling The capacity of hereditary characters to remain associated in several generations, without regard to the Mendelian principle of independent assortment.

The tendency of genetic factors to stay together in inheritance was discovered in 1906 by Bateson and Punnett. Like the mechanism of *repulsion,* it results in the formation of an excess of the parental combinations of genes and a deficiency of the new type of combinations, and is now regarded as an instance of the important phenomenon called *linkage* (q.v.).

cousin marriage See *intermarriage.*

couvade (kōō-vàd′) Among many primitive races, it is a custom, after the birth of his child, for the father to take to his bed, as if he had actually given birth to the child.

'One of my female patients through an accidental observation, happened upon the theory of the "couvade," . . . [which] probably has the purpose of contradicting that doubt about paternity that is never quite to be overcome. After the birth of his child, a rather strange uncle of hers remained for days at home and received visitors in his nightshirt, so she concluded that both parents had a share in the birth and must go to bed.' (Freud, S. *Collected Papers,* vol. 2, tr. by Riviere, J., Leonard and Virginia Woolf and The Institute of Psychoanalysis, London, 1924–25)

cover-memory *Screen-memory* (q.v.).

cramp, memory S. Paton says: 'In conditions of fatigue or exhaustion patients frequently complain of the constant and annoying recurrence of certain tunes, melodies, phrases, verses of poetry, etc., which they have heard. The more aggravated forms, on account of their sudden startling appearance in consciousness, are in many ways analogous to muscular cramps. Certain authorities have spoken of them as "reproduction" or "memory cramps." Ribot has referred to them as characterized by a semi-tetanized attention. . . .' (Paton, S. *Psychiatry,* Lippincott, Philadelphia and London, 1905)

cramp, musician's An occupation neurosis, affecting instrumentalists and usually named according to the instrument played.

cramp, reproduction See *cramp, memory.*

cramp, seamstress's An occupation neurosis, similar to writer's cramp, occurring in needlewomen.

craniosynostosis (krā-nē-ō-sin-os-tō′sis) A congenital anomaly in which there is premature closure of the cranial sutures, resulting in oxycephaly (the most frequent form, due to closure of the coronal and lambdoid sutures), scaphocephaly (due to closure of the sagittal suture), or acrocephaly (due to closure of the coronal suture).

cratomania (krat-ō-mā′ni-à) *Obs.* 'The monomania of power, preeminence, and superiority.' (Tuke, D.H. *A Dictionary of Psychological Medicine,* vols. 1–2. Blakiston, Philadelphia, 1892)

craving, acquisitive-assimilative An expression used by Kempf. 'The autonomic-affective craving for food, which is a typical *acquisitive-assimilative* craving and the autonomic-affective craving to urinate, which is a typical *emissive-avertive* craving, indicate that probably all the *acquisitive* or *avertive* emotions or affective cravings and the most delicate sentiments, such as hunger, love, fear, anger, grief, sympathy, pity, joy, can probably be best understood as having a peripheral origin in characteristic variations of postural tension of autonomic or visceral segments. In its essential respects this is the James-Lange theory of the emotions.' (Kempf, E.J. *Psychopathology,* Mosby, St. Louis, 1921)

craving, autonomic-affective This is an expression peculiar to the psychopathology of Kempf. 'The postural tensions of the hollow viscera, although they vary in degree, are also continuously active, and this gives rise to a continuous, complex, converging affective stream from all parts of the autonomic musculature, *to which the organism as a unity is constantly, reciprocally adjusting itself*. Most of the time this afferent affective stream from a visceral or autonomic segment is subliminally active and does not cause the organism to adjust overtly *as a unity*, that is, to become conscious of the segment's activities. When, however, the tension of some viscus is increased, the sensory stream is felt in the form of a *craving*, that is, a more or less intermittent, persistent *itching* (which in the stomach causes a craving or wish for food, or in the bladder causes a craving or wish to urinate).' (Kempf, E.J. *Psychopathology*, Mosby, St. Louis, 1921)

craving, conditioned By this expression Kempf refers to the conditioning of the autonomic segments 'through an endless variety of experiences.'

craving, emissive-avertive See *craving, acquisitive-assimilative.*

craving, segmental From the point of view of Kempf's psychopathology, affective cravings arise through increased tensions of different segments of the autonomic apparatus. 'The term "segmental craving" ' means that the craving 'originates in some autonomic segment, i.e., some viscus or organ such as the stomach, bladder, throat, heart or genitalia. As *physiological segments* they include their nerve and circulation division. As excised *anatomical segments* or dead organs we do not usually consider the circulatory and innervating systems, but in psychopathology we must deal with organs as they function in life.' (Kempf, E.J. *Psychopathology*, Mosby, St. Louis, 1921)

creation, replacement While discussing hysteria Jones says that 'in the production of neurotic symptoms the displacement process plays a fundamental part, and it must be regarded as one of the most characteristic peculiarities of the malady. The symptoms are replacement-creations (*Ersatzbildungen*), which take the place in consciousness of the painful and repressed complexes.' (Jones, E. *Papers on Psycho-Analysis*, 4th ed., Wood, Baltimore, 1938)

creeps See *fidgets.*

cremnophobia (krem-nō-fō'bi-à) Fear of precipices.

cretinism Cretinism is classified by Tredgold as one of the forms of deprivative amentia. Cretinism, which may be sporadic or endemic, is associated with the absence or insufficiency of secretion of the thyroid gland. The signs and symptoms are mental and physical, usually appearing at about the sixth month of life; among the symptoms may be mentioned apathy, lethargy, protrusion of tongue, skin changes, thickening of features, prominence of abdomen, breathing difficulties (the 'leathery' cry), defective speech, difficulty in posture and gait, generalized underdevelopment, and intellectual impairment.

cretomania (krē-tō-mā'ni-à) *Obs.* The form of insanity sometimes associated with the cretinoid state. Mania with lust and satyriasis.' (Tuke, D.H. *A Dictionary of Psychological Medicine*, vols. 1–2, Blakiston, Philadelphia, 1892)

Crichton, A. (1763–1856) British psychiatrist.

crime 'Defined legally as a violation of law.' (Sutherland, E.H. *Principles of Criminology*, Lippincott, Chicago, 1939)

Crime involves three elements: 'A value which is appreciated by a group or a part of a group which is politically important; isolation or cultural conflict in another part of this group so its members do not appreciate the value or appreciate it less highly and consequently tend to endanger it; and a pugnacious resort to coercion decently applied by those who appreciate the value to those who disregard the value.' (ibid.)

'Crime within the group is essentially and primarily antisocial in that the criminal who is expected to contribute positively to the welfare of his group acts instead against it and breaks the principles of social solidarity not merely by not doing what these principles prescribe, but by doing something exactly opposite.' (Thomas, W.I. and Znaniecki, F. *The Polish Peasant in Europe and America*, Knopf, New York, 1927)

crime, and mental disorders From the standpoint of criminal hygiene the relationship between mental disorders and the commission of criminal offenses presents a problem of primary importance. This is indeed a problem of many complexities and conflicting aspects. On one side we have the rigid legal rules of our existing system of criminal justice, and on the other side the technical limitations of the science of criminal psychiatry when 'insanity' becomes the issue of an offense against law. In this respect the verdict 'medically insane, but legally sane' is highly demonstrative of the dilemma confronting us in this relationship of crime and mental disorders.

The importance of this problem becomes even more apparent through the mere mention of statistics which emphasize the role of mental disorders in criminal offenses. 'A survey made by the American Prison Association some years ago disclosed that of approximately 8,500 inmates then in six New York penal institutions 25.5% were definitely feeble-minded. Almost 20% of younger offenders sentenced to one of the principal reformatories in New York are mental defectives. In 1937 the psychiatrist at one of those institutions reported that 54% of the inmates are psychopaths; that while only 2% are actually psychotic, almost 18% were potentially psychotic.' We should remember 'that criminal behavior is but a symptom of an underlying disorganization in the economic, social and psychological background of the offender.' (Seliger, R.V., *et al. Contemporary Criminal Hygiene,* Oakridge Press, Baltimore, 1946)

crime, preventives of This term applies to any program set up to attack crime and delinquent behavior at their sources. A program of this nature needs the constant and comprehensive collaboration of psychiatrists, social workers, educators, lawmakers, and public officials, since crime is a social problem and it should be treated as such.

'Some crime preventives which should be mentioned are as follows: (1) The insurance that every child will be decently born and that his home life be socially and economically adequate; without socially mature parents the child is handicapped at the start; thus parental education, integrated with the public school system, should be developed now. (2) A more meaningful educational program which would emphasize ideals of citizenship, moral integrity, and respect for the law and the police. (3) A periodic check made for potential delinquents throughout the public schools and treatment provided

if possible; and if not, proper segregation in institutions. (4) Careful attention paid to press, movies, and radio so that crime may no longer appear to be glamorous. This can be done by women's clubs, civic bodies, and other educational groups exerting pressure on the movie syndicates and broadcasting companies to free their productions of the tawdry and lurid characteristics of crime and criminals.' (Seliger, R.V., *et al. Contemporary Criminal Hygiene,* Oakridge Press, Baltimore, 1946)

criminal, from sense of guilt This term is used in reference to an individual with an unconscious need for punishment stemming from repressed oedipal wishes; this unconscious need propels the individual into commission of a crime for which punishment is certain.

criminal intent See *intent, criminal.*

criminalism, compulsive-neurotic Frequent repetition of criminal acts in a compulsive manner. Like most symptoms of the compulsive-neurotic, such antisocial acts are closely related to feelings of hostility and aggression, often against the father. Because these acts are symptomatic, they afford only temporary relief and are therefore repeated. One patient with compulsive-neurotic criminalism was apprehended after breaking into a hardware store and stealing money. He later confessed to many similar incidents over the preceding two years. At the same time it was apparent that he stole only for the sake of stealing. He did not need the money he thus obtained and had no special plans for using it.

criminology, biological In criminology, an approach that is concerned with the criminal in relation to his body-build as a factor in the crime committed. (Abrahamsen, D. *Crime and the Human Mind,* Columbia University Press, New York, 1944)

criminology, psychiatric The branch of criminology dealing with the components of the criminal's personality that precipitate the perpetration of the crime: the criminal's experiences, inherited traits, and the causes of the crime as they pertain to his mind. (Abrahamsen, D. *Crime and the Human Mind,* Columbia University Press, New York, 1944)

criminology, sociological That branch of criminology, or the science of crime, which investigates all aspects of environment as causes of crime. (Abrahamsen, D. *Crime and the Human Mind*, Columbia University Press, New York, 1944)

criminosis (krim-i-nō′sis) 'The writer [A.N. Foxe] and others have for some years used the word criminotic to describe the individual who commits crimes, and the word *criminosis* to [describe?] the condition of such an individual.' (Branham, V.C., and Kutash, S.B. *Encyclopedia of Criminology*, Philosophical Library, New York, 1949) The word *criminosis* is patterned after neurosis and psychosis in form, but differs in that it does not specifically connote mental illness. The criminotic individual is not necessarily emotionally or mentally ill, but the term criminosis would imply such a condition.

In his work as a prison psychiatrist Foxe encountered the problem of how to classify the prisoners who show none of the customary symptoms of mental disease. As a solution he suggested classifying criminals according to criminal behavior. 'Just as the psychiatrist studies mental symptoms as evidences of mental disease, so he must study criminal manifestations as evidence of criminality or *criminosis*.' (Foxe, A.N. *Studies in Criminology*, Nervous and Mental Disease Monographs No. 76, New York, 1948)

criminotic See *criminosis*.

crisis, adolescent This term denotes the emotional changes that take place during the period of life known as adolescence: the psychological events during this period constitute a kind of crisis, the last battle fought by the individual before reaching maturity. The ego must achieve independence, the old emotional ties must be cast off and new attachments made. Biological development brings in its train great qualitative and quantitative changes, in both the physiologic and the psychologic fields, and as a result the adolescent ego is confronted with new difficulties. Because they are closely connected with instinctual life, the emotions are affected more than is any other part of the personality by the problems of growth and therefore represent a challenging problem for the adolescent. (Stekel, W. *Compulsion and Doubt*, Liveright, New York, 1949)

crisis, catathymic (ka-ta-thī′mik) Usually, an isolated, non-repetitive act of violence which, though occurring suddenly, devel-

ops from a background of intolerable tension.

crisis, hemoclastic (hē-mō-klas′tik) Reversal of the normal white blood cell and blood pressure response to the ingestion of protein. In the normal, ingestion of protein results in leukocytosis and rise of blood pressure. In contrast, 'hemoclastic' patients show a fall in blood pressure, leukopenia, altered differential white blood count, and a reduction in the refractive index of the blood. Hemoclastic crisis is said to be particularly frequent in schizophrenia, depression, and anxiety states, and to be correlated with a poorer prognosis than in patients with a normal response.

crisis, physiologic Bender's term for any sudden change, endogenously produced, which occurs in the course of apparently normal maturation and development. Physiologic crisis is always seen in the history of childhood schizophrenics and is often a precipitating factor in onset of psychosis. The physiologic crisis appears to depend upon embryonal plasticity and a maturational lag.

crisis, psycholeptic (sī-kō-lep′tik) The term psycholeptic crisis is used by Baynes in a sense that irrational unconscious elements try to erupt into the consciousness of the person. He analogizes breaking in of unconscious material with the psycholeptic outbreak, which is essentially the feeling of a catastrophe, namely, the end of the world. Epileptic patients often have ideas of impending destruction. There, too, the breaking of unconscious material into the consciousness is assumed to be responsible for this ideation. (Baynes, H.G. *Mythology of the Soul*, Williams and Wilkins, Baltimore, 1940)

crispation (kris-pā′shun) Slight spasmodic or convulsive muscle-contraction—the creeps. A synonym for *dysphoria* (q.v.).

critical flicker (fusion) frequency See *flicker*.

criticizing faculty See *faculty, criticizing*.

cross-association, telepathic A psychiatric term which describes a phenomenon that occurs when a thought or phantasy in one mind suddenly intersects a thought or phantasy articulated by another. It is assumed that such factors as coincidence, intuition, suggestion, or sympathetic identification of the one individual with the other are not at play for the phenomenon, which is labeled telepathic cross-association. Jule Eisenbud ('Telepathy and Problems of Psychoanalysis,' *Psychoanalytic Quarterly 15*, 61, 1946) gives the following example of telepathic cross-association occurring in the course of his analysis of a patient: 'I had just come from a conference on hypertension and coronary thrombosis. During an analytic hour I began to ponder the question of differential organic neurotic adaptations. Why hypertension or coronary spasm in some cases and convulsive seizures or migraine in others? All have the factor of repressed aggression. So has the obsessive and depressed middle-aged patient on the couch before me; yet he has no physical symptoms and no clinically demonstrable organic difficulty. How is it that with his lifelong neurotic conflicts he has still managed to escape organic injury? Perhaps he is the "silent" type who will one day get a sudden coronary attack. At this point my patient, who had been weeping and complaining about his unhappy lot, said, "Why don't I die? Why don't I simply get a heart attack and die? Others do."' This phantasy was completely new to the patient and intersected the analyst's thoughts in two respects: the patient mentioned a heart attack, and also the fact that others under similar circumstances do get coronary disease.

cross-dressing Transvestitism.

crossing over This term designates the genetic mechanism by which a chromosomal linkage group is broken up, so that some of the linked genes are able to separate and to enter different gametes and new *recombinations*. Since this interchange of genes between members of a pair of homologous chromosomes tends to involve large parts of chromosomes, that is, blocks of genes rather than single genes, mixed chromosomes, composed of both paternal and maternal gene units, originate either by *single* or *double* crossing over.

That crossing over occurs only between chromatids is due to the fact that it does not take place until after the chromosomes have each split into a pair of chromatids, early in prophase.

The new linkage groups are again as permanent as those that preceded them. It is clear, however, that a second crossing over not only undoes the genetic effect of a

single crossing over, but also prevents single crossings over from occurring in more than 50 per cent. If exactly 50 per cent of crossing over took place, the numerical result would be the same as if free assortment were operating.

If there is only little crossing over between two genes, the linkage is said to be *strong* or *close*. If there is much crossing over taking place, it is said that the linkage is *weak* or *loose* (see *linkage*).

crossover See *recombination*.

croup, hysterical A hysterical cough accompanied by a croupy sound and paroxysms of dyspnoea.

crowd A group of persons in a state of sympathetic responsiveness to each other and with their attention focused upon a particular object or objective which leads to their consequent collective action.

Four types of crowd have been differentiated: the *casual* or street crowd; the *conventionalized* as spectators at college football games; the *acting* as the lynching mob; and the *expressive,* or dancing crowd observed in the origin of religious sects. (Blumer, E.H., and Park, R.E. *Principles of Sociology,* Barnes & Noble, New York, 1939)

crowding, thought By this expression Bleuler denotes what may be called enforced thinking. 'In superficial contradistinction to obstruction, schizophrenics often feel a "crowding of thoughts"; they are forced to think.' Bleuler adds that it is to be distinguished from obsessive thinking in that 'in the former the obsession lies in the subject-matter, while in the latter it is in the process.' (Bleuler, E. *Textbook of Psychiatry,* tr. by Brill, A.A., Macmillan, New York, 1930)

cruciata, hemiplegia See *hemiplegia cruciata*.

crush A popular term, denoting an amorous interest of an adolescent girl for an older girl or woman, but particularly for a teacher (woman or man).

cry, epileptic (ep-i-lep'tik) A peculiar discordant cry or yell occasionally uttered at the beginning of an epileptic fit, just before respiration is arrested. It is believed to be due to the expulsion of air through the glottis, which is narrowed at the time of the tonic spasm. The epileptic cry is sometimes referred to as the *initial cry*.

cry, initial See *cry, epileptic*.

cryptesthesia (krip-tes-thē'si-à) A general term for clairvoyance, clairaudience, and other types of paranormal cognition in which the sensory stimulus is unknown.

cryptomnesia (krip-tom-nē'zhi-à) When a forgotten experience is recalled, but it appears to the subject that the experience is completely new to him, the condition is known as cryptomnesia.

crystallophobia (kris-tal-ō-fō'bi-à) Fear of glass.

Cs. Abbreviated form of *conscious*.

culmen (kul'men) See *cerebellum*.

culture 'The totality of the social heritages viewed as an organized body of achievement.' (Reuter, E.B. and Hart, C.W. *Introduction to Sociology*, McGraw-Hill, New York, 1933)

'Culture comprises inherited artifacts, goods, technical processes, ideas, habits and values. Social organization cannot be understood except as a part of culture.' (Malinowski, B. 'Culture,' *Encyclopaedia of the Social Sciences*, vol. 4, Macmillan, New York, 1931, p. 621)

The distinction is made between *material* culture, including tools, shelter, goods, technology; and *non-material* culture, as values, customs, institutions, and social organization.

cunnilinction (kun-i-lingk'shun) Apposition of the mouth to the female genitals. 'The majority of clitoris fetishists are adherents of cunnilinction.' (Hirschfeld, M. *Sexual Pathology*, tr. by Gibbs, J., Emerson Books, New York, 1939)

cunnilingus (-ling'gus) One who practices the apposition of the mouth to the vulva or to any part of the external female genitals. Contact is perhaps more frequently established with the clitoris. From the woman's standpoint the act is completed when she achieves an orgasm. The practice is not common among psychiatric patients, though the impulse is frequently symbolized by them; in other words, with them, it is a common source of conflict. The Roman epigrammatist Martial (38 or 41–102 A.D.) mentions this type of individual (12,59,10).

curdling *Rare*. A term, coined by Masselon, for emotional dementia; it refers to the fixation of affects upon infantile or early childhood experiences.

curiosity, infantile Curiosity concerning matters of a directly sexual nature, in-

dulged in by most children at one time or another, is referred to by psychoanalysts as infantile curiosity. The children exhibit a kind of foolish, witless behavior, and inept kind of funniness and silliness, the motivation for which, says Jones, is 'to simulate innocence and often extreme childishness, even "foolishness," in order to delude their elders into regarding them as being "too young to understand" or even into altogether disregarding their presence. The purpose of the artifice is that by these means children can view and overhear various private things which they are not supposed to. It need hardly be said that the curiosity thus indulged in is in most cases concerned with matters of a directly sexual nature; even marital embraces are in this way investigated by quite young children far oftener than is generally suspected or thought possible.' (Jones, E. *Hamlet and Oedipus*, Norton, New York, 1949.) See *pseudoimbecility*.

curve, Lange's colloidal gold See *Lange's colloidal gold reaction*.

Cushing's syndrome (Harvey William Cushing, American surgeon and neurologist, 1869–1939.) *Basophil adenoma* (q.v.).

custom 'The word custom is used to apply to the totality of behavior patterns which are carried by tradition and lodged in the group, as contrasted with the more random personal activities of the individual.' (Sapir, E. 'Custom,' *Encyclopaedia of the Social Sciences*, vol. 4, Macmillan, New York, 1931, p. 658)

The customs of society become the habits of its individual members. W.G. Sumner classified customs into the *folkways* (q.v.) and the *mores* (q.v.).

cutting, braid See *braid-cutting*.

CWF Cornell Word Form. See *test, Cornell Word Form*.

cybernetics (sī-ber-ne'tiks) The study of messages and communication in humans, social groups, machines, etc., especially in reference to regulation and control mechanisms such as feedback. The field of cybernetics is particularly associated with the name of Norbert Wiener, who hypothesizes a similarity between the human nervous system and electronic machines.

cycle, life See *life-cycle*.

cycle, manic-depressive See *psychosis, manic-depressive*.

cycloid In psychiatry the term refers to the type of personality characterized by alternating states of increased psychic and motor activity, usually with feelings of well-being, and of diminution of the same factors. The personality is said to alternate from the one to the other. *Cycloid* commonly describes the normal or usual personality of individuals who subsequently develop manic-depressive psychosis, although the development of the psychosis is not a necessary result of such a personality.

Cycloid and cyclothymia are regarded by many as synonymous, although the latter term generally refers to personality problems that are more than cycloid and less than manic-depressive reactions.

cyclothemia (sī-klō-thē'mi-à) An older form for *cyclothymia.*

cyclothymia (-thī'mi-à, -thim'i-à) Mild fluctuations of the manic-depressive type that almost have the stamp of normal mood shifts come under the heading of cyclothymia. There need not be fluctuations from psychomotor overactivity to underactivity. Some individuals possess a history only of periodic excitements, while others have one of periodic depressions.

The depressive phase may be clouded by the predominance of physical complaints, to which the term neurasthenia may be applied. 'Here is a group of cases who during their attacks regularly seek the specialist and are subjected to all sorts of gastro-intestinal treatment, gastric lavage, special dietaries, gynecological manipulations of one sort and another, metabolism experiments, endocrine therapy, eye-strain and almost everything in the category of medical specialism. . . .' (Jelliffe, S.E., and White, W.A. *Diseases of the Nervous System,* 6th ed., Lea & Febiger, Philadelphia, 1935)

Jelliffe and White include certain paranoid reactions under the heading of cyclothymia. 'Another group of these cases are the paranoid type. These patients present typical paranoid symptoms with emotional accompaniments that seem to be hardly in excess of what is demanded as normal reactions to the delusional state.' (ibid.)

cyclothymic personality See *personality pattern disturbance.*

cyclothymosis (-thī-mō'sis) A term suggested by Southard for manic-depressive reactions.

cynanthropy (sī-nan'thro-pē) This is a symptom in which the patient believes himself to be a dog; it is sometimes seen in the hebephrenic form of schizophrenia.

cynobex hebetis (kē'nō-beks hē'bē-tis) See *cough, convulsive, of puberty.*

cynophobia (sī-nō-fō'bi-à) Fear of a dog, or of rabies. Cynophobia, sometimes called pseudo-hydrophobia, is a morbid mental state, usually hysterical in character, sometimes precipitated by the bite of a dog. The symptoms vary in different individuals.

cynorexia (-rek'si-à) Dog's appetite. Bulimia.

cypridophobia (sip-ri-dō-fō'bi-à) Fear of contracting venereal disease.

cytheromania (si-ther-ō-mā'ni-à) Nymphomania.

cytoarchitecture Cell structure; used primarily in neurohistology. See *isocortex.*

cytoplasm (sī'tō-plaz'm) The biological term *cytoplasm* refers to the outer protoplasmic substance of a cell, exclusive of the nucleus. According to Sinnott and Dunn, its groundwork is a clear, viscous, colorless liquid which contains, in addition to various differentiated protoplasmic structures, numerous bodies of nonprotoplasmic and chiefly nutritive nature, such as oil globules and starch grains.

A system of cytoplasmic rays, the *aster,* usually surrounds in animal cells the *centrosome* or *central body* which takes a leading part in cell division. Almost all cells also embrace smaller granular bodies of mainly lipoid composition, the *mitochondria* or *chondriosomes,* which are suspected by some biologists of having a certain function in heredity, too. The *Golgi apparatus* or *Golgi material* occurs only in animal cells as a special series of platelike bodies (fibrils), while the *plastids,* oblong bodies with specialized functions, are found exclusively in certain cells of plants. (Sinnott, E.W. and Dunn, L.D. *Principles of Genetics,* 3rd ed., McGraw-Hill, New York and London, 1939)

cytoplasmic, cytoplasmatic (sī-tō-plaz'-mik, -mat'ik) Pertaining to cytoplasm. *Cytoplasmic* originally referred to all biological qualities of the cytoplasm, but is now predominantly used in connection with that particular mode of non-Mendelian inheritance which is supposed to be based on a system of *plasmons* or gene-like entities in the cytoplasm.

Although evidence for the existence of a plasmon has been derived from various sources, it seems safe to say that the problem of *cytoplasmic inheritance* is still far from a satisfactory solution. It is generally recognized now that the cytoplasm is very closely associated with the nucleus and constitutes the most immediate and intimate part of the environment in which the genes operate, thus playing an important role both in the origin of differentiation and the development of hereditary char-

acters. According to Sinnott and Dunn, however, the part played in hereditary transmission by the cytoplasm alone is 'a relatively minor one and clearly subsidiary to the dominant genic mechanism in the nucleus,' while the operation of independent cytoplasmic determiners for characters other than those which have— like the plastids—their physical basis in the cytoplasm itself, must still be regarded as an open question. (Sinnott, E.W. and Dunn, L.D. *Principles of Genetics,* 3rd ed., McGraw-Hill, New York and London, 1939)

D

d Rorschach scoring symbol for a popular detail response.

dacrygelosis (dak-ri-jē-lō′sis) *Obs.* Condition characterized by spells of alternate weeping and laughing.

daemonophobia (dē-mon-ō-fō′bi-à) A morbid fear of ghosts, spirits, devils, etc.

D.A.H. An abbreviation for disordered action of the heart; the syndrome is known as neurocirculatory asthenia or effort syndrome.

Daltonism Red-green color blindness.

dance, St. Vitus' See *Saint Vitus' dance.*

danger-situation The term has special significance in psychoanalysis. As Freud puts it: 'Every *danger-situation* corresponds to a certain period of life or phase of development of the psychic apparatus and seems justified for it.' (Freud, S. *Collected Papers,* vol. 1, tr. by Riviere, J., Leonard and Virginia Woolf and The Institute of Psychoanalysis, London, 1924–25) From the standpoint of 'anxiety fixations' Freud describes three principal danger situations: anxiety concerning the loss of love, castration anxiety, and social anxiety.

Strivings from the id are an intimate part of dangerous situations, for it is their blind demand for expression which makes external situations dangerous. The id never learns from experience. The ego must be incessantly on guard to see that the demands of reality are satisfied and also that the tensions of the id are released. When the ego becomes partial and unduly favors the one faction or the other, a danger-situation is likely to arise, for both are very forceful entities. In the event of a real struggle, the ego must lose much of its narcissism. The ego may have to withdraw from the dangerous situation by severe inhibitions or by symptoms. See *anxiety.*

DAP Draw-a-person. See *test, draw-a-person.*

dart and dome The spike and wave type of electroencephalographic tracing seen in petit mal epilepsy. See *epilepsy.*

Dauerschlaf (dow′er-shlaf) Prolonged sleep treatment with drugs (usually barbiturates), used mainly in status epilepticus, acute psychotic episodes, and drug addiction.

Darwin, Charles Robert (1809–82) The scientific work of this famous British naturalist has received so much acclaim for having placed the principle of the *evolution* of living forms on a firm biological basis, that his name and the *evolutionary theory* have practically become inseparable.

Darwin was born at Shrewsbury on February 12, 1809, and there he received his early education. After he had completed his studies at the Universities of Edinburgh and Cambridge, he spent five years in a surveying expedition on the ship *Beagle,* which took him to all corners of the earth. His later life was equally active and extremely productive. His contributions to comparative zoology alone would have been sufficient to make him rank as one of the first biologists of all time. Moreover, in his *The Expression of the Emotions* he made an outstanding contribution to psychology. He died on April 19, 1882, and was buried in Westminster Abbey.

Darwin's works with their assumption of Man's descent from lowlier animal forms —particularly his *Origin of Species,* published in 1859—were interpreted by literalist theologians and religionists, including Wilberforce and Gladstone, as contradicting the biblical doctrine of the special creation of Man. He thus became the subject of hostile attacks in which his doctrines were misrepresented and caricatured, although he had an able defender in T.H. Huxley.

However, even if he could not support all of his postulates, Darwin certainly was the first to succeed in establishing the truth of organic descent and to place great importance not only on the hereditary transmission of well-established characters from parents to progeny, but also on the development of certain new characters which the old-style naturalist had ignored. He proved the value of breeding experiments as a means of settling problems of ancestry, and in doing so he anticipated *genetics,* the study by which the ways of descent are discovered (see *evolution*).

Darwinism, Darwinianism Both terms relate to the branch of biology that deals with, or is in favor of, the doctrine of

Charles Darwin postulating the evolution of all forms of living organisms from a few forms of primitive life (see *evolution*).

Dasein (däs-īn') 'The One'; Heidegger's term for the field of Being which is existence. See *existentialism*.

day-dream In general a *day-dream* is defined as an idle indulgence of the fancy during the waking hours. It usually implies what is known as wishful thinking. Often, as in schizophrenia, day-dreams assume pre-eminence in the mind of the patient, in whom they take the place of action in the real environment. In schizophrenia day-dreams acquire the value of reality for the patient; that is, they become symptoms of the psychosis. When the latter takes place one no longer speaks of the phantasies as day-dreams, because reality has been abandoned for the unconscious strivings and their presentation in the form of symptoms.

Freud says that day-dreams hover in a curious medley of the past, present, and future. Some thought of the present creates a desire; the desire courses back to some earlier pleasant experience, which is lived out again in the mind with the idea of future fulfilment.

The driving force behind day-dreaming is regarded as an unsatisfied unconscious wish or striving. Day-dreams serve an appeasing function (Maeder), in that they give partial release to strong, unconscious affects. The process involved is in the nature of abreaction (Varendonck). Federn says that abnormal day-dreaming is analogous to sexual fore-pleasure in that neither represents the fulfillment of the final aim. See *phantasy-life*.

day-dreamer One who indulges in conscious phantasies. The latter are in the nature of day-dreams united with the environment in thought or action, or both. They have a realistic value about them, in that they represent undisguised wishes. When the wishes are disguised and appear as symptoms of a psychic illness, they are not regarded as day-dreams. When an individual, angered at another, phantasies that he is injuring him, the individual is expressing a day-dream. When, however, the would-be avenger has a compulsion to go through certain rituals lest he hurt someone, the ideas are symptoms rather than phantasies.

daymare A condition 'of great temporary mental terror or distress, arising without apparent cause, or from very slight causes in a person in a state of wakefulness.' (Tuke, D.H. *A Dictionary of Psychological Medicine*, vols. 1–2, Blakiston, Philadelphia, 1892)

day-residue See *regression, topographical.*

Dd Rorschach scoring symbol for an unusual detail response.

dd Rorschach scoring symbol for a very small detail response.

Dds Rorschach scoring symbol for a detail response to a small white space on the card.

DdW Rorschach scoring symbol for an unusual detail response which is elaborated in such a way that the whole is perceived in the form of the detail.

de Rorschach scoring symbol for edge detail.

deadly nightshade poisoning See *poisoning, deadly nightshade.*

deafness, hysterical Inability to hear appearing as a symptom in and of hysteria. Hysteria is a neurosis and is a consequence of a conflict in the unconscious part of the psyche. When the mental struggle, unacceptable to the conscious mind, gains expression by means of physical symptoms, the condition is known as *conversion hysteria* (q.v.). Thus, deafness appearing as the physical symptom through which an emotional conflict is gaining expression is called hysterical deafness. An emotional conflict has simply been converted into a physical symptom. The symptom has an entirely emotional causation, not an organic one.

deafness, word Auditory aphasia. See *aphasia, auditory.*

de-analize Instincts are said to be *de-analized* when they are shifted from the anal region to another object or form of expression. For example, interests in feces may later be expressed as interests in mud, still later in money, securities, etc. Part of the interests may be expressed as a character trait (e.g. cleanliness).

death Cessation of life, physical and mental; total and permanent cessation of the functions or vital actions of an organism. Among certain psychiatric patients the term 'death' does not imply cessation of life, save in the sense that the patient ceases to continue in the environment in which he lives. Death is regarded simply as a preliminary step to re-birth, without any essential alteration of the body or psyche. This concept is common in schizophrenia. The belief in the immortality of the body and psyche is genuine to the schizophrenic individual.

In other individuals (e.g. hysterical women) death may be dramatically enacted in connection with the thought of punishment for carrying out a forbidden impulse (e.g. incest). Both the death and the incest are symbolically represented. Death thus comes to mean punishment, but not 'death' punishment or punishment by death. It is intimately connected with sado-masochism, as though the patient said to herself: 'I may have incest, if I am punished for it.' The hysterical woman, while reproducing (without knowing it) the motions of sexual congress, at the same time believes she is dying.

Death is often used synonymously with 'reunion' as one of the components of the Oedipus complex. In this sense it also carries with it the thought of incest.

Another symbolic meaning of death occurs in depressive states, in which suicide unconsciously represents the means by which the death of another is accomplished. The mental mechanism is in effect not dissimilar to that observed in hara-kiri.

death-instinct See *instinct, death.*

death-phantasy See *phantasy, death.*

death-rate See *rate, death.*

death-trance A state of apparent death; so-called suspended animation; not uncommon among psychiatric patients, especially hysteria and catatonic schizophrenia.

death-trend. See *suicide.*

death-wish It has been suggested by psychoanalysts that there is an aggressive instinct which leads to the death of the individual or of others when expressed in original and unmodified form. Jones says: 'It is well established that suicide is the result of murder wishes that have been directed from the objects of them in the other world and have been turned inward against the self.' (Jones, E. *Papers on Psycho-Analysis,* 4th ed., Wood, Baltimore, 1938)

debilitas animi (dā-bē′lē-tàs à′nē-mē) (L.

'infirmity of the spirit') An older term for imbecility.

debilitas erethisica (er-e-thē′zē-kà) Morbid irritability.

debilitas memoriae (me-mô′rē-ī) (L. 'weakness of memory') Defect or weakness of memory.

debilitas nervosa (ner-vō′zà) (L. 'nervous debility') *Obs.* Neurasthenia.

debility Asthenia.

decadence The retrogression of a person, group, or society which results from social rather than from physical or biological change (see *degeneration*).

'The apparent decline of any social phenomenon for which observation or philosophy suggests a serial development: races, nations, institutions, religions, manners, techniques, arts.' (Todd, E. *Encyclopaedia of the Social Sciences,* vol. 5, Macmillan, New York, 1931, p. 39)

decades, involutional Roughly, the period from 40 to 60 years of age; in women, the involutional period is usually considered to include the years between 40 and 55, in men the years between 50 and 65.

decapitation, fear of An adolescent's castration anxiety dread (that his penis will be cut off) which in the psychoanalytic context assumes the form of a fear that he will be decapitated. Castration anxiety appears in boys at the age when a high concentration of pleasurable sensations from the penis begins to arise. This anxiety may take many forms depending on the history of the particular person, and one of these forms is a fear of decapitation. This might occur when a boy witnesses the slaughtering of a fowl involving its decapitation. His resultant fear of decapitation would represent a form of his castration anxiety. (Fenichel, O. *The Psychoanalytic Theory of Neurosis,* Norton, New York, 1945)

deception Simulation; malingering.

deception, reduplicative memory This is an expression used by Pick to denote a form of false memory sometimes observed in patients with an organic brain disease. The patient claims, for instance, that he has already been examined by the same doctor, in the same examining room, with the same nurse in attendance, although the entire situation is in fact new to him.

decerebrate rigidity See *rigidity, decerebrate.*

decidentia (dā-kē-den'tē-à) *Obs.* Epilepsy.

decompose In a psychiatric sense: *to divide* oneself or another into separate and distinct personalities.

decomposition In psychoanalysis the expression refers to the 'dividing up' of an individual into separate components, or, more correctly, personalities. It is often observed among patients with the paranoid form of schizophrenia that they decompose or split the persecutor into separate entities.

'If we take a survey of the delusions as a whole we see that the persecutor is divided into Flechsig and God; in just the same way Flechsig himself subsequently splits up into two personalities, the "upper" and the "middle" Flechsig and God into the "lower" and "upper" God. In the later stages of the illness the decomposition of Flechsig goes further still.' (Freud, S. *Collected Papers,* vol. 3, tr. by Strachey, A. and J., Leonard and Virginia Woolf and The Institute for Psychoanalysis, London, 1925)

Storch says: 'Most remarkable, however, is the division and multiplication of the personality unit into various separate persons which appear to her as strange, though, as she also distinctly feels, they represent her own thought complexes and aspirations.' The patient described by Storch had described herself as a child, a pastor, etc. She said: 'Once it seemed to me that I was divided into eight persons. I saw seven forms coming out of me, one after the other.' (Storch, A. *The Primitive Archaic Forms in Schizophrenia,* tr. by Willard, C., Nervous & Mental Disease Publishing Company, New York and Washington, 1924)

'Where the hysterical dissociation becomes so extreme as to eventuate in amnesia in one state for another the different systems of complexes are easily recognized as so many phases of *multiple personality.*' (Prince, M. *The Unconscious,* Macmillan, New York, 1916)

Decomposition and *dissociation* appear to be synonymous in the foregoing sense.

decomposition, in dreams The gradual dissolution of the whole structure (i.e. its manifest content) of the dream into its component parts (i.e. its latent content) by the process of free association.

decomposition of ego See *ego, decomposition of.*

decomposition of movement This condition, described by Babinski, is characterized by irregularity in the successive flexion or extension at the various joints, instead of steady, well-timed movements.

de-erotize To remove the 'love' or erotic instinct from an object or its psychic representation.

defecation Act of discharging excreta. From the psychodynamic point of view defecation or the act of passing excreta has received considerable attention in the field of psychoanalysis. It is the opinion of psychoanalysts that the infant derives much pleasure from contact with his own warm excretions. Some infants exhibit this interest to a marked degree; they show their pleasure also in handling the product.

Abraham calls attention to the association between defecation and ideas of omnipotence. He says that 'the child believes that through defecation he can create and destroy every object.' (Abraham, K. *Selected Papers,* tr. by Bryan, D. and Strachey, A., Leonard and Virginia Woolf and The Institute for Psychoanalysis, London, 1927)

Jones maintains that 'the act of defecation constitutes one of the two greatest personal interests of the infant during the first year of life. . . .' (Jones, E. *Papers on Psycho-Analysis,* 4th ed., Wood, Baltimore, 1938). See also *analerotism.*

defect, field See *field defect.*

defectio animi (dā-fek'tē-ō à'nē-mē) (L. 'deficiency of mind') Mental deficiency.

defective, mental One who is subnormal intellectually; feebleminded. In New York State a mentally defective individual is defined as 'any person afflicted with mental defectiveness from birth or from early age to such an extent that he is incapable of managing himself and his affairs, who for his own welfare or the welfare of others or of the community requires supervision, control or care and who is not insane or of unsound mind to such an extent as to require his commitment to an institution as provided by this chapter.' (*Handbook of the Department of Mental Hygiene, New York State,* State Hospitals Press, Utica, N.Y., 1939)

defemination See *eviration.*

defense, defence A mental attribute or mechanism or dynamism, which serves to protect the individual against danger arising from his impulses or affects. See *anxiety*.

The ego arises in response to the frustrations and demands of reality on the organism; it learns to follow the reality principle. But the id follows the pleasure principle only, so that often there are conflicts between the two. This is the essential neurotic conflict. The superego may take either side, and if the world and external reality appear to the ego to be sources of temptation, the conflict may appear to be between the world and the ego. The mechanisms of defense are developed as a means of controlling or holding in check the impulses or affects which might occasion such conflicts. The various motives for the development of defense-mechanisms are: (a) anxiety, arising when the ego believes the instinct is dangerous; (b) guilt, with anxiety of the ego toward the superego and fear of annihilation or decrease of narcissistic supplies; (c) disgust, when the ego must reject the impulse or it will have to be vomited out, and (d) shame, a fear of being looked at and despised if the impulse is not rejected.

Various defense-mechanisms have been described. Anna Freud (*The Ego and the Mechanisms of Defence,* Hogarth Press, London, 1948) lists the following: regression, repression, reaction-formation, isolation, undoing, projection, introjection, turning against the self, reversal, and sublimation or displacement of instinctual aims. O. Fenichel (*The Psychoanalytic Theory of Neurosis,* Norton, New York, 1945) includes: regression, repression, reaction formation, isolation, undoing, projection, introjection, sublimation, displacement, denial, postponement of affects, affect equivalents, and change in the quality of affects. Evidently both Anna Freud and Fenichel use introjection and identification interchangeably, although technically introjection is the mechanism by which *identification* (q.v.) is accomplished. L. E. Hinsie (*Visual Outline of Psychiatry,* Oxford University Press, New York, 1940) lists 16 mental mechanisms: repression, reaction-formation, isolation, undoing, projection, introjection, identification, sublimation, displacement, condensation, rationalization, transference, symbolization and transposi-

tion, conversion, phantasy, and day-dreaming.

defense, character In the early 1920's, many psychoanalysts had become pessimistic about the value of therapy. Wilhelm Reich (*Character Analysis,* 3rd ed., Orgone Institute Press, New York, 1949) undertook an evaluation of therapeutic failures and pointed out that many chaotic analyses are the result of failure to recognize a latent negative transference.

This negative transference is commonly hidden behind the character traits of the individual, which serve as a protective armor against stimuli from the outer world and against the individual's own libidinous strivings. In the course of the conflict between instinctual demands and the frustrating outer world, the character armor develops in the ego and becomes a chronic and habitual pattern of reaction to threatened or actual frustration from the outer world. Also, in psychoanalytic treatment the character armor serves as a compact defense-mechanism, and this character resistance or character defense must be overcome if the analysis is to proceed properly. The ego employs other mechanisms of defense, such as repression, regression, reaction formation, isolation, undoing, introjection, turning against the self, reversal, and sublimation. Although any or all of these mechanisms may be involved in the development of the character defense, they correspond essentially to a single experience, whereas the character represents a specific way of an individual's being and is an expression of his total past.

There are four main types of character defense: (1) hysterical; (2) compulsive; (3) phallic-narcissistic; and (4) masochistic.

(1) In the hysterical (which includes the passive-feminine) character, obvious sexual behavior is combined with a specific kind of bodily agility which has a definitely sexual nuance. Such behavior traits are combined with outspoken apprehensiveness, which is increased when the sexual behavior comes close to attaining its goal. The hysterical character represents an apprehensive defense against incest wishes inhibited by the anxiety related to any genital expression.

(2) The compulsive character has a pedantic concern for orderliness, a tendency to collect things, and thriftiness or

avarice. Thinking is circumstantial and ruminative in type. This character armor is a defense against sadistic and aggressive impulses.

(3) The phallic-narcissistic character appears self-confident and arrogant; behavior is either cold and reserved or derisively aggressive. Most forms of active homosexuality and of schizophrenia fall into this group. Phallic-narcissistic attitudes are a defense against passive-feminine tendencies and represent an unconscious tendency of revenge against the opposite sex. The character resistance is seen in aggressive deprecation of the analysis and a tendency to take over the interpretation work.

(4) The masochistic character shows chronic tendencies to self-damage and self-depreciation and subjectively has a chronic sensation of suffering. The masochistic self-punishment is a defense against punishment and anxiety in that it represents a milder substitute punishment. The masochistic character avoids anxiety by wanting to be loved, but the excessive demand for love is disguised in grandiose provocation of the love-object. The purpose of this is to make the provoked person react with behavior which will justify the reproach: 'See how badly you treat me.'

The classification above is in terms of the clinical picture. There is another classification which stresses the libido origin of character. In this system, the character attitudes are assumed to be reaction formations or sublimations of the libido of the stage in question. Thus: (1) The oral receptive character is considered a sublimation of the earliest sucking stage of life. Such people are characterized by friendliness, optimism, and generosity and expect the whole world to mother them. When frustrated they become pessimistic and act as if the bottom had fallen out of the world.

(2) The oral aggressive character represents a sublimation of the oral biting stage. Aggressiveness, envy, ambition, and a tendency to exploit others are typical features.

(3) The anal character corresponds to the compulsive character described as (2) in the other classification above.

(4) The phallic character has also been described.

(5) The urethral character has burning ambition and a need to boast of achieve-ment, and is impatient; there is often a history of bed-wetting beyond the usual age.

(6) The mature or genital character is no longer dominated by the pleasure principle, shows features characteristic of the preceding stages, but in a combination conducive to the greatest effectiveness. The mature character is able to care for and contribute to the welfare of another.

defense-mechanism The means by which the organism protects itself against impulses and affects. See *defense.*

defense-neuropsychosis See *psychosis, defense.*

defense-neurosis See *psychosis, defense.*

defense, pathogenic A defense against instinctual demands, pathogenic in its nature, because the opposed unconscious impulse cannot find discharge.

For many reasons, as the individual develops, he learns to 'ward off' his own impulses, his instinctual drives. First, as an infant he required external help to satisfy these demands and since this help was not always immediately at hand, the infant found himself in traumatic situations as a result of his instinctual excitations. Secondly, both education and nature's own prohibitions (such as being burned upon touching a flame) engender fear of instinctual acts. Education is effective not only because of the adult's physical power, but also because of the child's need of affection from the adult. Thirdly, the child thinks animistically and, accordingly, believes that his own instinctual demands are identical with those of his environment. Also, since the child feels that any of his acts might provoke the same response from the environment, he will fear fantastic dangers from the environment in connection with his own instinctual impulses. For example, on meeting a rebuff in his phantasies of devouring the environment, the child may phantasy that he might be eaten by the parents. These are some of the reasons for the development of forces opposing the discharge of instinctual impulses. These forces are known as ego-defenses. When successful, the ego-defenses are called sublimations. The instinctual drives find an adequate discharge in these sublimations. When unsuccessful, however, these defenses are called pathogenic. The opposed pregenital impulses do not find discharge but remain in the unconscious and in fact keep on gaining strength, because of the continued functioning of their physiological sources. These warded-off instincts continue to seek discharge. 'A state of tension results and a breakthrough may occur.' This breakthrough is the basis of neurotic symptoms which express simultaneously both a repressed drive and the defense against it. An unsuccessful defense is therefore pathogenic, in the sense that it is the basis for the subsequent neurotic symptoms, in which the drive, formerly opposed by the defense, has broken through and is expressed in the neurotic symptom.

The pathogenic defenses are mechanisms which consist of 'a partial cessation of certain functions of the ego.' Some examples of these pathogenic defenses are denial, projection, introjection, repression, reaction formation, undoing, isolation, and regression. In many of these defenses the ego's function of reality-testing has been conspicuously suspended and, in some of them, old archaic modes of thinking, perceiving, and relating to reality have been utilized again. (Fenichel, O. *The Psychoanalytic Theory of Neurosis,* Norton, New York, 1945)

defense-psychoneurosis See *psychoneurosis, defense.*

defense-psychosis See *psychosis, defense.*

defenses, Ur See *Ur-defenses.*

defense-symptom See *symptom, defense.*

defensive-reaction See *reaction, defensive.*

deficiency, mental Intellectual inadequacy, feeblemindedness, hypophrenia, oligophrenia, oligergasia. In the 1952 revision of psychiatric nomenclature, mental deficiency refers to intellectual defect existing since birth, without demonstrated organic brain disease or known prenatal cause. As thus used, mental deficiency refers to cases previously classified as familial or idiopathic mental deficiency. Intellectual defect secondary to other organic brain diseases is classified under the known brain syndrome; e.g. 'chronic brain syndrome associated with congenital spastic paraplegia, with mental deficiency.' See *amentia; dementia.*

In regard to degree of defect: 'In general, *mild* refers to functional (vocational) impairment, as would be expected with I.Q.'s of approximately 70 to 85; *moderate* is used for functional impair-

ment requiring special training and guidance, such as would be expected with I.Q.'s of about 50–70; *severe* refers to the functional impairment requiring custodial or complete protective care, as would be expected with I.Q.'s below 50. The degree of defect is estimated from other factors than merely psychological test scores, namely, consideration of cultural, physical and emotional determinants, as well as school, vocational and social effectiveness.' (*Diagnostic and Statistical Manual, Mental Disorders,* American Psychiatric Association, Washington, D.C., 1952)

The more conventional differentiation of degree of mental deficiency includes the following grades: (a) borderline, with I.Q. of 70–80; (b) moronity, with I.Q. of 50–69; (c) imbecility, with I.Q. of 25–49, and (d) idiocy, with I.Q. below 25.

deficiency, mental, psychosis with Occasionally, mental defectives or those suffering from feeblemindedness may show psychotic reactions which are usually of an acute transitory nature. These psychotic manifestations include episodes of excitement with depression, hallucinatory attacks, or paranoid trends.

deficiency, moral An early term for moral insanity. Most psychiatrists today prefer to use the term *psychopathic personality* (q.v.) for such cases. See *anethopathy.*

definition of the situation The concept of the definition of the situation stresses the point that the group and the person react not to the objective environment, but to the way in which the environment has been defined by the group and by the person.

'The don'ts of the mother, the gossip of the community, epithets ("liar," "thief"), shrugs, sneers, and "bawlings out," the press, the pulpit, legal decisions, etc., are common methods of defining the situation.' (Park, R.E. and Miller, H.A. *Old World Traits Transplanted,* Harper, New York, 1921)

The definitions of the situation and the meanings of objects to which the person reacts are 'those which these things have acquired long ago in society and which the individual is taught to understand during his whole education as a conscious member of a social group.' (Thomas, W.I. and Znaniecki, F. *The*

Polish Peasant in Europe and America, Knopf, New York, 1927)

defloration The act of perforating the hymen during the first coitus of a virgin. From the psychiatric point of view, such an event is, of course, extraordinarily important, inasmuch as it constitutes an experience which, in general, is of vital consequence in the development of a woman's personality. A careful study of all the details concerning this act supplies to psychoanalytic theory and practice valuable material in which the analyst may unearth the clue for elucidating many emotional conflicts seemingly unrelated to defloration, but in fact linked with and stemming from this experience.

In the interpretation of dreams, defloration and its symbolic representations often play a role of paramount importance.

deformation While in general medicine this term is identical with *disfigurement* or *want of harmony,* in the field of constitutional medicine it refers to De Giovanni's particular hypothesis, the *'law of deformation,'* which is basic to his concepts of constitutional types: that individuals having a small trunk tend to assume a *longilinear* body which corresponds to the *phthisic habitus* (q.v.). Analogously, individuals having a large trunk are thought to be inclined to assume a *short* body which corresponds to the *habitus apoplecticus* (q.v.), and individuals having a normal trunk are said to be inclined to maintain *normal* proportions of the body.

defusion In psychoanalysis this term means the separation or detachment of the instincts, so that they operate independently.

In normal instinctual development, the component instincts are organized in the genitals and the aggressive or death instincts are fused with the sexual. With regression, however, this unification and organization of part-instincts crumbles; the libido is desexualized and the destructive instincts are freed and often work directly against the sexual instincts. This is the process of defusion, which in severe form will lead to such prepotency of the destructive instincts that negation of life is the result.

degeneracy Fact of being or becoming a degenerate. From the standpoint of the psyche, degeneracy may be defined as the more or less permanent appearance (in the conscious layer of the mind) of impulses that are considered harmful to the culture of the environment in which the individual lives. The concept of degeneracy usually implies conduct of an anti-social character. Moreover, it generally, though not always, contains an overt sexual reference, such as rape, pederasty, bestiality, exhibitionism, etc. Or it may seem to be free from sex, as in sadism and masochism.

The term is not in common use among psychiatrists, perhaps because degeneracy constitutes but a very small fraction of formal psychiatric symptoms. Phenomena of degeneracy are usually associated with the so-called borderline cases, e.g. psychopathic personality (as a diagnosis), epileptic equivalent, the criminal, etc.

Degeneracy may be defined from the standpoint of the individual himself, without essential reference to his environment. The individual, living alone, who displays unnatural interests in body excretions, is considered a degenerate, depending upon the nature, extent, and quality of those interests.

degeneration Deterioration. In psychiatry the term refers to a reduction to a lower type of personal and social conduct. The reduction is defined from the standpoint of the existing moral and organic laws to which the individual is expected to conform. The common implication of the term, degeneration, is a sexual offense or an offense allied to sex, which the individual actually carries out or tries to carry out.

When an individual reverts to some earlier phase of his existence, for example, when an adult thinks, acts, and feels like a child, one speaks of regression. Among his many tendencies there may be much sexual material of a so-called 'degenerate' nature, but if he makes no effort to translate his thoughts into action, he is not described as a degenerate, but as a psychotic individual.

degeneration, hepatolenticular (he-pa-tol-en-tik'ū-lĕr) Wilson's disease; tetanoid chorea of Gowers; Westphal's pseudosclerosis; progressive lenticular degeneration. A hereditary disorder of copper metabolism characterized by degeneration of the corpus striatum (especially the putamen) and cirrhosis of the liver, with decreased serum ceruloplasm and increased urinary excretion of copper and amino acids. The disease begins early in life (10 to 25 years of age) and is progressive. The initial symptom is usually tremor, which is increased by voluntary movement. This is followed by rigidity, similar to that seen in Parkinsonism, and including a vacant, expressionless appearance or a vacuous smile. Involuntary laughing and crying may occur and also some degree of mental deterioration. In a certain number of cases, a zone of golden-brown granular pigmentation (the Kayser-Fleischer ring) can be seen in the cornea; some would distinguish these patients from those with Wilson's disease and term the syndrome Westphal-Strümpell's pseudosclerosis. Untreated cases are invariably fatal, half of them within six years from onset of symptoms; more recently, treatment with BAL (British anti-lewisite) to remove copper from the body has afforded some hope of at least temporary amelioration.

degeneration, subacute combined See *sclerosis, posterolateral.*

degeneration, Wallerian (Augustus Volney Waller, English physician, 1816–70) Myelin sheath degeneration of the axon distal to the point of severance from the cell body.

dégénérés supérieurs (dā-zhā-nā-rā' sü-pā-ryēr') (F. 'high-class degenerates') An expression coined by the French sociologist Magnan to denote that class of sexual perverts in whom the perversions serve as an inspiration for great achievements in some special field of endeavor—social, artistic, ethical, etc. A patient strongly sadistic to children built and maintained a home for unfortunate children.

degenitalize (dē-jen'i-tal-īz) To remove affects from the genital organs or any of direct methods of expression. Instincts once connected with the genital area or any of its forms of expression may be combined with activities that seemingly have no relationship with genitality. For example, the impulse to explore the genitals may be put into the service of research investigations into scientific subjects (e.g. astronomy, mathematics, etc.).

degradation, senile *Obs.* for *senile deterioration.*

dehumanization Making or becoming inhuman. D.H. Tuke defines this as 'the mental and physical degradation which takes place in many insane persons, especially in chronic maniacs and melancholiacs, by which they are brought, as it were, to the level of beasts.' (Tuke, D.H. *A Dictionary of Psychological Medicine,* vols. 1–2, Blakiston, Philadelphia, 1892)

dehypnotize (dē-hip'nō-tīz) To bring one out of the hypnotic state.

déjà entendu (de-zhà'äN-täN-dü') (F. 'already heard, perceived') The feeling, not demonstrable in fact, because it never was associated with reality, that one had at some prior time heard or perceived something, is called *déjà entendu.*

déjà eprouvé (ā-proo-vā') (F. 'already experienced, tested, tried out') Many patients, on the basis of the wish, have the distinct feeling that an act or experience, in which they had actually never engaged, had already been carried out by them. It is not an uncommon delusional phenomenon among psychotic patients.

déjà fait (de-zhà' fā') (F. 'already done') Pierre Marie's term for a type of paramnesia in which the patient believes that what is happening to him now has happened to him before. Thus one hebephrenic believed he had experienced exactly one year before everything that was happening to him at the time. 'The very same visitor in exactly the same clothes was here one year ago today and said the same things.' This sort of paramnesia is common in schizophrenia. It is not clearly distinguishable from memory falsifications based on identification. One patient, for example, believed that he had painted a certain masterpiece 600 years before.

déjà pensé (päN-sā') (F. 'already thought [of]') A patient's feeling, verging on certainty, that he has already thought of the matter. 'The *déjà vu* and *déjà pensé* phenomena that are a part of many psychomotor attacks . . . suggest that many of them are associated with disorders localized to the temporal lobes.' (DeJong, R.N. 'Phenurone in the Treatment of Psychomotor Attacks,' *American Journal of Psychiatry CVII,* No. 11, May 1951)

déjà raconté (rà-kawN-tā') (F. 'already told, recounted') Sometimes, when a forgotten experience, particularly one from the distant past, is recalled, the individual may feel as if he had known all the time that the experience had been told to him. The phenomenon is known as *déjà raconté.*

déjà voulu (voo-lü′) (F. 'already desired') Pierre Marie's term for a type of paramnesia in which the patient believes that his present desires are exactly the same as the desires he had some time before. See *déjà fait; déjà vu.*

déjà vu (vü′) (F. 'already seen') Feeling of familiarity. When an individual, upon perceiving something that he has never seen before, has the distinct feeling that he had had the experience some time in the past, the expression *déjà vu* is used. It is not uncommon among psychiatric patients, particularly those with hysteria and epilepsy. A patient, for example, while visiting a town for the first time in his life may feel certain that he has been there on some previous occasion. The reason for the feeling, Freud believes, is an association, unknown to the individual, with something in the unconscious. Ferenczi observed the phenomenon in a patient in whom the feeling of familiarity was traceable to a forgotten dream.

dejectio animi (dā-yek′tē-ō ä′nē-mē) (L. 'depression of spirit') Melancholia.

dejection Melancholy. The word dejection refers to the mood-tone change which is part of a clinical depression and is approximately equivalent to the word depression as used by the layman. In psychiatry, depression has a more specific meaning and should not be used when only a lowered mood tone is meant.

Déjérine (dā-zhē-rēn′), **Jules-Joseph** (1849–1917) French neurologist and psychiatrist.

de Jong, H. Holland (1895–1956) Dutch psychiatrist, in later years in U.S.; production of symptoms of mental illness in animals (especially catatonia).

delibidinization (dē-li-bi-di-ni-zā′shun) Technically, the act of removing libido from an object. In practice, this term is used to refer to an interpersonal relationship which is predicated on spiritual, objective, or non-emotional grounds. In certain Jewish forms of culture, for example, the father's authority rests primarily on his status as an exponent of the religious and scholarly tradition, rather than on the status of comforter, nurse, or donor of material or emotional comforts. 'Insofar as is possible to a living creature, a father's personality is delibidinized.' (Landes, R. and Zborowski, M. 'Hypotheses concerning the Eastern European Jewish Family,' *Psychiatry 13,* 447, 1950)

delinquency The term delinquency, which includes faults, misdeeds, and certain types of misbehavior, is applied (*technically* speaking) only to the offenses of young people under the age of sixteen or eighteen, and refers to all offenses committed by them. Heredity, family influences, environmental competition, idleness and monotony in the life of the child, emotional maladjustment, and psychosexual development are among the more important factors to be studied as causes of delinquency. Nevertheless, one may assert that, in gross personality disturbances, the delinquent does not differ markedly from the general run of the population, and although the delinquent suffers less from the neuroses and is not sharply inferior (in mental deficiency rates) in comparison with the corresponding classes of the population, he is, on the other hand, more often the victim of psychoses and psychopathic states.

Immaturity, egocentricity, and inability to establish emotional relationship with others are characteristics of the delinquent personality.

Immaturity: This involves the inability to deny oneself a present pleasure, even though its indulgence may carry with it an immediate penalty or may interfere with the attainment of future aims.

Egocentricity: The delinquent selfishly seeks personal pleasure, has little or no consideration for others, has no sense of guilt, and often believes that he is right and the rest of society is wrong.

Inability to establish emotional relationship with others: The delinquent is pressed by family, school (or class), and communal competition and, as he fails to reach standards that are quite beyond him, his inadequate behavior becomes delinquent to compensate for his inadequacy. He develops an antisocial attitude through his inability to make the necessary healthy identifications, or through actual and direct hostility to adverse surroundings.

Heredity: 'Figures most prominently in the causes of crime through the production of feeblemindedness and the lessening of emotional inhibition.'

Family influences: 'The unharmonious atmosphere of the home whose members are constantly fighting and where the children are made a buffer between quarreling parents who have "fallen out of love" is much more likely to result in delinquency than are parental separations and family breakups. The emotional relationships in the family are most important, particularly those based on the child's feeling of rejection or on the manifestation of overprotection by a parent. The child's need for affection and sense of security and of personal adequacy, which is ordinarily satisfied in the normal family, is not so met in the psychologically broken home, whose bickering and disharmony is anything but reassuring to the sensitive child mind. The situation is particularly serious, if the youngster is made to feel that he is not wanted.'

Environment: The life of children in a 'bad' neighborhood atmosphere is likely to be hostile to the normal development of the individual. 'There is not sufficient opportunity for social activities and wholesome outdoor play. Delinquent schools, of which there are some, as a rule are closely associated with delinquent communities. The rigid, theoretical curriculum of the public school makes it difficult for non-bookish, non-academic youngsters to get along well. The final blunder of society is its failure to provide school activities that will interest and intrigue these peculiar types of youths, who are likely to turn delinquent when frustrated, disappointed, and discouraged.'

Idleness and monotony: Long periods of idleness in the life of children, especially in the slum districts of large cities, may be considered a factor of importance as a crime breeder. 'Monotony is unbearable to adventurous youth. . . Many times juvenile crime is nothing more or less than an unconscious attempt to escape boredom.'

Psychosexual development: While more complete sex instruction 'has done much to lessen sex worries and anxiety, it has done but little, if anything, to improve sexual morals. There is just about as much of the sex element in juvenile delinquency today as a generation ago. It represents one of the major divisions of juvenile crime; in fact, among girls, it is the outstanding delinquency. . . Many times sex offenses are committed by young people for the same reason that they resort to the use of alcohol—to convince themselves and others that they have "grown up." These abnormal sex drives are also exhibited by "rippers" and "slashers,"

those boys who cut pieces of clothing from girls' dresses or snip off locks of their hair. Many times these sexual delinquents are intelligent youths, good students, and otherwise very well-behaved socially . . . undoubtedly many sexual delinquents are on the borderline of insanity. This will explain certain types of sex perversion, criminal sexual assaults, and chronic exhibitionism. This group of psychotic sex offenders will not be helped very much by ordinary methods of treatment.' (Sadler, W.S. *Modern Psychiatry,* Mosby, St. Louis, 1945; Seliger, R.V. *et al. Contemporary Criminal Hygiene,* Oakridge Press, Baltimore, 1946)

delinquency area See *area, delinquency.*

delinquent, defective In some states it is recognized that 'there are individuals who are not of sufficiently low mentality to be called legally irresponsible for their anti-social acts, or incapable of standing trial, but who are, nevertheless, of more or less subnormal mentality, and who require special institutional treatment.' (Weihofen, H. *Insanity as a Defense in Criminal Law,* Commonwealth Fund, Oxford University Press, New York, 1933) Such individuals are known as defective delinquents and the condition is known as defective delinquency.

'The Massachusetts law provides that in any case involving an offense not punishable by death or life imprisonment, if the court shall find that the defendant is mentally defective and has shown himself to be an habitual delinquent or shows tendencies towards becoming such, and that such delinquency is or may become a menace to the public and that he is not a proper subject for commitment as an insane or feebleminded person, the court may commit him as a defective delinquent.' (ibid.)

deliquium animi (dā-lē′kwē-oom á′nē-mē) Mental deficiency.

deliramentum (dā-lē-rà-men′toom) (L. 'nonsense, absurdity') *Obs.* Delirium.

deliration (del-i-rā′shun) *Obs.* Delirium.

deliratio senum (-rä′tē-ō se′noom) (L. 'dotage of the old') Senile psychosis.

délire (dā-lēr′) (F. 'delirium') An uncertain term, which sometimes refers to *delirium* (q.v.), at other times to *delusion* (q.v.) or to *compulsion* (q.v.). In general, the term could best be described as referring to a complex or system of ideas which forms a prominent part of the patient's mental condition.

délire aigu (ā-gü′) (F. 'acute delirium') French term for acute mania.

délire alcoolique (àl-kô′lēk′) (F. 'alcoholic delirium') Delirium tremens.

délire ambitieux (äN-bē-syẽ′) (F. 'highfalutin delirium') Maniacal excitement with grandiosity.

délire à quatre (à katr′) (F. 'quadruple insanity, foursome insanity') A psychiatric constellation, usually consisting of systematized delusions of persecution, involving four people. The delusions are found first in one person, and then are taken over, as in a contagious disease, by a second, third, and fourth person. See *association, psychosis of.*

délire chronique à évolution systématique (krô-nēk′ à ā-vô-lü-syawN′ sē-stā-mà-tēk′) (F. 'chronic delirium with organized development') See *paranoia completa.*

délire crapuleux (krà-pü-lẽ′) (F. 'dissolute delirium') Delirium tremens.

délire d'emblée (däN-blā′) (F. 'delirium at one blow') Bleuler says: 'Some delusions, especially in schizophrenia, suddenly appear in consciousness as finished products (délire d'emblée, primordial delusion).' (Bleuler, E. *Textbook of Psychiatry,* tr. by Brill, A.A., Macmillan, New York, 1930)

délire de négation (dẽ ne-gà-syawN′) (F. 'delirium of negation') See *negation.*

délire de négation généralisé (zhā-ne-rà-lē-zā′) (F. 'generalized delirium of negation') Church and Peterson write: 'Another interesting form of depressed delusion is that of negation (délire de négation généralisé), which has its origin usually from an idea of having sinned. The patient thinks he must be the devil himself, his sin is so great; consequently he can never die, so he must suffer forever; then with the growing idea of the enormity of his sin, he comes to believe that God and mankind and the world exist no more.' (Church, A. and Peterson, F. *Nervous and Mental Diseases,* 8th ed., Saunders, Philadelphia and London, 1916)

délire d'énormité (dā-nawr-mē-tā′) (F. 'mania of vastness') Bleuler says that in

délire d'énormité 'the patients may not use a chamber because they would flood the entire institution or the whole world; they are swollen up so big that they fill up the entire house and city, and choke everybody. . . . In a certain sense the opposite of this is *micromania* which also occurs only in organic depressions.' (Bleuler, E. *Textbook of Psychiatry,* tr. by Brill, A.A., Macmillan, New York, 1930)

délire depressif (dā-pres-ēf′) (F. 'depressive delirium') Melancholia.

délire des grandeurs (dā-gräN-dēr′) (F. 'mania of grandeurs') Monomania of grandeur.

délire des persécutions (dā per-sā-kü-syawN′) (F.) 'Insanity' of persecution.

délire du toucher (dü tōō-shā′) (F. 'mania for touching') A neurosis characterized by the compulsion to touch things.

délire ecmnésique (ek-mnā-zēk′) (F. 'ecmnesic delirium') See *ecmnesia.* By this expression Pitres denotes preoccupation with events which transpired years before. He describes the condition in conjunction with hysteria, pointing out that the patient in this state lives almost entirely in the past.

délire en partie double (äN pàr-tē′dōō′-bl′) (F. 'double-entry delirium') Induced 'insanity'; *folie à deux.* See *association, psychosis of.*

délire onirique (aw-nē-rēk′) (F. 'oneiric delirium') See *deliria oneirica.* Dreamlike delirium. 'There is reason to believe that obsessions are of prime importance in the evolution of certain forms of melancholia; mental confusion, the *délire onirique,* and in certain systematized deliria.' (Paton, S. *Psychiatry,* Lippincott, Philadelphia and London, 1905)

délire terminal See *hysteria.*

délire tremblant (träN-bläN′) (F. 'trembling delirium') Delirium tremens.

délire vésanique (ve-za-nēk′) (F. 'insane delirium') A general term for 'insanity'; see *vesania.*

deliria (dā-lē′rē-à) An older term, meaning 'insanity' in general.

deliria oneirica (ô-nā′rē-kà) Bianchi says: 'These deliria are constituted of scenes from dreams, changing, varied, and uninterrupted, the subject being as if he were in a somnambulic dream. These occur generally at night, but sometimes they continue after waking. On recovery the patient has no recollection of his delirium.' (Bianchi, L. *A Text-Book of Psychiatry*, tr. by MacDonald, J.H., Baillière, Tindall & Cox, London, 1906)

delirious reaction See *syndrome, organic.*

delirium (dē-lir′i-um) The term was formerly used in essentially the same sense that we now use the terms insanity, psychopathy, mental derangement, etc. Hence, among older psychiatrists, there were such expressions as senile delirium, alcoholic delirium, grandiose delirium (délire ambitieux), depressive delirium (melancholia), délire des persécutions (now called paranoid reaction), délire du toucher (now one of the psychoneuroses), etc.

Later the expression was used 'in a much more limited sense, being made to signify that temporary disturbance which occurs in connection with other diseases, generally of a febrile kind; it therefore excludes the chronic mental affections which are usually included under the term insanity.' (Tuke, D.H. *A Dictionary of Psychological Medicine*, vols. 1–2, Blakiston, Philadelphia, 1892)

The clearest idea of the term delirium is gained by regarding it as a disorder of the sensorium, in which orientation is impaired, the critical faculty is blunted or lost and thought content is irrelevant and incoherent. From an etiological point of view delirium may be somatogenic (e.g. as in typhoid fever) or psychogenic (e.g. as in extreme states of schizophrenic or manic excitement).

All manner of ideas may be expressed in states of delirium. Thus they may be grandiose, persecutory, terrifying, or there may simply be incomplete references to natural acts of the individual's career. There is the so-called occupational delirium, in which the patient makes feeble and incomplete references to his workaday activities.

delirium, abstinence When a state of delirium, usually delirium tremens, follows the immediate withdrawal of alcohol from a chronically alcoholic individual, the condition is known as *abstinence delirium.* The syndrome may be observed in any form of drug addiction.

delirium, acute Bleuler says: 'The *delirium acutum* belongs to the infectious deliria of a different origin,' namely, 'it

is evidently based on different infections or on schizophrenic processes, and shows itself in deliria, convulsive manifestations, and in most cases in a rapidly ending death.' (Bleuler, E. *Textbook of Psychiatry*, tr. by Brill, A.A., Macmillan, New York, 1930)

delirium alcoholicum (dā-lē′rē-oom ăl-kō-hô′lē-koom) (Mod.L. 'alcoholic delirium') Delirium tremens.

delirium ambitiosum (dā-lē′rē-oom ăm-bē-tē-ō′zoom) (L. 'conceited delirium') *Obs.* Megalomania.

delirium, asthenic (as-then′ik) P. Janet thus denotes delirium occasioned by fatigue.

'I have no space here to record the innumerable incidents which have shown me that Sophie's obsessions are always the outcome of a lowering of psychological tension, and that delirium ensues when the lowering of tension is extreme. Always, in her, fatigue is the cause of the depression. Anything which necessitates a great expenditure of energy will induce delirium.' (Janet, P. *Psychological Healing*, vols. 1–2, tr. by Paul, E. and C., Macmillan, New York, 1925)

delirium, chronic (kron′ik) *Obs.* Insanity.

delirium, chronic alcoholic This is a nosologic term synonymous with *psychosis, alcoholic Korsakoff* (q.v.).

delirium, collapse Thus Kraepelin designates a condition, usually associated with high fever, characterized by marked disorientation, illusions, unsystematized delusions and emotional variability; the condition is marked by physical collapse.

This term is also sometimes used to refer to delirious mania (Bell's mania).

delirium, cyanotic (sī-an-o′tik) See *insanity, cyanotic.*

delirium ebriosorum (dā-lē′rē-oom ā-bri-ō-zō′room) (L. 'delirium of drunkards') Delirium tremens.

delirium, emotional This is a term used by Morel for the mental state in which the patient unqualifiedly accepts a false idea.

delirium e potu (dā-lē′rē-oom ā pō′tōō) (L. 'delirium from drinking') Delirium tremens.

delirium ferox (dā-lē′rē-oom fe′rôks) (L. 'wild, savage, fierce') A psychiatric state characterized by violence.

delirium furibundum (dā-lē′rē-oom foo-rē-boon'doom) (L. 'raging delirium') *Obs.* 'The delirium of insanity.' (Tuke, D.H. *A Dictionary of Psychological Medicine,* vols. 1–2, Blakiston, Philadelphia, 1892)

delirium furiosum (dā-lē'rē-oom foo-rē-ō'zoom) (L. 'furious delirium') *Obs.* Mania.

delirium grandiosum (dā-lē'rē-oom grån-dē-ō'zoom) Megalomania.

delirium grave (dā-lē'rē-oom grà've) Collapse delirium. Also used by some to refer to delirious mania (Bell's mania).

delirium, hysterical An old term, denoting what was known as hysterical mania.

delirium, idiopathic *Obs.* Name for psychiatric states occasioned by brain injury or toxic cerebral conditions.

delirium, intellectual An old term, designating what is now known as psychoneurosis. D.H. Tuke defines it as 'that form of mental disturbance in which the person suffers from the presence of groundless, causeless fears, ideas, or imaginations, without any hallucinations or illusions.' (Tuke, D.H. *A Dictionary of Psychological Medicine,* vols. 1–2, Blakiston, Philadelphia, 1892)

delirium maniacum (dā-lē'rē-oom mà-nē'à-koom) (Mod.L. 'maniacal delirium') Mania.

delirium melancholicum (dā-lē'rē-oom me-làn-kô'lē-koom) (Mod.L. 'melancholic delirium') Melancholia.

delirium metabolicum (dā-lē'rē-oom me-tà-bô'lē-koom) (Mod.L. 'Metamorphic delirium') *Obs.* The condition in which the patient believes himself to be another person.

delirium, metamorphosis *Obs.* The state in which the patient believes that his body is transformed into that of a beast.

delirium, micromaniacal (mī-krō-mà-nī'-à-kal) 'The form of insanity in which the patient believes himself to be a little child or a dwarf with shrunken limbs.' (Tuke, D.H. *A Dictionary of Psychological Medicine,* vols. 1–2, Blakiston, Philadelphia, 1892)

delirium mite (dā-lē'rē-oom mē'te) (L. 'mild, calm, gentle') A mental state characterized by low, delirious muttering.

delirium mussitans (dā-lē'rē-oom moos'-sē-tàns) Delirium mite.

delirium nervosum (dā-lē'rē-oom ner-vō'zoom) (L. 'nervous') This older term had many meanings, chief of which was delirium associated with organic brain disease.

delirium, oneiric Dream delirium; see *deliria oneirica.*

delirium palingnosticum (dā-lē'rē-oom pà-lēng-gnaws'tē-koom) 'A term applied to that form of insanity which is merely a translation into belief or actuality of a sensation sometimes experienced by anyone on first going into a new place, that he has been there before; the insane conversion of this sensation makes the patient assert that he has been for years in a spot to which he has only recently come, and that he has seen places which he has really never visited.' (Tuke, D.H. *A Dictionary of Psychological Medicine,* vols. 1–2, Blakiston, Philadelphia, 1892)

delirium persecutionis (per-se-kōō-tē-ō'nēs) (L. 'mania of persecution') Paranoid condition.

delirium placidum (dā-lē'rē-oom pla'kē-doom) (L. 'gentle, quiet, placid'.) Quiet delirium.

delirium, post-traumatic Adolf Meyer used this expression in 1904 (*American Journal of Insanity LX,* 1904). He described four subdivisions:
'a. Pre-eminently febrile reactions.
b. The delirium nervosum of Dupuytren, not differing from deliria after operations, injuries, etc.
c. The delirium of slow solution of coma with or without alcoholic basis.
d. Forms of protracted deliria usually with numerous fabulations, etc. (with or without alcoholic or senile basis).'

delirium potatorum (dā-lē'rē-oom pô-tä-tō'room) Delirium tremens.

delirium, psychasthenic See *delusion, psychasthenic.*

delirium, rhyming A symptom of the manic phase of manic-depressive reaction characterized by utterances in rhyme.

delirium, senile This is usually a syndrome superimposed upon other manifestations of senile dementia. The onset is usually acute. Its principal characteristics are: clouding of consciousness, hallucinations, restlessness, aimless wandering, insomnia, and delusions.

delirium, sensorial A mental state characterized by hallucinations and illusions.

delirium sine materia (dā-lē'rē-oom sē'ne mà-tē'rē-ä) (L. 'without matter, pus') *Obs.* 'Delirium without appreciable cerebral lesion; a term applied to various forms of insanity.' (Tuke, D.H. *A Dictionary of Psychological Medicine,* vols. 1–2, Blakiston, Philadelphia, 1892)

delirium, traumatic A mental disturbance characterized by an acute delirium occuring immediately after head or brain injury as a result of force directly or indirectly applied to the head. Other patients, following such injury, may show a protracted or chronic delirium with marked disorientation, confabulation, and memory defect, but with apparent superficial alertness. This latter condition may resemble the Korsakoff syndrome.

delirium tremefaciens (dā-lē'rē-oom treme-fà'kē-ens) (L. 'shaking delirium') Delirium tremens.

delirium tremens (dē-lir'i-um tre'mens) An acute brain syndrome, due to alcohol intoxication, characterized by an acute hallucinatory delirium and a coarse, generalized tremor which involves particularly the fingers, face, and tongue. Delirium may appear at any time in the chronic alcoholic, but it is usually precipitated by intercurrent infection, injury, or a prolonged debauch, or it may appear as an abstinence delirium in the malignant, addictive alcoholic.

The syndrome begins suddenly with fever, rapid pulse, leukocytosis, profuse perspiration, headache, anorexia, nausea, weakness, and dehydration. Along with the tremor there are seen ataxia and hyperreflexia, and all these appear to be due to an encephalosis involving mainly the fronto-ponto-cerebellar pathways. Increased cerebrospinal fluid pressure and increased globulin in the cerebrospinal fluid are usual, and in about 50 per cent of cases a mild transitory albuminuria is seen. Epileptiform convulsions may also occur.

The delirium itself begins within a few days after onset of the disorder. Persecutory delusions are common and are usually in reference to a gang of the same sex or some obvious castration fear. These delusions may lead to suicide or homocide. Illusions are frequent or are easily suggested. Visual hallucinations are the most common of the hallucinatory elements, and these are typically of animals, such as snakes or rats, which symbolize mainly sexual fears (pink elephants, incidentally, are most uncommon). Haptic hallucinations, of animals crawling over the skin, are also seen, but many of these are probably illusions based on paresthesiae. Auditory hallucinations, when they occur, are usually of a derogatory and/or homosexual nature. In the midst of the delirium, disorientation is marked; there is loss of attention and memory impairment, most marked for recent memory. There is an incontinence of emotions—panic, anxiety, and terror most commonly, although some few show euphoria or indifference to their hallucinations and illusions. Misidentification is common, and patients are highly suggestible and can easily be made to confabulate.

The delirium usually lasts three to six days; the patient usually has an amnesia for the delirium and frequently returns to his pattern of heavy drinking and thus there is often an early repetition of the syndrome. Auditory hallucinations usually indicate that the course will be prolonged. In uncomplicated cases, death is rare (3–4 per cent). If there is not full recovery, there is usually progression into a Korsakoff syndrome (in about 15 per cent of cases).

The pathological picture consists of nuclear destruction of the nerve cells, with all degrees of granular degeneration and disintegration of the nuclei. In most patients, the cortex is mainly affected, but in those tending clinically to progress into a Korsakoff psychosis, the brain stem is affected to a greater degree.

delirium verborum (dā-lē'rē-oom verbō'room) (L. 'delirium of words') Psychiatric state characterized by great loquacity.

delirium vesanicum (dā-lē'rē-oom vā-sä'nē-koom) (Mod.L. 'insane delirium') *Obs.* 'The delirium or incoherence, delusions, hallucinations, illusions, restlessness, watchfulness, etc., of insanity.' (Tuke, D.H. *A Dictionary of Psychological Medicine,* vols. 1–2, Blakiston, Philadelphia, 1892)

delta rhythm or wave See *electroencephalogram.*

delusion A false belief, born of morbidity. A belief engendered without appropriate external stimulation and maintained by one in spite of what to normal beings constitutes incontrovertible and 'plain-as-day' proof or evidence to the contrary. Further, the belief held is not one which is ordinarily accepted by other members of the patient's culture or subculture (i.e. it is not a commonly believed superstition).

A paranoid patient firmly believes that he is the Redeemer and as such he can turn night into day, he can cure all the ills of mankind, he can recall all the events that have ever happened since the dawn of civilization, with the unaided eye he can read newsprint from a distance of several thousand miles.

A delusion is almost invariably a product of forces in the sphere of the unconscious. When an impulse, arising in the unconscious, is rejected by any of the forces of the unconscious or conscious spheres, the individual fails to recognize the genuineness of the impulse. He may develop one or more beliefs about the impulse, beliefs which distort the facts. For example, the unconscious realm of the paranoid patient possesses a strong homosexual tendency, which constantly strives for expression in consciousness and in reality. The ego rejects the demands of the tendency, whereupon one or more of several compromises are developed.

First, the homosexual interests may be 'projected' onto other people, so that it is made to appear that others try to get the patient to indulge in homosexual practices. The patient holds the belief, born of morbidity, that others are persecuting him.

Second, unconscious homosexuality may reach the conscious level in the guise of symbols. The patient may believe that the picture of a pair of trousers, appearing really as an advertisement in the newspaper, was put there by his persecutors for its derogatory reference to him.

Third, the patient may believe that he has no genitals, again a false belief, based on a morbid set of ideas; in this instance, part of the homosexuality is 'projected' upon his own physique.

When the homosexual complex leaves the sphere of the unconscious, is projected upon others and then reaches the conscious part of the patient's mind through one or more of the sense organs (eyes, ears, nose, taste, skin), the false belief is called a hallucination.

Not all delusions, however, are known to stem from the unconscious. Some individuals develop conscious antipathies to the customs and habits of their environment. They come to believe with absolute certainty that they are justified in appropriating or destroying (illegally) the person and property of others. In many instances the delusional attitude toward society is traceable to the unconscious.

delusion, abortive Fenichel says: 'As to "abortive delusions," we may refer to erythrophobia, in which there is a feeling of being watched by persons to see whether one will blush—a state of mind reminiscent of delusions of reference.' (Fenichel, O. *Outline of Clinical Psychoanalysis,* tr. by Lewin, B.D. and Zilboorg, G., The Psychoanalytic Quarterly Press and Norton, New York, 1934)

delusion, allopsychic (al-ō-sī'kik) See *delusion, autopsychic.*

delusion, asthenic (as-then'ic) Psychathenic delusion (Janet).

delusion, autopsychic (aw-tō-sī'kik) When a delusional concept refers to the individual's own personality, it is called an autopsychic delusion; when it relates to the outside world, it is known as an allopsychic delusion; when it has to do with one's own body, it is called a somatopsychic delusion. This classification was suggested by Wernicke.

delusion, catathymic (kat-à-thī'mik) See *catathymia.* When a delusion is due to a complex in the unconscious is called a *catathymic delusion.* 'It alone or combined with hallucinations forms the *paranoid syndrome,* which is to be distinguished from the *paranoid constitution.*' (Bleuler, E. *Textbook of Psychiatry,* tr. by Brill, A.A., Macmillan, New York, 1930)

delusion, expansive See *megalomania.*

delusion, explanatory Bleuler uses this expression to refer to delusions that give reasons for the false belief. A patient who believes that men are persecuting him, explains the delusion by 'showing' that they open his mail, that they publish photographs of him, that they assemble to discuss methods of injuring him.

delusion, healthy In his review of *The Maggid of Caro,* C.B. Farrar feels that 'whether a hallucination is agreeable with health or symptomatic of illness seems to depend upon circumstances. A deranged person may express ideas regarding sin and future penalties that we unhesitatingly set down as pathologic delusions; but identical ideas are found in the Holy Writ and presumably accepted by persons whose mental health is not under suspicion. Are these then *healthy* delusions?' (*American Journal of Psychiatry CVII*, No. 9, March 1951, p. 720)

delusion, infidelity See *paranoia, amorous.*

delusion, interpretation According to Freud, as the expression implies, this is an interpretation or a meaning of a delusion as given by the patient himself.
'Paranoia . . . turns to another source in forming symptoms; the delusions which, by means of a compromise, succeed in becoming conscious (symptoms of the return of the repressed) absorb the thought-processes of the ego until they finally become accepted without contradiction. Since the delusions themselves are not to be influenced, the ego must accommodate itself to them; and thus the combinatory delusion-formations, such as *interpretation-delusions* ending in a *change within the ego,* correspond to the secondary defense in the obsessional neurosis.' (Freud, S. *Collected Papers*, vol. 1, tr. by Riviere, J., Leonard and Virginia Woolf and The Institute of Psychoanalysis, London, 1924–25)

delusion, Mignon (mē-ñoN′) The belief that one is the offspring of some distinguished family (e.g. royalty) rather than one's own parents. This delusion is seen most frequently in the schizophrenias, although it may appear as a more or less disguised wish in almost any psychiatric entity.

delusion of observation The phrase *delusion of observation* is synonymous with *delusion of reference.*
'Recognition of this institution [i.e. conscience] enables us to understand the so-called "delusions of observation" or, more correctly, of *being watched,* which are such striking symptoms in the paranoid diseases and may perhaps also occur as an isolated form of illness, or intercalated in a transference neurosis.' (Freud, S. *Collected Papers,* vol. 4, tr. by Riviere, J., Leonard and Virginia Woolf and The Institute of Psychoanalysis, London, 1924–25)

delusion, primordial See *délire d'emblée.*

delusion, psychasthenic (sīk-as-then′ik)

Janet's term for delusions occasioned by fatigue.

delusion, residual This is an expression used by Neisser to refer to delusions, formed in an acute state, which are carried over into a chronic state.

delusion, secondary With Bleuler this denotes a delusion that is based upon a primary one. 'When the patient is convinced that the physician wants to murder him and after taking medicine he feels indisposed, then it is a conclusion, based on logical probability, that the physician has prescribed poison (secondary delusion).' (Bleuler, E. *Textbook of Psychiatry,* tr. by Brill, A.A., Macmillan, New York, 1930)

delusion, somatic (sō-mat′ik) A psychiatric term that refers to a definite category of symptoms frequently found in the so-called 'functional psychoses,' particularly schizophrenia, but specifically to the subjective reports and complaints made by patients that their body is perceived, or felt, by them as disturbed or disordered in all, or individual, organs or parts. In 1935, Angyal reported that a depersonalized schizophrenic patient reported to him that he felt the floor waving. Angyal analyzed the phenomenon as an 'exteriorization' of the pulse in the plantar region of the foot. The complaints stemming from such somatic delusions in unrecognized ambulatory schizophrenics are frequently the source of much useless medical and surgical treatment, and thus of 'iatrogenic' illnesses. (Hunt, J. McV. *Personality and the Behavior Disorders,* vol. 2, Ronald Press, New York, 1944)

delusion, somatopsychic (sō-ma-tō-sī′kik) See *delusion, autopsychic.*

demand See *feeding, demand.*

dement (dē-ment′) A person with an absence or reduction of intellectual faculties in consequence of known organic brain disease. Earlier writers used the term for deteriorated schizophrenics. Thus the paranoid dements of Kraepelin are those with unstable and unorganized delusions, apparent marked reduction in intellectual capacities, and a break in psychic unity.

dementia (dē-men′shi-à) Absence or reduction of intellectual faculties in consequence of known organic brain disease.
In years gone by, the term dementia has had various meanings. It was once

synonymous with madness, insanity, and lunacy; in the early part of the 17th century it was synonymous with delirium. Nowadays, however, in recognition of the fact that many psychotic individuals possess very keen intelligence, the term is not used sweepingly for all psychiatric states. It is often limited to those who show primary memory loss due to disorders in brain tissue, and as used today the term stresses the irreversibility of the intellectual defects, whatever their origin. The term 'deterioration' also refers to progressive loss of intellectual faculties, but without intimating a specific cause and without stressing the permanency of the change. The term 'regression,' on the other hand, stresses the reversibility of the change, and with Freud this term came to refer primarily to emotional disturbances rather than to loss of intellectual ability. See *dementia, schizophrenic.*

dementia, acute Anergic stupor, such as is seen in catatonic stupor and hysterical trance states. The term is little used today; in the past, however, it was considered a distinct nosological entity.

dementia adventitia (dā-men'tē-à ȧd-ventē'tē-à) (L. 'adventitious dementia') *Rare.* A generic term denoting psychiatric conditions arising in individuals who had previously been mentally well adjusted.

dementia, affective (dē-men'shi-à) See *hebetude.*

dementia agitata (dā-men'tē-à ȧ-gē-tä'tà) This expression, introduced by Krafft-Ebing, refers to agitated states in patients with dementia praecox (schizophrenia).

dementia, alcoholic (dē-men'shi-à) This is the term used to refer to lack of recovery and progression of *Korsakoff's psychosis* (q.v.). Alcoholic dementia consists of impairment of memory and intellectual capacity, emotional instability, moral deterioration, carelessness in dress and personal cleanliness, and, frequently, delusions of marital infidelity.

dementia apathetica (dā-men'tē-à à-pàthā'tē-ka) (L. 'apathetic dementia') *Obs.* Dementia with listlessness.

dementia apoplectica (à-pô-plek'tē-kà) (L. 'apoplectic dementia') Apoplectic attacks, associated with cerebral arteriosclerosis, may be due to hemorrhage or to softening of brain tissue. Usually there are prodromes of variable duration; they may

appear as headache, dizziness, fainting attacks, together with ideational and emotional changes. Depending upon the nature and severity of the arteriosclerotic process, the apoplectic ('stroke') condition may be followed by diffuse cerebral atrophy, giving rise to the organic type of dementia. Clinically the last condition is known as apoplectic dementia.

dementia, apperceptive (dē-men'shi-à) Used by Weygandt to denote a type of dementia induced primarily by disorder in the volitional and intellectual spheres. Weygandt applied the term to dementia praecox (schizophrenia), conceiving the so-called deterioration in the light of 'disintegration' of the will, which in turn interrupted the normal train of thought, the final effect appearing as dementia.

dementia, arteriosclerotic See *psychosis, arteriosclerotic.*

dementia, ascending paretic General paresis with grandiose delusions. See *paresis, general.*

dementia, boxer's One type of chronic cerebral disorder seen in boxers, especially those who have sustained many head blows; also known as dementia pugilistica. Boxer's dementia is a chronic, slowly progressive disorder with pathologic changes similar to those seen in post-encephalitic Parkinsonism.

The other common cerebral disorders in boxers include (1) boxer's traumatic encephalopathy, where predominantly neurological defects are directly related to head blows, and (2) paranoid and catatonic psychoses, the nature of whose relationship to oft-repeated brain traumata is incompletely understood.

dementia, chronic *Obs.* Dementia praecox (schizophrenia).

dementia, circular Thus Kraepelin denotes a form of dementia praecox (schizophrenia) characterized by alternating phases of excitement and depression.

dementia, depressive Kraepelin's designation for a special subdivision of dementia praecox (schizophrenia). The syndrome resembles that of *simple depressive dementia,* save that all symptoms are more intense and the course of the illness is protracted. *Rare* in the United States.

dementia, driveling *Rare.* This is an expression used by Kraepelin to denote 'the general *decay of mental efficiency'* observed in the terminal states of certain syndromes of dementia praecox (schizophrenia).

'Here also are still found, as a rule, hallucinations and delusions, the senselessness of which distinctly proves the mental weakness.' (Kraepelin, E. *Dementia Praecox and Paraphrenia,* tr. by Barclay, R.M., Livingstone, Edinburgh, 1919)

dementia, endogenous (en-doj'e-nus) Kraepelin says that the endogenous dementias 'display two peculiarities, that they are in the first place, so far as can be seen, not occasioned from without, but arise from internal causes, and that secondly, at least in the great majority of cases, they lead to a more or less well-marked mental enfeeblement.' (Kraepelin, E. *Dementia Praecox and Paraphrenia,* tr. by Barclay, R.M., Livingstone, Edinburgh, 1919) When the latter is brought about by external agencies (e.g. injuries, infections, etc.), the dementia is said to be of exogenous origin.

Dementia praecox (schizophrenia) is an example of endogenous dementia; general paresis is one of exogenous dementia.

dementia, epileptic (ep-i-lep'tik) Two forms of psychoses are seen in epilepsy: typical 'organic psychoses' (acute and chronic brain syndromes) and a chronic form which progresses to a Korsakoff psychosis or an epileptic dementia.

Epileptic dementia refers to the progressive mental and intellectual deterioration seen in a small number of epileptics (not more than 5 per cent, and there are many famous epileptics who showed no such dementia: Helmholtz, Flaubert, Dostoyevsky). The resultant mental deficiency is more likely when the attacks have begun early in life. It is probable that both this and the convulsions are expressions of some unknown physiological abnormality, although some believe that the dementia is due to nerve cell degeneration secondary to vascular disturbances during the convulsive episodes.

In a small group of epileptics, more complicated clinical psychiatric syndromes are seen, with mainly depressive or mainly schizophrenic symptoms. It will thus be noted that epilepsy and schizophrenia are not antagonistic, even though a belief to the contrary afforded a rationale for the electro-convulsive treatment of schizophrenic psychoses.

dementia, exogenous (eks-oj'e-nus) See *dementia, endogenous.*

dementia, foolish Kraepelin's term for a form of dementia praecox (schizophrenia), called the hebephrenic by most psychiatrists.

dementia, hallucinatory (ha-lū'sin-à-tor-ē) See *dementia paranoides gravis.*

dementia, higher Van Guden's term (Hoch calls it *parlor dementia*) for a condition in individuals 'who absorb school material quite well, under given conditions even excellently, and can even use it in certain combinations, but in spite of great activity they are failures in life. Their behavior is the reverse of the oligophrenics; they have much knowledge and can do nothing.' (Bleuler, E. *Textbook of Psychiatry,* tr. by Brill, A.A., Macmillan, New York, 1930)

Bleuler refers also to *relative dementia,* which is not to be sharply distinguished from the foregoing. About it he says: 'There are people whose understanding suffices for a usual attitude of life, and often even for one a little above the average, who, however, are too active, and constantly adjudge to themselves more than they can grasp, and therefore commit many stupidities and suffer shipwreck in life.' (ibid.)

dementia infantilis (dā-men'tē-à ēn-fàn-tē'lēs) (L. 'infantile [or childhood] dementia) A term suggested by Heller to designate a variety of infantile schizophrenia. It has been also referred to as *Heller's disease.* In discussing it Kanner (*Child Psychiatry,* 2nd ed., Thomas, Springfield, Ill., 1948) writes: 'It was customary to list Heller's disease among the varieties of infantile schizophrenia. Corberi's findings make it more plausible that this condition represents a cerebral degenerative process akin to Tay-Sachs' disease and to "amaurotic idiocy without amaurosis" (Kufs-Walter).' Schilder stated categorically: 'I assume as a matter of course that *dementia infantilis* (Heller) has nothing to do with schizophrenia, but is an organic process.' (Schilder, P. 'Reaction Types Resembling Functional Psychoses in Childhood on the Basis of an Organic Inferiority of the Brain,' *Mental Hygiene 19,* 439–48, 1935)

Infantile dementia occurs in children at three to four years of age. The patient becomes resistive, whining, and anxious, shows a general loss of acquired functions with mutism, dementia, and posturing, but an intelligent facial expression is usually retained.

Up to the present time, no cases of infantile dementia have been reported in the American literature.

dementia naturalis (nä-tōō-rä′lēs) (L. 'natural, inborn dementia') *Obs.* Idiocy.

dementia paralytica (pà-rà-lē′tē-kà) (L. 'paralytic dementia') See *paresis, general.*

dementia paranoides (pà-rà-nô′ē-dās) Dementia praecox or schizophrenia, paranoid form.

dementia paranoides gravis (grà′vēs) Kraepelin's diagnostic term for the paranoid form of dementia praecox (schizophrenia), for 'those paranoid morbid states, which, it is true, begin with simple delusions,' but which as time goes on terminate in severe so-called deterioration, 'a *peculiar disintegration of the psychic life.*' (Kraepelin, E. *Dementia Praecox and Paraphrenia,* tr. by Barclay, R.M., Livingstone, Edinburgh, 1919)

The *milder* type of paranoid schizophrenia, hallucinatory feeblemindedness, Kraepelin called *dementia paranoides mitis,* when the patient has hallucinations and 'the substance of the personality seems to be less seriously damaged.' To-day Kraepelin's term is used only occasionally and even then not in the diagnostic sense assigned to it by Kraepelin.

dementia paranoides mitis (mē′tes) See *dementia paranoides gravis.*

dementia paratonita progressiva (pà-rà-tō′nē-tà prô-gres-sē′và) Alexander Bernstein suggested this term for *dementia praecox* (schizophrenia), in order to emphasize the motor symptoms occurring in the disorder. He referred particularly to the catatonic form. He also called it *paratonia progressiva.*

dementia, parlor (dē-men′shi-à) See *dementia, higher.*

dementia, partial *Rare.* A form of dementia praecox (schizophrenia) in which the patient retains some healthy mental components.

dementia, periodic See *dementia praecox, circular.*

dementia, post-traumatic (pōst-traw-mat′ik) An absence or diminution of intellectual faculties secondary to brain in-jury. Post-traumatic dementia comprises 0.6 per cent of annual admissions to mental hospitals. Less severe disturbances with memory impairment and minor personality changes are more frequent. Psychologic changes following head injury become prominent approximately two months after the injury and generally subside within the next three months. In 50 per cent of cases, symptoms persist for at least six months, and in 15 per cent, for a year or more. There is no correlation between severity of the injury and severity of the post-traumatic psychiatric sequelae. Persons with pre-traumatic psychoneurotic personalities, and those with many complicating factors, such as pending litigation, anxiety about compensation, occupational stresses, or associated bodily injuries, are more likely to develop post-traumatic psychiatric sequelae. Traumatic epilepsy develops within two years in about 10 per cent of cases who manifest psychiatric sequelae.

dementia praecocissima (dā-men′tē-à prī-kô-kēs′sē-mà) (L. 'premature dementia') In a paper on neuropsychiatric disorders in young children DeSanctis calls attention to a disorder named by him *dementia praecocissima.* (*Neuropsichiatria infantile,* Rome, Stock, 1925, pp. 623–61) According to DeSanctis this condition, occurring in young children, sometimes as early as the fourth year, is characterized by a more or less abrupt appearance of symptoms indicative of catatonia. Stereotypy, fixed postures, negativism, angry outbursts, echolalia, emotional blunting are particularly noticeable. Marked intellectual deterioration is present. DeSanctis ascribed the cause of the disorder to a hereditary predisposition due to paternal alcoholism. Its development was hastened by acute or chronic toxic diseases such as pertussis, rickets, pleurisy, and intestinal infections.

Kanner feels that the case material presented by DeSanctis as dementia praecocissima includes a variety of pathologic conditions. He writes: 'Some of the cases are indistinguishable from childhood schizophrenia (Bromberg), others represent rapidly progressing brain diseases (Lutz; Schilder). An autopsy performed by Ciampi showed chromatolysis of the pyramidal cortical cells.

'Rapid disorganization after a fairly normal start is encountered in small children on rare occasions and offers baffling problems of diagnosis. Some cases prove to belong to the group of Heller's disease (*dementia infantilis*), some few are cases of Tay-Sachs's disease with or without the characteristic eye ground findings, others are instances of even more unusual cerebral disease processes. The custom of including them under the heading of schizophrenia should be discouraged.' (Kanner, L. *Child Psychiatry,* Thomas, Springfield, Ill., 1948)

dementia praecox (dē-men'shi-à prē'koks) A term coined by Morel in 1857 to describe those psychoses ('vesania') with a poor prognosis, i.e. those ending in deterioration (dementia) and incurability. Praecox was meant to refer to the fact that the onset of the disorders was early in life—typically, in adolescence. In the years following the introduction of this term, various symptom complexes were described which later were included in the group, dementia praecox. Thus, Kahlbaum described catatonia, Hecker described hebephrenia, Pick and Sommer described simple deterioration, and Zieber described paranoia. In 1896, Kraepelin made the important differentiation between manic-depressive psychosis and dementia praecox, and he included the aforementioned entities as subgroups of dementia praecox. He, too, emphasized the poor prognosis in dementia praecox and believed that those cases which could be cured permanently or arrested for very long periods were really instances of manic-depressive psychosis.

In 1911, Bleuler introduced the term *schizophrenia,* which in present-day psychiatry has largely replaced the term 'dementia praecox.' Bleuler rejected the latter term because, in his experience, dementia is not a constant end-product of the disorder (or group of disorders), and because at least 40 per cent of cases did not manifest gross disturbances until after their twenty-fifth year.

Some contemporary authorities, and particularly European psychiatrists, continue to use the term dementia praecox in a fairly restricted sense to refer to 'nuclear' or 'process' schizophrenia, i.e. unquestionable cases with a high tendency to deterioration and little tendency to remission or recovery. See *schizophrenia.*

dementia praecox, agitated Certain schizophrenic patients show marked agitation.

Kraepelin classified them as having the agitated form of dementia praecox. As a rule psychiatrists have not accepted the classification. In America, patients with agitation are grouped in accordance with other phenomena. They may be classed as hebephrenic, catatonic, or paranoid.

dementia praecox, catatonic (ka-taton'ik) This term is equivalent to 'catatonic schizophrenia.' See *schizophrenia.*

dementia praecox, circular Kraepelin describes a circular form of dementia praecox, denoting the type that shows periods of a manic-like state, and at other times those of a depressive-like phase. The clinical syndrome is unmistakably one of dementia praecox (schizophrenia). American psychiatrists do not formally recognize the condition as a nosologic entity. Patients with the symptomatology are classed as having a catatonic or a mixed schizophrenic reaction.

dementia praecox, hebephrenic (hē-befre'nik) This term is equivalent to 'hebephrenic schizophrenia.' See *schizophrenia.*

dementia praecox, paranoid (par'à-noid) This term is equivalent to 'paranoid schizophrenia.' See *schizophrenia.*

dementia praecox, simple A subdivision of the group formerly called *dementia praecox* (q.v.) and now generally called *schizophrenia* (q.v.). Sometimes the word 'simplex' is substituted for 'simple.' It is also known as dementia simplex, schizophrenia simplex, and primary dementia.

dementia praesenilis (dā-men'tē-à prī-senē'lēs) See *senium praecox.*

dementia, precocious (dē-men'shi-à) Dementia praecox (schizophrenia).

dementia, premature *Obs.* Dementia praecox (schizophrenia).

dementia, primary Synonymous with *dementia praecox, simple* (q.v.).

dementia, psychasthenic (sī-kas-then'ik) P. Janet says: 'Sufferers from what is termed dementia praecox (which is often nothing more than severe psychasthenic dementia) are subject to agitations and are apt to be violent when living in the complicated environment of the family. . . .' (Janet, P. *Psychological Healing,* vols. 1–2, tr. by Paul, E. and C., Macmillan, New York, 1925)

dementia pugilistica (dā-men'tē-à pōō-gēlē'stē-kà) See *dementia, boxer's.*

dementia, relative (dē-men'shi-à) See *dementia, higher.*

dementia, schizophrenic (skiz-ō-fre'nik) One of the fundamental symptoms of the schizophrenias (Bleuler). Schizophrenic patients, despite generally adequate preservation of their intellectual potentialities, are often not able to make use of this potential in a constructive, appropriate, purposeful, goal-directed way. Knowledge, although present, is not always available to them at the moment it is called for. Schizophrenic dementia seems to be the result of disturbances of primary elemental functions, such as associations, affectivity, attention and concentration, and will.

Schizophrenic dementia reveals itself in various forms: e.g. stupid, foolish mistakes; senseless generalizations; gullibility; faddism; pseudomotivations; vacuity and banality of thought; an insipid, unintegrated, disconnected quality in thought and speech; difficulty in forming new concepts; ellipsis in thought and speech; treating the concrete as though it were abstract, etc. On psychological testing, probably the most frequent expression of schizophrenic dementia is 'scattering.'

dementia, secondary This is an expression, infrequently used today, referring to the schizophrenic syndrome that follows what was known as the initial 'acute' attack or dementia simplex. In the psychiatry of today no such differentiation is made, the entire course of the illness, whether periodic or continuous, being known merely as schizophrenia.

dementia sejunctiva (dā-men'tē-à sā-yoongk-tē'và) Dementia praecox; schizophrenia. The expression is rarely used.

dementia, semantic (dē-men'shi-à) The inability to experience or evaluate the meaning of things. In psychiatry this term has been used by Cleckley ('Semantic Dementia and Semi-suicide,' *Psychiatric Quarterly 16,* 521, 1942) to refer to the inability of the psychopathic personality to evaluate or experience life as a totally integrated organism. Although the psychopath can react verbally as though he understood love, pride, grief, shame, or the other emotions, he has no real experience of these human values or connotations. Cleckley believes that failure to function at this level provokes regression, which is expressed in a drive toward failure and folly, a destruction of the self at the personality or cultural level.

dementia, senile This term almost invariably refers to the psychic and cerebral manifestations of deterioration associated with old age. From the organic point of view the symptoms depend upon the intensity and extensity of involvement of the cerebral hemispheres. The dementia is characterized by impairment of intellectual functions. From the psychic standpoint there is in general a steady withdrawal of interests from the environment and a replacement of the withdrawn interests upon the individual himself. This is usually followed by regression which may reach the level of infantile mentality if it gains in force and depth.

The expression *senile psychosis* is usually considered to be synonymous with senile dementia, although the latter term often denotes a less intense involvement in the psychic sphere.

'The senile psychoses are progressive mental disorders, due to pathological old age, marked by defective mental functioning and notably by impairment of recent memory.' (Strecker, E.A. and Ebaugh, F.G. *Practical Clinical Psychiatry,* 4th ed., Blakiston, Philadelphia, 1935) The authors just quoted use the term *mental* to include psychic and somatic manifestations.

'In dementia senilis, as in paresis, catatonic-like forms have been spoken of, inasmuch as one observes stereotype movements and attitudes, verbigeration, flexibilitas cerea, stupor, and echolalia. Many of these cases, as the anamnesis and symptoms show, are undoubtedly (latent) schizophrenics that have become senile.' (Bleuler, E. *Textbook of Psychiatry,* tr. by Brill, A.A., Macmillan, New York, 1930)

dementia, sequential (sē-kwen'shal) *Obs.* Synonymous with *secondary dementia.*

dementia, simple depressive The expression *simple depressive (or stuporous) dementia,* one of the subdivisions of dementia praecox (schizophrenia), so denoted by Kraepelin, is not generally considered as a nosologic entity by psychiatrists. It is a clinical syndrome appearing in schizophrenic patients, but it is commonly subsumed under the heading of catatonia or of hebephrenia.

The syndrome is characterized by depression, resembling that seen in the depressive phase of manic-depressive disorder; the projection mechanism appears to a greater or lesser degree. The condition often tends toward periodicity, but not with the same sharpness that marks clear-cut depressive states.

dementia, simple senile From the psychiatric and neurologic point of view, simple senile deterioration is characterized by gradual intellectual impairment beginning in old age and consequent upon natural deterioration of cerebral structures. Memory defects are first encountered with regard to recent events; later the memory defects relate to experiences of the distant past. Often the memory lapses are filled in with confabulations. Orientation in all spheres is generally lost. Emotional instability is usually present, although there may be pronounced apathy.

dementia simplex (dā-men'tē-à sim'-pleks) See *dementia praecox, simple.*

dementia, traumatic (dē-men'shi-à, trawmat'ik) When dementia, intellectual or affective, or both, is directly or indirectly caused by an injury, usually to the head, the condition is known as traumatic dementia.

'Common to most of them are rapid exhaustion, irritability, tendency to spontaneous and reactive moods, up to the most intensive anger, which is in part labile and in part of a more torpid persistent affect. . . . Not rarely epileptic attacks appear in which the typical *epileptic dementia* may occur (traumatic epilepsy). Pictures similar to catatonia can last for a long time.' (Bleuler, E. *Textbook of Psychiatry,* tr. by Brill, A.A., Macmillan, New York, 1930)

demenza primitiva (dā-men'tsà prē-mē-tē'và) (It. 'primitive dementia') Dementia praecox (schizophrenia).

demissio animi (dā-mēs'sē-ō à'nē-mē) (L. 'lowering of the spirit') Melancholy.

demi-vierge (dē-mē'vyerzh') (F. 'semi-virgin') The French novelist Marcel Prevost describes women who, he says, are spiritually, not bodily, deflorated, that is, deprived of their virginity. The concept is common, for example, among schizophrenic patients, who express the delusion that men steal into their beds nightly and have sexual intercourse with them.

demon Literature is replete with demons from the psychiatric point of view.

'At the origin of all religions, as Otto has recently shown, before any elaboration of definite gods or demons, there are certain "numinous primordial feelings," i.e., fear for what is mysterious, awe of what cannot be understood, and the like. As the "precursors of religious ideas," these numinous feelings of fear of "demons" live in magic, fairy tales, and myths.' (Storch, A. *The Primitive Archaic Forms in Schizophrenia,* tr. by Willard, C., Nervous & Mental Disease Publishing Company, New York and Washington, 1924)

'Jung believes, as does Lévy-Bruhl, that primitive mentality is largely mystic; it thinks of its surroundings in terms of demons, ghosts, dragons, energy, gods, etc.' (Hinsie, L.E. *Concepts and Problems of Psychotherapy,* Columbia University Press, New York, 1936)

'Psychologically, demons are interferences from the unconscious, i.e., spontaneous irruptions into the continuity of the conscious process on the part of unconscious complexes. Complexes are comparable to demons which fitfully harass our thoughts and actions, hence antiquity and the Middle Ages conceived acute neurotic disturbances as possessions.' (Jung, C.G. *Psychological Types,* tr. by Baynes, H.G., Harcourt, Brace, New York and London, 1923)

'As is known, many authors, foremost among them Charcot, have recognized states of demoniacal possession and ecstasy. . . .' (Freud, S. *Collected Papers,* vol. 4, tr. by Riviere, J., Leonard and Virginia Woolf and The Institute of Psychoanalysis, London, 1924–25)

demonia (dē-mo'ni-à) Demonomania.

demoniac *Obs.* One affected with madness.

demonolatry (dē-mun-ol'à-trē) A form of mental deviation in which a patient worships a demon or devil.

demonomania (dē-mun-ō-mā'ni-à) Morbid dread of demons. Freud believes that the original pleasurable affect associated with an act, such as masturbation, is first repressed, then transformed into anxiety, which contains features of punishment in it and brings dread of an evil spirit as the next stage.

'The demonomania and the self-reproaches of the boy can be traced to the influences of a religious education which had acted upon him as a child.' (Quoted by Freud from Debacker's *Terreurs nocturnes des enfants,* 1881)

demono-melancholia (-mel-an-kō'li-à) Demonomania.

demonopathy (dē-mun-op'à-thē) Demonomania.

demophobia (dē-mō-fō'bi-à) Morbid fear of crowds; ochlophobia.

demoralization, personal The repudiation by the person in a crisis situation of 'old habits and restraints without reorganizing his life.' (Park, R.E. and Miller, H.A. *Old World Traits Transplanted,* Harper, New York, 1921)

'Demoralization is the decay of the personal life-organization of an individual member of a social group. . . . Prevalent social disorganization, in those periods when the old system which controlled more or less adequately the behavior of the group members is decaying so rapidly that the development of a new social situation cannot keep pace with this process of decadence, is particularly favorable for the growth of individual demoralization.' (Thomas, W.I. and Znaniecki, F. *The Polish Peasant in Europe and America,* Knopf, New York, 1927)

demorphinization (dē-mor-fin-i-zā'shun) The process of gradual or rapid withdrawal of morphine in the treatment of addicts.

demyelination (dē-mī-e-lin-ā'shun) The process of destruction of the myelin sheaths of the nerve fibers. There is a large group of neurologic diseases, the 'demyelinating diseases of the nervous system,' characterized by foci of demyelination. These foci are usually in the white matter and vary in size, shape, distribution, and in the acuteness of the pathological process. Classification of these disorders is unsatisfactory; their etiology is unknown, their differential pathology is indistinct, and clinical forms are often transitional, presenting features common to more than one of the specific diseases recognized. The four major forms, divided on the basis of clinico-pathologic manifestations, are: acute disseminated encephalomyelitis (following acute infections); disseminated myelitis with optic neuritis (Devic's disease); multiple sclerosis (disseminated sclerosis); and diffuse sclerosis (Schilder's disease, Balό's disease, etc.).

demyelination, concentric Balό's disease. See *sclerosis, diffuse.*

denarcissism (dē-när'si-sis'm) The state of being unselfish, altruistic. In early infancy instinctual energy is incorporated almost completely within the infant himself. In the very early stages it is bound to the soma. Later, with the development of the psyche, much of the energy is transferred to it. When psychic energy is devoted to one's own psyche, the condition is known as narcissism. Still later, for healthy mental growth, a part of the psychic energy must be objectivated, externalized, detached from its very personal value to the individual. When psychic energy exists in what may be called an impersonal state, that is, it exists in something not strictly related to the individual himself, it is said to be in a state of denarcissism.

dendrophilia, dendrophily (den-drō-fil'i-à, drof'i-lē) Love of trees. Psychiatrists consider it symbolic of the love for the phallus. Magnus Hirschfeld defines it as 'a sexual obsession for trees.' He reports: 'A few years ago a man confided in me who was having an "affair" with an oak tree in Machnow near Berlin. He had, as he said, an idolatrous veneration for it, and often in the darkness, when he felt quite safe from observation, he would press his naked member against the "venerable trunk," until an ejaculation resulted.' (Hirschfeld, M. *Sexual Pathology,* tr. by Gibbs, J., Emerson Books, New York, 1939)

dendropsychosis (den-drō-sī-kō'sis) Intense interest in trees.

'Now the significant fact is that most of both the childish animisms and also of these special dendropsychoses fall away or end completely at puberty. . . .' (Hall, G.S. *Adolescence,* vol. 2, Appleton, New York, 1908, p. 217)

denial A defense-mechanism (see *defense*) in which external reality is rejected and replaced by wish-fulfilling phantasy or behavior. The term has been used more loosely to refer also to blocking of awareness of internal reality (e.g. wishes, impulses, affects, etc.).

denotation See *connotation.*

de-orality De-orality is the state in which instinctual activity, formerly connected with the oral region, is expressed through some other agency. It is said by psychoanalysts that the pleasure of suckling at the breast may in later life assume the form of a pleasure in being morally dependent upon a maternal person.

depatterning D.E. Cameron uses this term almost synonymously with 'regressive' ECT. He uses intensive ECT and prolonged sleep with chlorpromazine and barbiturates to treat chronic paranoids.

dependence, oral The unconscious wish for maternal protection, to be encompassed by the mother, to regain the peace, protection, and security of her sheltering arms. This stems from the original intense and forgotten gratifications of the infantile nursing period, when the infant's prehensile mouth anchored it to the mother's nipple and breast. To the child, to be fed means to be loved, i.e. to be protected, ergo, to be secure. The nostalgic urge toward the reinstatement of such security has been found nuclear in asthmatics. (Alexander, F. *Psychosomatic Medicine,* Norton, New York, 1950)

dependency State of being dependent. With social workers this means 'a form of behavior which suggests inability to make decisions; marked inclination to lean on others for advice, guidance, support, etc.' (Hamilton, G. *A Medical Social Terminology,* Presbyterian Hospital, New York, 1930)

depersonalization The process of being dissolved, of losing the identity, personality, the I. A mental phenomenon, characterized by loss of the sense of the reality of oneself. It often carries with it loss of the sense of the reality of others and of the environment. The condition may be observed in psychoneurotic states, though it reaches its fullest and most lasting form in schizophrenia. It has been described in connection with all the formal diagnostic groups.

It appears in mildest form in the psychoneuroses. 'My whole body was not shrinking or invisible, but as if it were away from me, like a strange body.' (Feigenbaum, D. *Psychoanalytic Quarterly, VI,* 1937, p. 7)

Often, in the depressive phase of manic-depressive psychosis, the feeling that nothing exists may be observed; the condition may be so intense as to be associated with complete unawareness (amnesia) of oneself and the environment, though as a rule there is awareness of the nature of the immediate environment.

Depersonalization may be partial or complete. Among certain psychopathic individuals (e.g. epileptics) there may be loss of one's identity and of former life interests, with retention of the reality of the physical self and of the environment. These are the so-called 'amnesia victims,' the amnesia being the consequence of emotional forces rather than of tissue changes in the brain.

In schizophrenia, depersonalization may be complete and lasting. The patient denies the existence of everything, including himself, yet he places himself at the head of the universe. 'Nothing exists, unless I order it to exist.' Though it plays no essential part in his life, he is aware of the nature of his environment; there is no loss of memory, but there is a complete disinterest.

Properly, the term depersonalization refers to the sense of loss of oneself. The sense of loss of the environment is known as estrangement. (Freud, S. *Almanach für Psychoanalyse,* 1937)

depravity, insanity and An old medico-legal and psychiatric term dating back to the early nineteenth century and embodying mainly moralistic attitudes toward behavior disorders involving clashes with society and the law. The phrase is particularly used and applied to the borderline cases between personality deviation, habitual criminality, and perversion on the one hand, and those minimal ambulatory psychotics with predominantly acting-out trends on the other. The early concepts of 'moral insanity,' 'constitutional (inborn) psychopathic inferiority,' 'psychopathic personality,' 'psychopathic inferiority,' 'moral imbecility,' 'moral insanity,' 'moral lunacy' all refer to this borderline group, the fundamental understanding of which, even today, is an open question.

In 1908 Dr. Walter E. Fernald wrote: 'The patients described vary greatly in intelligence and in the amount of definite knowledge which they have acquired, but they greatly resemble each other in their childish tastes, excessive vanity, unreliability, aggressive, boastful egotism, selfishness, moral insensibility, fondness for malicious mischief and trouble-making, indolence, willingness to run great risks for the sake of some small gain, untruthfulness, lack of shame and remorse, and lack of sympathy, etc.' (Quoted from

Hunt, J.McV. *Personality and the Behavior Disorders,* vol. 2, Ronald Press, New York, 1944)

deprehensio (dā-prā-hen′sē-ō) *Obs.* Catalepsy.

depressio apathetica (dā-pres′sē-ō à-pà-thā′tē-kà) See *anxietas praesenilis.*

depression In psychiatry, depression refers to a clinical syndrome consisting of lowering of mood-tone (feelings of painful dejection), difficulty in thinking, and psychomotor retardation. The general retardation, however, may be masked by anxiety, obsessive thinking, and agitation in certain depressions, especially those of the involutional period ('involutional melancholia').

As used by the layman, the word depression ordinarily refers only to the mood element, which in psychiatry would more appropriately be labeled dejection, sadness, gloominess, despair, despondency, etc.

Depression, even as defined above, may occur in the course of any psychiatric disorder although it is most commonly seen in the psychotic group, particularly in the manic-depressive reactions, the involutional psychoses and the chronic brain disorders associated with senile, circulatory, or metabolic disease.

depression, acute See *melancholia.*

depression, adolescent J.T. MacCurdy says: 'Such depressions are so frequently seen in youth of both sexes that the term "adolescent depression" would not be out of place. But they occur whenever the adult sex problem becomes acute, for instance, following engagement or marriage. They are never pure depressions, because the repression is never complete. Symbolic outlets, representing unconscious solutions of the problem, carry off much of the libido and only what is left, which tends to appear in the form of crude infantilism, is repressed. There are, therefore, many anxieties and worries and much hypochondria, with only a general background of depression.' (MacCurdy, J.T. *The Psychology of Emotion,* Harcourt, Brace, New York, 1925)

depression, agitated Depressed patients generally exhibit reduction of motility, corresponding as a rule to the seriousness of the depression. Certain depressed individuals, notably those in the involutional period of life, are in more or less incessant activity, varying from mild restlessness to pronounced overactivity. The condition may be observed also in depressive states appearing before the involutional age. It has been found to be associated with depressed individuals who are intensely fearful that, as a result of their alleged guilt, both they and their loved ones are to suffer a horrible and painful death. The dread of impending punishment gives rise to the agitation. The patient in a retarded depression usually accepts the awfulness of his condition as a just penalty for alleged sins; the patient who is depressed and agitated tries to reject the anticipated and horrible penalty.

depression, ambivalent (am-biv′à-lent) Minkowski's term for cases of depression in which ambivalence is a prominent symptom (Minkowski, E. 'A Study of the Structure of Depressive States: The Ambivalent Depressions,' *Schweiz. Arch. f. Neurol. u. Psychiat.* 22: 230, 1930).

depression, anaclitic (an-à-klit′ik) A term used by Spitz to refer to the syndrome shown by infants who are separated from their mothers for long periods of time. Initially, the infant gives indications of distress, but after three months of separation '. . . the weepiness subsided, and stronger provocation became necessary to provoke it. These children would sit with wide open, expressionless eyes, frozen immobile face, and a faraway expression, as if in a daze, apparently not perceiving what went on in their environment. . . . Contact with children who arrived at this stage became increasingly difficult and finally impossible. At best, screaming was elicited.' (Spitz, R. *The Psychoanalytic Study of the Child,* vol. 2, International Universities Press, New York, 1946.)

In Spitz's series, the reaction occurred in children who were six to eight months old at the time of separation, which continued for a practically unbroken period of three months. This reaction was seen in full form only in children who had left a 'good' mother-child relationship; those with a 'bad' relationship did not develop the syndrome.

Bakwin noted a similar syndrome, with listlessness, emaciation and pallor, relative immobility, quietness, unresponsiveness, indifferent appetite, failure to gain weight despite adequate diet, frequent stools, poor sleep, an appearance of unhappiness, proneness to febrile episodes, and absence of sucking habits. Bakwin and others refer to this syndrome as 'hospitalism.'

The anaclitic depression is reversible if the mother is restored to the child within three months.

depression, anancastic (an-an-kas'tik) Lion uses this term to refer to dejection or depression accompanied by tension, perplexity, anxiety, and obsessive and paranoid ideas which occurs in individuals whose premorbid personality was of the rigid, obsessive, anancastic type. See *anancasm.*

depression, anxious See *depression, classification of.*

depression, autonomous (aw-ton'ō-mus) See *depression, classification of.*

depression, classification of In the 1952 revision of psychiatric nomenclature by the American Psychiatric Association, depression is considered in the following groups: (1) involutional psychotic reaction, (2) manic-depressive reactions (manic type; depressed type; other), (3) psychotic depressive reaction, (4) schizophrenic reaction, schizo-affective type, and (5) psychoneurotic depressive reaction.

An older scheme after Kraepelin classified manias and depressions (or melancholias) under the general heading Affective Psychosis, as follows:

(A) Manic-Depressive Psychosis
   (1) Manic phase
      (a) hypomania
      (b) acute mania
      (c) delirious mania
         (Bell's mania)
      (d) chronic mania
   (2) Depressive phase
      (a) simple depression
      (b) acute depression
      (c) depressive stupor
   (3) Periodical psychoses
      (a) recurrent mania
      (b) recurrent melancholia
      (c) alternating insanity
      (d) circular insanity
   (4) Mixed states
      (a) maniacal stupor
      (b) agitated depression
      (c) unproductive mania
      (d) depressive mania
      (e) depression with flight of ideas

      (f) akinetic mania
      (g) perplexity state
(B) Involutional Melancholia
   (1) Depressed type (agitated depression)
   (2) Paranoid type

Various authors have suggested other classificatory schemes, but these seem to compound rather than alleviate the difficulties inherent in categorizing disturbances whose etiology is only poorly understood. Thus Gillespie speaks of reactive, autonomous, and involutional depressions. Reactive depression, in this scheme, is characterized by lack of activity and thought; autonomous depression has more activity, restlessness, and self-accusatory tendencies; involutional depression is chiefly distinguished by a hypochondriacal trend.

Mira y Lopez differentiates the following types: (1) physiogenetic or symptomatic depression; (2) simple affective depression, (3) melancholic depression, with self-destructive tendencies; (4) anxious depression; (5) psychogenic depression; (6) depression associated with aboulia or other disturbances of the will; (7) schizophrenic depression.

depression, constitutional See *disposition, constitutional depressive.*

depression, cyclical (sī'kli-kal, sik'li-) A mental illness in which the patient's mood undergoes excessive periods of depression which may or may not alternate with periods of exaltation. Cases of cyclical depression can be divided into two groups, those in which 'outer exciting causes do not seem to play any decisive part' and can, therefore, be described as spontaneous; and those that can 'easily be traced back to mental traumata.' In their clinical manifestations the two types are markedly similar and both may end in mania.

In the second type the trauma, in the end, results in the real or emotional loss of a loved object (such as a failure of some sort, a monetary loss, the death of a loved person, a disappointment in love). From the psychoanalytical point of view the next step is the introjection of the lost object by the ego: the patient's ego becomes identified with the object. Finally, the ego-ideal, or superego, violently attacks both the ego and the object now identified with the ego. These rebukes and attacks upon the object are experienced by the patient as delusions of inferiority, as self-depreciation, and self-reproaches. At bottom, these symptoms represent the ego's revenge upon the lost object.

According to Freud, the just described rebellion of the ego against the ego-ideal is also at work in the spontaneous cyclical depression. In these patients, there is a sharp conflict between the ego and superego, 'a conflict in which the ideal, in an excess of sensitiveness, relentlessly exhibits its condemnation of the ego in delusions of inferiority and in self-depreciation.' This occurs as the ego periodically rebels against the ego-ideal. (Freud, S. *Group Psychology and the Analysis of the Ego,* International Psycho-analytical Press, London, 1922)

depression, ictal (ik'tal) See *emotions, ictal.*

depression, involutional (in-vō-lū'shun-al) See *psychosis, involutional.*

depression, melancholic (mel-an-kol'ik) See *depression, classification of.*

depression, psychasthenic (sī-kas-then'ik) Depression occurring in a psychasthenic person.

depression, psychogenic (sī-ko-gen'ik) See *depression, classification of.*

depression, (psycho)neurotic (sī-ko-nū-rot'ik) In the 1952 A.P.A. revision of psychiatric nomenclature, the diagnosis, psychoneurotic depressive reaction is synonymous with reactive depression (see *depression, reactive*). 'The anxiety in this reaction is allayed, and hence partially relieved, by depression and self-depreciation. The reaction is precipitated by a current situation, frequently by some loss sustained by the patient, and is often associated with a feeling of guilt for past failures or deeds.' *Mental Disorders: Diagnostic and Statistical Manual,* American Psychiatric Association, Washington, D.C., 1952) To be considered in differentiating this group from the corresponding psychotic reaction are the following points: '. . . (1) life history of patient, with special reference to mood swings (suggestive of psychotic reaction), to the personality structure (neurotic or cyclothymic) and to precipitating environmental factors and (2) absence of malignant symptoms (hypochondriacal preoccupation, agitation, delusions, particularly somatic, hallucinations, severe guilt feelings, intractable insomnia, suicidal ruminations, severe psy-

chomotor retardation, profound retardation of thought, stupor).' (ibid.)

It is recognized that attempts to differentiate between psychotic and neurotic depressions, either on phenomenological or on psychodynamic grounds, are inadequate. While it is obvious that severe dejection can be superimposed upon any nosologic entity (and is particularly common in phobics and obsessional neuroses), that this should justify a special diagnosis of depression is questionable.

depression, physiogenetic (fiz-i-ō-ge-net'ik) See *depression, classification of.*

depression, reactive When a depressive state is directly occasioned by some external situation and is relieved when the external situation is removed, the condition is known as a reactive depression. A mother, intensely joyous at the expectation of rejoining her children after a long absence abroad, was held by federal authorities until the legality of her admission to the country was established. She remained acutely depressed until a decision favorable to her was rendered.

'Reactive *depressions,* which become aggravated to a mental disease, are quite rare in the light of present views.' (Bleuler, E. *Textbook of Psychiatry,* tr. by Brill, A.A., Macmillan, New York, 1930)

Some use this term synonymously with psychoneurotic depressive reaction.

depression, retarded See *melancholia.*

depression, simple affective See *depression, classification of.*

depression, stuporous (stū'por-us) See *melancholia.*

depression, symptomatic (sim-tō-ma'tik) See *depression, classification of.*

depression, unreality J.T. MacCurdy says: 'Patients suffering from this psychosis do not labour with the diffuse inhibition assailing the retarded cases. In fact, they may seem to be perfectly normal, from an objective standpoint, and even intimates may fail to observe their trouble. Yet they tell a sad story. All kinds of activity to which they force themselves fail to reward them with any emotional satisfaction. They can make themselves laugh in company with others, but the joke does not feel funny, they only know it is. They can recognize intellectually the beauty in any work of art, but there is no glow of pleasure in the sight. Above all in their human relationship they feel themselves lacking. Affection for others who ought to be dearest to them simply will not come. Consequently they sum up their subjective woes in the expression *unreality.*' (MacCurdy, J.T. *The Psychology of Emotion,* Harcourt, Brace, New York, 1925)

deprivation, emotional (de-pri-vā'shun) Isolation of an infant from its mother to the degree that identification with the maternal figure is not made, with the result that personality development is impaired. The validity of the general proposition regarding the adverse effects of emotional deprivation has been established by two sets of observations—studies of children who were reared in institutional settings and whose adjustment difficulties reflected early distortions in personality development; and studies of infants' reactions to separation from their mothers. See *depression, anaclitic* for a description of the latter.

deprivation, perceptual (per-sep'choo-al) See *deprivation, sensory.*

deprivation, sensory Perceptual deprivation; perceptual or sensory isolation. These terms are ordinarily used to refer to experimental techniques which either reduce the absolute intensity of stimuli reaching the subject, or reduce the patterning of stimuli or impose a structuring of stimuli upon the subject. One of the methods employed to reduce intensity of stimuli, for example, is to suspend the subject, wearing only a blacked-out head mask for breathing, in a tank of water maintained at a constant temperature of 34.5°C. Such experimental sensory deprivation is considered to be similar to 'brainwashing' and the isolation experienced by many explorers and shipwrecked individuals, who under conditions of severe environmental stress are known to develop mental abnormalities. The following features are common to the various situations, whether 'naturally' or experimentally produced: intense desire for extrinsic sensory stimuli and bodily motion, increased suggestibility, impairment of organized thinking, oppression, depression and, in extreme cases, hallucinations, delusions, and confusion.

It is believed that such abnormalities may be explained as follows: the correspondence between external reality and sensory neuronal activity is not a one-to-

one relationship; perception is learned through motor interactions with objects in the environment, and when sleep or other states minimize or eliminate such interactions, percepts based upon previous experience will emerge from the brain itself in the form of hallucinations and delusions (e.g. in dreams). This may be because the sensory input from the viscera augments spontaneous neuronal activity, especially in the thalamus, to such an extent that impulses over relay tracts are initiated, giving rise to visceral hallucinations and similar phenomena.

deprivation, thought *Blocking* (q.v.).

depth-psychology (depth'sī-kol'ō-jē) The psychology relating to the realm of the unconscious, in contradistinction to the psychology of the conscious part of the mind. In psychoanalysis (Freud), depth-psychology may be represented by the id and superego; in analytical psychology (Jung), by the collective unconscious. It is simply a term indicative of a psychic level.

derailment Kraepelin frequently uses the term derailment, indicating abnormal deviation or disorganization of psychic processes. Thus, he speaks of derailment of volition, speech, thought, etc. Derailment is a basic symptom of schizophrenia.

derailment of volition In writing on *parabulia,* Kraepelin says that 'gradual transitions from the simple changes of every-day purposeful actions lead to those disorders of volition which we may gather together under the name of parabulia. The side impulses which at first bring about only flourishes in action may gradually become cross-impulses which lead to complete derailment of volition.' (Kraepelin, E. *Dementia Praecox and Paraphrenia,* tr. by Barclay, R.M., Livingstone, Edinburgh, 1919.) The phrase thus comes to mean disorganization and disintegration of volition.

derailment, speech See *derailment.* This is a phrase, used by Kraepelin, not in common use today, about which he says that '*derailments in linguistic expression* form an important domain in the speech disorders of dementia praecox. Vocal speech itself can be changed in the most varied way by side and cross impulses. The patients in speaking, bellow, screech, murmur or whisper, scarcely move their lips, keep their teeth closed, or often pass suddenly from low whispering to loud screaming.' (Kraepelin, E. *Dementia Praecox and Paraphrenia*, tr. by Barclay, R.M., Livingstone, Edinburgh, 1919)

derailment, thought Kraepelin used this expression to refer to 'a great many quite incomprehensible and disconnected utterances, in which it can scarcely be only a question of disorders of linguistic expression. . . .' (Kraepelin, E. *Dementia Praecox and Paraphrenia*, tr. by Barclay, R.M., Livingstone, Edinburgh, 1919)

deranged Mentally unsound.

Dercum, Francis Xavier (1856–1931) American neurologist.

derealization (dē-rē-al-i-zā'shun) The feeling of changed reality; the feeling that one's surroundings have changed. The symptom is usually (though not always) indicative of schizophrenia and is based on the sense of passivity toward the environment which is secondary to projection feelings. 'Everybody is doing things to me; something has happened to the whole world; the world has changed.' If severe enough, this feeling of changed reality may be expressed as a feeling of imminent or actual catastrophe. See *dereism*.

dereism (dē'rē-iz'm) Mental activity that deviates from the laws of logic and experience and fails to take the facts of reality into consideration. Among psychiatric patients dereism reaches its fullest development in schizophrenic states, in which psychic activity is largely expressed without respect to the realities of life. When a patient firmly believes that, as the Redeemer, he cures all illnesses by a simple gesture, his thinking is said to be out of harmony with facts, that is, dereistic.

'The separation of associations from experience naturally facilitates dereistic thinking in its highest degree, which is actually based on the very fact that natural connections are ignored.' (Bleuler, E. *Textbook of Psychiatry*, tr. by Brill, A.A., Macmillan Company, New York, 1930, p. 79) See *autism*.

derivation, psychological (sī-kō-loj'i-kal) P. Janet says: 'When analyzing agitation, I was led to consider the phenomenon of *psychological derivation*. I wrote: "Derivation occurs whenever the production of a superior phenomenon, one characterized by high tension, has begun, but when the production of the phenomenon has been checked by a lowering of mental tension which has rendered the appearance of phenomena of high tension impossible." When this happens, instead of the complete activation which culminates in decision, effort, and triumph, there occur convulsive paroxysms, tics, questionings, interminable debates, multifarious visceral agitations. . . . When one psychological phenomenon is superior to another, the force requisite for its production may be adequate to produce a lower-grade phenomenon a hundred times over.' (Janet, P. *Psychological Healing*, vols. 1–2, tr. by Paul, E. and C., Macmillan, New York, 1925)

derivative See *substitute-formation*.

dermatography, dermatographia (dĕr-mȧtog'rȧ-fē, -tō-graf'i-ȧ) Dermatography is commonly called skin-writing. It appears in exaggerated form, namely, as an urticaria, when the skin is stroked by a pointed instrument.

Dermatography 'may be divided into two types; one the dilator type, which is characterized by reddening, swelling and even exudation, following stimulation of the skin; the other, the constrictor type, characterized by pallor of the skin where it has been irritated by a firm stroke of the finger.' (Eppinger, H. and Hess, L. *Vagotonia*, 2nd ed., tr. by Kraus, W.M. and Jelliffe, S.E., Nervous & Mental Disease Publishing Company, New York, 1917)

dermatome (der'ma-tōm) The skin area supplied by the dorsal root of a single nerve segment.

dermatophobia (dĕr-mat-ō-fō'bi-ȧ) Fear of skin(-lesion).

dermatosiophobia (dĕr-mȧ-tō-si-ō-fō'bi-ȧ) Fear of (acquiring a) skin disease.

dermographia, dermographism, dermography (dĕr-mō-graf'i-ȧ, -graf'iz'm, dermog'ra-fē) See *dermatography*.

desaggressivization (des-ag-gres-iv-i-zā'shun) Neutralization of the aggressive drive (just as desexualization is neutralization of the sexual drive), so that the energy which would ordinarily be discharged is made available to the ego for carrying out its various tasks and wishes according to the secondary process.

desanimania (des-an-i-mā'ni-ȧ) *Obs.* Psychosis with mental deficiency.

desensitization (dē-sen-si-ti-zā'shun) The act of alleviating or removing a mental complex. 'Hand in hand with this analysis [i.e. distributive analysis] go corrective habit training, necessary specific treatment for somatic disorders, and the bringing to recognition and the enucleation of "sore-spots" or complex-determined topics, memories, associations and reactions which require desensitization and replacement by more wholesome resources and per-formances.' (Howard, F.E. and Patry, F.L. *Mental Health,* Harper, New York, 1935)

déséquilibrés (dā-zā-kē-lē-brā') (F. 'un-balanced persons') A term coined by Magnan for those affected by what was then known as inherited neurasthenia.

desexualization (dē-sek-shoo-al-i-za'shun) Neutralization of the sexual drive so that the energy which would ordinarily be expended in immediate id discharge (the primary process) is held up and made available to the ego for its various tasks and wishes according to the secondary process.

desire Until the introduction of modern concepts in psychopathology, the term desire was defined essentially from the standpoint of the conscious part of the mind. It meant, and continues to mean, a wish, a longing for, a craving, an incli-nation. With the development of fuller knowledge of the unconscious, the term desire was applied to many impulses or tendencies of that part of the psyche. There are forces in the unconscious that strive for expression in reality. To indi-cate this striving, the terms desire, wish, etc. have been retained, amid great oppo-sition, because it is not conceded in gen-eral that there is, for example, a wish to die, a wish for incest, for exhibitionism, etc. That is true, from the standpoint of consciousness; yet, in the unconscious are impulses, the antitheses of conscious de-sires or wishes, that press for overt expres-sion. They may be regarded as biological urges or 'wishes' or 'desires,' in contradis-tinction to the personal ones. To wish or desire generally carries the idea that it is done wittingly and consciously; we are not in the habit of thinking that we wish also unconsciously. It suits our morality to have unconscious impulses and con-scious wishes.

'In other words, the latter (unconscious) consists of thoughts, desires, and wishes of a kind that are highly unacceptable to the conscious personality. . . .' (Jones, E. *Papers on Psycho-Analysis,* 4th ed., Wood, Baltimore, 1938)

desire, psychical (sī-ki-kal) This is a term for a conscious sexual feeling.

'In whole groups of cases anxiety-neuro-sis is accompanied by a very noticeable abatement of sexual libido, i.e. of *psychi-cal desire.*' (Freud, S. *Collected Papers,* vol. 1, tr. by Riviere, J., Leonard and Virginia Woolf and The Institute of Psy-choanalysis, London, 1924–25)

desocialization (dē-so-shal-ī-zā'shun) The process of withdrawing or turning away from interpersonal contacts and relation-ships, such as is seen commonly in schizo-phrenics. These patients tend to replace social behavior and language habits with personal, highly individual behavior.

despeciation (dē-spē-shi-ā'shun) In the field of constitutional medicine this term refers to the presence in an individual of a number of extreme variants of physical characteristics, such as a scaphoid shoul-der-blade, a supernumerary breast, a de-formed ear lobe, an anomalous distribution of hair, etc. The variants, when alone, have little pathogenic value or meaning, but the accumulation of them in a single individual is regarded as a sign of biologi-cal inferiority or despeciation (Apert). J. Bauer uses the term *degeneration* to refer to such marked deviations from the type of the species.

'Today there can be no doubt whatever that these extreme variants from the average type are in effect constitutions physically, or, better, psycho-physically, inferior. . . .' (Pende, N. *Constitutional Inadequacies,* tr. by Naccarati, S., Lea & Febiger, Philadelphia, 1928)

despondency Melancholy.

destiny, neurosis of (nū-rō'sis) This type of neurotic ailment afflicts the individual who unconsciously arranges all of his life's experiences so that he is in the position of suffering continual reverses, while he consciously holds that destiny or fate brings them. His friends will always re-mark on his bad luck and continual ill fortune. Moreover, the patient invariably tends to blame his fate for his continual reverses, being unaware that he is respon-sible for them himself.

As the 'all-consuming task of his life' this neurotic has in the first place the 'mastery of guilt-feelings,' which he hopes to accomplish through his own suffering, and thus ingratiate himself with an implacable superego. Secondly, the patient turns all of his life's activities into situations where he can experience this suffering. In Fenichel's words, he uses his environment solely as 'an arena in which to stage his internal conflicts.' All real-life actions 'are repetitions of childhood situations or attempts to end infantile conflicts rather than rational undertakings.' (Fenichel, O. *The Psychoanalytic Theory of Neurosis,* Norton, New York, 1945)

destructive instinct See *instinct, death.*

destrudo (des-tro͞o′dō) Edoardo Weiss coined this term to denote the energy associated with the death or destructive instinct (*Imago, XXI,* 393, 1935). It is the opposite of *libido,* the energy of the instinct Eros. See *Thanatos.*

detachment Separation; in psychiatry, separation or divorce from emotional involvement. See *affect, detached.*

detector, lie A machine designed to record the various physiological changes which accompany changes in emotional tone, such as changes in respiratory rate, pulse rate, blood pressure, skin moisture, etc. 'The lie detector is based upon the fact that the impact of emotionally charged ideas or the conscious suppression of a true recollection and the substitution of a false statement cause detectable physiologic changes through stimulation of the autonomic nervous system, over which one has no voluntary control.' (Guttmacher, M.S. *Psychiatry and the Law,* Norton, New York, 1952) Although results are not always accurate, the technique of interpretation is constantly being improved; it appears that accurate diagnosis on the basis of the test is possible in 75–80 per cent of cases, that in 15–20 per cent results may be too indefinite for confident diagnosis, and that the remaining 5 per cent constitute the margin of probable error. Such errors as do occur are usually those on the side of failing to detect a guilty person rather than on the side of mislabeling an innocent person guilty.

detentio (dā-ten′tē-ō) *Obs.* The fixed attitude in catalepsy.

deterioration (dē-tēr-ē-or-ā′shun) In its current usage the term deterioration implies a chronic, progressive process from

which recovery may not take place. However, the degree of deterioration forms the better prognostic guide. Deterioration in a psychical sense is common among schizophrenic subjects.

Intellectual deterioration generally refers to diminution or impairment of the ability to remember, together with disorders attendant upon memory losses. Intellectual deterioration is usually observed in patients with destructive processes in the cerebral cortex. See *dementia.*

deterioration, chronic alcoholic This condition occurs in individuals who are chronically addicted to the use of alcohol and who show emotional blunting, organic memory defect, and deterioration in the moral and ethical spheres.

deterioration, emotional Emotional deterioration occurs mainly in patients suffering from schizophrenia: the patient becomes careless and indifferent about the surroundings and people around him, and shows no adequate emotional reaction to environmental stimuli. (Brill, A.A. *Basic Principles of Psychoanalysis,* Doubleday, New York, 1949)

deterioration, epileptic (ep-i-lep′tik) See *dementia, epileptic.*

deterioration, habit The abandonment of integrated and socialized behavior in favor of disintegrated and personal behavior. Habit deterioration is a reflection of regression.

'In all dementing psychoses, in dementia praecox and paranoides and in organic and senile dementias there occurs a failure of the habits appropriate to the patient's social standing. Habits of cleanliness; of decency in micturition, defaecation and eating, and of neatness in dress, together with the conventional social manners, all suffer degradation and are replaced either by the habits of a lower social level or by purely indifferent animal behaviour.' (Craig, M. and Beaton, T. *Psychological Medicine,* 4th ed., Churchill, London, 1926)

deterioration, post-traumatic mental (post-traw-ma′tik) A nosologic entity included under the psychoses due to trauma as indicated in the Standard Classified Nomenclature of Disease, 1935. It is now called chronic brain syndrome associated with trauma, with mental deficiency. Following a severe or an apparently slight injury to the head, with or without an acute or chronic delirium, some individuals may develop a progressively increasing dementia or mental enfeeblement. Many of the symptoms included under post-traumatic personality disorders may also be present.

deterioration, senile A slowly progressing decline in physical and mental health apparently due to natural causes attendant upon processes of aging. The symptomatology varies; from the neurological point of view the central symptoms are fatigue, diminution of concentration, impairment of memory and perhaps impairment of functions due to focal cerebral disorders; emotionally there is an incapacity toward sustained interests in the environment, with a gradual regression of interests to the period of childhood. Visceral functioning in general usually plays a part in the decline.

determinant See *determinant, dream.*

determinant, dominant See *determinant, dream.*

determinant, dream The real or principal motive or reason responsible for the production of the dream, since it is true that even if 'dreams are always abundantly overdetermined, one determinant is invariable in the dreams of neurotics.' This invariable factor is called the 'dominant determinant' and is in direct connection with the dreamer's most important conflict. To discover the dominant determinant is no easy task: most of the time it is not revealed through association and may be discovered only by the use of the interpreter's intuition. (Stekel, W. *The Interpretation of Dreams,* Liveright, New York, 1943)

determination, sex See *sex-determination.*

determining quality See *quality, determining.*

determinism (dē-tēr'min-iz'm) 'Determinism has been a subject of controversy for ages. It is the concept which states, first, that our actions can change nothing in the events of life which were firmly established through causal connection, and, second, that man is not free to dispose of his own will and to choose between good and evil in his actions.' (Bleuler, E. *Textbook of Psychiatry,* tr. by Brill, A.A., Macmillan, New York, 1930)

The same idea is stated by Thomas Hobbes: 'Nothing begins from itself. When

will arises, the cause is not the will itself, but something else, not in one's own disposing.'

Spinoza said: 'In the mind there is no absolute or free will, but the mind is determined by another cause, and this last by another cause, and so on to infinity." (Spinoza, B. de, *Ethic,* tr. by White, W.H.)

'The scientific point of view presupposes an irrevocable commitment to the concept of determinism in nature, as an article of faith.' (Rosanoff, A.J.)

'The feeling of conviction [that there is a free will] exists, but it is not incompatible with the belief in determinism.' (Freud, S.)

determinism, biological In the field of mental deficiency this term means that all individuals of the same intellectual level are not necessarily to be classed as feebleminded, and that only those who exhibit a quantitative difference in total organization, constitutionally determined—such as lack of common sense—should be classified as mentally defective. This is true of high grade defectives as well as the lower grades. 'According to this contention, morons and borderlines are physically, mentally, volitionally, socially, and educationally inferior to the intellectually subnormal of the same intelligence level, and the application of the term "feebleminded" to the latter group is highly unsound.' (*White House Conference on Child Health and Protection, IV,* 1933.) The clinical differentiation of constitutionally determined mental defectives from those defectives not so determined is frequently difficult, if not impossible. For example, the intellectually subnormal not constitutionally determined may become social failures because of unfavorable environmental factors, and the constitutionally defective may be socially successful in a favorable environment. This opinion contrasts with that of *biosocial determinism* (q.v.).

determinism, biosocial In the field of mental deficiency, the theory of biosocial determinism contrasts with that of biological determinism. The former maintains that feeblemindedness in the higher as well as the lower levels cannot be considered a clinically differentiable entity. 'It is claimed that there is no generally demonstrable biological difference between the higher levels of intellectual subnormality and the higher levels of feeble-mindedness as the latter term is used in the standard definitions, and that when social failure or inadequacy occurs it is a result of the combined action of biological and environmental factors in a total situation. According to this contention, morons as a class have the same potential capacity with the intellectually subnormal of the same intelligence level, because identical with them.' (*White House Conference on Child Health and Protection, IV,* 1933) Just as persons of average intelligence may be socially effective or inadequate because of environmental factors, so the higher grade mentally defective may behave according to accepted social standards or be forced into behavior viewed as being feebleminded in nature. The intellectually subnormal and the feebleminded do not differ as groups, except in the terms of social success or failure.

dethronement See *parents, dethronement of.*

detumescence (dē-tū-mes'ens) In the field of sex, this term now generally refers to the emptying of the blood vessels connected with the genitals following the stage of engorgement or tumescence.

'The second process [i.e., detumescence] has the object, directly, of discharging the tension thus produced and, indirectly, of effecting the act by which the race is propagated.' (Ellis, H. *Studies in the Psychology of Sex,* vol. 3, Davis, Philadelphia, 1903) See *tumescence; contrectation.*

deuteropathy (dū-tēr-op'à-thē) A secondary disease, disorder or symptom.

deutero-phallic (dū-tēr-ō-fal'ik) See *proto-phallic.*

developmentalism (dē-vel-op-men'tal-iz'm) The genetic, longitudinal view of human behavior. The term is used to describe Gesell's method at his center at Yale University, where the emphasis is on maturation as a biological process in a cultural setting. Each level of development of children's behavior is determined and standardized on the basis of long-term studies; there is little concern with interpretation of the inner life of the child.

development, genital-psychical (jen'i-tal-sĭ'ki-kal) A psychoanalytic term which stresses the importance of psychosexual, developmental, emotional maturation as a true basis for genito-sexual potency—

in contrast to mechanical, anatomical, physiological, and orgastic criteria which give rise to pseudo-potency and the masking of impotence. Genito-sexual potency is characterized by the ability to love in the adult sense and by a free, full, and satisfactory orgasm as well. Genito-sexual pseudo-potency is manifested in a masturbatory preoccupation with personal, orgastic, and tactile sensation. Even though orgasm in the pseudo-potent may be deceptively satisfactory, it is frequently entirely dependent upon thinly disguised perversion stimuli, and perversion auspices. Genito-sexual psuedo-potency is associated with self-love and self-satisfaction; in contrast the genito-sexual potency of the psychosexually mature is strongly marked by love of and consideration for the partner. E.F. Sharpe (*Collected Papers on Psycho-analysis,* Hogarth Press and The Institute of Psychoanalysis, London, 1950) writes: 'In our attempt to understand and resolve resistances [in analysis] we shall not accept sexual potency as a proof of psychical genital development.'

development, inhibition of See *pathogenesis.*

deviance, cultural A special term, springing from combined anthropological, sociological, psychiatric, and personality studies of personality types within a specific culture. In the setting of a specific culture, the norms of personality type, with specific traits, are present either in all individuals or in so many individuals that the trends appear as the normal stuff of the social life of that cultural community. In such a community, deviant, or differing, personality types 'stick out like a sore thumb' in their relative maladjustment to the group of norms, and in the hostile and critical reaction of the norms toward those with differing, or deviant, trends. Implicit in the term 'deviant' is the idea of standardization of the normal or 'normal.'

J.McV. Hunt (*Personality and the Behavior Disorders,* vol. 2, Ronald Press, New York, 1944) states: 'This typological approach to culture has been criticized on the lines that presuming some degree of standardization, it makes no allowance for deviance. To this type of criticism, the reply is, first, that the term "deviant" implies standardization; and, second, that deviance *is* allowed for and expected to occur in all cultures, though it is not expected that deviance will occur in the same directions in all cultures.'

deviation, average See *deviation, mean.*

deviation, conjugate (kon'jū-gāt) See *nerve, oculomotor.*

deviation, mean (M.D.) A description of the variability of a frequency distribution; also called *average deviation* (or A.D.). The mean deviation from the mean is computed by tabulating the amount by which each individual score in distribution differs from the mean score, considering all these deviations as positive, and then computing their mean.

The *standard deviation* (S.D.) is similar to the mean deviation, except that each deviation from the mean is squared, the squared deviations are totaled and averaged, and the square root of the average is then extracted. This gives a more reliable measure of variability than the mean deviation and is in wider use because other statistical measures are calculated on the basis of the S.D. In any distribution which approximates the normal curve in form, about 65 per cent of the measures will lie within one S.D. of the mean, and about 95 per cent will lie within two S.D.'s of the mean. When used as a measure of variability the S.D. is known as the *standard error.*

deviation, median A description of the variability of a frequency distribution; also called probable deviation or probable error (P.E.) The median deviation from the mean is computed by tabulating the amount by which each individual score in a distribution differs from the mean score, considering all these deviations as positive, and then computing their median. The median deviation is the absolute amount of deviations from the mean that is exceeded by half the measures in a distribution.

deviation, probable See *deviation, median.*

deviation, sexual See *sociopathic personality disturbance.*

deviation, skew Skew-deviation (Hertwig-Magendie phenomenon) is a rare cerebellar or collicular sign, characterized by downward and inward rotation of the eyeball on the same side of the lesion and upward and outward rotation of the eyeball on the opposite side.

deviation, standard (S.D.) The standard deviation is a summary of the variation of the items in a frequency distribution. It is the square root of the mean square of the deviation of each variable in the series from the mean of the series. See *deviation, mean.*

device, safety Karen Horney's term for any means of protecting the self from threat, especially the hostility of the environment; although a more general term, safety device is approximately equivalent to defense-mechanism.

Devic's disease Neuromyelitis optica; ophthalmoneuromyelitis; disseminated myelitis with optic neuritis. An acute demyelinating disease which is sometimes self-limited but which in 50 per cent of cases is relapsing, progressive, and fatal. It consists of massive foci of demyelination in the optic nerves and chiasma and spinal cord, which may undergo softening and cavitation. Etiology is unknown and there is no definitive treatment.

devil In psychoanalysis the concept *devil* is 'a personification of the unconscious instinctual forces.' While writing on *Character and Anal Erotism* Freud says: 'We know how the money which the devil gives his paramours turns to excrement after his departure, and the devil is most certainly nothing more than a personification of the unconscious instinctual forces. . . . Even in the early Babylon cult gold is "the excrement of Hell." '

In a later communication (*A Neurosis of Demoniacal Possession in the Seventeenth Century*) Freud reviews a brochure bearing the title *Trophaeum Mariano-Cellense*. The central theme of the story is the redemption of a pact entered into between the devil and a citizen, one Christoph Haitzmann. The object of Freud's review is to show that the devil is often a father-substitute. In the story 'the Devil binds himself for a period of nine years to take the place of his lost father to the painter [Haitzmann]. . . . The train of thought motivating this pact seems indeed to be as follows: Owing to my father's death I am despondent and can no longer work; if I can but get a father-substitute I shall be able to regain all that I have lost.' (Freud, S. *Collected Papers*, vol. 4, tr. by Riviere, J., Leonard and Virginia Woolf and The Institute of Psychoanalysis, London, 1924–25)

devolution (dev-ō-lū'shun) MacCurdy states, with regard to regression, that 'it is a fundamental principle of all pathology that adaptations or specializations of recent evolution are more unstable than ones of longer standing. This means that if the health of an organism be in any way affected, the first functions to be altered will be those of most recent acquisition and that the alteration will be in the direction of reinstatement of more primitive functions. This principle was elaborated for the nervous system by *Hughlings Jackson* in theories that have inspired the best modern work in neurology. He called the tendency "devolution" as it was an undoing, a reversal, of evolution. The cornerstone of psychoanalytic theory is just this principle applied to mental functions, here called "regression." ' (MacCurdy, J.T. *The Psychology of Emotion*, Harcourt, Brace, New York, 1925)

devotion, mania for This expression is used by P. Janet, who explains that some patients 'declare that they do not wish merely to be loved, but wish to love. They want to protect others, to do services to others, to pay compliments, to overwhelm the objects of their affection with flattery and delicate attentions. In a word, they want to devote themselves to others.' (Janet, P. *Psychological Healing*, vols. 1–2, tr. by Paul, E. and C., Macmillan, New York, 1925)

dextrality-sinistrality (deks-tral′i-tē-sin-is-tral′i-tē) These yoked terms refer to the clinically observed phenomenon that the 'uninfluenced' child will spontaneously favor and develop skill in the use of one hand, eye, and foot in a kind of primacy and choice over the other. The predominance of the right hand, eye, and foot is called *dextrality* (right-handedness), while that of the left hand, eye, and foot is called *sinistrality*. It is theoretically assumed that this motor predominance is correlated with a corresponding cerebral physiological pattern. Thus, the neuro-physiological theory concludes that the left cerebral hemisphere is predominant over the right in children with dextrality, while the right cerebral hemisphere is physiologically predominant over the left in those with sinistrality.

It is contended that 'handedness,' right or left, can be converted through educational means, but that 'eyedness' seems resistant to such conversion. Some observers ascribe learning difficulties, speech diffi-

culties, and other intellectual difficulties to this conversion process, which is usually the change of a 'natural' sinistrality into a converted dextrality. The validity of these correlations, as well as the neuro-physiological and psychological interrelationships theoretically implicit in these clinical states, are still moot questions.

Alexandra Adler (Harms, E.. *Handbook of Child Guidance*, Child Care Publications, New York, 1947) states: 'One of the most frequent "inferiorities" is left-handedness. Our present-day culture is righthanded. We have indications that this was not always so. . . The suggestion that changing a left-handed child over to the use of the right hand may produce stammering, could not be proven.'

dextrophobia (deks-trō-fō′bi-à) Fear of objects to the right.

DFP See *psychotomimetic*.

di Rorschach scoring symbol for inside detail.

diabetic exophthalmic dysostosis (dī-à-bet′ik ek-sof-thal′mik dis-os-tō′sis) *Xanthomatosis* (q.v.).

diaboleptics (dī-à-bō-lep′tiks) Maudsley coined this term for those individuals who claim to have supernatural communications.

diagnosis, negative Diagnosis by means of exclusion; 'wastebasket' diagnosis.

diagnosis, social Psychiatric social workers thus denote the conditions prevailing in the environment of the patient.

diamine (dī′à-mēn) Any substance that contains two amine groups. Such substances have recently received much attention in psychiatry because of certain indications that they may be of etiologic significance in the production of endogenously occurring psychoses. Thus, in the schizophrenias, 'The indications are that faulty enzyme production results in inadequate binding of amines, some of which are cerebrotropic, or exert their influence by reason of specific amino-sensitive cerebral areas. Both Baruk (France) and Buscaino (Italy) emphasize toxic and infectious (intestinal) causes, giving great importance to excessive or abnormal amine body production (especially diamines) due to liver or reticuloendothelial dysfunction or to gastro-intestinal diseases.' (Campbell, R.J., *Psychiatric Quarterly 32:* 318–334, 1958)

diaphragma sellae (dē-à-fràg′mà sel′lē) See *meninges*.

diaschisis (dī-as′ki-sis) A term introduced by Monakow to indicate that when one 'center' of the brain is affected another distant 'center' which has a definite relation to the affected one, becomes functionally disordered.

diastematomyelia (dī-as-tem-à-tō-mī-ē′lē-à) Partial duplication of the spinal cord, usually in the thoracolumbar segments, with a column of connective tissue which sometimes contains bone or cartilage in the cleft between the two halves of the cord. Myelography shows a filling defect and dilatation of the vertebral canal, and also congenital deformity of two or more vertebrae.

diathesis (dī-ath′ē-sis) This term refers to an old concept of general and constitutional medicine, which is now best understood as a constitutional disposition, or predisposition, to some anomalous or morbid condition 'which no longer belongs within the confines of the normal variability, but already begins to represent a potential disease condition.' These various *diathetic* conditions are distinguished by the fact that diathetic individuals respond with abnormal or truly pathological reactions to physiological stimuli, such as foods, or other ordinary conditions of life, such as sunlight, that are borne by the majority of individuals without injury.

'Hence the concept of diathesis enters into the larger concept of constitution, particularly of constitution so seriously anomalous that even ordinary exogenous stimuli may cause special forms of disease to breed on diathetic soil. But in the practical application of the diathetic concept we often speak of diathesis, when we have already entered the domain of diathetic disease.' (Pende, N. *Constitutional Inadequacies,* tr. by Naccarati, S., Lea & Febiger, Philadelphia, 1928)

diathesis, arthritic (är-thrit′ik) Constitutional morbid condition which, according to the Italian school, includes the closely related exudative and hypersecretory diathesis as well as arthritism and is said to occur especially in the *megalosplanchnic hypervegetative* (q.v.) constitution. Pende and Naccarati consider the hypersecretory diathesis as bearing out MacAuliffe's concept of a 'heavy type' and the chemical theories used to explain this type, although their own theory is based on neuro-chemism rather than on purely chemical principles.

Arthritic subjects are prone to syndromes grouped by the French school under the heading of diseases of *bradytrophism* (q.v.). Their organs have a tendency to sclerosis (fibroplastic diathesis) on account of the special primary hyperplasia and irritability of the visceral connective tissue.

Czerny's exudative diathesis readily becomes engrafted upon the overnourished megalosplanchnic constitution, inclined as it is to anomalies of metabolism, including those little-known anomalies which lie at the bottom of the exudative diathesis. This condition occurs in growing children and is so similar to the arthritic diathesis of adults that it has been called infantile arthritism.

There is general agreement that the arthritic manifestations differ somewhat in infancy because of the constitution peculiar to this age, namely, marked development of the connective and lymphatic tissue and a predominance of hormones stimulating the sympathetic nervous system, although the parasympathetic was originally predominant. The endocrine sympathetic condition accounts for the development and hardening of skin and mucosae, which are very delicate, fragile, and soft in the child, and for the ready appearance of phenomena due to the (originally predominant) parasympathetic nerves. It also explains the special localization of these neurovegetative disorders in the field of the skin and the mucosae as well as the special irritability and tendency to infection of the connective-lymphatic tissue, which functions actively in these first stages of life.

diathesis, colloidoclastic (ko-loid-ō-klas′-tik) In constitutional medicine, this term refers to a morbid condition in children which results from an imperfect albuminoid metabolism and leads to an unstable colloidoplasmatic equilibrium (colloidoclasia). The condition is believed to belong to the syndrome of *infantile arthritism* which is an *arthritic (exudative) diathesis* (q.v.) in children.

diathesis, eosinophilic (ē-ō-sin-ō-fil′ik) In constitutional medicine, this term designates a condition which is to be regarded a feature of the *arthritic diathesis* (q.v.) rather than a special constitutional state, as was originally assumed by Staeubli. The condition is characterized by various degrees of eosinophilia, which may range from 8 to 30 per cent and seems to depend on protein intoxication and anaphylactic crises.

diathesis, explosive This term is used to designate a clinical subdivision of the traumatic psychoses characterized by intense irritability, particularly after the ingestion of alcohol; the irritability sometimes leads to acts of violence which appear unmotivated, that is, automatic.

diathesis, exudative (eks-ū′dȧ-tiv) This term, introduced by Czerny, designates a form of arthritic diathesis occurring in growing children and characterized by a constitutional condition called colloidoclastic diathesis by Widal.

The syndrome of arthritism in children is produced by irritating toxic products, which result from the protein metabolism and accumulate in the blood and interstitial lymph of the tissues, and especially in the skin and mucosae which possess the power of neutralizing toxins. The products of imperfect albuminoid metabolism stimulate these tissues and render them abnormally sensitive. They affect particularly the parasympathetic nerves, which are already in a state of hypertonia in the normal child. An unstable colloidoplasmatic equilibrium follows which is upset by ingestion of ordinary articles of diet, inducing the phenomena of protein shock, colloidoclasia, anaphylaxis and blood alkalosis. It is precisely to these phenomena that the syndrome of exudative diathesis applies.

diathesis, fibroplastic (fī-brō-plas′tik) A constitutional anomaly characterized by a sclerotic degeneration of various organs, due to a primary hyperplasia and irritability of the visceral connective tissue, and occurring in the course of a general arthritic diathesis.

diathesis, glial (glē′al) With this term Pende denotes a constitutional condition characterized by a hyperplastic or neoplastic tendency of primitive or more differentiated glial cells. The condition is believed to underlie a series of 'heredo-familial nervous diseases that usually develop on the soil of the lymphatic or hypoplastic constitution, and which include cerebral tuberous sclerosis and gliomatous cerebral hypertrophy, spinal gliosis and syringo-myelia, glioma, neurofibromatosis, progressive lenticular degeneration, and other degenerative scleroses of the corpora striata.' (Pende, N. *Constitutional Inadequacies*, tr. by Naccarati, S., Lea & Febiger, Philadelphia, 1928)

'We may recall the relations, pointed out by Bartel, between cerebral glioma and status lymphaticus and status hypoplasticus, the coincidence of glioma with syringomyelia and the relations of the latter with proliferation of the ependymal cells of the glia in the walls of the spinal canal; the close relationship between tuberous sclerosis and neurofibromatosis shown by Verocay, Iczekowski and Nowicki, who speak of a central or peripheral or universal neurinomatosis, that is, a tendency to new growth of the primitive neuro-epithelial cells, occasionally associated with anomalies of other derivatives of the ectoderm (as, for example, multiple cutaneous moles); finally, that special glial hyperplasia, with atrophy of the nerve cells and disintegrative foci, that is demonstrated in Wilson's disease and its allied syndrome, cerebral pseudo-sclerosis of Westphal-Strümpell.' (ibid.)

diathesis, hypersecretory (hī-pĕr-sē-krē′-tō-rē) See *diathesis, arthritic.*

diathesis, lithic (lith′ik) This constitutional morbid condition is characterized by the metabolic anomaly of uricemia and a tendency to form urinary calculi. It is one of the most important manifestations of *arthritism* (q.v.) and is primarily a hereditary anomaly of metabolism rather than one of renal function, as it occurs especially in families in which various signs of a constitutional weakness of the urinary apparatus are found.

A uric acid diathesis is often found in the same family or individual to be combined or alternating with gout and an oxalic acid diathesis leading to oxaluria and oxalic lithiasis. It is the autonomic system, together with the endocrine system, which plays a significant part in the pathogenesis of oxaluria and the related phosphaturia and calcinuria.

diathesis, neoplastic (nē-ō-plas′tik) Tendency of certain constitutional types to develop neoplastic conditions, especially carcinoma. Some typologists assign the equivalent of the pyknic or megaloplanchnic constitutions to persons with this tendency, while others postulate an association of the arthritic and the neoplastic diathesis, or an association between the cancerous and the *exudative* diathesis (q.v.).

In the literature, the assumption of an antagonism between cancer and active tuberculosis is widespread. It is said that both conditions are rarely found in the same individual and that they favor different physiques, namely, the pyknic and asthenic types, respectively. The recent anatomical studies by Lewis have confirmed this assumption by revealing a high incidence of carcinoma in his hypercompensatory types and its absence in his regressive types. It must be mentioned, however, that the findings concerning a possibly genetic predisposition to cancer are still inadequate and contradictory, while there is already considerable evidence of the heredito-constitutional basis of the phthisic habitus.

diathesis, neuro-arthritic (nū-rō-är-thrit′-ik) Practically identical with *arthritic diathesis,* but the role of the autonomic system in this diathesis is stressed.

diathesis, neuropathic (nū-rō-path′ik) *Obs.* Neurasthenia.

diathesis, oxalic acid (oks-al′ik) See *diathesis, lithic.*

diathesis, traumatophilic (traw-mà-tō-fil′-ik) A predisposition to accidents, sometimes referred to as accident proneness. Fenichel considers this to be a manifestation of Freud's repetition compulsion. 'The repetition is desired to relieve a painful tension; but because the repetition is also painful, the person is afraid of it and tends to avoid it. Usually, therefore, a compromise is sought: a repetition on a smaller scale or under more encouraging circumstances. The ambivalence toward this repetition shows itself in the phenomena of traumatophilia and traumatophobia, in the fact that whatever these persons [of traumatophilic diathesis] undertake turns into a trauma; they fear this, and nevertheless they strive for it.' (Fenichel, O. *The Psychoanalytic Theory of Neurosis,* Norton, New York, 1945)

diathesis, uric acid (ū′rik) See *diathesis, lithic.*

diencephalon (dī-en-sef′à-lon) See *forebrain.*

diencephalosis (dī-en-sef-à-lō′sis) A term used to refer to any of the many possible disturbances or functional alterations of the diencephalon and/or its interconnections. The following symptom groups are included: (1) lack of restraint and inhibition, (2) paradoxical co-existence of opposed functional disturbances, (3) alterations of biological rhythm, (4) various endocrine dysfunctions, (5) abnormalities of growth and development, (6) certain forms of psychopathy, (7) vascular lability, (8) dysthermia, (9) electroencephalographic abnormalities, and (10) cranioradiographic abnormalities. (Pende, N. 'Introduction to the Clinical Pathology of the Diencephalon.' *Medicina* 6:197–206, 1957)

differentiation, sex See *sex-differentiation.*

diffuse sclerosis See *sclerosis, diffuse.*

dihybrid (dī-hī′brid) A hybrid individual differing in two hereditary characters, or hereditary traits based on two pairs of genes (see *hybrid*).

diisopropyl fluorophosphate (dī-ī-sō-prō′pil floo-ōr-ō-fos′fāt) See *psychotomimetic.*

dikephobia (dī-kē-fō′bi-à) Fear of justice.

dilapidation Deterioration; dementia.

'The minor degrees of incoherence are known as "scattering" and "dilapidation." ' (Henderson, D.K. and Gillespie, R.D. *A Text-Book of Psychiatry,* 4th ed., Oxford University Press, London, 1936)

dilution, transference The diminution of the intensive transference toward the therapist owing to the presence of sibling and identification transferences to other members of a group. See *therapy, dilution.*

dinomania (dī-nō-mā′ni-à) Dancing mania.

dioecious (dī-ē′shus) See *hermaphrodite.*

dionism (dī-on′iz′m) See *uranism.*

diplegia (dī-plē′ji-à) Bilateral paralysis of corresponding parts of the body.

diplegia, congenital spastic (kon-jen′i-tal spas′tik) Little's disease.

diploid (dip′loid) This genetic term refers to the original stage in the maturation of a reproductive cell, in which the number of chromosomes is full, that is, not yet halved by the reduction division following the first or equation division (see *maturation*).

diploidy (dip′loid-ē) In the meiotic process of cell division the genetic term diploidy signifies the original quota of chromosomes, that is, the *full* number resulting from the duplicating equation division, prior to their reduction to the halved or haploid number through the reduction division (see *haploidy*).

diplopia (di-plō'-pi-à) Double vision; due to paralysis of the ocular muscles, which causes the image of an object to fall upon non-corresponding portions of the two retinae. See *nerve, oculomotor.*

diplopia, monocular (mō-nok'ū-lĕr) A condition in which two images are seen with one eye. The existence of true monocular diplopia is questioned and when present is regarded as a sign of hysteria.

dippoldism (di'pol-diz'm) Flogging of (school) children. The German schoolteacher, Dippold, was tried and convicted of manslaughter. Thereafter the act of flagellation came to be known as dippoldism. See *flagellation.*

dipsomania (dip-sō-mā'ni-à) A periodic mental disorder occasioned by alcoholic excesses. It is characterized mentally by a variety of responses peculiar to the individual. Some individuals become shy and retiring; others quite boisterous and pugnacious; still others exhibit paranoid reactions. The alcoholic bout and its results last as a rule for several days, rarely for several weeks. 'In the intervals, that may last several weeks but also many months, most of these patients are temperate, and some are abstinent.' (Bleuler, E. *Textbook of Psychiatry,* tr. by Brill, A.A., Macmillan, New York, 1930) Dipsomania is usually regarded as a symptom or a syndrome of some more fundamental disorder, such as psychopathic personality, epilepsy, schizophrenia, etc. Bleuler includes dipsomania among the acute syndromes in the schizophrenias.

dipsosis avens (dēp-sō'zēs àv'ens) (Mod. L. 'craving desire for drink') Excessive craving for alcohol.

disaggregation, mental (dis-ag-rē-gā'shun) According to Janet, '. . . a special form of weakness owing to which an elementary idea is left in isolation, and is not combined with others to form a higher unity.' 'It is a condition of natural and perpetual distraction, which prevents these persons from appreciating any other idea than the one which actually occupies their mind.' (Janet, P. *Psychological Healing,* vols. 1–2, tr. by Paul, E. and C., Macmillan, New York, 1925)

disaster, reactions to See *neurosis, traumatic.*

disattach See *attachment, liquidation of.*

discharge, affective This term, employed by Freud, indicates an energetic reaction to an affective experience. This energetic reaction includes the whole range of voluntary and involuntary reflexes, by which, according to experience, the emotions—from weeping up to a clear act of revenge—are habitually worked off.

'If this reaction occurs with sufficient intensity a great part of the affect disappears; common speech bears witness to these facts of everyday observation in the expressions "to cry out," "to storm oneself out." ' (Freud, S. *Collected Papers,* vol. 1, tr. by Riviere, J., Leonard and Virginia Woolf and The Institute of Psychoanalysis, London, 1924–25)

discomfiture In social work, 'a failure in self-preservation in the sense of giving up the struggle; being overwhelmed by circumstances; defeatism.' (Hamilton, G. *A Medical Social Terminology,* Presbyterian Hospital, New York, 1930)

discriminanda (dis-krim-in-an'dà) See *intelligence.*

disease, American An expression, introduced in Europe, for neurasthenia.

disease, association Myoclonia and epilepsy co-existent in the same patient; myoclonus epilepsy.

disease, barbed wire A reactive mental disturbance of prisoners, held in barbed wire camps. The type of mental disorder is variable. Vischer coined the expression.

disease, Beard's (George M. Beard, American physician, 1839–1883) An old term for neurasthenia; named after the physician who introduced the name neurasthenia in 1869.

disease, Bell's Collapse delirium, delirious mania; the most severe of the manic type of manic-depressive psychosis.

disease, caisson Caisson disease (diver's paralysis, the bends, tunnel disease) is a circulatory disturbance occurring in the nervous system, observed when an individual, subjected to high air pressure (e.g. in diving or working under compressed air in a caisson) returns too suddenly to normal atmosphere. There is a question as to whether the sudden release of pressure causes air emboli in the brain and spinal cord or whether the blood vessels dilate, giving rise to congestion and stasis. Pathologically, the spinal cord shows softening and necrosis.

The symptoms are acute in onset with headache, pains in the epigastrium, limbs and back, sufficient to double the patient up (the bends), dizziness, dyspnea, nausea, vomiting, coughing and partial or complete paralysis, usually of both lower extremities. Cerebral symptoms may occur, such as aphasia, double vision, confusion, coma, and convulsions.

disease, flight into Gain through disease or disorder is commonly recognized by psychiatrists. 'By means of *flight into the disease* one achieves definite aims through the disease; by an attack of rage one achieves a yielding; by a fainting spell, a new hat; and by the more protracted disease one gets a pleasant sojourn in a sanatorium. By means of all these one can at the same time compel consideration, secure care and tenderness, obtain power over others who have to adjust themselves to the disease, extort an allowance, evade tasks from the simple household duties up to the terrors of the trenches.' (Bleuler, E. *Textbook of Psychiatry*, tr. by Brill, A.A., Macmillan, New York, 1930)

disease, Friedmann's (Max Friedmann, German physician, 1858–1925) *Narcolepsy* (q.v.).

disease, genetotrophic (ge-ne-tō-trō'fik) A disease 'in which the genetic pattern of the afflicted individual calls for an augmented supply of a particular nutrient (or nutrients) for which there develops, as a result, a nutritional deficiency.' (Williams, R.J., et al. in Podolsky, E., *Management of Addictions*, Philosophical Library, New York, 1955) 'On the basis of our studies with rats it seems likely that the basic etiologic factor in human alcoholism is genetotrophic, and that the sociological and psychological factors so generally considered as fundamental factors are only precipitating factors for the development of the clinical syndrome.' (ibid.) The factor described is believed to depend on one or more partial genetic blocks. 'Briefly described, such a block involves a heritable trait that is characterized not by a complete inability to carry out a specific enzymatic transformation, but by a diminished potentiality for producing the biochemical change. This in turn leads to an

augmented requirement for some specific nutritional factor or factors.' (ibid.)

disease, Heller's See *dementia infantilis*.

disease, Janet's (zhà-nāz') *Psychasthenia* (q.v.).

disease, Leber's (Theodor Leber, German ophthalmologist, 1840–1917) Hereditary familial primary optic atrophy, occurring between the ages of eighteen and thirty, more common in the male progeny, but transmitted from the female. It is a bilateral, slowly progressive condition, often remaining stationary or even regressing. There is a central scotoma and a normal peripheral field.

disease, Lindau's (Arvid Lindau, contemporary Swedish pathologist) An angioma of the brain occurring in connection with angiomatosis of the retina, occasionally familial and hereditary.

disease, Little's (William John Little, English surgeon, 1810–94) Includes the spastic diplegias, presumably due to bilateral congenital brain defects, involving especially the pyramidal motor system, or to lesions acquired at birth. Walking is retarded, the gait is spastic and the child walks on its toes (pes equinovarus). The thighs are adducted, the knees rub together, and the legs cross in progression (scissors gait). This spastic paralysis may involve both upper extremities as well. Frequently present are various grades of mental disturbance, ranging from hyperexcitability and irritability to imbecility or idiocy. Typical epileptic convulsions may occur. Strabismus, dysarthria, drooling, and abnormal involuntary and associated movements may be observed.

disease-narcissism (-när'sis-iz'm) See *narcissism, disease*.

disease, Pick's See *Pick*.

disease, pink *Acrodynia* (q.v.).

disease, sacred In Latin, *morbus sacer* (q.v.). Same as epilepsy.

disease, Saint Dymphna's (St. Dymphna, patron saint of the insane, a British noblewoman, murdered by her insane father, in Gheel, Belgium.) Any mental disease, insanity.

disease, Saint Mathurin's (St. Mathurin, patron saint of idiots and fools.) Epileptic psychosis.

disease, Saint Valentine's Epilepsy.

disease, sanatorium 'The habit of living in sanatoria can itself become a kind of disease that might be called *sanatorium-disease;* many people are by it completely estranged from their homes and occupations.' (Ferenczi, S. *Further Contributions to the Theory and Technique of Psycho-Analysis,* tr. by Suttie, J.I., Leonard and Virginia Woolf and The Institute of Psychoanalysis, London, 1926)

disease, Schilder's (Paul Schilder, American neurologist, 1886–) Schilder's disease, or encephalitis periaxialis diffusa, is a slowly progressive degenerative disease of the brain occurring mainly in children and young people; it is characterized essentially by slowly advancing cerebral blindness and progressive mental deterioration terminating usually in complete amentia.

diseases, demyelinating (dē-mī'e-lin-ā-ting) See *demyelination.*

disease, Simmonds's (Morris Simmonds, Hamburg physician, 1855–1925) See *cachexia, hypophysial.*

disease, Tay-Sachs's Amaurotic family idiocy; it was first described by Warren Tay in 1881, who referred principally to the ocular changes; in 1887 Bernard Sachs described the brain changes in a paper entitled *Arrested Cerebral Development.*

disease, tunnel *Disease, caisson* (q.v.).

disequilibrium, mental Dubois uses this expression for mental imbalance.

'It is often difficult to discover these causes of mental disequilibrium. Sometimes the patients dissemble, often they themselves do not know the causes of their strange condition. Sometimes, in the suggested freedom of hypnosis, they reveal their secret, but there are others who retain and preserve it for years, until some opportune occasion arises to bring it to an end.' (Dubois, P. *The Psychic Treatment of Nervous Disorders,* 7th ed., tr. by Jelliffe, S.E. and White, W.A., Funk & Wagnalls, New York and London, 1909)

disguise in wit Freud writes that 'the means which serve to make a person comical are transference into comic situations, imitations, disguise, unmasking, caricature, parody, travesty and the like.' (Freud, S. *The Basic Writings of Sigmund Freud,* tr. by Brill, A.A., Random House, New York, 1938). See *wit.*

disharmony, affective In writing on schizophrenia, White states: 'The lack of conformity of the emotional reaction and the ideational content—affective disharmony—is shown not only with reference to a given time, but in relations of succession. Moods and affects change in all possible ways without visible inner or outer causes.' (White, W.A. *Outlines of Psychiatry,* 12th ed., Nervous & Mental Disease Publishing Company, Washington, D.C., 1929)

disinfection, mental *Liquidation, mental* (q.v.).

disinhibition (dis-in-hi-bish'un) The inhibitory function of the cerebral cortex can be reduced by various agents—for instance, alcohol. If such a cortical function is impaired or reduced in its activity, the inhibitory influences of the cortex are diminished or removed and then a disinhibition takes place, indicating that without the high cortical control, lower vegetative or emotional functions are manifested. (Masserman, J.H. *Behavior and Neuroses,* University of Chicago Press, Chicago, 1943)

disintegration (dis-in-tē-grā'shun) Disorganization of psychic processes. 'We may therefore expect that a weakening or annihilation of the influence which general conceptions, higher emotions, and the permanent general trend of volition exercise on our thinking, feeling, and acting, must draw after it that inner *disintegration,* those "schizophrenic" disorders, which we meet with in dementia praecox.' (Kraepelin, E. *Dementia Praecox and Paraphrenia,* tr. by Barclay, R.M., Livingstone, Edinburgh, 1919) See *integration.*

disk, choked See *papilledema.*

disk, herniated lumbar intervertebral (hĕr'ni-ā-ted lum'bĕr in-tĕr-vĕr'te-bral) Protrusion of the central portion of the intervertebral disk (the nucleus pulposus) through the surrounding annulus fibrosus, which holds the bodies of the vertebrae together. Such herniation is usually due to trauma, induced typically by lifting a heavy object in a bent-forward position or by a fall in a similar posture. Almost half of the cases begin in the fourth decade, and approximately three-quarters of the cases are male. Most herniations are between the fourth and fifth lumbar bodies, or between the fifth lumbar and first sacral bodies. Herniation of the disk results in compression of the spinal nerve running to the foramen one segment below; the clinical result is *sciatica,* i.e. pain beginning in the lumbar region and spreading down the back of one lower limb to the ankle, usually intensified by coughing or sneezing.

Four symptom-phases are recognized: (1) back pain, muscle spasm, and trunk tilt; (2) compression of the spinal nerve resulting in sciatica, with paresthesiae in the lateral calf and foot, muscle spasm, focal tenderness, and diminution of the ankle jerk; (3) paresis of the lower extremity and muscle atrophy; (4) paralysis of the affected extremity, marked sensory loss, and bladder and bowel disturbances.

In most cases, conservative treatment with analgesics and mobilization is adequate; in about 10 per cent of cases, interlaminar operation is indicated.

dismemberment, fear of The depressive symptoms present in menopause and other involutional states 'dominated by the fear of the impairment of the body function in general, and of sex especially.' This generalized fear may culminate in a specific fear of death. In cases of this type, death is experienced 'as a slow or fast dismemberment.' This feeling that the patient has of losing part of his body is called the dismemberment complex, or fear of dismemberment. In a way, this fear represents the anxiety connected with the period in life when our existence seems to be coming to an end. The dismemberment complex may be combined with acute anxiety or with inhibitions. In some cases described by Schilder, the individual develops a strong feeling of persecution. This is explained in the following manner: Through the process of fear of dismemberment the individual projects to the outside world parts of his body, and then the endangered parts of the body retain their relation to the individual by coming back in the form of persecutors. Such a mechanism is clearly illustrated in the example of the depressive menopausic woman who feared she was going to cut off all her fingers every time she held a knife in her hand. She later developed a persecution complex in which five different enemies were following her. (Schilder, P. *Psychotherapy,* Norton, New York, 1938)

disorder, affective determined An expression used by Adolf Meyer as equivalent with manic-depressive psychosis.

disorder, behavior See *behavior disorders.*

disordered behavior, classification of Rado (*American Journal of Psychiatry, 110:* 406–416, 1953) offered the following provisional classification of disordered behavior, based mainly on the psychodynamic phase of etiology:

I. Over-reactive disorders. (1) Emergency dyscontrol; (2) Descending dyscontrol; (3) Sexual disorders; (4) Social overdependence; (5) Common maladaptation or combination of sexual disorder with social overdependence; (6) Expressive pattern; (7) Obsessive pattern; (8) Paranoid pattern.
II. Mood cyclic disorders.
III. Schizotypal disorders. (1) Compensated schizo-adaptation; (2) Decompensated schizo-adaptation; (3) Schizotypal disintegration marked by adaptive incompetence.
IV. Extractive disorders.
V. Lesional disorders.
VI. Narcotic disorders.
VII. Disorders of war adaptation.

disorder, personality See *personality-disorder.*

disorders, extractive See *psychodynamics, adaptational.*

disorders, impulse See *impulse disorders.*

disorders, moodcyclic See *psychodynamics, adaptational.*

disorders, over-reactive See *psychodynamics, adaptational.*

disorientation (dis-ō-ri-en-tā'shun) Impairment in the understanding of temporal, spatial, or personal relationships.

disorientation, autopsychic (aw-tō-sī'kik) Synonymous with impairment of insight; see *orientation, autopsychic.*

disparagement, mania for This is a term used by Janet, who says that 'one who feels himself to be a weakling and has a terrible dread of effort, has a different idea of competition. His aim is to triumph, not by raising himself, but by lowering his rival. Thus it is that the psychasthenic secures a partial and thrifty success by preventing others from acting. His opposition to all action on the part of his associates may arise out of a desire for immobility in his environment, out of a fear lest he himself should become involved in changes taking place in that environment; but, in many instances, an additional factor is his dread of others' success.' (Janet, P. *Psychological Healing,* vols. 1–2, tr. by Paul, E. and C., Macmillan, New York, 1925)

displacement The phenomenon of displacement is commonplace in normal and abnormal psychology. It is universal among psychiatric patients, in whom it appears with great clearness.

The term has two meanings. The first and usual meaning refers to the transference of the emotions (cathexes) from the original ideas to which they are attached —to other ideas. It is assumed in psychoanalysis that psychic energy may exist as an entity, such as 'free-floating' libido, that is, that it possesses a certain autonomy. It is sufficiently mobile to leave one set of ideas and go to another. By such an arrangement the affects may be able to gain the realm of consciousness, attaching themselves to ideas to which the patient is ordinarily indifferent. By such an arrangement the patient is spared the pain of knowing the original source of the affects. A patient had a morbid fear that illuminating gas was issuing from the jet in his room. The fear was not allayed in any way by logic. The patient recognized how ridiculous it was to let such an idea control his life. Upon analysis it was found that the fear was associated with the repressed wish for his father's death.

Schizophrenic patients exhibit displacement of affects to a remarkable degree. What are seemingly the most inconsequential thoughts may be heavily emotionalized. A schizophrenic patient used to get into a state of uncontrollable rage over his shoestrings. Another patient was ecstatic over the word 'there.'

The displacement of affects presupposes also the displacement of ideas.

The second, but perhaps a corollary, meaning of displacement has to do with the shifting of id impulses from one pathway to another. When, for instance, aggression cannot express itself through direct motor discharge, as in fisticuffs, it may take the pathway of verbalization.

Displacement manifests itself also with regard to organic zones. The instincts shift, for example, from the oral to the anal, to the genital zones, or to any other erotogenic zone. In conversion hysteria a psychic complex may be displaced upon any potentially acceptable organic structure. Or, all the issues connected with genitality may be displaced to the oral zone.

Displacement 'from below upward' is a common phenomenon.

Dreams afford notable examples of displacement. See *dream.*

displacement from below to above See *displacement; above and below.*

displacement in dreams See *dream-displacement.*

displacement of affect See *affect, transposition of.*

displacement, retroactive Unconscious displacement that reaches back into the patient's early life. When we begin to investigate how far memory can go back into life, we find that quite often memories are concealed. 'If the content of the concealed memory belongs to the first years of childhood, but the ideas it represents belong to a later period of the individual's life, we speak with Freud about a retroactive displacement.' (Brill, A.A. *Basic Principles of Psychoanalysis,* Doubleday, New York, 1949)

displacement-substitute See *substitute, displacement.*

displacement-wit See *wit, displacement.*

disposing mind and memory Singer and Krohn thus describe 'a sound mind, capable of making a will; remembering the property to be disposed of and the persons who are the natural objects of bounty, and comprehending the manner in which the property is to be distributed.' (Singer, H.D. and Krohn, W.C. *Insanity and Law,* Blakiston, Philadelphia, 1924)

disposition, brain See *neurogram.*

disposition, constitutional depressive Certain individuals are more or less consistently depressed throughout life. They are retarded in thinking and acting, show a protracted pessimism as regards all life experiences, have difficulty in making and completing decisions, and lack self-confidence. Bleuler says they display the *melancholic mood.*

The term 'constitutional depression' is used by some to indicate endogenous depression, i.e. one in which precipitating factors are not clear or definite.

disposition, constitutional manic This denotes the type of personality that is more or less of a 'manic' disposition throughout life.

'The manic temperament of such people disposes to over-hasty acts and to a thoughtless manner of living in general, when it is not restrained by a particularly sound understanding and a particularly good morality. For that reason we find here on the one hand snobbish, inconsiderate, quarrelsome and cranky ne'er-do-wells, who have no staying powers in their transactions, but on the other hand "sunny dispositions," and people endowed with great ability, amounting sometimes to genius, and not rarely gifted with artistic ability who possess a tireless energy.' (Bleuler, E. *Textbook of Psychiatry*, tr. by Brill, A.A., Macmillan, New York, 1930) Bleuler says these people have the *manic mood*.

The term 'constitutional mania' is used by some as an equivalent of 'endogenous mania,' or mania without clear-cut precipitating factors.

disposition, polymorphous-perverse (pol-i-mor'fus-per-vers') See *perverse, polymorphous*.

disposition-system See *subject-complex*.

disseminated sclerosis (dis-em'in-ā-ted skle-rō-sis) See *sclerosis, multiple*.

dissimilation See *assimilation*.

dissimulation 'In the same connection, let it also be stated that the mere assertion of an accused that he has feigned insanity is by no means sufficient of itself to justify a court in declaring him sane and criminally responsible. It is not uncommon for an insane person, on finding that his acquittal on account of mental disorder will entail a longer period of confinement than would a conviction for the crime of which he stands accused, to declare he has feigned the symptoms of insanity.' (Jacoby, G.W. *The Unsound Mind and the Law*, Funk & Wagnalls, New York and London, 1918)

dissimulator One who dissimulates, dissembles, or pretends that he is not. One who puts up a bold front while faint with terror—dissimulates or dissembles his fear; at the same time he simulates or feigns intrepidity or a stout heart.

dissociate To split off some part or component of mental activity, which component then acts as an independent unit of mental life. See *dissociation*.

dissociation MacCurdy says that dissociation, as a psychopathological term, means 'the segregation of a group of mental processes, separated off from conscious-ness, but functioning as a unitary whole, *as if* they belonged to another person. This, when greatly elaborated, may lead to a double personality, but only if the dissociated complexes displace the normal consciousness, becoming themselves conscious.' (MacCurdy, J.T. *The Psychology of Emotion*, Harcourt, Brace, New York, 1925)

Henderson and Gillespie state: ' "Double" and "multiple" personality are the terms applied when the same individual at different times appears to be in possession of entirely different mental content, disposition and character, and when one of the different phases shows complete ignorance of the other, an ignorance which may be reciprocal. Each "sub-personality" (for the personality in these conditions at least is compounded of a series of sub- or partial personalities or "monads," as McDougall calls them) is said to be "dissociated" from the total personality, and from the other sub-personalities, on each occasion when its activities are fully conscious and control the motor apparatus of the individual.' (Henderson, D.K. and Gillespie, R.D. *A Text-Book of Psychiatry*, 4th ed., Oxford University Press, London, 1936)

'Psycho-analysis, too, accepts the hypothesis of dissociation and of the unconscious, but sets them in a different relation to each other.' This quotation, taken from Freud's *Psychogenic Visual Disturbance According to Psycho-Analytical Conceptions*, has to do with another form of dissociation. Freud says: 'If, then, psychogenic visual disturbance, as we have learnt, is based on the segregation from consciousness of certain ideas connected with seeing, the psychoanalytical mode of thought constrains us to assume that these ideas have come in opposition with other more powerful ideas . . . and have therefore become repressed.' Any sense organ and its psychical representation may exhibit the phenomenon of dissociation.

Another form of dissociation is included in the definition framed by Strecker and Ebaugh: 'In effect, *dissociation is the separation of the mind or consciousness by a splitting off of one (sometimes more) component or system of ideas, the personality or remainder of the mind being unable to exert any control over the split-off portion*. This phenomenon of dissociation may be witnessed in the automatic writing of hysteria, in somnambulism, in double personality and in the many delusions of patients.' (Strecker, E.A. and Ebaugh, F.G. *Practical Clinical Psychiatry,* 4th ed., Blakiston, Philadelphia, 1935)

Another expression of dissociation has to do with the separation of ideas from their consonant affects. For example, a schizophrenic patient laughed heartily while discussing the idea that he was cut into millions of pieces.

dissociative reaction A type of conversion hysteria. See *conversion; hysteria.*

dissolution, insanity of See *insanity, dissolute.*

distemperature *Obs.* Mental derangement.

distortion Owing to the forces exerted by the several repressing or censoring agencies in the psyche, unconscious complexes are not permitted to become conscious in their original form. The various mechanisms of the mind co-operate to disguise, to distort the complex as it appears in the unconscious. To the conscious mind of an individual the unconscious complex as it originally exists is unacceptable and forbidden. It is permitted access to the field of awareness, however, after it has been adequately distorted.

Distortion is a daily process with normal and abnormal individuals. If we must tell a story that originally was objectionable because of its frankness, we repeat it, if we are embarrassed, with frequent inferences, but not with candor.

Dreams exhibit distortion to a remarkable degree. A neurosis is a distortion of the truth of the unconscious. 'I have already asserted that obsessional thoughts have undergone a distortion similar to that undergone by dream thoughts before they become the manifest content of a dream.' (Freud, S. *Collected Papers,* vol. 3, tr. by Strachey, A. and J., Leonard and Virginia Woolf and The Institute of Psychoanalysis, London, 1925)

'The forgetting of dreams is, like the distortion of the latent content, a manifestation of the activity of the censorship.' (Jones, E. *Papers on Psycho-Analysis,* 4th ed., Wood, Baltimore, 1938)

distortion, apperceptive (ap-er-sep′tiv) A subjective interpretation of a perception which is dynamically meaningful in that perception of the contemporary stimulus is influenced by memories of previous percepts. The various projective tests (Rorschach, TAT, etc.) deal with apperceptive distortions of different degrees.

distortion by transference This term, employed by Freud, indicates that 'When there is anything in the complex-material (the content of the complex) which can at all suitably be transferred on to the person of the physician such a transference will be effected, and from it will arise the next association.' (Freud, S. *Collected Papers,* vol. 2, tr. by Riviere, J., Leonard and Virginia Woolf and The Institute of Psychoanalysis, London, 1924–25)

distortion, compromise See *compromise-distortion.*

distortion, memory See *displacement.*

distortion, parataxic (par-à-tak′sik) Any attitude toward any other person which is based on a phantasied or distorted evaluation of that person or on an identification of that person with other figures from past life.

Freud defined transference as a repetition of the attitude toward the parents at the time of the Oedipus complex. Almost invariably in the course of analysis, the patient begins to concern himself with the analyst in terms of these transferred attitudes. There are some classical analysts today who would confine the term transference to this original meaning. Others, however, accept character attitudes also as a part of transference, for these, too, are reaction patterns from the past which are applied indiscriminately to the analytic situation, where they are not suitable. In an attempt to avoid confusion, Sullivan has used the term parataxic distortion to include this whole picture. 'Sullivan uses neither the libido concept nor the repetition compulsion as formulated by Freud. Parataxic distortions, according to Sullivan, develop from early but essentially nonsexual integrations with significant people. One develops ways of coping with these people and then tends to apply these ways in later interpersonal integrations. However, the need to repeat is by no means as rigid a compulsion as Freud formulated in the repetition compulsion. Later experiences can modify the pattern consciously and unconsciously. In fact, the process of cure is an example of such a modification. The analyst, by his objectivity and insight, fails to conform to the patient's expectations and this, when the patient realizes it, constitutes a new interpersonal situation which helps to make clear the irrational nature of his own behavior.' (Thompson, C. *Psychoanalysis: Evolution and Development,* Hermitage House, New York, 1950) One way to learn what is true and what is parataxic in thinking or feelings about another is to compare one's evaluations with those of others. Sullivan calls this comparison 'consensual validation.'

distractibility See *mania.*

distraction, suggestions by This is an expression used in discussing *suggestion* by Janet, who says that there has been the general tendency 'to avoid arousing attention when making suggestions. Many authorities have noticed that in certain patients suggestions made by insinuation, made gently without attracting attention, succeed better than imperative suggestions. I have myself written at considerable length about suggestions of this kind, terming them "suggestions by distraction." A great many subjects who are not ordinarily cataleptic will keep the arm raised if we raise it gently without their noticing it.' (Janet, P. *Psychological Healing,* vols. 1–2, tr. by Paul, E. and C., Macmillan, New York, 1925)

disturbances, psychographic (sī-kō-graf'-ik) See *psychographic.*

disulfiram See *Antabuse.*

ditention Burrow's term, used to indicate the intrusion of affect or bias into the process of attention. In his view, ditention now characterizes man's interrelational behavior throughout. Contrasted with co-tention. See *attention.*

divagation (dī-và-gā'shun) Rambling thought and speech.

division, cell In biology, cell division represents that genetically most important process by which new cells originate from old ones, following a definite order. The division of ordinary body cells takes place by *mitosis* and is initiated by the nucleus.

In the nucleus of a resting cell the chromatin is scattered and appears like a fine network. At the first indication of imminent division, however, it is formed in a long thread which breaks up into separate pieces, the *chromosomes.* The mitotic *prophase* is finished when each of the chromosomes splits longitudinally into two and the centrosome has also divided into

two halves, which migrate to opposite poles of the nucleus.

In the *metaphase* of mitosis, the nuclear membrane breaks down, and a spindle-shaped mass of fiber-like structures accumulates beside the nucleus, converging toward two opposite poles. The split chromosomes arrange themselves in a plane across the equator of the cell, in such a manner that a spindle fiber is attached to each half chromosome, apparently connecting it with the adjacent pole.

The next stage, known as the *anaphase,* is characterized by a polar migration of the separated two halves of each chromosome. 'The result of this activity is the aggregation at each pole of a group of chromosomes, similar in number and all other visible respects to the single set of mother cell chromosomes from which they arose.' (Sinnot, E.W., and Dunn, L.D. *Principles of Genetics,* 3rd ed., McGraw-Hill, New York and London, 1939)

The last stage of division, the *telophase,* completes the replacement of one old cell by two new ones. The chromosomes of each polar group become surrounded by new nuclear membranes and reorganize daughter nuclei exactly like those of the mother cells. Finally, the cytoplasmic cell body is divided between the new nuclei, in animals by a cleavage furrow going inward from the periphery, and in most plants by a row of pellets forming a wall across the middle of the cell.

divorce See *marriage, psychiatric aspects of.*

divorce, emotional The expression emotional divorce, while described by psychiatrists from the standpoint of instinctual psychology (psychoanalysis), is usually discussed also from the social point of view. When two people marry on a basis of some unresolved conflict in their unconscious, it is probable that marriage may not solve the conflict. Indeed, it may make the conflict less tolerable. Thus, if an emotionally immature girl of 18 who has a strong attachment to her father marries a bachelor of 45 who has always been inordinately attached to his mother, it is highly probable that the couple may soon become incompatible on the basis of a deeply lying and severe incestuous complex. One of several types of response may come about, each of which may be a reflection of emotional divorce.

Dix, Dorothea Lynde (1802–87) American reformer in the care of psychiatric patients.

dizygotic (dī-zī-got′ik) Pertaining to a twin pair produced by two eggs; preferable to the synonymous *fraternal, nonidentical.*

Do Oligophrenic detail; Rorschach scoring symbol for an impoverished response, indicative of low mental level.

dodge, insanity Fictitious defense of insanity designed to evade punishment for a criminal act.

'It has been pretty widely assumed that insanity was used very frequently as a plea to save the criminal when all other means failed, and the "insanity dodge" has come into existence by popular consent as a symbol of sharp practice by unscrupulous attorneys and none-too-honest medical men.' (White, W.A. *Insanity and the Criminal Law,* Macmillan, New York, 1923)

dolichocephaly (dol-i-kō-sef′a-lē) See *index, cephalic.*

dolichomorph (dol′i-kō-morf) An individual with long thin stature.

dolichomorphic (dol-i-kō-mor′fik) Relating to the long thin stature of an individual.

Dolichomorphic is equivalent to *microsplanchnic* of Viola and corresponds closely to Kretschmer's *asthenic* (q.v.).

dolichomorphy (dol′i-kō-mor-fē) The psychiatric field gains an advantage by adopting certain concepts from the school of constitutional medicine. Dolichomorphy, meaning the long, thin type of body build, is in part a reflection of the Law of Godin, or Law of Alternations, namely, that in normal growth, phases of growth in width alternate with phases of growth in length. There are at least two extremes in growth, representing excessive development in width or in length. Dolichomorphy refers to the latter and, in the psychiatric field, is frequently found in schizophrenic individuals.

doll, amputation A doll which can readily be taken apart; used in play therapy with children; introduced by David Levy, who uses the doll in a specific situation, where it represents the mother. 'It is suggested that breasts be made of clay and attached to the mother doll. A baby doll may then be put to the breast. A brother or sister doll representing the child under investi-

gation or treatment is added to the play setup. The child is encouraged to destroy the baby at the breast, the breasts, and also the mother. The patient may also punish the brother or sister doll.' (Bender, L. *Child Psychiatric Techniques,* Thomas, Springfield, Ill., 1952)

domatophobia (dō-ma-tō-fō′bi-a) Fear of being in a house.

dominance Within the various phenomena of Mendelian inheritance, this term denotes the genetic mechanism by which one member of an allelic pair of hereditary factors is endowed with the capacity of expressing itself so strongly that it prevails in the hybrids over the contrasting factor and determines the visible appearance of a hybridized individual either completely or, at least, predominantly. The phenotype of any hybrid inheriting a *completely dominant* character from one of the parents exhibits no manifestations of the suppressed, or *recessive,* factor and is thus enabled to appear as a pure-bred organism in spite of its heterozygosity (see *recessiveness*).

In this dominant or *direct* mode of inheritance we observe as a rule that the phenotypically healthy children are also germinally healthy. Once a descending stock is free of a dominant anomaly, it is free forever. A diseased carrier of a dominant trait must always have one diseased parent and, on the average, 50 per cent diseased siblings and children.

Since the heterozygotic hybrids of a dominant character appear phenotypically like the homozygotes, homozygosity of a trait-carrier can be assumed only if *both* parents are affected by the same trait. Such cases, of course, are very rare.

If a spontaneous interruption of the direct transmission of a dominant trait is found in some affected families, it must be concluded that the clinical pathology of the trait was either not diagnosed, or was inhibited by certain antagonistic factors, or could not be manifested because of the early death of the ordinary taint-carriers.

dominance, cerebral The tendency for certain functions of the brain to be concentrated on a single side of the brain. In right-handed individuals, such functions tend to be concentrated in the left cerebral hemisphere; this is spoken of as 'left cerebral dominance.' Cerebral dominance is certainly associated with handedness, and attempts to alter a natural dominance may cause intellectual disturbances and speech disorders. But that dominance is the primary factor in all speech disorders, as has been maintained by some, is questionable.

dominant In a strictly genetic sense, the term is limited and of a very distinctive nature. It describes the particular faculty of a hereditary factor, transmitted to a hybrid by one of the parents, to constitute the only expressible member of a given pair of contrasting characters and, thus, to appear in the hybrid to the exclusion of the contrasted character transmitted by the other parent.

dominant determinant See *determinant, dominant.*

donatism (don′à-tiz'm) Donato (professional name of the Belgian 'magnetizer' Alfred d'Hont, 1845–1900) demonstrated the role of imitation in hypnosis; the term donatism was given to that form of hypnosis in which imitation forms an important part.

Don Juan (don jōō′an *or* dōn hwän) (Sp. 'Sir John') The Chronicle of Seville relates that Don Juan Tenorio (a member of one of the city's 24 leading families) killed Commendatore Ulloa at night and carried off his daughter. The father was buried in the St. Francis monastery in the family chapel and his statue erected there. The statue and chapel were destroyed by fire. To end the profligate's debauchery the Franciscan monks lured and killed him and spread the rumor that Don Juan had insulted the Commendatore on his tomb and that the new statue had dragged the Don to hell. Tirso de Molina (1571–1648) dramatized the legend in 1630 and Mozart immortalized the story in his opera *Don Giovanni* (1787).

Psychoanalysts believe that the Don Juan type of man is such of the necessity for avenging himself on all women because of the disappointments he experienced in early life with his mother or her surrogate. He is said to stand in apposition to the prostitute type, who is said to avenge herself for the disappointments she incurred in her relations with her father. It may not be the experience of all people today 'that the noble hidalgo, Don Juan, is to be seen nowhere save in the theatre.' (Jung, C.G. *Contributions to Analytical Psychology,* tr. by Baynes, H.G. and C.F.,

Kegan Paul, Trench, Trubner, London, 1928)

Dora The patient on whom Freud reported in his 1905 paper, 'Fragment of an Analysis of a Case of Hysteria.' Dora was an 18-year-old unmarried female whose neurotic symptoms began at the age of eight—chronic dyspnea, hemicranial headaches, and attacks of nervous coughing. Her later symptoms included suicidal threats, amnesic episodes, and periods of aphonia. Analysis of the patient was incomplete since she withdrew from treatment after three months. She died many years later in New York City but had all her life suffered a multitude of neurotic symptoms.

doraphobia (dō-rà-fō′bi-à) Fear of skin of animals.

Dorian love See *love, Dorian.*

dotage Senile psychosis.

doubt The function of doubt in life and in the neuroses is, according to Adler, always to obtain a cessation of aggressiveness, to evade decisions, and to conceal this fact from one's self.

Adler states, 'I refrain from acting in order, if doubt develops, to weigh two possible future situations without coming to any decision.'

doubt, obsessive A doubt or uncertainty having the nature of an obsessional thought, i.e. one that persistently forces itself on the mind of the patient and cannot be banished or reasoned away. In obsessive doubts, says Noyes, 'the patient cannot decide between two courses of action, or if he has chosen he doubts if he has properly completed the act. He may, for example, lock the front door at night, but no sooner has he reached his bed than he is in doubt about the security of the door and must return and try the lock. Even then his doubts may return after he is again in bed and require further visits to verify that the door is locked . . . such doubts and indecisions have a dynamic psychopathological origin and significance . . . they originate from repressions and are protective or defensive in purpose.' (Noyes, A.P. *Modern Clinical Psychiatry,* Saunders Company, Philadelphia and London, 1943)

douche, fan Fan-shaped water spray produced by holding the finger at the nozzle of a hose from which water is emitting.

douche, jet A form of hydrotherapy, consisting of a single stream of water directed at parts of the body.

douche, rain Shower bath.

douche, Scotch Alternating warm and cold jet douche.

dr Rorschach scoring symbol for an unusual (rare) detail.

dramatogenic (dram-à-tō-jen′ik) Moreno's term to denote people 'especially sensitive for collective experiences and able to dramatize them easily . . . Just as there are some people who are photogenic, there are some individuals who are dramatogenic. . .' (Moreno, J.L. 'The Concept of Sociodrama,' *Sociometry VI*, 4, Nov. 1947, p. 448)

drapetomania (drà-pē-tō-mā′ni-à) Uncontrollable impulse to wander; dromomania.

drawing, automatic The execution of drawings without a person's conscious volition, but often after being directed to do so in a hypnotic trance. Automatic drawing constitutes an important aid and method in hypnoanalytical technique: 'Drawing is both a form of motor expressiveness and a means by which the individual can reveal inner problems, wishes, and fears. It is an excellent method of gaining access to deep material where the patient is unable or unwilling to associate freely. Drawings have many of the characteristics of dreams. They provide symbolic ways of representing unconscious impulses. The patient condenses into his creations material that is to him of great emotional significance. He also injects into his graphic productions meanings that reflect his unconscious fantasies; this is similar to what occurs in the Rorschach test.' Automatic drawing can be done in a hypnotic trance (hypnotic drawing), or after awakening if the patient has previously, during the state of hypnosis, been instructed to do so. (Wolberg, L.R. *Hypnoanalysis*, Grune and Stratton, New York, 1945)

drawing, Goodenough See *test, Goodenough*.

dread A term that denotes anxiety related to a specific danger-situation. In his analysis of the nature of anxiety, Freud points out that it originates as the reaction to helplessness in a traumatic situation. Later on, as the ego develops, it anticipates that a situation of helplessness will occur or it is reminded of a previous traumatic experience by the present situation. The situation that is the cause of this anticipation or reminder is called the danger-situation. And the ego will now react with anxiety in this danger-situation. Thus anxiety has become an expectation of trauma in a danger-situation.

However, the affect of anxiety 'is endowed with a certain character of indefiniteness and objectlessness.' This objectlessness and indefiniteness pertain 'to the traumatic situation of helplessness which is anticipated in the danger-situation.' Freud states that in proper usage the term anxiety should be reserved for the original reaction of helplessness in a traumatic situation where no specific danger-situation is expected. The term dread should be used for the anxiety that relates to a specific danger, i.e. 'when it has found an object.' Therefore, 'dread in an individual is provoked either by the greatness of a danger or by the cessation of emotional ties (libidinal cathexes); the latter is the case of neurotic dread.' (Freud, S. *The Problem of Anxiety*, Norton, New York, 1936; *Group Psychology and the Analysis of the Ego*, The International Psychoanalytical Press, London, 1922)

dread, talion A fear of 'retaliation in kind' as punishment for forbidden acts or impulses. Psychoanalysts are familiar with the talion (retaliation) principle of psychology and the exactness with which the punishment is made to fit the crime.

A most vivid example of the use of the term in psychiatric context is seen in the Oedipus situation, wherein the boy fears loss of his penis, i.e. castration by his father, as punishment for his misuse of it (in incestual relationship with his mother): 'the boy's *talion dread* born of his incestual wishes toward his mother.' Another example is to be seen in the neurotic's fear of death and in the hysterical attacks during which he feels he is dying. The talion relationship of these phenomena with unconscious wishes for the death of another will readily be seen.

dream A psychic phenomenon occurring during sleep in which thoughts, images, emotions, etc. present themselves to the dreamer, usually with a definite sense of reality. Dreams are not random psychic productions, for they fulfill a vital purpose in the mental economy. They safeguard sleep; they foster a solution in phantasy of needs and conflicts too dangerous for solution in reality; they provide an outlet for the discharge of instinctual tension; they allow a working through of destructive and traumatic experiences which defy the coping capacities of the waking state. Dreaming is a universal psychic function, typical of the human mind. It is one of the vehicles by which impulses from the unconscious reach the level of consciousness.

Because sleep includes a shutting out of sensory receptors and progressive cortical inhibition, the dream itself works in the manner of the primitive mental apparatus. Visual images tend to replace words, thinking becomes archaic and prelogical and distorted, and there is a tendency toward a universal language.

The recollected dream emerges as the 'manifest dream content,' which tends to be constructed out of events in the recent past. The 'latent dream content' is uncovered by analysis of the manifest content, usually by means of free association. Freud considered the dream a detour by means of which repression could be avoided. The day's residues (events of the waking day) establish contact with repressed, unconscious impulse(s), which attempt to find fulfillment in the material of the latent thoughts. Thus the latent content will include some or all of the following: early memories and experiences, attitudes and phantasies toward parents and siblings, defenses against early experiences and phantasies, present-day wishes (both acceptable and non-acceptable), and conflicts and defenses against these, habitual character strivings and character defenses, attitudes to therapy and attitudes toward the therapist. The unrecognizability, strangeness, and absurdity of the manifest dream are partly the result of translation of thought into archaic modes of expression and partly the result of the restrictive and disapproving dream-censorship.

The processes which transform the latent into the manifest content are called the 'dream work': condensation, displacement, symbolization, dramatization, and secondary elaboration.

The *condensation* of latent thoughts, memories, and phantasies in a dream operates like a magnet gathering together out of the whole reservoir of past and present-day experiences all those pertinent to the magnet. *Displacement* is achieved by giving high interest in the manifest content to an element which will have little significance when the latent thoughts are evoked, or by representing an important latent thought as an insignificant detail in the manifest content. Similarly, the affective accompaniment may be very strong with the least important dream thought, but feeble with the most important thought. Displacement may also be achieved by reversal; e.g. representing the inside as the outside, or the bottom as the top, etc.

Symbolism is the chief method of distorting the latent content. Psychoanalytic experience has shown that the ideas symbolized concern the fundamental factors of existence—our bodies, life, death, procreation—in relation to ourselves and our families. Dream symbolism has many mechanisms in common with formation of figures of speech. The simplest figure of speech is 'simile,' i.e. the equation of two dissimilar things by means of a common attribute, the similarity being indicated by 'as' or 'like.' When these words are omitted, the compressed simile is known as 'metaphor.' These devices also occur in dreams. Personal metaphor involves the transference of human activities to the non-human, such as 'sighing oak.' A flowing stream in a dream will suggest a stream of urine or a flow of talk; or a particular type of tree may have special significance, such as 'pine' tree meaning someone longed for, etc. Through 'metonymy,' a name that has a usual or accidental connection with a thing is used for the thing itself, such as the 'bar' for the profession of law. 'Synecdoche' employs a part to represent the whole, such as a factory accommodating so many 'hands.' When the sounds of the words echo the sense, the term is 'onomatopoeia.' 'Antithesis' appears in dreams in the form of opposition in position, as in sitting. Parallels are used to convey similarity of position, such as sitting alongside a person. The repetition of a dream element is similar to the repetition of phrases in diction to secure emphasis. Through the 'implied metaphor,' abstract ideas are expressed in terms of the concrete; e.g. 'food for thought,' 'hot temper.' Although words acquire a second meaning and convey abstract ideas, they do not lose their original concrete significance in the unconscious; language itself, therefore, may yield significant information. Thus, 'She is her mother's spoiled darling' may mean she is pampered; but to the unconscious, spoiled also means dirty or ruined.

Dramatization is the representation in the manifest dream of an action or situation evolved from the latent thoughts by the dream mechanisms. It is the subjective attempt within the psyche to project anxiety and control stimuli. The mechanisms may attempt to draw a unity from the conflicting forces of many years, balancing and neutralizing affects. Different persons may represent conflicting parts of the psyche. If a balance is not achieved, the dream may leave a disagreeable affect or anxiety. *Secondary elaboration* molds the latent thoughts and wishes, disguised by the processes of condensation, displacement, and symbolization, into the semblance of a logical story. Ernest Jones considers it as being closely allied to rationalization. (Sharpe, E.F. *Dream Analysis,* Norton, New York, 1938)

Every dream is capable of many meanings, on many different psychic levels, and not all of them will necessarily be interpreted by the analyst. There are several choices possible in the technique of dream interpretation: to proceed chronologically and in order, to start with one particular element, to ask the dreamer what events of the previous day are associated with the dream, or to let the dreamer begin where he will to free-associate. L. Wolberg (*The Technique of Psychotherapy,* Grune & Stratton, New York, 1954) lists the following techniques of interpretation: (a) summarizing for the patient the basic trends in the dream; (b) asking the patient for spontaneous associations; (c) tentative, unverbalized formulation of the dynamics based on the therapist's knowledge of the patient (which formulation will take account of the setting of the dream, the characters in the dream, underlying wish or need, personality traits disclosed in the dream, mechanisms of defense, conflicts expressed in the dream, the movement and outcome of the dream, and the resistance and transference manifestations expressed); and (d) encouraging further associations by focusing the patient's attention on particular problems or conflicts as they seem to be expressed in the dream.

According to Adler, the dream has an anticipatory, prescient function. It foreshadows the preparations developed in connection with actual difficulties encountered by the dreamer's life-plan and the safeguarding purpose is never lost sight of. In other words, the dream attempts to influence the future complexion of things. It is an attempt to solve a problem and has no sexual connotation. It is an indication of power, a sign and a proof that both body and mind are making an attempt at anticipatory thinking and at anticipatory groping in order to justify the personality of the dreamer in connection with some approaching difficulty. It provides a glimpse of the dreamer's unconscious life-plan by means of which he strives to dominate the pressure of life and his own feeling of uncertainty. In dreams all the transitional phases of anticipatory thinking occur as if directed by some previously determined goal and by the utilization of personal experiences.

He sums up: 'The main function of dreams consists of simplified early trials and of warnings and encouragements favorable to the life-plan; and to have as their object the solution of some future problem.' (Adler, A. *The Practice and Theory of Individual Psychology,* tr. by Radin, P., Kegan Paul, Trench, Trubner, London, 1924)

dream, absurd In this way Freud denotes what many investigators thought to be the essence of dreams, namely, absurdity, incoherence, senselessness. See *absurdity.*

dream activity See *activity, dream.*

dream, agreement in Freud states that dream-work is characterized, among other things, by the process of *condensation,* meaning that several components may be reduced to a unity. When, through some common feature, two or more persons are represented by one person, Freud uses the term *identification;* when two or more things are unified, he speaks of *composition.* Since things may symbolize, that is, stand for persons, composition may also involve persons. 'Localities are often treated as persons.'

'*Similarity, agreement, community,* are quite generally expressed in dreams by contraction into a *unity,* which is either already found in the dream-material or is newly created.' (Freud, S. *The Interpretation of Dreams,* 3rd ed., tr. by Brill, A.A., Macmillan, New York, 1933)

dream, alternative in Freud says that 'dreams are quite incapable of expressing the alternative "either-or"; it is their custom to take both members of this alternative into the same content, as though they had an equal right to be there.' (Freud, S. *The Interpretation of Dreams*, 3rd ed., tr. by Brill, A.A., Macmillan, New York, 1933) In dreams 'either-or' means 'and.'

dream, ambiguity of Many dreams appear quite ambiguous and are capable of more than a single interpretation. While referring to his analysis of a dream, Freud says: 'The two interpretations do not contradict one another, but rather dovetail into one another, and furnish an excellent example of the usual ambiguity of dreams, as of all other psychopathological formations.' (Freud, S. *The Interpretation of Dreams*, 3rd ed., tr. by Brill, A.A., Macmillan, New York, 1933)

dream, an objective process By this phrase Jung means that during sleep 'the mind is to a great extent withdrawn from our voluntary control. With the small portion of consciousness that remains to us in the dream state we can perceive what takes place, but we are no longer in the position to guide the course of psychic events according to our wish and purpose; hence we are also robbed of the possibility of deceiving ourselves. The dream is an automatic process resting upon the independent activity of the unconscious, and is just as much removed from our conscious control as, for example, the physiological action of digestion. In it, therefore, we have an absolutely objective process from the nature of which we can draw objective conclusions about the actual situation.' (Jung, C.G. *Contributions to Analytical Psychology*, tr. by Baynes, H.G. and C.F., Kegan Paul, Trench, Trubner, London, 1928)

dream, antithesis in (an-tith'ē-sis) Freud's earlier view was that 'the attitude of dreams to the category of *antithesis* and *contradiction* is very striking. This category is simply ignored; the word "no" does not seem to exist for a dream. Dreams are particularly fond of reducing antitheses to uniformity, or representing them as one and the same thing.' (Freud, S. *The Interpretation of Dreams*, 3rd ed., tr. by Brill, A.A., Macmillan, New York, 1933)

dream, anxiety An anxiety dream is one in which anxiety forms an important part. Freud says: 'That a psychic process which

develops anxiety may still be a wish-fulfilment has long ceased to imply any contradiction for us. We may explan this occurrence by the fact that the wish belongs to one system (the *Ucs*), whereas the other system (the *Pcs*) has rejected and suppressed it.' (Freud, S. *The Interpretation of Dreams*, 3rd ed., tr. by Brill, A.A., Macmillan, 1933)

dream, artificial The expression *artificial dream* is used to designate that dream which is apparently induced by sensory stimulation. Freud cites from Maury, who, when his neck was lightly pinched during sleep, dreamed that a blister was being applied. Freud holds that sensory stimuli may instigate a dream, but they cannot be held responsible for the content of the dream.

dream, biographical This is a type of dream in which the manifest content is mainly composed of fairly reasonable events connected with the life of the dreamer.

dream, castration The castration theme is frequently presented in dreams in a variety of ways. Freud relates a dream in which a son saw his head cut off by his mother.

dream-censorship See *censorship, dream*.

dream, comfort Synonymous with *dream, convenience* (q.v.).

dream, community in See *dream, agreement in*.

dream, compensatory nature of Jung says: 'It is an assured finding of scientific experience that dreams, for example, almost invariably have a content which can act as an essential corrective to the conscious attitude. Hence our justification for speaking of a compensatory function of the unconscious.' (Jung, C.G. *Contributions to Analytical Psychology*, tr. by Baynes, H.G. and C.F., Kegan Paul, Trench, Trubner, London, 1928)

dream, composition in See *dream, agreement in*.

dream, conceptual content of As a rule, ideas in dreams are expressed in the form of visual images.
　'The second quality peculiar to the dream alone, as distinguished from the day-dream, is that the conceptual content is not thought, but is transformed into visual images, to which we give credence, and which we believe that we experience.

Let us add, however, that not all dreams show this transformation of ideas into visual images.' (Freud, S. *The Interpretation of Dreams*, 3rd ed., tr. by Brill, A.A., Macmillan, New York, 1933)

dream, confession A dream which implies a confession. 'If we take into account this nurse's touchiness, her attitude to unlucky Fridays, etc., we should confirm the conclusion that the dream contained a confession. . . .' (Freud, S. *Collected Papers* vol. 2, tr. by Riviere, J., Leonard and Virginia Woolf and The Institute of Psychoanalysis, London, 1924–25)

dream, consolation When dreams contain an encouraging note, they are known as consolation dreams.

'There are consolation-dreams, directed against another anxiety perceived in dreams—the fear of death. "To depart" is one of the most frequent and one of the most readily established of the death-symbols. The dream therefore says consolingly: "Reassure yourself, you are not going to die (to depart)," just as the examination-dream calms us by saying: "Don't be afraid; this time, too, nothing will happen to you." The difficulty in understanding both kinds of dreams is due to the fact that the anxiety is attached precisely to the expression of consolation.' (Freud, S. *The Interpretation of Dreams*, 3rd ed., tr. by Brill, A.A., Macmillan, 1933)

dream-content By this Freud means the material of which the dream is composed. Dreams have a latent dream-content, made up of dream-thoughts and a manifest dream-content, usually presented in highly symbolic form. 'The dream-content is, as it were, presented in hieroglyphics, whose symbols must be translated, one by one, into the language of dream-thoughts.' (Freud, S. *The Interpretation of Dreams*, 3rd ed., tr. by Brill, A.A., Macmillan, New York, 1933)

dream, contradition in See *dream, antithesis in*.

dream, contrast in Freud says: 'I have already stated that the dream has no means of expressing the relation of contradiction, contrast, negation. I shall now contradict this assertion for the first time. A certain number of cases of what may be summed up under the word "contrast" obtain representation, as we have seen, simply by means of identification—that is,

when an exchange, a substitution, can be bound up with the contrast.' (Freud, S. *The Interpretation of Dreams*, 3rd ed., tr. by Brill, A.A., Macmillan, New York, 1933)

dream, convalescent Dreams can and do occur in *any* convalescence, but in no other period than the convalescence of traumatic neurosis is it true that *convalescent dreams* are of a specific type and *only* of that type. The nature and content of the dreams of a traumatic neurotic are characteristic of this particular disorder, so much so in fact that they may be taken as pathognomonic of the illness.

'In traumatic neurosis—especially in the early stages, within the first year of the trauma—the dream life is pathognomonic.' (Kardiner, A., and Spiegel, H. *War Stress and Neurotic Illness*, Hoeber, New York, 1947)

Moreover, in differential diagnosis this unique quality of the dream life in traumatic neurosis is a factor that may be used in differentiating this disorder from others which may resemble it (psychoneuroses, character neuroses, schizophrenia, malingering, etc.). The traumatic neurotic exhibits a stereotypy in his dream life. The most common content of the dream is the threat of annihilation, usually a representation of the original trauma. 'These . . . dreams say essentially the same thing in different ways; they all reproduce a helpless situation with its tremendous release of disorganized aggression. They all say: "I am as at birth, I perceive the world but can do nothing with it, hence it threatens me." ' (ibid.)

dream, convenience While saying about convenience dreams that 'in truth all dreams may claim this designation,' Freud stresses certain types as such.

'Such convenience-dreams came very frequently to me in my youth. Accustomed as I had always been to work until late at night, early waking was always a matter of difficulty. I used then to dream that I was out of bed and standing at the washstand.' (Freud, S. *The Interpretation of Dreams*, 3rd ed., tr. by Brill, A.A., Macmillan, New York, 1933) He calls this a lethargy-dream.

dream, corroborating A dream corroborating the material of a previous dream. 'In conclusion, I will mention a particular type of dream which, in the nature of the case, occurs only in the course of psycho-analytic treatment, and may bewilder or deceive beginners in practice. These are the corroborating dreams, which follow, as one may say, like "hangers-on"; they are easily translated, and contain merely what has been arrived at by analysis of the previous few days' material.' (Freud, S. *Collected Papers,* vol. 2, tr. by Riviere, J., Leonard and Virginia Woolf and The Institute of Psychoanalysis, London, 1924–25)

dream, counter-wish According to Freud certain dreams seem not to be associated with a wish; in fact they seem to be of the opposite character, that is, to convey a counter-wish. The wish may be concealed behind its opposite. An impotent patient dreamed he had syphilis. He said that if he had syphilis it would signalize potency to him. A second motive for a counter-wish dream is seen in dream-distortion. A patient, who had often punished his brother, dreamed that the brother had foreclosed his (the patient's) mortgage on a house highly prized by the dreamer. Under analysis it was evident that the dreamer, out of a sense of guilt, was expressing a hidden wish for punishment.

dream-day The day before the night of the dream. It is significant because it often contributes something that stimulates the occurrence of a dream.

dream, diagnostic capacity of Freud says: 'The "diagnostic" capacity of dreams becomes equally comprehensible, too—a phenomenon which is so universally acknowledged, but regarded as so puzzling; in dreams, incipient physical disease is often detected earlier and more clearly than in waking life, and all the current bodily sensations assume gigantic proportions.' (Freud, S. *Collected Papers,* vol. 4, tr. by Riviere, J., Leonard and Virginia Woolf and The Institute of Psychoanalysis, London, 1924–25)

dream-displacement In principle dream-displacement does not differ from the displacement observed in other psychic structures. 'That which is obviously the essential content of the dream-thoughts need not be represented at all in the dream. The dream is, as it were, *centered elsewhere;* its content is arranged about elements which do not constitute the central point of the dream throughts.' (Freud, S. *The Interpretation of Dreams,* 3rd ed.,

tr. by Brill, A.A., Macmillan, New York, 1933) See *displacement.*

dream-distortion Distortion is a common psychic phenomenon. When it occurs in dreams, it is called dream-distortion. Its motive is to prevent understanding of the issue that is distorted. Freud says: 'We feel justified in connecting the unpleasant character of all these dreams with the fact of dream-distortion, and in concluding that these dreams are distorted, and that their wish-fulfilment is disguised beyond recognition, precisely because there is a strong revulsion against—a will to repress—the subject-matter of the dream, or the wish created by it. Dream-distortion, then proves in reality to be an act of the censorship.' (Freud, S. *The Interpretation of Dreams,* 3rd ed., tr. by Brill, A.A., Macmillan, New York, 1933). See *distortion.*

dream, egoism of Freud says: 'It has been my experience—and to this I have found no exception—that every dream treats of oneself. Dreams are absolutely egoistic. In cases where not my ego, but only a strange person occurs in the dream-content, I may safely assume that by means of identification my ego is concealed behind that person.' (Freud, S. *The Interpretation of Dreams,* 3rd ed., tr. by Brill, A.A., Macmillan, New York, 1933)

dream, embarrassment Dreams of embarrassment usually take the form of shame associated with nakedness. 'But the dream of nakedness demands our attention only when shame and embarrassment are felt in it, when one wishes to escape or hide, and when one feels the strange inhibition of being unable to stir from the spot, and of being utterly powerless to alter the painful situation.' (Freud, S. *The Interpretation of Dreams,* 3rd ed., tr. by Brill, A.A., Macmillan, New York, 1933) The embarrassment dream is said to stem from similar experiences of childhood. Elsewhere Freud says: 'I hope that the examples given above will suffice—until some further objection appears—to make it seem credible that even dreams with a painful content are to be analysed as wish-fulfilment.' (ibid.)

dream, examination Examination-dreams (Freud), or matriculation - dreams (Stekel), are dreams connected with examinations. See *examination anxiety.*

dream, exhibition A dream of nakedness.

dream-forgetting During the waking stage there is 'an unmistakable intention to forget' dreams. During sleep there is a slackening of the censorship forces, the forces of resistance that keep unconscious material out of consciousness. The forces, however, gain their full powers when sleep is ended and they drive the memory of the dream into the unconscious sphere.

dream-formation The manner in which dreams are formed. Groups of unconscious impulses first undergo condensation, that is, some single symbolic representation is substituted for a large series of events. When an individual dreamed, for instance, that his law office, which in reality is well-lighted, neat, and clean, was dark, dirty, and disorderly, he had condensed, and, of course, distorted, a series of anal impulses about which he gave details during the analysis of the dream. In the dream he condensed another impulse which he connected with the first. In the dark office was the dimly outlined form of an elderly woman, perhaps a client. Analysis showed the woman to be his mother, about whom he related many Oedipus events.

'In respect of the great majority of the groups of thoughts revealed by analysis, we are obliged to admit that they have already been active in the formation of the dream, for if we work through a succession of such thoughts, which at first sight seem to have played no part in the formation of the dream, we suddenly come upon a thought which occurs in the dream-content, and is indispensable to its interpretation, but which is nevertheless inaccessible except through this chain of thoughts.' (Freud, S. *The Interpretation of Dreams,* 3rd ed., tr. by Brill, A.A., Macmillan, New York, 1933)

dream, fractional interpretation of Freud states that 'the interpretation of a dream cannot always be accomplished in one session; after following up a chain of associations you will often feel that your working capacity is exhausted; the dream will not tell you anything more that day; it is then best to break off, and to resume the work the following day. Another portion of the dream-content then solicits your attention, and you thus gain access to a fresh stratum of the dream-thoughts. One might call this the "fractional" interpretation of dreams.' (Freud, S. *The In-*

terpretation of Dreams, 3rd ed., tr. by Brill, A.A., Macmillan, New York, 1933)

dream-function Freud says: 'The dream is the (disguised) fulfilment of a (suppressed, repressed) wish.' (Freud, S. *The Interpretation of Dreams,* 3rd ed., tr. by Brill, A.A., Macmillan, New York, 1933)

Jung holds that the general function of dreams is to reflect 'certain fundamental tendencies of the personality, either those whose meaning extends over the whole life, or those that are momentarily of most importance. The dream gives an objective statement of these tendencies, a statement which does not trouble itself about conscious wishes and convictions.' (Jung, C.G. *Contributions to Analytical Psychology,* tr. by Baynes, H.G. and C.F., Kegan Paul, Trench, Trubner, London, 1928)

While referring to Freud's dream theory Adler says: 'In reality these infantile wishes already stand under the compulsion of the imaginary goal and themselves usually bear the character of a guiding thought suitably arrayed, and adapt themselves to symbolic expression purely for reasons of thought economy.' (Adler, A. *The Neurotic Constitution,* tr. by Glueck, B. and Lind, J.E., Moffat, Yard, New York, 1917)

dream, functional According to Silberer, this expression refers specifically to dreams that originate in physical disturbances of mental origin. On the other hand, Stekel uses the term in a looser sense to denote dreams that symbolize the function of the psyche, whether normal or morbid.

dream, general function of According to Jung dreams reflect 'certain vital fundamental tendencies of the personality, either those whose meaning extends over the whole life, or those that are momentarily of most importance. The dream gives an objective statement of these tendencies, a statement which does not trouble itself about conscious wishes and convictions.' (Jung, C.J. *Contributions to Analytical Psychology,* tr. by Baynes, H.G. and C.F., Kegan Paul, Trench, Trubner, London, 1928)

dream, hallucinatory Excitation in a dream 'communicates itself not to the motor end of the apparatus, but to the sensory end, and finally reaches the system of perception. If we call the direction which the psychic process follows from the unconscious into the waking state progressive, we may then speak of the dream as having a regressive character.' (Freud, S. *The Interpretation of Dreams,* 3rd ed., tr. by Brill, A.A., Macmillan, New York, 1933) The 'complex' arouses the system of perception, producing an hallucinatory dream.

dream, hyper-determination of Most dreams have multiple determinants. 'In dream-formation the essential elements, those that are emphasized by intensive interests, may be treated as though they were subordinate, while they are replaced in the dream by other elements, which were certainly subordinate in the dream-thoughts.' (Freud, S. *The Interpretation of Dreams,* 3rd ed., tr. by Brill, A.A., Macmillan, New York, 1933) See *dream-displacement*.

dream, hypermnesia in (hī-pẽrm-nē′zhi-à) Exaggerated degree of memory in a dream is particularly common. Freud says: 'The hypermnesia of the dream and its ability to dispose of infantile material have become the main foundations of our doctrine.' (Freud, S. *The Interpretation of Dreams,* 3rd ed., by Brill, A.A., Macmillan, New York, 1933)

dream, hypocritical According to Freud certain dreams, those which repeat disagreeable experiences in the life of the individual, seemingly refute the theory of wish-fulfillment. Such dreams are called hypocritical dreams, for upon analysis they are found to sustain that theory.

dream, identification in See *dream, agreement in.*

dream-illusion A dream may be precipitated by an objective sensory stimulus. A ringing alarm clock may set a dream in motion that has nothing to do with ringing or an alarm clock. The ringing stimulated a patient to dream of a locomotive swiftly passing by him. He was panic-stricken lest he be drawn into the path of the locomotive. The ringing of the clock had aroused a painful complex in him, that of castration. Of course, the locomotive was the illusory symbol.

Dream-illusions may be engendered also by subjective sensory stimuli. 'They are those very vivid and changeable pictures which with many people occur constantly during the period of falling asleep, and which may linger for a while even after the eyes have been opened. . . . According to Maury, if one wakes up shortly after such an experience (of hypnagogic hallucinations), it is often possible to trace in the dream the images which one has perceived before falling asleep as hypnagogic hallucinations.' (Freud, S. *The Interpretation of Dreams,* 3rd ed., tr. by Brill, A.A., Macmillan, New York, 1933)

Dream-illusions may come about as a consequence of organic, visceral stimulation. Thus, an organ, activated by disease or by any physiological urge, may stimulate memory-images that superficially have nothing in common with the source of the stimulus.

dream-images During sleep psychic activity occurs principally in the form of images, of pictorial representations, called dream-images.

dream-inciter See *dream-stimulus.*

dream-instigator See *dream-stimulus.*

dream-interpretation The meaning given to a dream is dream-interpretation. The only kind of dream-interpretation used in current psychiatric practice is derived from the formulations of Freud, who includes many of the findings of others within his discipline. The Freudian form of dream-interpretation assumes that the dream has two contents: the manifest content is the dream as it actually appears to the dreamer; the latent content is made up of the hidden, disguised meaning of the manifest content. Dream-interpretation involves the application of the free-association method to the material comprising the manifest content for purposes of revealing the basic impulses resident in the latent content.

Usually dreams are analyzed by the 'fractional' method, that is, each item of the dream is considered separately for free-association. When this process is completed, the separate parts are used, in order to piece together a whole.

But the task is not finished when all of the details have been interpreted. Freud speaks of over-interpretation. He says: 'It is really not easy to form an idea of the wealth of trains of unconscious thought striving for expression in our minds, or to credit the adroitness displayed by the dream-work in killing—so to speak—seven flies at one stroke, like the journeyman tailor in the fairy-tale, by means of its ambiguous modes of expression.' (Freud,

S. *The Interpretation of Dreams,* 3rd ed., tr. by Brill, A.A., Macmillan, New York, 1933)

'It is always a strict law of dream-interpretation that an explanation must be found for every detail.' (ibid.)

dream, inversion in The peculiar but very common phenomenon of a latent dream-thought's element being represented by its very opposite in the manifest or actual dream. This turning into the opposite 'is one of the most favoured and most versatile methods of representation which the dream-work has at its disposal.' First of all, it enables the ego to react against a disagreeable dream-thought by wish-fulfillment. For, wish-fulfillment is the replacing of an unpleasant thing by its opposite. And through inversion wish-fulfillment can prevail against unpleasant dream-thoughts. Second, inversion is a very important technique of dream censorship: the representation in a dream of some dream-thoughts by their opposites adds greatly to the distortion of the dream. Now, inversion applies not only to concrete images but also to the affects of dream-thoughts. Thus in a dream a feeling of affection for someone may stand for a feeling of hatred and vice versa. This distortion is also the work of dream censorship.

Freud points out that 'transformation into the contrary is made possible by the intimate associative ties which in our thoughts connect the idea of a thing with that of its opposite.' He mentions the fact that in primitive languages one word frequently refers to both extremes in a series of attributes or activities; thus one word would mean both strong and weak, old and young, far and near, high and deep, etc. (Freud, S. *The Interpretation of Dreams* in *The Basic Writings of Sigmund Freud,* Modern Library, Random House, New York, 1938)

dream, keystone of the Freud says: 'In the best interpreted dreams we often have to leave one passage in obscurity, because we observe during the interpretation that we have here a tangle of dream-thoughts which cannot be unravelled, and which furnishes no fresh contribution to the dream-content. This, then, is the keystone of the dream, the point at which it ascends into the unknown. For the dream-thoughts which we encounter during the interpretation commonly have no termi-

nation, but run in all directions into the net-like entanglement of our intellectual world. It is from some denser part of this fabric that the dream-wish then arises, like the mushroom from its mycelium.' (Freud, S. *The Interpretation of Dreams,* 3rd ed., tr. by Brill, A.A., Macmillan, New York, 1933)

dream, lethargy See *dream, convenience.*

dream-life The activity of the mind, recorded in sensory images during sleep.

dream, lying According to Freud 'a dream is not the "unconscious" itself; it is the form into which a thought from the preconscious, or even from waking conscious life, can, thanks to the favouring conditions of sleep, be recast. . . . With our dreamer, the intention to mislead me, just as she did her father, certainly emanated from the preconscious, or perhaps even from consciousness; it could come to expression by entering into connection with the unconscious wish-impulse to please the father (or father-substitute), and in this way it created a lying dream.' (Freud, S. *Collected Papers,* vol. 2, tr. by Riviere, J., Leonard and Virginia Woolf and The Institute of Psychoanalysis, London, 1924–25)

dream, made-to-order A dream that the patient seems to produce at the analyst's direct suggestion, as if the patient dreams in response to the urgent demands of the psychiatrist. Of course, determined as they are by the relationship between the patient and the analyst, such dreams are often extremely distorted, and usually express a derisive attitude toward the physician.

dream, manifest The name given by Freud to the dream itself, as reported by the dreamer. The dream-text or manifest dream in itself is not intelligible as far as gaining new information about the patient is concerned. In the process of analysis of the manifest dream, however, information concerning the patient, which would otherwise be inaccessible, is obtained. This information which lies behind the dream is termed the latent dream-thoughts. The technique by which the latent dream-thoughts are derived from the manifest dream is called dream interpretation. This technique utilizes the associations of the patient to the various parts of the manifest dream and the meaning of certain symbols with which the patient often is unable to associate. The process by which the latent dream-thoughts become the manifest dream in the dreamer's mental life is called the dream-work. The two major techniques by which the dream-work is accomplished are condensation and displacement. (Freud, S. *New Introductory Lectures on Psycho-analysis,* Norton, New York, 1933)

dream, matriculation See *dream, examination.*

dream, motive power of See *system.*

dream, nonsensical A dream seemingly senseless or void of logic is termed a nonsensical dream by Stekel. The illogicality of a dream does not necessarily mean that the patient himself is illogical in his waking life. 'On the contrary, the dreams that appear logical enough may be the fruit of a sick brain.' In the opinion of Stekel, a person of frank disposition, one who has nothing to hide (insofar as that is possible), will have dreams that are not essentially distorted, in opposition to persons who are perpetually fleeing from self-awareness and need distorted, so-called nonsensical dreams which are almost insoluble enigmas.

Of course, the analyst's failure to understand a dream does not inevitably imply that the dream is nonsensical. 'The dream has its own secret logic, so that we are justified in speaking of the inner logic of the dream,' because sometimes the apparently nonsensical parts of a dream are, as a matter of fact, the very spots that contain a clue to its meaning. (Stekel, W. *The Interpretation of Dreams,* Liveright, New York, 1943)

dream-pain Hypnalgia; pain occurring during the dream state.

dream, paramnesia in (par-am-nē′shi-à) See *paramnesia.*

dream, perennial According to Freud, a dream 'which, being first dreamt in childhood, recurs again and again in adult years.' (Freud, S. *The Interpretation of Dreams,* 3rd ed., tr. by Brill, A.A., Macmillan, New York, 1933)

dream-phantasy The manifest content of the dream, that is, the picture presented to the dreamer, is called the dream-phantasy. Freud says: '. . . that activity of the psyche which may be described as *phantasy,* freed from all rational governance, and hence no longer strictly con-

trolled, rises to absolute supremacy in our dreams. To be sure, it borrows all its building-material from the memory of the waking state, but with this material it builds up structures which differ from those of the waking state as day differs from night.' (Freud, S. *The Interpretation of Dreams,* 3rd ed., tr. by Brill, A.A., Macmillan, New York, 1933)

There is a second meaning to the term dream-phantasy. When dreams are 'particularly well-constructed, flawless and clear,' and are not 'subject to the mechanism of condensation and distortion,' the type of dreams described as 'phantasies during sleep,' they are called *dream-phantasies* (ibid.). Freud abandoned the idea of erecting such a category, but later wondered if he had been justified in doing so.

dream-problem The nature and meaning of dreams constitute dream-problems.

dream processes See *dream-work.*

dream, prophetic Stekel considers it justifiable to use the term 'prophetic' for describing those dreams that seem to forecast a wish of the dreamer and later on come true. To illustrate a dream of this type Stekel gives the example of the individual who was attached to his mother and his family with unduly strong ties and expressed symbolically, in a dream, his wish to break these bonds. After the meaning of the dream was explained to him, he was able to fulfill his wish and become engaged to a girl with whom he had been in love for a long time. (Stekel, W. *The Interpretation of Dreams,* Liveright, New York, 1943)

dream-psychosis The mental state of the dreamer is called a dream-psychosis. Freud calls that state a psychosis, emphasizing that it is transitory, harmless, and disappears when relations with the external world are resumed.

dream, punishment Freud says that certain dreams are quite disagreeable in content, since they often reproduce painful experiences of the past. 'I see no objection to regarding such dreams as *punishment-dreams,* as distinguished from wish-fulfilling dreams. I should not see in this any limitation of the theory of dreams hitherto as presented, but merely a verbal concession to the point of view to which the convergence of contraries seems strange.' (Freud, S. *The Interpretation of Dreams,*

3rd ed., tr. by Brill, A.A., Macmillan, New York, 1933)

dream, reconstruction In Levin's terminology, a dream in which a succession of events culminate, seemingly by chance, in a stimulus coinciding with an external stimulus of like nature which wakes the dreamer. Thus a dream that ends with a bell ringing when the ringing of an alarm clock wakes the sleeper is a reconstruction dream. It is probable that such dreams are mainly instances of the dynamic and 'economizing' purpose of dreams to protect the sleeper from disturbances. There seems to be no reason to doubt that reconstruction dreams are further utilized, as is any other dream, in the symbolic expression of unconscious conflicts: that is, reconstruction dreams are subject to psychoanalytic interpretation. (*Psychoanalytic Quarterly 10,* 685, 1941)

dream, secondary elaboration of The account of a dream given by the dreamer upon awakening, insofar as it differs from the original content, is referred to as secondary elaboration of the dream.
'This process continues even in the waking state, so that the account of a dream as related directly after waking differs from that related some time after.' (Jones, E. *Papers on Psycho-Analysis,* 4th ed., Wood, Baltimore, 1938)

dream, similarity in See *dream, agreement in.*

dream, Sisyphus Frustration dream. See *neurosis, traumatic.*

dream-source See *dream-stimulus.*

dreams, paired Alexander calls attention to what he describes as 'paired' dreams. They are based upon the concepts of punishment and gratification, in the sense that one is allowed to indulge in a forbidden act, if he has already paid the penalty for it. During the same night the individual may first dream that he is being punished; later he dreams that he is engaging in a forbidden act.

dream, speech in Freud says: 'The dream-work cannot compose a new speech. No matter how many speeches and answers, which may in themselves be sensible or absurd, may occur in dreams, analysis always shows us that the dream has merely taken from the dream-thoughts fragments of speeches which have really been delivered or heard, and has dealt

with them in the most arbitrary fashion.' (Freud, S. *The Interpretation of Dreams,* 3rd ed., tr. by Brill, A.A., Macmillan, New York, 1933). The dream-work actually produces neologistic sentences. What appears in the dream as speech often represents a command or prohibition stemming from the superego.

dreams, semantics in Dreams represent the language of the unconscious—the language of ancient mankind. Dreams are largely pictorial and perceptual, and over the ages newer and different meanings have been given to the pictorial language. Semantics in dreams refers to such language evolution. According to Freud, the language of dreams would be understood better and translated more easily if more were known about the development of language, for the thought-expression in dreams has the same regressive archaic character as is shown by primitive thought and its expression in language.
Freud gives the example of inversion in dreams—the process by which an element of the manifest dream may represent its opposite in the latent dream-thoughts. In many old and primitive languages, a fair number of the words have opposite meanings. This is true of the oldest roots of language, for, as the language develops, double meanings often disappear. For example, the Latin *altus* means both 'high' and 'deep,' and other examples may be drawn from other languages. Thus the prototype of the mechanism of inversion in dreams can be seen in the antithetical sense of many primitive words. (Freud, S. *The Antithetical Sense of Primal Words* in *Collected Papers,* vol. 4, Hogarth Press, London, 1925)

dream-stimulus An exciting cause of a dream is a dream-stimulus. It may be (1) an external sensory stimulus, (2) an internal (subjective) sensory stimulus, (3) an internal (organic) physical stimulus, or (4) a stimulus from the psyche itself.

dream-symbolism The manifest content of a dream, according to psychoanalysis, is always a substituted or symbolic way of expressing something that is unacceptable to the conscious mind of the dreamer. 'When one has familiarized oneself with the extensive employment of symbolism for the representation of sexual material in dreams, one naturally asks oneself whether many of these symbols have not a permanently established meaning, like the signs in shorthand; and one even thinks of attempting to compile a new dream-book on the lines of the cipher method.' (Freud, S. *The Interpretation of Dreams,* 3rd ed., tr. by Brill, A.A., Macmillan, New York, 1933)

dream-synthesis A term used by Havelock Ellis to designate a study of dreams from the standpoint of statistics.

dream, telepathic By this expression Stekel describes a certain type of dream which seems to be engendered in the mind of the dreamer by transmission from other dreamers near him. The existence of such a type of dream is unquestionable according to Stekel, who asserts that he has collected 'numerous instances to show that persons who sleep in the same room influence one another's dreams.' The interpretation of this kind of dream, according to Stekel, is very valuable in the joint analysis of husband and wife, as they do transmit to each other their oneiric influences, and, furthermore, this is the only type of dream which does not represent a wish element. (Stekel, W. *The Interpretation of Dreams,* Liveright, New York, 1943)

dream-text The manifest part of the dream, in contradistinction to its latent significance.

dream-thought An expression referring to the ideas that give rise to the dream-content. 'The dream-thoughts and the dream-content present themselves as two descriptions of the same content in two different languages; or, to put it more clearly, the dream-content appears to us as translation of the dream-thoughts into another mode of expression, whose symbols and laws of composition we must learn by comparing the origin with the translation.' (Freud, S. *The Interpretation of Dreams,* 3rd ed., tr. by Brill, A.A., Macmillan, New York, 1933) For example, the dream-thought may be an intra-uterine phantasy, presented as being in a cave, which is the dream-content.

Dream-thought also refers to the character by which unconscious motives are expressed. Dreams reproduce primitive, archaic modes of thought. Freud cites Havelock Ellis's remark that the dream is 'an archaic world of vast emotions and imperfect thoughts.' Freud also quotes Sully to the effect that 'our dreams bring back again our earlier and successively developed personalities, our old ways of regarding things, with impulses and modes of reaction which ruled us long ago.' (Freud, S. *The Interpretation of Dreams,* 3rd ed., tr. by Brill, A.A., Macmillan, New York, 1933) Suppressed material is 'the mainspring' of the dream. The dream-thought, then, is the idea or ideas behind the dream and the special ways by which the material is expressed.

dream, unity in See *dream, agreement in.*

dream-waking *Obs.* Illusion or hallucination.

dream-wish From the psychoanalytical point of view the dream-wish represents an unfulfilled desire or impulse. 'Let me, therefore, set aside the view previously expressed, and it matters little whence the dream-wish originates, and replace it by another, namely: *the wish manifested in the dream must be an infantile wish.* In the adult it originates in the Ucs. (unconscious), while in the child, in whom no division and censorship exist as yet between the Pcs. (preconscious) and Ucs., or in whom these are only in process of formation, it is an unfulfilled and unrepressed wish from the waking state.' (Freud, S. *The Interpretation of Dreams,* 3rd ed., tr. by Brill, A.A., Macmillan, New York, 1933)

dream within a dream Sometimes part of a dream is regarded during the dream state as having been dreamed; the dreamer therefore does not consider that the dream within a dream belongs to the dream. He continues to dream, looking upon the continuation only as the real dream.

'The inclusion of a certain content in "a dream within a dream" is therefore equivalent to the wish that what has been characterized as a dream had never occurred.' (Freud, S. *The Interpretation of Dreams,* 3rd ed., tr. by Brill, A.A., Macmillan, New York, 1933.) The attitude that the dreamer assumes toward it constitutes a repudiation of it.

dream-work Many phenomena are involved in the production of dreams, from the time that the unconscious impulse is set in motion until the impulse appears in final form as the manifest content of the dream. Freud described many processes: condensation, displacement, inclusion of the real memory and the wish ('a dream within a dream'), pictorial representation, symbolism, absurdity, secondary elaboration, etc. Each of the phenomena is called dream-work, that is, the way in which a dream is evolved.

dreamy-state See *state, dreamy.*

drift, genetic A change in succeeding generation of the frequency of certain genes, due to chance rather than to selection.

drinker, problem See *alcoholism, chronic.*

drive 'A drive, then, is a genetically determined, psychic constituent which, when operative, produces a state of psychic excitation or, as we often say, of tension. This excitation or tension impels the individual to activity, which is also genetically determined in a general way, but which can be considerably altered by individual experience. . . . Thus we see that there is a sequence which is characteristic of the operation of the drive. This sequence we may call either tension, motor activity, and cessation of tension, or need, motor activity, and gratification, as we prefer. The former terminology deliberately neglects the elements of subjective experience, while the latter explicitly refers to it.' (Brenner, C. *An Elementary Textbook of Psychoanalysis,* International Universities Press, New York, 1955)

In present day psychoanalytic psychology, two drives are distinguished—the sexual or erotic (the energy of which is the libido), and the aggressive or destructive (the energy of which is the aggressive energy or, less commonly, destrudo).

driveness, organic Kahn and Cohen's term for the overactivity of the brain-damaged individual, which is attributed to defective brain-stem organization.

driving, photic See *electroencephalogram.*

driving, psychic Continuously repeated playback of psychodynamically significant material which has been recorded on a device such as a tape recorder. Described by D.E. Cameron (*American Journal of Psychiatry 112*:502–9, 1956): 'Since this compels a continued response within a field largely limited by the cue material selected, it has been termed "psychic driving." The term "cue" is used to indicate that the material was selected because it triggers into expression a whole community of related topics.'

If the psychic driving is in response to the patient's own verbal cues, it is termed 'autopsychic'; if it is in response to cues verbalized by others but based on his known psychodynamics, it is termed 'heteropsychic.' The values of psychic driving are said to include penetration of defenses, elicitation of hitherto inaccessible material, and the setting up of a dynamic implant (see *implant, dynamic*).

dromolepsy (drom'ō-lep-sē) A short spurt of running occurring just prior to and generally ending in an epileptic attack. By many it is believed to be the beginning of the attack. It is known also as *procursive epilepsy.*

dromomania (drō-mō-mā'ni-à) An abnormal impulse to travel is called dromomania; the term is frequently used by Hirschfeld to denote the desire to escape from a disagreeable sexual situation. It is also known as *vagabond neurosis.*

dromophobia (drom-ō-fō'bi-à, drō-mō-) Fear of (running across) a street.

drudge, household In social work, 'a person so tied down by housework or family cares as to have little time for rest, recreation, or self-development. There is usually lack of sympathy or understanding on the part of others of the household.' (Hamilton, G. *A Medical Social Terminology,* Presbyterian Hospital, New York, 1930)

drug, abreactive Any of the preparations, usually barbiturates, used in narcocatharsis. See *narcotherapy.*

drug, addicting See *addiction.*

drugs, psychosis due to (sī-kō'sis) Certain drugs such as bromides, cocaine, acetanilide, chloral phenacetin, trional, sulphonal, etc. may by brief, excessive, or long continued use give rise to mental symptoms. Apathy and dullness may be apparent initially, sometimes followed by toxic delirium with confusion, auditory and visual hallucinations, confabulation, flight of ideas, misidentification, or paraphasia. When the drug is withheld, the symptoms usually disappear. In the 1952 revision of psychiatric nomenclature, these psychoses are classified as acute or chronic brain syndomes associated with drug or poison intoxication.

drunkards, acute hallucinosis of Wernicke's name for alcoholic hallucinosis. See *alcoholism.*

drunkards, hallucinatory insanity of Kraepelin's expression for alcoholic hallucinosis. See *alcoholism*.

drunkenness, maudlin Intoxicated state characterized by mawkish, silly, and blissful behavior. Bleuler speaks of *maudlin drunkenness*, regarding it as 'an abnormal reaction,' but not as a psychosis.

drunkenness, pathological This expression is commonly used for a variety of clinical states, induced by alcohol, usually of short duration and not of such severity as to be called a psychosis, although some authorities regard it as such. It is believed, however, as the expression indicates, to be pathological. It is also known as *pathological intoxication*.

Ds Rorschach scoring symbol for an associative response to a white space on the card.

dualism, psychic This term refers to the co-existence of double consciousness or of two fairly distinctly formed superego streams (double conscience). Such psychic dualism is particularly notable in cases of multiple personality, where one personality may alternate with a second with complete amnesia of the active personality for the behavior of the inactive one, or where the two personalities live side by side, one or the other being predominant periodically but still influenced by the inactive one. But such co-conscious mentation may also be a normal phenomenon, as when one writes a letter and at the same time listens to the radio. Usually, however, when the co-conscious thinking is pathological, each of the co-conscious organizations strives to drive the ego in a different direction. Such psychic dualism is an obsessional symptom involving thinking itself. Psychic dualism is perhaps responsible for critical self-observation, the ability of one conscious stream to observe the remainder of the personality. See also: *personality, alternating; personality, split*.

dual leadership See *psychotherapy, multiple*.

Dubois, Paul-Charles (1848–1918) (dü-bwá') French psychiatrist; psychotherapy.

dullard See *moron*.

dullness, mental Tredgold says: 'The group comprised by the term "dull or backward" consists of those children who, at about the middle of their school career, are behind the normal average of their age to the extent of two years or two classes. This corresponds to a retardation of between 15 and 20 per cent of their age, or to about twice the "standard deviation," and roughly to an I.Q. of between 80 and 85.' (Tredgold, A.F. *A Textbook of Mental Deficiency*, 6th ed., Wood, Baltimore, 1937)

dumbness, word See *aphasia, motor*.

dumpish A popular term meaning dull, stupid, morose; dumpy.

dunce (John *Duns* Scotus, a pedantic schoolman and theologian [died 1308].) Popular term for a stupid person.

dura mater (dōō'rà mà'ter) See *meninges*.

Durham decision, Durham test This refers to a 1954 ruling by the United States Court of Appeals that 'an accused is not criminally responsible if his unlawful act was the product of mental disease or mental defect.' Prior to this decision, psychiatric testimony relating to the mental status of the accused was confined to a determination of whether the accused could distinguish right or wrong, or acted under an irresistible impulse at the time of the offense. Under the Durham test, however, the psychiatrist may give any relevant testimony concerning the mental illness at issue. See *impulse, irresistible; rule, M'Naghten*.

DW Rorschach scoring symbol for a response to a part of the card elaborated in such a way that the whole is perceived as having the form of the part.

dwarfism Extreme deficiency in stature (under 105 cm. in white racial groups). It is identical with *microsomia* (q.v.) and is usually divided into the following three special forms:

(a) dwarfs with regular physical proportions and normal psychic development, going under such names as *nanosomia primordialis, heredo-familial essential microsomia*, and *pygmeism* (qq.v.);

(b) dwarfs with a serious hypogenesis of the skeleton except for a very large skull, falling under the heading of Paltauf's *nanism* (q.v.);

(c) dwarfs with a combination of infantilism and premature senility, known as Gilford's *progeria* or the *senile nanism* (q.v.) of Variot and Pirronneau.

In addition to these specific forms, there is a heterogeneous group of '*infantil-*

istic' dwarfisms, or nanisms, of endocrine origin, which are said to 'assume different clinical forms according to the glands principally attacked by dysfunction.'

'In these infantilistic dwarfisms we are naturally dealing with infantilisms in which a serious defect in stature and in the total bodily mass is the outstanding feature. Owing to this predominance of mass hypoevolutism they form a group by themselves, distinct from other glandular infantilisms in which bodily mass and proportions seem more evenly retarded in development. We do not fully understand the reason why in some cases the syndrome of infantilistic dwarfism and in others that of true infantilism develops. One group of hormones may be particularly predisposed to stimulate the organism's ponderal growth, and another to stimulate the growth of the proportions, so that in certain cases the first group is harder hit than the second.' (Pende, N. *Constitutional Inadequacies,* tr. by Naccarati, S., Lea & Febiger, Philadelphia, 1928)

dynamic In psychiatry *dynamic* relates to the operation of mental forces.

dynamics The word is used interchangeably with dynamism(s).

dynamism In psychiatry, the term *dynamism* refers to the action of psychic structures and to the forces behind the action. A dynamism 'is a specific force operating in a specific manner or direction.' (Healy, W., Bronner, A.F., and Bowers, A.M. *The Structure and Meaning of Psychoanalysis,* Knopf, New York, 1930.) While the authors just cited prefer *dynamism* to *mechanism,* the latter is more commonly used. See: *mechanism.*

dynamogeny (dī-nà-moj'ē-nē) This term, used by P. Dubois, means 'the evolution of physical force.'

dynamophany (-mof'à-nē) The expression of psychic force (P. Dubois).

dynamopsychism (dī-nà-mō-sī'kiz'm) Geley's theory of libido or energy. The unconscious is the seat of both lower and higher functions, but the latter are purposely kept in abeyance during normal life in order to maintain the sense of limitation and deficiency necessary for ambition and progress. Thus a person forgets, because too much knowledge would remove the spurring to further efforts. But with impending death, the sense of

limitation and deficiency is no longer necessary, so that the higher faculties are allowed to appear. The mind then becomes clearer and sharper, and certain manifestations such as clairvoyance and telepathy may occur. (Geley, G. *From the Unconscious to the Conscious,* tr. by S. De Brath, Harper, New York, 1921, p. 353)

dysapocatastasis (dis-ap-ō-kà-tas'tà-sis), *Obs.* Restless discontent.

dysarthria (-är'thri-à) Difficulty in articulation; partial impairment of articulatory speech.

dysautonomia (dis-aw-tō-nō'mi-à) Dysfunction of the autonomic or vegetative nervous system, as a result of brain abnormality. Dysautonomia is often familial and bears many resemblances to childhood schizophrenia; the affected child is tense, irritable, subject to recurrent physical crises, defective in organizing complex behavior and adapting to change, and as a result typically develops any number of emotional disturbances.

dysbasia (dis-bā'zhi-à) Any form of difficult or distorted walking is called dysbasia. It may be organically or psychically determined. As examples of the latter one may mention the great variety of abnormal gaits observed in schizophrenic patients. A patient had to take very short and quick steps, in order, as he said, 'to bring the world into rhythm.' Another patient had to walk with the lower extremities rigid, 'so that no one can enter my body.'

dysbulia, dysboulia (dis-bōō'li-à) Disturbance in the will or in the volitional aspects of the personality. See *will, disturbances of the.*

dyschezia (dis-kē'zhi-à) Inadequate evacuation of the stool from the rectum, commonly found in children who suffer from constipation on what is presumed to be an emotional basis.

dyscontrol, descending See *disordered behavior, classification of; psychodynamics, adaptational.*

dyscontrol, emergency See *disordered behavior, classification of; psychodynamics, adaptational.*

dyseneia (dis-e-nē'à) Defective articulation secondary to deafness.

dysergasia (dis-ēr-gas'i-à) A term used by Adolf Meyer to designate those psychiatric syndromes which are presumably associated with disordered physiology of the brain. The dysergasias are generally known as toxic psychoses, one of the chief symptoms of which is delirium.

dysesthesia (-es-thē′zhi-à) Distortion of the sense of touch. It may be organically or psychically determined.

dysesthesia interna (dēs-es-thā′zē-à ēn-ter′nà) (Mod.L. 'internal dysesthesia') Amnesia.

dysgenesia (dis-jē-nē′zi-à) A morbid condition of the generative organs or functions.

dysgenesis (-jen′e-sis) (1) Faulty development and infertility in general or, (2) more specifically, a condition in which hybrids are sterile among themselves, but fertile with members of either parent stock.

dysgenic (-jen′ik) This term, specifically genetic, applies to various biological conditions which have a detrimental effect on the hereditary qualities of a stock or tend to counteract racial improvement through influences bearing on reproduction. In a more general sense, the term denotes any factor which is in contrast with *eugenic* principles by tending to impair the racial qualities of future generations (see *eugenics*).

dysgenics *Obs.* Term used by some eugenicists in reference to the study of 'racial degeneration.'

dysgeusia (dis-gū′si-à) E. Tanzi says: 'As to transitory perversions of taste that are to be observed in adolescents and hysterical patients, which impel these persons to eat ashes, earth, salt, vinegar, etc., they do not correspond to unusual or latent needs of a chemically imperfect organ, but are aberrations devoid of any biological purpose (*dysgeusia*).' (Tanzi, E. *A Text-Book of Mental Diseases,* tr. by Robertson, W.F. and Mackenzie, T.C., Rebman, New York, 1909)

dysgnosia (-gnō′si-à) A general term for any intellectual impairment or anomaly.

dysgraphia (-graf′i-à) Defective ability to write. As seen clinically, the dysgraphia is often dissociated in that the patient is unable to write spontaneously but is able to copy from printed material to script or vice versa. Dissociated dysgraphia is an almost constant finding in patients with primary reading retardation and in the Gerstmann syndrome.

dyskinesia (-ki-nē′si-à) Distortion of voluntary movements; involuntary muscular activity such as a tic, spasm, or myoclonus.

dyskinesis, professional (-ki-nē′sis) Professional neurasthenia.

dyslalia (-lā′li-à) Impairment of, partial disorder in, or specific inability for uttering (speaking).

dyslexia (-lek′si-à) Distorted speech; the ability to read may be intact, but there is little or no understanding of what is read. See *reading, disabilities of.*

dyslogia (-lō′ji-à) Bianchi writes: 'Incoherence of speech, which coincides with incoherence of thought, corresponds to the so-called *dyslogia,* which is divided into *alogia* and *paralogia.*' Dyslogia means abnormality of speech. (Bianchi, L. *A Text-Book of Psychiatry,* tr. by MacDonald, J.H., Baillière, Tindall & Cox, London, 1906)

dysmetria (-mē′tri-à) Inability to gauge distance for bodily movements; elicited by asking patient to raise both arms and bring them quickly to a stop at the horizontal level; when one arm sinks below the horizontal level, correction is required for the dysmetria.

dysmimia (-mim′i-à) This term is generally used to denote inappropriate mimicry. E. Tanzi says that '. . . there is manifested a strange contrast between the thoughtful brow and the gay or indifferent expression of the face (*dysmimia*).' (Tanzi, E. *A Text-Book of Mental Diseases,* tr. by Robertson, W.F. and Mackenzie, T.C., Rebman, New York, 1909)

dysmnesia (-nē′si-à) Impaired memory.

dysmorphophobia (-mor-fō-fō′bi-à) Fear of physical deformity or impairment.

dysneuria (-nū′ri-à) *Obs.* Mental weakness.

dysnusia (-nū′si-à) *Obs.* Mental enfeeblement.

dysorexia (-ō-rek′si-à) Impaired or perverted appetite.

dysostosis, diabetic exophthalmic (-os-tō′sis, dī-a-bet′ik eks-of-thal′mik) *Xanthomatosis* (q.v.).

dyspareunia (-pa-rōō′ni-à) Dyspareunia is painful sexual intercourse. It is generally held that the pain is not due to any local condition, but is associated with matters of the psyche. Furthermore, the term is commonly used to refer to pain in women.

'Pain at the beginning of intercourse generally indicates a lack of lubrication of the vaginal canal, and this, since it is functional, is generally due to an absence of sexual desire on the part of the female, or a fear of the results of a coitus even though the desire be present.' (Behan, R.J. *Pain*, Appleton, New York, 1920)

Jones defines dyspareunia as 'pain during intercourse; an hysterical symptom.' (Jones, E. *Papers on Psycho-Analysis*, 4th ed., Wood, Baltimore, 1938)

dysphagia (-fā′ji-à) Difficulty in eating; it may be organically or psychically determined. Very often in psychiatric patients there is refusal of food due to many and various reasons; a patient rejects food because he believes it is poisoned; another protests he will choke to death if he eats; a third patient insists she will become pregnant if she eats; a fourth believes he should take only liquid nourishment. Indeed, there are many morbid ideas associated with eating, yet the term dysphagia is more commonly used from the standpoint of organic etiology.

dysphagia globosa (glô-bō′zà) (Mod.L. 'spherical dysphagia') *Globus hystericus* (q.v.).

dysphagia hysterica (hēs-te′rē-kà) (Mod. L. 'hysteric dysphagia') Globus hystericus.

dysphagia spastica (spàs′tē-kà) (Mod.L. 'spastic dysphagia') Impairment in swallowing, sometimes observed in hysterical subjects; it may also be due to organic causes.

dysphemia (-fē′mi-à) Stuttering; stammering.

dysphoria (-fō′ri-à) Dysphoria is defined by C.A. Mercier as 'misery in various degrees'; he says that it 'is perhaps the most frequent and widespread of all disorders of the mind, and that with the most numerous associations with other disorders. . . . The most frequent mental accompaniment of dysphoria is abasement, or underestimation of self on any or every level—physical, mental, possessive, or moral.' (Mercier, C.A. *A Text-Book of Insanity*, George Allen & Unwin, London, 1914)

dysphoria nervosa (ner-vō′zà) (Mod.L. 'nervous dysphoria') Fidgets.

dysphrasia (dis-frā′zhi-à) Impaired speaking due to intellectual defects.

dysphrasia, imitative Echolalia; echophrasia.

dysphrasia imitatoria (dēs-frà′zē-à ē-mē-tä-tō′rē-à) (Mod.L. 'imitative dysphrasia') Echolalia; echophrasia.

dysphrenia (dis-frē′ni-à) An old and general term for mental disorder. Wolff used the term synonymously with dementia praecox (schizophrenia).

dysplasia (-plā′zhi-à) Abnormal tissue development. The term came into prominence in psychiatry particularly through the studies of Kretschmer on body configuration. According to him, there are three basic types of physique among psychiatric patients: the asthenic, athletic, and pyknic. The fourth, called the dysplastic, is a heterogeneous group, 'varying much among themselves, of which any one group contains only a few members.' Among the types described under this heading may be mentioned elongated eunuchoids, those with polyglandular syndromes, infantilism, and hypoplasia.

dysplastic (-plas′tik) See *type, dysplastic; dysplasia.*

dyspnea, neurotic (disp′nē-à nū-rot′ik) The symptom of shortness of breath or other related breathing difficulties associated with the implication that the symptom is an expression of unconscious emotional conflict or neurosis. The neurotic or psychogenic etiology of this symptom demands careful diagnosis through the exclusion of all possible organic causes by the usual physical diagnostic methods, as well as a careful personality study and evaluation. Neurotic dyspnea is frequently associated with symptoms of weakness and exhaustion, and seems closely related to long-standing repressed, denied, and undischarged hostility and resentment. When patients have adequately faced and 'aired' (abreacted) their resentment, the symptoms are frequently alleviated.

A 25-year-old young woman always complained of 'a smothering feeling and an inability to get the proper amount of air' and deeply resented the diagnosis that there was no organic cause for her symptoms. It became obvious that she harbored a great deal of resentment toward her brother and his wife. After the relationship between her exhaustion and the great amount of energy it had cost her to remain unaware (unconscious) of her denied and repressed hostility to her brother had been consciously established in her mind, it became possible for her to 'air' her hostility—and she began to breathe better. She then began to 'relax and let more air in,' and then seemed to gain energy. (Weiss, E., and English, O.S. *Psychosomatic Medicine,* 2nd ed., Saunders, Philadelphia and London, 1949)

dyspraxia (dis-prak'si-à) Partial impairment of the ability to perform skilled movement, with no associated defect in the motor apparatus.

dysrhaphic (-raf'ik) Dysontogenetic; referring to disturbances of development and particularly to developmental disorders of the central nervous system such as the Arnold-Chiari malformation.

dysrhythmia, dart and dome (-rith'mi-a) See *pyknolepsy.*

dysrhythmia, paroxysmal cerebral (pa-rok-sis'mal ser'e-bral) *Epilepsy* (q.v.).

dyssocial reaction See *sociopathic personality disturbance.*

dys-symbole (dis-sim'bō-lē) This psychiatric term denotes a state of mind characterized by the inability to formulate conceptual thoughts upon personal topics or to discriminate the gradations of personal emotions in language intelligible to others. Dys-symbole is certainly apparent in some schizophrenics, but many physicians believe that it is present in all schizophrenics. Whether dys-symbole represents a defect in the patient's semantic power or is indicative of a more basic emotional deficiency is not known.

dyssynergia (-si-nĕr'ji-à) A failure to work in unison or harmony, such as is seen in the motor and gait disturbances that follow cerebellar lesions.

dysthymia (-thim'i-à, -thī'mi-à) Certain forms of cyclothymia are characterized by depressions associated with hypochondriasis. These states possess the clinical symptomatology of the depressive form of manic-depressive psychosis, but the expressions are less intense.

'In the dysthymic types are found the depressions which are attributed in large part to neurasthenia and to various visceral disturbances.' (Jelliffe, S.E. and White, W.A. *Diseases of the Nervous System,* 6th ed., Lea & Febiger, Philadelphia, 1935)

dysthymic (-thim'ik, -thī'mik) Pertaining to certain cyclothymic reactions that have the appearance of neurasthenia.

dystonia (dis-tō'ni-à) A state of abnormal tension or tonicity. It may be general, as in catatonic, or local, as in gastric, muscular, psychic, cerebral dystonia.

dystonia musculorum deformans (mus-kū-lor'oom dē-for'mans) See *dystonia, torsion.*

dystonia, torsion Oppenheim's dystonia musculorum deformans. Torsion dystonia is usually familial and is particularly common among Russian Jews. The characteristic lesion is status marmoratus (a disorder of glial formation leading to hypermyelination and giving a marble slab appearance), particularly in the caudate nucleus and putamen. The disease has its onset in childhood or adolescence and consists of involuntary movements which produce a torsion spasm of the limbs and spine. There is no muscular wasting, sensory loss, or reflex changes, and no mental deterioration. It appears that torsion dystonia is a symptom-complex rather than a specific disease, for it may occur in a number of disorders.

dystonic (-ton'ik) From the organic point of view *dystonic* means 'relating to abnormal (muscular) tension.' The psyche or personality is said to be dystonic when it is not in harmony either with itself or with its environment.

dystrophia myotonica (-trō'fi-à mī-ō-ton'i-kà) Myotonia atrophica; a hereditary disorder characterized by atrophy of the sternocleidomastoid muscles and the muscles of the face (leading to a 'hatchet-face' appearance), shoulder, forearm, and hand and of the quadriceps muscles. There is also myotonia and, usually, other dystrophic disturbances such as cataract and gonadal atrophy. Males are more commonly affected, between the ages of 20 and 30 years. Affected patients usually succumb to intercurrent illness in late middle life. The disease was first described by Déléage in 1890.

dystrophy, pseudohypertrophic muscular (dis'tro-fē, sū-dō-hī-pĕr-trō'fik mus'kū-lĕr) The commonest form of muscular dystrophy, first described by Duchenne in 1868. It is inherited as a sex-linked recessive and affects males six times as often as females. Onset is gradual, beginning at about five years of age. The child is noted to be clumsy and falls frequently. There is pseudohypertrophy, but weakness, of the muscles of the calves, the glutei, quadriceps and deltoids; the face and hands always escape. The patient adopts a waddling gait and an attitude of lordosis when standing; characteristically, he rises from the ground by climbing up on his own legs. Further progression of the disease leads to contractures in the muscles and fatal termination within 10 to 15 years.

dystropy (dis′trō-pē) This is a term used by Adolf Meyer, meaning abnormality of behavior.

E

Earle, Pliny (1809–92) American psychiatrist.

ear-pulling See *pulling, ear.*

eaten, fear of being Whether conscious or unconscious, the fear of being eaten originates early in the development of the infant's ego during what is termed the oral stage. During this stage the infant develops the normal aim of pleasure or satisfaction through eating and, in a more general sense, through the incorporation of objects. Frustrations of this erotic aim of eating or incorporating and fears of such frustration are of frequent occurrence. These anxieties take the form of a fear of being eaten, because of infantile animistic thinking which assumes that what the infant feels and does will also take place in the world around it. Clinically, it has been found that the archaic fear of being eaten may have another function—may be used as a cover for castration anxiety, disguised by being distorted through regression into the older fear of being eaten. Moreover, the patient's anxiety may contain both a fear of being eaten and a fear of being castrated. (Fenichel, O. *The Psychoanalytic Theory of Neurosis,* Norton, New York, 1945)

eaten, phantasy of being The phantasy of being eaten or incorporated frequently occurs as part of a certain type of relationship to a love-object. In this relationship the patient's only aim is 'to become part of a more powerful personality' whom he overestimates to an enormous degree, though having at the same time no interest in or idea about the partner's real personality. Patients who have this sort of aim, attitude, and phantasy are characterized by an overwhelming feeling of inadequacy and inordinate need for self-esteem. As a result they can never give love but have an extreme need to feel loved, and this they achieve in the way described above. In Fenichel's words, they 'never become complete individuals in their own right and, therefore, need participation in a greater union in order to be able to feel their own existence.' (Fenichel, O. *The Psychoanalytic Theory of Neurosis,* Norton, New York, 1945)

ebriecation (ē-bri-ē-kā′shun) A term coined by Paracelsus to denote mental disorder associated with alcoholism.

ébriécation celeste (ā-brē-ā-kȧ-syawN′ sā-lest′) (F. 'heavenly intoxication') A Paracelsian term, meaning religious excitement and enthusiasm in psychiatric patients.

eccentricity (ek-sen-tris′i-tē) Henderson and Gillespie refer to a group of individuals 'who have been from childhood or early youth abnormal in their emotional reactions and in their general behavior, but who do not reach, except perhaps episodically, a degree of abnormality amounting to certifiable insanity, and who show no intellectual defect. They exhibit lack of perseverance, persistent failure to profit by experience, and habitual lack of ordinary prudence.' The authors discuss this type of individual under the heading of *psychopathic personality,* calling attention to the eccentricities of the group. An individual in this class is sometimes called eccentric.

ecdemomania (ek-dē-mō-mā′ni-ȧ) Morbid impulse to travel or wander about.

ecdemonomania (-nō-mā′-ni-ȧ) *Obs.* Uncontrollable impulse to wander; dromomania.

ecdysiasm (ek-di′si-az′m) A morbid tendency to disrobe in order to provoke useless erotic stimulation in the opposite sex.

écho des pensées (ā-kō′ dā päNsā′) (F. 'echo of thoughts') The imagined sound-reproduction of the patient's thoughts. 'A special form of auditory hallucinations is that in which the acoustic verbal images of the thought itself are projected outside in such a way that whatever the subject thinks, he hears repeated in speech. This *écho des pensées* not only repeats the patients' thoughts, but announces their future actions.' (Jacoby, G.W. *The Unsound Mind and the Law,* Funk & Wagnalls, New York and London, 1918)

echoing, thought Same as *écho des pensées* (q.v.).

echokinesis (ek-ō-ki-nē′sis) *Echopraxia* (q.v.).

echolalia (-lā′li-ȧ) The repetition by imitation of the speech of another is called echolalia in its most morbid form. It is not uncommon in patients with the catatonic form of schizophrenia.

[242]

echomatism (ek-om′ă-tiz′m) *Echopraxia* (q.v.).

echomimia (ek-ō-mim′i-ă) *Echopraxia* (q.v.).

echopalilalia (-pal-i-lā′li-ă) The morbid repetition (re-echoing) of words spoken by another person.

echopathy (ĕ-kop′ă-thĕ) Echopathy is a morbid condition, characterized by the repetition through imitation of the actions or speech of another. It is encountered in vivid form in the catatonic phase of schizophrenia, when the patient assumes the postures, gestures, and speech of another in 'mirror' form, so to speak. See *echopraxia, echolalia.*

echo-phenomena By this expression Kraepelin refers to echolalia and echopraxia.

echophrasia (ek-ō-frā′zhi-ă) *Echolalia* (q.v.).

echopraxia (-prak′si-ă) Echopraxia, a common symptom in the catatonic form of schizophrenia, is the repetition by imitation of the movements of another. Thus, a patient acted as the 'mirror image' of his physician in that he assumed the physician's postures and gestures as he saw them.

'Contrasting with negativism is the so-called *automatic obedience,* showing itself in echopraxia (repetition of actions seen), echolalia (repetition of words heard), and flexibilitas cerea (the maintenance of imposed postures).' (Henderson, D.K. and Gillespie, R.D. *A Text-Book of Psychiatry,* 4th ed., Oxford University Press, London, 1936)

'The echopractic patients imitate whatever strikes them in the actions or words of their surroundings. As far as we know, it is partly a question of hysteria-like mechanisms, as seen in the echopraxia of primitive people, and certainly in most cases of schizophrenia, and partly a matter of an incapacity to get away from a conceived idea, so that instead of giving an answer the question is repeated or instead of a new action the preceding act is imitated.' (Bleuler, E. *Textbook of Psychiatry,* tr. by Brill, A.A., Macmillan, New York, 1930)

echo-sign See *sign, echo.*

echo-speech Synonymous with *echolalia.*

eclactisma (ek-lak-tiz′mà) A synonym for epilepsy, in part descriptive of the move-ments of the lower limbs during the grand mal seizure.

eclimia (ek-lim′i-ă) Bulimia.

eclipse, mental This is an expression used by Janet to denote the 'stealing' of ideas from patients, particularly from patients with schizophrenia, who claim that whenever they have an idea, someone takes it away.

ecmnesia (ek-mnĕ′zhi-ă) *Rare.* Synonym for anterograde amnesia.

ecnoea (ek-nō-ĕ′à) *Obs.* Mental disorder or disease.

ecology, human (ĕ-kol′ō-jĕ) The study of 'the special aspects of the symbiotic relations of human beings and human institutions.' (McKenzie, R.D. *Encyclopaedia of the Social Sciences,* vol. 5, Macmillan, New York, 1931, p. 314)

Poverty, insanity, delinquency, crime, and other social phenomena show characteristic distributions definitely related to the ecological pattern of the city.

ecomania (ĕ-kō-mā′ni-ă) An infrequently used term for a morbid attitude toward the members of one's family. It used to be considered somewhat in the nature of a nosologic entity, but today, it is generally regarded as only one component of a syndrome. Also *oik(i)omania.*

economic The term *economic* has special meaning in psychoanalysis. 'We see how we have gradually been led to introduce a third point of view into the scheme of mental phenomena—beside the dynamic and the topographical we take the *economic* standpoint, one from which we try to follow out the fate of given volumes of excitation and to achieve, at least relatively, some assessment of it.' (Freud, S. *Collected Papers,* vol. 4, tr. by Riviere, J., Leonard and Virginia Woolf and The Institute of Psychoanalysis, London, 1924–25) See *economy.*

Economo's disease (Konstantin von Economo, Austrian neuropathologist, 1876–1931) Encephalitis lethargica.

economy In psychiatry the term *economy* has been considered extensively by psychoanalysts. Freud studies mental phenomena from three points of view, that of dynamism, of topography and of economy. The latter has to do with 'the fate of given volumes of excitation' and 'some assessment of it.' (Freud, S. *Collected Papers,* vol. 4, tr. by Riviere, J., Leonard and Virginia Woolf and The Institute of Psychoanalysis, London, 1924–25)

'By an *economic* point of view Freud means one in which the attempt is made to ascertain the laws covering the production, distribution, and consumption of definite quantities of physical excitation or energy, according to the economic principle of the greatest advantage with the least effort.' (Jones, E. *Papers on Psycho-Analysis,* 4th ed., Wood, Baltimore, 1938)

ecophobia (ē-kō-fō′bi-à) See *oikophobia.*

écouteur (ā-kōō-tēr′) One who obtains inordinate gratification through listening to sexual accounts. See *voyeur.*

ecphoria (ek-fō′ri-à) It is maintained 'that everything that has been psychically experienced leaves behind a lasting trace, or *engram.*' Memory involves 'the recurrence of a function resembling a previous experience, like an idea of something perceived, or of a function almost like it, like the repetition of a practiced motion. We designate this as an *ecphoria* of the engrams.' (Bleuler, E. *Textbook of Psychiatry,* tr. by Brill, A.A., Macmillan, New York, 1930)

ecphorize (ek′fō-rīz) To revive memories or engrams.

ecphronia (ek-frō′ni-à) *Obs.* Mann said in 1883 that 'Mason Good made the order *Phrenetica,* in the class *Neurotica,* and subdivided it into *ecphronia* (mania and melancholia), *empathema* (ungovernable passion), *alusia* (illusion), *aphelxia* (reverie), *paroniria* (sleep disturbance), and *moria* (fatuity).' (Mann, E.C. *A Manual of Psychological Medicine and Allied Nervous Diseases,* Blakiston, Philadelphia, 1883, p. 44)

ecplexis (ek-plek′sis) A term used by Galen to denote stupor.

ecstasy From the psychiatric point of view, this term was formerly used to denote a clinical syndrome 'in which a person presents opposite phases of mental action, some faculties being exalted and others depressed, sensation and locomotion being suspended. It is so allied to catalepsy that the term "cataleptic ecstacy" is often employed'; it was also known as *ecstatic trance* (Tuke, D.H. *A Dictionary of Psychological Medicine,* vols. 1–2, Blakiston, Philadelphia, 1892) and *contemplatio.*

In present-day psychiatry, the term ec-

stasy is confined for the most part to trance-states in which religious ideation or similar ideas of dedication and complete surrender occupy almost the entire field of consciousness.

E.C.T. Abbreviation of *electric convulsion therapy.* See *therapy, electric convulsion.*

ectoderm (ek′tō-dĕrm) In medicine and embryology, this name is given to the first, or outer, germ layer which in the embryo's monodermic *blastula* (q.v.) stage consists of an epithelial layer of more or less columnar cells, or to the primary tissues which are subsequently derived from this layer and, thus, are characteristically distinguished from the organs and tissues developed from the other germ layers, the *entoderm* and the *mesoderm* (qq.v.).

The *ectoderm* is early differentiated into a thickened axial *neural plate,* and thinner lateral portions. When the neural canal has become closed, the surface ectoderm forms a continuous layer which gives rise to the *epidermis;* while the entire nervous system originates in the thickened walls of the dorsally situated axial groove which is subsequently converted into a canal (see *cephalogenesis*).

In addition to the epidermis, with hair and nails, and all neurons and neuroglia of the nervous system, the ectodermal tissue derivatives include the epithelium of mouth, anus, nostrils, conjunctiva, and lacrimal glands; the lens of the eye and the epithelium of the membranous ear labyrinth; the epithelium lining the central canal of the spinal cord and the ventricles of the brain; certain ductless glands such as the pineal, the nervous portion of hypophysis, and the medulla of suprarenal.

ectomorphic (-mor′fik) In Sheldon's system of constitutional types this means characterized by a predominance of its third component (linearity), that is, the physical structures developed from the *ectodermal* layer of the embryo. Persons of this type are contrasted with the *endomorphic* and *mesomorphic* types and correspond roughly to Kretschmer's *asthenic* type.

ectopia pupillae (ek-tō′pi-à pū-pil′ē) Displacement of pupil.

E.C.T., regressive See *therapy, electroconvulsive, regressive.*

ectype (ek'tīp) Outstanding or unusual type. Types of physical or mental constitution that vary considerably from the average are called ectypes. From the physical point of view two ectypes are recognized, first the megalosplanchnic (brevilineal, brachymorphic) and, second the microsplanchnic (longilineal, dolichomorphic). There are likewise two personality ectypes, the introverted and the extraverted.

eczema, nervous (ek'zē-mà) A mixed dermatological and psychiatric diagnostic term for a skin disorder in which psychogenic character or personality-determined factors are paramount in the etiology, understanding, and treatment of the condition. This concept does not exclude organic, chemical, irritant, or contact factors in the etiology. It does, however, emphasize the interaction of the psychogenic or emotional factors with the chemical or organic.

edema, angioneurotic (e-dē'mà an-ji-ō-nū-rot'ik) Angioneurotic edema (Quincke disease) is a condition which is said to represent an allergic or anaphylactic reaction to infectious, toxic, or autotoxic processes, occurring frequently in neurotic individuals with a hereditary predisposition. The disease is characterized by a circumscribed edematous swelling of the skin and subcutaneous tissue and, less frequently, of the mucous membranes.

Edinger-Westphal nucleus See *accommodation.*

edipism (ed'i-piz'm) (From Oedipus, King of Thebes, who beat out his own eyes.) *Rare.* Self-inflicted injury to the eyes.

EDR Electrodermal response. See *reflex, psychogalvanic.*

education, progressive A movement within the field of education, founded by John Dewey, which emphasizes the needs of the individual and the individual's capacity for self-expression and self-direction.

EEG *Electroencephalogram* (q.v.).

effect, placebo See *placebo.*

effeminated man See *man, effeminated.*

effemination Krafft-Ebing says: 'In this group are fully developed cases in which males are females in feeling; and *vice versa* women, males. This abnormality of feeling and of development of the character is often apparent in childhood. The boy likes to spend his time with girls, play with dolls, and help his mother about the house; he likes to cook, sew, knit; he develops tastes in female *toilettes,* and even becomes the adviser of his sisters.' (Krafft-Ebing, R.v. *Psychopathia Sexualis,* Login, New York, 1908)

effort, sustained In occupational therapy, this term denotes a continued exertion or attempt on the part of a patient to apply himself to some activity or achievement.

effort syndrome A type of anxiety-neurosis or anxiety reaction, approximately equivalent to soldier's heart, neurocirculatory asthenia, etc.

egersis (ē-gēr'sis) Intense wakefulness.

egg The genetic term *egg* is synonymous with *ovum* and signifies those germ cells in the process of sexual reproduction which are produced by the female. An egg is passive and relatively large as compared with the very small and actively motile germ cells of the male.

The most important biological characteristic of eggs is the phenomenon known as *meiosis* or *maturation.* In typical meiosis such a cell experiences two successive divisions, during which the number of chromosomes is reduced to one-half. The finally resulting egg only has one chromosome from each chromosome pair.

Prior to the commencement of meiosis, the female reproductive cells or *oögonia* multiply by repeated cell divisions of the ordinary duplicating type. After these cells cease to divide by ordinary division and become *primary oöcytes,* in which the pairing of the chromosomes takes place, they grow considerably in size.

The first meiotic division produces two very unequal cells. Only the large daughter cell, or *secondary oöcyte,* is functional. The other cell, which is very small and is usually called the *polar body,* gradually disintegrates and disappears (see *meiosis*).

The next division is again very unequal, the large cell being the *mature egg,* the small cell another, or the *second,* polar body. In most sexually reproducing animals a mature egg must be fertilized before it can develop into a new individual (see *fertilization*).

ego (ē'gō) In psychoanalytic psychology, the ego is that part of the psychic apparatus which is the mediator between the individual and reality. Its prime function is the perception of reality and adaptation to it. The ego is the executive organ of the reality principle and is ruled by the secondary process. The various tasks of the ego include: perception; motor control (action); adaptation to reality; use of the reality principle and the mechanism of anxiety to ensure safety and self-preservation; replacement of the primary process of the id by the secondary process; memory; affects; thinking; and a general synthetic function manifested in assimilation of external and internal elements, in reconciling conflicting ideas, in uniting contrasts, and in activating mental creativity. Unlike the id, the ego has an organization (i.e. it is not chaotic), it can generate co-ordinated action, and it is ruled by the secondary rather than the primary process. Its functions develop gradually, dependent upon physical maturation (and particularly, the genetically determined growth of the central nervous system) and upon experiential factors.

Beginning at birth, stimuli from the external world act upon the organism; over the ensuing months and years, with the accumulation of more and more experiences, certain mental events have a peculiar intimacy and a new psychic structure, the ego, is formed. The ego mediates between the individual and reality; it is a clearing-house for stimuli from both the unconscious and from conscious reality. It develops on the basis of unsatisfied instinctual demands (thus, if there were always to be satisfaction, there would be no development of reality). Birth floods the individual with excitation, and this becomes the model for all later anxiety. But the infant is still in the primary undifferentiated phase of consciousness; he is ignorant of any sources of pleasure other than himself and there is, at this stage of objectivation, no differentiation of the mother, or other objects, from himself. The breast is thought of as a part of his own body, and his slightest gestures are followed by satisfaction of his instinctive nutritional needs. This gives rise to the autarchic fiction of false omnipotence, and this is the stage of primary narcissism. The infantile ego only unwillingly orients itself to objects, which at this stage are seen only as ego-substance which satisfies instinctual demands. Thus, there is only ego and non-ego. Soon, however, reality makes increasing demands. Perceptions and memory system are dif-

ferentiated, and the ego defends itself against stimulation by shutting off the perceptive system, by mastery through 'fascination' (empathy), or by mastery through swallowing and introjection. The infant develops the attitude that objects exist only for the ego's satisfaction, and the purified pleasure ego perceives anything which is unpleasant as non-ego. The ego believes itself to be omnipotent, but this is disproved by experience and frustration. The ego then comes to believe that the parents are omnipotent and partakes of their omnipotence by introjection. This is the primary identification: the putting into the mouth results in perception, and the ego imitates what is perceived in order to master the object. The imitation of the external world by oral incorporation is the basis for that primitive mode of thinking called magic. Even though reality destroys the feeling of omnipotence, the longing for this primary narcissism remains—the narcissistic needs—and self-esteem is the awareness of how close the ego is to the original omnipotence. The desire to partake of the parental omnipotence, even though it arose originally from the basic desire for the satisfaction of hunger, soon becomes differentiated from the hunger itself, and the ego craves affection in a passive way (passive object love), being willing to renounce other satisfactions if rewards of affection are promised.

By substituting actions for mere discharge reactions, the ego achieves the stage of active mastery. This is achieved through the interposing of time, the development of a tension tolerance, and the development of judgment (the ability to anticipate the future in the imagination by testing reality). Primary anxiety is the passive experiencing of excitation which cannot be mastered but which must be endured; with judgment, the ego declares that a certain situation might give rise to this primary anxiety, and instead of the original panic itself being experienced, a moderated, tamed fear is experienced which is anxiety in anticipation of what might happen.

The first fear is of a recurrence of the primal anxiety, and from this develops the fear that the child's own instinctual demands, which gave rise to the overwhelming excitation beyond his capacity to master, are dangerous in themselves. This fear is complicated by animistic thinking (the belief that the external environment has the same instincts as the self), for if the desire to recapture the primary narcissism is to be achieved by eating the parents, the child feels that the deed will be undone by his being devoured himself (talion principle). This is how anxieties of physical destruction originate; the most important representative of this group is castration anxiety.

The development of speech initiates a further decisive step in the development of reality testing, for tying up words and ideas makes thinking proper possible. Thinking is an anticipatory acting out done with reduced energy. The faculty of speech changes archaic, prelogical thinking ('primary process') into logical and orderly ('secondary process') thinking. With the arrival of speech and logical thinking, a final differentiation of conscious and unconscious is made. Now prelogical thinking will be used as a substitute for logical thinking only when the latter cannot master unpleasant reality.

The maturing ego must not only postpone action, but on occasion it must inhibit action completely. Thus the ego develops reactions of defense against instinctual impulses and turns against its own instinctual demands (countercathexis). There are various reasons for the development of these defenses: (1) instinctual demands that cannot be satisfied become traumatic in themselves; (2) prohibitions from the outside world, through education, experience, etc.; (3) the danger is phantasied because of a projective misunderstanding of the world; (4) the ego becomes dependent upon the superego (which has meanwhile developed), and anxiety is transformed into guilt.

The above paragraphs outline the gradual development of the ego as theorized by the psychoanalytic school of psychology. Others conceive of the ego in somewhat different ways.

Jung says that the ego 'consists of record-images from the sense functions that transmit stimuli both from within and from without, and, furthermore, of an immense accumulation of images of past processes.' The record-images are innumerable. 'Therefore, I speak not merely of the ego, but of an ego-complex, on the established presupposition that the ego, having a fluctuating composition, is changeable, and therefore cannot be just simply *the* ego.' (Jung, C.G. *Contribu-*

tions to Analytical Psychology, tr. by Baynes, H.G. and C.F., Kegan Paul, Trench, Trubner, London, 1928)

From the standpoint of analytical psychology (Jung) the ego is 'a complex of representations which constitutes the centrum of my field of consciousness and appears to possess a very high degree of continuity and identity.' The ego 'is not identical with the totality of my psyche, being merely a complex among other complexes. Hence, I discriminate between the ego and the Self, since the ego is only the subject of my consciouseness, while the Self is the subject of my totality: hence it also includes the unconscious psyche. In this sense the Self would be an (ideal) factor which embraces and includes the ego. In unconscious phantasy the Self often appears as a super-ordinated or ideal personality. . . .' (Jung, C.G. *Psychological Types,* tr. by Baynes, H.G., Harcourt, Brace, New York & London, 1923)

'I take it, then, that "the censor" on the one hand, and "the Ego" (together with "the Ego-Ideal") on the other, are two alternative designations for that part of the developed personality which I have called the sentiment of self-regard.' (McDougall, W. *Outline of Abnormal Psychology,* Scribner, New York, 1926)

According to the formulations of Kempf the ego 'is constituted of the inherent segmental functions that have become *conditioned* to seek stimuli in a manner that not only obtains gratification but also wins social justification and esteem. Hence, this egoistic unity must keep the asocial segments under control.' In another section of his book Kempf says: 'This general, incessant, autonomic compensation becomes essentially integrated into a unity to prevent any division from jeopardizing the unity. *This unity, having the capacity of reacting so as to be conscious or aware of any segment's activities constitutes the ego, and learns to speak of itself, as "I," "me," "myself," "I am," "I wish," etc.'* (Kempf, E.J. *Psychopathology,* Mosby, St. Louis, 1921)

ego-alteration, reactive A type of anticathexis—that is, expenditure of energy in maintaining the repression of libidinal impulses—in which the ego is altered by a reaction-formation against the particular libidinal impulses. Freud gives the example of the compulsion-neurosis in which an exaggeration of the normal character traits of pity, conscientiousness, and cleanliness is found. These character traits are the antithesis of the anal-sadistic instinctual impulses repressed by the compulsion-neurosis. Thus the ego is altered through an exaggeration of the above-mentioned character traits which are a reaction against the repressed instinctual impulses; that is, some of the energy spent in repressing these anal impulses is spent in reactive ego-alteration.

Another type of reactive ego-alteration occurs in hysteria. Freud gives as an example the way in which 'the ambivalency conflict in hysteria is resolved: hate for a loved person is kept submerged by an excess of tenderness towards him and anxious concern about him.' Unlike the compulsion-neurosis in which the reaction-formation takes the guise of a character trait, the reaction-formation in hysteria is confined to a specific situation, as illustrated by the hysterical woman who treats with an excess of tenderness the children she really hates, but who is therefore more tender neither in general nor toward other children. Freud contrasts the two types of reactive ego-alteration as follows: 'the reaction-formation of hysteria adheres tenaciously to a specific object and is not elevated to the status of a general disposition of the ego. Of compulsion-neurosis it is precisely this universalization, the looseness of object relationships, the displaceability marking object choice, which are characteristic.' (Freud, S. *The Problem of Anxiety,* Norton, New York, 1936)

ego-analysis See *analysis, ego.*

ego, auxiliary 'The auxiliary ego is an individual who identifies himself consciously with all the subject's expressions and purposes as far as organic limitations permit, thus strengthening the ego of the subject. The auxiliary ego, acting in the subject's behalf, is a genuine prolongation or extension of the subject's ego.

'An auxiliary ego operating upon the instinctive level is a function known as an "alter-ego." Illustrations of an alter-ego are the mother to her child, the lover, or the friend. This function received a new distinction when it became a conscious tool in therapeutic situations. In the case of an interpersonal difficulty, the consulting psychiatrist becomes an auxiliary ego of two or more persons involved. His function is to accept uncritically the subjective attitude of the patients and to stimulate their subjectivity and thus become ready to act in their behalf.

'In the psychodrama the function of the auxiliary ego is to enact such roles which the patient may require for presenting his situation adequately. Such roles may be upon the private level or the auxiliary ego may have to assist in embodying concrete persons in the patient's milieu, such as a specific father, wife or child. Or, the roles may be upon a symbolic level, such as God, Judge, or Satan. Finally, the auxiliary ego may embody delusionary roles or peculiar symbolic combinations characteristic for the patient's world.' (Moreno, J.L. *Sociometry, 1,* 17, 1937)

ego, body That part of the perceiving portion of the ego around which all concepts of one's own ego are grouped. The body ego consists of the psychic representations of one's body and self—the memories and ideas connected with the body along with their cathexes. At first the various parts of the body, and eventually the body as a whole, occupy a particularly important place in the psyche throughout life.

The ego perceives not only external stimuli '. . . but also inner, mental processes (ideas, wishes, thoughts, strivings, sensations, and fantasies). External stimuli are intercepted by the sense organs and led to the central nervous system. Here they leave traces in the form of memories and ideas whose nature depends upon the particular sense organ which has received the stimulus (sight, hearing, touch). These precipitates in the psyche of external experiences, together with the internal processes, such as thinking, imagination, feelings, emotions, and visceral sensations, form what we call the psychic body scheme or image. The nucleus around which all concepts of one's own ego are grouped is the *body ego,* whose main function is perception.' (Nunberg, H. *Principles of Psychoanalysis,* International Universities Press, New York, 1955)

Federn used the term 'bodily ego-feeling' to refer to the body ego.

ego boundary See *boundary, ego.*

ego-cathexis (-kà-thek′sis) See *cathexis.*

ego-center Schilder's term for the nucleus, or inner part of the ego, surrounded by a peripheral part of the ego in the same manner that the nucleus of a cell is enclosed by the protoplasm.

The word 'ego' is used here not in the psychoanalytical sense but rather as a general psychological concept. According to Schilder, the various experiences of our life are at different distances from the center of the ego, some being closer than others. 'Our problems, emotions, feelings and attitudes, in this respect, belong closer to the nucleus of the ego than experiences relating to the outward world, and to our body.' Some sensations are particularly close to this hypothetical nucleus of the ego, and specifically pain, sexual excitement, and anxiety seem to be in the very center of the personality. The fact that certain parts of the body are nearer than others to this center should be kept in mind during the study of post-operative neurosis and psychosis. It is worth while to point out that the importance of surgical operations varies in accordance with the part of the body operated upon: operations on genitals, breasts, or eyes threaten the body parts that are nearer than others to the center of the ego. In schizophrenia and neurosis, the complexes are in the center of the personality, yet the experiences of organic brain lesions concern material which is rather impersonal. Individuals with organic diseases are generally much more objective toward their infirmity than are psychogenic cases. In support of this theory, Schilder gives numerous examples, of which the following may suffice: 'A nineteen-year-old girl, who was feeling ill three days before admission and complained of headache and vomiting, did not talk at the time of admission. The somatic picture and the spinal-fluid findings were typical for meningococcus meningitis. Her stupor and drowsiness subsided, and twelve days after admission she answered—to the question "How do you feel?"—"Pretty good. I don't know what happened to me." She minimized the headaches she had had, and had no idea that she was seriously ill.' (Schilder, P. *Psychotherapy,* Norton, New York, 1938)

egocentrism Healy, Bronner, and Bowers ask whether the term *egocentrism* might not be clearer and less confusing than *egoism.* The latter means self-centeredness, yet it is often used synonymously with narcissism. Freud makes a distinction when he says: 'I believe narcism is the libidinous complement of Egoism.' He states that one may be egoistic and still retain strong interest in libido-objects or 'one can be egoistic and at the same time preponderantly narcistic, that is, have a very slight need for an object.' (Freud, S. *Collected Papers,* vol. 4, tr. by Riviere, J., Leonard and Virginia Woolf and The Institute of Psychoanalysis, London, 1924–25) See *egoism.*

ego, collective The ego is 'not only a product of the individual but, at the same time in the measure that it reflects the group and its concepts and expresses its mentality, it is also the product of the group. Thus, as a whole, it is a composite of a collective ego and an individual ego.' (Laforgue, R. *The Relativity of Reality,* Nervous and Mental Disease Monographs, No. 66, New York, 1940)

ego-complex See *complex, ego.*

ego, decomposition of The ego appears in the dream split up in its various tendencies, and represented by different persons, actions, things, or localities.

ego, dream With this expression Jung (analytical psychology) designates 'a mere fragment of the conscious ego' that is active during the dream stage. 'In a dream, consciousness is neither fully awake nor fully extinguished; there is still a small remnant of consciousness. There is, for instance, nearly always some consciousness of the ego, but rarely of the ego as it appears to the consciousness of waking life. It is rather a limited ego, sometimes peculiarly transformed or distorted. . . . The psychic contents of the dream appear to the ego very like those external phenomena which appear to it in the waking state. Hence it happens that we find ourselves in situations like those in real life, but rarely exercise thought or reason about them.' (Jung, C.G. *Contributions to Analytical Psychology,* tr. by Baynes, H.G. and C.F., Kegan Paul, Trench, Trubner, London, 1928)

ego-drive Impulse toward self-preservation, ego-maximation, and group conformance, the development of which is deeply rooted in biological constitution and markedly influenced by the social nature of man's existence. Also called *ego-instinct* (q.v.).

ego, duplication of See *personality, multiplication of.*

ego-dystonic (-dis-ton'ik) Anything that is unacceptable to the ego is called ego-dystonic. If an instinctual urge finds the ego unprepared to receive it, the impulse is said to be ego-dystonic. Stimuli from any source that are rejected by the ego or that are prevented from reaching the ego for its consideration are called ego-dystonic. Its opposite is ego-syntonic.

ego, effective In his theory of traumatic neurosis, Kardiner introduced this term to denote the ego that has learned how to adapt itself to the environment and deal with it *effectively,* as differentiated from the infantile ego—helpless at birth and, therefore, *ineffective* in this respect. This learning process consists in the acquisition of adaptive techniques and manipulations and the integration of them into effective tools. To Kardiner, adaptation is 'a series of maneuvers in response to changes in the external environment, or to changes within the organism, which compel some activity in the outer world in order to continue existence, to remain intact or free from harm, and to maintain controlled contact with it. At birth only the automatic functions—anabolic and catabolic—are effective, with the aid of a few reflexes, the chief of which is sucking. The infant's adaptation is passive as far as the outer world is concerned; it has no controlled contact with the outer world except insofar as this is mediated through the mother. It cannot choose, avoid, or seek out objects in the outer world necessary for its survival.' (Kardiner, A., and Spiegel, H. *War Stress and Neurotic Illness,* Hoeber, New York, 1947)

ego-erotism (-e′rō-tiz′m) Narcissism. See *ego-libido.*

ego, escape from the A phenomenon of psychic displacement by which the compulsive-neurotic shifts the goals of his own ego to another person by way of identification or differentiation. This is, for instance, the case of the rich man, suffering from a compulsion, who 'identifies himself with the man who sweeps the streets every day. The patient shares his life with the street-cleaner, he experiences his feelings, he participates in his humiliations, his deprivations, his small pleasures. This may go so far that the compulsive does not permit himself to enjoy a good meal at a restaurant, because the street-cleaner can afford only a modest one. On the other hand, the street-cleaner is under no obligation to maintain a high cultural standard. For this identification, the com-

pulsive is rewarded with the pleasure that he does not have to restrain himself in certain other aspects: he may swear, curse, or tell vulgar stories in public, since it is the street-cleaner talking, not he, the man of his social position. In this way he can escape the culture-ego, even if he does so by denying himself luxury and many conveniences. However, he enjoys making these sacrifices, although he claims that he is troubled by this annoying compulsion, and threatens suicide, as all these patients do.' For another, and far more prevalent, mechanism of escape from the ego, see *ego, negation of the.* (Stekel, W. *Compulsion and Doubt,* Liveright, New York, 1949)

ego, extinction of A psychoanalytic term referring to the relationship between a punitive superego and a guilt-ridden ego. The guilt of the ego stems from the strength of denied and repressed unconscious hostility (or sexuality) of an infantile and primitive nature. The obsessional neurotic, for example, must constantly neutralize his infantile omnipotent destructive powers through equally omnipotent magical means, so that he can protect his loved objects from his repressed hostility. In this way he attains the right, or justification, for his own ego to continue to exist. When these ritualistic and magical processes fail, extreme guilt with deep inhibition, feelings of painful dejection, apathy, and nihilistic unworthiness overwhelm the ego (individual). It is this state that is tantamount to extinction of the ego through the wrath of the superego. E.F. Sharpe (*Collected Papers on Psycho-analysis,* Hogarth Press, and The Institute of Psychoanalysis, London, 1950) states: 'The ritual [of the obsessional neurotic] must never cease, or his unconscious destructive power will bring about the extinction of his ego . . .'

ego-function See *ego.*

egohood Personality; individuality.

ego, ideal The ideal ego is the ego which feels as one with the id, as is the case with the unorganized ego of the child. This ideal condition begins to disappear with the first opposition to the gratification of his needs, and while all individuals presumably strive to recapture this state it is for the most part only in certain psychoses (e.g. manic and catatonic episodes) that the patient grants himself everything pleasurable and rejects everything unpleasurable. The phantasy of a return to the womb is an expression of the desire to return to the state of the ideal ego.

ego-ideal In psychoanalysis the term ego refers to a psychic structure that undergoes gradual evolution from the time that it makes its embryonic appearance as a modification of a part of the id until it acquires more or less final form late in life. As the ego expands, as it develops new structures and functions, its limits extend from the id to reality. The individual is constantly identifying himself with others. The first important identifications are connected with the parents; hence, a part of the developing ego is set aside, so to speak, to contain the mental images of the parents. Later the composite image, constituting the superego, occupies a position in the unconscious, where it continues to act as the 'inner conscience' and controlling agency of the id. 'During the course of its growth, the super-ego also takes over the influence of those persons who have taken the place of the parents, that is to say of persons who have been concerned in the child's upbringing and whom it has regarded as ideal models. Normally the super-ego is constantly becoming more and more remote from the original parents, becoming as it were more impersonal.' (Freud, S. *New Introductory Lectures on Psycho-Analysis,* tr. by Sprott, W.J.H., Norton, New York, 1933) That part of the ego devoted to the development of parental substitutes (parental imagos) and in which the parental imagos are laid down is called the ego-ideal. 'Identifications take place with these later editions of the parents as well, and regularly provide important contributions to the formation of character; but these only affect the ego, they have no influence on the super-ego, which has been determined by the earliest parental imagos.' (ibid.) The ego-ideal is a precipitation of the superego.

The ego-ideal may change from time to time as newer identifications are made. When the individual's own narcissism is threatened, it is usually withdrawn from the ego-ideal of later development and regresses to what is called the narcissistic ego-ideal, namely, the mental image of perfection that the child constructs of himself.

See *ego; superego.*

ego-ideal, narcissistic See *ego-ideal.*

ego-instinct In psychoanalysis it is said that 'every instinct seeks to come to expression by activating those ideas which are in accordance with its aims.' (Freud, S. *Collected Papers,* vol. 2, tr. by Riviere, J., Leonard and Virginia Woolf and The Institute of Psychoanalysis, London, 1924–25) Freud goes on to say that the instincts are not always in agreement with one another; the disagreement leads to conflicting interests. He adds: 'Of quite peculiar significance for our efforts towards elucidation is the undeniable opposition between the instincts which serve the purpose of sexuality, of gaining sexual pleasure, and those others which aim at the self-preservation of the individual, the ego-instincts.' (ibid.)

Jones defines the ego-instincts as 'all the non-sexual instincts.'

Freud states: 'The hypothesis of separate ego instincts and sexual instincts rests scarcely at all upon a psychological basis, but is essentially supported upon the facts of biology.' (Freud, S. ibid.) For Freud's latest revision of the dual-instinct theory, see *instinct, death.*

ego, integrated A psychoanalytic term usually employed in reference to a specific and important goal or aim of the psychoanalytic procedure. The psychoanalytic task is to help the patient face the truth about himself, the truth of which he is unaware and to which unawareness large areas of his personality have been devoted. Through this painfully achieved *self-consciousness* (in the full literal sense) harmonious functioning of the personality may be established under the primacy of the conscious ego so that finally the patient learns to be afraid of neither his infantile and primitive instinctual urges nor the terrorizing force of his guilt-ridden conscience. E.F. Sharpe (*Collected Papers on Psycho-analysis,* Hogarth Press, and The Institute of Psychoanalysis, London, 1950) states: 'If patients can externalize in the analysis the many roles the unconscious plays in phantasy, then they too can build an integrated ego in actual life.'

egoism Selfishness. *Egoism* refers to the condition of evaluating things in terms of oneself, of one's personal interests. When ideas concerning an object are recognized for their value to the individual possessing them, one speaks of egoism. 'Egoism is the feeling that demands for self an increase of enjoyment and a diminution of discomfort. Altruism is that which demands these results for others.' (Ward, L.F.) An effort is made today to define egoism without reference to the quantity or quality of feeling or affect associated with ideas. When the self-centeredness is heavily intermixed with the sense of self-importance, it is called egotism.

egoity (ē-gō'i-tē) Egohood; personality; individuality.

egoize (ē'gō-īz) To give excessive consideration to one's self.

ego-libido (-li-bēd'ō) When libido is attached to the ego it is called ego-libido. It is generally used in contradistinction to the expression *object-libido*. It is synonymous with ego-cathexis, when the latter refers to libidinal qualities. The ego may be cathected with libido (constructive instinctual quality) or with destrudo (destructive instinctual quality). The latter term (destrudo) has not found favor in psychoanalysis, though its meaning (sado-masochism) is extensively described.

In the early stages of the development of ego-libido the outside world is 'generally speaking, not cathected with any interest and is indifferent for purposes of satisfaction.' (Freud, S. *Collected Papers*, vol. 4, tr. by Riviere, J., Leonard and Virginia Woolf and The Institute of Psychoanalysis, London, 1924–25)

Ego-libido and narcissism (narcism) refer to same conditions, namely, in the words of Karl Abraham, 'that stage in the development of the libido in which the child is himself the center of his own narrow world and in which he receives proofs of love from other persons without himself giving any return.' (Abraham, K. *Selected Papers*, tr. by Bryan, D. and Strachey, A., Leonard and Virginia Woolf and The Institute of Psychoanalysis, London, 1927)

egology (ē-gol'ō-jē) A term devised by S. Rado to mean study of the ego, the 'I.'

ego, loss of boundaries of Often, as in schizophrenia, the usual sharp delineation of the ego is lost, the patient's ego merging with that of another or with the entire world (cosmic identity). A patient, quoted by Storch, said: 'Sometimes I cannot tell myself from other people. I just cannot understand it—sometimes she was my sister and sometimes I was the doctor.' Storch comments as follows: 'Here the ego of the patient had lost its stability

and independent completeness to such a degree that it could not separate itself with certainty from the personality of another—that it confounded itself with the "thou." The intimate bond of affection connecting her with another drew her ego into that of the other, extinguishing differences and melting both together.'

Storch also says: 'We often found ourselves confronted by experiences in which the discrimination between the consciousness of self and the consciousness of the object were entirely suspended, the ego being no longer separated from the non-ego; the subject no longer distinct from the object; the self and the world were fused in an inseparable total complex.' This is a common phenomenon in schizophrenia and in primitive mentality. (Storch, A. *The Primitive Archaic Forms in Schizophrenia*, tr. by Willard, C., Nervous and Mental Disease Publishing Company, New York and Washington, 1924)

egomania (ē-gō-mā'ni-à) Exaggerated self-centeredness.

ego-maximation Ego drives to maintain feelings of personal adequacy in competitive situations. See *self-maximation*.

ego, mental See *ego, body*.

egomorphism (ē-gō-mor'fiz'm) A term that designates the attributing of one's own needs, desires, motives, etc., to someone else; the tendency to build a system of thought and interpret the reactions of others in terms of one's own ego needs—*projection* (q.v.). It has been suggested that the interpretations a psychiatrist makes to his patient are based on the egomorphism of the physician. This is one factor which has led psychoanalytic training institutes to require their students to undergo psychoanalysis.

ego, motor control of the The control exerted by the ego over the individual's motor activities. The mastery of the motor apparatus is a task gradually learned by the human infant. It learns to substitute 'actions for mere discharge reactions,' by acquiring a tolerance for the tension which arises from stimuli and which results in immediate reaction impulses. In addition, the infant must develop the function of judgment as a 'prerequisite for an action . . . This means the ability to anticipate the future in the imagination.' According to Fenichel, learning to walk, to control the sphincter, and to speak 'are the main steps in the development of the mastery of physical motor functions.' See *ego*.

Disturbances in the ego's motor control can be seen in certain types of symptoms. One example of this type of symptom is 'psychogenic dystonia.' The individual suffers from either localized or general muscular spasms or hypotonic muscular attitudes. In some cases hypertonic and hypotonic states alternate. Whichever is the case, there is 'a partial weakening of the voluntary mastery of motility.' (These symptoms are a defense aimed at 'barring warded-off impulses from motility.')

Another example is the tic. Here, 'instead of acting as a means for voluntary and directed action, the musculature has become again . . . an instrument for immediate discharge.' This is another instance in which 'the ability for ego control of motor disturbances seems lacking or insufficient.' (Fenichel, O. *The Psychoanalytic Theory of Neurosis,* Norton, New York, 1945)

ego-narcissism (-när-sis′iz'm) In the earlier months of development the id has unqualified control over existing erotogenic zones. There is nothing to curtail its organ-pleasure aims. Some time later the embryonic ego, budding, as it were, from the id, comes into being and it, too, for a considerable period of time is under the domination of the id. As the ego slowly evolves, it gains power step by step and as a consequence of repeated experiences it comes to learn how to satisfy the demands of the id. During the process of growth the ego gains a certain measure of control, variable in each individual, over the instinctual qualities. Indeed, it 'steals' a fair volume of the instincts and appropriates that volume for its own use. In other words, the ego has now achieved power; it can now do things under its own guidance. When mature, the ego can negotiate with reality and with the id. The investment of gratifying power in the ego system is called ego-narcissism.

'Throughout its dealings with the Id the Ego's own narcism must always be reckoned with.' (Healy, W., Bronner, A.F., and Bowers, A.M. *The Structure and Meaning of Psychoanalysis,* Knopf, New York, 1930)

ego, negation of the A mental mechanism through which the compulsive-neurotic avoids the responsibilities of his own ego by putting himself in the place of another person (identification) and then trying with all his might to differentiate himself from the chosen person (differentiation). The object in this case may be called a 'negative ruler of the soul.' The patient achieves the negation of his own ego through a negative and antagonistic attitude toward the person chosen as object. He will tell himself: 'I have no free will. I must do the opposite of what my object does. My actions are determined by his, but in such a manner that I become his opposite.'

This may be illustrated by the following example given by Stekel: 'A compulsive girl utilizes her neighbor for differentiation. This neighbor goes to her office at eight o'clock every morning. The patient anxiously watches for her behind the curtain. What kind of dress will the neighbor wear? What mood will she be in? Has she taken an umbrella along? The object appears, the patient inspects her closely—thus, the order of the day is given. The neighbor wore a dark dress. The patient will wear a light one. It is raining. The object carries an umbrella. The patient decides to go without one.' The mechanism of the negation of the ego constitutes a type of flight from the ego. See *ego, escape from the.* (Stekel, W. *Compulsion and Doubt.* Liveright, New York, 1949)

ego-neurosis See *neurosis, ego.*

ego-nuclei (-nū′klē-ī) The smaller component elements of the ego. 'According to Edward Glover, the ego, at first but loosely organized, consists of a considerable number of ego-nuclei. In his view, in the first place an oral ego-nucleus and later an anal ego-nucleus predominates over the others.' (Klein, M. *Contributions to Psycho-analysis* 1921–1945, Hogarth Press, London, 1948)

egopathy (ē-gop′á-thē) Hostile behavior due to a psychopathically exaggerated sense of self-importance. This expression is applied to the ailment of one of the most interesting and common groups of psychopaths. The individuals belonging to this group are characterized by a strong egocentric trend which compels them to deprecate others in their constant aggressive and unconceding attitude. The egopathic reaction, in a way, 'is not only characteristic of the psychopathic criminal, but also of the normal one.' Egopathic reactions are of different types and differ in their clinical significance. As an example of one of the types of egopathic reaction, Ralph Brancale gives 'the gunman who, with his compelling need to assert himself at the expense of others and to reassure himself of his strength and masculinity, works off his problems through aggression. He presents a different type of egocentricity than that of the relatively unaggressive, narcissistic swindler who tries to enact his vainglorious role through verbalism and deception.' (Seliger, R.V., *et al. Contemporary Criminal Hygiene,* Oakridge Press, Baltimore, 1946)

ego, perception Schilder's term for the censoring forces emanating from the ego and preventing certain psychic material from becoming conscious: 'the repressive forces originating from the ego are the representatives of the social functions of perception, action, and reality testing.' For this capacity of the ego, Schilder prefers the term 'perception ego,' instead of the widely current *repression* (q.v.), saying that, 'it is difficult to forget that the term ego has been used for generations to denote the totality of one's experiences, equivalent to the term person or personality.' In his opinion, the repressive forces are connected with logical thinking, i.e. the thinking directed to the community. In the analytic sense, these repressive forces constitute conscious material which is socially approved, and, therefore, also accepted by the individual himself. (Schilder, P. *Psychotherapy,* Norton, New York, 1938)

ego, phantasy-life of A psychoanalytic term referring specifically to one aspect of the transference situation. Transference is the blank slate of the relationship between analyst and analysand (patient) upon which the patient inevitably and invariably projects out his own thoughts and feelings of an unconscious and 'repressed' nature. These thoughts and feelings of an unconscious nature relate to his primitive infantile instinctual urges (id), as well as to the terroristic demands of his conscience (superego). In addition, the entire gamut of the phantasy life of thoughts and wishes that relate to reality and social adjustments and ideal control over instinctual forces appears in the ego-phantasy formations projected out upon the screen

of the transference situation. E.F. Sharpe (*Collected Papers on Psycho-analysis,* Hogarth Press, and The Institute of Psychoanalysis, London, 1950) states: 'Transference is this ever-shifting interchange of rôles in the present or past life of reality, or the phantasy-life of super-ego, ego, id, played out with the analyst on whom some [one?] of these rôles is constantly being thrust.' See *transference.*

ego, pleasure The part of the ego made up of components agreeable with instinctual impulses. See *ego, reality.*

ego, preschizophrenic This term denotes the prepsychotic personality of the schizophrenic. The personality is characterized by impairment of ego synthesis; that is, the individual does not give the impression of a personal oneness which the normal person gives. The preschizophrenic child daydreams excessively, and the phantasies here have the aim of withdrawal from reality; in the normal child, phantasies have the goal of experimentation and preparation for mastery of reality. Often, during sleep, the preschizophrenic child has dreams of its own death; there is a predominance of regressive (even prenatal) phantasies; exaggerated conscience, bizarre somatic sensations, frequent severe temper tantrums, and a pervasive aggressiveness are typical. 'The boundaries of the prepsychotic ego are progressively constricted by aimless aggressiveness, whatever may be the serious obstacles preventing the healthy transformation of primitive aggressive drives into activity suitable for mastering reality, and adapting the "normal" individual to social existence. The inability adequately to test reality is closely connected with the limitation of the boundaries of the ego, a basic disturbance in schizophrenia . . . Thus, intrapsychic object representations and instinctual derivatives are detached from the ego, and come to be regarded as "real," as belonging to the outside world.' (Bychowski, G. 'The Preschizophrenic Ego,' *Psychoanalytic Quarterly 16,* 225, 1947)

ego, purified pleasure A psychiatric term that designates 'a stage in the development of the ego in which anything unpleasant is considered non-ego, anything pleasant is considered ego.' Both the ego and the sense of reality originate in the infant's awareness that, to satisfy its needs, there is something outside which is necessary, which must be present. The perception of this something outside which satisfies needs as being different from the self who has the needs establishes the first demarcation between self and non-self, between the ego and objects—in a word, the sense of reality.

The primitive infantile need out of which arise the concepts of ego and object is, of course, hunger. Thus, when the infant has learned to recognize objects, his first reaction will be to put them into his mouth, for the experience through which he first got rid of the tension that disturbed his sleep and forced him to become aware of the outside world was satiation. His first way of handling reality was by swallowing. Likewise, when, instead of helping to gain satisfaction, something raises tensions, it is spat out. Therefore, the ego's first experience of judgment distinguishes between edible and non-edible objects.

Now at about this stage in the development of the ego, everything pleasurable is experienced as belonging to the ego and something to be swallowed, and everything painful is experienced as being non-ego and something to be spat out. Freud called this stage 'the purified pleasure ego.' This purified pleasure ego strives to reverse the separation of ego from non-ego, thus expressing a longing for the original objectless state of affairs. By swallowing anything pleasant, the infant adjoins pleasurable stimuli to the ego and attempts to make parts of the external world flow into the ego. By 'spitting out' anything painful, the infant adjoins unpleasant stimuli to the non-ego and puts unpleasant sensations into the external world. See *ego*.

These mechanisms of the state of the purified pleasure ego may be used by the ego for defensive purposes. For example, projection is a derivative of the first negation of unpleasurable stimuli described above. Psychotics show the use of this mechanism most clearly, for, by narcissistic regression, the reality testing of their egos has been severely damaged. The boundaries between ego and non-ego are no longer clear. The psychotic perceives emotions or excitements which are unpleasant to him as being outside the ego. 'The offensive impulse is perceived in another person instead of in one's own ego.'

Also in childhood, as the ego develops, the projection derived from the purified

pleasure ego is important as the source of the early animistic way of thinking and feeling. (Fenichel, O. *The Psychoanalytic Theory of Neurosis,* Norton, New York, 1945)

ego, reality When the ego is autoerotic, that is, when the individual is self-contained, it has no need of the outside world, 'but, in consequence of experiences undergone by the instincts of self-preservation, it tends to find objects there and doubtless it cannot but for a time perceive inner instinctual stimuli as painful.' (Freud, S. *Collected Papers,* vol. 4, tr. by Riviere, J., Leonard and Virginia Woolf and The Institute of Psychoanalysis, London, 1924–25) When the objects of reality are pleasurable they are absorbed by (introjected into) the ego. Hence, an object of reality, incorporated into the ego, helps to constitute that part of the ego known as reality-ego.

The ego absorbs both painful and pleasurable objects, but it separates them, retaining the pleasurable to form the *pleasure-ego* and projecting the painful back into the outer world as a hostile object.

'Thus the original *reality-ego,* which distinguished outer and inner by means of a sound objective criterion, changes into a purified *pleasure-ego,* which prizes above all else the quality of pleasure.' (Freud, S., ibid.)

ego, reality life of A psychoanalytic concept referring to the practical everyday life of the patient with all its reality problems, in contrast to the goals and aims of the psychoanalytic procedure, as confined to the analyst's office. In the analyst's office, the patient's relationship to the analyst per se (i.e. the transference situation) is of paramount concern. The main task of the analyst is directed not at helping the patient with his reality problems but at assisting the patient in acquiring the courage to face the truth about himself. This is achieved mainly through the analysis of what are called defensive resistances. In this way, insuperable conflicts between powerful and primitive instinctive forces on the one hand, and horror-filled guilt-feelings on the other, stemming from childhood conscience pressures, can eventually be resolved. When this resolution has been brought about, symptomatic improvement in the reality life of the ego will usually ensue. (Sharpe, E.F. *Collected Papers on Psy-*

cho-analysis, Hogarth Press and The Institute of Psychoanalysis, London, 1950)

ego, reasonable 'Lack of a reasonable ego' is discussed by Fenichel as a major factor to be considered in deciding whether or not psychoanalysis should be tried with a given patient. 'The method of psychoanalysis is based on the cooperation of a reasonable ego.' A part of the ego must be split off into a reasonable, judging portion. And 'this cleavage is accomplished by utilizing positive transference and transitory identifications with the analyst.'

In certain cases it may be difficult or even impossible to establish this co-operative reasonable ego. Some patients actually refuse to co-operate. In these cases the analyst must try to convince the patient that it is not that he simply does not wish to co-operate but that he is incapable of doing it. An interest in this inability to co-operate then becomes the patient's first motive for co-operation and other motives may follow. An extreme example of this type of patient is the generally frigid character who avoids emotions altogether. He does not understand the psychology of emotions and emotional connections and accepts only logical connections. Another example of this sort of patient is the pseudo-emotional type of character whose intense and uncontrollable emotions have flooded everything. Such patients find 'reality full of representatives of the feared instincts' and 'lack the necessary detachment to form judgments' about their own emotions. Other patients in whom a reasonable ego may also be lacking are the schizophrenics. In these cases the problem is to establish a transference. A pre-analytic procedure may accomplish this and the transference thus formed will then be the basis of a later analysis. (Fenichel, O. *The Psychoanalytic Theory of Neurosis,* Norton, New York, 1945)

ego-resistance See *resistance, ego.*

ego-retrenchment The act of diminishing or removing the need for a given function of the ego is called ego-retrenchment. Thus, inhibitions may make it unnecessary for the ego to form symptoms in order to appease an unconscious impulse. 'Inhibitions are sometimes to be explained as Ego-retrenchments in the service of defense, when, through regression, a sexual phantasy begins to take on a stronger cathexis and to demand motor discharge.

Thus, inhibitions may obviate the need for symptom-formation.' (Healy, W., Bronner, A.F., and Bowers, A.M. *The Structure and Meaning of Psychoanalysis,* Knopf, New York, 1930)

ego, safety of A psychoanalytic term that refers to the function of conscious and unconscious ego defense-mechanisms in allaying or fending off anxiety. The ego is more or less constantly threatened from three different directions: (1) the objective reality of the outer world; (2) the severity of archaic and infantile conscience (superego); and (3) the urgent impulsive and compulsive power of instinctual drives. The safety and freedom of the ego from anxiety depends on the unconscious magic inherent in the illusions fostered by the ego defense-mechanisms.

When unable to reach the longed-for grapes by jumping, the hungry fox said: 'The grapes are sour, and besides I'm not hungry'—a nice example of the defense of the ego by the creation of two ideas, both false and contrary to fact or reality. E.F. Sharpe (*Collected Papers on Psycho-analysis,* Hogarth Press and The Institute of Psychoanalysis, London, 1950) states: 'The safety of the ego will depend upon its ability to deal with incorporated imagos. We know from the mechanism of melancholia that when the ego itself becomes identified with the reproached love object, super-ego sadism, reinforced by id sadism, may destroy the ego.'

ego, satanic This expression refers to the amoral, antisocial, unethical trend of the ego functions, in which the self is manifested as 'the result of repressive impulses and of suppressed criminality.' The influences conducive to the development of satanic ego are defined by Stekel under the denomination of 'katagogic trends' or 'downward-leading.' (Stekel, W. *The Interpretation of Dreams,* Liveright, New York, 1943)

ego, second See *alteregoism.*

ego, split in the By this term Freud designates the phenomenon in which the ego may develop several divergent yet co-existing attitudes toward the same thing. This situation exists (1) in the normal personality; (2) in neuroses; and (3) in psychoses.

(1) In the normal person, 'The ego can take itself as object, it can treat itself like any other object, observe itself, criticize

itself, and do Heavens know what besides with itself. In such a case one part of the ego stands over against the other. The ego can, then, be split; it splits when it performs many of its functions, at least for the time being. The parts can afterwards join up again.' In particular, Freud describes that faculty of the ego which observes and criticizes the ego and he names it 'super-ego.' This is one example of a split in the ego, and the self-observation and self-criticism demonstrate the existence of two attitudes toward whatever is being done by the person at the time.

(2) In neuroses, two contrary and independent attitudes are always present as regards some particular behavior, for the ego's defensive efforts to ward off danger are never completely successful and the weaker attitude which is repressed nevertheless leads to 'psychological complications,' such as the neurotic symptoms. This split in the ego is most vividly demonstrated when an effort is made to deny certain perceptions of the external world which represent painful demands of the external world on the person. The detachment from reality is always incomplete and the rejection is coupled with an acceptance. For example, the fetishist is trying to reject his perception of the fact that women have no penis, because then he must admit the fact that he, too, could be castrated. The fetish, a symbolic penis, is usually something that was seen at the same moment the women's genitals were seen or it is something suitable as a symbol for a penis. But many fetishists have a dread of castration. Thus these patients must also recognize the fact that women have no penis. The co-existence of fetishism and a dread of castration may be classified as a split in the ego.

(3) In psychotic episodes, the patients frequently verbalize the fact of a split in the ego when they relate that even during acute hallucinatory and delusional states one part of their mind was watching in an objective way the remainder of the patient and his feelings, behavior, and thoughts. This is particularly clear in those catatonic patients who, after the attack has ended, can report coherently on all their behavior and upon all that was going on about them during a catatonic episode in which they appeared to be completely out of contact. Here one attitude, the stronger one, arising from instincts has detached the patient from reality, represented by a

now weaker attitude. When the psychosis has been cured, the normal attitude which takes account of reality has become stronger and the attitude represented by the psychosis has become weaker and is now unconscious. (Freud, S. (1) *An Outline of Psychoanalysis,* Norton, New York, 1949; (2) *New Introductory Lectures on Psychoanalysis,* Norton, New York, 1933)

ego, stability of A psychoanalytic term referring to a symptomatic quality indicating degree of health, strength, maturity, or 'normality' of the ego. It is a concept particularly useful in contrasting the ego of the so-called 'normal' individual with that of the neurotic. The usual differentiating criteria of the more normal ego, in contrast to the neurotic one, are the following: (1) less severe primitive or infantile hostility (id); (2) less severe self-punitive archaic conscience drive (superego); (3) fewer magical defensive systems; (4) less infantile omnipotent (wishful) thinking; (5) enhanced object reality functioning. In addition (6), E.F. Sharpe *(Collected Papers on Psycho-analysis,* Hogarth Press and The Institute of Psychoanalysis, London, 1950) states: 'The one essential difference I find between neurotic and normal . . . is a *reality system* of some kind in which the conflict is played out, or annulled, in connection with *real* people and *real* things.'

ego-strength The effectiveness with which the ego discharges its various functions. A strong ego will not only mediate between id, superego, and reality and integrate these various functions, but further it will do so with enough flexibility so that energy will remain for creativity and other needs. This is in contrast to the rigid personality in which ego functions are maintained, but only at the cost of impoverishment of the personality.

ego-subject When the ego is the object of its own instincts (ego-instincts), the ego is called the ego-subject. 'Originally, at the very beginning of mental life, the ego's instincts are directed to itself and it is to some extent capable of deriving satisfaction from them on itself. This condition is known as narcissism and this potentiality for satisfaction is termed autoerotic. The outside world is at this time, generally speaking, not cathected with any interest and is indifferent for purposes of satisfaction. At this period, therefore, the ego-subject coincides with what is pleasurable and the outside world with what is indifferent (or even painful as being a source of stimulation).' (Freud, S. *Collected Papers,* vol. 4, tr. by Riviere, J., Leonard and Virginia Woolf and The Institute of Psychoanalysis, London, 1924–25)

ego-suffering One of the functions of the superego is to criticize the ego and to inflict punishment upon it, whenever the ego conspires with the id to carry out some urge to which the superego strenuously objects. Punishment may be the result of only allowing the instinctive impulse to gain the sphere of consciousness. An individual, 'conscience stricken' (that is, struck down by the superego) because he 'allowed' himself to think or act in a way considered immoral by him, may suffer severely for the 'infraction.' It is said that the ego suffers. Freud reserves the expression 'consciousness of guilt' to a conscious condition, and that of 'need for punishment' to the unconscious ego (superego).

Ego-suffering is a common phenomenon in psychiatric syndromes, being very vividly expressed in states of depression.

ego, supportive This term was first introduced by S.R. Slavson to denote one who is dynamic in activity group psychotherapy. In therapy groups it refers to the relation in which one member—because of his greater strength or maturity—helps a fellow-member to gain status in a group or to work out his intrapsychic problems. It has been observed that supportive-ego relations are temporary and progressive in nature. A weak child may attach himself to another weak child in order to forward his own adaptation to a group, but, growing stronger and less fearful, he makes friends with the stronger members of the group. Finally, the child functions on his own, without support from any one of his fellow-members.

ego-syntonia (-sin-tō′ni-à) Ego-syntonia is a condition of the mind, characterized by the acceptability of ideas or impulses to the ego. It means that the ego receives the impulses as consonant and compatible with its principles.

egotheism (ē′gō-thē-iz′m) Self-deification.

egotism See *egoism.*

egotropy (ē-got′rō-pē) Adolf Meyer's term for egocentricity or narcissism.

egregorsis (ē-grē-gor′sis) Egersis.

egrimony (eg′ri-mō-nē) *Obs.* Sadness, sorrow.

egritude (ē′gri-, eg′ri-tūd) *Obs.* Mental sickness.

eidetic (ī-det′ik) Pertaining to or characterized by clear visualization (even by a voluntary act) of objects previously seen. Eidetic images (also known as primary memory images) are clearer and richer in detail than the usual memory images and are also more intense and of better quality. Except that the individual recognizes the eidetic image as a memory experience, the phenomenon is analogous to a hallucination. Visual eidetic imagery is more common than auditory. Such imagery is rare in adults.

eisoptrophobia (ī-sop-trō-fō′bi-à) Fear of mirrors.

ejaculatio deficiens (ā-yà-koo-lä′tē-ō dā-fē′kē-ens) (Mod.L. 'failing ejaculation') Absence of ejaculation.

ejaculation (ē-jak-ū-lā′shun) From the sexual point of view ejaculation is the expulsion of semen and seminal fluid from the urethra.

ejaculatio praecox (ā-yà-koo-lä′tē-ō prī-kôks) The ejaculation of semen and seminal fluid during the act of preparation for sexual intercourse, i.e. before there is penetration.

Ejaculatio praecox (premature ejaculation) is usually based on a feminine orientation and/or a sadistic desire to soil the woman and/or intense urethral eroticism. Typically, such patients have marked masturbatory guilt. The sexual partner is identified with the mother, and the patient aims to have his genitals touched by the woman and then to ejaculate as though he were passing urine. This is in part determined by infantile narcissism, in that the penis and urinary activities are thought to exercise an irresistible charm over the woman. The praecox patient can only receive love, and his exhibitionism is a hostile attitude of contempt for the woman. In ejaculatio praecox there is a defiant relapse into the infantile uncontrolled emptying of the bladder; in this way, the person takes revenge on every woman for the disappointments in love he suffered as a child at the hands of his mother.

ejaculatio retardata (rā-tàr-dä′tà) (Mod.

L. 'retarded ejaculation') When ejaculation during sexual intercourse is unduly delayed, the condition is known as *ejaculatio retardata*. It is not uncommon in anxiety neuroses.

elaboration, secondary One of the four mechanisms of dream-making. These are: (1) condensation, (2) displacement, (3) dramatization, (4) secondary elaboration. The psychic material from which the dream is derived is transformed by these four mechanisms into the picture of the dream as it appears to the dreamer. In the process of transformation the psychic material undergoes great distortion. Jones writes: 'This [secondary elaboration] is the product of consciousness, and is brought about by the alteration undergone by the dream processes during their apprehension in consciousness. To it is due whatever degree of order and consistency there may be found in a dream. It particularly affects those parts of the dream that have been insufficiently distorted during the dream-making; its action continues after waking, so that a memory of a dream becomes more altered the greater is the period that has elapsed since it was experienced.' (Jones, E.J. *Papers on Psycho-Analysis,* Williams and Wilkins, Baltimore, 1949)

élan vital (ā-laN' vē-tàl') Bergson's term for the creative life-force or life-impulse, the basis of evolutionary progress.

electric convulsion therapy See *therapy, electric convulsion.*

electrodermal response See *reflex, psychogalvanic.*

electroencephalogram (ē-lek-trō-en-sef'à-lō-gram) The graphic record of the electrical activity of the brain, usually obtained by means of electrodes attached to the scalp. The regular, spontaneous oscillations of the electrical potential of the brain are amplified and recorded on an oscillograph. Characteristic changes in type, frequency, and potential of the brain waves occur in various intracranial lesions.

The alpha wave or rhythm (also known as the Berger wave) is the most common wave form of the adult cortex. It is found mainly in the parieto-occipital area when the subject is at rest and consists of smooth, regular oscillations at a frequency of 8 to 12 per second. It is usually diminished ('blocked') by sensory stimulation and mental activity.

The beta rhythm has a frequency of 18 to 30 c./s. and is associated with alertness. The delta rhythm is an abnormal rhythm with a frequency slower than 4 c./s.; it is often found when the subject is in light sleep. The theta rhythm is a 4 to 7 c./s. rhythm, seen not uncommonly in the temporal region.

Various techniques are used to accentuate abnormal waves or to bring out latent abnormalities, among them overventilation, natural or drug-induced sleep, photic driving (rhythmic optic stimulation with a stroboscope), chemical stimulation (especially with metrazol, and often combined with photic driving) and hydration induced by pitressin, alcohol, hypoglycemia, or oxygen lack. Such activated EEGs, however, often give false positives and are, therefore, even more difficult to interpret than the standard record.

electroencephalograph The apparatus used in making a graphic record of the electrical activity of the brain.

electroencephalography (-en-sef-à-log'rà-fē) The process or method of making (by a special electrical apparatus) a graphic record of the electrical activity of the brain (encephalon); a specific technique of investigation, neurophysiological in the main, consisting basically of the elaboration, recording, observation, and interpretation of the minute electrical action currents of the functioning cerebrum, or brain. These action currents, the result or concomitant of cerebral neurophysiological activity, are tapped off from the underlying brain tissue through fine electrodes inserted into the scalp, thus obviating the necessity of trephining or opening the skull.

Through an elaborate system of electrical amplification, the low-voltage electrical impulses are made discernible and readable through transformation into kymographic drum recordings. These kymographic drum records make visible the transformation of electrical impulses into the movements of a light-weight stylus over a revolving drum, covered with smoke soot, and are called electroencephalograms. Organic pathological and pathophysiological variations of the action currents of the brain have been standardized and can be compared with the standardized norms of the 'average,' the 'healthy,' or the 'normal.' The electroencephalogram (abbreviated *EEG*) is now an accepted and integral tool in the organic and physiological examination of the central nervous system, especially the brain. (Harms, E. *Handbook of Child Guidance,* Child Care Publications, New York, 1947)

electronarcosis (-när-kō′sis) A form of shock therapy requiring an electrical machine with electrodes which are applied to the patient's temples. 'Once the switch is thrown, the patient becomes unconscious immediately and tightens up (without breathing) for half a minute. The current is then turned off; the patient immediately relaxes, moves, and begins breathing. Then the current is carefully regulated to increase gradually till the patient reacts by sleeping, generally quiet and breathing easily. This procedure continues for five to seven minutes, after which the current is cut off and treatment is terminated.' (Polatin, P., and Philtine, E. *How Psychiatry Helps,* Harper, New York, 1949.) This treatment is used mainly in schizophrenia, but its effect is inferior to the effects of insulin in such diseases.

The electrical machine used for electronarcosis is more complicated technically than the electroconvulsive apparatus, but it has similar electrodes to apply the current.

electrophobia (ē-lek-trō-fō′bi-à) Fear of electricity.

electroplexy (ē-lek′trō-plek-sē) Electroconvulsive treatment; ECT.

elementary process See *process, elementary.*

eleuthomania (ē-lū-thēr-ō-mā′ni-à) *Rare.* Excessive zeal for freedom.

ellipsis (e-lip′sis) In psychiatry, essentially as in grammar: 'The omission of one or more words, leaving the whole to be understood or completed by the reader or hearer.' (The Century Dictionary)

In psychoanalysis Freud has stressed the omission of ideas, which are supplied by analysis. He quoted the following sentence from a patient: *'If you indulge in a coitus, something will happen to Ella.'* Freud writes: 'Here is another instance in which a solution can be reached by filling out an ellipsis. . . . When the omissions have been made good, we have: "Every time you copulate, even with a stranger, you will not be able to avoid the reflection that in your married life sexual inter-

course can never bring you a child (on account of the lady's sterility). This will grieve you so much that you will become envious of your sister [Ella's mother] on account of little Ella, and you will grudge her the child. These envious impulses will inevitably lead to the child's death." ' (Freud, S. *Collected Papers,* vol. 3, tr. by Strachey, A. and J., Leonard and Virginia Woolf and The Institute of Psychoanalysis, London, 1925)

Ellis, Henry Havelock (1859–1939) British sexologist.

emancipation In psychiatry the term means detachment of instinctual qualities with particular reference to the Oedipus complex as it reappears at puberty. According to psychoanalysis the Oedipus situation loses many of its original manifestations at the close of the period of infantile sexuality and remains dormant during the latency period. At puberty it is reanimated and to it 'there is added a powerful current of unmistakable sensuality, which always at first attaches itself in the unconscious to the early incestuous objects of affection.' (Jones, E. *Papers on Psycho-Analysis* 4th ed., Wood, Baltimore, 1938) The child is obliged to relive the earlier complex, following which in normal instinctual growth he frees himself from the libidinal attachment to the parents and from dependence upon parental authority. The emancipation leads to heterosexual object-choice.

emasculation Castration; physical eviration; eunuchism.

embolalia (em-bō-lā′li-à) Embololalia.

embolism, cerebral (em′bō-liz'm ser′ebral) Brain obstruction. Emboli (i.e. plugs or stoppers, usually detached clots) arising from the pulmonary circulation, from thrombosis of the arteries of the neck and head, or from vegetations on the heart valves, may interfere with cerebral circulation, causing cerebral softening and neurological or psychotic symptoms. This condition, however, is comparatively rare. Stupor or coma may be present with focal signs of hemiplegia or paralysis. Irritability and anger, dulling of general intelligence, and memory defects may occasionally be observed. See *accident, cerebrovascular.*

embololalia (em-bō-lō-lā′li-à) A type of speech disorder, frequently associated with stuttering. in which the patient interpolates short sounds or words which are out of place in the structure of the sentence.

embolophasia (-fā′zhi-à) Embolophrasia.

embolophrasia (-frā′zhi-à) Bianchi writes: 'A melancholic subject in my clinique became quite oppressive, because he interlarded his speech with "really, now." "Really, now, you cannot understand, really now, how much I suffer, really now. . . ." This dysphrasic disorder goes under the name of *embolophrasia.*' (Bianchi, L. *A Text-Book of Psychiatry,* tr. by MacDonald, J.H., Baillière, Tindall & Cox, London, 1906)

emergence The theory that mind or consciousness arises from living matter which has reached a certain state of complexity; the term emergence is used to indicate that such an end result is not predictable from a consideration or knowledge of its constituent parts.

emetomania (em-ē-tō-mā′ni-à) Morbid desire to vomit, usually a hysterical symptom.

emetophobia Morbid dread of vomiting, not an uncommon symptom in hysteria.

emission, nocturnal See *ejaculation; wet-dream.*

emotion Agitated strong feeling. The most commonly accepted definition of emotion today includes reactions of an instinctive character that have both physical and psychical manifestations. 'It is surely of the essence of an emotion that we should feel it, i.e., that it should enter consciousness.' (Freud, S. *Collected Papers,* vol. 4, tr. by Riviere, J., Leonard and Virginia Woolf and The Institute of Psychoanalysis, London, 1924–25) Freud maintains that the true aim of repression is to suppress the development of emotion, that is, to keep the emotion in the unconscious sphere. This means also that the ideas associated with the emotion are repressed. Apparently when both ideas and their associated emotions are relegated to the unconscious, the ideas continue 'as an actual formation' therein, but the emotion exists only as 'a potential disposition. Hence, there are no unconscious affects in the sense in which there are unconscious ideas. . . . The whole difference arises from the fact that ideas are cathexes —ultimately of memory-traces—whilst af-

fects and emotions correspond with processes of discharge, the final expression of which is expressed as feeling.' (Freud, S., ibid.)

'Emotional expressions are objective phenomena which may qualify instinctive behavior or betray an attitude. They consist of gestures, postures, movements of parts of the face, vocal expressions, modulations of the voice and many visceral changes.' (MacCurdy, J.T. *The Psychology of Emotion,* Harcourt, Brace, New York, 1925)

'The usual way of thinking about the emotional experiences and their facial or other bodily manifestations is that the emotional experience is excited by the perception of some object, and that the emotional feeling then expresses itself in the bodily manifestations in question.' (*Encyclopaedia Britannica,* 14th ed., vol. 12, p. 885)

The James-Lange Theory of Emotions states that the so-called expressions or bodily changes are the direct results of the perception of the exciting object, and that the emotion is just the feeling of these bodily changes as they occur.

emotionalism, respiratory See *pseudoasthma.*

emotionality, pathologic (ē-mō-shun-al′-i-tē, path-ō-loj′ik) A variety of emotional responses characterizing one type of psychopathic personality, which are usually held under control in the presence of superior strength or police force. The commonest pathologic emotion is pugnacity. A person afflicted with this type of malady is uncivil and bullying, and scorns the rights of others. Pathologic emotionality is also shown by inordinate bragging, by the individual's acting 'the part of beggars in order to gain money or favors,' or by his enacting 'sadness for purposes of attention.' In all these instances there is a certain slyness or cunning. (Hinsie, L.E. *Understandable Psychiatry,* Macmillan, New York, 1948)

emotionally unstable personality See *personality trait disturbance.*

emotion, conversion of The psychosomatic process through which an unconscious emotional conflict concerning the function of one organ is displaced upon and expressed, vicariously, through the energizing of the functional disturbance of another organ. In this process symbolic representation of organ function plays a major role.

Blushing is a good example of the displacement of the erotic functions of congestion, tumescence, and erection from their primary phallic (clitoral or penile) glans, or head, onto the head (caput) of the body as a whole. In this process the body, as a whole, functions symbolically and unconsciously as a phallus, and is utilized to express and carry out conflicts that relate primarily to the genital area, and not primarily to the organ involved. (Weiss, E., and English, O.S. *Psychosomatic Medicine,* 2nd ed., Saunders, Philadelphia and London, 1949)

emotion, Papez' theory of A modification of Cannon's hypothalamic theory. According to Papez, the hippocampus, fornix, mammillary bodies of the hypothalamus, anterior thalamic nuclei, and gyrus cinguli form a circle ('Papez' circle') which elaborates the functions of central emotion and participates in emotional expression. The midbrain reticular formation is connected indirectly to Papez' circle by means of the olfactory tubercle and the amygdaloid and septal nuclei.

emotions, Cannon-Bard theory of See *Cannon hypothalamic theory of emotion.*

emotions, emergency See *psychodynamics, adaptational.*

emotions, ictal (ik'tal) Any suddenly occurring and quickly disappearing emotional reactions, but especially depression and anxiety. While affective disturbances may accompany almost any organic cerebral disorder, they are most frequently associated with disorders of the temporal lobe. A.A. Weil (*American Journal of Psychiatry, 113:* 149–157, 1956) suggests that such disturbances may be due to sub clinical 'hippocampalamygdaloid-temporal lobe epilepsy' and/or after-discharge from these areas following manifest seizure activation.

emotion, sources of A psychoanalytic term that is particularly used and useful in emphasizing the root origins, in the unconscious, of the personal shibboleths and prejudices of so-called 'normal' individuals. This is especially important for those with pretensions toward objective scientific observations and judgments. By working through the defensive resistances rooted in the character, a degree of self-knowledge is achieved, which is, in a way,

the ideal goal of the personal analysis. Through this process the emotional sources of rationalizations, self-delusions, self-deceptions, and confused obstructions to lucidity and clear understanding are uncovered. It is only through the intimate knowledge of one's own unconscious life that the emotional sources of bias and prejudice can be recognized and overcome.

E.F. Sharpe (*Collected Papers on Psycho-analysis,* Hogarth Press and The Institute of Psychoanalysis, London, 1950) upbraids an imagined self-satisfied analyst: ' "I am a normal person, and I do not need psychoanalysis." To think that, especially if the thinker is a practitioner, it is to be a conjurer or worker of magic. It is to be blind to the fact that we are all enmeshed in the magical thinking and doing that lies under the veneer of our civilization.'

emotions, welfare See *psychodynamics, adaptional.*

empathema (em-pà-thē'mà) *Obs.* Ungovernable passion.

empathema atonicum (à-tô'nē-koom) (Mod.L. 'atonic empathema') Mason Good's term for melancholy.

empathema entonicum (en-tô'nē-koom) (Mod.L. 'enteric empathema') Mason Good's expression for what is now known as the manic phase of manic-depressive psychosis.

empathema inane (ē-nä'ne) (Mod.L. 'empty empathema') Mason Good's term for psychomotor 'violence.'

empathetic (em-pà-thet'ik) Relating to intellectual, in contrast to emotional, identification.

empathic (em-path'ik) In Burrow's phylobiology the organism's primary feeling-motivation and response. Contrasted with affects or projective feeling. (Burrow, T. *The Biology of Human Conflict,* Macmillan, New York, 1937, p. 385)

empathize (em'pà-thīz) To diagnose, that is to recognize and identify the feelings, emotions, passions, sufferings, torments through observing their symptoms is to *realize intellectually,* to *understand* them, in a remote way to identify oneself with the patient, without ever having personally experienced those feelings,—to *empathize,* as it is known in psychiatry.

On the other hand, to place oneself in the position of the patient, to get into his skin, so to speak, to be able to duplicate, live through, *experience* those feelings in a vicarious way, is closely to identify oneself with another, to *share his feelings with him,* to *sympathize,* from the Greek *sýn,* together with, and *páthos,* suffering, passion.

empathy (em'på-thē) From the standpoint of psychoanalysis, empathy is defined as an 'intellectual understanding of what is inherently foreign to our own Ego in other people.' (Freud, S.) Empathy is thus a form of identification; it may be called intellectual identification in contrast to affective identification.

emphrensy (em-fren'zē) *Obs.* Same as *enfrenzy.*

empiricism (em-pir'i-siz'm) A school of philosophic thought which holds that the only source of knowledge is observable fact or objective experience. Watson's behaviorism is a form of empirical psychology.

empresiomania (em-prē-si-ō-mā'ni-à) Pyromania.

emprosthotonos (em-pros-thot'ō-nos) A forward bending of the body. It is the opposite of opisthotonos. See *arc de cercle.*

emulation Conscious, willful copying or imitating of another. Emulation is to be differentiated from *identification* (q.v.), which is an unconscious process.

enantiodromia (ē-nan-ti-ō-drō'mi-à) Jung says: 'Enantiodromia means "a running counter to." In the philosophy of Heraclitus this concept is used to designate the play of opposites in the course of events, namely, the view which maintains that everything that exists goes over into its opposite.' Jung quotes from Zeller (*History of Greek Philosophy*) to wit: 'From the living comes death, and from the dead, life; from the young, old age; and from the old, youth; from waking, sleep; and from sleep, waking; the stream of creation and decay never stand still.' (Jung, C.G. *Contributions to Analytical Psychology,* tr. by Baynes, H.G. and C F., Kegan Paul, Trench, Trubner, London, 1923)

enantiopathic (-path'ik) Tending to induce an opposite passion.

encatalepsis (en-kà-tà-lep'sis) Hippocratic term for catalepsy.

encephalasthenia (en-sef-al-as-thē'ni-à) Mental exhaustion; *obs.* for *psychasthenia.*

encephalitis, acute serous (en-sef-à-lī'tis) See *psychosis, infective-exhaustive.*

encephalitis, acute toxic See *psychosis, infective-exhaustive.*

encephalitis, arsphenamine hemorrhagic See *arsphenamine hemorrhagic encephalitis.*

encephalitis, epidemic This condition includes those mental disturbances which are associated with the acute phases of epidemic encephalitis such as delirium or stupor. It also includes those chronic cases of encephalitis, such as the parkinsonian syndrome, where residual defects of the character and emotional processes are observed. Post-encephalitic residual symptoms may include a diminution of voluntary attention, of spontaneous interest, and of initiative. Irritability, lack of concentration, forgetfulness, delusions of infidelity and excessive sexual desire may develop. In children, conduct disorders, memory defects, and mental deterioration may be observed. The behavior disorders may include tantrums, sexual aberrations, cruelty, homicidal tendencies, destructiveness, lying, and stealing. Schizophrenia may be simulated. In the adult, one may observe a great variety of mental states and syndromes.

encephalitis periaxialis diffusa (en-sef-à-lē'tēs pār-ē-ak-sē-à'lēs dē-fōō'sà) Schilder's disease. See *sclerosis, diffuse.*

encephalitis, purulent (en-sef-à-lī'tis) Brain abscess.

encephalitis, traumatic (traw-ma'tik) A term suggested by Osnato and Giliberti to replace *postconcussion neurosis,* because of actual cerebral injury in cases of concussion. (Osnato, M. and Giliberti, V. *Postconcussion Neurosis—Traumatic Encephalitis.* Archives of Neurology & Psychiatry *18,* 181–214, 1927)

encephalization (en-sef-al-i-zā'shun) In higher mammals the cerebral cortex has taken over more and more the task of controlling and exerting a regulative function on bodily processes and on emotions. In the human being this process of encephalization has reached its highest degree. In humans, the cerebral cortex governs not the somatic system alone, but all systems involved in emotional expression, psychological tensions, fears, and phobias. It is possible that the complexity of such a regulation is due to the functioning of the cerebral cortex. The lower animals are regulated by the hypothalamus and other centers. In the human, the lower centers co-operate in directing the behavior, but are themselves increasingly dominated by the cortex. (Masserman, J.H. *Behavior and Neurosis,* University of Chicago Press, Chicago, 1943)

encephalocele (en-sef'a-lō-sēl) Hernia of the brain. A developmental anomaly of cerebral substance protruding through a cleft in the skull.

encephalogram An X-ray of the skull following replacement of cerebrospinal fluid by air by means of lumbar puncture.

encephaloleukopathia scleroticans (en-sef-à-lō-lōō-kō-path'i-à   sklĕr-o'tē-kàns) See *sclerosis, diffuse.*

encephalomalacia (-mà-lā'shi-à) Softening of the brain.

encephalomyelitis, acute disseminated (-mī-e-lī'tis, -lē'tis) Acute perivascular myelinoclasis; an acute demyelinating disease occurring in the course of infection with the causal virus of one of the exanthemata (e.g. measles, mumps, smallpox, chickenpox, vaccination, antirabic inoculation).

encephalomyelomalacia chronica diffusa (-mī-e-lō-mà-lā'shē-à kro'ni-kà di-foo'zà) See *sclerosis, diffuse.*

encephalopathia literatorum (en-ke-fà-lō-pà'thē-à lē-te-rä-tō'room) (Mod.L. 'brain disease of the learned') *Obs.* Mental disorder due to overstudy.

encephalopathia puerperalis (poo-er-pe-rä'lēs) (Mod.L. 'puerperal brain-disease') Puerperal psychosis.

encephalopathy (en-sef-à-lop'à-thē) Disease of the brain.

encephalopathy, acute toxic See *psychosis, infective-exhaustive.*

encephalopathy, boxer's See *dementia, boxer's.*

encephalopathy, lead A diffuse brain disease due to chronic lead poisoning. It is usually occupational in origin, occurring in painters, plumbers, plasterers, and typesetters. Children may develop the disease from licking painted toys. Such substances as hair dyes, cosmetics, lead plasters, and salves, used over a long period of time, may cause lead poisoning.

Clinically, the disease may be characterized by headache, memory defects, convulsions, delirium, hallucinations, hemiplegia, and blindness. Lead encephalopathy in children is characterized by increased intracranial pressure, convulsions, hypertension, and cerebral edema.

encephalopathy, progressive degenerative subcortical See *sclerosis, diffuse.*

encephalopathy, traumatic (traw-ma'tik) A diffuse organic brain disease due to injury to the brain. Clinical symptoms are: persistent headache, dizziness, spots before the eyes, poverty of memory, general mental and physical fatigability, poor concentration, loss of energy, irritability, outbursts of anger, and either drowsiness or insomnia; personality changes are commonly a part of the syndrome.

encephalopsychosis (en-sef-à-lō-sī-kō'sis) A term suggested by Southard to refer to psychosis associated with cerebral lesions.

encephalopyosis (-pī-ō'sis) Brain abscess.

encephalosis (-lō'sis) A degenerative brain process produced by infectious disease. Clinically, it is characterized by headache, irritability, apathy, stupor, and convulsions. Pathologically, there occur petechial hemorrhages, anemic infarcts, endarteritis of small vessels, degeneration of ganglion cells, and brain hydration. Winkelmann introduced the term.

encopresis (en-kop-rē'sis) Involuntary defecation not due to organic defect or illness. Encopresis in a child over two years old is a result of faulty training, mental retardation, or regression on a psychogenic basis.

endocrinopathy (en-dō-kri-nop'à-thē) In general, a pathological state or abnormal functioning of an endocrine gland, with the clinical symptoms occurring in other parts of the body, although they are referable to the disturbance of the internal secretion of the gland in question.

Endocrinopathic conditions are usually named in accordance with the quantitative or qualitative alteration in the internal secretion of the gland involved, unless they are named after their discoverer (Basedow's disease, Graves' disease) or are given special names (myxoedema, acromegaly). In the case of the thyroid, for instance, we have hyperthyroidism where there is oversecretion; hypothyroidism where there is undersecretion; and dysthyroidism where qualitative alteration (underiodized thyroxin) is alleged.

Constitutional medicine views these various endocrinopathic syndromes from the standpoint of constitutional type rather than of disease. In fact, some authors go so far as to regard the glandular changes as secondary to other constitutional traits, denying them a causal role in the symptomatology commonly attributed to them.

The glandular constitutions of chief practical importance in constitutional medicine are the *hyper-* and *hypothyroid,* the *hyper-* and *hypopituitary,* the *hyper-* and *hypoadrenal* and the *hyperthymic* constitutions. Most of these types show features which have been included by Kretschmer in the description of his *dysplastic type* (see *type, dypsplastic*).

endocrinotherapy (-krin-ō-ther′ȧ-pē) Treatment with preparations from the glands of internal secretion, namely, the thyroid, thymus, gonads, pituitary, etc.

endoderm (en′dō-dĕrm) Entoderm.

endogamy (en-dog′ȧ-mē) Restriction of marriage to members of one's own social, religious, or cultural group.

endogenous, endogenic, endogenetic (en-doj′ē-nus, -dō-jen′ik, -jē-net′ik) In the modern era of psychiatry and physiological genetics, the term *endogenous* is preferably used for the general clinical classification of mental disorders, which are based primarily on special heredito-constitutional factors, thus originating predominantly *within* the organism itself and affecting the nervous system *directly.*

Schizophrenic and manic-depressive psychoses are the most characteristic types of endogenous disorders, while the so-called '*symptomatic*' psychoses which arise —as a secondary symptom of organic diseases in parts of the body other than the nervous system—from causes *outside* of the nervous system, even though *within* the body, are quite reasonably classified today as exogenous (see *exogeny*).

endogeny, endogenism, endogenesis (en-doj′ē-nē, -niz′m, -jen′ē-sis) The term *endogeny,* relating in biology to any process of 'growing from within,' is used in medicine to denote physical and mental conditions which are known or suspected to arise predominantly from causes *within* the body, and more specifically, from causes inherent in that system of the body which

is the seat of the morbid character in question.

The latter narrower definition seems to be preferred in the province of psychiatry, particularly. In the case of mental disorders it has become customary to classify them as exogenous rather than as endogenous, if their primary causes act from within the nervous system, even though they may have originated within, or may have been brought into, another part of the organism. From this point of view, a traumatic psychosis would be no more an exogenous disorder than a case of alcoholic hallucinosis or a symptomatic psychosis due to pernicious anemia or cancer of the liver.

If this definition is accepted, the psychiatric meaning of endogeny becomes almost concordant with a heredito-constitutional etiology, even if the significance of this classification was not clear in its essential aspects when the theoretical distinction between endogenous and exogenous psychoses was introduced. The same view explains why the term *autogeny* has been used as synonymous with endogeny.

In any case, since psychiatric knowledge of the genetic and constitutional factors operating in the origin of 'autogenic' psychoses has meanwhile been considerably improved, it seems now more adequate to limit the application of the term endogeny to such disorders as are predisposed to by specific hereditary factors and cannot be produced, without their pre-existence, by purely external causes, for instance, the disease groups of schizophrenia or manic-depressive psychosis (see *exogeny*).

endomorphic (-mor′fik) In Sheldon's system this term describes the type characterized by a predominance of its first component (circularity), that is, the physical structures developed from the *endodermal* layer of the embryo. Persons of this type are contrasted with the *mesomorphic* and *ectomorphic* (qq.v.) types and correspond roughly to Kretschmer's *pyknic* (q.v.) type.

endopsychic (-sī′kik) This term, characterizing something as being within the mind or psyche, is applied to those mental mechanisms that occur completely within the mind; thus *psychic suicide* is determined by the same processes that determine physical suicide, but in the case of the former the processes work endopsychically. Endopsychic structure refers to the structure of the psyche itself: the conscious, the preconscious, and the unconscious, the ego, the superego, and the id are all parts of the endopsychic structure.

end-pleasure The expression *end-pleasure,* taken from psychoanalysis, refers to the final organization of libido at the genital stage. It is pointed out by psychoanalysts that during growth libido passes from one erotogenic zone to another, always leaving behind a quantum of libido in each zone that is relinquished in favor of the next one. The earlier erotogenic areas later enter as *fore-pleasures* to the culmination of the sexual act or *end-pleasure.*

At puberty 'the excitations, mechanical and other, that gave satisfaction to the child's desires, now come to contain a disagreeable component (*Unlust*) due to the feeling of tension experienced. Thus they constitute merely a "fore-pleasure" (*Vorlust*), which impels to further activities destined to produce the "end-pleasure" (*Endlust*) that relief of tension brings about.' (Jones, E. *Papers on Psycho-Analysis,* 4th ed., Wood, Baltimore, 1938)

In the pre-genital stage of development the pleasures associated with erotogenic zones are end-pleasures.

enelicomorphism (en-el-i-kō-mor′fizm) *Adultomorphism* (q.v.).

energy, affective See *affective-energy.*

energy, capitalized See *canalization.*

energy, kinetic (ki-net′ik) See *canalization.*

energy, psychic (sī′kik) Freud emphasizes the dynamic nature of mental processes. The psyche has structure or form, with many departments or divisions, each of which has its own special architecture, so to speak. Each special division, however, is an intimate part of the total. The psyche has functions to perform. Sometimes the functions are the resultant of activities of the psyche as a unit, while at other times only certain departments are in action. The propelling force behind psychic action is called psychic energy. According to psychoanalysis the source of psychic energy is the id.

'Accompanying every mental process is a varying amount of psychical energy, which roughly corresponds with what we term the affect.' (Jones, E. *Papers on Psycho-Analysis,* 4th ed., Wood, Baltimore, 1938)

'If we disregard anatomical or etiologi-cal considerations concerning which little is as yet known, and if we confine ourselves to a descriptive treatment of symptoms and to the field of psychological analysis, all these troubles can be presented as different grades of a mental depression which reduces the energy or the tension of mental activity.' (Janet, P. *Psychological Healing,* vols. 1–2, tr. by Paul, E. and C., Macmillan, New York, 1925)

'Instinctive mental processes have, for their emotional goal, bodily action. These processes are, then, a vehicle for expression of the energy of the whole organism, which they direct in somewhat the same way as an elaborate switch-board directs electrical energy.' (MacCurdy, J.T. *The Psychology of Emotion,* Harcourt, Brace, New York, 1925)

'The energic viewpoint on the other hand is in essence final; the event is traced from effect to cause on the assumption that energy forms the essential basis of changes in phenomena, that it maintains itself as a constant throughout these changes, and finally leads to an entropy, a condition of general equilibrium. The flow of energy has a definite direction (goal), in that it follows the fall of potential in a way that cannot be reversed.' (Jung, C.G. *Contributions to Analytical Psychology,* tr. by Baynes, H.G. and C.F., Kegan Paul, Trench, Trubner, London, 1928)

enfrenzy *Rare.* To madden, to make frenzied.

engram In neurology this term designates a neuronal pattern of an acquired skilled act. The term has been used somewhat loosely in psychiatry to refer to the persisting psychical traces (usually in the form of an unconscious or latent memory) of any experience.

engram, function See *function-engram.*

enomania (ē-nō-mā′ni-à) *Oinomania* (q.v.).

enosimania (en-ō-si-mā′ni-à) Obsessional belief of the patient that he has committed an unpardonable sin.

enosiophobia (en-ō-si-ō-fō′bi-à) A morbid dread of having committed 'an unpardonable sin.'

entatic (en-tat′ik) Invigorating, aphrodisiac.

entelechy (en-tel′ē-kē) Teleological impulses are integrative impulses. (Carrel, A. 'The Relation of Cells to One Another,' Cowdry, E.V., ed., *Human Biology and Racial Welfare,* Hoeber, New York, 1930, p. 205) A. Carrel has demonstrated an integrative or teleological element, that is, an impulse to integration in cell groups in the nutrient medium. He says: 'These cells have, as it were, the magical power of setting themselves in order and making a wall, even when there is no house to be erected and no mason to build it.' Similar observations can be made in relation to the nervous system, which is capable of self-regulation, and this gives the coherent logical connection to its apparently integrative and purposeful functioning. (Dunbar, F. *Emotions and Bodily Changes,* Columbia University Press, New York, 1946)

enterocolitis (en-tĕr-ō-kō-lī'tis) Inflammation of the mucous membrane of the intestines. Déjérine and Gauckler say: 'the patients afflicted with this disease are, for the majority, neuropaths, characterized as such even by those specialists who are determined to refer the symptoms to an organic origin. There are no physicians who do not recognize that mucomembranous enterocolitis is almost certain to develop on a neuropathic soil.' (Déjérine, J. and Gauckler, E. *The Psychoneuroses and Their Treatment by Psychotherapy,* 2nd ed., tr. by Jelliffe, S.E., Lippincott, Philadelphia & London, 1915)

enteroptosis (en-tĕr-op-tō'sis) See *habitus, ptotic.*

entheomania (en-thē-ō-mā'ni-à) Demonomania.

entoderm (en'tō-dĕrm) In medicine and embryology, this term designates either the second primitive germ layer which is developed in the embryo's didermic *gastrulation* (q.v.) and is also called *hypoblast;* or the primary tissues which are subsequently derived from this layer and, thus, are characteristically distinguished from the organs and tissues developed from the other primitive germ layers, the *ectoderm* and the *mesoderm* (qq.v.).

In contrast to the *ectodermal* tissues, which eventually take over protective and neural functions, the *entoderm* becomes further specialized to subserve chiefly trophic functions. The blastopore, or primitive mouth, marks the future site of the anus, while the definitive mouth develops at approximately the opposite end, as soon as the embryo has attained a bilateral symmetry.

The entodermal tissue derivatives mainly consist of the epithelium of the digestive tract and associated glands, including pancreas, liver and gall bladder; epithelium of the respiratory system, thyroid, middle ear and auditory tube; epithelium of the urinary bladder, female urethra, proximal part of the male urethra, and the prostatic and bulbo-urethral glands.

entomophobia (en-tō-mō-fō'bi-à) Fear of insects.

entropy (en'trō-pē) Freud uses the term *entropy* with respect to the mobility of the affects. He says that as one grows older there is a 'striking diminution' in the movements of 'mental cathexes.' Some individuals lose mental plasticity very prematurely, while others retain it far beyond the usual age-limit. 'So that in considering the conversion of psychical energy no less than of physical, we must make use of the concept of an *entropy,* which opposes the undoing of what has already occurred.' (Freud, S. *Collected Papers,* vol. 3, tr. by Strachey, A. and J., Leonard and Virginia Woolf and The Institute of Psychoanalysis, London, 1925) Entropy means a 'turning inward' of energy; apparently it is a form of *fixation* (q.v.).

enuresis (en-ū-rē'sis) In general, the involuntary passage of urine. It may be the result of some physical disorder or it may be psychically determined. According to psychoanalysis, enuresis may acquire the significance of nocturnal masturbation (Jones), of exhibitionism (Abraham), of penis-envy in women (Abraham). Freud believes there is a relationship between incontinence of the bladder and fire. Ferenczi noted that bed-wetting and incendiarism where often connected with one another. He regarded enuresis as a urethral-erotic trait.

C.M. Pierce *et al.* (*U.S. Armed Forces Medical Journal 7:* 208–219) suggest an organic basis for enuresis on the strength of their findings of a significant preponderance of abnormal electroencephalograms and high incidence of familial history of enuresis in known enuretics. They suggest that sleep disturbances may be characteristic of the enuretic and may be a direct and measurable result of an inherited gene pattern.

enuresis nocturna (-nok-tĕr'nà) Bed-wetting; nocturnal enuresis; technically, urinary incontinence at night. Enuresis nocturna is more often psychic than physical in origin, although it may be secondary to urinary tract pathology, spina bifida, or other spinal cord anomalies. See *enuresis.*

environment 'Those forces or situations, or more strictly those stimuli, which reach and affect the human beings from the outside.' (Young, K. *An Introductory Sociology,* American Book Company, New York, 1934)

Bernard classifies the social environments of man as: (1) *physico-social,* including tools, weapons, ornaments, machines, transportation and communication systems, household and office equipment; (2) *bio-social,* as domesticated plants and animals, and human beings performing services; (3) *psycho-social,* as the inner behavior of individuals with whom we come in contact, uniformities of behavior as customs, folkways, conventions, traditions, beliefs, mores, externalized language symbols, and inventions such as books, magazines, newspapers, motion pictures and radio; and (4) *institutionalized derivative control* environments, as economic, political, racial, esthetic, ethical, educational, cultural, nationalistic, regional, religious, revolutionary, conservative, masculine, etc.' (Bernard, L.L. *Introduction to Social Psychology,* Holt, New York, 1926)

'Our real environment consists of those images which are most present to our thoughts, and in the case of a vigorous, growing mind, these are likely to be something quite different from what is most present to the senses. The group to which we give allegiance, and to whose standards we try to conform, is determined by our own selective affinity, choosing among the personal influences accessible to us.' (Cooley, C.H. *Human Nature and the Social Order,* Scribner, New York, 1902)

Both heredity and environment 'are indispensable to every phase of life, and neither can exist apart from the other; they are co-ordinate in importance and incommensurable in nature.' (Cooley, C.H. *Social Organization,* Scribner, New York, 1912)

environment, neutral A physical and social environment which aims to impose no specific or rigid limitations or make demands upon the patient. 'Psychological determinants for what appear to be the same maladjustments may be quite different, and because of that, they require different situations. Since a therapy group supplies a neutral environment, each member can take from it whatever his needs may be. The aggressive child finds relief from his anxiety . . . while the shy and withdrawn one overcomes his fears.' (Slavson, S.R. *An Introduction to Group Therapy,* The Commonwealth Fund, Oxford University Press, New York, 1943, p. 84)

environment, permissive A social and physical environment in which acting out and verbalization is permissible but not necessarily sanctioned or approved.

envy, penis This is a psychoanalytic concept. It is said that when the little girl finds out that the boy has a genital organ that she does not possess, she begins to envy the boy and to long for a penis.

'From the analyses of many neurotic women we have learnt that women go through an early phase in which they envy their brothers the token of maleness and feel themselves handicapped and ill-treated on account of the lack of it (really, on account of its diminutive form). In our view this "penis-envy" forms a part of the castration complex.' (Freud, S. *Collected Papers,* vol. 4, tr. by Riviere, J., Leonard and Virginia Woolf and The Institute of Psychoanalysis, London, 1924–25)

'If for brevity you will allow me purposely to exaggerate the differences of opinion, one might say that according to one view the girl hates her mother, because she had disappointed her wish that her clitoris were a penis, whereas according to the other view the reason that the girl wishes that her clitoris were a penis is that she feels hatred for her mother which she cannot express.' (Jones, E. *Papers on Psycho-Analysis,* 4th ed., Wood, Baltimore, 1938)

Freud says that when the little girl realizes she has no penis, she reacts either by hoping that some day she will have one or by denying that she does not have one. In the latter case she may be 'compelled to behave as though she were a man.'

Penis-envy is responsible for 'a loosening of the girl's relation with her mother as a love-object,' because the girl blames her mother for the alleged loss. At this stage the girl is prepared for the further development of the Oedipus situation. The wish for the penis is displaced upon the wish for a child, 'With this object in view, she takes her father as a love-object. Her mother becomes the object of jealousy.'

eonism (ē′on-iz′m) The adoption of the female role by a male. See *transvestitism; sexo-esthetic inversion.*

eosophobia (ē-ō-sō-fō′bi-à) Fear of dawn.

ephialtes (ef-i-al′tēz) *Obs.* Nightmare.

ephialtes vigilantium (e-fē-àl′tās vē-gē-làn′tē-oom) (L. 'nightmare of those awake') Daymare.

epicritic sensibility (ep-i-krit′ik) The ability to appreciate light touch and its localization; point discrimination; discrimination of moderate variations; distinguished from protopathic. 'To test epicritic or gnostic sensibility the light touch is employed. . . . Either a wisp of cottonwool should be used or a fine camel-hair brush.' (Jelliffe, S.E. and White, W.A. *Diseases of the Nervous System,* 6th ed., Lea & Febiger, Philadelphia, 1935)

epilempsis (ep-i-lemp′sis) Hippocratic term for epilepsy.

epilentia (e-pē-len′tē-à) *Obs.* Epilepsy.

epilepsia corticalis continua (e-pē-lep′sē-à kôr-tē-kä′lēs kôn-tē′nōō-à) See *epilepsy, continuous.*

epilepsia cursiva (koor-sē′và) (Med. L. 'running epilepsy') *Obs.* A symptom of epilepsy with apparently aimless running about.

epilepsia dromica (drô′mē-kà) (Mod.L. 'fleet [-footed] epilepsy') A term used by Semmola to denote a syndrome of epilepsy resembling chorea.

epilepsia gravior (grà′vē-ôr) (L. 'severer epilepsy') *Obs.* Grand mal epileptic seizure.

epilepsia mitior (mē′tē-ôr) (L. 'milder epilepsy') *Obs.* Petit mal form of epilepsy.

epilepsia partialis continua (pär-tē-ä-lēs kôn-tē′noo-à) (L. 'partial continuous epilepsy') S.A.K. Wilson says that Kozhevnikoff originally described this 'doubtless somewhat rare' motor variant of epilepsy. Wilson states that 'it differs from the general myoclonic type in that the twitching is limited to one segment of the body, nearly always a peripheral part such as the wrist and fingers, is practically continuous between the paroxysmal fits, and on the whole partakes of the form less of move-

ments than of irregular, individual muscular contractions.' (Wilson, S.A.K. *Modern Problems in Neurology,* Wood, New York, 1929)

epilepsia procursiva (prō-koor-sē′và) (Med. L. 'procursive epilepsy') See *epilepsy, procursive.*

epilepsia trochaica (trô-kà′ē-kà) (L. 'trochaic [i.e. choreic] epilepsy') Epilepsia cursiva.

epilepsia vertiginosa (ver-tē-gē-nō′zà) (L. 'vertiginous epilepsy') Epilepsia mitior; it also refers to the dizziness that occasionally precedes or replaces a grand mal attack.

épilepsie larvée (ā-pē-lep-sē′ lar-vā′) (F. 'masked epilepsy') Masked epilepsy; epileptic equivalent.

epilepsy (ep′i-lep-sē) A paroxysmal, transitory disturbance of brain function which develops suddenly, ceases spontaneously, and exhibits a conspicuous tendency to recurrence. The typical epileptic attack, or fit, or convulsion, consists of the sudden onset of loss of consciousness, with or without tonic spasm and clonic contractions of the muscles. There are many forms of epilepsy, which vary depending upon the site of origin, the extent of the area involved, and the nature of the etiological factors; at the present time the term also includes transient episodes of sensory or psychic disturbances. Epilepsy, in short, is not a disease but a symptom, consisting of recurrent episodes of changes in the state of consciousness, with or without accompanying motor or sensory phenomena. Epilepsy has also been called paroxysmal cerebral dysrhythmia.

The average frequency or expectancy of epilepsy in the general population is 1 in 200; but individuals with one epileptic parent have a higher expectancy (1 in 35), and those with both parents epileptic have a much higher expectancy (1 in 10). For each person who develops seizures during his lifetime, it is said that there are 20 more with a predisposition to the affliction. There is no difference in incidence between the sexes, although epilepsy tends to begin earlier in the female.

Today it is customary to divide epilepsy into two major groups on the basis of etiology: (1) *genuine* or *idiopathic* or *cryptogenic epilepsy,* in which there is no known local, general, or psychologic cause; and (2) *symptomatic epilepsy,* in which an organic basis is demonstrable. Approximately 25 per cent of all epileptics fall clearly within the symptomatic group. But as the horizons of neurology widen to include the more recent pathological, physiological, and biochemical advances, it can be anticipated that specific etiologic agents will be demonstrable in an increasing number of cases. Electroencephalograph studies, for example, show that epilepsy is an uncontrolled discharge of cortical and/or subcortical neurones, i.e. an abnormal conversion of the potential energy of the neurones into kinetic energy. Epilepsy can thus be considered a physicochemical disturbance, which could be produced by any number of agents.

Within the *symptomatic* group of epilepsies are those due to: (a) local causes —intracranial infection, brain trauma, congenital abnormalities, degenerative diseases such as Pick's disease, various circulatory disturbances of the brain, etc.; (b) general causes—exogenous poisons, anoxemia, endocrine disorders, metabolic disorders (uremia, hypoglycemia, alkalosis, eclampsia, and hypertension in pregnancy), etc.; and (c) psychogenic causes.

In regard to the psychogenic group: there is little evidence that epileptic seizures, as distinct from hysterical fits, are ever purely psychogenic, but it is well recognized that the individual attack may be precipitated by fear, excitement, or other strong emotions. In his article "Dostoevsky and Parricide," (1928) Freud suggested that epilepsy was an organic discharge mechanism which could be brought into play by any number of factors, and that hystero-epilepsy represented an instance of the mechanism being called into play for impulse discharge in hysteria. See also *personality, epileptic; deterioration, epileptic.*

The *idiopathic epilepsies* have no known local, general, or psychologic cause; this is a large and heterogeneous group which suffers from a predisposition to convulsions, the nature of which is not yet understood. This predisposition in some cases seems to be largely hereditary in origin, but not all workers would subscribe to the view that idiopathic epilepsy is essentially a hereditary disorder. What is inherited is not epilepsy itself, but rather a predisposition to the development of convulsions under certain conditions, i.e. the physical basis of a cortical dysrhythmia. And only

a small proportion of those with this cortical dysrhythmia become epileptic.

Gibbs and Gibbs, and Lennox, feel that the cortical dysrhythmia is inherited as a Mendelian dominant; it often remains latent, however, and the condition appears only in a collateral line. Lilienfeld and Pasamanick, on the other hand, feel that epilepsy is a result of complications of pregnancy and delivery, and these writers postulate a continuum of reproduction casualty composed of a lethal component (stillbirths, neonatal deaths), a severe sublethal component (cerebral palsy), and a less severe sublethal component (epilepsy).

The onset of epilepsy is often difficult to determine, for minor attacks may not be recognized, and major attacks (25%) may be only nocturnal, especially in children. The first seizure occurs before the age of 20 in 75 per cent of cases.

Epilepsy is divided into types on the basis of etiology, as discussed above; it may also be subdivided on the basis of physical manifestations, and when considered in this way, three major seizure types are distinguished: (1) *major epilepsy, grand mal epilepsy;* (2) *minor epilepsy, petit mal epilepsy,* and (3) *psychomotor epilepsy* (also known as *psychic equivalents,* or *temporal lobe seizures).* Various types of prodromata may precede major attacks or a series of minor attacks, and an *aura* (q.v.) precedes grand mal attacks in 60 per cent of cases.

In *grand mal epilepsy,* the convulsion or fit consists of a tonic spasm of all the limbs, rarely lasting longer than 30 seconds. This is followed by the clonic phase —a series of sharp, short, interrupted jerks which result from a series of interruptions of the tonic phase. Following cessation of these spasms, the patient may pass into a heavy sleep lasting for hours; some patients, in this 'post-ictal phase,' evidence post-epileptic automatism in which they wander, completely amnesic and disoriented, from the scene of attack (this may last for hours or days). Other patients become psychotic, maniacal, or even homicidal.

Petit mal epilepsy may be associated with major seizures or may occur without them. Laymen know them as faints, sensations, or spells. They consist of one or more of the following: mild attacks of dizziness, faintness, queer sensations, dazed states, hot flashes, pallor, vomiting, belching, temper tantrums, sudden relaxation of musculature (so that the patient drops anything in his hand and stops speaking for a moment), momentary confusion and change of color, dreamy sensations, sudden visual or auditory or gustatory sensations, peculiar rushing sensations through the body, sudden jerks and starts. Petit mal attacks are usually extremely brief in duration and often there is no memory of the loss of consciousness so that the patient is only dimly aware of the occurrence of a spell. These minor spells sometimes take the form of the patient's aura preceding his major attacks, as if the attack were incomplete; patients will often spontaneously label them their frustrated or incomplete spells. Petit mal epilepsy occurs typically in young people and only rarely begins after the second decade. Associated psychiatric symptoms are rare and there is almost never an aura. Usually there is immobility during an attack, and the patient is mentally clear immediately after the attack. Incontinence is infrequent in petit mal epilepsy.

Petit mal epilepsy is sometimes further subdivided into *myoclonic, akinetic* and *short stare types*. Petit mal is associated with a spike and wave complex (also known as dart and dome complex) in the electroencephalogram, usually at a frequency of three per second. Some workers use the term *pyknolepsy* (q.v.) synonymously with petit mal.

The group called *psychomotor epilepsy* includes a bewildering variety of recurrent periodical disturbances which usually take the form of some mental disturbance during which the patient carries out movements of a highly organized but semiautomatic character. These seizures are rare in children, and the attack itself is marked by confusion rather than loss of consciousness, and there is later amnesia. Psychomotor attacks last longer than petit mal attacks, with which they are easily confused; but incontinence and post-ictal confusion, which do not occur in petit mal, are seen frequently in psychomotor epilepsy. About two-thirds of the psychomotor group also have grand mal seizures, but only about 3 per cent also have petit mal attacks. There is general agreement that the great majority of psychomotor seizures are the epileptic manifestations of temporal lobe lesions.

Classification of psychomotor epilepsy is arbitrary. Lennox pr^poses the following subdivisions: (a) psychomotor seizures proper (43%), with an excess or absence of involuntary motor activity, combined with amnesia for the events that transpire during attack; (b) automatic seizures (32%), where activity of a purposeful or semi-purposeful nature is carried out, with amnesia for the event; these seizures are also known as primary automatisms, or primary ictal automatisms, so long as they are not preceded by an aura; and (c) psychic or subjective seizures (25%), including déjà vu or dream states, hallucinations, episodes of confusion or stupor, or feelings of depression or exaltation without motor components.

epilepsy, acoustico-motor See *epilepsy, reflex.*

epilepsy, affective This is an expression used by Bratz to designate a form of epilepsy characterized by exaggerated emotional responses, which generally culminate in an epileptiform seizure. Bonhoeffer referred to such states as *reactive epilepsies* and Kraepelin classified many of them as *epileptic swindlers.*

epilepsy, akinetic (à-kin-et'ik) A type of petit mal epilepsy. See *epilepsy.*

epilepsy, alcoholic This is an ill-defined clinical disorder, including a variety of manifestations associated with alcoholism and so-called epilepsy.

An alcoholic individual may experience an epileptiform seizure; or an individual with the epileptoid personality may try to solve his personality difficulties through alcohol; or the alcoholism and epilepsy may be more or less independent of each other.

epilepsy, autonomic (aw-tō-nom'ik) Diencephalic epilepsy; sympathetic epilepsy; parasympathetic epilepsy. Autonomic epilepsy refers to symptoms of sudden, diffuse discharge of the autonomic nervous system in otherwise normal individuals. In some, symptoms are primarily of sympathetic discharge; in others, symptoms of primarily of parasympathetic discharge. Usually, however, symptoms are mixed.

Penfield, in 1929 under the name 'diencephalic autonomic epilepsy,' described predominantly sympathetic seizures consisting of fever, flushing, tearing, sweating, salivation, hiccoughing, and shivering. In this case, a ball valve tumor of the third ventricle had resulted in compression of adjacent hypothalamic nuclei.

Cushing, in 1932, reported on parasympathetic outbursts occurring in response to intraventricular injections of pituitrin and pilocarpine. Symptoms included profuse sweating, flushing, fall in blood pressure, lowering of temperature and basal metabolic rate, and increased peristalsis in the stomach and intestines.

epilepsy, continuous This is a form of epilepsy, including the polyclonia epileptoides continua of Choroschko, the epilepsia corticalis continua of Kozhevnikoff and the epilepsia partialis continua of Wilson, characterized by myoclonic attacks in single muscular groups; it is limited to one side of the body and consciousness is retained during the attacks.

epilepsy, co-ordinated S.A.K. Wilson says: 'By this term—possibly not the most appropriate that might be devised—the intention is to denote those cases where the movements seen during the attack are coördinated and seemingly purposive, exhibiting objectively to a large extent the features of "voluntary" movements. They may, however, be aimlessly repeated and in any case do not attain the end to which they may be supposed to be directed.' (Wilson, S.A.K. *Modern Problems in Neurology*, Wood, New York, 1929)

epilepsy, cryptogenic (krip-tō-jen'ik) Epilepsy without known etiology and pathology.

epilepsy, diencephalic (dī-en-se-fål'ik) See *epilepsy, autonomic.*

epilepsy, erotic A type of epileptiform focal seizure in which the patient experiences spells of intense erotic sensation; first reported by T.C. Erickson (*Archives of Neurology & Psychiatry 53*: 226–231, 1945) in a 43-year-old housewife, in whom a small vascular tumor was later disclosed on the medial surface of the cerebral hemisphere, impinging upon the motor and sensory representation of the genitalia.

epilepsy, essential Idiopathic epilepsy.

epilepsy, gelastic (je-las'tik) A form of epilepsy in which laughter is a part of the seizure pattern, usually due to a lesion in the left temporal region.

epilepsy, genuine Same as *idiopathic epilepsy.*

epilepsy, hallucinatory A type of focal epilepsy in which complex hallucinations are the main part of the attack. The hallucinations are short-lived, paroxysmal, and irresistible in quality; they tend to be identical in each attack.

epilepsy, inhibition of See *epilepsy, reflex.*

epilepsy, inhibitory A rare form of petit mal epilepsy in which transitory loss of power occurs in a limb or on one side of the body without preceding tonic spasm or clonic movements; there may be an associated impairment of consciousness.

epilepsy, Jacksonian A variant of grand mal epilepsy described by John Hughlings Jackson. The convulsion begins with clonic movements which increase in severity and spread (the 'cortical march') to involve large segments of the limb, then the other limb on the same side, then the face, and finally sometimes the other side, at which point consciousness is usually lost. The spread is along anatomical and/or physiological lines, and this type of epilepsy almost always indicates organic disease of the precentral cortex. Jacksonian epilepsy usually begins in one of three foci: thumb and index finger; angle of the mouth; or the great toe.

epilepsy, larvated Epileptic equivalent.

epilepsy, major Same as epilepsy, grand mal. See *epilepsy.*

epilepsy, masked Epileptic equivalent.

epilepsy, minor Same as epilepsy, petit mal. See *epilepsy.*

epilepsy musicogenic (mū-si-ko-gen'ik) See *epilepsy, reflex.*

epilepsy, myoclonic (mī-ō-klon'ik) A type of petit mal epilepsy. See *epilepsy.*

epilepsy, myoclonus (mī-ō-klō'nus) A variant of grand mal epilepsy first described by Unverricht in 1891. This type of epilepsy is usually familial and occurs in several siblings. Symptoms usually begin between 6 and 16 years. Generalized epileptiform attacks with loss of consciousness appear first, often only at night. After several years, the characteristic myoclonic contractions develop; they involve simultaneously the symmetrical muscles on both sides of the body and are strong enough to produce movements of limb segments. The face, trunk, and upper and lower limbs are most commonly involved. The contractions disappear during sleep and are intensified by emotional excitement. They tend to increase in severity before a generalized epileptic attack; sudden contraction of the lower limbs may throw the patient to the ground. For a period of years, myoclonic contractions and epileptic attacks are associated; during this time, a progressive dementia develops and there is a passing into a third stage, where the grand mal attacks tend to disappear. Then dysarthria and dysphagia increase and death often follows progressive cachexia.

epilepsy, nocturnal Jelliffe and White state that 'the possibility of exclusively nocturnal attacks—*nocturnal epilepsy*—should be borne in mind. It is suspicious if the patient awakes tired and lame, as if his muscles had been beaten, particularly if he shows conjunctival ecchymoses, a wounded tongue and flecks of blood on the pillow. A localized muscular weakness that passes off promptly would add certainty to the diagnosis.' (Jelliffe, S.E. and White, W.A. *Diseases of the Nervous System*, 6th ed., Lea & Febiger, Philadelphia, 1935)

Exclusively nocturnal attacks occur in approximately 25 per cent of known epileptics; both day and night attacks occur in another 25 per cent of patients. Exclusively nocturnal attacks are more common in children.

epilepsy, parasympathetic (pà-rà-sim-pathet′ik) See *epilepsy, autonomic.*

epilepsy, photic (fot′ik) See *epilepsy, reflex.*

epilepsy, procursive An epileptic symptom, characterized by sudden, impulsive running forward.

epilepsy, psychic (sī′kik) The epileptiform convulsion may be replaced by any one of the many epileptic equivalents. 'These attacks of *psychic epilepsy* frequently take the form of so-called *epileptic automatism* or *epileptic dream states*. In these conditions the patient may do almost anything and when he comes to himself he has absolutely no recollection of what has happened.' (Jelliffe, S.E. and White, W.A. *Diseases of the Nervous System,* 6th ed., Lea & Febiger, Philadelphia, 1935) Other manifestations of psychic epilepsy are states of depression, excitement, delirium, stupor, paranoid reaction, etc.

epilepsy, psychomotor See *epilepsy.*

epilepsy, psychopathology of (sī-kō-pathol′ō-jē) See *personality, epileptic.*

epilepsy, reactive Bleuler speaks of 'the rare "reflex epilepsy," whose attacks are set free by the irritation of a scar or some other pathological focus. . . .' (Bleuler, E. *Textbook of Psychiatry,* tr. by Brill, A.A. Macmillan, New York, 1930)

epilepsy, reflex This is used to refer to epileptic convulsions precipitated by some external stimulus, such as a sudden loud noise (acoustico-motor epilepsy), music (musicogenic epilepsy), visual (photic epilepsy) or cutaneous stimuli. Reflex inhibition of the fit is an allied phenomenon: if, for example, a focal convulsion begins with movement in one limb, a strong stimulus such as a firm grip applied to the limb will often abort the attack if this is begun immediately after onset of the attack.

epilepsy, reflex inhibition of See *epilepsy, reflex.*

epilepsy, regional See *epilepsy, myoclonic.*

epilepsy, residual This infrequently used expression, coined by Kraepelin, refers to a form of epilepsy characterized by recurring epileptiform seizures without such other phenomena as dementia, marked personality changes, etc.

epilepsy, retropulsive An epileptic symptom, characterized by sudden, impulsive running backward.

epilepsy, sensory A type of petit mal epilepsy consisting of paresthesiae involving part or the whole of one side of the body, often without loss of consciousness. Sensory epilepsy is usually due to a contralateral lesion in the parietal lobe.

epilepsy, short stare A type of petit mal epilepsy. See *epilepsy.*

epilepsy, sleep *Obs.* Narcolepsy.

epilepsy, sympathetic See *epilepsy, autonomic.*

epilepsy, symptomatic The term symptomatic epilepsy refers to a condition in which the convulsions represent a symptom of an underlying organic disease process. This may occur in such conditions as congenital defects of the brain, intracranial hemorrhages, meningitis, brain abscess, senile degeneration, carbon monoxide poisoning, etc.

epilepsy, tetanoid (tet′à-noid) Pritchard introduced this expression to refer to the form of epilepsy in which the spasm is tonic only.

epilepsy, tonic Epileptic fits 'characterized by tonic contractions only, to the exclusion of the clonic element, have long been known.' (Wilson, S.A.K. *Modern Problems in Neurology,* Wood, New York, 1929)

epilepsy, true Same as *idiopathic epilepsy.*

epilepsy, visceral (vis'er-al) A form of focal epilepsy in which the fit is manifested as visceral sensations, usually referable to the gastrointestinal tract, the cardiorespiratory system, or the genitourinary system. The principal loci of lesions in such cases have been found to be in the frontotemporal and mid-frontal parasagittal regions, indicating that the visceral sensations arise from some central location, probably the amygdalohippocampal portion of the temporal lobe.

epileptic character See *personality, epileptic.*

epileptic clouded states Epileptic clouded states are psychotic reactions occurring in epileptics. At times, either preceding or following a convulsive attack, the epileptic may manifest a dazed reaction with deep confusion or excitement, anxiety, and bewilderment. Associated with this, there may be violent outbreaks, hallucinations, fears, or ecstatic moods with religious exaltation.

epileptic cry See *cry, epileptic.*

epileptic deterioration See *deterioration, epileptic.*

epileptic equivalent See *equivalent, epileptic.*

epilepticism (ep-i-lep'ti-siz'm)   *Obs.* Status epilepticus.

epileptic psychopathic constitution See *constitution, epileptic psychopathic.*

epileptic psychoses (sī-kō'ses) See *dementia, epileptic.*

epileptic, pyknic (pik'nik) One who has epilepsy and a physique of the pyknic type. The majority of persons having epilepsy are of the athletic or dysplastic type; the pyknic type is encountered the least often. Westphal analyzed a large group of epileptics from the standpoint of body type. According to this analysis the percentages of incidence were as follows: dysplastic type, 29.5 per cent; athletic type, 28.9 per cent; asthenic type, 25.0 per cent; pyknic type, 5.5 per cent; 11.1 per cent were unclassified. (Hoch,

P.H., and Knight, R.P. *Epilepsy,* Grune and Stratton, New York, 1947)

epileptoid (ep-i-lep'toid)   Resembling epilepsy.

epileptoidism The state of being epileptoid. Some psychiatrists hold that epileptic patients show personality traits and behavior patterns which they believe are characteristic and indicative of a developing epileptic disorder. The presence of these mental manifestations is referred to as epileptic character (see *personality, epileptic*). These mental traits appear in some epileptics after the occurrence of epileptic fits. In some, however, they are present before the epilepsy occurs. If it is a forerunner of epileptic manifestations, it is called epileptoidism in the same sense as schizoidism is present in many before the appearance of schizophrenia, cycloidism before the development of manic-depressive psychosis. (Hinsie, L.E. *Understandable Psychiatry,* Macmillan, New York, 1948)

epileptoid, orthostatic (or-thō-stat'ik) Children who have fainting spells and occasional convulsions when forced to stand for a long time or after getting up in the morning are referred to as *orthostatic epileptoids* by Husler. (Husler, J. 'Bemerkungen zur genuinen Epilepsie im Kindesalter,' *Zeitschrift für Kinderheilkunde 66,* 237–50, 1920)

epileptology (-tol'ō-jē) The science or study of epilepsy.

epileptosis (-tō'sis) A term suggested by Southard to refer to the various manifestations of epileptic psychoses.

epiloia (e-pi-loi'ä) *Tuberous sclerosis* (q.v.).

epinephrine (e-pin-e'frin) The active principle of the medullary portion of the adrenal glands, $C_9H_{13}O_3N$, often referred to by its proprietary name, adrenalin. Epinephrine is the most powerful vasopressor drug known; it increases blood pressure, stimulates heart muscle, accelerates heart rate, and increases cardiac output.

Stimulation of sympathetic nerve fibers releases a substance similar to epinephrine which is known as sympathin. Sympathin is the chemical mediator of the excitatory processes initiated by sympathetic nerve impulses at neuroeffector junctions. Like epinephrine, sympathin has both excitatory and inhibitory effects; that released when excitatory responses are stimulated is sympathin E, and that released when inhibitory responses are stimulated is sympathin I.

It has been suggested that epinephrine or products in its metabolism may be involved in the natural occurrence of mental disorders. Some doubt is cast on this by the fact that epinephrine itself is present in the brain only in small quantities. A closely related substance, norepinephrine (noradrenalin, arterenol), which is also present in the adrenal medulla, is known to occur in significant amounts in the brain, particularly in the hypothalamus, and derivatives of this substance might therefore be more likely as possible precursors of clinical psychoses. For these same reasons, it seems more likely that norepinephrine is the central sympathetic neurohumor.

Both epinephrine and norepinephrine are normally present in the blood only in low concentration, but in response to stress both increase markedly. When the stress agent is removed, the circulating blood level of these catecholamines falls quickly back to normal. This rapid disappearance might be achieved by storage in tissues or by enzymatic destruction, and evidence to date favors the latter mechanism. It seems most likely that the important mechanism for in vivo inactivation of these catecholamines is breakdown by the particular enzyme monoamine oxidase (MAO, amine oxidase).

epinosic, epinosis (e-pin-o'sik, -ō'sis) See *gain, epinosic.*

epistasis (e-pis'tȧ-sis) This term designates a genetic mechanism by which the phenotypical expression of one hereditary factor masks, or prevents, the manifestation of another factor which concerns the same organ, although it is not allelic to the factor with the greater expressivity. The factor exercising the masking effect is called *epistatic,* while the factor which is hidden is said to be *hypostatic.*

The result of *epistasis* is similar to that produced by a *dominant* character. However, there is a significant difference between the phenomena of dominance and epistasis. While a dominant and a recessive factor are always alleles of each other, an epistatic and a hypostatic factor are merely related to the same trait or

organ, but they are not the two members of an allelic pair (see *dominance*).

epistemophilia (ē-pis-tē-mō-fil'i-ȧ) The love of knowledge or the impulsion to inquire into things is said by psychoanalysts to receive its earliest important stimulation during the phallic phase, although preliminary preparation is gained through interests in other and earlier erotogenic zones, particularly the oral and the anal. Freud believed that during the stage of so-termed 'phallic primacy,' 'the epistemophilic impulses are now largely occupied with the new center of sexual sensations, the penis, and that the boy's interest is concentrated upon this organ.' (Healy, W., Bronner, A.F., and Bowers, A.M. *The Structure and Meaning of Psychoanalysis,* New York, 1930) The many subsequent manifestations of the impulse to learn are regarded as sublimations of the several varieties of infantile sexuality.

epithalamus (e-pi-thal'ȧ-mus) A zone of brain tissue above the thalamus composed of: (1) *habenular ganglion* or *trigone,* a depressed triangular area anterior to the superior colliculus; (2) *pineal body* which lies between the superior colliculi; (3) *posterior commissure,* some of whose fibers connect the two superior colliculi.

equation, personal The individual or 'personal' peculiarities or variations (in both the experimenter and the person experimented upon) which must be discounted or deducted in order to 'equate' or correct the results of an observation.

equilibrium, homeostatic (hō-mē-ō-stat'ik) See *instinct, aim of.*

equilibrium, narcissistic (när-si-sis'tik) A state of harmony between the demands of the superego and the capabilities of the ego; derived from the original harmony between the obedient child and its loving parents. 'Both ego and super-ego are made up of identifications. Where the latter are harmoniously integrated in the personality we have the state of narcissistic equilibrium. The super-ego does not demand of the ego more than it can produce. The ego is not terrified by the threat of the super-ego severity.' (Hart, H.H. 'Narcissistic Equilibrium,' *International Journal of Psychoanalysis 28,* 106, 1947)

equivalent, anxiety See *anxiety-attack, equivalent of.*

equivalent, epileptic The manifestations

of genuine epilepsy are many. When an epileptic patient has an 'attack' that is neither of the grand or petit mal type, he is said to have an *equivalent,* that is, a 'substitutive' attack. For example, a twilight state may take the place of a grand mal attack. A patient about to have a major seizure developed a condition in which he believed that he was in heaven, curing all the ailments of the universe. 'More frequent are those with an anxious or angry effect which readily lead to brutal acts of violence against the individual himself and others; sexual excitements are the basis of Ripper murders or frequent exhibitionism. Besides fearful visions of hell and the devil, there occur much more rarely ecstasies which are completely beyond the reach of reality and blissful erotic-religious hallucinations of all the senses.' (Bleuler, E. *Textbook of Psychiatry,* tr. by Brill, A.A., Macmillan, New York, 1930)

Some authors use this term to refer to psychomotor epilepsy. See *epilepsy.*

equivalent, onanistic (ō-nan-is′tik) Ferenczi uses this expression to refer to a great variety of acts that act as substitutes for (manual) masturbation. For example, rhythmic movements of the legs, resulting in genital stimulation, constitute an onanistic equivalent.

'Transition stages are here discoverable between symptomatic acts and certain forms of *tic convulsif,* of which as yet we possess no psychoanalytic explanation. My expectation is that on analysis many of these tics will blossom forth as stereotyped onanistic equivalents.' (Ferenczi, S. *Further Contributions to the Theory and Technique of Psycho-Analysis,* tr. by Suttie, J.I., Leonard and Virginia Woolf and The Institute of Psychoanalysis, London, 1926) See *onanism, larval.*

equivalent, psychic (sī′kik) Psychomotor epilepsy. See *epilepsy.*

erectio deficiens (ā-rek′tē-ō dā-fē′kē-ens) (L. 'deficient erection') Absence of (genital) erection.

eremiophobia (ē-rē-mi-ō-fō′bi-à) Fear of a lonely place or solitude.

eremophilia (er-ē-mō-fil′i-à) Morbid desire to be alone.

eremophobia Fear of being alone

erethism (er′ē-thiz′m) Morbid excitability. Erethism is initiated generally

through psychical influences. Ellis mentions that 'a medical friend tells me of a lady considerably past middle age who experienced sexual erethism after listening to a heated argument between her husband and a friend on religious topics.' (Ellis, H. *Studies in the Psychology of Sex,* vol. 3, Davis, Philadelphia, 1903 p. 143)

Erethism means an exaggerated degree of irritability or sensitivity in any part of the body. While the term refers to excitement or stimulation of any organ or tissue of the body, it more commonly relates to the organs of reproduction, when used in psychiatry nowadays.

The term, originally meaning excitement, used to be followed by some word indicative of the cause of the excitement. Hence *erethismus ebriosorum* meant excitation from drink; later it was used synonymously with delirium tremens. In constitutional medicine *erethism* denotes overactivity in general. Thus, Pende says: 'Generally, however, the animal nervous system shows erethism, great instability and a tendency to crises of exhaustion.' (Pende, N. *Constitutional Inadequacies,* tr. by Naccarati, S., Lea & Febiger, Philadelphia, 1928) When psychic reactions, for example, are exaggerated, the condition is sometimes known as *tachypragia.*

Sexual erethism may be displayed as nymphomania, satyriasis, erotomania, etc.

erethismus ebriosorum (e-re-thēz′moos ā-brē-ô-zō′room) (Mod. L. 'drunkards' irritability') Delirium tremens.

erethistic (er-ē-this′tik) Same as erethismic. See *erethism.*

erethitic (-thit′ik) Characterized by excitement.

erethizophrenia (er-ē-thiz-ō-frē′ni-à) Exaggerated cortical excitability.

erethizophrenic (-fren′ik) Pertaining to or suffering from erethizophrenia. A term introduced by Hunt equivalent to *cycloid.* (Hunt, J.R. *American Journal of Psychiatry 12,* 475–92, 1932–33)

ereuthophobia (ē-rōō-thō-fō′bi-à) Same as *erythrophobia* (q.v.).

ergasia (ēr-gas′i-à) This term, introduced into psychiatry by Adolf Meyer, is designed to express the total of functions and reactions of an individual, in contradistinction to the functions of individual organs or parts of the human organism. It embraces the concept known as *the personality as a whole* and refers to those responses of an individual that represent the results of the activity of many of his parts. It stands for the action of the total organism.

ergasiatry (ĕr-gas-ī′à-trē) Adolf Meyer's term for psychiatry.

ergasiology (-i-ol′ō-jē) See *psychology*.

ergasiomania The term, infrequently used today, denotes a morbid impulse to work, to keep busy. It is observed in pronounced form in the manic state of manic-depressive psychosis.

ergasiophobia Fear of functioning or acting. It is not uncommon and generally associated with an underlying dread that if movement takes place something disastrous will happen. There is a strong sadistic component in the fear. When the sadism is turned outwardly, its unconscious meaning is the equivalent of injury or death to another; when directed inwardly upon the subject himself, it has the same motive. The fear is often associated with the castration phantasy of the Oedipus complex. It is related to the magical feeling that what happens to oneself also happens to the environment. A patient may believe that if he stops functioning or moving, the world will do the same. The fear is said to be the conscious representation of an unconscious wish.

ergasthenia (ĕr-gas-thē′ni-à) A condition of fatigue or debility due to overwork or excessive functioning. Although the term is not in common use today, the condition is frequently encountered, particularly in extreme cases of excitement in the manic phase of manic-depressive psychosis.

ergastic (ĕr-gas′tik) Ergasic.

ergetic (ĕr-jet′ik) Janet says: 'In the carrying out of resolutions, in the continuance of actions, we are no longer concerned, as a rule, with reflective tendencies, but with tendencies of a lower grade for which I have proposed the name "ergetic" for they are characterized by effort and work.' (Janet, P. *Psychological Healing,* vols. 1–2, tr. by Paul, E. and C., Macmillan, New York, 1925)

ergodialeipsis (ĕr-gō-dī-à-lāp′sis) This is a term introduced by Moravsik, referring to action which ceases before it is completely carried out. The term is not in common use today. It is believed to be one of the characteristics of schizophrenia and is synonymous with *blocking* (q.v.).

erogeneity (er-ō-jē-nē′i-tē) The state or quality of being erogenous. See *orality; anality.*

Eros (ē′ros, er′os) (Gr. *Eros,* Eros, the god of love) In psychiatry *Eros* is synonymous with *libido.* Freud defines libido as 'the energy . . . of those instincts which have to do with all that may be comprised under the word "love." ' See *libido.*

erotic, anal See *anal-erotic.*

erotic-cathexis See *cathexis.*

eroticism (ē-rot′i-siz'm) See *erotism.*

eroticism, olfactory (ē-rot′i-siz'm, ol-fak′tō-rē) The pleasurable sensations associated with smelling. Along with the sexual impulses of hearing and tasting, olfactory eroticism 'participates to a relatively great extent in the general orientation of the child.' Thus these senses are filled with pleasurable erotic excitement for the infant or, in Fenichel's words, 'are highly cathected with infantile sexuality.' Also they show a close relationship to pregenital eroticism as a whole. More specifically, phenomena of smell sexuality coincide, for the most part, with anal eroticism.

Owing to repressed pregenitality, the average adult's sense of smell is much duller than it was in childhood. Olfactory eroticism, however, that has undergone repression becomes revived in certain pathological states. 'Emotions which originally were connected with infantile sexuality may later be remobilized in a conflict situation around sensations of smelling, tasting, or hearing.' A revival of nasal eroticism will occur whenever there is a regression toward anal and respiratory eroticism, as happens, for example, in bronchial asthma. Also, conflicts concerned with smelling and hearing are particularly prominent in states of narcissistic regression. The hallucinations of paranoid schizophrenics are very frequently linked with offensive sounds and odors. (Fenichel, O. *The Psychoanalytic Theory of Neurosis,* Norton, New York, 1945)

eroticize (ē-rot′i-sīz) To charge with libidinal or erotic energy. Any part of an individual may be invested with the erotic instinct, that is, eroticized (libidinized).

erotic, organ See *organ-erotic.*

erotic seizure See *epilepsy, erotic.*

erotism, eroticism (er′ō-tiz′m) Erotism is a condition characterized by the instinctual quality called 'love' or Eros. Thus, one speaks of erotism relating to body zones, such as anal, oral, and genital erotism; or to psychic structures, such as ego-erotism (narcissism); or to objects outside of the body or mind such as alloerotism.

erotism, anal See *anal erotism.*

erotism, ego See *narcissism, ego-libido.*

erotism, muscle Any part of the body may contain the erotic instinct. Sadger referred to *muscle erotism,* meaning by the expression to convey the idea of pleasure associated with muscular activity (dancing, posturing, walking, etc.). He also described the skin as especially susceptible to the incorporation of erotic impulses. Thus, he spoke of 'skin erotism.'

erotism, oral The pleasure and gratification derived from using the mouth above and beyond the utility value of taking in food and drink. In the child it means the pleasure experienced when close to the mother's warm body, when sucking her breast or the nipple of the bottle and thus feeling secure and protected.

erotism, organ See *organ-erotism.*

erotism, urethral See *urethra.*

erotization (ē-rot-i-zā′shun) The act of erotizing or state of being erotized. During infancy the body becomes erotized, notably those parts of the body called erotogenic zones. All forms of activity subsequent to the stage of infantile sexuality may and usually do undergo erotization. Character traits, ideas, actions of all sorts, hobbies, recreations, etc. are erotized.

The term is synonymous with *libidinization.*

erotocrat (ē-rō′tō-krat) A man of powerful sexuality. A term, coined by George Hirth, more common in popular literature.

erotodromomania (-drō-mō-mā′ni-à) Hirschfeld uses this term to denote the morbid impulse to travel as an escape from some painful sexual situation.

erotogenesis (-jen′ē-sis) The springing or origination of libidinal or erotic impulses.

In *Three Contributions to the Theory of Sex,* Freud shows that the sexual instincts in man are complex and result from impulses coming from several sources. Hence, there is, for instance, the oral component. Impulses stemming from the oral region constitute a partial contribution to sexuality.

erotogenetic (-jē-net′ik) Same as *erotogenic.*

erotogenic (-jen′ik) Relating to or having its origin in the libidinal or erotic instinct; commonly applied to libidinal impulses that are expressed through special body areas or erotogenic zones (genitals, mouth, anus, urethra). Freud says: 'The genitals are the latest of these *erotogenic* zones. . . .' (Freud, S. *New Introductory Lectures on Psycho-Anlysis,* tr. by Sprott, W.J.H., Norton, New York, 1933)

erotographomania (-graf-ō-mā′ni-à) A morbid impulse to write love letters. Usually love is expressed in sublimated terms, often having a vivid religious background. The letters are generally written anonymously. Magnus Hirschfeld cites the letters of the monk Abélard and the nun Héloïse as classical examples of erotographomania.

erotolalia (-lā′li-a) Sexually obscene speech, especially in reference to the use of such speech during sexual intercourse as a means of enhancing gratification. This term emphasizes the sexual content of speech in contrast to the obscene or socially tabu speech of coprolalia, which term is more properly limited to verbal expression of excretory processes. (MacDougald, D., in A. Ellis and A. Brandt, *Encyclopedia of Sexual Behavior,* Hawthorn Books, New York, 1959)

erotomania (-mā′ni-à) Inordinate or morbid inclination to love. Its usual implication is love of genital relations with members of the opposite sex. It is closely related, however, to unconscious homosexual impulses, which in turn stem from the stages of infantile sexuality, particularly those identified with the Oedipus situation.

'Many cases of erotomania might give an impression that they could be satisfactorily explained as being exaggerated or distorted heterosexual fixations, if our attention were not attracted by the circumstance that these infatuations invariably begin, not with any internal perception of loving, but with an external perception of being loved.' (Freud, S. *Collected Papers,* vol. 3, tr. by Strachey, A. and J., Leonard and Virginia Woolf and The Institute of Psychoanalysis, London, 1925). The quotation is taken from *A Case of Paranoia (Dementia Paranoides),* which deals largely with the projection mechanism and homosexuality.

erotopathy (ē-ro-top′ȧ-thē) Any abnormality of the sexual impulse.

error Freud states: 'Errors of memory are distinguished from forgetting and false recollections through one feature only, namely, that the error (false recollection) is not recognized as such but finds credence.' He adds that 'we speak of "erring" instead of "falsely recollecting" where the character of the objective reality is emphasized in the psychic material to be reproduced—that is, where something other than a fact of my own psychic life is to be remembered, or rather something that may be confirmed or refuted through the memory of others. The reverse of the error in memory in this sense is formed by ignorance.' (Freud, S. *The Basic Writings of Sigmund Freud,* tr. by Brill, A.A., Random House, New York, 1938)

Freud says: 'Back of every error is a repression. More accurately stated: the error conceals a falsehood, a disfigurement which is ultimately based on repressed material.' (ibid.)

erythrism (ē-rith′riz′m) In medicine and anthropology this term denotes a condition characterized by the presence of red hair in certain regions of the body, notably in the beard and pubic zone, where it contrasts with the color of the remainder of the body hair. This condition attains its significance for constitutional medicine from the theory that in analogy to *flavism* (q.v.) it constitutes a stigma of the *asthenic, microsplanchnic* physique and its tendency to tuberculosis. See *type, asthenic.*

erythroblastosis fetalis (er-rith-rō-blas-tō′-sis fē-tal′is) See *icterus gravis neonatorum.*

erythroedema polyneuritis (er-rith-re-dē′-mȧ pol-ē-nū-rī′tis) *Acrodynia* (q.v.).

erythrophobia (ē-rith-rō-fō′bi-ȧ) Fear of red. This is most commonly associated with blood, although, as with other fears, anything identified with the original fear may act as a substitute for it. For example, the fear of blood may be expressed as the fear of red, of anything that is red; the fear may then spread to all colors; the fear of colors may then give way to that of certain localities in which colors are prominent. Fears amass with great facility; moreover, as fears grow they tend to appear less associated with the original one, until finally the fear seems thoroughly illogical and unrelated to any previous experiences.

The conscious fear is symbolic of an unconscious and antithetic impulse. Thus, the fear of blood is related unconsciously to a wish for it. The wish is a sadistic expression connected with the castration phantasy or one of its many subsequent symbolic expressions.

Not infrequently *erythrophobia* appears as a fear of blushing. It is said that the latter is related to exhibitionism and that it means genitalization of the face or head. The individual fears the red face as if it were the penis.

escapism In psychoanalytic therapy, this term denotes the tendency to escape from reality functioning to the relative security of childhood, a tendency often manifested by an accentuation of neurotic symptoms. It is a form of resistance.

Eshmun complex See *complex, Eshmun.*

esophoria (ē-sō-for′i-ȧ) See *heterophoria.*

E.S.P. Abbreviation of *extra-sensory perception* (q.v.).

esprit de corps (âs-prē′ dē kôr′) (F. 'group spirit, corporate feeling') 'An organization of group-feeling and essentially as a form of group enthusiasm.' (Blumer, H.E., in Park, R.E., *Principles of Sociology,* Barnes & Noble, New York, 1939)

Esquirol, Jean Étienne Dominique (1772–1840) (es-kē-rôl′) French psychiatrist.

EST Abbreviation of electro-shock therapy. See *therapy, electric convulsion.*

esthesia (es-thē′z[h]i-ȧ) Sensibility; capacity for sensation. Used frequently as a combining form.

esthesiogenesis (es-thē-si-ō-jen′ē-sis) The production of a reaction in a sensory zone.

estrangement, kinship Social workers' term for 'the state of being out of touch or not on friendly terms with one's relatives because of disagreement or indifference.' (Hamilton, G. *A Medical Social Terminology,* Presbyterian Hospital, New York, 1930)

estromania See *oestromania.*

état marbré (ă-tă′ măr-brā′) Status marmoratus. See *dystonia, torsion.*

eternity, fear of By this term Fenichel designates one in the group of fears of 'surroundings that imply the loss of the usual means of orientation,' such as fear of cessation of customary routine, fear of death, fear of uniform noises, etc. The patient who has such fears is particularly afraid of a loss of control over infantile sexual and aggressive impulses, and then projects onto the outside world his own fears of losing control. Thus, he will see situations in which there is a loss of the customary spatial or temporal orientation not only as situations where there is a loss of normal control over, or usual organization of, the real world. He will also identify himself with such a situation, referring this loss of control to his own personal situation. Then a concept such as eternity, in which the normal assessment of time loses its significance, is seen as a great threat to him, for it means a loss of the forces protecting him against his own unconscious unmastered sexual and aggressive impulses. (Fenichel, O. *The Psychoanalytic Theory of Neurosis,* Norton, New York, 1945)

ethnology (eth-nol′ō-jē) The branch of *anthropology* which deals with the division of mankind into races and studies the origin, history, customs, and institutions of the various racial groups.

etiology (ē-ti-ol′ō-jē) The division of medical science relating to the cause of disease. The cause of general paresis is the germ of syphilis; not all patients with syphilis develop general paresis. Etiological studies involve also investigations into the nature and response of the tissues of the host as well as of the response of the total personality to the results of the disease.

eu- (ū-) prefix meaning good, well, advantageous, from Gr. *eŭ,* well.

eudemonia, affective (ū-dē-mō′ni-à) Flight into mental illness as an escape from frustrating or frightening reality. The *Ganser syndrome,* certain cases of *hypochondriasis,* and *faxen-psychosis* (qq.v.) are instances of affective eudemonia. This term emphasizes secondary gains, which are particularly prominent in these cases.

euergasia (ū-ĕr-gas′i-à) Adolf Meyer's term for wholesome or normal mental functioning.

eugenic (ū-jen′ik) Properly used in its original sense, the term relates only to the ideology or methods of preventive medicine in *applying* genetic principles to human health conditions as postulated by eugenics.

eugenics This term was coined by Francis Galton to denote the systematically organized efforts of preventive medicine to improve average human qualities through the observation of *heredity.* Galton's introduction of the word 'study' into his final definition: 'the study of agencies under social control that may improve or impair the racial qualities of future generations, either physically or mentally,' makes it clear that he was thinking of such studies as would be the foundation of plans. Eugenics is thus complementary to *euthenics,* which aims at the betterment of the human race by studying the *environmental* conditions of human beings and differs from *genetics,* which is the branch of natural science that studies the origin, transmission, and manifestation of hereditary characters.

Eugenic measures are (1) *positive,* to encourage reproduction by persons biologically most highly qualified ('aristogenic'), or (2) *negative,* for the reduction or stoppage of parenthood among those least qualified physically and mentally ('cacogenic'). While positive eugenic activities consist mainly of educational propaganda and practical help to biologically sound families, negative eugenic procedure is devoted to the restriction of marriage and birth rates in the lowest class of family stocks through eugenic advice, contraceptive birth control measures, and voluntary or compulsory sterilization.

Accordingly, the *positive* aim of eugenics is to improve the human capacity for responding favorably to contemporary standards of culture and civilization, in order to obtain a general stabilized level of resistance to the dysgenic and antisocial influences of inferior family stocks; whereas the chief task of *negative* eugenics is to determine and prevent biological incapacity to thrive even in a favorable environment.

eumorphic (ū-mor′fik) According to the classification of constitutional types by the Italian school, this term means 'built along normal lines' and refers to a type intermediate between *dolichomorphic* and *brachymorphic* and is equivalent to Viola's *normosplanchnic* type.

Etymologically the term eumorphic is derived from the structure or shape of the body as a whole, whereas normosplanchnic is derived from the size of the viscera and their effect on the contour of the body. It is held nevertheless that there is a complete correspondence between the eumorphic build and the normosplanchnic visceral status.

eunuch In general usage as well as in medicine this term designates a man *castrated before puberty* and subsequently developing the secondary sexual characteristics of a female. See *castrate.*

In Oriental harems the male supervisors were *eunuchs,* to prevent their sexual relations. However, the belief that the removal of the testes after puberty necessarily prevents sex functioning is erroneous: in neither sex does removal of the gonads *after puberty* invariably produce such an effect. 'Eunuchs' may therefore have sex relations as other men whose testes are removed after puberty.

Real eunuchs may be recognized by not growing bald, since they do not produce the hormones which make other men susceptible to the genetic tendency to baldness.

eunuchism A medical term for the state of being eunuched or of being a eunuch, that is, a man castrated before puberty.

eunuchoid In constitutional medicine this term describes the physical appearance of a male whose secondary sexual characteristics resemble those of a female. See *type, hypogenital.*

eunuchoidism In the classificatory system of constitutional medicine, the concept of *eunuchoidism* applies to a male resembling a *eunuch,* that is, a man who develops after castration the secondary sexual characteristics of a female: large hips, narrow sloping shoulders, absence of beard and body hair, and high-pitched feminine voice.

Eunuchoidism sometimes results from early derangement of the sex glands without operative castration before puberty. It may even occur in mature men, especially in old age, following drastic changes in their glandular balance, and is easily recognizable by high-pitched voice. See *castration.*

euphoria (ū-fō′ri-à) In psychiatry, a morbid or abnormal sense of well-being.

'Euphoria is a generalized feeling of well-being, not amounting to a definite affect of gladness.' (Henderson, D.K. and Gillespie, R.D. *A Text-Book of Psychiatry,* 4th ed., Oxford University Press, London, 1936) While the condition may be observed in many psychiatric states, it gains distinction in the manic state of manic-depressive psychosis.

euphoria, indifferent Elation and cheerfulness which lack emotional depth. Bleuler applies this term to apparent euphoria in the schizophrenic, where seemingly marked euphoria is often expressed in the same sentence, side by side with marked depression or indifferent expressions. Indifferent euphoria is an instance of the lack of homogeneity of mood and of the dissociation between mood and verbal expression which are almost pathognomonic of schizophrenia.

euphoriants See *psycholeptica.*

eupraxia (ū-prak′si-à) Normal ability to perform co-ordinated movements.

eurhythmia (ū-rith′mi-à, ū-riTH′) In constitutional medicine, harmonious body relationships. 'There is no doubt that the original evolutional spurt of the organism or of the separate organs may from the start be deficient or excessive, and yet we may have a just distribution of the two resultants of such a spurt, namely, the ponderal and the morphological, so that the result will be *eurhythmic, microsomic* and *megalosomic* individuals.' (Pende, N. *Constitutional Inadequacies,* tr. by Naccarati, S., Lea & Febiger, Philadelphia, 1928)

eurotophobia (ū-rō-tō-fō′bi-à) Fear of female genitals. Paton says: 'A distressing tendency to blush is noted in many psychasthenics, and is often sufficiently pronounced to make the patient averse to going into society. In the exaggerated cases it is excited whenever the patient encounters a stranger—eurotophobia. This term must be carefully distinguished from erythrophobia, or the fear of a red color.' (Paton, S. *Psychiatry,* Lippincott, Philadelphia and London, 1905)

euryplastic (ū-ri-plas′tik) This term characterizes a type described by Bounak and corresponding to the *pyknic* type in Kretschmer's system, the *megalosplanchnic hypervegetative* constitution of Pende.

eusthenic (ū-sthen′ik) In comparison with the *oligosthenic* and *phthinoid* divisions of the *asthenic* type in Kretschmer's system of constitutional types, this denotes the asthenic variety which is relatively the most vigorous and the closest to the *athletic*.

eutelegenesis (ū-tē-lē-jen′e-sis) This term is used in genetics, synonymously with *artificial insemination,* to denote the technical process of artificially impregnating a female with the sperms of a male without any contact between the two.

In the breeding of domestic animals this technique has long passed the experimental stage, and is now being widely used in many countries. 'Sperms are drawn off, transferred to vials and kept under refrigeration for days, to be used as needed.' (Scheinfeld, A. *You and Heredity,* Book of the Month Club, New York, 1939)

It is expected by some biologists that the practice of eutelegenesis will soon be applied to human beings also. It may be utilized for eugenic purposes as well as for the control of the proportionate birth rate of the sexes.

euthanasia (ū-thȧ-nā′z[h]i-ȧ) This term applies mainly to the measures by which physicians alleviate, or seek to remove, the distress attending the approach of death in the course of a chronic disease. According to this concept, the removal of pain is regarded as essential for an 'easy death.'

In a more specific sense, the term implies not only an easy, painless death, but also the means of bringing one on by legally putting to immediate death every sufferer from an incurable disease who prefers this kind of death to being tormented for a lengthy period before an eventual, painful death. This particular procedure is commonly known as 'mercy killing' and has been advocated by small groups of physicians subscribing to the belief that, with adequate safeguards, euthanasia should be legalized 'to allow incurable sufferers to choose immediate death rather than await it in agony.' These advocates of euthanasia hold that most of the legal and religious arguments against mercy killing are founded on emotion rather than on reason.

Within the province of eugenics, it is the method of infanticide—that is the destruction of infants with marked congenital defects—which has at certain times been practiced as a form of euthanasia which seemed advisable for the particular purposes of race betterment. It was in Plato's Republic and in ancient Sparta—whose population was essentially military and had become accustomed to looking at marriage chiefly as a means of supplying new soldiers—that infanticide was urged for the first time and actually practiced, upon the decision of the ephors, when a child was unlikely to turn out a vigorous citizen (soldier). Following the pattern of Sparta, numerous tribes and nations have also contrived, at one time or another, to destroy their unfit, in order to prevent them from becoming a burden to themselves and to society.

At present and in all civilized countries, of course, any kind of euthanasia is contrary to ethical and humanitarian concepts and is punishable as a felony (see *eugenics*).

euthenics (ū-then′iks) In contrast to *eugenics,* which aims at improving the biological qualities of future human generations with the aid of data gained from the observation of heredity, the term *euthenics* relates to the study of environmental conditions tending to improve the human race (see *peristasis*).

euthymia (ū-thim′i-ȧ, ū-thī′mi-ȧ) Joyfulness or mental tranquility.

evaluation, false This term is used by Adler to include under-evaluation of other persons or objects and over-evaluation of personal achievement or aims.

As an example of under-evaluation, Adler presents the story of the 'fox and the sour grapes.' He states that, 'instead of realizing his own inferiority the fox deprives the grapes of their inherent value—and thus *retains his high spirits.* He is prepared for his *megalomania.* These types of psychical procedure primarily serve the maintenance of "free will" and of personal worth. The same purpose is served by the over-evaluation of *personal achievements* and aims caused by the individual's flight from the pessimistic feeling of his own inferiority. They are thus "arranged" and arise out of an *exaggerated safety-tendency* directed against the feeling of "being below." ' (Adler, A. *The Practice and Theory of Individual Psychology,* tr. by Radin, P., Kegan Paul, Trench, Trubner, London, 1924) evasion See *paralogia*.

event, traumatic A term that in the evolution of psychiatry and psychiatric terminology was introduced for the purpose of designating a special variety of the concept already included without a qualifying adjective under the undifferentiated broader term *trauma;* the physical or psychic injury specifically precipitating emotional or mental illness of the injury-caused type, i.e. the traumatic neuroses or psychoses. The illness may be caused by a single injury, as in the case of a workman caught in a construction cave-in, or by a series of traumatic incidents, as a soldier participating in protracted warfare. In any case, the designation *traumatic event* is reserved for denoting *the* injury that precipitates the illness and finds representation in its clinical picture.

'As soon as the organism encounters an unfamiliar stimulus in the effective environment, it must assay this stimulus, and a new adaptive maneuver must be set into motion. If the maneuver is successful, the organism continues to thrive and adds the new pattern to its armamentarium. The stimulus may, however, be too strong, or the time too brief, to permit a successful maneuver, e.g. a temperature of 160 degrees F., an exploding shell, or a plane with one wing shot off. In this case a series of events takes place within the organism which indicates its failure to adapt to the new conditions. Although sometimes the organism ceases to exist, more often it continues to exist, its reaction to the failure becoming the starting point for a new adaptation. An *event* which creates conditions to which the organism cannot adapt may be called *traumatic,* and the point at which the organism's adapted capacities fail may be called the breaking point. . . .

'The traumatic neurosis is the record of the lasting consequences of an abrupt change in the external environment to which the resources of the individual are unequal. This situation we designated as a trauma [traumatic event]. The neurosis is, therefore, the record of the disturbance created by the trauma on the previously established adaptations.' (Kardiner, A., and Spiegel, H. *War Stress and Neurotic Illness,* Hoeber, New York, 1947)

evil, St. John's An old term for epilepsy.

eviration (ev-i-rā'shun) Krafft-Ebing writes: 'If, in cases of antipathic sexual instinct thus developed, no restoration occurs, then deep and lasting transformations of the *psychical* personality may occur. The process completing itself in this way may be briefly designated *eviration (defemination* in women). The patient undergoes a deep change of character, particularly in his feelings and inclinations, which thus become those of a female. After this, he also feels himself to be a woman during the sexual act, has desire only for passive sexual indulgence, and, under certain circumstances, sinks to the level of a prostitute.' (Krafft-Ebing, R.v. *Psychopathia Sexualis,* Login, New York, 1908)

Eviration is also defined as emasculation from the physical point of view.

evolutility (ev-ō-lū-til'i-tē) With biologists, the term means the capability of an organism to exhibit change in growth and other aspects of the physical structure as a result of nutrition.

evolution Vague rudimentary notions of evolution, as a transition from simplicity to complexity, appeared already in Greek philosophy; but it was only with the demonstration in a scientific manner of its working in the realm of biology by Darwin and Wallace that it became of real interest in science. Since then it has been assigned an important role in anthropology, ethnology, history, comparative religion, and psychology. As a philosophy in modern times *emergent evolution* has a great vogue. Its central notion is that a sum is more than its parts, and that in the evolution of higher organisms from lower, some new emergent qualities arise.

Evolution may be of a positive or negative kind, progressive or regressive, and it may take form in a broad generalization. Some biologists restrict the meaning of the term 'evolution' so that it is applicable only to plants and animals. Others extend the meaning to apply throughout nature and interpret mental progress in terms of evolution. According to C. Lloyd Morgan, any condition, physical or mental, which exemplifies evolution is a temporary phase in an orderly series of events, and its relations to preceding, subsequent, and surrounding events may be determined by scientific methods.

In biology it has become customary to limit the meaning of the term to the evolution of living forms, first placed on a scientific footing by the observations made independently but almost simultaneously by Charles Darwin and A.R. Wallace. From their study of fauna and fossils in many lands they were able to form a picture of the distribution of animal life in space and time which forced each to the conclusion that the more complex forms of living beings including man are descended from more primitive forms (see *Darwinism*).

The great reputation of Darwin for the demonstration of the biological facts underlying this *theory of evolution* was scarcely diminished by the subsequent discovery of his mistakes in interpreting the mechanism of this evolutionary process. From the present genetic standpoint it may be said that regarding Natural Selection acting through Survival of the Fittest as a mechanism bringing new types into existence, in addition to favoring the better-adjusted types already in existence, Darwin implied the heinous genetic heresy of the inheritance of acquired characters. Modern genetics has not only discredited this heresy but, in revealing the frequency of *mutations* has provided a substitute for Darwin's false notion. When a new type has arisen by mutation, the principles of natural selection and survival of the fittest can work to preserve or destroy it. See *mutation*.

exaltation, reactive See *mania, reactive*.

examination, mental See *mental status*.

examination, psychiatric social 'The psychiatric social examination has as its immediate end as complete an understanding as possible of the patient's personality and behavior. It approaches the problem from a developmental point of view, bringing together data concerning the individual's heredity, his physical and mental make-up, his social and material environment, the personalities in his family group and his reactions to them, from the time of his childhood to the present.' (*Vocational Aspects of Psychiatric Social Work,* Mental Hygiene, 1925)

examinations, psychometric Various psychological tests that are administered to the individual in order to test one, several, or all of the following factors in his mental make-up: intelligence, special abilities and disabilities, manual skill, vocational aptitudes, interests, and personality characteristics.

exanthropia (ek-san-thrō'pi-à) An old

term for what was called the third stage of melancholia, namely, dislike for society.

excandescentia furibunda (eks-kàn-des-ken'tē-à foo-rē-boon'dà) (L. 'furious irascibility') Plattner's term for psychosis characterized by violent reactions.

exceptions See *type, 'the exceptions'*

excitation From the standpoint of Janet excitation is a form of psychotherapy: it 'has the opposite sense to that of depression.' He adds: 'We must not confuse excitation with agitation, as often happens. . . . Its essential characteristic is a rapid increase in psychological tension above the degree at which the tension has remained for a considerable time. This rise can obviously occur in either of two ways. There may be a real elevation above the level typical of what is regarded as normal. Excitation must, then, correspond to the phenomenon which passes by the name of joy—enthusiasm, inspiration, ecstasy. It must play a part in works of genius, in inventions, and in the progress of thought. But this form is rare, and we have little experience of it in our therapeutic observations. The other form of excitation is more familiar; it is that which we shall find in our patients, the form in which the psychological tension, previously lowered, rises to the level which is regarded as normal.' (Janet, P. *Psychological Healing*, vols. 1–2, tr. by Paul, E. and C., Macmillan, New York, 1925)

Appreciation of the meaning of the concept *excitation* may be gained when one knows that Janet refers to excitation by action, by betrothal, by changes in mode of life and occupation, by traveling and athletics, by intellectual work, etc.

excitation, deflection of By this term Freud indicates the turning aside of a response to stimulation from the psychical sphere to the somatic. In discussing hysteria and anxiety-neurosis he states: 'In each of them there occurs a deflection of excitation to the somatic field instead of psychical assimilation of it.' (Freud, S. *Collected Papers*, tr. by Riviere, J., Leonard and Virginia Woolf and The Institute of Psychoanalysis, London, 1924–25)

excitation, somatic sexual With Freud this term means a continuous visceral excitation produced by pressure on the walls of the seminal vesicles, which are lined with nerve-endings.

excitation, subliminal See *summation*.

excitation, unconscious While discussing dreams Freud says that in children 'a wish unfulfilled during the day may instigate a wish,' but wishes of that nature seldom induce dreams in adults. In the latter 'the source is in the unconscious. I believe that *the conscious* wish becomes effective in exciting a dream only when it succeeds in arousing a similar unconscious wish which reinforces it. From the indications obtained in the psycho-analysis of the neuroses, I believe that these unconscious wishes are always active and ready to express themselves whenever they find an opportunity of allying themselves with an impulse from consciousness, and transferring their own greater intensity to the lesser intensity of the latter.' (Freud, S. *The Interpretation of Dreams,* 3rd ed., tr. by Brill, A.A., Macmillan, New York, 1933)

excitatory state, central See *summation.*

excitement, anniversary Bleuler used this term to refer to episodes of agitation which appear on specific calendar dates and which usually disappear after a few repetitions. He included anniversary excitements among the acute syndromes of the schizophrenias. On analysis it is found that the anniversary excitement is related to something which had happened to the patient on a certain day which had some connection with his complex or complexes.

excitement, catatonic (ka-ta-ton′ik) See *schizophrenia, catatonic.*

excitement, constitutional An older term used by Kraepelin for *manic temperament.* See *temperament, manic.*

exhaustion, combat See *shell-shock.*

exhaustion, nervous An older term for *neurasthenia.*

exhaustion psychosis See *psychosis, infective-exhaustive.*

exhaustion, stage of See *syndrome, general adaptation.*

exhibitionism According to psychoanalysis, early sexual impulses, that is, those occurring during the period of infancy, gain gratification through physical or somatic expression. There are three principal zones, called erotogenic zones—the oral, anal, and genital—that serve to provide outlet for the instinctual qualities.

During the infancy period the sexual instinct consists of several 'component' or partial impulses, each of which tries to achieve independent satisfaction, chiefly through the erotogenic zones. One of the partial impulses is exhibitionism. This impulse, manifested early in the form of genital exhibitionism, is later subject to all the modification that may take place with any of the instincts. It may be progressively displaced from the genital zone to the body as a whole, to the oral zone (the pleasure of speaking), to clothes, to dramatics, to the possession of material assets, etc. Or, it may be expressed in terms of reaction-formation, that is, there may be aversion to display of any kind.

Psychiatric patients express the exhibitionistic impulse in a variety of ways. In its severest form the genitals are exposed, usually to some person who represents to the patient the parent of the opposite sex. Exhibitionism is thus associated with the Oedipus complex.

'Most of these phantasies were plainly of an exhibitionistic order: thus he moved the crowd by his marvelous oratory or ravished an audience by his violin-playing; oftener it was a wind instrument, horn or a flute, which he played in a way that the world had never known before. . . .' (Jones, E. *Papers on Psycho-Analysis,* 4th ed., Wood, Baltimore, 1938)

'The *turning around* of an instinct *upon the subject* is suggested to us by the reflection that masochism is actually sadism turned round upon the subject's own ego, and that exhibitionism includes the love of gazing at the subject's own body.' (Freud, S. *Collected Papers,* vol. 4, tr. by Riviere, J., Leonard and Virginia Woolf and The Institute of Psychoanalysis, London, 1924–25)

existence, intra-uterine See *intra-uterine.*

existentialism A system of philosophy particularly associated with the names of Jean-Paul Sartre, Martin Heidegger, Karl Jaspers, and Sören Kierkegaard. Existential philosophy is essentially of European origin and is a reaction to the realization that technology and a belief in pure rationalism, Logical Positivism, or similar philosophies have only alienated man from society and from himself. Existentialism rejects the Hellenic view of man as a man of detached, logical reason and instead emphasizes the Hebraic view of man as a man of faith and a concrete, individual doer.

Philosophy in the Western world before the time of Kierkegaard tacitly accepted

Parmenides' belief that if a thing cannot be thought, it cannot be real. Yet existence cannot be thought, it can only be lived; thus reason must ignore existence completely or reduce it to nothingness. For Kierkegaard, existence was not a matter of speculation but a reality in which the individual is personally and passionately involved; the decisive encounter with the Self is in the Either/Or of choice. For Heidegger, existence is a Being spread over a field or region which is the world of its care and concern. This field of being is called Dasein (the One). In the everyday world, none of us is a private Self confronting a world of external objects; we are simply one among many—'the One,' a fallen state in that we have not yet become a Self and recognized our mortal, feeble, impotent nature. Sartre and his followers, representing a small part of existential philosophy, emphasize the despair of a world from which God has departed, and their themes include: 'Alienation and estrangement; a sense of the basic fragility and contingency of human life; the impotence of reason confronted with the depths of existence; the threat of Nothingness, and the solitary and unsheltered condition of the individual before this threat.' (Barrett, W. *Irrational Man,* Doubleday, New York, 1958)

In psychiatry, existentialism forms the philosophic background for 'existential analysis,' which in the main is represented by Europeans trained originally as psychoanalysts. The existential group does not consider itself divorced from the body of orthodox psychoanalytic theory and method, but it looks to existentialism rather as a more extensive and practicable approach to the patient and his world. Existential analysis is considered to have appeared in reaction to existing inadequacies in the various schools of thought in psychopathology.

For example: 'The existentialists conceive of schizophrenic episodes as moments when it is impossible for the patient to conduct his own life within the stream of existence around him. The question is, how can one conduct a life impossible to conduct?—by substituting for the uninterrupted, objective sequence of experience a subjective sequence. Experience takes on a non-sequential character in the schizophrenic, who aims for misguided ideals which are contradicted by experience. Thus the sequential character of experience is shattered and the schizophrenic becomes embroiled in alternatives which are impossible to fulfill. This leads to masking, imitation, eccentricity and mannerisms. Not being able to cope with life gives rise to anxiety for the attempt at masking fails and the misguided ideals cannot be achieved. Existential analysis consists of looking behind the symptoms for the specific modes of existence which determine those symptoms, and guiding the patient from an uncharted existence into new roads which allow existence to proceed in an orderly sequence.' (Campbell, R.J. *Psychiatric Quarterly 32:* 318–34, 1958)

exogenism (eks-oj'ē-niz'm) State of being generated or born or caused by conditions or factors outside of the body. Thus, general paresis is exogenic in the sense that the original cause, the spirochete, is transmitted to the body from an outside source.

exogenous, exogenetic, exogenic (eks-oj'ē-nus, ek-sō-jē-net'ik, -jen'ik) In modern medical classification, the term *exogenous* relates to physical or mental disorders which are caused predominantly by factors acting either from outside of the body or from another part of the body (outside of the system), which is the very seat of the morbid condition in question. See *endogenous.*

exogeny, exogenism, exogenesis (eks-oj'ē-nē, -niz'm, ek-sō-jen'ē-sis) Although the medical term *exogeny* relates originally to the pathogenetic process of only those morbid conditions which are caused by factors acting from *outside* of the body, it is used in psychiatry in a more specific sense. The psychiatric classification includes disorders which are at least predominantly due to influences of pathological processes outside of the nervous system, and are not inherent in its particular genetic constitution.

According to this definition, a '*symptomatic*' psychosis which originates within the body, but arises primarily from morbid factors outside of the nervous system, thus constituting merely a secondary symptom of an organic disease affecting parts of the body other than the nervous system itself, must similarly be classified as exogenous, as the more obvious cases of traumatic psychosis, alcoholic hallucinosis or reactive depression (see *endogeny*).

exophoria (ek-so-for'i-à) See *heterophoria.*

exophthalmic dysostosis (eks-of-thal'mik dis-os-tō'sis) *Xanthomatosis* (q.v.).

expansiveness From the psychiatric point of view *expansiveness* is usually synonymous with megalomania. Bleuler cites delusions of grandeur as expansive forms of delusions. 'In the mildest cases they rather take the form of over-estimation of the ego; the patient surpasses other people in health, ability, beauty to an extent greater than the corresponding reality.' (Bleuler, E. *Textbook of Psychiatry,* tr. by Brill, A.A., Macmillan, New York, 1930) In severer instances, patients believe they are God or that they are endowed with supernatural powers.

expectancy, life The number of years that individuals of a given age will, on the average, live beyond that age, is called the expectation of life at that age.

Example: According to the life table for continental United States, 1929 to 1931, prepared by the U.S. Bureau of the Census, the expectation of life at birth for white males was 59.12 years. At age 40 the expectation of life was 29.22 years.

Patients with mental disease have an expectation of life less than half that of the general population. In 1930, male patients in the New York civil State hospitals had an expectation of life of 19.17 years at age 20, compared with 46.02 years for white males in the continental United States. Female patients had an expectation of life of 18.06 years at age 20, compared with 48.52 for white females in the continental United States. See *table, life.*

expectation, anxious Freud says: 'primitive man is a prey to a perpetual "anxious expectation," to a lurking sense of apprehension, just like those suffering from the anxiety-neurosis classified by us in the psychoanalytical theory of the neuroses. This "anxious expectation" shows itself most intensely on all occasions that depart from what is usual, in regard to anything that involves something novel, unexpected, unexplained, uncanny.' (Freud, S. *Collected Papers,* tr. by Riviere, J., Leonard and Virginia Woolf and The Institute of Psychoanalysis, London, 1924–25) See *neurosis, expectation.*

experience, accidental See *accidental.*

experience, corrective emotional One of the briefer and more direct techniques advocated by Alexander to expedite psychotherapy. In this technique, the therapist temporarily assumes some particular role to bring the patient more quickly to an awareness of transference relationships and to other personal insights and reorientations.

experimental neurosis See *neurosis, experimental.*

experiment of nature See *nature, experiment of.*

explosion-readiness See *readiness, explosion.*

exposure, indecent See *exhibitionism.*

expressible Synonymous with *penetrant.*

expression, exchange of the verbal This is a psychoanalytic concept. Freud speaks of *'an exchange of the verbal expression for the thought in question'* as a form of displacement.

'Displacement usually occurs in such a way that a colourless and abstract expression of the dream-thought is exchanged for one that is pictorial and concrete. The advantage, and along with it the purpose, of this substitution is obvious. Whatever is pictorial is *capable of representation* in dreams and can be fitted into a situation in which abstract expression would confront the dream-representation with difficulties not unlike those which would arise if a political leading article had to be represented in an illustrated journal.' (Freud, S. *The Interpretation of Dreams,* 3rd ed., tr. by Brill, A.A., Macmillan, 1933)

expressive pattern See *psychodynamics, adaptational.*

expressivity See *penetrance.*

extension, symbolic The investment (through extension) of new situations or objects with the same meaning and values as were engendered by experience with older situations or objects, to which the new ones bear no actual resemblance. The original connection is forgotten, so that meaning and values have become dissociated from the experiential material, which originally determined them, and are now associated with the new material, which only *stands for or symbolizes* the original. Thus the original conceptions are extended by their application to symbols, and the process itself is known as symbolic extension. For example, psychoanalysis has demonstrated that in some individuals a belief in God represents a symbolic extension of the original ideational material concerning the individual's own father.

exteriorization (eks-tē-ri-ō-ri-zā'shun) This term, used frequently in psychiatry, refers to the act of objectivating one's interests and affects. While speaking of treatment of schizophrenic individuals, Henderson and Gillespie say that '. . . we must encourage, stimulate, explain and try to "exteriorise" those who tend to day-dream and to lead asocial seclusive lives.' (Henderson, D.K., and Gillespie, R.D. *A Text-Book of Psychiatry,* 4th ed., Oxford University Press, London, 1936)

externalization (eks-tern-al-i-za'shun) In discussing the Thematic Apperception Test, Bellak (in Abt, L.E., and Bellak, L., *Projective Psychology,* Knopf, New York, 1950) defines externalization as '. . . those apperceptive processes which function on a preconscious level and can therefore readily be made conscious.' The writer thereby differentiates between, on the one hand, projection as an unconscious defense mechanism which leads to extreme and pathological distortion of reality, and, on the other, the apperceptive distortions which make up the subject's responses in 'projective' tests.

extinction In neurophysiology, disappearance of excitability to a previously adequate stimulus. Immediately after application of a stimulus to a nerve, there occurs a progressive depression of excitability of that nerve; at the point at which the nerve or focus becomes completely inexcitable, extinction is said to have occurred.

For the meaning of extinction in psychoanalysis, see *ego, extinction of.*

extinction, order of In genetic family studies, the statistical estimate of families dying out in a certain generation because of lack of reproduction.

extractive disorders See *psychodynamics, adaptational.*

extrapunitive See *intropunitive.*

extrapyramidal system A functional system of nerve tracts whose main action is concerned with automatic movements involved in postural adjustments and with autonomic regulation. It is usually considered to include three layers of integration: cortical, basal ganglia, and midbrain (tegmental). Parkinsonism, athetosis, chorea, and torsion spasms are all possible results of extrapyramidal dysfunction. The mechanisms involved in the production of these syndromes are only poorly understood, but many believe that they are a result of release from suppressor action.

extrasensory perception See *perception, extrasensory.*

extraversion (eks-trȧ-vēr'shun) Disposition to turn one's interests upon or find pleasure in external things. 'An outward-turning of the libido. With this concept I denote a manifest relatedness of subject to object in the sense of a positive movement of subjective interest towards the object. Everyone in the state of extraversion thinks, feels, and acts in relation to the object, and moreover in a direct and clearly observable fashion, so that no doubt can exist about his positive dependence upon the object. In a sense, therefore, extraversion is an outgoing transference of interest from the subject to the object.' (Jung, C.G. *Psychological Types,* tr. by Baynes, H.G., Harcourt, Brace, New York and London, 1923)

Jung speaks of *active* extraversion, when the libido is 'deliberately willed,' and *passive* extraversion 'when the object compels it, i.e., attracts the interest of the subject of its own accord, even against the latter's intention.' (ibid.)

The act or process of extraverting is *exteriorization* (q.v.).

extraversion, active See *extraversion.*

extraversion, passive See *extraversion.*

extremity, phantom See *limb, phantom.*

extroversion, extrovert less correct, but equally frequent spellings of *extraversion, extravert.*

eyelash sign See *sign, eyelash.*

F

F Rorschach scoring symbol for a form response, i.e. a response determined primarily by the form of the inkblot.

f Frequency.

F minus Rorschach scoring symbol for a form response (see *F*) of poor quality.

F plus Rorschach scoring symbol for a good form response.

fabrication See *confabulation, opportune; psychosis, Korsakoff.*

fabulation Adolf Meyer used this term in the sense of confabulation or fabrication. He spoke of 'forms of protracted deliria usually with numerous fabulations. . . .' (*American Journal of Insanity LX,* 439, 1904)

facial hemiatrophy See *hemiatrophy, facial.*

facies, ironed-out (fā′shē-ēz) This expression is usually applied to the facial expression of patients with general paresis. The loss of tone of the muscles of expression gives the face the appearance as if it has been 'ironed-out,' flattened.

factor In genetics, practically identical with *gene.*

factorial (fak-tō′ri-al) Pertaining to a genetic factor or a combination of factors.

factor, intrinsic See *sclerosis, posterolateral.*

faculty, criticizing Freud says that '*conscience* is a criticizing faculty. In this disease [i.e. melancholia] . . . the most remarkable characteristic is the way in which the super-ego—you may call it, but in a whisper, the conscience—treats the ego. The melancholiac during periods of health can, like any one else, be more or less severe towards himself; but when he has a melancholic attack, his super-ego becomes over-severe, abuses, humiliates and ill-treats his unfortunate ego, threatens it with severest punishments, reproaches it for long forgotten actions which were at the time regarded quite lightly, and behaves as though it had spent the whole interval in amassing complaints and was only waiting for its present increase in strength to bring them forward, and to condemn the ego on their account.' (Freud, S. *New Introductory Lectures on Psycho-Analysis,* tr. by Sprott, W.J.H., Norton, New York, 1933)

faeces amicae in os proprium inicere (L.) The phrase (quoted from Stekel) refers to a form of sexual perversion, namely, the oral incorporation of rectal contents.

faith-cure Improvement (much less frequently, cure) as a result of faith or confidence of the patient in the therapist and/or the therapeutic method. Usually, faith-cures occur in favorable responses to the supportive type of psychotherapy, and particularly in the types known as prestige suggestion and persuasion.

fallacia (fal-lä′kē-à) (L. 'deceit, trick, deception') An illusion or hallucination.

fallacia optica (ôp′tē-kà) (L. 'optical deception') *Obs.* Optical illusion or hallucination.

fallectomy (fal-ek′tō-mē) See *salpingectomy.*

falling sickness A popular term for epilepsy.

Falret, Jean-Pierre (1794–1870) (fàl-rā′) French psychiatrist; in 1854, Falret and Baillarger independently described recurring attacks of mania and melancholia in the same patient.

Falret, Jules Ph.J. (1824–1902) French psychiatrist; in 1879 described 'folie circulaire' and 'mixed states,' which he considered to be transitory stages between attacks of mania and depression.

falsehood, unconscious A false or untrue statement made by an individual without intention or without his being aware of its false nature. 'There is a large group of individuals who are not deliberately falsifying their situation as they describe it, but are unconsciously falsifying, who have come to believe some things about themselves or others or about the situation which are not true.' (Levine, M. *Psychotherapy in Medical Practice,* Macmillan, New York, 1943)

falsification, memory See *confabulation, opportune; psychosis, Korsakoff.*

falsification, retrospective When an individual adds false details and meanings to a true memory, it is said that he engages in retrospective falsification. The condition is particularly common among patients with the paranoid form of schizophrenia, who in reviewing experiences of their past explain many of those experiences from a delusional point of view, though the experiences happened before their delusional system was formed.

falx cerebelli (falks se-re-bel′ī) See *meninges.*

falx cerebri (se′re-brī) See *meninges.*

fames bovina (fà′mes bô-vē′nà) (L. 'ox-like hunger') *Obs.* Bulimia.

fames canina (kà-nē′nà) (L. 'doglike hunger') *Obs.* Bulimia.

fames lupina (loo-pē′nà) (L. 'wolfish hunger') *Obs.* Bulimia.

familial This term is generally used in medicine to characterize a normal or morbid trait tending, or observed, 'to run in families.' As the hereditary origin of such a trait is not proved by the mere observation of its occurrence in several members of the same family, the use of the expression 'familial' is to be interpreted in the sense that in the particular case of a disease or another trait the genetic basis is either not to be stressed or as yet unknown. See *heredity.*

familianism (fà-mil′i-an-iz′m) A sociological and psychological term emphasizing the tendency to maintain strong intrafamilial bonds, ties, and demands, culturally transmitted and inherited, and making for intensely compact family life and solidarity. This phenomenon, pointed to by some authors as characteristic of Jewish cultural tradition, tends as a result of centuries of enforced isolation and persecution to make for neurotic over-attachments, emotional maladjustments, and relative difficulty in the establishment of independent, adult, emotional maturity of the individual scions. On the plus side, however, it probably also accounts for the relative infrequency of delinquency and criminality in the Jewish portion of the population. In this ethnic group delinquency and criminality is statistically less frequent—in contrast to other groups where family solidarity is less marked and broken homes more frequent. (Harms, E. *Handbook of Child Guidance,* Child Care Publications, New York, 1947)

famille névropathique (fa-mēy′ nā′vrô-pa-tĕk′) (F. 'neuropathic family') A group of degenerative diseases in which Charcot

included hysteria, since heredity, he felt, was the unique originating cause.

family social work See *social work, family.*

fancy, tendency to A tendency to fancy is present in many normal individuals, but is especially common in shut-in, seclusive personalities who have never come into normal contact with other people and generally lead an abnormal existence. Such individuals resort to the fairy tale as a mode of emotional gratification. If the tendency to fancy and day-dreaming is morbid, it is detrimental to the individual's psychic development, because he will not be able to cope with an inexorably real world, living as he does in a world of fancy. (Brill, A.A. *Basic Principles of Psychoanalysis,* Doubleday, New York, 1949)

fantasy See *phantasy.*

fantasying, active This psychiatric term denotes a psychotherapeutic procedure in which the patient is asked to relate his spontaneous imagery. An analysis of these fantasied images enables the physician to find out the roots of the patient's conflicts. If it becomes possible to show the patient these unconscious connections, he is in a position to recognize the source of his conflicts and is able to bring the conflict within the sphere of conscious insight and control. (Baynes, H.G. *Mythology of the Soul,* Williams and Wilkins, Baltimore, 1940)

fasciculus cuneatus (fà-sik′ū-lus koon-ā-à′tus) Tract of Burdach, located in the posterior white column of the spinal cord between the fasciculus gracilis and the posterior gray column. The fasciculus cuneatus carries proprioception and vibratory sensation fibers from the upper limbs. These fibers terminate in the nucleus cuneatus at the medulla, whence arise internal arcuate fibers, some of which proceed to the homolateral restiform body and most of which cross to form the medial lemniscus of the opposite side.

fasciculus gracilis (grà′si-lis) Tract of Goll, located in the posterior white column of the spinal cord next to the posterior (dorsal) median septum. The fasciculus gracilis carries proprioception and vibratory sensation fibers mainly from the lower limbs. These fibers terminate in the nucleus gracilis at the medulla, whence arise internal arcuate fibers, some of which proceed to the homolateral restiform body and most of which cross to form the medial lemniscus of the opposite side.

fascination When a desire for mastery of some factor in the environment cannot be gratified, a partial mastery of it is sometimes achieved by means of identification with it. This reaction is called *fascination*. For example, if an infant is seen paying rapt attention to a rattle which the mother waves before it, a phase preliminary to mastery can be assumed. But if mastery is not possible because the rattle is beyond reach, or perhaps because the knack of reaching has not yet been learned, there still remains the rapt attention, which becomes greatly intensified. The infant, so to say, loses itself in the sight and sound of the rattle and thus becomes one with it, and, through identification, a partial mastery is achieved by way of fascination.

fascinum (fàs'kē-noom) (L. 'witchcraft') This concept involves the belief, carried from the ancients, that certain individuals possess 'the evil eye,' because of which they are capable of fascinating and injuring others by looking at them. Patients with the paranoiac form of schizophrenia often express such a belief.

Among the Romans it also meant the membrum virile, because images of it were hung round the necks of children as a preventive against witchcraft (Varro, died B.C.27, *De Lingua Latina,* 7, §97, Müll.)

fashion Fashion refers to changes in dress, manners, the arts, literature, and philosophy 'based fundamentally on differentiation and emulation.' (Blumer, H.E., in Park, R.E. *Principles of Sociology,* Barnes & Noble, New York, 1939)

Styles set by the social elite with the object of differentiation are imitated by classes lower in the social structure, which in turn causes the upper class to make fresh innovations in fashion.

fastidium cibi (fàs-tē'dē-oom kē'bē) Loathing of food.

fastidium potus (pō'tōōs) Loathing of drink.

father-fixation See *mother-fixation.*

father-ideal A psychoanalytic term for the father component of the ego-ideal. Jones writes: 'If we inquire into the matter and origin of the ego-ideal, we discover that it is compounded of two constituents,

derived from the Father and the Self respectively—the original (primal) narcissism of the infant becomes in the course of development distributed in four directions, the actual proportion in each of these varying enormously with different individuals. *One* portion remains in an unaltered state attached to the real ego; this is probably the one concerned in the genesis of hypochondria. A *second* portion is deflected from any direct sexual goal and becomes attached to the idea of the parent, leading to adoration, devotion, and general over-estimation. It is important to bear in mind that to begin with this process is much more a matter of narcissistic identification than of any form of object-love. A *third* is transferred on to an ideal ego, and is one of the constituents of the "ego-ideal." The *fourth* is gradually transformed into object-love. Now the second and third of these commonly fuse during the latency period of childhood or even earlier. The form assumed by the resulting ego-ideal is largely derived from the ideas and mental attitudes of the father, the bond being effected through the second portion of the narcissistic libido mentioned above—that attached to what may be called the *father-ideal*. On the other hand, the energy that gives the ego-ideal its significance is wholly derived ultimately from narcissistic libido. There are three routes for this: (1) directly from the original narcissism of the primary ego (third portion mentioned above); (2) via the attachment to the *father-ideal* (second portion); (3) via the regression of narcissistic identification with the father that often takes place after a disappointment at the lack of gratification of object-love (fourth portion).' (Jones, E.J. *Papers on Psycho-Analysis,* Williams and Wilkins, Baltimore, 1949)

father-imago (-ē-mä'gō) See *image.*

father-substitute See *surrogate, mother.*

father-surrogate See *surrogate, mother.*

fatigue, battle See *shell-shock.*

fatigue, combat See *shell-shock.*

fatigue-state See *hypoglycemia.*

fatuity (fà-tū'i-tē) Feeblemindedness; sometimes used synonymously with dementia of any kind.

fatuous Stupid.

faunorum ludibria (fou-nor'oom loo-dē'-

brē-à) An old term, sometimes meaning nightmare, at other times referring to epilepsy.

faute de mieux (fōt dē mew) (F. 'for want of anything better') In psychiatry, this term is ordinarily used to refer to so-called accidental homosexuality, in which a male chooses another male as a sexual object when no women are available.

faxen-psychosis (fak′sen-sī-kō′sis) The German psychiatric term, literally in its English equivalent *buffoonery-psychosis* (q.v.).

FC Rorschach scoring symbol for a form response determined by the colored areas of the card.

Fc Rorschach scoring symbol for a form response in which any shading or color on the card is perceived merely as giving texture or surface appearance to the form.

fear Fear may be of a twofold nature, namely, real fear and neurotic fear. The latter arises whenever an instinctual urge is felt which is unacceptable to the conscious mind and creates the feeling of fear, if the demand for expression is too great.

Freud says that in the study of small children there is nothing that leads him to believe that there is any such thing as 'an instinctive perception of externally threatening danger.' It is true, he says, that external circumstances may combine with internal or endogenous fears, but the latter are primary. He further adds that there are three practically universal childhood fears that 'may be termed almost normal'; they are the fear of being alone, the fear of strangers, and the fear of darkness, each of which is associated with the unconscious dread of losing the protecting influences of the mother.

Freud seems to use the terms *fear, phobia,* and *anxiety* synonymously. He says: 'The most frequent cause of anxiety-neurosis is undischarged excitation. A libidinal excitation is aroused, but is not satisfied or used; in the place of this libido which has been diverted from its use, anxiety makes its appearance. I have even thought it was justifiable to say that this unsatisfied libido is directly transformed into anxiety. This view found some support in certain almost universal phobias of small children.' (Freud, S. *New Intro-*

ductory Lectures on Psycho-Analysis, tr. by Sprott, W.J.H., Norton, New York, 1933)

Neurotic anxiety may come about as a direct transformation of libido; or the ideas, associated with the affect, may be repressed, while the affect is converted into anxiety.

To psychoanalysts there is no basic difference between neurotic anxiety and objective anxiety. 'What one fears is obviously one's own libido. The internal danger is transformed into an external one.' Freud says, for instance, that 'the agoraphobiac is always afraid of his impulses in connection with temptations aroused in him by meeting people in the street. In his phobia he makes a displacement and is now afraid of an external situation. What he gains thereby is obvious; it is that he feels that he can protect himself better in that way. One can rescue oneself from an external danger by flight, whereas to attempt to fly from an internal danger is a difficult undertaking.' (ibid.)

'It is customary to distinguish anxiety in this sense [intense morbid dread] from fear, but it would seem that the resemblances between the two emotions are great enough to predicate at least a common biological source for them, and there is little doubt but that the differences between the two are due rather to the respective circumstances under which they arise than to more fundamental divergences.' (Jones, E. *Papers on Psycho-Analysis,* 4th ed., Wood, Baltimore, 1938)

'The present confusion is partly due to the ambiguous use of the words "anxiety" and "fear." British and American authors have habitually translated the word *Angst* as "anxiety"; whereas, although the German word involves the same confusion between fear and anxiety, it carries, more positively than the word "anxiety," the meaning "fear." ' (McDougall, W. *Outline of Abnormal Psychology,* Scribner, New York, 1926.) See *anxiety.*

fear-hypnosis See *hypnosis, father.*

fear, impulse An 'impulse-fear' is one that arises within the individual, more or less directly from an instinctual source. It is contrasted with real fear, which is associated with some real object in the environment. The fear of being in a dark place is a real or a 'reality' fear. The fear of imminent collapse and death, while in excellent health, is an impulse-fear.

fear of:
air: aerophobia
animals: zoöphobia
anything new: kaino(to)phobia; neophobia
bacilli: bacillophobia
barren space: cenophobia; kenophobia
bearing a monster: teratophobia
bees: apiphobia; melissophobia
being alone: autophobia; eremiophobia; monophobia
being buried alive: taphephobia
being enclosed: clithrophobia
being locked in: claustrophobia; clithrophobia
being looked at: scopophobia
being touched: (h)aphephobia; haptephobia
birds: ornithophobia
blood: hematophobia; hemophobia
blushing: ereuthophobia
brain-disease: meningitophobia
bridge: gephyrophobia
carriage: amaxophobia
cat: ailurophobia; galeophobia; gatophobia
change: kainophobia; kainotophobia; neophobia
childbirth: maieusiophobia
choking: anginophobia; pnigophobia
cold: cheimaphobia; psychrophobia
color(s): chromatophobia; chromophobia
comet: cometophobia
confinement: claustrophobia
contamination: molysmophobia; mysophobia
corpse: necrophobia
(crossing) street: dromophobia
crowds: demophobia; ochlophobia
dampness: hygrophobia
darkness: achluophobia; nyctophobia; scotophobia
dawn: eosophobia
daylight: phengophobia
death: thanatophobia
definite disease: monopathophobia
deformity: dysmorphophobia
demons: demonia; demonomania; entheomania
depth: bathophobia
devil: demonophobia; satanophobia
dirt: mysophobia; rhypophobia; rupophobia
disease: nosophobia; pathophobia
dog: cynophobia
dolls: pediophobia
dust: amathophobia
eating: phagophobia

electricity: electrophobia
emptiness: kenophobia
everything: pamphobia (obs.); panphobia; panophobia; pantophobia
examination: examination phobia
excrement: coprophobia
eyes: ommatophobia
failure: kakorrhaphiophobia
fatigue: kopophobia
fearing: phobophobia
feathers: pteronophobia
female genitals: eurotophobia
fever: febriphobia; pyrexeophobia
filth: mysophobia; rhypophobia; rupophobia
filth (personal): automysophobia
fire: pyrophobia
fish: ichthyophobia
flash: selaphobia
flogging: mastigophobia
floods: antlophobia
flute: aulophobia
fog: homichlophobia
food: cibophobia; sit(i)ophobia
forest: hylophobia
frog(s): batrachophobia
functioning: ergasiophobia
ghosts: phasmophobia
girls: parthenophobia
glass: crystallophobia; hyelophobia
God: theophobia
gravity: barophobia
hair: trichopathophobia; trichophobia
heat: thermophobia
heaven: uranophobia
height: acrophobia; hypsophobia
hell: hadephobia; stygiophobia
heredity: patroiophobia
high objects: batophobia
house: domatophobia; oikophobia
ideas: ideophobia
infinity: apeirophobia
injury: traumatophobia
innovation: neophobia
insanity: lyssophobia; maniaphobia
insects: acarophobia; entomophobia
jealousy: zelophobia
justice: dikephobia
knife: aichmophobia
large objects: megalophobia
left: levophobia
light: photophobia
lightning: astraphobia; astrapophobia; keraunophobia
machinery: mechanophobia
man: androphobia
many things: polyphobia
marriage: gamophobia
materialism: hylephobia

medicine(s): pharmacophobia
metals: metallophobia
meteors: meteorophobia
mind: psychophobia
mirror: eisoptrophobia; spectrophobia
missiles: ballistophobia
moisture: hygrophobia
money: chrematophobia
motion: kinesophobia
mouse: musophobia
myths: mythophobia
naked body: gymnophobia
name: onomatophobia
needles: belonephobia
Negro(es): negrophobia
night: noctiphobia; nyctophobia
northern lights: auroraphobia
novelty: kainophobia; kainotophobia; neophobia
odor (personal): bromidrosiphobia
odor(s): olfactophobia; osmophobia; osphresiophobia
open space(s): agoraphobia
pain: algophobia; odynophobia
parasites: parasitophobia
people: anthropophobia
place: topophobia
pleasure: hedonophobia
points: aichmophobia
poison: iophobia; toxi(co)phobia
poverty: peniaphobia
precipice(s): cremnophobia
punishment: poinephobia
rabies: cynophobia
railroad or train: siderodromophobia
rain: ombrophobia
rectal excreta: coprophobia
rectum: proctophobia
red: erythrophobia
responsibility: hypengyophobia
ridicule: catagelophobia
right: dextrophobia
river: potamophobia
robbers: harpaxophobia
rod: rhabdophobia
ruin: atephobia
sacred things: hierophobia
scabies: scabiophobia
scratch: amychophobia
sea: thalassophobia
self: autophobia
semen: spermatophobia
sex: genophobia
sexual intercourse: coitophobia
shock: hormephobia
sin: hamartophobia
sinning: peccatiphobia
sitting: thaassophobia
sitting down: kathisophobia

skin disease: dermatosiophobia
skin lesion: dermatophobia
skin (of animals): doraphobia
sleep: hypnophobia
small objects: microphobia; microbiophobia
smothering: pnigerophobia
snake: ophidiophobia
snow: chionophobia
solitude: erem(i)ophobia
sounds: acousticophobia
sourness: acerophobia
speaking: lal(i)ophobia
speaking aloud: phonophobia
spider: arachnephobia
stairs: climacophobia
standing up: stasiphobia
standing up and walking: stasibasiphobia
stars: siderophobia
stealing: kleptophobia
stillness: eremiophobia
stories: mythophobia
stranger(s): xenophobia
street: agyiophobia
string: linonophobia
sunlight: heliophobia
symbolism: symbolophobia
syphilis: syphilophobia
talking: lal(i)ophobia
tapeworms: taeniophobia
taste: geumaphobia
teeth: odontophobia
thinking: phronemophobia
thunder: astra(po)phobia; brontophobia
time: chronophobia
travel: hodophobia
trembling: tremophobia
trichinosis: trichinophobia
tuberculosis: phthisiophobia; tuberculophobia
vaccination: vaccinophobia
vehicle: amaxophobia
venereal disease: cypridophobia; cypriphobia
void: kenophobia
vomiting: emetophobia
walking: basiphobia
water: hydrophobia
weakness: asthenophobia
wind: anemophobia
women: gynophobia; horror feminae
work: ponophobia
writing: graphophobia

fear, real See *fear, impulse.*

febriphobia (fe-bri-fō′bi-à) Pyrexeophobia; fear of fever.

febris hysterica (fe′brēs hēs-te′rē-kà) Hysterical fever.

feces-child-penis concept See *concept, feces-child-penis.*

Fechner, Gustav Theodor (1801–87) (feK′nēr) German physicist, psychologist, philosopher.

feeblemindedness Mental deficiency; oligophrenia; hypophrenia.

feeblemindedness, affective When the affects are so vividly in the ascendancy as to give rise to general inhibition of thought, Ferenczi uses the expression *affective feeblemindedness.* For example, anxiety may be so overpowering in an individual that he cannot think, nor do ideas occur to him. For the duration of the anxiety he seems to be feebleminded. When the anxiety is relieved, his usual thinking capacity is restored. Depressed patients often complain that they cannot think owing to the intensity of their feelings.

feeblemindedness, epileptic (ep-i-lep′tik) Often during the course of epilepsy there is a steady decline of intelligence which may eventuate in a greater or lesser degree of feeblemindedness.

feeblemindedness, hallucinatory See *dementia paranoides gravis.*

feedback Knowledge of one's own performance or the results of one's own behavior. Feedback thus includes kinesthesia and proprioception in the animal, and the term is used also with machines to refer to automatic registration of performance. The term is mainly used in the field of *cybernetics* (q.v.).

feeding, demand Feeding an infant when he gives evidence of being hungry rather than by a predetermined, rigid schedule; also known as self-demand schedule.

feeding problem A common type of behavior disorder in which the child will not eat at all, or only under certain conditions, or shows any number of untoward and unusual reactions if and when he does eat.

feeding, self-demand In infant feeding, the modern concept that the infant is a reacting human being and should be fed whenever he is hungry. Everything else being equal, the child will cry when hungry and at that time he should be fed. This is opposed to the Spartan attitude which requires that the infant be fed every four hours, regardless of his physiological needs, and that, even when hungry, he should be made to wait until the scheduled feeding time. During the first two or three weeks of life, hunger stimuli make themselves apparent at rather irregular intervals, but thereafter the normal infant settles gradually into a time schedule of his own.

feeding, tube Patients who resist the taking of food may be fed through a nasal catheter that terminates in the stomach.

feeling The term is used by many 'with special reference to one only of the three kinds of process into which mental life is now usually classified—that part which deals with "feeling" in the narrower sense, as distinct from "knowing" or "wishing." In this sense it is sometimes also called "affection" and is contrasted with "cognition" and "conation." ' (Flugel, J.C. *Encyclopaedia Britannica,* 14th ed., vol. IX, p. 143)

According to Burrow, the total, spontaneous response of the organism to stimuli naturally affecting the empathic system. The sensations arising as a spontaneous reaction within the organism as a whole. Contrasted with affect or projected feeling. Synonym: empathic reaction. (Burrow, T. *The Biology of Human Conflict,* Macmillan, New York, 1937, p. 160)

feeling-apperception Jung says: 'The nature of feeling-valuation may be compared with intellectual apperception as an *apperception of value.* An *active* and a *passive* feeling-apperception can be distinguished. The passive feeling-act is characterized by the fact that a content excites or attracts the feeling; it compels a feeling-participation on the part of the subject. The active feeling-act, on the contrary, confers value from the subject—it is a deliberate evaluation of contents in accordance with feeling and not in accordance with intellectual intention. Hence active feeling is a *directed* function, an act of will, as for instance, loving as opposed to being in love. This latter state would be *undirected,* passive feeling, as, indeed, the ordinary colloquial term suggests, since it describes the former as activity and the latter as a condition. Undirected feeling is *feeling-intuition.*' (Jung, C.G. *Psychological Types,* tr. by

Baynes, H.G., Harcourt, Brace, New York and London, 1923)

feeling, ataxic (à-tak'sik) See *ataxia, intrapsychic.*

feeling, bodily ego See *ego, body.*

feeling, directed See *feeling-apperception.*

feeling, discharge of See *discharge, affective; abreaction.*

feeling-into This is a literal translation of the German *Einfühlung.*

'Feeling-into, therefore, is a kind of perception process, distinguished by the fact that it transveys, through the agency of feeling, an essential psychic content into the object; whereby the object is introjected.' (Jung, C.J. *Psychological Types,* tr. by Baynes, H.G., Harcourt, Brace, New York and London, 1923, p. 359)

Worringer used 'feeling-into' and *empathy* as synonymous. (ibid., p. 358)

feeling-intuition See *feeling-apperception.*

feeling, oceanic See *omnipotence; nautomania.*

feeling-sensation This expression, used in analytical psychology, is defined by Jung as follows: 'Ordinary "simple" feeling is *concrete,* i.e., it is mixed up with other function-elements, frequently with sensation for instance. In this particular case we might term it *affective,* or (as in this book, for instance) *feeling-sensation,* by which a well-nigh inseparable blending of feeling with sensation elements is to be understood.' (Jung, C.G. *Psychological Types,* tr. by Baynes, H.G., Harcourt, Brace, New York and London, 1923)

feelings, insanity of the *Obs.* Synonymous with *moral insanity.*

feeling, superiority The boy's feeling that he is superior to a girl in the domain of sex. 'The amalgamation of the desire for a child with the epistemophilic impulse enables a boy to effect a displacement on to the intellectual plane; his sense of being at a disadvantage is then concealed and over-compensated by the superiority he deduces from his possession of a penis, which is also acknowledged by girls.' (Klein, M. *Contributions to Psycho-analysis,* 1921–45, Hogarth Press, London, 1948)

feeling, undirected See *feeling-apperception.*

fellatio (fel-lä'tē-ō) Fellatio is the apposi-

tion of the mouth to the penis. The mucous membrane of the lips and mouth are regarded by Freud as a primary erotogenic zone. 'An intense activity of this erotogenic zone at an early age thus determines the subsequent presence of a somatic compliance on the part of the tract of mucous membrane which begins at the lips.' The original object of the lips and mouth is the nipple. 'It then needs very little creative power to substitute the sexual object of the moment (the penis) for the original object (the nipple) or for the finger which did duty for it later on, and to place the current sexual object in the situation in which gratification was originally obtained. So we see that this excessively repulsive and perverted phantasy of sucking at a penis has the most innocent origin.' (Freud, S. *Collected Papers,* vol. 3, tr. by Strachey, A. and J., Leonard and Virginia Woolf and The Institute of Psychoanalysis, London, 1925)

fellation See *fellatio.*

fellator, self- See *auto-fellatio.*

fellatrice (fe-là-trēs') A female who takes the oral part in fellatio.

feminine traits in male See *traits, feminine, in male.*

femininity In contrast to the concept of *femaleness* which is primarily related to the proper sex chromosome structure of XX individuals, *femininity* preferably means a female individual's possession of the typical and well developed *secondary* sex characteristics of a woman (see *sex determination*).

Ferenczi, Sandor (1873–1933) (fe'ren-sē) Hungarian psychoanalyst.

Féré phenomenon See *reflex, psychogalvanic.*

Ferri, Enrico (1856–1929) (far'rē) Italian forensic psychiatrist.

fertility, net In human genetics this statistical concept is used for determining the reproduction and survival in tainted families. It applies to the number of those children of the carriers of a certain trait who reach the age group assumed to be the manifestation period of the trait in question.

fertilization This biological term refers to that creative process in sexual reproduction which brings a sperm and an egg into union and enables them to form one single cell, the fertilized egg or *zygote*. By a series of cell divisions, this new cell develops into an embryo and finally into an adult organism (see *reproduction*). The essential feature in fertilization is the fusion of the nuclei of the gametes.

festination (fes-ti-nā'shun) Involuntary inclination to hurry one's gait.

fetish (fē'tish) A fetish is a material object regarded as endowed with special magical powers. Literally it refers to an object of any kind (idol, charm, talisman) which embodies mysterious and awesome qualities and from which supernatural aid may be expected.

The fetish acquires great significance in psychiatry. It is often seen in its most primitive form in patients with schizophrenia, who deify much of the inanimate world about them. Or they personalize the inanimate: a patient conversed with an old rag as if it were a human being. Other patients, principally those with a psychoneurosis, who are unable to love a real person to whom they are attached, may carry out all the pleaures of love through the agency of some object belonging to or associated with the love-object. A lock of hair may be held in the same esteem as is the person from whom the hair was taken. A handkerchief, a shoe, a glove, anything, may be looked upon as the embodiment of the loved one.

'The tendency to overestimate the attractive value of anything belonging to the loved person—her hair, hand, glove, etc. —may be localized to a given part, such as the foot, and thus constitute a fetishism.' (Jones, E. *Papers on Psycho-Analysis*, 4th ed., Wood, Baltimore, 1938)

fetishism Worshipping, adoring, or loving something that serves as a substitute for the original object. A fetish may be a part of the body such as the hair, foot, hand, or it may be some object owned by the loved one, such as a handkerchief, shoe, purse, etc. The fetish stands as a substitute for the loved person.

fetishism, acoustic The pleasure of listening to sexual stories when it has acquired the quality of fetishism, is known as acoustic fetishism.

fetishism, adherent Magnus Hirschfeld uses this expression to refer to the form of fetishism in which clothing is donned by the fetishist. See *fetishism, coherent*.

fetishism, beast Animals often exert an

aphrodisiac influence over human beings.

'The transmitting medium of this fetishism may, perhaps, be found in a peculiar idiosyncrasis of the tactile nerves which, by touching furs or animal skins, produces peculiar and lustful emotions (analogous to hair-, braid-, velvet-, and silk-fetishism).' (Krafft-Ebing, R. v. *Psychopathia Sexualis*, Login, New York, 1908)

fetishism, coherent By this term Magnus Hirschfeld refers to 'the attraction which is exercised, for many people far more than is normal, by stuffs, and objects which are not donned or thrown over the body as clothing, but are brought into immediate contact with the body surface.' (Hirschfeld, M. *Sexual Pathology*, tr. by Gibbs, J., Emerson Books, New York, 1939)

fetishism, foot See *retifism*.

Feuchtersleben, Ernst von (1806–1849) (foiK'tĕrs-lā-ben) German psychiatrist; author of *Lehrbuch der aerztlichen Seelenkunde*.

fever, Christmas Malingering is often associated with holidays. Stappert uses the term *Christmas fever* to denote the varied syndromes connected with holidays. See *neurosis, Sunday*.

fever, erotic The 'fever' accompanying erotomania.

fever, psychogenetic Fever induced by psychical means is called psychogenetic fever. Body temperature may be elevated by hypnotic suggestion and in certain susceptible individuals by suggestion without hypnosis. The condition is more easily produced in hysterical than in other subjects.

fibrillation (fi-bri-lā'shun) Slow, vermicular twitchings of individual muscle fibers or bundles, occurring anywhere in the body, without producing movements of muscles or joints; the condition is mainly indicative of slow degeneration of anterior horn cells (nuclear masses of motor cells).

fiction, autarchic (aw-tär'kik) The false belief of the child in its own omnipotence. At the beginning of extra-uterine life the infant is ignorant of any sources of pleasure other than those within itself: the infant even thinks of the breast as a part of its body. Ferenczi has called this the period of unconditional omnipotence. The infant tries to cling to this feeling of omnipotence and only unwillingly orients itself to objects. This is the basis for the frequency of masturbation in children when they are weaned: they turn to themselves for pleasure rather than recognize their dependency upon the environment.

fiction, directive This term is used by Adler to describe the phantasy or idea of superiority which the individual originally conceives as a subjective compensation for a feeling of inferiority. This phantasy or idea he utilizes and reacts to as if it were an absolute truth.

fidgetiness Fidgety state. Increased motor activity, more frequently used in reference to children than to adults. Winnicott distinguishes three types of fidgetiness: common fidgetiness due to anxiety, tics, and chorea.

fidgets Vague uneasiness, usually accompanied by restless movements. Fidgets or creeps were colloquial terms for 'the disease or morbid symptom called dysphoria.' (Tuke, D.H. *A Dictionary of Psychological Medicine*, vols. 1–2, Blakiston, Philadelphia, 1892); dysphoria nervosa.

field defect The field of vision is the limit of peripheral vision, the area within which an object can be seen while the eye remains fixed on some one point. The normal visual field has a definite contour, any change in which from the normal constitutes a field defect.

The various visual field defects (with their common causes) are: (1) *circumferential blindness* or *tubular vision* (hysteria, optic or retrobulbar neuritis), consisting of a concentric contraction of the visual fields; (2) *total blindness* in one eye (complete lesion of optic nerve on same side); (3) *hemianopia* or *hemianopsia,* loss of one-half of the visual field, which may be (a) homonymous, i.e. loss of vision in the temporal half-field on the same side as the lesion and loss of vision in the nasal half-field of the other eye (lesions posterior to optic chiasm i.e. optic tract or optic radiation); or (b) heteronymous with loss of vision in the same half-field (usually the temporal) of both eyes (chiasmal lesion); or (c) unilateral hemianopia with loss of vision in the nasal or temporal half-field of one eye (perichiasmal lesion); (4) *quadrantic hemianopia* or *quadrantanopia* (partial involvement of optic radiation), with loss

of vision in one quadrant of the visual field, usually homonymous.

fields of Forel See *Forel, fields of; subthalamus.*

figure In psychoanalytic psychology particularly, this term, in combination with other nouns denoting familial or close interpersonal relationships (e.g. father-figure, mother-figure, authority-figure) is approximately equivalent to substitute, replacement, representative, or surrogate.

figure, helpful In the child's world of phantasy, a male or female fairy-creature with so much love, understanding, and sympathy that the child could turn to it for help in any need. 'I discovered in him identifications which corresponded more closely to his real parents, though not by any means identical with them. These figures, who appeared good and helpful and ready to forgive, he called his "fairy papa and mama," and, when his attitude towards me was positive, he allowed me in the analysis to play the part of the "fairy mama" to whom everything could be confessed.' (Klein, M. *Contributions to Psycho-analysis,* 1921–1945, Hogarth Press, London, 1948)

finding, object Object-finding is a psychoanalytic concept. It is said that during the pregenital stage of development the child incorporates much of his libido in somatic or erotogenic zones, such as the oral, anal, dermal, nasal, ocular, and muscular areas. With the coming of the latency period most of the libido is deflected from these zones into new channels in the environment. Object-finding is the process of transferring and finally placing libido upon environmental objects. The libido, formerly invested in erotogenic zones, may exhibit externalization in various forms.

'Adult object-finding is frequently determined by fetishism; the love-object must possess certain colored hair, wear certain clothing, or perhaps have certain physical blemishes.' (Healy, W., Bronner, A.F., and Bowers, A.M. *The Structure and Meaning of Psychoanalysis,* Knopf, New York, 1930)

finger-painting See *painting, finger.*

fingers, insane Stoddart says: 'The name *insane fingers* has been applied to a low form of whitlow to which the insane, especially general paralytics, are liable. The condition appears to be less common than formerly, probably on account of improved hygienic surroundings and greater cleanliness on the part of the attendants.

finger-sucking See *pleasure-sucking*.

first admission See *admission, first*.

first attack See *attack, first*.

fit, cerebellar (ser-ē-bel'ēr) Tonic or cerebellar fits were originally described by Hughlings Jackson in connection with tumors of the vermis. The patient suddenly loses consciousness, falls to the ground, develops cyanosis; the pupils are immobile and dilated. There is no tongue biting or incontinence. The head is retracted, the back arched, upper extremities extended and adducted with forearm pronated, the wrist and hand flexed and everted. The lower extremities are extended and the toes plantar flexed. There is no clonic phase; the phenomenon is one of decerebrate rigidity.

fit, tonic See *fit, cerebellar*.

fit, uncinate (un'si-nāt) A subjective disturbance (hallucination) of smell and taste, characteristic of deep, mesial lesions involving the tip of the temporal lobe, at times accompanied by champing movements of the jaw—due to lesion of uncinate gyrus.

fixate (fik'sāt) In psychoanalysis: to retain instinctual qualities in one or more of the infantile structures to which they were originally attached.

fixatio mononoea (fēk-sä'tē-ō mô-nô-noi'ȧ) *Obs.* Melancholia.

fixation In psychiatry the term *fixation* is generally used as meant by Freud. Psychoanalysts claim that some quantity of psychic energy always remains in all the psychic structures, even when those structures are abandoned in favor of newer development. The unconscious of the normal adult always contains some traces of infantile libidinal cathexes. The psychic energy that remains attached to components of the infantile period gives rise to the expression *fixation*. It is believed that psychiatric manifestations are due in part to the fixation of inordinate quantities of energy to infantile psychic organizations.

The organizations just mentioned usually include one or more of the early erotogenic zones and the activities of those zones. Fixation implies the incomplete desexualization or sublimation of the infantile mode of pleasure-finding. The incompleteness may be the result of constitutional or developmental factors.

'Each stage in the development of psychosexuality affords the possibility of the occurrence of a fixation, and thus for the laying down of a disposition to illness (neurosis) in later life.' (Freud, S. *The Basic Writings of Sigmund Freud,* tr. by Brill, A.A., Random House, New York, 1938)

Rickman explains that fixation is an inhibition in the development of the libido. It differs from a dynamism in that the latter is related to the changes in libidinal cathexes.

As used in social work, the term has been defined as 'a form of aberrancy of affection in which there is exaggerated devotion to someone, usually in the parental role; as mother fixation.' (Hamilton, G. *A Medical Social Terminology,* Presbyterian Hospital, New York, 1930)

fixation, anxiety Freud believes that the etiology of a neurosis is closely associated with libidinal fixations and ego fixations, both of them stemming from the early years of development. He says: 'Every danger situation corresponds to a certain period of life or phase of development of the psychic apparatus and seems justified for it.' The danger situations are responsible for 'anxiety fixations.' (Freud, S. *The Basic Writings of Sigmund Freud,* tr. by Brill, A.A., Random House, New York, 1938)

fixation, cannibalistic The fixation of the libido at the late oral or biting phase. This may lead to later cannibalistic impulses, which connote the phantasy of biting and eating, swallowing, and incorporating a hated object.

fixation, father See *fixation, mother*.

fixation, infantile level of 'There are some women who remain fixated at infantile levels as indicated by their constant use of "baby talk" even in ordinary conversation. There are men who take a childlike pleasure in being members of secret organizations and attach great importance to the "signs," "passwords," etc.' (Kraines, S.H. *The Therapy of the Neuroses and Psychoses,* Lea & Febiger, Philadelphia, 1948)

fixation, libido (li-bēd'ō) The retention of libido or the erotic instinct in an early level of psychic growth is called libido-fixation.

fixation, mother Among psychiatrists today great emphasis is placed upon the affective relationships between parents and children. When a child is inordinately attached to its mother the condition is known as mother-fixation. In psychoanalysis mother-fixation is said to stem from the period of infantile sexuality of the child.

When the fixation is upon the father, the expression *father-fixation* is used. See *fixation; complex, Oedipus.*

fixation-point It is the opinion of psychoanalysts that the different neuroses and psychoses are reflections of a fixation of psychic energy at given foci or *fixation-points.* Schizophrenia, for example, is believed to have its fixation-point at the auto-erotic stage of development; paranoia signifies fixation at the narcissistic and homosexual levels; melancholia at the oral sadistic phase; hysteria at the early genital level; obsessional neurosis at the anal stage.

'If you think of a migrating people who have left large numbers at the stopping places on their way, you will see that the foremost will naturally fall back upon these positions when they are defeated or when they meet with an enemy too strong for them. And, again, the more of their numbers they leave behind in their progress, the sooner will they be in danger of defeat.' (Freud, S. *Collected Papers,* vol. 3, tr. by Strachey, A. and J., Leonard and Virginia Woolf and The Institute of Psychoanalysis, London, 1925)

fixity, social The plan in which the role and status of each individual are rigidly fixed or defined as in feudal and caste societies. Social fixity also appears in modern society and in social and other groups where the place of members is defined and fixed. See *mobility, social.*

flagellantism (flaj′e-lant-iz′m, flà-jel′ant-) Erotic pleasure or stimulation derived from whipping or being whipped.

flagellation (flaj-e-lā′shun) Flagellation is the act of whipping as a sexual excitant. 'As for erotic flagellation, pure and simple, we know that it has existed from a remote antiquity, and that it was a recognized part of the love ritual of the ancients, a preparation for the rites of Eros, and as such, known to every debauchee.' (Put-nam, S. in *Encyclopaedia Sexualis,* edited by Robinson, V., Dingwall-Rock, New York, 1936)

A patient was capable of sexual excitation only when his wife whipped him to the point of bleeding. He owned a unique collection of whips, each of which was given a proper name by him.

flare, histamine See *histamine.*

flattening In psychiatry, this term is ordinarily used to refer to a disturbance of affectivity. Flattening of affect (or 'flat affect') is rarely seen outside the schizophrenic group, although affect-block, which is seen also in obsessive-compulsive patients, may be difficult to distinguish from flattening. Flattening of the affect consists of a general impoverishment of emotional reactivity or failure to react appropriately to affect-tinged stimuli. The affect-flattened patient is often described as emotionally bleak or dull, colorless, flat, unresponsive, cold, removed, apart, uninvolved, or unconvincing. The patient himself may complain that reality seems far away, that nothing has meaning for him or that his emotional responses seem forced, false, and unreal.

flattery, mania for Certain patients 'have to be everlastingly encouraged and stimulated; and, since nothing produces the desired effect so well as praise and compliments, they demand a constant flow of flattery; their vanity is as colossal as their sensitiveness. Sometimes this vanity inspires them with boastfulness, and then they recount the glorious deeds of their own doing, and expect their hearers to be full of admiration for their prowess and never to show any skepticism as to their veracity. Others, again, display their vanity by the assumption of a whining personality of demeanor. Such persons are forever repeating that they are "no good," that they are not intelligent, have no talents.' (Janet, P. *Psychological Healing,* vols. 1–2, tr. by Paul, E. and C., Macmillan, New York, 1925)

flavism (flā′viz′m) The presence of yellow hair in certain regions of the body in contrast with the stronger, darker hair on other parts of the body. This condition attains its significance for constitutional classification from the theory that, like the phenomenon of *erythrism,* it constitutes a stigma of the *asthenic, micro-*

splanchnic physique and its tendency to tuberculosis.

flexibility, waxy See *catalepsy.*

flicker Flutter; rapid change in frequency of stimulation (usually auditory or visual) producing corresponding periodic change in the visual or auditory perception. In the case of vision, for example, a flickering light will be perceived as such until brightness of the light and/or frequency of the flicker is increased to a certain point (critical flicker frequency); at this point, the stimulus will be perceived as a single, continuing stimulus (fusion).

flight Act of fleeing or running away, as to escape danger. See *fugue.*

flight into disease Same as *conversion;* the flight away from threatening reality by means of the conversion symptoms represents the paranosic or primary gain of the illness.

flight of ideas A near-continuous flow of speech which is not disjointed or bizarre, but which jumps rapidly from one topic to another, each topic being more or less obviously related to the preceding or to adventitious environmental stimuli. Flight of ideas is characteristic of acute manic states; consequently, it is seen most commonly in the manic phase of manic-depressive psychosis but can also be seen in the acute manic syndrome of schizophrenia. Cameron terms flight of ideas 'topical flight': 'The manic makes rapid shifts from topic to topic, but the alert, attentive listener can keep up with the changes because they do not differ fundamentally from the changes in subject a normal elated person might make. The shifts in schizophrenic talk . . . are confused by the indiscriminate overinclusion of material belonging to both shared social and private fantasy contexts. The manic in his talk keeps to social trails of communication, even though he may change his direction on them at every moment; the schizophrenic does not keep to social paths, but makes his own trail as he goes.' (Cameron, N. *The Psychology of Behavior Disorders,* Houghton Mifflin, Boston, 1947)

flight, topical Cameron's term for *flight of ideas* (q.v.).

floccillation (flok-si-lā'shun) *Carphology* (q.v.); aimless picking or plucking.

flogger One who whips; flagellator.

FM Rorschach scoring symbol for a response of animal movement.

folie (fô-lē') French term for insanity. The French distinguished *mental alienation* and insanity (*folie*), considering the former in a generic sense, while they used *folie* to denote a psychiatric condition acquired by an individual who had previously been in good mental health.

folie à deux (à dü') (F. 'double insanity') Folie à deux has been known by a number of names: communicated insanity, induced insanity, double insanity (Tuke, D.H.), folie simultanée (Régis), folie imposée (Lasègue and Falret), folie induite (Lehmann).

'Suggestibility plays a part, among other factors, in the genesis of folie à deux or "communicated insanity," which is the term applied when two persons closely associated with one another suffer a psychosis simultaneously, and when one member of the pair appears to have influenced the other. The condition is not of course necessarily confined to two persons, and may involve three or even more (*folie à trois,* etc.).' (Henderson, D.K. and Gillespie, R.D. *A Text-Book of Psychiatry,* 4th ed., Oxford University Press, London, 1936)

'It happens that paranoid or paranoiac and rarely hypomanic patients not only can make those with whom they live close together believe in their delusions, but they so infect them that the latter under conditions themselves continue to build on the delusion. . . .' (Bleuler, E., *Textbook of Psychiatry,* tr. by Brill, A.A., Macmillan, New York, 1930) See *association, psychosis of.*

folie à double forme (à dōō'bl' fawrm') (F. 'insanity in double form') An older term for what is now called manic-depressive psychosis.

folie à formes alternes (fawrm' àl-tern') (F. 'insanity in alternate forms') An older term for manic-depressive psychosis.

folie ambitieuse (äN-bē-syēz') (F. 'pretentious insanity') An older generic expression, equivalent to 'insanity with grandiose ideas.'

folie à quatre (fôlē' à kat'r) (F. 'quadruple insanity') The appearance of the same delusions in four members of a family. Bleuler cites the following case: 'At one time we had in Burghölzli four siblings (two brothers and two sisters) who all had the same persecutory and religious delusions. It turned out that one sister, the most intelligent of the four, was the first to become ill; she imposed her delusions on the others. She deteriorated severely and later developed catatonic symptoms. The second sister could eventually be released, but had to be readmitted later. The two brothers managed to maintain themselves outside the hospital. There was no doubt that the two sisters were really schizophrenic; and we had excellent reasons for believing that the two brothers were also schizophrenic, not only because they never recovered completely afterwards, but also because of their peculiar modes of life already before the acute attack.' (Bleuler, E. *Dementia Praecox or the Group of Schizophrenias,* International Universities Press, New York, 1950) Bleuler considers this a form of *induced schizophrenia.* See *association, psychosis of.*

folie à trois (trwà) (F. 'triple insanity') The appearance of the same delusions in three members of a family. See *schizophrenia, induced; association, psychosis of.*

folie avec stupeur (à-vek′ stü-pĕr′) (F. 'insanity with stupor') The expression, not used today in American psychiatry, means insanity characterized by a stuporous state. At the time, however, that the term was a nosological entity, it included among other conditions that which is now considered as advanced 'deterioration' in schizophrenia.

folie circulaire (sēr-kü-lâr′) (F. 'cyclic insanity') Falret's term for the condition known today as manic-depressive psychosis, circular or alternating type.

folie communiquée (kô-mü-nē-kā′) (F. 'infectious insanity') Synonymous with folie à deux.

folie d'action (dàk′syawN′) (F. 'madness of movement, action') Brierre de Boismont's term for moral and emotional insanity.

folie de la puberté (dē là pü-ber-tā′) (F. 'insanity of adolescence') Dementia praecox; schizophrenia.

folie démonomaniaque (dā-mô-nô-mà-nē-àk′) (F. 'demonomaniacal insanity') Demonomania.

folie dépressive (dā-pre-sēv′) (F. 'depressive insanity') Melancholy.

folie des femmes en couches (dā fam′ äN kōōsh′) (F. 'insanity of women in childbirth') Puerperal psychosis.

folie des grandeurs (dā gräN-dēr′) (F. 'insanity of greatness') Megalomania.

folie de spéculation (dē spā-kü-là-syawN′) (F. 'insanity of speculation') An old term, which, like many other analogous expressions, had the weight of a clinical entity, but which today is recognized as a part of a larger syndrome.

folie des persécutions (dā per-sā-kü-syawN′) (F. 'insanity of persecutions') Paranoid psychosis.

folie du doute (dü doot′) (F. 'insanity of doubt') This French term is not in common use in American psychiatry today. What used to be called *doubting mania,* when it was considered to be a nosological entity, is today usually subsumed under the heading of anxiety-neurosis or obsessive-compulsive reaction.

'The fear of responsibility expresses itself in the compulsion to examine repeatedly whether a match thrown away no longer burns, whether the doors of closets are locked, whether letters are sealed, or whether a mistake was made in calculating (doubting mania, *folie du doute*).' (Bleuler, E. *Textbook of Psychiatry,* tr. by Brill, A.A., Macmillan, New York, 1930)

'On the basis of chronic apprehensiveness (anxious expectation) on the one hand, and a tendency to attacks of vertigo, with anxiety on the other, two groups of typical phobias develop, the first relating to common physiological dangers, the other to locomotion. To the first group belongs the fear of snakes, thunderstorms, darkness, vermin and so on, as well as the typical moral over-sensitiveness, and the forms of "*folie du doute*". . . .' (Freud, S. *Collected Papers,* vol. 1, tr. by Riviere, J., Leonard and Virginia Woolf and The Institute of Psychoanalysis, London, 1924–25)

Falret introduced the expression as a nosological entity, calling it *la maladie du doute.* At an earlier date Esquirol termed the same condition *monomanie raisonnante;* Baillarger referred to it as *monomanie avec conscience;* at other times it was known as *aliénation partielle;* Oscar Berger named the condition *Grübelsücht.*

folie du pourquoi (pōōr-kwà′) (F. 'craze of "why."') Question-asking insanity. This is a manifestation of the compulsive-obsessive form of psychoneurosis, in which the patient has the morbid urge to ask questions.

'The intrusion of these irrepressible ideas into consciousness often gives rise to a great variety of mental, motor, and emotional anomalies. Among the first are the various questions which the patient very frequently feels impelled to ask (*folie du pourquoi*). . . . Not uncommonly, especially in the intellectual class of patients, this interrogatory mood drives them to the discussion of abstruse themes. They feel themselves compelled to spend much time in debating why God made the world, why they were put on the earth, the origin of right and wrong, and various other metaphysical inquiries.' (Paton, S. *Psychiatry,* Lippincott, Philadelphia and London, 1905)

folie gémellaire (zhā-me-lâr′) (F. 'twin-insanity') Psychoses in twins occurring simultaneously.

folie hypocondriaque (ē-pô-kawN-drē-āk′) (F. 'hypochondriacal insanity') Neurasthenia.

folie hystérique (ēs-tā-rēk′) (F. 'hysteric insanity') Hysteria.

folie imitative (ē-mē-tà-tēv′) (F. 'imitative insanity') Folie à deux.

folie imposée (eN-pō-zā′) (F. 'imposed insanity') See *association, psychosis of; folie à deux.*

folie induite (eN-dwēt′) (F. 'induced insanity') See *folie à deux.*

folie instantanée (eN-stäN-tà-nā′) (F. 'momentary insanity') Mania transitoria.

folie morale (maw-ral′) (F. 'moral insanity') See *insanity, moral.*

folie morale, acquired Certain individuals who are referred to as *psychopathic personalities,* may eventually develop a well-defined psychotic condition. Kraepelin calls the psychotic state an acquired form of *folie morale* or *moral insanity.*

'Numerous patients, who on account of moral incapacity either become habitual criminals, or fall into prostitution, or who, become incapable of earning a living, drift into a vagrant life, are for many years disciplined and punished, if the more striking symptoms of dementia praecox are absent, till the appearance of more severe disorders, states of excitement and stupor, hallucinations of hearing, and delusions, makes clear the morbidity of their

state.' (Kraepelin, E. *Dementia Praecox and Paraphrenia,* tr. by Barclay, R.M., Livingstone, Edinburgh, 1919)

folie paralytique (pà-rà-lē-tēk′) (F. 'paralytic insanity') General paresis.

folie pénitentiaire (pā-nē-täN-syâr′) (F. 'penitentiary insanity') Prison psychosis.

folie puerpérale (pwer-pe-ràl′) (F. 'puerperal insanity') Puerperal psychosis.

folie raisonnante (rā-zaw-näNt′) (F. 'reasoning insanity') See *insanity, reasoning.*

folie raisonnante mélancolique (me-läN-kaw-lēk′) (F. 'melancholic reasoning insanity') Griesinger's expression for what was called in his time hypochondriacal melancholia.

folie simulée (sē-mü-lā′) (F. 'feigned insanity') Feigned psychosis.

folie simultanée (sē-mül-tà-nā′) (F. 'simultaneous insanity') See *folie à deux.*

folie sympathique (seN-pà-tēk′) Sympathetic insanity.

folie systématisée (sis-te-mà-tē-zā′) (F. 'systematized insanity') An old term, synonymous with *primary delusional insanity* and with *paranoia.*

folie utérine (ü-tā-rēn′) (F. 'uterine insanity') A general term, denoting psychiatric conditions supposedly associated with uterine disorders; also nymphomania.

folie vaniteuse (và-nē-tēz′) (F. 'conceited insanity') Megalomania.

folklore Folk-wisdom or folk-learning. A term suggested by Thoms, in 1846. In the present-day life of civilized peoples, folklore is the sum-total of meager, often fragmentary relics (that have survived, through tradition, from earlier primitive-culture stages) of cultural monuments in word and art: historical accounts, legends and myths, adages and sayings, beliefs, customs, magic practices, folk-remedies, household prescripts, fairy tales, fables and songs (words, music, dances).

Folklore occupies a position of great significance in the psychiatry of today. It is a subdivision of ethnological psychology. Psychiatric patients, especially those who show deep regression, vividly produce psychic material that may be said to have intimate parallelism with folklore.

'It is scarcely possible to estimate too highly the value of these ideas to psychopathology. The extension of the field of individual psychology into that of racial psychology, the psychological analysis of the myths, fairy tales, and magic practices of primitive peoples and early societies opened up to the clinician a surprising perspective and gave rise to a multitude of new and stimulating problems.' (Storch, A. *The Primitive Archaic Forms in Schizophrenia,* tr. by Willard, C., Nervous and Mental Disease Publishing Company, New York and Washington, 1924)

folk soul See *soul, folk.*

folkways 'Group habits or customs.' (Davie, M.R. 'Folkways,' *Encyclopaedia of the Social Sciences,* vol. 6, Macmillan, New York, 1931, p. 293)

Folkways are 'the whole system of behavior patterns characteristic of a group.' (McIver, R.M. *Society, Its Structure and Changes,* Macmillan of Canada, Toronto, 1931)

Folkways 'are developed out of experience, reach a final form of maximum adaptation to an interest, are handed down by tradition and admit of no exception or variation, yet change to meet new conditions, still within the same limited methods, and without rational reflection or purpose.' (Sumner, W.G. *Folkways,* Ginn, New York, 1906)

folly The clinical syndrome known in the early part of the 19th century as *folly* was roughly the equivalent of what is today known as *schizophrenia;* Guislain (early 19th century) used the terms *folly* and *paraphrenia* interchangeably.

fomes ventriculi (fō'mes ven-trē'koo-lē) (L. [foreign body as] contagium-carrier of the stomach') Hypochondriasis.

force, anti-instinctual See *anti-cathexis; counter-cathexis.*

force, central In his book on the psychology of Jung, Dr. Jacobi refers to 'the central force out of which at one time the individual psyche has been differentiated. This central force goes through all further differentiations and isolations, lives in them all, cuts through them to the individual psyche, as the only one that goes absolutely unchanged and undivided through all layers.' (Jacobi, J. *The Psychology of C.G. Jung,* Kegan Paul, Trench, Trubner, London, 1942) This central force (which Jung calls primal libido) lies at the very bottom of the whole structure of an individual's total psychic system. It is synonymous with

undifferentiated energy, is psychical in nature, and has the general meaning of a life force.

force, psychic Mental power, a force generated by thought or mental action, apart from energy or physical force.

forebrain Prosencephalon, from which develop the telencephalon (which forms the cerebral cortex, striate bodies, rhinencephalon, lateral ventricles, and the anterior portion of the third ventricle) and the diencephalon (which forms the epithalamus, thalamus, metathalamus, hypothalamus, optic chiasm, tuber cinereum, posterior lobe of hypophysis, mammillary bodies, and most of the third ventricle).

foreconscious, fore-conscious See *co-conscious.*

Forel, fields of (Auguste Forel, Swiss psychiatrist, 1848–1931). See *subthalamus.*

fore-pleasure In psychoanalysis, the pleasure that precedes final genital pleasure or end-pleasure. During the phase of infancy libido is invested in many erotogenic zones, the mouth, anus, skin, muscles, eyes, nose, etc. During the so-called pregenital stage, stimulation of these zones constitutes an end-pleasure, but with the advent of genital stimulation which will eventually culminate in adult genital behavior, the pregenital zones are subordinated to the genital; hence, they later become a fore-pleasure. The many physical and psychical antecedents to final genital action are called fore-pleasure.

'The increment of pleasure which is offered us in order to release yet greater pleasure arising from deeper sources in the mind is called an "incitement premium" or technically "fore-pleasure." ' (Freud, S. *Collected Papers,* vol. 4, tr. by Riviere, J., Leonard and Virginia Woolf and The Institute of Psychoanalysis, London, 1924–25)

forgetfulness, organic According to Brill, there is but one kind of forgetfulness— that which is organic. Memory disturbances based on organic disorders have various etiologies. Diseases of the brain such as arteriosclerosis, syphilis, tumor, metabolic, or inflammatory diseases—all can lead to organic memory disturbances. If there is no organic condition, actually no true forgetfulness takes place, but an unconscious wish not to remember. We often forget what we do not wish to do, if the act is unpleasant or repugnant. (Brill, A.A. *Basic Principles of Psychoanalysis,* Doubleday, New York, 1949)

forgetting, mechanism of Freud has given the following outline for the mechanism of the normal process of forgetting. In general, all memory material falls under two influences, condensation and displacement. The memories to which little emotion is attached are those that easily 'merge into a process of condensation.' On the other hand, the memories that are more emotionally charged resist condensation and then succumb to distortion. However, 'the tendencies of distortion also feed on the indifferent material, because they have not been gratified when they wished to manifest themselves.' Since these processes are always at work, the memory content will continue to be transformed by fresh experiences as time goes on. In this way time will blur memory and make it uncertain and indistinct. When repressed memories are recovered as in analysis, however, 'it can be verified that they suffer no changes even in the longest periods.' Although impressions assume many different forms in their development in the course of time, none of these forms is lost, and each of them is retained, including the form in which the memory was originally received. (Freud, S. *Psychopathology of Everyday Life* in *The Basic Writings of Sigmund Freud,* Modern Library, Random House, New York, 1938)

forgetting, motivated In psychiatry, this term means forgetting that is motivated by the desire to avoid painful memories. There are many cases of forgetting in which the individual feels that the impression or experience is so well known that it should not have been forgotten at all. In these and other cases the thing forgotten is often one that would be painful to the individual if remembered. As a defense against experiencing this pain, the individual forgets the experience in question. The capacity for forgetting disagreeable things is differently developed in different persons: the individual will therefore often find it impossible to rid himself of painful memories or emotions, hard as he might strive to do so. On the other hand, things that have associative connection with the disagreeable material may frequently be forgotten. (Freud, S. *Psychopathology of Everyday Life* in *The*

Basic Writings of Sigmund Freud, Modern Library, Random House, New York, 1938)

formation, character See *formation, personality.*

formation, habit See *training, habit.*

formation, inhibition Inhibition-formation refers to the organization of inhibiting or restraining influences. 'Freud refers to the fact that general inhibition is very characteristic of depressive states, especially of melancholy. He thinks his theories of inhibition-formation should be a beginning towards the better understanding of these states.' (Healy, W., Bronner, A.F., and Bowers, A.M. *The Structure and Meaning of Psychoanalysis,* Knopf, New York, 1930)

Inhibition-formation is one type of mental activity that serves to restrain the appearance in consciousness of impulses unacceptable to it. Symptom-formation is a method by which the unacceptable impulses gain the level of consciousness, but in symbolic form.

formation, personality This expression, used extensively in psychoanalytic literature, refers to the structure or arrangement of the constituents of the personality. It possesses the same meaning in any of the schools of psychological thought.

Psychoanalysts employ *personality-formation* and *character-formation* synonymously.

formation, ready-made While writing on *The Psychology of the Dream-Processes,* Freud emphasizes that the unconscious division of the psyche contains preformed dream-content. 'As for the riddle of the superabundant dream-content compressed into the briefest moment of time, we have been able to contribute the explanation that the dream seizes upon ready-made formations of the psychic life.' (Freud, S. *The Interpretation of Dreams,* 3rd ed., tr. by Brill, A.A., Macmillan, New York, 1933)

formation, replacement An idea or set of ideas that serve to substitute for another or other ideas.

'The generalization can be safely hazarded that all members of the family group, from brother to grandfather, from sister to aunt, are all replacement-formations of the image of the original trinity of father, mother and child.' (Jones, E.

Papers on Psycho-Analysis, 4th ed., Wood, Baltimore, 1938)

formation, reticular The primitive, diffuse system of interlacing fibers and nerve cells which forms the central core of the brainstem; also called the bulbotegmental reticular formation. The reticular formation projects to the thalamic intralaminar nuclei via the reticulothalamic, tegmentothalamic, and tectothalamic tracts. From the reticular nucleus of the thalamus, nonspecific fibers project to all parts of the cerebral cortex. It is believed that these fibers can activate the cortex independently of specific sensory or other neural systems, and the reticular formation is thus considered a part of the 'reticular activating system' (R.A.S.), which also includes subthalamus, hypothalamus, and medial thalamus. The R.A.S. seems to be essential for the initiation and maintenance of alert wakefulness, for alerting or focusing of attention, perceptual association, and directed introspection. Impaired function of the R.A.S. may be associated with anesthesia and comatose states. There is evidence to indicate that the primary site of action of certain of the so-called tranquillizing drugs is in the R.A.S.

formes frustes (fawrm′ früst′) (F. 'defaced, worn, blurred forms') Relating to indefinite or less significant or atypical symptoms or types of a disease.

formication (for-mi-kā′shun) An abnormal subjective sensation (referred to skin areas) of ants (or other small insects) creeping in or under the given skin area; while the condition may occur in the so-termed psychogenic mental states, it is perhaps most commonly seen in those patients in whom there is some organic agent, usually in the form of narcotic drugs (alcohol, cocaine, morphine, etc.).
'*Hallucinations of touch* (haptic hallucinations) and other skin sensations are common (*formication*—the "cocaine bug").' (Henderson, D.K. and Gillespie, R.D. *A Text-Book of Psychiatry,* 4th ed., Oxford University Press, London, 1936)

form, pre-psychic This term is used by Adler to indicate that many conceptions and especially sexual theories 'can persist in a *pre-psychic* form, i.e., that all the conditions for the development exist and yet that these tentative beginnings never mature into a conscious judgment.' (Adler, A. *The Practice and Theory of Individual Psychology,* tr. by Radin, P., Kegan Paul, Trench, Trubner, London, 1924)

fornication (for-ni-kā′shun) Sexual intercourse on the part of an unmarried person.

fornicator (for′ni-kā-tĕr) A male person who participates in illicit sexual intercourse.

fornicatrix (-triks) A female person who engages in illicit sexual intercourse.

fornix (for′niks) An arched white fiber tract lying beneath the corpus callosum, extending from the hippocampus and terminating in the mammillary body.

Foster Kennedy syndrome (Foster Kennedy, New York neurologist, 1884–1955) See *nerve, olfactory.*

Fothergill's neuralgia (Samuel Fothergill, English physician, 19th century) See *tic douloureux.*

fouetteuse (fwȧ-tēz′) A female flogger or flagellator.

Fournier tests (Jean Alfred Fournier, French dermatologist, 1832–1914) Occasionally an ataxic gait may be absent in normal walking; to overcome this, the Fournier tests may be utilized to verify the presence of equilibratory ataxia in walking; the patient is commanded to rise quickly from a sitting position; he is asked to rise and walk, then stop quickly on command; he is requested to walk and turn about quickly on sharp command.

Foville's syndrome (Achille L. Foville, French neurologist, 1799–1878) A form of *hemiplegia alternans* (q.v.) with contralateral hemiplegia and homolateral paralysis of the abducens and facial nerves.

fractional interpretation of dream See *dream, fractional interpretation of.*

Fragesucht (frȧ′ge-sookt) Compulsion to ask irrelevant questions even though not particularly interested in the answers.

fragmentation White defines this expression as 'molecular splitting of the psyche' and says that it is 'an obvious psychological characteristic of dementia praecox at the descriptive level.' See *thinking, fragmentation of.*

free will The term for the concept that man is free to dispose of his own will; that he can choose between alternatives in such manner that the choice is entirely uninfluenced by factors not consciously controlled by him.

Discussing the subject of free will and its opposite, determinism, Ernest Jones writes: 'One of the psychological arguments against the belief in a complete mental determinism is the intense feeling of conviction that we have a perfectly free choice in the performance of many acts. This feeling of conviction must be justified by something, but at the same time it is entirely compatible with a complete determinism. It is curious that it is not often prominent with important and weighty decisions. On these occasions one has much more the feeling of being irresistibly impelled in a given direction (compare Luther's "Hier stehe ich, ich kann nicht anders"). On the contrary, it is with trivial and indifferent resolutions that one is most sure that one could just as well have acted otherwise, that one has acted from non-motivated free will. From the psychoanalytical point of view, the right of this feeling of conviction is not contested. It only means that the person is not aware of any conscious motive. When, however, conscious motivation is distinguished from unconscious motivation, this feeling of conviction teaches us that the former does not extend over all our motor resolutions. What is left free from the one side receives its motive from the other—from the unconscious— and so the physical determinism is flawlessly carried through. A knowledge of unconscious motivation is indispensable, even for philosophical discussion of determinism.' (Jones, E.J. *Papers on Psycho-Analysis,* Williams and Wilkins, Baltimore, 1949) The interrelation of conscious and unconscious mental processes provides the key to the problem of psychological *determinism* (q.v.).

frenetic Phrenetic.

frenzy *Obs.* Extreme excitement and mental agitation; it was sometimes considered synonymous with *mania.*

frequency The number of individuals with a given character, for example, the number of persons aged 20–24 years, is termed its frequency. See *table, frequency.*

frequency, flicker (fusion) See *flicker.*

Freud, Sigmund (1856–1939), Austrian psychiatrist; founder of psychoanalysis; concepts of the libido, regression, transference, repression, sublimation, id, ego, superego, Oedipus complex, etc.; psychopathology of dreams; evaluation of infantile experiences and impressions.

friction In social work, the term means 'conflicts arising out of unlike temperaments or emotional needs which, instead of resolving themselves in a constructive manner, continue on a level of chafing and irritation. *Family Friction*—a generalized tension or irritation in any combination of family life, excepting when otherwise distinguished; *Marital Friction* —the spouse being the patient; *Parental Friction*—between the parents of a minor child, the child being the patient; *Parent-Child Friction*—between parent and child, either being the patient.' (Hamilton, G. *A Medical Social Terminology,* Presbyterian Hospital, New York, 1930)

friction, wet mitten K.M. Steele says: 'This is a friction given with a coarse burlap or loofah bath mitten moistened in cold water. . . . Small areas of the body are uncovered, rubbed, dried, and covered. Rubbing is started at the chest, then abdomen, arms, legs, back. Rub until a pink glow is obtained.' (Steele, K.M. *Psychiatric Nursing,* Davis, Philadelphia, 1937)

Friedmann's complex (Max Friedmann, German neurologist, 1858–1925). See *constitution, post-traumatic.*

Friedreich's ataxia See *ataxia, Friedreich's.*

fright The reaction to an unexpected danger. According to Freud, 'fright is the name of the condition to which one is reduced if one encounters a danger without being prepared for it; it lays stress on the element of surprise.' This element of surprise distinguishes fright from both fear and apprehension. 'Apprehension denotes a certain condition of expecting a danger and preparation for it, even though it be an unknown one; fear requires a definite object of which one is afraid.'

Also, the element of surprise appears to be the essential causal factor in the traumatic neurosis. Apprehension cannot produce a traumatic neurosis, for 'in apprehension there is something which protects against fright and therefore against the fright-neurosis.' Apprehension prepares the organism for 'oncoming masses of excitation' and it can therefore defend itself, whereas in fright the organism, taken unawares, is overwhelmed by the excitation. (Freud, S. *Beyond the Pleasure Principle,* Boni and Liveright, New York, n.d.)

frigidity, sexual From the medical point of view, the absence of sexual feelings, with special, though not exclusive, reference to the genitals. It is commonly defined as want of natural heat and vigor of the body. In modern usage it generally implies absence of the sexual aspect of love in women. The same condition in men is called impotence.

From the psychogenic point of view, frigidity may appear only under special circumstances. When, for instance, the partner in sexual congress reanimates the incestuous complex, the woman may become frigid; or, she may be frigid under a strong homosexual urge. Stekel reports the case of a woman who used to dress in men's clothes. 'I wanted to put on father's clothes, as I have a few of them in my possession, and to go to mother's bed at night. I acquired a sort of apparatus . . . for the purpose.' The patient had become frigid to her husband after the death of her father. It is held by psychoanalysts that a woman must be frigid to become a prostitute.

As a rule, a frigid woman is so only so long as sexual intercourse or love is identified with, that is, stands for, a so-called infantile Oedipus situation. When a man does not arouse such an unconscious impulse, intercourse may be accompanied by all the manifestations of sexual excitation, culminating in an orgasm.

Abraham feels that frigidity may be traced back to the castration complex. Some women who consciously desire to participate in sexual union may become frigid just as the act is about to begin. He believes the frigidity is then occasioned by the unconscious impulse to take revenge on the man. It is a commonplace observation that prostitutes hate men.

'The sexual frigidity of women, the frequency of which seems to confirm this last point, i.e., the achievement of the biological aim is entrusted to the aggressiveness of the male, is still a phenomenon which is insufficiently understood. Sometimes it is psychogenic, and, if so, it is accessible to influence; but in other cases one is led to assume that it is constitutionally conditioned or even partly caused by an anatomical factor.' (Freud, S. *New Introductory Lectures on Psycho-Analysis,*

tr. by Sprott, W.J.H., Norton, New York, 1933)

Freud believes that 'penis-envy' is a very important cause for frigidity. Behind it is the wish to be a boy. 'The hostility thus aroused may lead to a desire for revenge on the man who finally and definitely made them into a woman.' (Jones, E. *Papers on Psycho-Analysis,* 4th ed., Wood, Baltimore, 1938)

Some authorities restrict the term *frigidity* to the inability to achieve vaginal orgasm. In her love life, a woman may obtain satisfaction, sexual in nature, though not associated with genital excitation.

From the standpoint of sexology *anhedonia* denotes complete frigidity.

fringe A term used by Morton Prince, generally in the combination of *fringe of consciousness.* He says: 'If you were asked to state what was in your mind at a given moment it is the vivid elements, upon which your attention was focused, that you would describe. But, as everyone knows, these do not constitute the whole field of consciousness at any given moment. Besides these, there is in the background of the mind, outside the focus, a *conscious margin or fringe* of varying extent (*consisting of sensations, perceptions, and even thoughts*) *of which you are only dimly aware.* It is a sort of twilight zone in which the contents are so slightly illuminated by awareness as to be scarcely recognizable.' (Prince, M. *The Unconscious,* Macmillan, New York, 1916)

fringe, subliminal See *summation.*

Fröhlich's syndrome (Alfred Fröhlich, Viennese neurologist, 1871–   ) Fröhlich's syndrome or *dystrophia adiposogenitalis* described in 1901 is caused by a chromophobe adenoma which destroys the anterior lobe of the pituitary gland occurring mainly in individuals in the pre- or postadolescent period. The syndrome is characterized by a eunuchoidal obesity, alteration of the secondary sex characters, metabolic disturbances, change in bodily growth—gigantism, hypoplastic genitals, polyuria, polydipsia, and increased sugar tolerance.

Froin's syndrome (Georges Froin, French physician, 1874–   ) High protein content of the cerebrospinal fluid (0.5 per cent or more) associated with xantho-

chromia, massive coagulation, and pleocytosis. Froin's syndrome is seen mainly in
chronic meningitis, especially syphilitic,
in obstruction of the spinal subarachnoid
space by cord tumor or epidural abscess,
and in cases of polyneuritis and Landry's
paralysis.

Fromm-Reichmann, Frieda (1890–1957)
German-born psychoanalyst; to U.S. in
1934; director of psychotherapy, Chestnut
Lodge Sanitarium; Washington School of
Psychiatry and Psychoanalysis; psycho-
therapy of schizophrenia.

frottage (frot'ij) A form of sexual perversion in which the orgasm is induced
by rubbing against the clothing of an
individual of the opposite sex, as occurs
when the subject is pressed close to others
in a throng or crowded public conveyance. An individual so afflicted is a
frotteur (q.v.).

frotteur (frô-těr') (F. 'one who rubs')
One who gains sexual excitement through
the sense of touch by rubbing up against
somebody. The term usually implies that
the act of touching or being touched is
not directly or overtly of a genital character, or at least that there is some
measure of disguise. For example, some
individuals are sexually stimulated when
they are pressed closely by others as often
happens when they are in a crowd. Some
authorities use the term to mean direct
genital or sexual activity, not including
the union of the genital organs.

frustration From the standpoint of instinctual psychology (psychoanalysis),
frustration generally refers to the denial
of gratification by reality. Sometimes it is
spoken of as external frustration to distinguish it from the thwarting of impulses
by forces in the unconscious or also in
consciousness.

When in a mentally healthy individual
the environment is not prepared for the
acceptance of a libidinal urge, the latter
may be held in suspension until reality is
suitably arranged or until some form of
substitutive gratification may present itself. Frustration may be eluded by means
of sublimation.

When the instinctual urge cannot be
handled normally by the individual, he
may summon all his energies to the satisfaction of the urge, disregarding the mores
of his surroundings. Or he may regress,
that is, the frustrated libido may be with-

drawn from objects in reality and take
'refuge in the life of phantasy where it
creates new wish-formations and reanimates the vestiges of earlier forgotten
ones.' (Freud, S. *Collected Papers,* vol. 2,
tr. by Riviere, J., Leonard and Virginia
Woolf and The Institute of Psychoanalysis, London, 1924–25, p. 114)

Internal frustration means the checking of instinctual impulses by forces in
the unconscious, chiefly by the superego.
Jones says: 'The ego defends itself against
external danger by repressing the genital
impulses [the topic under discussion by
Jones] directed towards the love-object.
Regression to the anal-sadistic level ensues, but the relation of this process to the
frustration and to the influence of the ego-
instincts is not clear.' (Jones, E. *Papers
on Psycho-Analysis,* 4th ed., Wood, Baltimore, 1938)

frustration tolerance The ability to withstand tension arising from a buildup in
instinctual demand which is not immediately relieved or gratified. Development
of tension or frustration tolerance is an
essential for achieving active mastery by
the ego; low frustration tolerance and/or
the need for immediate instinctual gratification are indicative of severe ego weakness.

fugue In psychiatry today, this term means
a flight, so to speak, from reality in the
sense that the individual becomes more
or less completely unmindful of his environment and often of himself. He enters into a phase of so-called psychological
amnesia, in which he may frequently seem
to possess all his mental faculties, but
questioning may reveal complete or partial
amnesia for certain experiences.

Strecker and Ebaugh define a fugue as
'a state during which the patient for a certain period of time seemingly acts in a
conscious way, perhaps traveling, buying
food, and in general comporting himself
in a natural manner; yet, afterward he has
no conscious remembrance for this period
of time and his behavior during it.'
(Strecker, E.A. and Ebaugh, F.G. *Practical Clinical Psychiatry,* 4th ed., Blakiston,
Philadelphia, 1935)

The syndrome may occur in a number
of psychiatric states. For example, Henderson and Gillespie, writing about
hysteria, say: 'These last [i.e. episodic
mental states] are the fugues, somnambulisms, dream-states and hypnotic states

in which a greater or smaller part of the personality takes command and dictates the general behavior, the rest of the normal personality becoming apparently incapable of consciousness for the time being and having no influence on conduct.' (Henderson, D.K. and Gillespie, R.D. *A Text-Book of Psychiatry,* 4th ed., Oxford University Press, London, 1936)

fulfillment, punishment Freud employes this term to indicate self-punishment.

fulfillment, wish See *wish-fulfillment.*

function From the psychic point of view the psyche has organization, that is, structure. The operation of the structure is called function. The ego, as a structure of the psyche, has capacities for working or functioning.

Jung says: 'By psychological function I understand a certain form of psychic activity that remains theoretically the same under varying circumstances. From the energic standpoint a function is a phenomenal form of libido, which theoretically remains constant, in much the same way as physical force can be considered as the form or momentary manifestation of physical energy.' (Jung, C.G. *Psychological Types,* tr. by Baynes, H.G., Harcourt, Brace, New York and London, 1923)

functional Relating to performance or execution. The heart has structure; when the structure works it is functioning; the psyche has structure; when the psychic structure works it is functioning. According to the most acceptable doctrines today, the psyche is an organ of the body, intimately associated and correlated, as are the physical organs, with other bodily structures. Each organ has its own special constitution or organization, designed to operate in its own way and to produce particular end-results.

Nowadays, psychiatric states are sometimes referred to as 'functional disorders'; the expression meets the requirements of current psychiatric knowledge when it means what it says, namely, that the psychiatric condition observed is a manifestation of disordered function of the psyche, a disorder from a somatic standpoint, that is, instigated from the soma, or from a psychic point of view. The heart may show abnormal functioning, not because of any pathology of the heart, but because of some abnormal stimulation from a distant source. An analogous situation prevails

with respect to the psyche. Or the functioning of the heart may be disturbed because of something unusual about the heart itself. Again, the psyche may exhibit an analogous condition.

It is not clearly known today what the more intimate relations are between the soma and the psyche. When it is said that the heart possesses a functional disorder, it is usually meant that the cause is traceable as far as the heart; the source of disorder may be even more distant; likewise, when it is maintained that the psyche is functionally disturbed (as when we speak of a functional psychosis) the scope of the term *functional* is determined by our present state of knowledge. Thus, the best information we have today regarding, for instance, the psychoneuroses, carries us as far back as the psyche. Hence, a functional mental disorder is one which, insofar as knowledge permits, stems from the psyche.

A conservative description of *functional disorders* is given by William McDougall: 'There are two great classes of disorders of our mental life, those that are directly due to organic lesions of the nervous system and those which seem to imply no such lesion, no gross injury to the structure of the brain, and which are therefore called "functional disorders." ' (McDougall, W. *Outline of Abnormal Psychology,* Scribner, New York, 1926)

functional inferiority See *inferiority, functional.*

function, auxiliary See *function, principal.*

function-complex See *complex, function.*

function, directed See *intellect.*

function, dream See *dream-function.*

function-engram This is an expression used in analytical psychology by Jung. 'The symbol is always derived from archaic residues, or imprints engraven in the very stem of the race, about whose age and origin one can speculate much, although nothing definite can be determined. It would certainly be quite wrong to look to personal sources for the source of the symbol, as for instance repressed sexuality. At best such a repression could only furnish the libido-sum which activates the archaic imprint. The imprint (engram) corresponds with a functional inheritance whose existence is not contingent upon ordinary sexual repression, but proceeds from instinct differentiation in general.' (Jung, C.G. *Psychological Types,* tr. by Baynes, H.G., Harcourt, Brace, New York and London, 1923)

function, Gestalt See *psychology, Gestalt.*

function, inferior See *function, superior.*

function, irrational See *irrational.*

function pleasure See *pleasure, function.*

function, principal Among the many aspects of *function,* Jung speaks of the *principal* and *auxiliary* functions. 'For all the types appearing in practice, the principle holds good that besides the conscious main function there is also a relatively unconscious, auxiliary function which is in every respect different from the nature of the main function. From these combinations well-known pictures arise, the practical intellect for instance paired with sensation, the speculative intellect breaking through with intuition, the artistic intuition, which selects and presents its images by means of feeling judgment, the philosophical intuition which, in league with a vigorous intellect, translates its vision into the sphere of comprehensible thought, and so forth.' (Jung, C.G. *Psychological Types,* tr. by Baynes, H.G., Harcourt, Brace, New York and London, 1923)

function, rational See *rational.*

functions, seriatim (ser-ē-ā'tim) Organization or synthesis of skilled acts or thoughts into an orderly series; such organization requires ability to anticipate a goal and ability for temporal organization. The seriatim functions are generally disturbed in the schizophrenias.

function, superior This is a phrase common to the field of analytical psychology. According to Jung, there are four basic psychological types—thinking, feeling, intuitive, and sensational. Any one of the functional types may predominate as the means by which the individual adjusts himself to the problems of living. The predominating is called the *superior* function, while the remaining three functions are *inferior* in varying degrees.

function-type The generic name for Jung's various types: feeling, thinking, intuitive, and sensation. The characters of introversion and extraversion are ways of regarding reality rather than methods

of adaptation to reality; hence they are called attitude-types.

function-way, archaic In analytical psychology this expression designates thinking, acting, and feeling characteristic of the primitive type of mind. While discussing *regression* Jung says: 'The draining of libido involves their gradual relapse below the threshold of consciousness, their associative connection with consciousness gets loosened, until they sink by degrees into the unconscious. This is synonymous with a regressive development; namely, a recession of the relatively developed function to an infantile and eventually archaic level. But, since man has spent relatively only a few thousand years in a cultivated state, as opposed to many hundred thousand years in a state of savagery, the archaic function-ways are correspondingly extraordinarily vigorous and easily reanimated. Hence, when certain functions become disintegrated through deprivation of libido, their archaic foundations begin to operate in the unconscious.' (Jung, C.G. *Psychological Types,* tr. by Baynes, H.G., Harcourt, Brace, New York and London, 1923)

Funkenstein test (Daniel Hertz Funkenstein, American psychiatrist, 1910—   ) See *test, adrenalin-mecholyl.*

fureur genitale (fü-rẽr' zhā-nē-tàl') (F. 'genital rage') *Obs.* Bruisson's term for nymphomania and satyriasis.

furibundus (fū-ri-bun'dus) *Obs.* 'Maniacal, mad, raging.' (Tuke, D.H. *A Dictionary of Psychological Medicine,* vols. 1–2, Blakiston, Philadelphia, 1892)

furiosi (foo-rē-ō'zē) (L. 'those full of madness, raging, fury') This is one of the two subdivisions of the insane recorded in the old Roman laws. Those who were violent and maniacal were called *furiosi;* those exhibiting dementia or feeblemindedness were termed *mente capti.*

furor epilepticus (foo'rôr e-pē-lāp'tē-koos) (L. 'epileptic rage') 'While observed in association with exaltation, as just noted, and among the prodromata of various insanities, it [irritability] is particularly characteristic of a primary emotional state of congenital and acquired mental weakness, neurasthenic insanity, and the epileptic psychoses. In the latter it not infrequently becomes a true *furor epilepticus.*' (Church, A. and Peterson, F.

Nervous and Mental Diseases, 6th ed., Saunders, Philadelphia and London, 1916)

furor uterinus (oo-te′rē-noos) (L. 'uterine rage') *Obs.* Nymphomania.

fusion The term *fusion* is used in psychoanalysis to refer to the union of the instincts. Normally during the early infantile months the two primal instincts, life and death, are separated from one another, each operating alone. Later the two fuse to a greater or lesser extent. In psychiatric conditions there is usually more or less defusion of the instincts.

For example, when the ego is threatened by an external danger associated with a genital impulse, the latter is repressed and regression to the anal-sadistic level follows. Several possibilities then occur regarding the redistribution of libido. 'A part regresses and fuses with the hate instincts to constitute sadism.' (Jones, E. *Papers on Psycho-Analysis,* 4th ed., Wood, Baltimore, 1938) See *instinct.*

fusion See *flicker.*

G

G Rorschach scoring symbol for a response that includes the entire inkblot.

gain, epinosic (ep-i-nō′sik) Secondary or superimposed gain proceeding from the symptoms or general conditions of the underlying illness. Epinosis is a state of illness secondary to an original illness. It has been given much attention by psychoanalysts, who stress the psychic significance of a real or a fancied sickness. One speaks of a 'wish for illness' with the implication that the illness serves as a release phenomenon for repressed material. Thus, an individual with a castration complex acquires relief from it, when anything hurtful happens to him such as a disease or an injury. He may at the same time live through an unresolved Oedipus situation. A patient sick in a hospital abreacts the Oedipus situation. He submits to the aggressive father (substitute), in the form of the surgeon, and is nursed as a helpless individual by the maternal surrogate, the nurse. All of these things are regarded as secondary gains, associated with an original illness.

gain, morbid Gain, advantage, or profit by illness. This neurotic symptom serves as an emotional outlet. It enables the patient to realize his wish. Upon experiencing some misfortune certain individuals cannot resign themselves to the present reality. They would like to draw benefit from it and they fall sick—and that fulfills their wish to escape reality. This constitutes a morbid gain. If two people fall sick, the one who derives the greater morbid gain from the neurosis will remain sick for a much longer time. (Brill, A.A. *Basic Principles of Psychoanalysis*, Doubleday, New York, 1949) See *advantage by illness; gain, epinosic.*

gain, secondary See *gain, epinosic.*

gait, cerebellar (se-re-bel′ēr) In diseases of the cerebellum, the patient walks unsteadily with a 'drunken,' wobbly gait. There is lack of association between the movements of the legs and body, so that in walking, the body either lags behind, or is abruptly brought forward.

gait, hemiplegic (he-mi-plē′jik) In patients with hemiplegia, the lower extremity is held stiffly and circumducted in walking.

gait, myopathic (mī-ō-pa′thik) A waddling gait is characteristic of the myopathies.

gait, paralysis agitans (pà-rà′lē-sēs à′gē-tàns) In the paralysis agitans syndrome, the patient walks stooping forward, rigidly, with loss of associated swinging of the arms. In sitting or rising, he does so stiffly, the head, limbs, and trunk appearing as a rigid unit. The head is held fixedly and the arms hang stiffly by his sides, or perhaps assume a semi-flexed position.

gait, scissors In patients with bilateral spastic limbs, there is crossed progression, in the process of walking; the legs cross in scissors fashion.

gait, spastic (spas′tik) The patient walks stiffly with legs extended and feet shuffling.

gait, steppage A condition in which the patient must raise the legs high while walking; due to weakness or paralysis of the perineal group of muscles; patient cannot stand on his heels.

gait, stuttering A disorder in walking, usually, though not necessarily, psychogenic. It is characterized by a hesitancy in walking analogous to that observed in speech stuttering. It is sometimes seen in hysterical and in schizophrenic subjects. Bleuler mentions it with the expectation neuroses.

galeanthropy (gā-lē-an′thrō-pē) A symptom when the patient imagines himself a cat.

galeophobia (gā-lē-ō-fō′bi-à) Fear of cats; also *ailurophobia, gatophobia.*

gallows humor See *humor, gallows.*

Galt, John Minson 2nd (1819–62) American psychiatrist.

galvanic skin response See *reflex, psychogalvanic.*

game, hallucinatory In his discussion of hallucinations Kanner (*Child Psychiatry*, 2nd ed., Thomas, Sprinfield, Ill., 1948) mentions that in young infants the same factors that are responsible for illusions may produce reactions which Stern called hallucinatory games. (Stern, W. *Psychologie der Frühen Kindheit*, 5th ed., Quelle und Meyer, Leipzig, 1928, p. 237) These hallucinations differ from real hallucinations in their being actively created by the child instead of being felt as something foreign and passive. The infant literally makes a *game* of deliberately creating objects out of phantasy and amusing itself thereby. It is at all times fully aware of the unrealness of these self-created objects and can easily banish them when tiring of them, or for any reason whatever. A very young child's 'playing store' is largely a hallucinatory game: the business of the 'store' is playfully transacted through pantomime and the use of hallucinated merchandise and money.

gamete (gam′ēt) Special sex-cell. In genetics, the term signifies a specialized sexual cell which unites with another germ cell to form a zygote. Among animals the male gametes are known as spermatoza and the female gametes as *eggs* or *ova*.

Gametes are always haploid and genetically pure, because they contain only one member of a given factor pair. Since the formation of a gamete involves a reduction of 50 per cent in the amount of genetic material carried, each gamete has only half of the factorial equipment of an ordinary body cell and never shows the hybrid character of the individual producing it.

gammacism (gam′ȧ-siz′m) Common speech defect (the 'baby talk') of young children who replace the *velars* (g,k) with corresponding *dentals* (d,t).

gamo- (gam′ō-) combining form meaning marriage, (sexual) union, from Gr. *gámos*, wedding, marriage.

gamonomania (ga-mo-nō-mā′ni-ȧ) Morbid desire to marry.

gamophobia (gam-ō-fō′bi-ȧ) Fear of marriage.

gang 'The gang, whether developed out of lawless crowd behavior of adults or from the neighborhood play groups of children, is always a conflict group at war with other groups or with the forces of organized society.' (Reuter, E.B., and Hart, C.W. *Introduction to Sociology*, McGraw-Hill, New York, 1933)

The gang is an interstitial group originally formed spontaneously, and then integrated through conflict. It is characterized by the following types of behavior: meeting face to face, milling, movement through space as a unit, conflict, and planning. The result of this collective behavior is the development of tradition, unreflective internal structure, *esprit de corps,*

solidarity, morale, group awareness, and attachment to a local territory.' (Thrasher, F.M. *The Gang*, University of Chicago Press, Chicago, 1927)

Boy groups in American cities are an important factor in juvenile delinquency, in the beginnings of criminal careers, in organized crime, and in political corruption.

ganglia, basal See *basal ganglia.*

Ganser syndrome (Sigbert Joseph Maria Ganser, German psychiatrist, 1853–1931) Syndrome of deviously relevant answers, popularly called the 'nonsense syndrome'; it is often observed among prisoners, who, it is held, hope to be treated leniently by the court in virtue of their malady. It is described by many investigators as a hysterical reaction. The patient seldom does anything correctly. When shown a watch, reading 3:30, the patient may say it reads 5:00; when shown a glove he says it is a hand; he designates a 50-cent piece as a dollar bill; calls a key a lock.

gargalesthesia (gȧr-gal-es-thē′zhi-ȧ) Sensation of tickling.

gargoylism (gär′goil-iz′m) Tredgold says: 'From time to time cases have been reported by various writers which presented a combination of mental defect, peculiar abnormalities of the osseous system, corneal opacities, and enlargement of the liver and spleen.' (Tredgold, A.F. *A Text-Book of Mental Deficiency*, 6th ed., Wood, Baltimore, 1937) Ellis, Sheldon, and Capon suggested the name *gargoylism* for this syndrome.

G.A.S. General adaptation syndrome. See *syndrome, general adaptation.*

gases, psychosis due to Poisonous gases, such as carbon monoxide found in illuminating gas and in exhausts from automobiles, may produce mental disturbances. There is usually a preliminary period of unconsciousness followed by more or less protracted delirium after which the patient may experience increased fatigability and difficulty in concentration. Sometimes the symptoms clear up entirely; a normal interval of many weeks may ensue, to be followed by symptoms of mental defect from which the individual may not recover. These patients then remain in a chronic state of moderate or severe mental enfeeblement.

gastropaths, false (gas′trō-paths) Déjérine

and Gauckler so designate those who express *food phobias.*

gastro-psychiatry (gas'trō-sī-kī'a-trē) A psychiatric term for a patient's preoccupation with his digestive system. The patient's mind can be preoccupied with any organic system of his body. He can concentrate on his eyes, on his genitals, etc. Preoccupation with the gastrointestinal system, the stomach, the bowels is particularly common. (Hinsie, L.E. *Understandable Psychiatry,* Macmillan, New York, 1948)

gastrulation (gas-troo-lā'shun) In embryological development of a human organism, the stage characterized by the conversion of the monodermic *blastula* into a didermic *gastrula.* The gastrulating process is effected by the invagination, in the form of a blind tube, of the vegetal pole into the segmentation cavity. The wall of this tubular invagination is constituted by the primitive *entoderm* while its opening, or primitive mouth, is known as the *blastopore.*

gatophobia (ga-tō-fō'bi-a) Fear of cats; also *ailurophobia, galeophobia.*

Gaupp, Robert E. (1870–) (goup') German psychiatrist.

gaze, fascinating In hypnosis this term refers to the fixation of the eyes of the hypnotist upon the subject.

gazing, crystal A technique used in hypnoanalysis consisting of having the hypnotized subject observe a glass ball or a mirror and then produce associations. The patient is instructed to look at the glass and told that he will see in it things that he will describe to the analyst afterward. 'Crystal and mirror gazing are technics that can be used only with subjects who are capable of entering very deep hypnotic states. Where a crystal is not available, a glass of water will serve as an adequate substitute. If a mirror is used, it should be so placed that it reflects the blank ceiling. The patient is instructed as follows: "You will now be able to open your eyes, even though you are deeply asleep. You will not awaken, until I give you the command to do so. On the table, in front of you, you will see a mirror. Look into the mirror and you will see things before you. Describe to me what you see." Peering into a crystal or mirror, the patient may be able to reconstruct events in his past life by hallucinating them as they happened.' (Wolberg, L.R. *Hypnoanalysis,* Grune and Stratton, New York, 1945)

gelasmus (jē-laz'mus) Spasmodic laughter, observed in hysteria and the schizophrenias.

gelatio (ge-lä'tē-ō) *Obs.* Rigid state of the body in catalepsy, as though it were frozen.

Gélineau's syndrome (Jean Baptiste Édouard Gélineau, French neurologist, born 1859.) Idiopathic narcolepsy.

gene Whether the ultra-microscopically minute structure of a *gene,* as yet invisible, is made up of still smaller particles or constitutes in itself the ultimate unit of living substance, the concept of the gene is as serviceable in genetics as is the atom in physics. Though as yet a gene has not been isolated or analyzed, some geneticists believe that it acts like an enzyme, producing certain biochemical changes in a compound without itself being affected. However, so much is already known as to what genes do and how they do it, that genetically they are viewed as the basic Mendelian units carrying all the inheritable characters of living organisms rather than as mere chemical substance (see *Mendelism*).

Morphologically a gene is best understood as a particular state of organization of the chromatin at a particular point in the length of a particular *chromosome.* This state of organization is to be regarded as the physical basis explaining how a hereditary character passes as a unit from parent to offspring, while it is the parallelism between the behavior of chromosomes and genes which supports the assignment of a physical basis in the chromosomes to the Mendelian units.

Both chromosomes and genes behave in inheritance as though they were individual units, and the principles of segregation and independent assortment apply to chromosomes in precisely the same way in which they have been demonstrated to apply to genes. It is assumed that the genes always occur in pairs, and that one member of each pair is contributed by one parent of an individual and the other by the other parent. Owing to the phenomenon of *crossing over* it has even been possible not only to map each chromosome in certain organisms, but also to assign the genes to their relative positions on the chromosome, and to establish the fact of the *linear order* of the genes. In the chromosomes of Drosophila, for instance, 'individual gene loci have been identified with individual bands, suggesting that these are or contain the actual genes.' (Sinnott, E.W. and Dunn, L.D. *Principles of Genetics,* 3rd ed., McGraw-Hill, New York and London, 1939)

In accordance with these experimental findings, Morgan's *theory of the gene* is formulated as follows:

(1) The hereditary characters of the individual are referable to paired elements [the genes] in the germinal material [the chromosomes] which are held together in a definite number of linkage groups;

(2) In accordance with Mendel's first law, the members of each pair of genes separate when the germ cells mature and in consequence each ripe germ cell comes to contain one set only;

(3) The members of different linkage groups assort independently in accordance with Mendel's second law;

(4) An orderly interchange, or crossing over, also takes place between the elements in corresponding linkage groups;

(5) The frequency of crossing over furnishes evidence of the linear order of the genes in each linkage group and of the relative position of genes with respect to each other.

genealogy (jē-nē-al'ō-jē) Although in a sense identical with the actual pedigree of an individual or with the demonstration of such a pedigree in the form of a genealogical family tree, the term applies to the scientific study, or the proper historical account, of the biological descent of a person, or a group of persons, from a certain number of ancestors. These studies aim to provide a complete list of ancestors for as many generations as possible and to clarify the relationship of a person with the families of a given population group, rather than to investigate either the biological qualities of these families or the variations of certain hereditary family traits in successive generations.

generalization Applying to a whole group or class conclusions, ideas, judgments, etc. based upon experience with a limited number of the class. While generalization is an essential element of conceptualization in the processes of normal thought, it attains particular significance in psychiatry in that one of the many thought-disorders

in schizophrenia is the tendency to overgeneralize, and to treat the concrete as though it were abstract.

general paralysis of the insane See *paresis, general.*

general paresis See *paresis, general.*

general paresis, juvenile See *paresis, juvenile.*

generation Even in the field of biology, this term has several meanings. It denotes the act of producing offspring, or the biological process by which reproduction is accomplished, or a group of individuals produced. In the last sense the term may mean that the given individuals are: (1) of the same genealogical rank, as a stage in the succession of natural descent; (2) a series of siblings within one family, as the offspring of the same parents; (3) a particular group of individuals within the general population, living at the same time; or (4) people of the same period.

As a statistical concept the term refers to the average duration of life in a species or group.

generative (jen'ẽr-ā-tiv) *Biol.* Having the function, or power, of reproducing.

generativity (jen-ẽr-à-tiv'i-tē) The impulse for procreation, general in the human race. 'Generativity is primarily the interest in establishing and guiding the next generation or whatever in a given case may become the absorbing object of a parental kind of responsibility.' (Erikson, E. *Childhood and Society,* Norton, New York, 1950, p. 231)

generic (jē-ner'ik) *Biol.* Pertaining to a *genus,* as compared with *specific.*

genetic, genetical (jē-net'ik, -'i-kal) While *genetical* is used exclusively in the sense of pertaining to the province of genetics, the term *genetic* has two meanings: (1) it is synonymous with *genetical;* and (2) it means: produced or predetermined by a gene or a combination of genes, and is then practically identical with *hereditary.*

genetic block See *disease, genetotrophic.*

genetics Bateson introduced this term to designate that portion of biology which seeks to account for the resemblances and the differences in organisms related by descent. It is the science which simply *studies* in living organisms such genetic phenomena as heredity and evolution, development and variation, whereas the doctrinal movement which tries to anticipate or enforce the practical utilization of the scientific principles studied is eugenics.

Genetic investigation seeks the cause, the material basis, and the manners of maintenance of the specificity of the germinal substance: it strives to clarify the problems of how the characters of parents and offspring are related, how those of the adult, latent in the egg, become patent as development proceeds.

It is the method of *experimental breeding* that is most successfully employed by genetics in its scientific investigations, in addition to the more general biological disciplines of physiology, morphology, cytology, and biochemistry. It is an obvious disadvantage for human genetics that breeding experiments are available only to research in plants and animals, while the direct observation of the operation of genetic mechanisms in human individuals is limited to the study of normal development or morbidity in population averages, in properly selected kinships and in unselected groups of twin pairs (see *twin*).

All scientific theories underlying the present genetic knowledge have been derived from facts accumulated by accurate experimentation. The basic theories of modern genetics are the laws of segregation and independent assortment propounded by Gregor Mendel and usually called the *Mendelian law,* Morgan's *theory of the gene,* Goldschmidt's *balance theory* of sex differentiation, and the *mutation theory* (q.q.v.).

genetotrophic disease See *disease, genetotrophic.*

genial *Biol.* Pertaining to or having the particular genetic quality or the individual manifestations of a *genius.*

genic (jen′ik) Pertaining to, or produced by, a gene or a combination of genes.

geniculate (jen-ik′ū-lät) **bodies** The medial and lateral geniculate bodies are part of the posterior nuclei of the thalamus. The medial geniculate body receives auditory fibers from the cochlear nuclei (via the lateral lemniscus) and from the inferior colliculus. It sends fibers to the temporal cortex (Heschl's gyrus) via the auditory radiation, which ascends through the internal capsule. The lateral geniculate body receives most of the fibers of the optic tract; it sends fibers to the visual

cortex (around the calcarine fissure) via the optic or geniculocalcarine radiation, which ascends through the internal capsule.

genidentic (jen-i-den′tik) Having identical genes.

genital (jen′i-tal) Pertaining to the organs of reproduction.

genitality (jen-i-tal′i-tē) A general term referring to the genital components of sexuality, and sometimes used to refer to adult sexuality; but genitality is evident before genital primacy is complete, as in childhood and adolescent genital masturbation. 'Infantile sexuality differs from adult sexuality in several respects. The most impressive difference lies in the fact that the highest excitation is not necessarily located at the genitals, but that the genitals, rather, play the part of *primus inter pares* among many erogenous zones. The aims, too, are different; they do not necessarily lead toward sexual intercourse, but linger at activities that later play a role in forepleasure. . . . In time, however, the genitals begin to function as a special discharge apparatus, which concentrates all excitation upon itself and discharges it no matter in which erogenous zone it originated. It is called genital primacy when this function of the genitals has become dominant over the extragenital erogenous zones, and all sexual excitations become finally genitally oriented and climactically discharged.' (Fenichel, O. *The Psychoanalytic Theory of Neurosis,* Norton, New York, 1945, p. 61) Unlike orality and anality, genitality probably cannot be sublimated, for the genitals represent an apparatus for achievement of a full, unsublimated orgastic discharge. See *character, genital; primacy, complete genital.*

genitalize (jen′i-tal-īz) To displace genital libido, as onto a non-sexual (but predisposed) organ in hysteria, where libido is discharged, but inadequately and incompletely.

genital love See *love, genital.*

genitals Organs of reproduction; sex organs.

genius (jēn′yus) (L. tutelar deity of a person or place; wit, talent, genius) A generic, non-specific term used loosely to denote an individual child or adult of markedly superior intellectual, emotional, volitional, affective, or creative abilities. At the present time, there exists no unanimity of opinion about the origin or development of such outstanding abilities in these superior individuals. One school of thought emphasizes that so-called 'genius creative ability' appears as a symptom of, or alternative to, the development of neurosis or psychosis. Another school tends to emphasize that superior traits in varying degree appear as incident to, and an index of, normal development, as a concomitant to rounded superior health and endowment.

The term superior individual is more general, less controversial, and less emotionally charged than 'genius.' For purposes of classification, superiorly endowed children, or superior children, have been divided into the following four categories: (1) the bright child; (2) the gifted child; (3) the superior child; (4) the prodigy. In our present loose usage of the term (in both scientific and lay parlance) any individual child, in any of the four categories above, may aptly be called 'a genius child.' (Harms, E. *Handbook of Child Guidance.* Child Care Publications, New York, 1947) See also *child, bright.*

genome (jē-nōm') The special biological term proposed by von Wettstein for the genes in the nucleus to differentiate them from an alleged system of analogous entities in the cytoplasm, called *plasmons.*

genophobia (jen-ō-fō'bi-à) Fear of sex.

genotropism (jen-ō-trō'piz'm) Szondi's hypothesis that latent recessive genes determine instinctive or spontaneous choice reactions. This is manifested in one way by attraction of libido between individuals possessing similar gene stock. The Szondi test (see *test, Szondi*) was constructed to demonstrate this hypothesis experimentally, and it is Szondi's belief that the test subject chooses a particular picture because the corresponding need-system within himself is in a state of tension.

genotype (jen'ō-tīp) The term was coined by the Danish botanist Johannsen in connection with his pure-line theory, in order to distinguish the factorial structure of an organism from its manifested *phenotype.* According to this theory, all individuals descended from a common ancestor by asexual reproduction have an identical *genotype* (q.v.) and will continue to breed true, regardless of environmental differences, forming lines genetically pure for all their characters.

Although originally the term meant the sum of all inherited predispositional characters of an individual, it has become customary to use it now in the sense of a particular *predisposition* (q.v.) underlying an individual morbid condition.

genotypical Pertaining to the *genotype.*

genus (jē'nus) (L. 'birth, descent, offspring, race, stock, species') In biology this term signifies a group of related *species* and classifies the group as ranking above a species and next below a subfamily (see *species*).

geography, psychological 'Psychological geography is the mapping of a whole community in which the interrelations of its inhabitants and the interrelations of its collectives or groups are depicted in respect to (a) its locality and (b) the psychological currents between them.' (Moreno, J.L. *Who Shall Survive?* Nervous & Mental Disease Publishing Company, 1934, p. 233)

geophagy (jē-of'à-jē) Dirt-eating.

gephyrophobia (je-fi-rō-fō'bi-à) Fear of (crossing a) bridge or river.

geriatrics (jer-i-at'riks) The science of curing or healing disorders and ailments of old age.

geriopsychosis (jer-i-ō-sī-kō'sis) A term suggested by Southard for psychoses of the senescent period; senile psychoses.

germ cell See *cell, germ.*

germinally affected See *affected, germinally.*

germ plasm See *plasm, germ.*

gerontology (jer-on-tol'ō-jē) The study of old age.

gerontophilia (jer-on-tō-fil'i-à) Love for old persons. Magnus Hirschfeld calls this 'an infantile fixation on elderly individuals.'

'Some of the resultants of the "grandfather-complex" may now be mentioned. The most striking is the tendency to gerontophilia—i.e., a special fondness for old people. This may also come about from the father being well over middle age when the child was born.' (Jones, E. *Papers on Psycho-Analysis,* 4th ed., Wood, Baltimore, 1938)

gerophilia (jer-ō-fil'i-à) Same as *gerontophilia.*

Gerstmann syndrome (J. Gerstmann, contemporary American neurologist) A symptom complex described by Gerstmann in 1940 consisting of finger agnosia, right-left disorientation, acalculia, and agraphia. There may be various additional features, such as constructive apraxia, amnestic reduction of word finding, disturbed ability to read, impaired color perception, absence of optokinetic nystagmus, and disturbance of equilibrium. The agraphia often takes the form of dissociated dysgraphia.

Presence of the Gerstmann syndrome implies definite parietal lobe pathology.

Gestalt (Ge-stalt′) See *psychology, Gestalt.*

geumaphobia (gū-má-fō′bi-à) Fear of taste.

Gheel Colony A colony in Gheel, Beligum, which has existed since the 13th century for the treatment of a large number of psychotic patients residing in private homes in the community.

gibberish Gibberish is commonly defined as unintelligible and incoherent language. In psychiatry it achieves its most florid form in patients with schizophrenia, who, as Storch and others have shown, often regress to the stage in which language is founded on the principles of primitive mentality. The language of the patient is gibberish to those who cannot understand it, in much the same sense that dreams are 'gibberish,' or that any mode of communication, foreign to one, is gibberish. The term was appropriate when the 'language' of the patient was undecipherable; it is not in use today because the language of schizophrenia is often recognizable and translatable.

'The tendency to silly plays on words and neologisms can get the upper hand in our patients to such an extent, that they fall into a wholly *incomprehensible gibberish.*' (Kraepelin, E. *Dementia Praecox and Paraphrenia,* tr. by Barclay, R., Livingstone, Edinburgh, 1919)

gifted As used in child psychiatry, this term is meant to refer to a child whose intelligence is in the upper 2 per cent of the total population of his age. Often, however, the term is used more loosely to refer to a child who shows outstanding ability in any single area. See *child, bright.*

gigantism (jī-gan′tiz'm) The constitutional anomaly is characterized by a stature greatly above the average (any height above 205 cm. in white population groups) and by a corresponding excess of body mass. It is due either to a heredito-constitutional hyperplasia of the entire endocrine system or to a particular form of hyperfunction in the anterior lobe of the hypophysis during the period of growth of the individual affected. This condition of hyperpituitarism may be primary or it may be secondary to genital hypofunction. Only in rare cases, glands other than the pituitary may be primarily implicated, for instance, the adrenal cortex or the pineal gland.

Among the various forms of gigantism are Berlinger's *gigantosomia primordialis,* Pellizzi's *precocious macrogenitosomia,* and *eunuchoid small gigantism.* The latter consists of excessive growth, especially of the lower extremities, which takes place just before puberty and is associated with a hypogenesis of the secondary sexual characteristics. It is often found in the phthisic or dolichomorphic types of constitution and may correct itself in later years, unless it leads to active pulmonary tuberculosis.

gigantism, eurhythmic (ū-riTH′mik) *Gigantosomia primordialis* (q.v.).

gigantosomia primordialis (gē-gàn-tô-sō′-mē-à prē-môr-dē-ä′ēs) Berlinger introduced this term for the extremely rare syndrome best described as a well-proportioned form of *gigantism* with normal sex development. Some authors attribute this condition to the effect of an excessive idiopathic energy in the development of the entire organism, while others consider it as a special form of gigantism with similar etiology.

gigolette (ji-gō-let′) Hirschfeld defines a gigolette as a young woman of 'easy virtue'; a woman who participates in promiscuous love affairs.

gigolism (ji′gōl-iz'm) This term refers to serving as a professional escort usually to members of the opposite sex. As a rule the escort is a male, a gigolo, defined by the French as a fop, a lounge-lizard, a dandy, with implications of sexual immaturity, often of homosexuality.

Gilles de la Tourette syndrome (Georges Gilles de la Tourette [jēl du là toor-et′] Paris physician, 1857–1904) A syndrome which usually has its onset in childhood, first described in 1885. It begins with facial movements and throat noises; the involuntary jerkings become more generalized and progressive, and later phrases or sentences may be ejaculated. Coprolalia and echolalia have also been reported. Prognosis is unfavorable, and most of these patients are considered to fall within the schizophrenic group.

girl, phallus The unconscious symbolic equivalence of girl with phallus. Such a situation arises most frequently in a particular type of disturbance, the perversion. One example is found in transvestitism. The male transvestite has phantasied that the woman has a penis. Having thus overcome his castration anxiety, he identifies with this phallic woman. He himself represents the phallic woman under whose clothes a penis is hidden. Moreover, the female identification frequently represents an identification not with the mother but with a 'little girl,' for example, with a little sister. On the other hand, on a deeper level, the identification is with one's own penis. 'At deeper levels, fantasies of introjections are found in which the penis is equated with an introjected woman.' Thus, occasionally in these cases, 'girl' comes to have the symbolic meaning 'penis.'

Another example in which 'girl' has the symbolic significance of 'penis' occurs in the urethral-erotic perversion in which men have a sexual interest in female urination. As always in perversions, the interest in female urination is used to achieve reassurance against castration fears. In one case that was analyzed 'the perversion meant primarily an intense rejection of any idea of a penis.' As a child the patient had thought women had only one opening and urinated from the anus. 'The perversion was conditioned by a simultaneous prohibition against looking which enabled the patient to cling to the fantasy of women urinating through the anus and thus to avoid again being reminded of castration by the sight of a urinating woman.' On a deeper level, moreover, 'the interest in watching urinating women meant the hope of finding out that they, too, have a penis. The "urinating girl" herself had the significance of a "urinating penis." '

This equation may also occur in heterosexual individuals who are not overtly perverse. Certain narcissistic men who in childhood liked to think of themselves as girls may fall in love with more or less

boyish 'little girls,' in whom they see the reincarnation of themselves. They treat these girls with the tenderness with which they would like to have been treated by their own mothers. They love them not as individuals but they love in them the feminine parts of their own ego. As a result of 'a castration anxiety, similar to that in cases of homosexuality . . . the narcissistically chosen girl "may represent" not only one's own person in adolescence but specifically one's own penis.' Here again we see the unconscious symbolic equation of girl with penis. (Fenichel, O. *The Psychoanalytic Theory of Neurosis,* Norton, New York, 1945)

Gjessing's syndrome (jes'ing) Recurrent episodes of catatonic stupor or excitement occurring in schizophrenics and associated with phasic variations in the nitrogen metabolism; first described by R. Gjessing in 1938. The syndrome is related to inadequate metabolism of dietary protein, leading to periods of nitrogen retention which are concurrent with hyper- or hypokinetic episodes. Dietary regulation is sometimes enough to control such patients; in others, thyroid administration increases nitrogen output with corresponding improvement in mental state.

glia (glē'-à) *Neuroglia* (q.v.).

glioma (glī-ō'mà) The generic name for one of the commonest types of brain tumor. The gliomata (gliomas) account for approximately 50 per cent of all intracranial tumors. They arise from glial cells and are composed predominantly of astrocytes or their embryonal precursors (medulloblasts, spongioblasts, astroblasts). By common usage, nearly all tumors of neuroepithelial origin are included in this term. In general, prognosis is unfavorable because gliomata tend to grow deep into the neural tissue; the more adult cell types (astrocytoma, oligodendroglioma, ependymoma) grow more slowly and are relatively benign, while the more immature cell types (medulloblastoma, spongioblastoma, or glioblastoma) tend to grow more rapidly, are more invasive, and are more malignant.

globus hystericus (glô'boos hēs-ter'ē-koos) (L. 'hysteric globe, or ball') A term for the sensation of a ball or globe that arises in the stomach area and progresses upwardly, being finally felt in the throat where it produces the feeling of strangulation.

Globus hystericus and other 'esophageal neuroses' are often based on an unconscious rejection of incorporation secondary to aggressive impulses, which are often of a sexual nature (such as castration wishes) and which are connected with eating and swallowing. Disgust plays an important role and is probably a combination of temptation and rejection along with an ambivalent attitude toward incorporation.

globus pallidus (pa'li-doos) See *basal ganglia.*

gloss, metallic Tschisch (Journal of Mental Pathology, 1903) asserts that there is a characteristic facial expression in patients suffering from essential epilepsy. He called it a *metallic gloss* or *metallic look.*

glosso- combining form meaning speech, language, from Gr. *glóssa,* tongue, language.

glossodynia (glos-ō-din'i-à) An itching, burning sensation in the tongue and buccal mucous membranes.

glossolalia (glos-ō-lā'li-à) Tongue jabbering. Unintelligible jargon.

glossospasm (glos'ō-spaz'm) Rapid protrusion and retraction of the tongue; the spasm generally lasts for several minutes.

glossosynthesis (glos-ō-sin'the-sis) Neologism.

glow, salt This is a procedure designed as a circulatory stimulant. 'About two pounds of coarse salt are moistened with cold water and allowed to stand for a short time. The treatment should be given in a wet room or bathtub. A towel is pinned about the waist and the patient stands in a tub in which water at 105° F. covers the ankles. Each section of the body as it is treated is moistened with water from the tub, or the entire surface may be moistened by immersion or spray at a temperature of 100° to 105° F. Standing in front of the patient, take a small amount of the wet salt in each hand, spread it evenly over the neck and chest, give vigorous alternate circular friction of the neck and cross-stroking to the chest, until the skin is in a glow.' (Bailey, H. *Nursing Mental Diseases,* 3rd ed., Macmillan, New York, 1935) The same procedure is followed with other areas of the body.

gluco-corticoid (gloo-kō-kor'ti-koid) See *syndrome, general adaptation.*

gnostic (sensation) A term applied by the Dutch school of neurologists (Brouwer, Kappers) to designate the deep and epicritic sensations in contradistinction to the protopathic sensations which are considered as vital or *paleosensations.*

goal, life This term is used by Adler to describe the *secret* strivings of the individual, implicit in everything he thinks and does, for a superiority which compensates the chief inferiority. This phantasy of what he thinks he could be acts as a striving from 'below' (ideas of his own disadvantages) to 'above' (ideas of how to gain advantages).

'This constant striving from below to above . . . is the basis of all individual orientation. . . . Individuality itself, in the human sense, depends upon this fact that there is always inferiority, against which a goal of superiority is erected.' (Mairet, P. *ABC of Adler's Psychology,* Kegan Paul, Trench, Trubner, London, 1928)

'Whether he regards his suffering as the most important thing in the world to which everyone must show obeisance, whether he is chasing after unattainable ideals or old deities, over-stepping all limits and norms, at every part of his way he is guided and spurred on by his longing for superiority, the thought of his godlikeness, the belief in his special magical power.' (Adler, C. *The Practice and Theory of Individual Psychology,* tr. by Radin, P., Kegan Paul, Trench, Trubner, London, 1924)

god-man See *anthropos.*

gold curve See *Lange's colloidal gold reaction.*

Goldflam, (gōld'flàm) **Samuel** (1852–1932) Polish neurologist.

Goldstein (gōld'shtīn) **Kurt** (1878–) German psychiatrist and neurologist; aphasia.

Golem (gō'lem) According to the widespread medieval tradition among the Jews, the Golem is a huge, man-shaped brute created from clay by the supernatural power of the Shem, the 'ineffable name' committed to writing, through the agency of a human being. The first man credited with this achievement was Elijah of Chelm (middle of sixteenth century), hence known as the Ba'al Shem, i.e.

Goll, Column of

master of 'the Name.' The best-known Golem was created by Rabbi Judah Löw ben Bezalel of Prague (end of sixteenth century). A modern Yiddish play built around this latter event represents the rabbi to have conceived the idea of making this Gargantuan mass of flesh and brawn as a bulwark for the Jews of Prague against a threatened pogrom and then taught the new monster how to use an axe. For a time the Golem was a passive obedient servant who did various kinds of minor chores. Later on, however, he began to show a sexual interest in the rabbi's niece and also insisted on joining the congregation in the synagogue—'the two most valued relations of the rabbi.' The aroused rabbi denied him entrance to the synagogue, and the enraged Golem seized an axe and started a pogrom on his own. The rabbi tried to regain mastery of the Golem by using his rabbinical knowledge and authority to invoke the magic powers of cabala, but all to no purpose. 'Not until he is driven by sheer necessity to meet the Golem with the whole force of his human passion can he gain the upper hand,' and lay the fiend—an earlier Frankenstein's monster—low. (Baynes, H.G. *Mythology of the Soul*, Williams and Wilkins, Baltimore, 1940)

Goll, column of (Friedrich Goll, Swiss anatomist, 1829–1904) *Fasciculus gracilis* (q.v.).

gonad (gō'nad) A germ-gland; sexual gland.

gonadocentric (gō-nà-dō-sen'trik) Relating to the genitals as focal points. 'At puberty the sex urge becomes fully gonadocentric, with masturbation at the threshold and fringe of object love.' (Tenenbaum, J. *Encyclopaedia Sexualis*, edited by Robinson, V., Dingwall-Rock, New York, 1936)

good and evil test See *test, good and evil.*

Goodenough test See *test, Goodenough.*

good object See *object, good.*

Gordon Holmes, rebound phenomenon of (Gordon Holmes, British physician, 1876–) A test for ataxia, specifically illustrating the loss of cerebellar 'check' on co-ordinated movement; if an attempt is made to extend the flexed forearm against resistance and suddenly let go, the hand or fist flies unchecked against the mouth or shoulder.

Gordon reflex (Alfred Gordon, American neurologist, 1869–) Dorsal extension of the great toe, induced by compression of the calf muscle.

government, patient See *patient-government.*

Gowers' tetanoid chorea (Sir William R. Gowers, English neurologist, 1845–1915) See *degeneration, hepatolenticular.*

Graefe's disease (Albrecht von Graefe, German ophthalmologist, 1828–1870) See *nerve, oculomotor.*

Graftschizophrenia (grâft-skiz-ō-frē'ni-à) *Propfschizophrenia* (q.v.).

grande attaque hystérique (gräNd à-tàk ē-stà-rēk) See *hysteria.*

grande hystérie (gräNd ē-stà-rē') (F. 'great hysteria') See *hysteria, major.*

grande nevrose (gräNd' nē-vrōz') (F. 'grand, great neurosis') *Obs.* French term for epilepsy.

grandeur See *megalomania.*

grandiose Characterized by showing feelings of great importance.

grand mal (gräN màl') (F. 'great malady') See *epilepsy.*

Grantham lobotomy See *lobotomy, Grantham.*

grapho- (graf'ō-), combining form meaning writing, from Gr. *gráphein*, to write.

graphomania (graf-ō-mā'ni-à) Inordinate impulse to write. 'Many persecuted patients react with evasion, threats, scolding, insulting letters, and appeals to the authorities. Those suffering from grandiose delusions often use the press in a prolific manner. In general many paranoiacs actually become "graphomaniacs."' (Bleuler, E. *Textbook of Psychiatry*, tr. by Brill, A.A., Macmillan, New York, 1930)

graphophobia Fear of writing.

graphorrh(o)ea (-rē'à) Stoddart says: 'The writing of the insane is disordered in exactly the same way as their speech. Garrulous, voluble patients, who are sometimes said to be suffering from "logorrhoea," often write many sheets of foolscap daily ("graphorrhoea").' (Stoddart, W.H.B. *Mind and Its Disorders*, 5th ed., Lewis, London, 1926)

grasping, forced See *lobe, frontal.*

Gray, John Perdue (1825–86) American psychiatrist.

gray-out A relatively mild or partial loss of consciousness due to anemia of the brain. A condition often observed in pilots of high-speed airplanes. A more complete or total loss of consciousness is known as *black-out*.

gregariousness (gre-gâr'i-us-nes) See *instinct, herd.*

grief See *mourning; melancholia.*

Griesinger, Wilhelm (1817–68) German psychiatrist.

groping, forced Same as forced grasping, grasp reflex or instinctive grasp reaction. See *lobe, frontal.*

group 'Any number of people, larger or smaller, between whom such relations are discovered that they must be thought of together.' (Small, A.W. *General Sociology,* University of Chicago Press, Chicago, 1905)

'Any group is constituted by the fact that there is some interest which holds its members together.' (Sapir, E. *Group; Encyclopaedia of the Social Sciences,* vol. 7, Macmillan, New York, 1932, p. 179)

A social group is a collection of persons 'capable of consistent action.' (Park, R.E., and Burgess, E.W. *Introduction to the Science of Sociology,* University of Chicago Press, Chicago, 1921)

Groups have been variously classified as: (1) *primary,* characterized by intimate face-to-face associations, and *secondary,* where the members, typically without presence, are formally and impersonally associated; (2) *in-groups* of which the person is a member and *out-groups* those to which he does not belong and with which his group is often in conflict; (Sumner, W.G. *Folkways,* Ginn, New York, 1906) (3) as *homogeneous* and *heterogeneous;* (4) *conflict* groups, e.g. nationalities, parties, reds, labor unions, and gangs, and *accommodation* groups, e.g. classes, castes, vocations, denominations.

group-analysis See *analysis, group.*

group, blanket A psychiatric term characterizing a group that is formed with no criteria for grouping. See *group, structured.*

group, closed A term describing a therapy group to which no new patients are added in the course of treatment or after treatment has proceeded for a time. See *group, open.*

group, continuous Same as *open group.*

group-feeling Same as *instinct, herd.*

group-formation See *instinct, herd.*

group, open A term describing a therapy group to which new patients are added at any time during the course of treatment. Sometimes this is referred to as a *continuous group.*

group, structured A term introduced by S.R. Slavson to emphasize the fact that the selection and combining of patients is essential for group psychotherapy, though some group psychotherapists pay little or no attention to it. Since in group psychotherapy the group is an important factor and the major therapeutic agency, it must be planned in such a way that, according to Slavson, the patients, individually and as a group, would have therapeutic effect upon every other constituent member. He has described some of the criteria for selection and grouping in his *Analytic Group Psychotherapy* (Columbia University Press, New York, 1950, Chapter XIV). This term is opposed to *blanket group,* in which no criteria for grouping are employed.

group, transitional A therapy group devised for children (in latency period and puberty) who do not require intensive group psychotherapy but are unable to participate with confidence in ordinary social clubs. A form of 'protective groups' has been developed for these young patients. (Slavson, S.R. *An Introduction to Group Therapy,* The Commonwealth Fund, Oxford University Press, New York, 1943, pp. 327ff.)

group-work, social 'Social group-work may be defined as a type of educational process carried on in voluntary groups during leisure time and with the assistance of a group leader. It aims at the growth and development of individuals through the group experience, and at the use of the group by its members for social purposes which they consider desirable. . . . The use of the term group-work is increasingly coming to mean a kind of guided group experience in which individuals are helped to meet their needs and develop their interests along socially acceptable lines, with the assistance of a group leader.' (Coyle, G.L. *Social Work Year Book 1939,* edited by Kurtz, R.H., Russell Sage Foundation, New York)

Grübelsucht (grü'bel-sookt) Brooding over trifles; seen most commonly in obsessive-compulsive psychoneurosis and in depressive psychoses.

Gruhle, Hans Walther (1880–   ) (grōō'lĕ) German psychiatrist.

grumbling mania See *mania, grumbling.*

GSR Galvanic skin response. See *reflex, psychogalvanic.*

guidance A form of supportive psychotherapy in which the patient is counseled and instructed in ways to set and achieve specific goals and in ways to recognize and avoid areas of conflict and anxiety-provoking situations. Educational guidance refers particularly to helping the patient find the school or courses best suited to him on the basis of his intelligence, aptitudes, preferences, and available opportunities. Vocational guidance refers particularly to helping the patient find a job which is realistically suited to his capacities.

Guidance is a relatively superficial type of psychotherapy and makes little attempt to deal with the unconscious motivants of behavior. It is based upon an authoritarian relationship in which the patient often overvalues the therapist and in which he must suppress any doubts or hostility against the therapist.

guidance, child See *child-guidance.*

guidance, parental 'The reader who considers some of the problems of parental unadjustment reflected in the cases alluded to in the present volume will appreciate the fact that child guidance implies parental guidance as well. It is only fair to the parent group to call attention to the fact that many of the problems which they find themselves burdened with are the products of their own past experience; for just as truly as with the child, the personality adjustments of the parents must be interpreted in terms of cause and effect in their own experience.' (Lee, P.R. and Kenworthy, M.E. *Mental Hygiene and Social Work,* The Commonwealth Fund, Division of Publications, New York, 1929)

Guillain-Barré syndrome (gē-yaN' bȧr-rā') (Georges Guillain, 1876–   , and J.A. Barré, French neurologists) Acute infective polyneuritis; acute toxic polyneuritis; rheumatic polyneuritis; polyradiculoneuritis. An acute, diffuse disease of the nervous system, probably due to a virus, consisting of chromatolysis of the anterior horn cells and the posterior roots and of myelin degeneration of the peripheral nerves. Most cases occur in males between the ages of 20 and 50 years. Initial symptoms are headache, vomiting, fever, and pain in the back and legs. These are followed by sudden paralysis of the limbs, in all segments, and of the facial muscles. The paralysis is flaccid in type and the deep reflexes are lost. There is pain, numbness, and tingling in the limbs. Cerebrospinal fluid protein is markedly elevated, but there are few or no cells. In sporadic cases the prognosis is good, but in some epidemics the mortality (usually from respiratory paralysis) is high. No specific treatment is known.

guilt The sense of guilt is a concept of great significance in psychoanalysis. 'One may say that a sufferer from compulsions and prohibitions behaves as if he were dominated by a sense of guilt, of which, however, he is ignorant—an unconscious sense of guilt, as one must call it in spite of the apparent contradiction in terms.... The protestations of the pious that they know they are miserable sinners in their hearts correspond to the sense of guilt of the obsessional neurotic.' (Freud, S. *Collected Papers,* vol. 2, tr. by Riviere, J., Leonard and Virginia Woolf and The Institute of Psychoanalysis, London, 1924–25) Freud says that the expression 'unconscious feeling of guilt' is psychologically incorrect and suggests the phrase 'need for punishment' as a substitute.

Consciousness of guilt is 'an expression of a tension between ego and super-ego. The ego reacts with feelings of anxiety (pangs of conscience) to the perception that it has failed to perform the behests of its ideal, the super-ego.' (ibid.)

Freud later says (*New Introductory Lectures on Psycho-Analysis,* tr. by Sprott, W.J., Norton, New York, 1933) that the origin of the unconscious need for punishment 'behaves like a part of the conscience, like the prolongation of conscience into the unconscious; and it must have the same origin as conscience, that is to say it will correspond to a piece of aggressiveness which has been internalized and taken over by the super-ego.'

It is said that the superego is heir of the Oedipus complex; one of the consequences of the dread of castration is privation or frustration, which alone is often regarded as adequate cause for the genesis of guilt. Jones says: 'Guilt, and with it the superego, is as it were artificially built up for the purpose of protecting the child from the stress of privation—i.e., of ungratified libido—and so warding off the dread of aphanisis that always goes with this; it does so, of course, by damping down the wishes that are not destined to be gratified.' (Jones, E. *Papers on Psycho-Analysis,* 4th ed., Wood, Baltimore, 1938)

The sense of guilt, so often associated with masturbation, is rooted in the phantasies connected with the Oedipus complex. It is obvious that masturbation, castration dread, guilt, and anxiety form a continuum.

guilt, unconscious sense of See *punishment, unconscious need of.*

Guislain, Joseph (1797–1860) (gē-lâN') French psychiatrist.

gumma, intracranial This condition is a form of cerebral syphilis and occurs rarely. The predominating pathological process is the gumma or syphiloma. This is an irregular or round granulomatous nodular growth, varying in size from that of a pinhead to a walnut; it is generally multiple. Occasionally when single and of large size, it may produce symptoms of intracranial pressure with or without focal signs. The mental symptoms include the acute organic type of reaction, and consist of delirium, with a memory defect for recent events, and emotional lability. When there is evidence of increased intracranial pressure, a dull, stuporous state is common, with a loss of sphincter control. The blood and spinal fluid findings may be similar to those observed in cerebral syphilis, and response to antisyphilic treatment is fairly successful.

Gunther-Waldenstrom syndrome *Porphyria* (q.v.).

gustatism (gus'tà-tiz'm) See *sensation, secondary.*

gymnophobia (jim-nō-fō'bi-à) Fear of a naked body.

gynander, gynandromorph (ji-nan'dĕr, -drō-morf) This biological term designates an individual of a bisexual species, exhibiting a 'sexual mosaic' of male and female characters as a result of the development of both types of sex tissue in the same organism.

Most specimens are *lateral* or *bilateral* gynandromorphs, male on one side of the mid-line of the body, and female on the other, with a sharp demarcation between the two kinds of tissue. In some instances the distribution is in a ratio of about 1:3, or the head may be female and the rest of the body male.

It is assumed that on the male side there appear the sex-linked characters received from either the mother or the father; while the characters of the female parts show the presence in these parts of both the maternal and paternal X chromosomes, as though one of the X chromosomes had been eliminated from the male parts, leaving them XO, while the female parts are XX. 'Such a gynander appears to have begun development as an XX female and at some early cell division to have lost one of the X chromosomes from part of the tissues.' (Sinnott, E.W., and Dunn, L.D. *Principles of Genetics,* 3rd ed., McGraw-Hill, New York and London, 1939)

gynandrian A biological term relating to the class of *Gynandria* as classified in the Linean system of botany.

gynandroid, gynandromorphic, gynandrous (-'droid, -drō-mor'fik, -'drus) Usually in biology these terms refer to the *hermaphroditic* combination, or the resemblance to such combination, of male and female characteristics in the physical and mental make-up of one individual. In a more specialized sense, in contrast to *androgynous,* they also indicate predominantly female features in a hermaphrodite with some male characteristics (see *androgynoid, androgynous*).

gynandromorphism (-drō-mor'fiz'm) This biological phenomenon is characterized by a 'mosaic' of male and female characters in the same individual of a bisexual species, and probably results from abberation in the distribution of the X chromosomes. It is assumed that if in the mating which produces a gynandromorph, sex-linked characters are involved and if the sex-linked characters of the two parents are dissimilar, then the sex-linked characters of the male parts are those either of the father or of the mother; whereas the sex-linked characters of the female parts are a combination of those of both parents.

If the gynandromorph starts life as a

female, XX in constitution, and at some stage, during the early divisions of the fertilized egg, a daughter X chromosome fails to enter one of the daughter cells, then this cell, unlike its sister, will contain one X instead of two, becoming XO instead of XX. It will thus come to possess the sex-chromosome constitution of male tissue.

If the X chromosome of paternal origin is lost, the sex-linked characterization of the male part of the gynandromorph will be like that of the mother.

gynecomania (jin-ē-kō-mā'ni-à) Morbid desire for women.

gynephobia (jin-ē-fō'bi-à) Fear of women.

gyno- (jin'ō-, jī'nō-) combining form meaning woman, female, from Gr. *gyné'*, woman.

gynomonoecism (jin-ō-mō-nē'siz'm) A genetic female's capacity for developing spermatozoa in the ovary, at certain times. See *hermaphroditism*.

gynophobia (jin-ō-fō'bi-à) Morbid fear of women.

gyrectomy (jī-rek'tō-mē) The name given to one of the several surgical operations on the brain performed as a therapeutic measure in certain cases of mental illness. In the gyrectomy procedure bilateral symmetrical removals of frontal cortex are carried out along fissure lines in order to leave the normally functioning gyri. For a more detailed discussion of psychosurgical operations see *topectomy*.

gyrus, angular (jī-rus) The posterior portion of the lower parietal region; the left angular gyrus is associated with speech function.

gyrus, postcentral See *lobe, parietal*.

gyrus, precentral See *lobe, frontal*.

H

H Rorschach scoring symbol for a human figure response.

habenular ganglion (hȧ-ben'u-lär gang'glē-on) See *epithalamus*.

habit, accident See *proneness, accident*.

habit, act See *act-habit*.

habit, complaint This is an expression used by Kanner in discussing hypochondriasis in children. He says that 'hypochondriasis is a chronic *complaint habit*.' At various times and in connection with a variety of situations children are known to complain of various aches and pains which clearly are emotionally rather than physically caused. For example, one child may complain of severe headache the morning of a day on which a severe test is to be given at school; another may complain of stomach-ache when some particularly disliked kind of food is served. But these are *isolated*, not habitual, complaints. The child complaining of headache on a school day which is to include a test does not *always* react to a test in this way. The child who complains of a stomach-ache at the sight of a disliked food will on some other occasion partake of that same food with no thought of stomach-ache.

The complaint habit refers to a *habitual* way of reacting by means of complaints of bodily disorder, according to definite patterns. In some instances the pattern has been set by the child himself, out of certain material from his own experience. If a real stomach-ache or a real cough has kept the child from school, which he happens to dislike, and has brought all sorts of kindly attentions, comforts, and privileges not ordinarily forthcoming, it may be found thereafter that a great desire for all this as a relief from some stress or other will be heralded by a stomach-ache or cough which, though felt and complained about, is *not* real. More often the pattern is suggested to the child by observation of his environment. If he notices that mother or father seems always to be relieved of this or that chore by reason of the complaint of headache or backache, the child, too, will be found feeling and complaining of headache or backache when the performance of some hated task is expected. (Kanner, L. *Child*

Psychiatry, 2nd ed., Thomas, Springfield, Ill., 1948)

habit-disorder See *behavior disorders*.

habit-formation See *training, habit*.

habit-forming This term, when used with a drug, usually refers to the fact that the drug leads to *addiction* (q.v.).

habit, hysterical Kretschmer distinguishes two kinds of hysteria, *reflex hysteria* (q.v.), and *hysterical habit*. The latter means a hysterical reaction that begins as a conscious, voluntary process and gradually becomes automatic by repetition.

habit-residual, hysterical This is Kretschmer's expression for a reflex hysteria which continues because of the patient's lack of desire to get well. It is distinguished from simple reflex hysteria in that the latter usually occurs upon occasions when there is something to be gained by the reaction.

habit-training See *training, habit*.

habituation See *addiction*.

habitus (hab'i-tus) (L. 'condition, state, nature, character, disposition') In general medicine this term originally meant a 'constitutional disposition or tendency' to some specific disease, in the sense of the *habitus phthisicus* and *habitus apoplecticus* as described by Hippocrates.

Later the meaning of the term was extended also to the type of physique associated with such tendencies by different typological schools of constitutional medicine, and to the general characteristic appearance of the human body.

habitus, affective An individual's organization or constitution from the standpoint of the affects. 'Many mere psychopaths have the same affective habitus as pronounced *epileptoid* or as the less correctly designated *epileptic* character. . . . (Bleuler, E. *Textbook of Psychiatry,* tr. by Brill, A.A., Macmillan, New York, 1930)

habitus apoplecticus (hä'bē-toos ȧ-pô-plek'tē-koos) (L. 'apoplectic constitution') Hippocrates used this term for the tendency of a certain group of persons to apoplexy. He ascribed a thick set, rounded physique to such persons, and this has become the actual meaning of the term. In this derived sense, the term indicates the type of physique corresponding to Kretschmer's *pyknic type* and its equivalents in other systems.

habitus, asthenic See *asthenic; type, asthenic.*

habitus phthisicus (fthē′zi-koos) (L. 'consumptive constitution') By this term Hippocrates denoted the tendency of certain persons to *pulmonary tuberculosis.* He ascribed a slender, flat-chested physique to such persons, and the term is used in a derived sense to indicate the type of physique corresponding approximately to Kretschmer's *asthenic type* and its equivalents in other systems.

habitus, ptotic ([p]tō′tik) In constitutional medicine, this refers to a special body type described by Stiller as associated with the constitutional anomaly *enteroptosis*— a sagging or a dropped condition of the intestines.

According to Pende, this particular condition of enteroptosis exerts secondary effects on the digestive functions, and also— through lack of diaphragmatic support— on the respiratory and circulatory systems and on the configuration of the thorax, thus contributing to the production of the 'general *dolichomorphic-asthenic* constitution.' (Pende, N. *Constitutional Inadequacies,* tr. by Naccarati, S., Lea & Febiger, Philadelphia, 1928)

habromania (hab-rō-mā′ni-à) *Obs.* General term for morbid gaiety.

hadephobia (hā-dē-fō′bi-à) Fear of hell.

Haeckel's biogenetic law (Ernst Heinrich Haeckel, German naturalist, 1834–1919) According to this formula, 'the child is on a lower developmental level of mankind than the adult.' In other words, the child is 'universally criminal.' In the child all the criminal drives of humanity are latent. Following Haeckel's conception, Stekel asserts that 'phrases about purity and innocence in the child are empty.' Compulsive acts are protective measures against the evil of one's self. A neurosis arises when the instinctual criminal drives are too powerfully developed. This means a regression to the infantile level. (Stekel, W. *Compulsion and Doubt,* Liveright, New York, 1949) See *law, biogenetic mental.*

haem(at)o- See *hem(at)o-.*

'half-show' A modification of puppet show technique in psychotherapy of children in which the patient sees only that part of the puppet show which presents or states a problem in dramatic fashion. When the conflict is at its height, the show is stopped with the promise that it will be continued later. Then the subject or group is asked what should happen. The solutions suggested, of course, are colored by the child's own problems, and the child will try to unravel the conflict in terms of his own constitution, background, emotional involvement, and general level of maturity.

Hall, G(ranville) Stanley (1844–1924) American psychologist and sexologist.

hallucinate (ha-lū′si-nāt) To have a sense perception for which there is no external reality.

hallucinatio hypochondriasis (hàl-loo-kēnä′tē-ō hē-pô-kôn-drē-ä′zēs) An obsolete expression for *hypochondriasis.*

hallucination (ha-lū-si-nā′shun) An apparent perception of an external object when no such object is present. A paranoid patient, sitting alone in a quiet room, complains that his persecutors who are miles away speak directly to him in derogatory terms; moreover, he believes implicitly that he feels electrical stimuli over the entire body, the stimuli coming, he alleges, from a machine operated by his persecutors. The auditory and tactile stimuli have no source in the environment; rather they are sensations arising within the patient himself. A hallucination is a *sense perception* to which there is no external stimulus. In the instances cited the *sensations* are *hallucinations.* The *false beliefs* regarding persecutors are *delusions;* a delusion is a *belief* that is obviously contrary to demonstrable fact.

When the same paranoid patient, sitting alone in an otherwise quiet room, upon hearing the crackling of the floor-boards, is firmly 'convinced' that the crackling sounds like those of a telegraph ticker are messages from the persecutors to him (the patient), he misinterprets actual stimuli from the environment. An *illusion* is a false impression from a real stimulus. But the text he thereupon reads into these messages is a *delusion.* See also *illusion; delusion.*
Obs. Fallacia.

hallucination, auditory (aw′di-tō-rē) See *hallucination, haptic.*

hallucination, auditory peripheric (per-ifer′ik) An auditory illusion (mainly hearing of voices) experienced as a result of auditory sensory stimulation, as the pouring of water, rumpling of paper, a person's walking, etc.

hallucination, diminutive visual *Hallucination, Lilliputian* (q.v.).

hallucination, elementary 'As *elementary hallucinations* in the optic field we designate such unformed visions as lighting, sparks, and cloudlike partial darkening of the visual field, and in the acoustic field, the simple noises such as murmurs, knocks, and shooting.' (Bleuler, E. *Textbook of Psychiatry*, tr. by Brill, A.A., Macmillan, New York, 1930)

hallucination, extracampine (eks'trà-kam'pīn) 'Remarkable are the "extracampine" hallucinations which are localized outside of the sensory field in question. In the nature of the thing one deals mostly with visions, the patient sees with perfect sensory distinctness the devil behind his head, but it may also concern the sense of touch; thus the patient feels how streams of water come out from a definite point of his hand.' (Bleuler, E. *Textbook of Psychiatry*, tr. by Brill, A.A., Macmillan, New York, 1930)

hallucination, genital A hallucination regarding which 'patients complain that they are the victims of obscenity.' (Magnan, V. 'Chronic Delusional Insanity of Systematic Evolution,' *American Journal of Insanity LII*: 46, 1895–96.) *Obs.*

hallucination, gustatory See *hallucination, haptic.*

hallucination, haptic (hap'tik) A haptic hallucination is one associated with the sensation of touch. A paranoid patient complained that his persecutors, operating an electrical apparatus hidden in the walls of the building, induced very disagreeable sensations over his body through the machine.

Alleged persecutors reach the patient's body through many avenues, among which are the sensory zones. In clear-cut cases of schizophrenia the persecutors aspire to tempt the patient to engage in homosexual practices. Indeed, they constantly stimulate him sexually through the several sense areas. 'He operates a machine that masturbates me' is a common expression among paranoid schizophrenic patients. The persecutors are said also to surround the patient with 'bad sexual odors' (olfactory hallucination); they put 'scum' (sem-

inal fluid) in his food (gustatory or taste hallucination); they call him a sexual pervert with men (auditory hallucination); they grimace at him, meaning he is homosexual (visual hallucination).

hallucination, hypnagogic (hip-nà-goj'ik) Same as *imagery, hypnagogic.*

hallucination, induced A hallucination aroused in one individual by another, such as may occur, for example, during hypnosis. See *association, psychosis of.*

hallucination, Lilliputian (lil-i-pū'shan) (From the six-inch-tall inhabitants of the island of Lilliput, in Jonathan Swift's (1667–1745) *Gulliver's Travels*) As a rule Lilliputian hallucinations occur in psychiatric states associated with febrile or intoxicating conditions. They may be observed in the absence of recognizable organic disorders. When objects, generally persons, appear greatly reduced in size, it is said that the patient has Lilliputian or microptic hallucinations. The term should be used only when true hallucination is present, that is, when there is no object in the environment that stimulates the perception. When a real object is misinterpreted by a patient, the condition is called an illusion. Certain patients, notably those with idiopathic epilepsy, while actually looking at objects, may believe them to be extremely diminutive; this constitutes an illusion.

hallucination, macroptic (mak-rop'tik) See *macropsia.*

hallucination, memory When material repressed into the unconscious returns to consciousness in disguised form, that is, in the form of a visual image, Freud calls the latter a memory-hallucination. He says: 'The paranoiac memory-hallucination undergoes a distortion similar to that of the obsessional neurosis—an analogous current image takes the place of the repressed one. . . .' (Freud, S. *Collected Papers*, vol. 1, tr. by Riviere, J., Leonard and Virginia Woolf and The Institute of Psychoanalysis, London, 1924–25)

hallucination, microptic (mī-krop'tik) See *hallucination, Lilliputian.*

hallucination, motor An older term for *hallucination, psychomotor* (q.v.).

hallucination, negative A *negative hallucination* is not a hallucination at all; the expression refers to the condition in which an individual fails to see an object while apparently looking at it. It is a phenomenon that can be induced through hypnosis.

hallucination, negative memory This expression designates a denial (of a so-called hallucinatory character) of something that the patient really has experienced. 'Thus a patient, like all the others, received cigars for Christmas; he smoked them quickly and then began to scold, because cigars were given to all patients except to him.' (Bleuler, E. *Textbook of Psychiatry,* tr. by Brill, A.A., Macmillan, New York, 1930)

hallucination of conception See *hallucination of perception.*

hallucination of perception An auditory hallucination in which the patient hears the sound or noise as coming from outside himself, in contrast to hallucination of conception (or, in Baillarger's terminology, psychic hallucination), in which inner voices are heard.

hallucination, olfactory See *hallucination, haptic.*

hallucination, psychic (sī′kik) *Obs.* 'An hallucination which is purely mental, having no relation to any supposed external object.' (Tuke, D.H. *A Dictionary of Psychological Medicine,* vols. 1–2, Blakiston, Philadelphia, 1892) This is in essence the current definition of the word *hallucination,* used alone.

Some authorities today use the expression *psychic hallucinations* for 'inspired' thoughts. (Bleuler, E. *Textbook of Psychiatry,* tr. by Brill, A.A., Macmillan, New York, 1930) See *hallucination of perception.*

hallucination, psychomotor (sī-kō-mō′tĕr) A patient's sensation that certain parts of his body are being transferred to body regions distant from their natural location.

hallucination, psycho-sensorial (sī-kō-sen-sō′ri-al) Baillarger distinguished two kinds of hallucinations—psycho-sensorial and psychic. He said that the first are the result of the combined action of the imagination and of the organs of sense, while the second are the result of the imagination without the interposition of a sensory stimulus.

hallucination, reflex A sensory impression induced through stimulation of a distant and different sensory area is called a *reflex hallucination.* 'An auditory sensation may in this way arise from irritation in the

region of the inferior alveolar nerve (carious tooth).' (Henderson, D.K. and Gillespie, R.D. *A Text-Book of Psychiatry,* 4th ed., Oxford University Press, London, 1936.) The use of the term *hallucination* in this sense is obsolete.

hallucination, retroactive (ret-rō-ak′tiv) Synonymous with *memory-hallucination.*

hallucination, slow-motion The sensation of inordinate slowness of body motion. One of Lippman's patients described it as 'a sensation of "slowing down." All my motions seem very slow. I try to move faster, and seem to move even more slowly. At the same time, everything around me seems to move very fast.' (Lippman, C.W. 'Hallucinations in Migraine,' *American Journal of Psychiatry CVII,* No. 11, May 1951)

hallucination, space-motor Lippman defines this form of hallucination as the 'sensation of acceleration involving the entire body.' (Lippman, C.W. 'Hallucinations in Migraine,' *American Journal of Psychiatry CVII,* No. 11, May 1951)

hallucination, teleologic (tel-ē-ō-loj′ik, or tē-lē-) When a patient is advised through a hallucination about what course he should take, it is said that he has a teleologic hallucination.

hallucination, unilateral (ū-ni-lat′ĕr-al) A term used when 'the hallucination is unilateral and affects only one side of the bilateral sensorial apparatus. The patient is influenced only through one eye, one ear, or one side of the body.' (Magnan, V. 'Chronic Delusional Insanity of Systematic Evolution,' *American Journal of Insanity LV:* 44, 1895–96)

hallucination, vestibular (ves-tib′ū-lĕr) (L. *vestibulum,* forecourt, our *vestibule,* anteroom, in Anat. the approach to the cochlea of the internal ear) In psychiatry this term describes false sensory perceptions that come from irritation of the vestibular apparatus. This form of hallucination is referred mainly to visual and tactile organs. The better to understand the mechanism by which this particular hallucination arises, we have only to consider the strong influences of the vestibular apparatus on the spheres of vision and touch. Visual images (real or imaginary) are affected by vestibular function. Under vestibular irritation these images show changes such as occur when the individual is submitted to passive rotating movement.

In such experimental circumstances, there are certain typical movements, or deviations of the optic image. In one experiment, related by Bibring-Lehner, the individual, while turning, imagines a child: this image seems to turn in the same direction as the subject under experiment. Sometimes a half of the image disappears and often the colors become gray during the turning, but the most remarkable features are the multiplication of the image, and its reduction in size. According to Schilder, this is very important, 'because it shows that turning induces the same changes in optic images as in optic vision.' In alcoholic hallucinations one may also observe vestibular phenomena. Indeed, Schilder describes the case of a patient who said: 'Sometimes I saw three or four people on the street instead of one. I saw three faces in glaring white; faces of Negroes and whites. They moved forwards and backwards and when I saw them they started to chase me. I felt them behind me.' In psychosis, the vestibular influences are not related exclusively to the visual sphere, but one also encounters marked changes in the feelings that the patient has about his own body. It should be mentioned that sensations of the body's lightness or heaviness are closely related to vestibular functions. (Schilder, P. *Mind, Perception and Thought*, Columbia University Press, New York, 1942)

hallucination, visual See *hallucination, haptic.*

hallucinogen (ha-lū-sin'ō-jen) Any substance capable of producing hallucinations in an experimental subject. See *psychotomimetic.*

hallucinosis (ha-lū-si-nō'sis) The state of experiencing sensory stimuli to which there is no discoverable reality. Thus, a paranoid patient who hears voices, who feels the electricity that his persecutors send forth at him, who smells the bad odors that they force upon him and who tastes poison in the food, when there is no possible validity to any of these assertions, is said to be in a state of hallucinosis.

hallucinosis, acute The sudden appearance of a psychotic picture with hallucinations. Confusion, panic, and excitement frequently ensue. Acute hallucinosis most commonly appears after traumata, such as operations or childbirth, and drug intoxication, as in alcoholism and opiate addiction. In these cases, hallucinations usually represent wish-fulfillments and the abandonment of reality testing. When the individual is not fully able to rid himself of the awareness of his own defects, the hallucinations may also be a projection of these defects onto his environment.

The clearest example of acute hallucinosis is *alcoholic hallucinosis.* This term is probably a misnomer, alcohol being only a symptom of the underlying instability that gives rise to the syndrome called alcoholic hallucinosis. The syndrome itself is presumably a reaction type dependent upon constitutional and emotional factors, rather than upon alcohol, which is merely a precipitating factor. It is likely that this is also the case in other examples of acute hallucinosis and that the term should be considered as purely descriptive, referring to a reaction pattern determined basically by the psychological constitution of the individual. In acute hallucinosis, there is ordinarily a slow return to normal within a period of weeks. If the symptoms become chronic, it is usually considered to be a schizophrenic reaction.

hallucinosis, alcoholic It is the custom to describe alcoholic hallucinosis as a clinical entity. The onset of the disorder is usually acute, following heavy indulgence in alcohol, or the hallucinosis may appear in a predisposed individual after a relatively small intake. The hallucinations are principally auditory and as a rule the voices he hears talk about him rather than to him. They plot to harm him, enumerate his sins, and plan measures for torturing and punishing him. Often the patient is intensely frightened, seeking the protection of authorities, such as the police. Not infrequently there are auditory illusions, the patient misinterpreting, for example, the sound connected with the closing of a door as a pistol shot directed at him. Likewise there may be visual illusions; a patient may interpret anything hazy to his vision as the form of an enemy. Delusions of persecution are common, though they are not well systematized. Orientation and memory are not necessarily disturbed.

The affects are often characterized by an admixture of anxiety and humor; it appears that the patient at times understands the incongruity of his ideas and emotions and laughs at their absurdity.

hallucinosis, diabetic Hallucinatory state associated with diabetes.

hallucinosis, uremic Hallucinatory states associated with kidney disease.

hamartophobia (hà-mär-tō-fō′bi-à) Fear of error or sin. 'Hamartophobia is intensified by calamity that brings out the next world, prompting self-stupration and the misologism that loves to see reason collapse and often plunges the soul into deep melancholy and despair. Horror of sin may make self-mortification a frenzy.' (Hall, G.S. *Adolescence,* Appleton, New York, 1908, p. 310)

Hand-Christian-Schüller's syndrome *Xanthomatosis* (q.v.).

handicap, collective life A term used in social work to refer to 'any disability (physical, mental, or emotional) which limits or threatens the patient's normal range of social intercourse, association, and enjoyment of fellowship.' (Hamilton, G. *A Medical Social Terminology,* Presbyterian Hospital, New York, 1930)

handicap, family life In social work this means 'any disability (physical, mental, or emotional) which definitely interferes with or limits either one's capacities for home making or for marriage.' (Hamilton, G. *A Medical Social Terminology,* Presbyterian Hospital, New York, 1930)

handicraft Manual art or trade, used as a means of treatment in occupational therapy.

hand-to-mouth reaction See *reaction, hand-to-mouth.*

Hans The patient on whom Freud reported in his 1909 paper, 'Analysis of a Phobia in a Five-Year-Old Boy.' The initial phobia of little Hans was directed to horses, and analysis revealed that the phobia represented the father, against whom Hans nourished jealous and hostile wishes because of rivalry for the mother. One interesting feature of this case is that the analytic treatment was carried out by the father, who corresponded with Freud and received the latter's suggestions about interpretation and technique by mail.

haphalgesia (haf-al-jē′zi-à) See *aphalgesia.*

haphephobia (haf-ē-fō′bi-à) See *haptephobia.*

haploid (hap′loid) In the maturation of a reproductive cell this genetic term refers to the stage in which the number of chromosomes is halved following the reduction division. This reduced number is called haploid as constrasted with the original or *diploid* number (see *diploid*).

haploidy (hap′loid-ē) The genetic process known as the reduction division of reproductive cells results in *haploidy* as the stage of meiosis at which the number of chromosomes per cell is reduced to half. Consequently, the haploid number of chromosomes in all daughter cells is just half as large as their original or *diploid* number in the cells from which they are derived (see *diploidy*).

haplology (hap-lo′lō-jē) Omission of syllables in words because of speed in speech; seen often in mania and in schizophrenic syndromes in which there is pressure of speech.

haptephobia (hap-tē-fō′bi-à) Fear of being touched.

haptophonia (hap-tō-fō-ni-à) The hearing of noises or voices in response to tactile or haptic stimulation. One patient, for example, complained of hearing voices coming from his forearm, where there was the scar of an old injury.

harmatophobia (här-mà-tō-fō′bi-à) A common misprint for *hamartophobia* (q.v.).

harmine (har′mēn) See *psychotomimetic.*

harpaxophobia (här-pak-sō-fō′bi-à) Fear of robbers.

hate, fetish Antifetishism.

haut mal (ō màl′) (F. 'high disease') Major (epileptic) attack; grand mal.

'During an epileptic fit the patient is unconscious; and, after it, he has no memory whatever of the events of the fit. His mind is a blank from the moment the fit begins until he wakes from the sleep which usually succeeds the attack of *haut mal.*' (Mercier, C. *Criminal Responsibility,* The Clarendon Press, Oxford, 1905)

Hd Rorschach scoring symbol for a response of parts of the human figure.

headache, histamine See *histamine.*

headache, lead-cap In describing neurasthenic symptoms Church and Peterson write that 'one describes a sensation as if the head were splitting or the skull lifting; another has a terrible weight or a severe constriction about the head. This *lead-cap headache* is very common.' (Church, A. and Peterson, F., *Nervous and Mental Diseases,* 8th ed., Saunders, Philadelphia and London, 1916)

head-banging One of the many typical physical exertions commonly observed during a temper-tantrum in small children. The child works itself up to a pitch of excitement and by almost every conceivable physical or muscular movement literally 'throws itself all over the place.'

head-knocking A habit developed by some infants which consists of bumping the head against the crib sides or other objects. (Pearson, G.H.J. *Emotional Disorders of Children,* Norton, New York, 1949)

head-rolling A psychiatric term denoting the rhythmical, semi-circular movement of the head exhibited by some children. When sufficiently constant, this movement may be considered similar to tics in its nature. In some instances, the rolling of the head may be attributed to restraint of movement in the crib and, in other instances, to absence of play material (monotony). It seems that in other cases it may have as its origin the passivity of the foetus during intra-uterine life. In these cases the rolling of the head will represent a hyperactive function which serves as a balance for the intra-uterine inactivity. (Pearson, G.H.J. *Emotional Disorders of Children,* Norton, New York, 1949)

health-conscience See *conscience, health.*

hearing, color Color hearing is usually believed to be a hallucinatory disturbance, characterized by a sensation of color when sounds are heard. A schizophrenic patient said that people talked to him in colors, meaning that colors occurred to him when he heard voices.

heart, soldier's See *neurasthenia, war.*

hebephrenia (hē-be-frē'ni-à) A symptom-complex now considered a chronic form of schizophrenia. In 1871 Hecker described hebephrenia and the heboid, and in 1896 Kraepelin included hebephrenia in the group dementia praecox. See *schizophrenia.*

hebephrenia, depressive Some patients with the hebephrenic form of schizophrenia run, for some time, a course that resembles the periodic changes observed in manic-depressive psychosis. When the constituents of a depression appear in hebephrenia, the state is known as *depressive hebephrenia.* When there is similarity to a manic phase, it is known as *manic hebephrenia.*

hebephrenia, engrafted Thus Kraepelin calls the cases of schizophrenia superimposed 'upon an already existing disease.' By 'existing disease' he referred to 'a considerable degree of psychic weakness' beginning in childhood. From his description it appears that when he refers to 'existing disease' he has in mind what is today called schizoidism, which is not regarded as a 'disease' in the sense that the term 'disease' has in medicine commonly. (Kraepelin, E. *Dementia Praecox and Paraphrenia,* tr. by Barclay, R.M., Livingstone, Edinburgh, 1919)

hebephrenia, manic See *hebephrenia, depressive.*

hebephrenic schizophrenia See *schizophrenia, hebephrenic.*

hebetude (hē'be-tūd) In current psychiatry this term usually means emotional dullness or disinterest. It is most characteristically expressed in schizophrenia in which the pronounced withdrawal of interest from the environment and apparently, in late cases, from the patient himself causes the patient to appear thoroughly listless; unemotional, disinterested, apathetic.

'In the severer forms of schizophrenia the *"affective dementia"* is the most striking symptom. In the sanatoria there are patients sitting around who for decades show no affect no matter what happens to them or to those about them. They are indifferent to maltreatment; left to themselves they lie in wet and frozen beds, do not bother about hunger and thirst. They have to be taken care of in all respects. Toward their own delusions they are often strikingly indifferent.' (Bleuler, E. *Textbook of Psychiatry,* tr. by Brill, A A., Macmillan, New York, 1930)

An older meaning of hebetude included listlessness or apathy from any cause, physical or mental. It is still sometimes used in this sense.

hebetudo animi (he-be-tōō'dô à'nē-mē) (L. 'dullness of spirit') *Obs.* Imbecility.

hebetudo mentis (men'tēs) (L. 'dullness of mind') *Obs.* Imbecility.

heboidophrenia (hē-boid-ō-frē'ni-à) This

term, not too common today, was first used by Kahlbaum for the simple form of dementia praecox (schizophrenia).

heboid praecox See *praecox, heboid.*

Hecker, Ewald (1843–1909) German psychiatrist; known from his studies in hebephrenia, which term was coined by him.

-hedonia (-hē-dō'ni-à) combining form meaning pleasure, from Gr. *hēdonē'*, delight, enjoyment, pleasure.

hedonic level See *psychodynamics, adaptational.*

hedonism (hē'don-iz'm) A philosophic doctrine in which pleasure or happiness is presented as the supreme good. In psychiatry, hedonism refers to the seeking of certain goals because they afford some type of gratification. Hedonism, then, is in opposition to the doctrine that goals may be sought as ends in themselves, irrespective of the pleasure or gratification they give the individual. See *hormism.*

hedonophobia (hē-don-ō-fō'bi-à) Fear of pleasure.

heel-to-knee test See *test, heel-to-knee.*

Heine-Medin disease (Jacob Heine, German physician, 1800–1879, and Karl Oshar Medin, Swedish physician, 1847–1928) *Poliomyelitis* (q.v.).

heir of the Oedipus complex The expression is common in psychoanalysis. 'Throughout, he appears to assume that the superego, which we know to be the heir of the Oedipus complex, results in this way from the incorporation of the parental figure that had to be given up in its sexual connection.' (Jones, E. *Papers on Psycho-Analysis,* 4th ed., Wood, Baltimore, 1938)

heliophobia (hē-li-ō-fō'bi-à) Fear of sunlight.

Heller's disease (Theodore Heller, German neuropsychiatrist, early twentieth century) See *dementia infantilis.*

helmet, neurasthenic (nū-ras-thē-nik) A feeling of pressure over the entire cranium in certain cases of neurasthenia, as if from a tight-pressing helmet.

Helmholtz See *accommodation.*

helper, magic Fromm's term describing a particular form of interpersonal relationship. Man has today become aware of himself as a separate entity. The growing realization of his separateness gives him a

sense of isolation and a longing to return to the earlier feeling of solidarity with others. So he uses certain irrational methods of relating back to the group, and these are termed mechanisms of escape. One method is to seek to lean on another for support. The other person represents a power or authority who can be used for that purpose. Sometimes the individual expects the other person to solve all his problems for him and endows the person with almost magical omnipotence. This other person is then termed the 'magic helper.' It is obvious that the person so endowed with magical power must himself be affected by it and to a degree be dependent on it. The power he has illustrates a form of *irrational authority* (q.v.), which is based not on competence but on a neurotic need for power.

helplessness, psychic A term used by Freud to characterize the state that occasions the first expression of anxiety in early infancy. Freud describes anxiety as a state of unpleasure in which there is an increase of excitation relieved through physiologic discharge phenomena such as an increase in the respiratory and pulse rates, rise in blood pressure, etc. The prototype of this experience of anxiety is seen as the experience of birth, in which the above-described sensations and responses first occur. All later anxiety states are reproductions of this earliest experience. Anxiety as experienced in later life, however, is clearly a response to a danger-situation. Thus some type of danger is understood to be associated with the production of anxiety from the time of its earliest appearance.

Initially, in birth, this danger is merely the increased quantity and intensity of stimuli which necessitates a discharge through respiratory, cardiovascular, and other pathways. Later, this increase in unpleasurable stimuli will occur in the infant every time his needs for food, warmth, etc. are not gratified. The infant is psychically unable to cope with these needs and thus provide for their discharge. This is 'a situation analogous to the birth experience, a repetition of the danger-situation; what the two situations have in common is the economic disturbance brought about by an increase in stimuli demanding some disposition be made of them, this common factor hence being the very essence of the "danger." In both cases the reaction of anxiety appears. . .' Freud describes as psychic helplessness this anxiety-invested danger-situation in which the small infant is powerless to gratify his needs. Later on, as the infant experiences the fact that 'an external and perceptible object, i.e. the mother, may put an end to the danger-situation reminiscent of birth,' the content of the danger becomes object loss or loss of the mother. What is now dangerous for the infant is absence of the mother, who satisfies his needs. Without her, it is possible that he might again be swept with the unpleasurable stimuli reminiscent of birth and associated with nongratification.

As the child continues to develop, other danger-situations arise, such as castration threats and dread of the superego. The early danger-situation of psychic helplessness is important chiefly in the 'period of immaturity of the ego' and grows less important as the ego develops and the later danger-situations of object loss, castration, and others successively emerge. The earliest danger-situations such as psychic helplessness may persist, however, and cause the ego to react with anxiety at a later period. Freud suggests that the form of the neurosis that develops in a given patient may be closely related to the variety of danger-situation typical of that particular patient. (Freud, S. *The Problem of Anxiety,* Norton, New York, 1936)

hematidrosis (hem-à-ti-drō′sis) Bloody perspiration.

hemato- (hē′mà-tō-, hem′à-) combining form meaning blood, from Gr. *haïma, -atos,* blood.

hematophobia (hem-à-tō-fō′bi-à) See *hemophobia.*

hemeralopia (hem-ẽr-à-lō′pi-à) Day-blindness; vision is poor by day, in bright light, and good in dim light; the opposite of *nyctalopia.*

hemeraphonia (-fō′ni-à) Voicelessness during daytime, usually a symptom of hysteria.

hemi- (hem′i-) a prefix meaning, *half-, semi,* from Gr. *hēmi-,* half.

hemianopia, hemianopsia (i-an-op′i-à, -op′si-à) See *field defect.*

hemianopsia, heteronymous (het-ẽr-on′imus) Bitemporal or binasal loss of vision.

hemianopsia, homonymous (hō-mon′imus) Loss of vision in the similarly situated (*both right,* or *both left*) halves of

one's eyes, i.e. in the nasal half of one eye and in the temporal half of the other.

hemianthropia (hem-i-an-thrō′pi-à) *Obs.* Insanity.

hemiatrophy, facial (-a′tro-fē) Parry-Romberg's syndrome. A trophic disorder, perhaps due to disturbance of the sympathetic nervous system, in which there is progressive wasting of some or all of the tissues of one side of the face, which as a result looks old and wrinkled. The disorder usually begins during the second decade; it causes no disability.

hemiballism (-bal′iz′m) Violent, uncontrollable shaking, twisting, and rolling movements involving one side of the body, occurring as a result of hemorrhage into the subthalamic body.

hemichorea (-kō-rē′a) Chorea affecting one side of the body only.

hemichorea, hysterical Hemichorea due to hysteria.

hemichorea, paralytic (par-à-lit′ik) Hemichorea associated with hemiplegia.

hemichorea, post-hemiplegic (post-hem-i-plej′ik, -plē′jik) Hemichorea following an attack of hemiplegia.

hemichorea, preparalytic (prē-par-à-lit′-ik) A condition in which unilateral choreic movements precede an attack of hemiplegia.

hemichorea, rheumatica (hà-mē-kô-rā′à rew-mà′tē-kà) Hemichorea coexistent with 'rheumatism.'

hemichorea, syphilitic (sif-i-lit′ik) Hemichorea due to syphilis.

hemicrania (-krā′ni-à) Migraine; see *megrim, magrums.*

hemiparesis (-par′ē-sis) Slight paralysis or weakness of only one side of the body.

hemiplegia (-plē′ji-à) A symptom-complex and not a disease, characterized by paralysis of one side of the body.

hemiplegia alternans (al′ter-nans) Crossed paralysis; paralysis of one or more cranial nerves and paralysis of the arm and leg of the opposite side. Hypoglossal hemiplegia alternans involves the twelfth cranial nerve; Weber's syndrome involves the oculomotor (third cranial) nerve.

hemiplegia cruciata (hà-mē-plā′gè-à kroo-kē-ä′tà) (Mod.L. 'crossed hemiplegia') Paralysis of an upper extremity and of the lower extremity on the side opposite to that of the upper extremity.

hemo- (hē′mō-, hem′ō-) Same as *hemato-*.

hemophobia, hematophobia (hē-mō-, hem-à-tō-fō′bi-à) Fear of blood.

hemoptysis, hysterical (hē-mop′ti-sis; hem-op′) Vomiting of blood, caused originally through psychic disorder.

hemorrhage, cerebral (hem-ēr-rēj) See *accident, cerebrovascular.*

hemothymia (hē-mō-thim′i-à, -thī′mi-à) Passion for blood; morbid impulse to murder.

hepatolenticular degeneration Wilson's disease. See *degeneration, hepatolenticular.*

herbivorous (hēr-biv′ō-rus) While in zoology this term applies to animals (herbivora) subsisting on herbaceous plants or vegetables, in constitutional medicine it designates a type described by Bryant and corresponding roughly to Kretschmer's *athletic* type and its equivalents in other systems.

Herculeus morbus (her-koo′le-oos môr′-boos) (L. 'Herculean disease') An old term for epilepsy, supposedly because of the epileptic's Herculean violence and strength.

herd See *instinct, herd.*

hereditary, hereditarial (he-red′i-ter-ē, -târ′i-al) The term is used with reference to both the Mendelian mechanism by which physical or mental attributes are transmitted from one generation to another, and to the inherited attributes to which an individual is predisposed by the presence of a certain gene or combination of genes.

hereditary cerebellar ataxia of Marie See *ataxia, Marie's hereditary cerebellar.*

hereditary spastic paraplegia See *paraplegia, hereditary spastic.*

heredito-constitutional (he-red′i-tō-kon-sti-tū′shun-al) In the modern era of physiological genetics this term denotes those genetic elements in the individual constitution of an organism which have been derived from its original genotype (see *constitution*).

heredity (he-red′i-tē) As it has become customary to use the terms *inheritance* and *transmission* for designating the actual genetic process by which physical or mental traits are transmitted from parents to offspring, *heredity* has a more general and abstract sense—of classifying the process of inheritance as a biological phenomenon and identifying it with the forces responsible for the resemblance between an individual and his ancestors, insofar as this resemblance is due to the operation of predisposing gene units rather than to the similarity of environmental influences.

The morphological equivalent of heredity is the *Mendelian* mechanism based on the integrity of the chromosomes and their continuity from one cell generation to the next, while the science dealing with the study of heredity is usually called *genetics.* See *Mendelism.*

heredo-familial essential microsomia (mī-krō-sō′mi-à) See *dwarfism.*

heritable (her′it-à-b′l) A general genetic term synonymous with *inheritable* (q.v.).

hermaphrodism (hēr-maf′rō-diz'm) Hermaphroditism.

hermaphrodism, psychical Adler's term for the constant striving of the individual to free himself from feelings of weakness, inferiority, and futility to attain self-confidence, superiority and self-gratification. It is the conflict in each individual, between the masculine and feminine components.

'The normal craving of the child for nestling, the exaggerated submissiveness of the neurotically-disposed individual, the feeling of weakness, of inferiority protected by hyper-sensitiveness, the realization of actual futility, the sense of being permanently pushed aside and of being at a disadvantage, all these are gathered together into a feeling of femininity. On the contrary, active strivings, both in the case of a girl as of a boy, the pursuit of self-gratification, the stirring up of instincts and passions are thrown challengingly forward as a masculine protest. On the basis of a false evaluation, but one which is extensively nourished by our social life, there thus develops a *psychical hermaphrodism* of the child, "logically" dependent upon its inward opposition. From within itself is then unfolded that frequently unconscious urge toward a reinforced masculine protest which is to represent the solution for the disharmony.' (Adler, A. *The Practice and Theory of Individual Psychology,* tr. by Radin, P., Kegan Paul, Trench, Trubner, London, 1924)

hermaphrodite (-dīt) One who has the

reproductive organs of both sexes; a bisexual individual.

hermaphroditism (hĕr-maf'rō-dit-iz'm) State of being a hermaphrodite; bisexuality. This term signifies the biological phenomenon of *bisexuality* (q.v.) occurring either synchronously or heterochronously and originating in the production of both male and female gametes by the same individual. There are two types of hermaphroditism:
I. The *non-functional,* when both male and female germ cells are provided transiently or permanently, yet only one kind of germ cells functions. Of this type there are 3 forms:
(1) *accessory,* when, in addition to the testis there is a *rudimentary ovary,* which, however, does not reproduce ova.
(2) *accidental,* with sporadic occurrence of ova in the testis or of spermatic tissues in the ovary.
(3) *teratological* (common in birds and mammals) when the reproductive system presents an intimate mixture of male and female structures.
II. The *functional,* when both male and female gametes, produced by one and the same individual, are functioning. Of this type which is characterized by *monoecism* (q.v.), also, there are 3 forms:
(1) *unisexual monoecism,* when at certain times a genetic female develops spermatozoa in the ovary (*gynomonoecism*) or a genetic male develops ova in the testis (*andromonoecism,* less common), so that one sex becomes hermaphroditic, i.e. the individual previously functioning as (1) female (2 male) now functions as (1) male (2 female).
(2) *consecutive monoecism,* when a male later functions as a female, or (less commonly) a female later becomes a male. Genetically these organisms are either males or neutrals.
(3) *spatial monoecism,* manifesting real functional hermaphroditism is characterized by the presence of both male and female reproductive organs.

hermaphroditism, psychic (sī-kik) Bisexuality from the mental point of view.

herniation, lumbar disk (hĕr-nē-ā-shun) See *disk, herniated lumbar intervertebral.*

hero-birth, primordial image of Jung says: 'We can be certain only that, when a man is identical with his persona, the individual qualities are associated with the soul.

It is this association which gives rise to the symbol, so often appearing in dreams, of the soul's pregnancy; this symbol has its source in the primordial image of the hero-birth. The child that is to be born signifies the individuality, which, though existing, is not yet conscious. Hence in the same way as the persona, which expresses one's adaptation to the milieu, is as a rule strongly influenced and shaped by the milieu, so the soul is just as profoundly moulded by the unconscious and its qualities.' (Jung, C.G. *Psychological Types,* tr. by Baynes, H.G., Harcourt, Brace, New York and London, 1923)

heroinomania (her-ō-in-ō-mā'ni-à) Morbid craving for heroin.

hero-worship From the psychoanalytic point of view, hero-worship is a product of the need of the great majority of people 'for authority which they can admire, to which they can submit, and which dominates and sometimes even ill-treats them.' The need for such an authority is simply the longing of each individual for the father, for a father figure, this longing having persisted since childhood days. As a result of this need it is possible for a great man to rise to extraordinary significance in the lives of large masses of people so that he is regarded as a hero. This hero will have in particular the traits that are characteristic of the father. 'The decisiveness of thought, the strength of will, the forcefulness of his deeds, belong to the picture of the father; above all other things, however, the self-reliance and independence of the great man, his divine conviction of doing the right thing, which may pass into ruthlessness. He must be admired, he may be trusted, but one cannot help also being afraid of him.' (Freud, S. *Moses and Monotheism,* Hogarth Press, London, 1939)

Hertwig-Magendie phenomenon (hert'-viK-mà-zhäN-dē') (Oscar Hertwig, German physiologist, 1849–1922, and François Magendie, French physiologist, 1783–1855) See *deviation, skew.*

hetaera (hē-tē'rà) A classical synonym for mistress or concubine.

hetaerism (-'riz'm) *Rare.* Concubinage; a state of common law or natural, as opposed to civil marriage.

hetero- (het'ĕr-ō-) combining form, meaning *other, different,* from Gr. *héteros,* the other, one of two.

heterocentric (-sen'trik) Directed away from oneself; opposed to autocentric.

hetero-erotic (-e-rot'ik) Relating to the attachment of libido (Eros) to objects outside of oneself, and specifically to objects of the opposite sex.

hetero-erotism (-er'ō-tiz'm) The attachment (cathexis) of the energy of the erotic instinct to objects outside of oneself, and specifically to objects of the opposite sex. If one uses the term *libido* synonymously with *Eros,* then hetero-erotism is hetero-libido or object-libido.

heterogamous (-og'à-mus) This is a genetic term relating to the structural and functional differences between the male and female gametes, as they appear in most animals and plants. See *syngamy.*

heterogeneity, heterogeny (-ō-jē-nē'i-tē, -oj'ē-nē) Dissimilarity in the genotypical structure of individuals originating through sexual reproduction. See *homogeny.*

hetero-hypnosis (-hip-nō'sis) Hypnosis induced by another, in contradistinction to auto-hypnosis. 'Hypnosis generally takes place in consequence of some incident by means of which the idea of hypnosis is induced; this often happens when the subject has been frequently hypnotized. Certainly it is not always possible to make a sharp distinction between auto-hypnotism and hetero-hypnosis.' (Moll, A. *Hypnotism,* tr. by Hopkirk, A.F., Scribner, New York, 1909)

heterolalia (-lā'li-à) The substitution of meaningless or inappropriate words for those meant or intended.

heteronymous hemianopia (het-er-on'i-mus hem-i-an-op'i-à) See *field defect.*

heterophasia (-fā'zhi-à) Heterolalia.

heterophemy (-of'ē-mē) The saying of one thing when another is meant.

heterophonia (-ō-fō'ni-à) Heterolalia.

heterophoria (-for'i-à) Deviation of one eye because of muscular imbalance. Inward deviation is known as esophoria; outward deviation is exophoria; downward deviation is hypophoria; upward deviation is hyperphoria.

heterorexia (-rek'si-à) Alibert's term for morbid appetite; dysorexia.

heterosexuality Sexuality (in all its manifestations, normal and morbid) directed to the opposite sex. Jones defines it as 'love for a member of the opposite sex.'

From the psychoanalytic standpoint there are many factors that lead to heterosexuality; the final fate of inherent bisexuality (psychical and physical) comprises one of the basic factors. The structure of the superego is an important determinant; it is said that when the superego is derived from the parent of the same sex the result is heterosexuality. (Jones, E. *Papers on Psycho-Analysis,* 4th ed., Wood, Baltimore, 1938)

'If we assume that love for the opposite sex is inborn in the greater part of humanity, we must deduce that analogous phenomena hold true of the lesser part of mankind and that homosexual love is also inborn.' (Hirschfeld, M. *Encyclopaedia Sexualis,* edited by Robinson, V., Dingwall-Rock, New York, 1936)

'Real heterosexual object-love means that the love-object is realized and loved as another distinct personality, not as the reflection of the lover's self.' (Healy, W., Bronner, A.F., and Bowers, A.M. *The Structure and Meaning of Psychoanalysis,* Knopf, New York, 1930)

heterosis (het-ēr-ō'sis) The favorable influence of crossing on growth and other developmental properties of animals and plants, as exercised by an increase in heterozygocity in contrast to the decrease in vigor following inbreeding. *Genet.* The beneficial effect of heterosis is observed and utilized by breeders of animals and plants all over the world. It is best evidenced in the generation immediately following the cross, by: greater size, larger parts, increased longevity, and higher resistance to disease. As significant is also the fact that any form of hybrid vigor disappears rapidly under inbreeding.

The mule is commonly cited as a hybrid animal whose vigor, hardiness, and resistance to disease are due to heterosis.

heterosociality (-sō-shi-al'i-tē) Social relationship between members of the opposite sex (J.C. Fluegel).

heterosome (het'ēr-ō-sōm) In genetics, the pair of chromosomes which is differently related to the determination of sex. So named in order to distinguish it from all other chromosomes called *autosomes* (see *sex-determination*).

In human beings each sex has 24 pairs (=48) of chromosomes, known under the alphabet letters A, B, C, up to and including X. Each pair consists of two identical chromosomes having a special function to perform in the growth of a human being: to form hair or nails or teeth, etc. Each pair in a woman is identical with the corresponding (i.e. designated by the same alphabet letters A, K, P, etc.) pair in man in the first 23 pairs. The 24th pair (whose function is sex-differentiation) of a woman again has two identical chromosomes (XX); but in man the 24th pair consists of one X chromosome, identical with the woman's two, whereas the other, smaller in size, is different and is denoted by the letter Y. When this Y from the male sperm enters into the (X of the) female's egg for impregnation a male offspring is the result—otherwise a female is born.

hetero-suggestibility The state of influencing another; the opposite of auto- or self-suggestibility.

hetero-suggestion See *auto-suggestion*.

heterotopia (-tō′pi-à) Congenital displacement of gray matter of the spinal cord into the white substance.

heterozygocity (-zī-, zi-gos′i-tē) *Heterozygousness* (q.v.).

heterozygosis (-zī-, zi-gō′sis) *Heterozygousness* (q.v.).

heterozygote (-zī′gōt, -zig′ōt) A zygote which has been produced by the union of two dissimilar gametes and is heterozygous with respect to any pair of allelomorphs. In the case of a recessive factor, the heterozygotes transmit its predisposition to the offspring but do not develop the character in question themselves.

heterozygousness (-zī′gus-nes) This term (identical with *heterozygosity* or *heterozygocity*) relates to the genetic condition of an individual whose two genes of a given factor pair are *different*.

Only dominant characters can appear in the state of heterozygousness, while the heterozygotic condition of a recessive trait affects the organism merely 'germinally.' A heterozygotic individual transmits the trait to the offspring but is not able to manifest the trait in his own phenotype. See *inbreeding; heterosis*.

H.I. Hyperglycemic index. See *index, hyperglycemic*.

hibernation This term has been used to refer to prolonged sleep therapy, especially when this was accompanied by a lowering of the body temperature. High dosages of chlorpromazine, for instance, were used to keep patients in a continuous semi-somnolent state with a lowered body temperature; such treatment was called hibernation therapy.

hibernation (of ament) L. Down remarked that 'many cases of imbecility, particularly those of the Mongolian variety, lose a large amount of intellectual energy in the winter—go through, in fact, a process of hibernation, their mental power being always directly as the external temperature.' (Cited from Tredgold, A.F. *A Text-Book of Mental Deficiency,* 6th ed., Wood, Baltimore, 1937)

hiccough, hiccup A spasmodic myoclonous of the diaphragm producing a sudden inhalation of air which is interrupted by a spasmodic closure of the glottis, thus producing a sound which may simulate an ordinary cry or an unpleasant crow; also known as *singultus*.

hiccup, hysterical The hiccoughing due to mental causes. Déjérine and Gauckler say: 'A purely neuropathic hiccough is hardly ever found except in hysterics. After examining very carefully everything that pertains to this phenomenon . . . we could not help but believe that . . . it was due to a more or less voluntary—or, if you prefer it, a quasistimulated—contraction.' (Déjérine, J. and Gauckler, E. *The Psychoneuroses and Their Treatment by Psychotherapy,* 2nd ed., tr. by Jelliffe, S.E., Lippincott, Philadelphia and London, 1915)

hidden self See *personality, secondary*.

-hidrosis (-hi-drō′sis) Perspiration.

hieromania (hī-ēr-ō-mā′ni-à) *Obs.* Religious insanity.

hieronosus (-nō′sus) Linnaeus's term for epilepsy.

hierophobia Fear of sacred or religious things.

hindbrain Rhombencephalon, from which develop the metencephalon (cerebellum, pons, part of the fourth ventricle) and the myelencephalon (medulla oblongata and part of the fourth ventricle).

hindering, mania for Janet describes the symptom thus: 'Instead of simply resisting orders by refusing to perform the action which is commanded, the action which they dread, these patients try to check the activities of the persons with whom they come into contact, even when the latter ask nothing of them.' (Janet, P. *Psychological Healing,* vols. 1–2, tr. by Paul, E. and C., Macmillan, New York, 1925)

Hinkemann (hing′kē-män) This proper name is widely used in Germany for a castrated male. Hinkemann, the principal character of a play by the same name, written by Ernst Toller (1893–1939) lost his genitals as a result of injury sustained in the World War.

hippanthropy (hip-an′thrō-pē) A symptom in which a patient imagines he is a horse.

hippocampus (hip-ō-kam′pus) See *rhinencephalon.*

hippus (hip′us) A condition in which the pupil alternately contracts and dilates on stimulation with light.

Hirschfeld, Magnus (1868–1935) (hērsh′-felt) German sexologist.

histamine (his′ta-mēn) An amine occurring in all animal and vegetable tissues. Histamine dilates capillaries and arterioles, constricts the bronchioles, stimulates the smooth muscles of the uterus, and stimulates many glands of external secretion, especially the gastric glands. Intracutaneous injection of histamine produces focal erythema within 1–5 seconds, and within 30–50 seconds is seen a spreading flush (the histamine flare) and, later, a wheal. The flare reaction is dependent upon an intact arteriolar circulation and an intact axon reflex; hence it has been used in diagnosis of peripheral nerve lesions. Histamine has also been used in the determination of circulation time, in various gastric function tests, and in the diagnosis of histamine headache (histaminic cephalalgia, Horton's syndrome). The latter is a unilateral headache associated with redness of the eye, lacrimation, rhinorrhea or stuffiness of the nostril, swelling of the temporal vessels of the affected side, and dilatation of the vessels of the pain area (usually the orbital area).

Histamine has been used in the treatment of peripheral vascular disease, rheumatoid arthritis and Ménière's disease.

hoarding The practice of collecting any number of objects, generally of limited size and of no practical use. Hoarding is seen most commonly in deteriorated schizophrenics and in other organic cerebral disorders. Hoarding is one of the behavioral manifestations on which an opinion of *incompetency* (q.v.) may be based.

Hoch, August (1868–1919) (hōK) American psychiatrist.

Hoche, Alfred (1865–1943) (hō′Kē) German psychiatrist.

Hoch, Paul Henry (1902–) Hungarian-born psychiatrist; in U.S. since 1941; experimental psychiatry, treatment in psychiatry.

hodophobia (hod-ō-fō′bi-à) Fear of travel.

Hoffmann (or Tromner's) sign (Johann Hoffmann, 1857–1919, German neurologist.) In hemiplegia, due to organic brain disease, snapping of the index or ring finger produces flexion of the thumb.

hog A slang expression to describe a morphine or heroin addict who takes progressively increasing doses in order to be 'loaded.' See *user.*

holergasia (hol-ēr-gas′i-à) A psychiatric disorder of such a nature as to involve the *whole* person, so to speak. For example, schizophrenia and manic-depressive psychosis ordinarily are associated with a disorganization of the entire personality and the syndromes are, therefore, known as holergastic reactions.

holism (hō′liz'm) Holism is used in the sense of *Gestalt totality* and similar expressions. It also means in general that the study of parts cannot explain the whole, because the whole is something different from the simple summation of its parts. The application of the holistic principle to the study of human beings has far-reaching implications. We have a number of sciences *relating to* the person, but no science *of* the person. Physiology, psychology, and sociology deal with artificially separated single aspects of the human organism, but at present there is no single science that studies the human person in its totality. From a holistic point of view the human being is more than a mere aggregation of physiological, psychological, and social functions: the person as a whole has attributes that cannot be explained by the attributes of its constituent parts. (Angyal, A. *Foundations for a Science of Personality,* The Commonwealth Fund, Oxford University Press, New York, 1941)

Holmes, Gordon, rebound phenomenon of See *rebound.*

Homburger, August (1873–1930) (hôm'-boor-gĕr) German psychiatrist; known from his studies in psychopathology of children.

home, loveless From the standpoint of mental hygiene, this term is used to describe those homes in which an inharmonious atmosphere is prevalent as the result of constant discord among the members of the family, and where the children are made buffers between quarreling parents who have 'fallen out of love.' This is the type of surrounding that breeds delinquency. In these loveless homes the children are constantly exposed to traumatic experiences which have a definite influence in the development of neuroses and other mental disturbances. Furthermore, it is an established fact that such loveless homes have a much more deleterious effect upon the children's mental development than have the so-called 'broken homes' which seem to play a rather secondary role in this respect. (Seliger, R.V., *et al. Contemporary Criminal Hygiene,* Oakridge Press, Baltimore, 1946)

homeostasis (hō-mē-os'tā-sis) The status quo; the tendency of an organism to maintain a constancy and stability of its internal environment; the result of the various autonomic mechanisms which adjust and adapt the body as a whole to changes in the external or internal environment. Homeostasis is Cannon's term for a steady, balanced, internal constitution; Claude Bernard's term for this was 'milieu intérieur.' 'Autonomic adjustments, while allowing for necessary responses of the organism, must maintain a physiological state adequate for the needs of the tissues. . . . The physiological requirements of any tissue must be balanced against those of all others, and with minor fluctuations, a steady "internal constitution" maintained. . . . Forces pulling in opposite directions are equilibrated so as to give an appearance of rest.' (J.F. Fulton, *Physiology of the Nervous System,* 3rd ed., Oxford University Press, New York, 1949) In general, rapid adjustments are made by the autonomic nervous system while slower adjustments occur through chemical and hormonal influences.

homeostasis, psycho-affective See *affect-tonus.*

homesickness An acute separation syndrome appearing in dependent individuals when for any reasons they are removed from their usual sources of dependency gratification.

homichlophobia (hō-mik-lō-fō'bi-à) Fear of fog.

homicidomania (hom-i-sīd-ō-mā'ni-à) See *mania, homicidal.*

homilophobia (hom-il-ō-fō-bi-à) Fear of sermons; also, fear that in a group of people the others in the group might find something wrong with one's appearance, attire, or demeanor.

homo- (hō'mō-) Combining form from Gr. *homós,* one and the same, common; opposed to *hetero-.*

homoerotic Relating to or manifesting the erotic or libidinal instinct toward one of the same sex.

homoerotism, homoeroticism (-er'ō-tiz'm, -e-rot'i-siz'm) A general term for the objectivation of erotic or libidinal interests upon a member of the same sex. The impulse is subject to all the modifications of erotic impulses. It may be expressed directly (homogenitality); it may be sublimated (homoerotism or homosexuality); it may be severely repressed; if so, the impulses may be subjected to reaction-formation, that is, they may appear as aversions against the homoerotism; or they may be transferred into reality in symbolic form (delusions, hallucinations, etc.).

homogamy In contrast to *panmixia,* this genetic term applies to the *inbreeding* conditions in an isolated population group composed of individuals with the same hereditary characteristics.

homogeneity, homogeny (hō-mō-jē-nē'i-tē, hō-moj'ē-nē) Identical genotypical structure of two or more organisms of common descent, as found in the case of pure lines or in monozygotic sets of twins.

homogenital (-jen'i-tal) Relating to interest in the genital organs of one's own sex.

homogenitality (-jen-i-tal'i-tē) Interest in the genitals of one's own sex. See *homosexuality.*

homologous (hō-mol'ō-gus) This genetic term classifies the gene units which belong to the same pairs of *homologues.* See *allelic.*

homologue (hom'ō-log) If one form or condition of a genetic character is contrasted with another form or condition of the same character, such as two eye colors or two color patterns, the genes which are responsible for these two conditions are said to belong to the same pair of *homologues.*

'They are so related that in the reduction division of maturation they regularly go to different cells, each germ cell receiving one, but not both.' (Shull, A.F. *Heredity,* 3rd ed., McGraw-Hill, New York and London, 1938)

homonymous hemianopia (hō-mon′i-mus hem-i-an-op′si-à) See *field defect.*

homonymous quadrantic field defect See *field defect.*

homosexual Relating to or directed toward one of the same sex.

homosexuality The state of being in love with one belonging to the same sex. Until the early part of the 20th century, this generally meant a form of sexual perversion. With the development of psychoanalysis, however, there came to be laid less emphasis on sex proper and a correspondingly broader connotation assigned to the term sexual. In current usage, overt homosexuality is used to refer to physical, sexual contact between members of the same sex, while latent homosexuality is used to refer to impulses and desires toward a member of the same sex which are unconscious or, if conscious, are not openly expressed. Some writers differentiate between homogenitality (genital relations); homosexuality (sexual relationship, but not expressed genitally); and homoerotism (erotic relationship which is well sublimated). See *homosexuality, female; homosexuality, male.*

In general, the term inversion is equivalent to homosexuality. When 'sex-role inversion' is used, however, it must be differentiated from homosexuality. Homosexuality refers to sexual desires and/or activity between members of the same sex, while sex-role inversion refers to adoption of the sex role and introjection of the psychologic identity of the opposite sex. Occasionally the two may co-exist, but more frequently one or the other is present alone.

homosexuality, female Erotic, sexual, or genital contact between females (see *homosexuality*). While it is generally believed that homosexuality is more frequent in the female than in the male, specific data on relative incidence do not support this belief (Bromley and Britten; Gilbert Youth

Research; Hamilton; Kinsey). 'The incidences and frequencies of homosexual responses and contacts, and consequently the incidences of the homosexual ratings, were much lower among the females in our sample than they were among the males on whom we have previously reported. Among the females, the accumulative incidences of homosexual responses had ultimately reached 28 per cent; they had reached 50 per cent in the males. The accumulative incidences of overt contacts to the point of orgasm among the females had reached 13 per cent; among the males they had reached 37 per cent.... Moreover, compared with the males, there were only about a half to a third as many of the females who were, in any age period, primarily or exclusively homosexual.

'A much smaller proportion of the females had continued their homosexual activities for as many years as most of the males in the sample.

'A much larger proportion (71 per cent) of the females who had had any homosexual contact had restricted their homosexual activities to a single partner or two; only 51 per cent of the males who had had homosexual experience had so restricted their contacts. Many of the males had been highly promiscuous, sometimes finding scores or hundreds of sexual partners.' (Kinsey, A.C., *et al. Sexual Behavior in the Human Female,* Saunders, Philadelphia, 1953)

'The institutions which have developed around male homosexual interests include cafés, taverns, night clubs, public baths, gymnasia, swimming pools, physical culture and more specifically homosexual magazines, and organized homosexual discussion groups; they rarely have any counterpart among females. Many of these male institutions, such as the homosexually oriented baths and gymnasia, are of ancient historic origin, but there do not seem to have been such institutions for females at any time in history. The street and institutionalized homosexual prostitution which is everywhere available for males, in all parts of the world, is rarely available for females, anywhere in the world. All of these differences between female and male homosexuality depend on basic psychosexual differences between the two sexes.' (ibid.)

Female homosexuality is often referred to as 'lesbian' or 'sapphic' after Sappho, a female homosexual who lived on the Isle of Lesbos in ancient Greece.

homosexuality, latent A psychiatric term often used interchangeably with 'unconscious homosexuality'; it denotes an erotic impulse toward a member of the same sex, present in the unconscious, though not felt or overtly expressed.

homosexuality, male Erotic or genital relationship between two (or more) males; see *homosexuality*.

Data on the frequency of male homosexuality are difficult to obtain. Havelock Ellis (1936) estimated the incidence at 2 to 5 per cent; Hirschfeld (1920) at 2 to 3 per cent; but these and many other estimates are biased by the belief that to qualify as a homosexual the individual must be exclusively homosexual. Kinsey's data are based on sexual contact resulting in orgasm; that is, his statistics do not include those who engage in sexual activity without coming to climax, or those who are erotically aroused by a homosexual stimulus without ever having overt relations. As thus defined, Kinsey found that 37 per cent of the male population has some homosexual experience between the beginning of adolescence and old age; and of unmarried males who are 35 years of age or over, almost 50 per cent have had a homosexual experience since the beginning of adolescence. Kinsey finds that 4 per cent of the white male population are exclusively homosexual throughout their lives.

Accidental homosexuality, the choice of a man as sexual object when no women are available (faute de mieux), indicates that most males are probably capable of a homosexual object choice. But the true homosexual must exclude women as his object choice for some other reason. Freud pointed out that fear of castration, intense Oedipal attachment to the mother, narcissism and narcissistic object choice, and identification with sibling rivals with secondary overcompensatory love for them are important etiological factors in male homosexuality. The sight of the female genitalia provokes castration anxiety by providing concrete evidence that castration is a reality and, through association with old oral anxieties, by perception of the genitalia as a castrating instrument. Such castration anxiety may make the individual retire from rivalry with the father by a denial and renunciation of all women. Castration anxiety is seen in non-homosexual neurotics, too; the decisive factor in the homosexual is the type of reaction to the castration shock—refusal to have anything more to do with such frightening sights.

The non-homosexual neurotic also shows an Oedipal attachment to the mother; but in the homosexual, the castration anxiety makes the mother and the female genitalia disappointing as a love object. Following such a disappointment, there is regression from object love to identification, and the homosexual identifies with the frustrating mother in a particular aspect—like his mother, he loves men. Then, if his fixation is predominantly narcissistic, he will choose young men or boys as love objects who represent himself, and he loves them in the way he wanted his mother to love him. These are 'subject homoerotic' individuals, one of whose conditions of love is often that the homosexual object be of the same age as the person himself when the change into overt homosexuality occurred. If, on the other hand, his fixation is predominantly anal (i.e. passive-receptive), he will choose the father or masculine father-substitutes as love objects and attempt to enjoy sex in the same way as his mother; such 'object homoerotics' cover with superficial passivity and submissiveness the unconscious idea of depriving the object choice of his 'secrets' or of his genitals. Narcissistic and anal fixations may, of course, occur in the same individual, in which case a combination of the above types would be seen.

F.J. Kallmann (*Heredity in Health and Mental Disorder,* Norton, New York, 1953) presents evidence that the major factors in such a development as outlined above are genetically determined.

homosexuality, masked This psychiatric term denotes the strong unconscious homosexual impulses that an individual may have; often they are disguised. For example, a married man, complaining that his wife was frigid, insisted on having solely anal intercourse with her, since this was much more gratifying to him than genital relations. The unique pleasure found exclusively in anal contact represented his masked homosexuality.

homosexuality, unconscious See *homosexuality, latent.*

homosociality A term coined by J.C.

Fluegel to denote social relationship between members of the same sex.

homozygocity (hō-mō-zī-gos'i-tē) *Homozygousness* (q.v.).

homozygosis (-zī-, zi-gō'sis) Homozygousness.

homozygosity (-zī, zi-gōs'i-tē) Homozygousness.

homozygote (-zī'gōt, -zig'ōt) A zygotic organism produced by the union of two similar gametes and therefore possessing two like genes of a given factor pair. In the case of *recessive* Mendelian inheritance, a hereditary character can be manifested only by those individuals who have inherited its predisposing factor from both parents and thus are homozygous for the character in question.

homozygousness (-zī'gus-nes) This rather obsolete term (identical with *homozygosity* or *homozygocity*) relates to the 'germinally pure' condition of an individual who inherits the same gene factor from each parent, so that in his organism the two genes of the given pair are *alike*.

Homozygousness of a dominant anomaly is very rare, as it can be assumed only when both parents of a diseased person are also patients. In the case of a recessive anomaly which can only appear in the phenotype of a homozygote, all trait-carriers must be homozygotes. Consequently, the occurrence of such a recessive anomaly is not possible, unless *both* parents are either homozygotes or heterozygotes for the anomaly in question (see *recessiveness*).

Certain deleterious effects of inbreeding are now assumed to be due chiefly to the attainment of homozygousness rather than merely to the process of inbreeding itself. The frequent mating of individuals closely related in descent must automatically result in a reduction of heterozygosity unless new mutations occur in these inbred lines. If the mutation rate is high, this may defer or prevent the attainment of homozygousness. See *inbreeding; heterosis*.

homunculus (hō-mung'kū-lus) (L. 'little man') According to Paracelsus (1493–1541), a tiny man produced artificially, and hence endowed with magic power; dwarf; manikin. Herbert Silberer wrote a monograph on 'Der Homunculus' (*Imago, III*, 37–79, 1914) in which he made an extensive survey of the concept from the standpoint of folklore and from

that of the clinician. In folklore homunculus means a little man created artificially out of dung or gold. In folklore dung and gold are equated. The homunculus continues to gain magical power, until finally he is master of his creator.

According to psychoanalysts, the homunculus is related to onanism, in the sense that it is the result of onanism. The product of onanism is transformed (i.e. sublimated) into a little man. This concept appears frequently in dreams. Silberer cites the case of a girl who masturbated by rubbing the genitals against the edge of a wooden table; she then dreamed of wooden children.

Hoover's sign (Charles F. Hoover, 1865–1927, American physician.) Observed in organic hemiplegia and is used for differentiating organic from hysteric hemiplegia; if the patient, lying on his back, attempts to raise the paretic leg, he unconsciously presses down forcibly the heel of the healthy leg; this accentuation does not occur in hysteria.

hormephobia (hor-mē-fō'bi-à) Fear of shock.

hormism (hôr'miz'm) A term used in the writings of the school of psychology which holds that goals are sought for their own sake because of some intrinsic value, regardless of any pleasure attendant upon their attainment. McDougall believes that in man and animals there are present certain tendencies or urges which account for all forms of behavior, including abstract mental processes. Each tendency leads to a definite end, or purpose. Hormism is thus opposed to hedonism, which states that goals are sought only because they give pleasure or gratification to the individual. See *hedonism*.

hormone (hor'mōn) In the higher organisms, this term designates a variety of internal chemical secretions which enter the blood from the ductless glands and provide a very important part of the *'internal environment'* in which biological development takes place through the actions of the genes.

Some hormones correlate the general processes of development, others regulate growth or are responsible for the attainment of normal maturity. 'A hormone itself may often be one channel through which a gene affects general characters; and there is undoubtedly a complex series of interactions between the genetic factors, the endocrine secretions, and the other agencies of the internal environment during development.' (Sinnott, E.W., and Dunn, L.D. *Principles of Genetics,* 3rd ed., McGraw-Hill, New York and London, 1939)

Horner's syndrome See *syndrome, Horner's.*

Horney, Karen (1885–1952) American psychoanalyst; the Horney school emphasizes environmental and cultural factors in the genesis of neurosis. Horney and H.S. Sullivan represent the two chief branches within the 'dynamic-cultural' school of psychoanalysis.

horror feminae (hôr′rôr fā′mē-nī) 'The essential feature of this strange manifestation of the sexual life is the want of sexual sensibility for the opposite sex, even to the extent of horror, while sexual inclination and impulse toward the same sex are present.' (Krafft-Ebing, R.V. *Psychopathia Sexualis,* Login, New York, 1908)

horrors Delirium tremens

hospitalism See *depression, anaclitic.*

hospitalitis A humorous term coined to emphasize the complete hospital-conditioning (or dependency on the hospital) of a patient, who is usually an utterly helpless or incompetent person before his admission to the hospital. It may be difficult for him to leave the hospital, and each attempt to prepare the patient for discharge results in an aggravation of symptoms.

HTP See *test, House-Tree-Person.*

Hübner, Arthur (1878–   ) (hüb′nẽr) German forensic psychiatrist.

humor, gallows Galgenhumor; this is a term, infrequently used in psychiatry, to refer to humorous and comical behavior in the face of disaster or death. Gallows humor is seen most frequently in the organic psychoses, and particularly in delirium tremens cases.

hunger, affect Indiscriminate and insatiable demand for attention and affection, seen often in children who have suffered *emotional deprivation* (q.v.). Affect hunger frequently takes the form of aggressive, hostile, antisocial behavior with an inability to accept limitations or recognize the needs of others.

hunger, nervous Urge to eat (orally in-corporate) as a method of allaying anxiety or tension and of gratifying frustrated pleasure cravings. Obesity is frequently the secondary symptomatic result of such chronic and intense nervous hunger. Nervous hunger is an expression of intense dependence and stems back to the oral incorporative stage of infantile development.

Food addiction, as well as cigarette addiction, is a closely related phenomenon. Thumb-sucking, which is closely related to the use of 'pacifiers' in infancy, with the thumb replacing the 'pacifier,' is an early infantile prototype of nervous hunger. Edward Weiss and O. Spurgeon English (*Psychosomatic Medicine,* 2nd ed., Saunders, Philadelphia and London, 1949) report the case of a woman who had been married twelve years, was childless and twenty pounds overweight. She stated that whenever she was unhappy and depressed she felt that she must have a good meal: "I didn't know I was eating much, when I was really eating and nibbling the whole day. It was like having company to eat a little something.'

hunger, social 'The desire to be accepted by the group . . . which is one of the strongest drives in human beings. It is also the major incentive for improvement in a therapy group.' (Slavson, S.R. *An Introduction to Group Therapy,* The Commonwealth Fund, Oxford University Press, New York, 1943, p. 15)

hunger-strike, neurotic Adler thus denotes the fear of eating, occurring mainly in females at about the age of seventeen. There follows usually a rapid decrease in weight. The goal, to be inferred from the whole attitude of the patient, is the rejection of the female role.

'In other words, it is an attempt by means of an exaggerated abstinence—as is so generally the case—to retard the development of the female bodily form.' (Adler, A. *The Practice and Theory of Individual Psychology,* tr. by Radin, P., Kegan Paul, Trench, Trubner, London, 1924)

Huntington's chorea See *chorea, Huntington's.*

Hurd, Henry Mills (1843–1927) American psychiatrist.

hybrid (hī′brid) The inbred offspring of two parents who differ with respect to one gene factor or a combination of factors or even belong to different species. *Genet.* Used also as an adjective. The hybrids which constitute the first filial generation are heterozygotic individuals originating from the cross of parents who carry a given hereditary stock in a pure, unmixed form. When such hybrids differ with respect to only *one* character, they are called *monohybrid.* When they differ in two characters, they are *dihybrid;* analogously, the other hybrid individuals are *trihybrid* or *polyhybrid.*

'It is not always, not even usually, possible to cross species, for there is a strong tendency for species to be intersterile. Some of them will not mate, or their germ cells will not unite, or the hybrid does not reach maturity. Other species leap all these hurdles, cross, and yield offspring, but the hybrids are sterile. There are, however, many grades of interfertility between species, and some such crosses are as fruitful as matings within species.' (Shull, A.F. *Heredity,* 3rd ed., McGraw-Hill, New York and London, 1938)

The genetic mechanism leading to developmental disharmony in hybridization is still by no means well understood. It is assumed that in the case of unlike chromosomes of the two parents, normal pairing at meiosis cannot take place and gametes consequently fail to be produced. 'This may result from differences in the number or size of the chromosomes, in the character of the genes that they contain, or in the arrangement of these genes.' (Sinnott, E.W., and Dunn, L.D. *Principles of Genetics,* 3rd ed., McGraw-Hill, New York and London, 1939)

hybridization (hī-brid-i-zā'shun) Genetic term for the process of increasing the variability in a species or group of plants or animals through the production of *hybrids.* The increase in variability is reflected in the appearance of many new character combinations and enables the breeders of animals and plants, by practicing selection among them, to develop new and valuable types.

Hybridization also accounts for the well-known fact that 'hybrids or mongrels, whatever their own excellent qualities, do not breed true and hence are valueless for breeding purposes where uniformity of type is desired.' (Sinnott. E.W., and Dunn, L.D. *Principles of Genetics,* 3rd ed., McGraw-Hill Book Company, Inc., New York and London, 1939)

hydro- (hī'drō-) Combining form meaning water; hydrogen, from Gr. *hýdōr,* water.

hydrocephalus (hī-drō-sef'à-lus) An increase in the volume of cerebrospinal fluid within the skull. If cerebrospinal fluid pressure is normal, the condition is termed *compensatory hydrocephalus,* since the excess fluid compensates for brain atrophy, as in congenital cerebral hypoplasia and in acquired cerebral atrophy due to diffuse sclerosis, general paralysis, and senile or presenile degeneration. If pressure is increased, the condition is termed *hypertensive hydrocephalus,* which may be (1) obstructive, when an obstruction to the circulation of cerebrospinal fluid within the ventricles or at the outlet from the fourth ventricle prevents free communication between the ventricles and the subarachnoid space; or (2) communicating, when communication between ventricles and subarachnoid space is free and hydrocephalus is due to increased fluid formation (as in meningitis, certain toxic states, and after head injury), decreased absorption (as in compression of venous sinuses by tumor, products of infection, etc., or in impaired venous drainage secondary to increased intrathoracic pressure in cases of pulmonary neoplasm, aneurysm of the aorta, or severe emphysema) or to obstruction within the subarachnoid space (as in the case of tumor, adhesions following trauma, inflammation or hemorrhage, or congenital abnormalities such as platybasia or the Arnold-Chiari malformation).

Hypertensive hydrocephalus may be congenital or acquired. In congenital hydrocephalus, the most conspicuous symptom is enlargement of the head, which usually is slowly progressive. The cranial sutures are widely separated and the anterior fontanelle is greatly enlarged. Convulsions are common, and also optic atrophy due to pressure on the optic nerves. Mental deficiency is seen in severe cases. Most cases die by the age of four; in the survivors, mental deficiency, epilepsy, and blindness are the usual sequelae.

In acquired obstructive hydrocephalus, increased intracranial pressure causes headache, vomiting, and papilledema. In time, there is usually some mental deterioration, often with emotional lability, hallucinations, and delusions. Cranial nerve palsies may occur.

hydrocephalus, toxic See *pseudotumor cerebri.*

hydrodipsomania (-dip-sō-mā′ni-à) Periodic attacks of incontrollable thirst often found in epileptic patients.

hydro-encephalocele (-en-sef′à-lō-sēl) A developmental anomaly of the brain in which the brain protruding through the skull contains a cavity which communicates with the cerebral ventricles.

hydromania (-mā′ni-à) *Obs.* Impulse to commit suicide by drowning.

hydromyelia (-mī-ē′li-à) An increase of fluid in the dilated central canal of the spinal cord or elsewhere in the cord substance where congenital cavities may be present.

hydromyelocele (-mī′el-ō-sēl) The protrusion of a portion of the spinal cord, thinned out into a sac which is distended with cerebrospinal fluid, through a spina bifida.

hydrophobia (-fō′bi-à) Fear of water; rabies. The symptoms of rabies are: (1) in the premonitory stage, irritability, general malaise, anorexia, headache, insomnia; tingling, numbness, or pain in the course of the nerves radiating from the site of the wound; spasms of the muscles of the larynx and pharynx; huskiness; difficulty in swallowing; (2) in the stage of excitement there is exaggeration of the premonitory symptoms; intense excitement with terror; intense thirst, but every effort to drink is forthwith followed by choking and dyspnea; elevation of temperature and pulse. As the disease progresses, convulsions become generalized; (3) in the stage of paralysis, restlessness abates, convulsions cease, the musculature becomes limp and paralytic.

hydrophobophobia (-fō-bō-fō′bi-à) Fear of hydrophobia; in severe cases, the symptoms of hydrophobia are actually paralleled.

hydropsychosis (-sī-kō′sis) Keen attraction to water. 'To the simple animisms of children water lives, sings, laughs, moans, beckons, and often talks in words and phrases of which Bolton collected many. . . . Youth works a sea change and the hydropsychoses strike inward.' The curve of runaways to go to sea rises steeply, and a sailor's life now makes its strongest appeal. (Hall, G.S. *Adolescence,* vol. 2, Appleton, New York, 1908, p. 196)

hydrorrhoea, nasal (-rē′à) A 'running nose.' Déjérine and Gauckler say: 'This is a phenomenon which may be observed not only in hysterics, but also, much more frequently, under certain special circumstances, in the neurasthenic. The nasal secretion is, as a matter of fact, liable to be directly influenced by the psychism. And the latter, on the other hand, is capable of directly creating sensations identical to those which result from a real nasal secretion. It is so true, that, in an individual with the least tendency toward any neuropathic traits, it is only necessary for him to notice that he has forgotten his handkerchief in order to have this simple idea cause him the most intense and legitimate desire to use one.' (Déjérine, J. and Gauckler, E. *The Psychoneuroses and Their Treatment by Psychotherapy,* 2nd ed., tr. by Jelliffe, S.E., Lippincott, Philadelphia and London, 1915)

hydrotherapy (-ther′à-pē) 'The treatment of disease by water. This may be administered internally or externally. It may be given of the same temperature as that of the body, or of lower or higher temperature.' (Sands, I.J. *Nervous and Mental Diseases for Nurses,* 3rd ed., Saunders, Philadelphia and London, 1937)

hyelophobia (hī-ē-lō-fō′bi-à) Fear of glass.

hygiene, criminal This expression defines the branch of mental hygiene of which the object is the 'study and investigation related to the causes, prevention and treatment of the social-medico-psychological illness known for centuries as crime.'

In taking into consideration the complexity of this problem in modern society, the science aiming at the study of crime has necessarily to deal with many aspects of the individual: heredity, environment, home, social, economical, and political factors, legal aspects, emotional and physical development, psychiatric investigation, and many other matters. (Seliger, R.V., *et al. Contemporary Criminal Hygiene,* Oakridge Press, Baltimore, 1946)

hygiene, mental The science and practice of maintaining mental health and efficiency—for a twofold purpose: first, to develop optimal modes of personal and social conduct in order to produce the happiest utilization of inborn endowments and capacities; and second, to prevent mental disorders.

hygiene, social 'Social hygiene deals with problems which have a direct or indirect origin in the phenomena of sex. Its goal may be said to be a healthy sex life for individuals and a healthy and scientific attitude toward sex by society. It fosters every measure which has been devised to strengthen and preserve marriage and family relations. These measures may be roughly divided into three groups: medical and public health, educational, and legal and protective.' (Edwards, M.S. *Social Work Year Book,* edited by R.H. Kurtz, Russell Sage Foundation, New York, 1939)

hygrophobia (hī-grō-fō′bi-à) Fear of moisture or dampness.

hylephobia (hī-lē-fō′bi-à) Fear of the result of materialistic doctrines, 'now often regarded as a sacred madness as epilepsy used to be'; (*obs.*) epilepsy.

hylophobia (hī-lō-fō′bi-à) Fear of forest.

hypacusia (hī-pà-kū′zi-à) Hypoacusia; partial deafness.

hypacusia hysterica (hē-pà-koō′zē-à hēs-te′rē-ká) In hysteria, hearing 'not up to the mark'; apparently psychogenic.

hypalgia, hysterical (hī-pal′ji-à) A psychogenically induced decrease in the normal sensitivity to pain in any body area. This psychogenic basis has two elements: (1) As in all hysterical symptoms, the hypalgia is a defense against unconscious instinctual demands. Sexual or aggressive sensations that would be painful—that is, would cause anxiety—are repressed. These anxiety-causing impulses are often linked to specific memories. Hypalgia helps suppress these memories by decreasing the sensitiveness to pain in the body areas connected with these particular memories. (2) The decrease in painful sensation permits this body area to be used for unconscious phantasies and thus the repressed material can be expressed without the concomitant painful anxiety. (Fenichel, O. *The Psychoanalytic Theory of Neurosis,* Norton, New York, 1945)

hypapoplexia (hī-pà-pō-pleks-i-à) A mild form of apoplexy.

hypengyophobia (hip-en-ji-ō-fō′bi-à) Fear of responsibility.

hyper- (hī′pĕr-) combining form meaning *over, above, beyond, more than* (the normal), from Gr. *hypér,* over, beyond.

hyperacusia, hyperacusis (-à-kū-si-à, -sis) Inordinate acuteness of the sense of hearing. Among certain psychiatric individuals,

as, for example, patients in the manic phase of manic-depressive psychosis, the special senses (hearing, sight, touch, etc.) may be particularly sensitive. Among others, also, especially those with a fearful reaction, the sense organs are unusually acute.

'The other striking persistent symptom of these war neuroses is the more or less marked *hyperesthesia of all the senses,* photophobia, hyperacusis, and the dread of passive contact.' (Ferenczi, S. *Further Contributions to the Theory and Technique of Psycho-Analysis,* tr. by Suttie, J.I., Leonard and Virginia Woolf and The Institute of Psychoanalysis, London, 1926, p. 138)

hyperalgesia (-al-jē′zi-à) Inordinate sensitiveness to pain.

hypercathexis (-kà-thek′sis) See *cathexis.*

hypercedemonia (-sē-dē-mō′ni-à) *Obs.* Excessive grief or anxiety.

hypercenesthesia (-sen-es-thē′z[h]-i-à) A feeling of exaggerated well-being.

hyperechema (-ē-kē′mà) Auditory magnification or exaggeration.

hyperephidrosis (-ef-i-drō′sis) Excessive sweating.

hyperepidosis (-ē-pid′ō-sis) An abnormal or excessive growth of any part of the body.

hyperepithymia (-ep-i-thī′mi-à, -thim′i-à) Inordinate desire.

hyperesthesia (-es-thē′zhi-à) Inordinate sensitiveness to a tactile stimulus.

hyperesthesia psychica (hē-per-es-thā′zē-à psē′kē-ká) *Obs.* Hypochondriasis.

hyperevolutism (e-vol′ū-tiz′m) In constitutional medicine, this term means excessive morphological, physiological, and psychological development and may be applied to the whole or parts of the psyche as much as to the somatic side of the human being.

According to Pende, *hyperevolute* physiques result from an evolution of the individual constitution, which develops more rapidly than is normal or usual for the average individual. Such a rapid evolution may be *general* or *local;* for instance, the structural and functional advance of the heart may exceed the development of the other organs of the body, or certain tissues within a single organ may evolve unequally, or the entire habitus of an individual may be hyper-evolute.

In distinguishing between *ontogenetic* and *phylogenetic hyperevolutism,* Pende relates the concept of hyperevolutism to the evolutionary theory and such specula-tive questions as genius, superman and moral genius. (Pende, N. *Constitutional Inadequacies,* tr. by Naccarati, S., Lea & Febiger, Philadelphia, 1928)

hyperfunction Activity or functioning above the subject's own or a standard group's average.

hypergenitalism (-jen'i-tal-is'm) This term denotes various forms of overdevel-opment of the genital system.

hyperglycemic index See *index, hypergly-cemic.*

hypergnosis (-gnō'sis) Exaggerated per-ception, such as the expansion of an iso-lated thought into a philosophical system. (Feigenbaum, Dorian. 'On Projection,' *Psychiatric Quarterly 5,* 307, 1936)

hyperhidrosis (-hi-drō'sis) Excessive sweating.

hyper-independence In social work: 'ex-aggerated desire to live one's own life in one's own way; extreme individualism and disregard of the advice of others or limita-tions imposed by the situation.' (Hamilton, G. *A Medical Social Terminology,* Presby-terian Hospital, New York, 1930)

hyperinsulinism, functional (-in'sul-in-is'm) See *hypoglycemia.*

hyperkinesis (-ki-nē'sis) Excessive muscu-lar activity, observed in many disordered states, physical and psychical. For ex-ample, in the condition known as epi-demic encephalitis, due to definite organic changes, exaggerated motility is often ob-served. Excessive activity is likewise associated with psychical disorders, such as manic-depressive and schizophrenic psychoses.

'Hyperkinetic movements with twitch-ings, myoclonias, especially of the dia-phragm and abdominal muscles (hiccough types) are usual.' (Jelliffe, S.E. and White, W.A. *Diseases of the Nervous System,* 6th ed., Lea & Febiger, Philadelphia, 1935)

When the hyperkinesis is psychically de-termined, it is usually purposeful. In the manic phase of manic-depressive psycho-sis, the individual tends to express his ideas in action; since he has a wealth of ideas, he also has a wealth of action. The

schizophrenic patient, in a catatonic ex-citement, may perform many stereotyped actions, usually in symbolic forms.

hyperkinetic impulse-disorder See *im-pulse-disorder, hyperkinetic.*

hyperlogia (-lō'ji-à) Morbid loquacity.

hypermanic (-man'ik) See *mania.*

hypermetamorphosis (-met-à-mor'fō-sis) An excessive tendency to attend and react to every visual stimulus; noted in monkeys by Bucy and Kluever following bilateral removal of the temporal lobes.

hypermimia (-mim'i-à) Excessive mimetic movements.

hypermnesia (-mnē-z[h]i-à) Exaggerated activity of memory. It is not uncommon in patients, particularly those with the manic form of manic-depressive psychosis.

'Hypermnesia for previously forgotten infantile events is sometimes seen in the manifest content [of a dream], and much more frequently in the latent content.' (Jones, E. *Papers on Psycho-Analysis,* 4th ed., Wood, Baltimore, 1938)

hypernea, hypernoia (-nē'à, -noi'à) *Obs.* Exaggerated mental activity; hyperpsycho-sis.

hyperontomorph (-on'tō-morf) In con-stitutional medicine, this term designates one of the two constitutional types distin-guished by Beau. Persons of this type are characterized by long, lanky bodies with short intestines, in contrast to the *mes-ontomorph* and correspond roughly to Kretschmer's *asthenic type.*

hyperopia (-ō'pi-à) Far-sightedness, long-sightedness. As a result of an error in refraction or flattening of the globe of the eye, parallel rays are focused behind the retina.

hyperorexia (-ō-rek'si-à) Bulimia.

hyperosmia (-oz'mi-à) Exaggerated sensi-tiveness to odors.

hyperpathia (-path'i-à) Sensation of pain in a hypesthetic zone; it is not uncom-monly observed in association with lesions of the thalamus.

hyperpathia, thalamic (thà-là'mik) See *thalamus.*

hyperphoria (-for'i-à) See *heterophoria.*

hyperphrenia (-frē'ni-à) Of this term's two different meanings, one has morbid implications. First, it refers to excessive mental activity, such as occurs in the manic phase of manic-depressive psychosis or in the severe preoccupations associated with the psychoneuroses. Secondly, it means intellectual capacity far above the average, and some consider it then synonymous with *genius*. See *phrenalgia*.

hyperpituitary constitution See *constitution, hyperpituitary.*

hyperplasia (-plā′z[h]i-à) In pathology this term applies to an increase in the bulk of a part or organ of the body, due to an increase in the number of the individual tissue elements, excluding tumor formation.

Some pathologists make this increase in *number* the criterion for sharply distinguishing *hyperplasia* from *hypertrophy* (q.v.), which is defined by them as an increase in bulk due to the increase in *size* of the individual tissue elements. Others restrict the usage of the concept of hyperplasia to cases in which the proliferative changes mentioned are not occurring to meet a demand for increased functional activity or to compensate for an organic inferiority elsewhere, which would fall under their definition of hypertrophy.

It is worth mentioning, however, that from the standpoint of tissue pathology, as opposed to cell pathology, such eminent pathologists as Aschoff and Lubarsch consider hypertrophy and hyperplasia practically identical, although hyperplasia is the preferable term.

hyperpragia (-prā′ji-à) In constitutional medicine this term, probably coined by Pende, means excessive mentation, and refers to the type of mental activity commonly observed during the manic phase of manic-depressive psychosis, namely, an excess of thinking and feeling.

hyperpragic (-praj′ik) Relating to or characterized by excessive mental activity; in constitutional medicine, by excessive or increased activity of various systems and organs of the body, with a *miopragic* type.

hyperprosessis (-prō-ses′is) Exaggerated attention. Bianchi says: 'Some consider that there is *hyperprosessis* in the malady of fixed ideas. Certainly we have here [i.e. in instances of fixed ideas] neither voluntary concentrative hyperprosessis, because in these cases the power of convoking images in consciousness, of selecting and eliminating them, is defective; nor distributive hyperprosessis, for this is al-most abolished. On full consideration we shall find there automatic sensory hyperprosessis; therefore we may speak of hyperprosessis, and so avoid falling into an erroneous interpretation of the facts.' (Bianchi, L. *A Text-Book of Psychiatry*, tr. by MacDonald, J.H., Baillière, Tindall & Cox, London, 1906)

Diminished attention is called *hypoprosessis.*

hyperprosexia (-sek′si-à) Exaggerated attention. It is almost a universal phenomenon among psychiatric patients, for they give inordinate attention to their symptoms.

hyperpselaphesia (-sē-là-fē′zhi-à) Eulenburg's term for tactile over-sensitiveness.

hyperpsychosis (-sī-kō′sis) Hypernoia; see *apsychosis.*

hypersensibility The social worker's term for 'a degree of sensitivity, physical, or psychological, or both, which calls for simplification of environment and protection.' (Hamilton, G. *A Medical Social Terminology*, Presbyterian Hospital, New York, 1930)

hypersexuality A disturbance of sexuality in which there is a greatly or morbidly increased sexual activity. Since all neurotics are unable to attain complete sexual satisfaction, any neurotic individual may show this symptom. He might try to gain satisfaction through persistent repetition of the sexual act, yet never achieve that quelling of desire which comes with complete orgasm. Also he may boast about the frequency with which he can perform the sexual act, or behave in an 'oversexed' way, giving sexual connotations to many of his relationships or activities. This occurs for two reasons: (1) the dammed-up sexuality will come out 'in unsuitable places and at inconvenient times,' just because it cannot be satisfied with orgasm; (2) there is a narcissistic need to prove through such activity that the individual is not impotent or frigid.

In case the symptom of hypersexuality is so marked as to dominate the clinical picture, additional factors are at work. The genital apparatus is being used to discharge 'some nongenital, warded-off, and dammed-up need.' These needs might be various: (1) The primary purpose of the sexual activity might be to obtain self-esteem by contradicting an inner feeling of inferiority with erotic 'successes.'

Whether the individual is a Don Juan or a nymphomaniac, 'analysis shows that the condition depends on a marked narcissistic attitude, on a dependency on narcissistic supplies, on an intense fear over loss of love, and a corresponding pregenital and sadistic coloration of the total sexuality. . . . The sadistic attitude is manifest in the attempt to coerce the partner by violence into "giving" complete sexual satisfaction and therewith a re-establishment of self-esteem.' As soon as the sexual act has been performed, the patient is no longer interested in his partner, but must find another, both because his narcissistic needs demand that he continually prove his ability to excite other partners, and because this partner has failed to satisfy him completely. (2) Another source of hypersexuality which can be traced to nongenital needs is an unconscious homosexual inclination. Though aroused, the patient cannot, through increased heterosexual activity, obtain the satisfaction he seeks. (3) Still another source, operative in women, might be an intense penis-envy. Through nymphomaniac activities the patient seeks to fulfill the wish phantasy of depriving the man of his penis. (Fenichel, O. *The Psychoanalytic Theory of Neurosis,* Norton, New York, 1945)

hypersomnia (-som'ni-à) Sleep of excessive duration. For example, certain patients with so-called lethargic encephalitis sleep for unusually long periods.

hypersthenic (-sthen'ik) In constitutional medicine, the meaning of this term implies excessive tension and strength or indicates a hyperfunction of the lymphatic elements and organs, in contrast to an 'asthenic lymphatic' condition.

In Pende's constitutional system, the term is used in connection with the *hypertonic* type to designate a sub-group of both the *megalosplanchnic hypervegetative* constitution and the *microsplanchnic hypovegetative* constitution.

In Mills's system, the term has a sense which corresponds roughly to the characteristics of the *pyknic* type of Kretschmer.

hypertelorism (-tel'ō-riz'm) Excessive distance between two parts or organs. D.M. Greig's term denotes a form of mental deficiency characterized by general mental and physical retardation, not very dissimilar to the essential features of mongolism.

hypertension, essential Abnormally high blood pressure without known cause. In psychiatry, many consider essential hypertension to be a psychophysiologic (psychosomatic) cardiovascular disorder. Alexander believes that the specific dynamic pattern is the repression of all hostile, competitive tendencies which are intimidating because of fears of retaliation and failure; this general readiness for aggression is combined with a passive-receptive, dependent longing to be rid of the aggression. But these dependent longings arouse inferiority feelings and thereby reactivate the hostile competitiveness; this leads to anxiety and the need for further inhibition of aggressive, hostile impulses. This vicious circle is the basis for arterial hypertension, but the syndrome probably occurs only in those whose vasomotor system (and/or kidneys and/or endocrine constitution) is predisposed to instability, perhaps by virtue of inherited factors. Essential hypertension is probably so frequent in the American businessman because in business a great amount of aggression is necessary even though the culture as a whole greatly depreciates aggression.

'A fully consummated aggressive attack has three phases. At first there is the preparation of the attack in phantasy, its planning and its mental visualization. This is the conceptual phase. Second, there is the vegetative preparation of the body for concentrated activity: changes in metabolism and blood distribution. . . . Finally there is the neuromuscular phase, the consummation of the aggressive act itself through muscular activity. . . . If the inhibition takes place as early as the psychological preparation for an aggressive attack, a migraine attack develops. If the second phase, the vegetative preparation for the attack, develops but the process does not progress further, hypertension follows. And finally if the voluntary act is inhibited only in the third phase, an inclination toward arthritic symptoms or vasomotor syncope may develop.' (Alexander, F. *Psychosomatic Medicine, Its Principles and Applications,* Norton, New York, 1950)

hyperthymia (-thī'mi-à, -thim'i-à) State of overactivity, greater than average and less than the overactivity of the manic stage of manic-depressive psychosis.

'The hyperthymic types show exaggerated activities in the way of the usual business occupations, writing letters and the like.' (Jelliffe, S.E., and White, W.A. *Diseases of the Nervous System,* 6th ed., Lea & Febiger, Philadelphia, 1935)

Hyperthymia is a subdivision of cyclothymia. It is probably very close to hypomania, but occupies a position between normal overactivity and hypomania.

hyperthymic (-thī'mik, -thim'ik) Relating to states of overactivity akin to the manic phase of manic-depressive psychosis, but less intense than it.

hypertonia (-tō'ni-à) Extreme tension of the muscles; spasticity or rigidity.

hypertrophy (hī-per'trō-fē) In pathology this term means the process of overgrowth, or the kind of increase in the bulk of an organ or part of the body which is not due to tumor formation.

Some pathologists restrict its usage to denote greater bulk through increase in *size,* but not in *number,* of the individual tissue elements; it is then contrasted with *hyperplasia.*

Other pathologists limit the term *hypertrophy* only to those cases in which the increase in size meets a demand for increased functional activity or compensates for an organic inferiority elsewhere. The other cases fall under their definition of hyperplasia.

In the field of constitutional medicine, the term is used by some typologists to indicate undue size of a body area relative to other parts of the body.

hypertropia (-trō'pi-à) A type of strabismus in which the affected eye deviates upward.

hyperventilation Overbreathing. See *syndrome, hyperventilation.*

hypesthesia (hip-es-thē'zhi-à) Subnormal sensitiveness to a tactile stimulus.

hyphedonia (hif-ē-dō'ni-à) A state in which the individual experiences slight pleasure from what normally gives great pleasure.

hypnagogic (hip-nà-goj'ik) Inducing sleep; hypnotic. See *imagery, hypnagogic.*

hypnagogic intoxication See *intoxication, hypnagogic.*

hypnalgia (hip-nal'ji-à) Dream-pain.

hypnenergia (hip-nē-nēr'ji-à) *Obs.* Somnambulism.

hypnic (hip'nik) Relating to or causing sleep; hypnotic.

hypno- (hip'nō-) combining form meaning sleep, from Gr. *hýpnos,* sleep.

hypnoanalysis (-an-al'i-sis) The use of hypnosis in psychoanalytic therapy as an aid to removing resistances that prevent awareness of unconscious material. Regression and revivification under hypnosis may open up pathways to memories which are not available to the patient at an adult, waking level. It is obvious, however, that no matter what material is elicited in the trance state, in order to be effective it must be integrated and incorporated into the more conscious layers of the psyche.

hypnobades (hip-nob'à-dēz) *Obs.* Somnambulist.

hypnobadicus (hip-nō-bad'i-kus) *Obs.* Pertaining to or affected by somnambulism.

hypnobadisis (-bad'i-sis) *Obs.* Somnambulism.

hypnobasis (hip-nob'à-sis) *Obs.* Somnambulism.

hypnobat (hip'nō-bat) A sleep walker; somnambulist.

hypnobatesis (hip-nō-bà-tē'sis) *Obs.* Somnambulism.

hypnobatia (-bat'i-à) The performance, during sleep, of actions that take place in the waking stage.

hypnocatharsis (-kà-thär'sis) 'Essentially, this method consists of hypnotizing the patient and having the patient free-associate while in this state. Often memories will flow more easily under such circumstances. The difficulties, however, lie in the fact that all patients are not hypnotizable and that hypnosis casts a shroud of mystery about the process, making a "mystic" affair of that which one desires the patient to be very clear about.' (Kraines, S.H. *The Therapy of the Neuroses and Psychoses,* Lea & Febiger, Philadelphia, 1948)

hypnodia (hip-nō'di-à) Somnolence.

hypnogenic spot (hip-nō-gen'ik) See *spot, hypnogenic.*

hypnograph (hip'nō-graf) An instrument to measure sleep. The basic hypnograph consists of a recording pen attached to a coil of the sleeper's bed so that any movement of his is communicated to the instrument and traced in a graph. This gives a measure of the amount of gross motor activity during sleep. In the same manner other functions may be tested during sleep, and there are modifications of the hypnograph which will measure any or all of the following: blood pressure, pulse, temperature, respiration, metabolic rate, muscle tone, reflexes, urine volume, sweating, gastric secretion, lacrimal and salivary secretion, etc.

hypnoid (hip'noid) See *hysteria, dispositional.*

hypnolepsy (hip'nō-lep-sē) Narcolepsy.

hypnology (hip-nol'ō-jē) The science of sleep and hypnotism.

hypnonarcosis (hip-nō-när-kō'sis) Narcosis (a state of deep sleep) induced through hypnosis.

hypnonergia (-nēr'ji-à) See *hypnenergia.*

hypnopathy (hip-nop'à-thē) Hypnolepsy.

hypnophobia (hip-nō-fō'bi-à) Fear of falling asleep.

hypnophrenosis (-frē-nō'sis) A general term, introduced by C.H. Schutze, for various forms of sleep disturbance.

hypnopompic (-pom'pik) Sleep-dispelling. Relating to or ushering out the semiconscious state between the stages of sleep and awakening.

hypnosigenesis (-si-jen'e-sis) Induction of hypnosis.

hypnosigenic (-si-jen'ik) Pertaining to the induction of hypnosis.

hypnosis (hip-nō'sis) The state or condition induced through hypnotism. The subject to be hypnotized usually lies in the recumbent position. He is commanded to fix his attention, usually by staring at an object, while the hypnotist gently strokes the brow of the subject and keeps repeating in a monotonous manner that the subject is growing tired, drowsy, and sleepy. The purpose is to induce a trance-like state in which, in deep hypnosis, the conscious mind of the subject no longer functions, as in sleep, yet the subject is completely obedient to the commands of the hypnotist.

Therapeutic hypnosis or hypnotherapeusis may be of two degrees, superficial or deep. During the former 'he has not been asleep, and has heard all my words. He has felt fatigue and a heaviness in the limbs, but might have opened his eyes and moved about, had he wished. . . . This is the type of a very superficial hypnosis.'

(Schilder, P. and Kauders, O. *Hypnosis,* tr. by Rothenberg, S., Nervous & Mental Disease Publishing Company, Washington, D.C., 1927) The same authors state that in deep sleep 'the outcome is the same, with the exception that the patient declares, after awaking, that she cannot remember what was said to her.'

hypnosis, catalyzing action of This psychiatric term denotes the accelerating influence of hypnosis upon the various phases of analytical proceedings. The hypnosis is induced as an adjunct to psychoanalysis, and then used in order to hasten the uncovering of unconscious material which might otherwise take a long time to come to the awareness of the patient. (Wolberg, L.R. *Hypnoanalysis,* Grune and Stratton, New York, 1945)

hypnosis, cathartic (kà-thär'tik) See *hypnotism.*

hypnosis, coaxing See *hypnosis, father.*

hypnosis, dependency in The patient under hypnosis may establish an exaggerated transference to the analyst based upon an overvaluation of the power and authority of the hypnotist. This exaggerated identification is called dependency in hypnosis. The patient plunges himself into a subordinate position in order to achieve his objectives, but such a position is incompatible with normal self-esteem. 'It tends to destroy assertiveness, to sap independence, and to vitiate activity and creative self-fulfillment. It may render the patient progressively more helpless—an automaton who lives without a self and is secure and confident only insofar as the omniscient hypnotist can shield him from harm and gratify his needs for him. Unable to achieve his goals through his own efforts, the patient may become increasingly hostile and finally may interrupt the therapy with a return to his neurotic symptoms.' (Wolberg, L.R. *Hynoanalysis,* Grune and Stratton, New York, 1945)

hypnosis, father Ferenczi says: 'We could maintain that hypnotic submission is to be traced back to blind obedience, but this again to the transference of paternal fixation. There are only two kinds of hypnosis: father-hypnosis (that might also be called fear-hypnosis) and mother-hypnosis (in other words, coaxing-hypnosis).' (Ferenczi, S. *Further Contributions to the Theory and Technique of Psycho-Analysis,* tr. by Suttie, J.I., Leonard and Virginia

Woolf and The Institute of Psychoanalysis, London, 1926)

hypnosi-therapeutics (hip-nō-si-ther-à-pū'-tiks) *Obs.* Treatment by hypnosis.

hypnotherapeusis, hypnotherapy (-ther-à-pū'sis, ther'à-pē) Treatment by means of hypnosis. See *hypnotism.*

hypnotism (hip'nō-tiz'm) The theory and practice of inducing hypnosis or a state resembling sleep induced by psychical means. It is also known as braidism (or Braidism) and induced somnambulism.

'Hypnosis may be applied therapeutically in many ways. We shall distinguish for the present between three such applications:

'1. The hypnotically induced sleep is used directly as a healing factor.

'2. The suggestion given in hypnosis is directed outright against the psychic or physical symptom which is to be eliminated.

'3. Forgotten experiences are brought back to memory in hypnosis and are made accessible to the consciousness (cathartic hypnosis).' (Schilder, P. and Kauders, O. *Hypnosis,* tr. by Rothenberg, S., Nervous & Mental Disease Publishing Company, Washington, D.C., 1927)

hypnotizability (hip-nō-tīz-à-bil'i-tē) Susceptibility to hypnosis.

hypnotization, collective (-ti-zā'shun) Simultaneous hypnosis of several individuals.

hypo- hyp- (hī'pō-, hip'ō-) A combining form meaning: under, below, less than (the normal), from Gr. *hypó,* under.

hypoaffective type See *type, hypoaffective.*

hypoalgesia (hī-pō-al-jē'zi-à) Lessened sensibility to painful stimuli.

hypoboulia, hypobulia (-bū'li-à) Deficiency or inadequacy of the will or willpower, seen primarily in schizophrenic patients. See *will, disturbances of.*

hypocathexis (-ka-thek'sis) See *cathexis.*

hypochondria (-kon'dri-à) *Hypochondriasis* (q.v.).

hypochondriac language See *speech, organ.*

hypochondriasis (hī-pō-kon-drī'à-sis) A more frequent term for *hypochondria.* Today this term denotes symptoms referable to physical structure and function when no causal relationship can be established between the part complained of and the complaints of symptoms. The name is derived from the region (upper part of the abdomen) which was formerly held to be the seat of the disorder. Although the exact etiology of the condition is undetermined, the symptomatology is often traceable as far as the psyche, with which it is often found to be intimately associated. Treatment by psychic measures often causes the symptoms to disappear.

Hypochondriasis is not described as a so-called functional disorder of an organ or organic system of the body. The term is gradually being restricted to refer to the use by the psyche of an organ as the medium through which the pathology of the psyche is expressed. The principle is well illustrated, for example, when the dread of contracting syphilis leads to sexual impotence. The dread in this instance is, of course, in consciousness. But an unconscious conflict may and often does produce impotence. When a woman, without clear or even vague knowledge on the part of the man, stimulates an unconscious fear of incest, the result may be impotence. When the man then complains of his genitals or some part of the reproductive apparatus as the cause for his impotence, he is said to manifest hypochondriasis.

Any part of the body may be the object of hypochondriasis. The gastro-intestinal tract is a favorite location for the disguise of psychic complexes or conflicts. But any organ may serve.

There is also another mechanism known as hypochondriasis. When, for instance, a sexual conflict, say over masturbation, is carried over to another part of the body, which then serves as a substitute for the sexual organ itself, the condition is known as hypochondriasis. It is not at all uncommon for a patient symptomatically to solve the masturbatory conflict by transferring the identical conflict and its complaints to the nose (a centrally placed, unpaired organ) and also to give to the nose the same attributes he had given to the penis. To him, though he does not know it, the nose becomes the penis.

'Hypochondriasis is a chronic complaint habit. It may arise from a variety of sources. Imitation of observed adult patterns, the desire to retain privileges derived during a period of actual illness, unhappiness at home or at school, ill-treatment, overwork with no recreational outlets, solitary life, parental oversolicitude, feeling of insecurity, medical mismanagement, and fear of punishment may all contribute to the development of somatic complaint on a psychogenic basis.' (Strecker, E A. and Ebaugh, F.G. *Practical Clinical Psychiatry,* 4th ed., Blakiston, Philadelphia, 1935)

Freud regards hypochondriasis as an *actual neurosis,* as he does *neurasthenia* and *anxiety-neurosis.* He says: 'Hypochondria, like organic disease, manifests itself in distressing and painful bodily sensations and also concurs with organic disease in its effect upon the distribution of the libido. The hypochondriac withdraws both interest and libido—the latter specially marked—from the objects of the outer world and concentrates both upon the organ which engages his attention. A difference between hypochondria and organic disease now becomes evident: in the latter, the distressing sensations are based upon demonstrable organic changes; in the former, this is not so. But it would be entirely in keeping with our general conception of the processes of neurosis if we decided to say that hypochondria must be right; organic changes cannot be absent in it either.' (Freud, S. *Collected Papers,* vol. 4, tr. by Riviere, J., Leonard and Virginia Woolf and The Institute of Psychoanalysis, London, 1924–25)

hypochondriasm, hypochondrism, hypochondriacism (-kon′dri-az′m, -′driz′m, -kon-drī′à-siz′m) *Obs.* Hypochondriasis.

hypochondrophthisis (-kon-drof′thi-sis) An infrequently used term for the wasting away of the body in hypochondriasis.

hypochoresis (-kō-rē′sis) Defecation.

hypodepression Simple depression, i.e. mild depression occurring as an episode in manic-depressive psychosis. This form of depressive episode may be difficult to distinguish from normal grief and from so-called psychoneurotic depressive reaction. As in all clinical depressions, however, lowering of the self-esteem and self-depreciatory, self-accusatory thought content are seen in hypodepression but do not occur in normal grief (mourning). For differentiation of hypodepression from psychoneurotic depression, see *depression, (psycho)neurotic; depression, reactive.*

hypoergasia (-ĕr-gas′i-à) The depressed type of manic-depressive psychosis.

hypoevolutism (-ev′ō-lū-tiz′m) Deficient morphological, physiological, and psychological development. The term is appli-

cable to the body as a whole, to particular systems, organs, and tissues, as well as to the psyche and aspects thereof. One usually distinguishes between *ontogenetic* and *phylogenetic* hypoevolutism.

hypofunction Reduced action or function.

hypogenitalism (hī-pō-jen′i-tal-iz′m) Various forms of underdevelopment of the genital system.

hypoglossal hemiplegia alternans (-glos′-sal) See *hemiplegia alternans.*

hypoglycemia (-glī-sē′mi-à) Concentration of blood sugar below the normal range. In psychiatry, hypoglycemia is of interest (1) in insulin coma treatment, where the blood sugar is deliberately lowered by injection of insulin; and (2) in functional hypoglycemia (functional hyperinsulinism), which is believed by some to be the psychophysiologic disturbance at the basis of many fatigue states. Franz Alexander (*Psychosomatic Medicine, Its Principles and Applications,* Norton, New York, 1950) believes that under the influence of emotional protest and regression, the vegetative functions of these individuals also regress toward a state of passivity and relaxation characterized by a preponderance of parasympathetic tonus. The organism is then forced either by external pressure or by the internal voice of conscience to undertake activity, even though he is physiologically in a state of relaxation. Alexander calls this 'vegetative retreat.' The specific psychodynamic constellation is the conflict between passive, dependent wishes and reactive aggressive ambition—a conflict, to be sure, almost universal in our civilization, but in fatigue states the following factors are more specific: little hope of success in a struggle against insuperable odds; no genuine incentive; the inconstancy of anxiety; and in many male cases a feminine identification which opposes aggressive, ambitious attitudes.

hypokinesis (-ki-nē′sis) Slow or diminished movement. It may be physically or psychically determined.

Depressed patients are generally slow in all their actions.

hypolepsiomania (-lep-si-ō-mā′ni-à) A general term, coined by Andral, to denote the various forms of monomania.

hypologia (-lō′ji-à) Reduction in speech, used usually to refer to cases of organic origin in which capacity for speech is limited.

hypomania (-mā′ni-à) See *mania*.

hypomelancholia (-mel-an-kō′li-à) Mild case of the depressed form of manic-depressive psychosis.

hypomotility (-mō-til′i-tē) Diminished or slowed-down movement.

hyponoia (-noi′a) *Rare.* Deficient mental activity; hypopsychosis.

hyponoic (-nō′ik) Kretschmer's term for hysterical reactions that stem from the deeper psychic layers. 'If the stimulation of the experience is overstrong or the personality, as a result of degeneration, is dissociable with abnormal ease, the deeper psychic layers, which we have already begun to study in hysterical volitional processes, are not always laid bare by simple repression, but through a splitting of the personality. These deeper layers, now working separately, in the field of ideational content furnish us with *hyponoic formations* belonging to an early ontogenetic functional type. We recognize these hyponoic formations in mythology and the art of primitives; in the modern normal adult person, we can study them, above all in the dream, and, aside from hysteria, very frequently in the schizophrenias.' (Kretschmer, E. *Hysteria,* tr. by Boltz, O.H., Nervous and Mental Disease Publishing Company, New York and Washington, 1926, p. 98)

hypophoria (hī-pō-for′i-à) See *heterophoria*.

hypophrenosis (-frē-nō′sis) A term suggested by Southard for feeblemindedness in general.

hypophysial cachexia See *cachexia, hypophysial*.

hypoplasia (hī-pō-plā′z[h]i-à) In pathology, the underdevelopment of a tissue or organ, whether due to deficient number or deficient size of the cells which constitute the body structure in question.

The usage of the term in constitutional medicine is somewhat different, and varies. Kretschmer applies it to underdevelopment of certain body areas; for instance, to a hypoplastic condition of the midface. Other typologists distinguish between relative and absolute hypoplasia.

When hypoplasia is *uniform* and relates to an organism as a whole, it results in a manikin or dwarf. However, it occurs

more frequently as a *selective* condition, and in this case it practically implies *dysplasia*.

hypoplastic (-plas′tik) Pertaining to the condition of hypoplasia or, in constitutional medicine, to a type characterized by Bartel's *status hypoplasticus* and equivalent to Rokitansky-Beneke's *habitus phthisicus* (qq.v.).

hypoprosessis (-prō-ses′is) See *hyperprosessis*.

hypopsychosis (-sī-kō′sis) Hyponoia; see *apsychosis*.

hyposomnia (-som′ni-à) The term has usually an implication of the time element. When an individual sleeps for shorter periods than is his wont he is said to manifest hyposomnia.

hypostasis (hī-pos′tà-sis) When used in a specifically genetic sense, this term denotes the obstructive mechanism by which one hereditary factor is prevented by the manifestation of another factor from being phenotypically expressible. The masking effect itself is known as *epistasis*, while the factor which is hidden is called *hypostatic* (see *epistasis*).

hyposthenia (hī-pos-thē′ni-à) Deficient strength.

hyposthenic (-then′ik) Pertaining to or suffering from hyposthenia.

In the systems of constitutional types described by Mills and by Pende the term is used in a sense which contrasts the *hyposthenic* with the *hypersthenic* variety of constitution and corresponds roughly to the characteristics of Kretschmer's *asthenic* type.

hypotaxia (hī-pō-tak′si-à) Durand introduced this term for the emotional rapport existing between the subject and the operator in a hypnotic setting. Ernest Jones refers to the relationship as *affective suggestion*.

hypotaxis (-tak′sis) Light, hypnotic sleep.

hypothalamotomy (-thal-à-mot′ō-mē) A psychosurgical procedure, employing the same technique as in *thalamotomy* (q.v.) and producing partial ablation of the hypothalamic area—performed subsequently in thalamotomy cases that have not responded to the original operation.

hypothalamus (-thal′à-mus) A phylogenetically old constellation of nuclei lying in the ventral part of the diencephalon just above the optic chiasm and sella turcica. 'It is the principal centre in the forebrain for integration of visceral functions involving the autonomic nervous system. The constituent nuclei may be divided into four groups: (1) anterior including the paraventricular and the supraoptic nuclei, (2) the middle including the tuber, dorsomedial and ventromedial hypothalamic nuclei, (3) the lateral area, and (4) the posterior group including the posterior hypothalamic nucleus and mammillary bodies. Pervading the whole area are ill-defined neurons, grouped under the general heading of "substantia grisea centralis." ' (Fulton, J.F. *Physiology of the Nervous System*, 3rd ed., Oxford University Press, New York, 1949)

Functions of the hypothalamus include regulation of sexual activity, water, fat, and carbohydrate metabolism, and heat regulation. The posterior hypothalamus is concerned primarily with the sympathetic system, the middle and anterior nuclei with the parasympathetic system; but all levels of the structure are subject to regulation from thalamic, striatal, and cortical levels.

The following hypothalamic syndromes are recognized: hypothermia, hypersomnia, the adiposogenital syndrome, diabetes insipidus, and autonomic epilepsy.

hypothesis, mediumistic (hī-poth′ē-sis, mē-di-um-is′tik) Baynes puts forth the hypothesis that the schizophrenic patient is closer than others to the collective unconscious and is strategically in a position to recognize forthwith the early signs of his own disintegration: *eo ipso* he is able to foresee the unconscious trend of events better than can those whose firm clinging to existing forms and conditions renders them insensible for discerning such signs.

hypothymia (hī-pō-thī′mi-à, -thim′i-à) While discussing emotions F.M. Barnes, Jr. says: 'The simplest and probably the most frequently met variation in the affective or emotional state is in the nature of a diminution in its intensity. We may speak of this as hypothymia.' (Barnes, F.M. *An Introduction to the Study of Mental Disorders*, 2nd ed., Mosby, St. Louis, 1923)

hypotonia (-tō′ni-à) Subnormal tension of the muscles; flaccidity.

hypotonic (-ton′ik) In Tandler's system this term denotes a type characterized by a low degree of tone of the voluntary muscles. This condition qualifies both the *pyknic* and the *asthenic* types in Kretschmer's system.

hypovegetative (-vej′ē-tā-tiv) In contradistinction to the *hypervegetative* (q.v.) biotype of Viola and Pende, this term designates the constitutional type in which the 'animal system' (muscular, nervous, and skeletal systems) predominates in forming contact with the external world, over the organs in the trunk, which represent the nutritional system and are associated with the vegetative life of an individual.

The biotype thus described corresponds exactly to the *dolichomorphic* and *microsplanchnic* types and approximately to Kretschmer's *asthenic*.

hypovigility (-vi-jil′i-tē) Pathological subnormal awareness or response, or complete lack of it, to external stimuli. Hypovigility is the opposite of exaggerated distractibility. Although exaggerated distractibility sometimes occurs in catatonic excitement, hypovigility is more characteristic of the schizophrenic group as a whole. 'The [schizophrenic] patients converse only rarely with those around them even when they are talking a great deal. The incitement to speech as well as its content originates for the most part autistically from inner sources.' (Bleuler, E. *Dementia Praecox or the Group of Schizophrenias*, International Universities Press, New York, 1950) Bleuler considers this an important point in the differential diagnosis of manic schizophrenia and true mania.

hypsophobia (hip-so-fō′bi-à) Fear of a high place.

hysteria (his-tē′ri-à) Unless modified by the word *anxiety* (i.e. anxiety-hysteria), the word hysteria usually refers to conversion hysteria. Clinically, the characteristic features of hysteria are: (1) a physical manifestation without structural lesion; (2) a calm mental attitude (called 'la belle indifférence' by Janet); and (3) episodic mental states, in which a limited but homogeneous group of functions occupies the field of consciousness, often to the complete exclusion of the usual contents of consciousness—fugues, somnambulisms, dream-states, hypnotic states, etc. There is, in other words, a dissociation of the mental or bodily functions, and the dissociated function may operate in co-existence with normal consciousness, or it may operate to the exclusion of the other functions. In hysteria, the split-off function is ordinarily a unity and the splitting is seldom into more than two parts; thus it is commonly said that in schizophrenia the splitting is molecular or fragmentary, while in hysteria it is molar or massive.

There are no physical symptoms in hysteria that cannot be produced by volition or by emotion, although it may ordinarily be possible to maintain these symptoms for only a short time. Further, the physical symptoms correspond strikingly with the usual lay concepts of disease. Thus hysterical paralysis shows an exact delimitation and an excessive intensity, and it is more frequently accompanied by sensory disturbances than organic paralysis.

The *motor symptoms* include paralysis with or without contracture, tics, tremors, etc. The *sensory symptoms* include anesthesiae, paresthesiae, and hyperesthesiae; their distribution is rarely according to anatomical lines; they vary at different examinations; and they are susceptible to suggestions. Blindness and deafness are also seen. The *visceral symptoms* include anorexia, bulimia, vomiting, hiccough or respiratory tic, various abdominal complaints, flatulence, etc.

The *mental symptoms* include amnesiae, somnambulisms, fugues, trances, dream-states, hysterical 'fits' or 'attacks,' etc. The amnesia is commonly for a circumscribed series of events and occasionally is for the entire period of life up to a certain recent point. In a fugue, the patient suddenly leaves his previous activity and goes on a journey which has no apparent relation to what he has just been doing, and for which he has amnesia afterward. Somnambulisms are fugues which begin during sleep and are usually of shorter duration than fugues. The movements of the somnambulist are in response to the manifest or latent content of the dream; the meaning may be an escape from the temptation of the bed, or a movement toward a positive goal which represents gratification or reassurance. In double or multiple personalities, there is further elaboration so that the groups of dissociated functions when fully conscious and in charge of the motor apparatus can at least superficially appear as a complete personality. Hysterical spells are a pantomimic expression of

(mainly Oedipal) phantasies; in them can be seen condensation, displacement, representation by the opposite, exaggeration of details which represent the whole, reversal of the sequence of events, multiple identification, and suitability for plastic representation. Dream-states are similar to these, but here the pantomimic discharge is lacking; dream-states may represent repression, or orgasm, or death-wishes turned against the ego, or the blocking of any hostile impulse.

Until Freud advanced his theory of hysteria, there had been few attempts at explanation. Charcot had described the 'grande attaque hysterique' with its four phases: (1) epileptoid phase; (2) large movement phase; (3) phase of 'attitudes passionelles'; (4) the 'délire terminal.' Janet's theories of restriction of the field of consciousness and the hereditary tendency to dissociate at moments of great emotion did not explain what it was that brought the dissociation to pass. Freud's earlier theory was that the hysterical attack was a symbolic representation of a repressed sexual trauma. He believed that the patient had undergone a passive sexual experience in childhood, but that this psychical experience could not find adequate discharge because the nervous system was incapable of dealing with it at that time; the experience was forgotten, but with puberty the memory of it was reawakened. But adequate discharge ('abreaction') was still not possible, because the memory conflicted with the conscious strivings of the personality and/or his culture. Instead, the strong affect associated with the memory is diverted into the wrong somatic channels (conversion) and the hysterical symptom results. Freud and Breuer found that 'catharsis'—reactivation of the childhood memory, at that time by means of hypnosis, and allowing abreaction—removed the hysterical symptom. This theory was later revised when it was discovered that the sexual traumata uncovered in hysterical patients were really fictitious memories designed to mask the autoerotic activities of childhood.

The hysterical attack itself may be aroused (1) associatively, if the content of the complex is stirred by a conscious occurrence; (2) organically, if for any reason the libidinal cathexis exceeds a certain amount; (3) in the service of the primary tendency (paranosic gain) as an expression of 'flight into illness' if reality becomes painful or frightening; (4) in the service of the epinosic gain, to achieve some end through an attack. To the hysterical patient, all sexuality represents infantile incestuous love, so he cannot love fully if the genitals are present because of Oedipal fears. The conversion symptom is a distorted substitute for sexual (and/or aggressive) gratification; but because of the effectiveness of repression, the symptom leads to suffering rather than gratificatory pleasure.

The choice of the afflicted region is determined by (1) the unconscious sexual phantasies and the corresponding erogeneity of the area; (2) somatic compliance ('locus minori resistentiae'); (3) the situation in which the decisive repression occurred; (4) the ability of the organ to symbolize the unconscious drive in question.

hysteria, acquired Freud says: 'Our observations show that a severe trauma (such as that in a traumatic neurosis) or a troublesome suppression (for instance, of sexual affect) can effect a splitting of groups of ideas in people previously free from it, and this would constitute the mechanism of psychically acquired hysteria.' (Freud, S. *Collected Papers,* vol. 1, tr. by Riviere, J., Leonard and Virginia Woolf and The Institute of Psychoanalysis, London, 1924–25) See *hysteria, dispositional.*

hysteria, anxiety See *anxiety-hysteria.*

hysteria, artificial It used to be said that 'hypnosis is an artificial hysteria.' (Freud, S. *Collected Papers,* vol. 1, tr. by Riviere, J., Leonard and Virginia Woolf and The Institute of Psychoanalysis, London, 1924–25) In one of his early communications Freud suggested that the phrase be changed to read: 'The existence of hypnoid states forms the foundation and condition of hysteria.' (ibid.)

hysteria, combat See *shell-shock.*

hysteria, conversion *Hysteria* (q.v.).

hysteria, defense To Freud defense hysteria is a form of acquired hysteria, because there is in this condition 'no question either of grave hereditary taint or of individual atrophic degeneration.' (Freud, S. *Collected Papers,* vol. 1, tr. by Riviere, J., Leonard and Virginia Woolf and The Institute of Psychoanalysis, London, 1924–25)

'These patients whom I analyzed had enjoyed good mental health up to the time at which an intolerable idea presented itself within the content of their ideational life; that is to say, until their ego was confronted by an experience, an idea, a feeling, arousing an affect so painful that the person resolved to forget it, since he had no confidence in his power to resolve the incompatibility between the unbearable idea and his ego by the process of thought.' (ibid.)

hysteria, degenerative See *psychosis, degenerative.*

hysteria, dispositional Freud holds that in every case of hysteria there is a splitting of consciousness, not necessarily to the same degree that exists in cases of double consciousness; generally the splitting exists 'in a rudimentary fashion' in hysteria. When that is the case Freud uses the term *hypnoid* to denote the state and says: 'the existence of hypnoid states forms the foundation and condition of hysteria.' (Freud, S. *Collected Papers,* vol. 1, tr. by Riviere, J., Leonard and Virginia Woolf and The Institute of Psychoanalysis, London, 1924–25) He then adds: 'If such hypnoid states exist before the manifest illness, they provide a foothold upon which the affect establishes itself with its pathogenic recollection and its subsequent somatic manifestations. This situation corresponds to dispositional hysteria.' (ibid.)

hysteria, epidemic Hysteria or hysteroid disturbances apparently acquired by association with hysterical patients.

hysteria, fixation W.A. White says: 'In fixation hysteria, while there is a like tendency to replace the mental by a physical symptom, there seems to be a tendency for a particular part of the body to become involved. Excellent examples were seen during the war in those cases in which the localization of the hysterical symptoms was determined by a wound. The fixation is upon external parts of the body as distinguished from hypochondria in which the fixation is upon some internal organ.' (White, W.A. *Outlines of Psychiatry,* 12th ed., Nervous & Mental Disease Publishing Company, Washington, D.C., 1929)

E. Jones writes: 'With a chronic disease this process [concentration of libido on the self] may lead to local regressions and the formation of hysterical symptoms—an example being a nervous cough as a sequel to whooping cough—a condition to which Ferenczi would give the name "patho-hysteria"; it differs from the rather closely allied "fixation-hysteria" in that the libido disturbance is secondary to the organic disease instead of being primary to it, as it is in the latter condition.' (*International Journal of Psychoanalysis I,* 1920, p. 170)

hysteria, hypnoid (hip'noid) According to Freud there are three forms of hysteria: (1) defense, (2) retention, and (3) hypnoid. When the splitting of consciousness in hysteria exists in a rudimentary state the expression hypnoid hysteria is used.

hysteria, major The expression major hysteria (grande hystérie) refers to a clinical syndrome of hysteria, perhaps first described at length by Charcot, later by Richer. It is characterized by several stages: first, the aural stage; second, the stage of epileptoid convulsions; third, the phase of tonic, then clonic spasms; fourth, the phase of intense and dramatic emotional expressions; fifth, the stage of delirium. The total attack lasts from several minutes up to half an hour. There are many modifications in the form and order of the above-enumerated states.

Some authorities use the expression *major hysteria* synonymously with *hystero-epilepsy* (q.v.).

hysteria, masked *Obs.* A form of hysteria in which the symptoms resemble those of organic disease.

hysteria, non-traumatic (non-traw-mat'ik) See *hysteria*.

hysteria, reflex Kretschmer uses this expression for a hysterical sign in which an automatic nervous process, that is, a reflex, plays a dominant part, while the will plays a minor role. Examples of reflex hysteria are: simple spasm, tremors, and tics.

hysteria, retention Freud says that the splitting of consciousness is not a primary process in hysteria; according to J. Breuer, the basis is in the hypnoid state. In certain forms of hysteria 'the splitting of consciousness plays an insignificant part, or perhaps none at all. These are the cases in which all that had happened was that the reaction to traumatic stimuli had failed to occur, so that they are accordingly dissolved and cured by "abreaction" —they are the pure "retention" hysterias.' (Freud, S. *Collected Papers,* vol. 1, tr. by

Riviere, J., Leonard and Virginia Woolf and The Institute of Psychoanalysis, London, 1924–25)

hysteria, traumatic (traw-mat'ik) A neurotic illness developing in consequence of an injury (a traumatic neurosis) is termed traumatic hysteria when the manifestations consist chiefly of symptoms characteristic of hysteria.

Most of the traumatic neuroses of civil life should be classified among the hysterias. As in other hysterias, factors that will serve some psychological purpose operate in their production, but sometimes the continuance of an original disability and the elaboration of symptoms are due to some gain which the injury incidentally brought the patient, 'such as escape from dreary or wearisome conditions of employment,' or the affective satisfaction of spiting or otherwise punishing wife or employer. 'The traumatic or accident neuroses rarely occur when the victim of the injury must bear the brunt of the financial responsibility for the accident, as in the case of injuries in sports. There is usually an incubation period between the injury, which may be quite slight, and the appearance of the mentally determined symptoms. This interval before the development of the chronic disabilities is of value in excluding an organic source. It is usually occupied with vague ruminations which tend to be of an imaginative, affective, wish-determined and suggestive nature.' (Noyes, A.P. *Modern Clinical Psychiatry,* Saunders, Philadelphia and London, 1940)

Any group of cases diagnosed as war neuroses doubtless would include instances of traumatic hysteria. 'It is recognized that the conditions of war and warfare may (1) cause neurosis in an individual who is subjected to sufficient violence; (2) precipitate a neurosis in one already susceptible to it. In both instances external situations played the dominant role. (3) In a third sub-division, however, there are individuals who cannot master their fear of injury or cannot bear the removal from their usual places and ways of living. Though in it, they 'escape' military service by way of one or more of the multiple symptoms observed in hysteria.' (Hinsie, L.E. *Understandable Psychiatry,* Macmillan, New York, 1948)

hysteria vaga (hēs-te'rē-à và-gà) (L. 'rambling hysteria') *Obs.* Hysteria.

hystericism (his-tĕr'i-siz'm) *Obs.* Tendency or predisposition to hysteria.

hysterics (his-tĕr'iks) A popular term for a mild hysterical reaction.

hysteriform (his-ter'i-form) Resembling or having the character of hysteria. 'This chapter will be devoted to certain types of neurosis known as "hysteriform conditions," which in some respects resemble hysteria, but which in other respects differ from it considerably, and at times present clinical states that are transitions from hysteria to psychoses.' (Fenichel, O. *Outline of Clinical Psychoanalysis*, tr. by Lewin, B.D., and Zilboorg, G., The Psychoanalytic Quarterly Press and Norton, New York, 1934)

hystero-demonopathy (his'tĕr-ō-dē-mon-op'à-thē) Demonomania in a hysterical person.

hystero-epilepsy (-ep'i-lep-sē) Not infrequently the symptoms of hysteria resemble closely those of epilepsy, and *vice versa.* Some psychiatrists term this state hystero-epilepsy.

'The clumsy name *hystero-epilepsy* originated at a period when epileptiform attacks were still looked upon as neuroses, and when they could not be differentiated. Besides the ordinary epilepsies with lesser striking hysterical symptoms, there are such who in addition show hysteroid attacks. Furthermore, there are hysteriacs, though they are extremely rare, who can imitate or produce an epileptiform attack. . . . *What is usually called hystero-epilepsy is hysteria with severe motor attacks,* which were falsely added to the side of epilepsy.' (Bleuler, E. *Textbook of Psychiatry*, tr. by Brill, A.A., Macmillan, New York, 1930)

hystero-erotism (-er'ō-tiz'm) *Rare.* Erotism in hysteria.

hysterofrenic, hysterofrenatory (-fren'ik, -fren'à-tō-rē) Aborting or arresting a hysterical attack. For example, when digital pressure is applied to some part of the body to check a hysterical episode, the pressure is called hysterofrenic.

hysterogenic spot (-je'nik) See *spot, hysterogenic.*

hysteromania (-mā'ni-à) The term is not in common use today. It is sometimes used synonymously with nymphomania and metromania. It has also been used to describe states of psychomotor overactivity in hysteria.

hystero-neurasthenia (-nū-ras-thē'ni-à) *Obs.* A state characterized by 'a mixture of symptoms showing shades of both diseases, which naturally occurs frequently.' (Bleuler, E. *Textbook of Psychiatry*, tr. by Brill, A.A., Macmillan, New York, 1930)

hysteropathy (his-tĕr-op'à-thē) Hysteria.

hysterophilia (his'tĕr-ō-fil'i-à) Lewandowsky applies the term to certain clinical conditions resembling hysteria, such as migraine, epileptiform attacks, asthma, membranous enteritis, occupational cramps, etc.

hysteropnix (his-tĕr-op'niks) *Obs.* Same as *globus hystericus.*

hysterosyntonic (-sin-ton'ik) A term used for describing a special personality type which represents a mixture of the hysterical personality type and the syntonic personality type.

I

iatrogeny (ī-à-troj′e-nē) The inducement of a psychiatric condition by a physician, as when the physician tells the patient that the latter has an enlarged heart, or low blood pressure, or a glandular disorder, or gives any diagnosis that serves as the nucleus around which the patient builds a neurosis or psychosis.

In an individual who is on the verge of a neurosis or psychosis, and who simply needs confirmation of its alleged origin, information given by the physician may be instrumental in inducing a so-called iatrogenic neurosis or psychosis.

'Not entirely unimportant, unfortunately, is the iatrogenic origin of neurotic manifestations. The physician solemnly diagnoses "enlargement of the heart," whereupon the patient is frightened and breaks down until the x-ray photograph resorted to by another physician relieves him of his nightmare.' (Bleuler, E. *Textbook of Psychiatry,* tr. by Brill, A.A., Macmillan, New York, 1930)

I.B. See *body build, index of.*

ichthyophobia (-ik-thi-ō-fō′bi-à) Fear of or aversion to fish.

'I'-complex See *'I'-persona.*

iconomania (ī-kon-ō-mā′ni-à) Morbid impulse to worship images.

ictal emotions (ik′tal) See *emotions, ictal.*

icterus gravis neonatorum (ik′ter-oos grà′-vis nē-ō-nà-tō′room) Kernikterus; a manifestation of erythroblastosis fetalis in which the infant becomes jaundiced two or three days after birth and, if untreated, develops convulsions, rigidity, and coma. Mortality is high (75%) in untreated cases, and those who survive manifest residua such as mental defect, epilepsy, chorea, or athetosis. Treatment is exchange transfusion with Rh-negative whole blood. Those in whom jaundice is severe, however, even when so treated show some degree of mental deficiency; follow-up studies indicate that such children have an I.Q. which averages 23 points below that of their siblings. (Day, R., and Haines, M.S., *Pediatrics 13:* 333–338, 1954)

ictus (ik′tus) (L. 'blow, stroke') An acute apoplectic stroke.

ictus epilepticus (e-pē-lep′tē-koos) *Obs.*

(L. 'epileptic stroke') An epileptic seizure with sudden onset and no premonitory aura.

id The id, as a psychoanalytic formulation, is part of the energy system of the psyche. It is regarded as the reservoir of psychic energy or libido; it contains all phylogenetic acquisitions and is the source of instinctive energy. The pleasure-principle reigns supreme in it and has control over the erotic and thanatotic (death) instincts. The id resides in the unconscious, far removed from reality, to which the id pays no attention. The id recognizes only its own needs and does not itself undertake to modify its needs in any way. Modifications of id impulses are brought about through other agencies, the superego and ego.

'It is the obscure inaccessible part of our personality; the little we know about it we have learned from the study of dreamwork and the formation of neurotic symptoms, and most of that is of a negative character, and can only be described as being all that the ego is not. We can come nearer to the id with images, and call it chaos, a cauldron of seething excitement. We suppose that it is somewhere in direct contact with somatic processes, and takes over from them instinctual needs and gives them mental expression, but we cannot say in what substratum this contact is made. These instincts fill it with energy, but it has no organization and no unified will, only an impulsion to obtain satisfaction for the instinctual needs, in accordance with the pleasure-principle.' (Freud, S. *New Introductory Lectures on Psycho-Analysis,* tr. by Sprott, W.J.H., Norton, New York, 1933) Freud goes on to explain that the id knows no laws of logic; it knows no negation; it is timeless; it is 'virtually immortal'; 'it knows no values, no good and evil, no morality.' 'Instinctual cathexes seeking discharge,—that, in our view, is all that the id contains.' (ibid.)

idea An idea is a constituent of the psyche. It is a mental image or picture.

In psychiatry ideas gain significance in proportion to the quantity and quality of affect accompanying them. From the psychoanalytic point of view an idea may exist without charge of affect. It may be charged or cathected with varying amounts of one or both of the instincts—the erotic and the destructive.

'But it amounts to an approximate fulfilment of this task if the ego succeeds in transforming a strong idea into a weak one, in depriving it of its affect—the quantity of excitation with which the idea is charged.' (Freud, S. *Collected Papers*, vol. 1, tr. by Riviere, J., Leonard and Virginia Woolf and The Institute of Psychoanalysis, London, 1924–25) When an idea is 'painful,' the affective charge may shift to another idea (in consciousness or in the unconscious), or it may shift from the idea to some part of the soma (producing, for example, rapid heart beat, flushing, etc.), or it may be relegated to the realm of the id. The idea may lessen its affective charge through natural somatic activity, that is, there is normal fulfilment of the impulse contained in the idea. An idea seems to be a psychic vehicle or receptacle for affects. At least that is one of its functions to which psychiatrists give much attention. It may be said also that an idea has structure or composition; the latter is representative of the stimulus giving rise to it. When the stimulus, for example, raises in the gastric zone, the idea of hunger, food, starvation, etc. appears.

For an idea to become conscious it must 'be coupled with a word presentation.' (Freud, S.)

idea, autochthonous (aw-tok′thō-nus) A psychic disturbance of a delusional character in the sphere of judgment, characterized by the existence of a persistent idea which the patient believes is put into his mind by an influence foreign to him. The idea seems to exist by itself, beyond the control of the patient, who, most of the time, attributes the existence of such ideas to some malevolent cause. (Selling, L.S. *Synopsis of Neuropsychiatry*, Mosby, St. Louis, 1947)

idea, by See *by-idea.*

idea-chase This is an old term, translated from the German *Ideenjagd*, used to denote the rapidity of ideas in the manic reaction; the ideas were said to 'chase one another.'

idea, co-conscious See *unconscious*, as viewed by Morton Prince.

idea, dominant *Obs.* Obsessive thought.

idea, fixed See *idée fixe.*

idea, imperative Obsession.

ideal ego See *ego, ideal.*

ideales (ē-de-ä′lās) (pl. of L. *idealis*, existing in idea, ideal) Linnaeus formulated three subdivisions of mental disorders, one of which he termed the ideales —disturbances of the intellectual faculties.

idealization (ī-dē-al-i-zā′shun) Process or act of idealizing. The term has a special meaning in psychoanalysis. Freud says that idealization is 'sexual over-estimation' of the love-object. It is 'the origin of the peculiar state of being in love.' Emphasis is placed upon the object rather than the aim. As Freud maintains, the love-object 'is aggrandized and exalted in the mind.'

Idealization may be related to object-libido, as stated above, or to ego-libido. In the latter case 'some of the self-love which in childhood is directed to the Ego (primary narcism) is transferred or displaced onto a substitute [ego-ideal, superego] which now instead of the infantile Ego is looked upon as "the possessor of all perfections."' (Healy, W., Bronner, A.F., and Bowers, A.M. *The Structure and Meaning of Psychoanalysis*, Knopf, New York, 1930)

Idealization is to be distinguished from *sublimation* and *identification*. The process of sublimation involves the *deflection* of the sexual *aim,* whereas idealization concerns the *object,* not the aim. Identification necessitates a partial alteration of the ego, in the sense that the ego is patterned after the love-object, whereas idealization constitutes 'an impoverishment of the Ego in respect of libido' in favor of the love-object.

idealize (ī-dē′al-īz) From the psychoanalytic point of view this means to transfer an inordinate quantity of libido from the ego to a love-object. The latter is hypercathected, over-evaluated.

idea, obtrusive An obsessive idea that persistently repeats itself in the patient's mind and disturbs the normal flow of his thoughts. The patient considers the obtrusive idea as foreign to his ego and vainly attempts to renounce it. The obtrusive idea is comprised in the general group of obsessions. In the obsessive-compulsive system of certain neuroses, obtrusive ideas play an important role from the point of view of diagnosis as well as in the technique of analytical treatment. (Stekel, W.

Compulsion and Doubt, Liveright, New York, 1949)

idea of reference A morbid impression that the conversation, smiling, or other actions of other persons have reference to oneself.

idea, overcharged A term for a dreamer's central idea or conflict which has been exceptionally endowed with inner repressed psychic energy and consequently appears in the dream in the form of various symbols and several identifications. When this type of idea is present, one speaks in terms of 'overcharged idea.' (Stekel, W. *The Interpretation of Dreams,* Liveright, New York, 1943)

ideas, complex of Morton Prince says: '. . . the elemental ideas which make up the experiences of any given moment tend to become organized (i.e., synthesized and conserved) into a system or complex of ideas, linked with emotions, feelings and other innate dispositions, so that when one of the ideas belonging to the experience comes to mind the experience as a whole is recalled. We may conveniently term such a system, when in a state of conservation, an *unconscious complex or neurogram, or system of neurograms.*' (Prince, M. *The Unconscious,* Macmillan, New York, 1916)

ideas, concatenated (kon-kat'ē-nāt-id) Interconnected or interdependent ideas.

ideas, flight of See *flight of ideas.*

ideas, inheritance of Psychiatrists are not inclined to believe that ideas are inherited; or even that ideas, as they exist in consciousness, are similarly presented in the unconscious. They are said to appear in the latter as phantasies, as pictorial representations of impulses. Dream material exemplifies the manner by which the unconscious expresses itself. Jung says: 'I do not by any means assert the inheritance of ideas, but only of the possibilities of germs of ideas, something markedly different.' He asserts elsewhere: 'I must own I have never yet found indisputable evidence of the inheritance of memory-images, but I do not regard it as positively excluded that besides these collective deposits, which contain nothing specifically individual, the psyche may also inherit memory acquisitions of a definite individual stamp.' (Jung, C.G. *Psychological Types,* tr. by Baynes, H.G., Harcourt, Brace, New York and London, 1923)

The schizophrenic individual reveals the nature of so-called inherited ideas. 'The ideational formations in schizophrenics are much more completely saturated with perceptual elements' than is the case in ordinary thought.' (Storch, A. *The Primitive Archaic Forms in Schizophrenia,* tr. by Willard, C., Nervous and Mental Disease Publishing Company, New York and Washington, 1924)

'Morbid mental conditions presenting themselves as a reflection of a disease of the organism, are rendered more comprehensible if we look upon them as the reappearance of a peculiar form of life which is normal for a lower level of organic development.' (Carus, C.G.)

ideas, insanity of irrepressible Kraepelin's expression for what is now called the compulsive-obsessive form of psychoneurosis.

ideas, overproductive See *mania.*

idea, undesired Freud thus denotes an idea unacceptable to consciousness.

'On falling asleep the "undesired ideas" emerge, owing to the slackening of a certain arbitrary (and, of course, also critical) activity, which is allowed to influence the trend of our ideas.' (Freud, S. *The Basic Writings of Sigmund Freud,* tr. by Brill, A.A., Random House, New York, 1938)

idée fixe (ē-dā' fēks') (F. 'obsession') The expression denotes the particular idea characteristic of a psychic disorder. 'For dreams belong to the same category of psychopathological formations as the *idée fixe* of hysteria, obsessions and delusions.' (Freud, S. *Collected Papers,* vol. 1, tr. by Riviere, J., Leonard and Virginia Woolf and The Institute of Psychoanalysis, London, 1924–25)

It also means *fixed idea.* Thus, a patient, feeling the necessity to carry out a certain act incessantly, lest something disastrous befall a loved one, is said to have a fixed idea. Quite apart, however, from the nature of the morbidity, any idea that controls the psyche to a greater or lesser degree may be called a fixed idea.

identical (ī-den'ti-kal) In genetics this term is used in the biological classification of twins from the standpoint of zygocity. It is then synonymous with *monozygotic* and contrasts these one-egg twins with *dizygotic,* or *fraternal,* twin pairs arising from two eggs. It is incorrect, therefore, to speak of 'almost identical' twins.

identification (ī-den'ti-fi-kā'shun) Literally, the process of making (or considering to be) the same. In psychoanalytic psychiatry it carries a similar connotation. When an individual incorporates within himself a mental picture of an object and then thinks, feels, and acts as he conceives the object to think, feel, and act, the process is called identification, but the process is largely an unconscious one.

It is a common misconception that conscious emulation can somehow lead to unconscious identification. That this is not primarily true can easily be seen from a consideration of the events that lead to identification in the first place. In the beginning of extra-uterine life, the infant is ignorant of any sources of pleasure other than in himself. The mother's breast is thought of as a part of the child's body. This is probably the first identification and represents no emulation of a pleasure-giving object but a reluctant admission of frustrating reality. When hungry the infant is not fond of the mother's breast but angry with it because the breast has allowed him to become hungry. Frustration at the hands of this object is mastered by identification with the object. 'Identification is the most primitive method of recognizing external reality; it is, in fact, nothing less than mental mimicry. Its necessary preconditions are an unbroken narcissism, which cannot bear that anything should exist outside itself, and the weakness of the individual, which makes him unable either to annihilate his environment or to take flight from it.' (Balint, A. 'Identification,' *The Yearbook of Psychoanalysis I*, 317, 1945) The child, then, uses identifications to transform what is strange and frightening in the external world into what is familiar and enjoyable. The same process holds true in identification at the Oedipal stage. Balint says: 'According to the schematic formula of the Oedipus complex, a small boy should love his mother and identify himself with his father. And, in general, this is the case. The boy's mother is after all the source of gratification and his father is the powerful rival against whom he cannot defend himself successfully either by attack or by flight, so that he is eventually obliged to resort to identification. . . What I have said applies also, *mutatis mutandis,* to little girls.' In other words, the male identifies with his father not because he emulates him, but because his

father is to him a source of frustration in reality. And later in life, the sensitive person protects his self-esteem and can continue to love himself by identification with his frustrating and humiliating environment. This is the basis for the well-known mechanism of 'identification with the aggressor.' Identification, then, operates in the interest of and clings to the defense of narcissism.

According to Balint: 'After we have taken mental possession of a portion of the external world by means of identification, mental material which has thus been assimilated can itself serve as a basis for further identifications. So there would seem to be no essential distinction between ego-identification (i.e. identification of the ego with an object) and object-identification (i.e. identification of one object with another). For it is only objects which have already been identified with ourselves that can become the starting-point for further identifications.'

From the psychoanalytic point of view there are two forms of identification, *primary* and *secondary*. The *primary* form, arising during the oral phase, represents 'oral mastery of the object.' (Freud) It is first associated with the erogenous zones. Thus, the child identifies itself with the parent on the oral, then the anal, and still later on the genital basis, depending upon the area in which reality frustrations operate. Subsequently the child identifies itself with the character traits of the parents, and this leads to the formation of the superego. These early identifications with the parent or parents are called primary identifications. The energy of the child flows out to the real object. It is a manifestation of object cathexis, of object identification. Balint says: 'The outcome of the struggle round an individual's narcissism is one of the most important events of his development. As a result of identification with the various commands and prohibitions, his ego undergoes a decisive transformation Since obedience takes place not through understanding but through identification, the command becomes a part of the child's ego, which he defends henceforward just as much as his own will. . . The consequence is a splitting of the ego into two parts, of which one is the vehicle of the original instinctual wishes, while the other is the vehicle of the wishes that have been incorporated by means of identification.

This second, transformed part of the ego, is called by Freud the "super-ego." '

Secondary identification is the consequence of incorporating the object within the psyche of oneself. The psychic energy now becomes attached to the object as it is represented in the mind of the individual. The libido (psychic energy) is withdrawn from the object as it exists in reality. 'The Ego itself becomes the Id's libidinal-object.' (Healy, W., Bronner, A.F., and Bowers, A.M. *The Structure and Meaning of Psychoanalysis as Related to the Personality and Behavior,* Knopf, New York, 1946) It is as if the instinctual impulses were asked to take a substitute (namely, the introjected object) for the real object. Secondary identification serves the purpose of detaching libido from an object outside of oneself; it makes it easier for an object to be given up.

It seems that *secondary identification* and *introjection* are synonymous in psychoanalysis; Freud himself interchanges them. During the early stages of introjection, however, an introjected object is apparently recognized by the individual as foreign to his ego, whereas an object of identification is regarded as an original, not a borrowed, expression of his ego. Prolonged introjection, as in depressed states, may eventually bring about the quality of identification. It would be technically more correct to say that introjection (incorporation) is the mechanism whereby identification takes place; but this distinction is often not carefully drawn in present-day writings.

identification, cosmic Belief that one is the universe. A condition, not uncommon in schizophrenia, often characterized by the loss of the knowledge of any discrimination between the patient and all things external to him.

'At a remotely earlier level man felt himself to be the immediate center of the universe; he did not discriminate between himself and the all; it was only through repeated experience of obstacles and resistances that he became conscious of his limitations. Just as in the feeling of magic omnipotence he imagined he was the living power in everything, because he was ignorant of the limits of his power, so he also felt as if he penetrated all things, lived in everything, was ubiquitous.' '. . . In schizophrenics . . . there is a direct demolition of the limits of the self and there-

with a cosmic extension which resembles the original identification with the cosmos.' (Storch, A. *The Primitive Archaic Forms in Schizophrenia,* tr. by Willard, C. Nervous and Mental Disease Publishing Company, New York and Washington, 1924)

identification, multiple Identification with more than one model or object, seen most commonly in hysterical seizures wherein the patient simultaneously or serially plays the part of various persons with whom he has identified. Such seizures may even represent the enactment of a whole drama. Multiple identification is also seen in cases of multiple personality.

identify In psychiatry the term is used today in its psychoanalytic meaning, namely, to incorporate an object into one's ego system and to act toward the object as if it were originally one's own self and not something borrowed from the environment.

identity, ego That sense of identity which 'provides the ability to experience one's self as something that has continuity and sameness, and to act accordingly.' (Erikson, E. *Childhood and Society,* Norton, New York, 1950, p. 38)

identity, organic See *organic persona.*

ideogenetic (ī-dē-ō-jē-net'ik) Relating to mental processes in which images of sense-impressions are employed, rather than ideas that have reached the form or stage of being ready for verbal expression.

ideoglandular (-glan'jū-lēr) Relating to the effect of mental impression on glandular functions.

ideology (ī-dē-ol'-ō-jē, id-ē-) A systematic scheme of ideas.

ideometabolic (ī-dē-ō-met-à-bol'ik) Relating to the effect of emotional impressions on the metabolic processes.

ideophobia (-fō'bi-à) Fear of ideas.

ideophrenia (-frē'ni-à) Guislain's term for delirium, characterized by ideational disorders.

ideoplastic See *stage, ideoplastic.*

ideoplasty (ī'dē-ō-plas-tē) Durand's term for the process of molding, making plastic, the subject's mind by means of ideas suggested by the hypnotist. It takes place as a so-called process. It is called *verbal suggestion* by Ernest Jones.

ideosynchysia (-sin-kis'i-à) *Obs.* Delirium.

idio- (id'i-ō-) Combining form meaning own, private, personal, distinct, from Gr. *idios,* one's own, private, personal.

idioctonia (id-i-ō-ktō'ni-à) *Obs.* Suicide.

idiocy, absolute Tredgold writes: 'In this condition we see humanity reduced to its lowest possible expression. Although these unfortunate creatures are, indeed, the veritable offspring of *Homo sapiens,* the depth of their degeneration is such that existence —for it can hardly be called life—is on a lower plane than even the beasts of the field, and in many respects may almost be described as vegetative. They come into the world without even the hereditary instinct of sucking. As they grow up they have to be fed, and would die of inanition amid abundance of food were it not put into their mouths. They respire, assimulate, and excrete, but they have no sexual instinct.' (Tredgold, A.F. *A Text-Book of Mental Deficiency,* 6th ed., Wood, Baltimore, 1937)

idiocy, amaurotic family See *amaurotic family idiocy.*

idiocy, cretinic (krē-tin'ik) Idiocy in cretins.

idiocy, cretinoid (krē'tin-oid) Idiocy with cretinic characteristics.

idiocy, developmental Idiocy due to arrested brain development.

idiocy, eclamptic (ek-lamp'tik) Idiocy associated with convulsions in children.

idiocy, epileptic (ep-i-lep'tik) Idiocy caused by epilepsy.

idiocy, genetous, congenital (jen'e-tus, kon-jen'i-tal) See *amentia, primary.*

idiocy, hydrocephalic (hī-drō-sē-fal'ik) Idiocy due to congenital or acquired hydrocephalus.

idiocy, hypertrophic (hī-per-trof'ik) Idiocy associated with hypertrophy of the brain.

idiocy, inflammatory See *idiocy, hypertrophic.*

idiocy, Kalmuk (kal'muk) (Kalmuk, member of a nomad Tartar tribe.) Mongolism.

idiocy, moral See *insanity, moral.*

idiocy, plagiocephalic (plā-ji-ō-sē-fal'ik) Idiocy due to cranial distortion.

idiocy, scaphocephalic (skaf-ō-sē-fal'ik) A form of idiocy in which the head is boat-shaped.

idiocy, sensorial Intellectual deficiency due to abnormality in a sense organ.

idiocy, toxic Idiocy due to opium, alcohol or other toxic drugs effective in early life.

idiocy, traumatic (traw-mat'ik) Idiocy due to injury of brain.

idiogamist (id-i-og'à-mist) 'One who is capable of coitus only with his own wife, or with a few individual women, but is impotent with women in general.' (*Encyclopaedia Sexualis,* edited by Robinson, V., Dingwall-Rock, New York, 1936)

idiokinesis (id-i-ō-ki-nē'sis) This obsolete term refers to the 'spontaneous' origin of a new hereditary character by means of *mutation* (q.v.), or more specifically, by mutation which takes place without determinable cause.

idiolalia (-lā'li-à) Development of one's own language, such as is seen with some children who suffer from auditory aphasia (word-deafness).

idioneurosis (-nū-rō'sis) *Obs.* Neurosis.

idiopathic (-path'ik) When the etiology of a disease or disorder is undetermined, but its *functional* phenomena are known, it is said that the condition is idiopathic. The National Conference on Nomenclature of Disease refers to 'diseases due to unknown or uncertain causes, the functional reaction to which is alone manifest.' For example, the syndrome called *narcolepsy* is well-known, but its etiology is unknown; hence, the symptom-complex is named *idiopathic narcolepsy.*

idiophrenia (-frē'ni-ā) *Obs.* A psychiatric disorder associated with an organic brain disease.

idiophrenic (-fren'ik) Originating in one's own mind, psychogenic.

idioplasm, idioplasma (-plaz'm, id-i-ō-plaz'mà) This term was introduced into biology by Naegeli, to distinguish from the nutritive parts of the protoplasmic substance that portion of a cell upon which its specific qualities depend. Genetically it corresponds closely to the *germ plasm* (q.v.) of a germ cell while its more general meaning embraces all the special hereditary equipment of an organism.

From the genetic standpoint, the transmission of hereditary characters from parents to offspring depends on the fact that the latter have, entirely or partially, the same idioplasmic structure as the parents, while all the genetic variations among adult individuals must be primarily the outcome of structural or chemical differences in the idioplasm. Minute idioplasmic differences between two ova may produce, in the course of their individual processes of development, a whole series of differences in various parts of the adult organism.

idiosome (id′i-ō-sōm) This term denotes the idioplasmic unit as the theoretically ultimate element of living matter carrying hereditary characteristics. See *idioplasm*.

idiosyncrasia olfactoria (ē-dē-ō-sēn-krä′-zē-à ôl-fàk-tō′rē-à) (Mod.L. 'olfactory idiosyncrasy') Perversion of the sense of smell.

idiosyncrasy, antifetishistic (id-i-ō-sing′-krà-sē, an-ti-fē-tish-is′tik) Special mental disposition expressing itself in antifetishism or hate of a fetish.

idiot See *amentia, degree of; deficiency, mental.*

idiotism (id′i-ut-iz′m) State of being an idiot. Pinel divided insanity into four subdivisions, namely, mania, melancholia, dementia, and idiotism. By the last term he meant 'advanced dementia.'

idiotropic (id-i-ō-trō′pik) Introspective; egocentric.

idiot-savant (-sà-väN′, -sav′ant) (F. *savant,* man of learning, scholar) W.A. White says: 'These are rare cases, who, although idiots, still have some special faculty wonderfully developed. It may be music, calculation, memory for some certain variety of facts, etc.

'The calculators can name the answer to mathematical problems almost instantly; the musical prodigies often play well and even improvise; one of my cases could instantly name the day of the week for any date for years back.' (White, W.A. *Outlines of Psychiatry,* 12th ed., Nervous & Mental Disease Publishing Company, Washington, D.C., 1929)

idiovariation (id-i-ō-vā-ri-ā′shun) This biological term covers the genetic phenomenon of *mutation* and signifies a constant change in the genotypical structure of an organism. Mutated genes necessarily lead to the appearance of new hereditary characters and, thus, to the origin of

hereditarily distinct new groups of a species and new races (see *mutation*).

idolatry, sexual (ī-dol′à-trē) See *partiality, sexual.*

idolism, sexual (ī′dul-iz′m) Sexual fetishism.

idolomania (ī-dul-ō-mā′ni-à) Passionate idolatry.

idolum (ē-dō′lum) *Obs.* A false idea, illusion, or hallucination.

Ilberg, Georg (1862–) (il′bĕrk) German psychiatrist.

illness, advantage by This expression indicates that the ego derives some satisfaction or gratification from every neurotic symptom, even if in a morbid manner. Freud states: 'Psycho-analysis recognized early that every neurotic symptom owes its existence to a compromise. Every symptom must therefore in some way comply with the demands of the ego which regulates repression, must offer some advantage, admit of some profitable utilization, or it would undergo the same fate as the original impulse itself which is being kept in check.' (Freud, S. *Collected Papers,* vol. 1), tr. by Riviere, J., Leonard and Virginia Woolf and The Institute of Psychoanalysis, London, 1924–25) See *paranosis; epinosis.*

illness as self-punishment This psychiatric term denotes the neurotic's utilization of his neurosis for the purpose of punishing himself. In the neurotic the superego has not developed normally, and it deals with the ego 'like a strict father with a child': the ego must submit to punishment by the superego by means of the illness. Only through this self-punishment, in the guise of the illness, can the neurotic relieve himself of his guilt-feeling, which is generated by his strict superego. Because of his need to relieve himself of this unconscious guilt, the neurotic clings to his illness. Indeed, unconscious guilt is the most powerful type of resistance against analytic treatment. This type of resistance is termed the resistance from the superego. (Freud, S. *The Question of Lay Analysis,* Norton, New York, 1950)

illuminism (i-lū′mi-niz′m) A state of mental exaltation in which the subject's hallucinations generally assume the form of conversations with imaginary, especially supernatural, beings.

illusion (i-lū′zhun) An erroneous perception, a false response to a sense-stimulation; but in a normal individual this false belief usually brings the desire to check or verify its correctness, and often another sense or other senses may come to the rescue and satisfy him that it is merely an illusion.

When a small ball or bead is rolled on the table between the tips of the crossed middle finger and index finger, one has the tactical illusion of rolling *two* balls instead of one. But our own eyes convince us that our tactile sensations are misleading, that *two* balls are but an illusion.

If a straight glass tube is lowered into a tumbler of water, we have the visual illusion that the submerged portion of the tube has bent and forms an angle with its free upper part. This unexpected sight impels us to pull the tube out and convince ourselves that there is nothing the matter with the tube, merely our eyes have misinterpreted the situation into an illusion: it merely looks, but actually is not bent.

Similarly a line-segment with $>$ $<$ at its ends ($>$————$<$) appears to us definitely longer than an equal segment with $<$ $>$ at its ends ($<$————$>$). But the simple application of a ruler dispels this visual illusion.

But the fact that in all these illusions the stimulus and the illusion (i.e. the reaction) involve the identical sense and can be disproven, makes it so much harder to realize that it is not an illusion when, sitting alone in a room, we suddenly start because we have 'heard' somebody else in the room, only to convince ourselves that we are still alone in the room and that no sound had actually been heard.

This absence of a sense-stimulus places the reaction in a different class from those cited above—it is a *hallucination* (q.v.). *Obs.* Fallacia.

illusion, memory When an individual ascribes to himself the experience of others and believes implicitly that the experiences are his own, he is said to have *memory illusion,* with a curiously loose, but well-established use of the term illusion.

'Whoever considers himself Christ, believes that he had been crucified, and, under certain conditions can delude himself into remembering the details of it with perceptible acuteness . . .' shows memory illusions. (Bleuler, E. *Textbook of Psychi-*

atry, tr. by Brill, A.A., Macmillan, New York, 1930) See *appersonification.*

illusion, necessary A literary term used in psychoanalytic literature in reference to an individual's special character defenses as they make for healthy and effective adjustment in the practical and real-life world. In their functioning in relation to the real world these character defenses will make for illusional, private evaluations of what is important and unimportant, what is of great value and of little value—evaluations that represent private predilections in private lives. It is important that an analyst be free of the tendency to confuse his private predilections, and his own unconsciously determined illusions, with the aims and goals of his patient's needs.

E.F. Sharpe (*Collected Papers on Psycho-analysis,* Hogarth Press and The Institute of Psychoanalysis, London, 1950) states: 'We may privately prefer beech trees to cedars, that type of character to this, and have our private evaluations of what a worthy life really is. . . . But these things, eminently useful as they are to us as individuals and to our necessary illusions, are of small importance to the world outside us, and most assuredly they are of no use in the consulting-room.'

illusion, proofreader's Failure to detect an error in spelling, punctuation, construction, etc. because of familiarity with the subject matter; a tendency to see things 'as they ought to be' rather than as they are.

illusio sensus (ĕl-lōō′zē-ō sen′sōōs) (L. 'illusion of sense') Hallucination.

image, imago (im′ij, i-mā′gō) The term *image* or *imago* is used most frequently in psychoanalysis, but it appears often also in analytical psychology (Jung). In the former it refers to the image or likeness of someone, usually not of the subject himself, constructed in the unconscious and remaining therein. The commonest imagos are those of the parents and of those who stand for the parents. Jones defines *imago* as 'an image preserved indefinitely in the unconscious and often identified with persons other than the original one.' (Jones, E. *Papers on Psycho-Analysis,* 4th ed., Wood, Baltimore, 1938)

'The mother-child relation is certainly the deepest and most penetrating one we know; the child in fact for a long time is, so to speak, a part of the maternal body! Later it is really a continuum of the psychic atmosphere of the mother for years, and in this way, all that is primordial in the child, so to speak, indissolubly fused with the mother image.' (Jung, C.G. *Psychological Types*, tr. by Baynes, H.G., Harcourt, Brace, New York and London, 1923)

Jung speaks of *primordial images*. 'Thus there naturally exists in the archetype, in the collectively inherited mother-image, that extraordinary intensity of relationship which first impels the child instinctively to cling to its mother.' (ibid.)

'Her inclination towards elderly married men (always platonic) is also traceable to her father *Imago*' (Stekel, W. *Frigidity in Woman*, vols. 1–2, tr. by van Teslaar, J.S., Boni & Liveright, New York, 1926)

Sometimes the person whose image is mirrored in the unconscious is spoken of as the *imago*. This use of the word is not encouraged.

image agglutinations See *agglutinations, image*.

image, body In psychiatry, a term for the concept which each individual has of his own body as an object in space, independently and apart from all other objects. The body is always in space and experiences are not possible without this conception of our body, or body image, since we live 'as human beings with a body.' At the same time, the body itself, in many respects, 'remains always outside the ego-environment boundary.' In Schilder's opinion, 'the accent of the various experiences (of our life) can be on the body image, i.e. on the *outer* world.' This body image is a dynamic concept subject to modification under the influence of various elements. In this regard Schilder states that 'in the dance, and by vestibular irritation, we try to get rid of the configuration of the body which we have created.' According to Strauss, 'in the dance, the center of the ego seems to wander from the head toward the trunk.' This is considered as 'one step in the direction of a new construction of the body image.' Apart from that, the body, as an object, is not only something for the individual but also an object for others. From this fact Schilder draws the conclusion that the formation of the body image is a social creation: 'an action which is merely in connection with oneself is senseless and

does not exist.' The image of the body extends in space and implies space perception. Indeed, it is a fact that 'there is not only a space outside of the body, but also a space which is filled by the body,' and 'this outer space and the space of the body, are the necessary basis for the unfolding of narcissistic tendencies.' (Schilder, P. *Mind, Perception and Thought*, Columbia University Press, New York, 1942)

image, idealized The term introduced by Horney, who was among the first to give a detailed description of the role of cultural pressures in producing neurosis. Though constituting the base from which attitudes toward authority in general develop, the early attitude toward the father is added to and modified by subsequent experiences with father figures. In the relationship to the father, or to subsequent father figures, difficulties often arise, and to circumvent them, neurotic defenses may be developed. For instance, if the patient adjusts to a difficult father by becoming submissive, submissiveness itself becomes a problem. Thereupon, some sort of periodic aggressiveness may be developed to circumvent the problem of submissiveness. This new difficulty, in turn, produces new defenses and the adult patient now presents a complicated defensive system. Thus the patient is sick because of what happened to him and also because, in coping with it, he establishes goals which lead him to pursue false values. The idealized image is the defense of having a false picture of one's virtues and assets. The more unrealistic (idealized) this image is, the more vulnerable is the person amid the vicissitudes of life.

image, memory Speaking of Pavlov's famous experiments with dogs, in the demonstration of conditioned reflex, Reik surmises that we are justified in assuming that the image of food comes into the mind of the animal when the bell rings during the experiment. Now, by submitting human beings to a similar test, for instance giving the individual an electric shock five seconds after a signal and then repeating the experiment, one may easily prove that the electric shock can be psychologically anticipated. This anticipation of the recurrence of a past experience, immediately before its recurrence, is what Reik describes as memory image. According to him, 'the past situation returns in the service of the present,' and it can even be reproduced with hallucinatory vividness. In such cases the memory image may be said to be a part of the conditioned reflex in Pavlov's sense, that is, the memory image is an ingredient of the inner preparedness for the stimulus, and is part and parcel of the individual's total reaction.

image, percept See *percept-image.*

image, personal When an image possesses archaic character, Jung calls it a *primordial* image. 'I speak of its archaic character when the image is in striking unison with familiar mythological motives. In this case it expresses material primarily derived from the collective unconscious, while, at the same time, it indicates that the momentary conscious situation is influenced not so much from the side of the personal as from the collective.' (Jung, C.G. *Psychological Types,* tr. by Baynes, H.G., Harcourt, Brace, New York and London, 1923)

'A *personal* image has neither archaic character nor collective significance, but expresses contents of the personal unconscious and a personally conditioned, conscious situation.' (ibid.)

image, primary memory Eidetic image. See *eidetic.*

image, primordial (prī-môr′di-al) 'The primordial image is a mnemic deposit, an *imprint* ("engramm"—Semon), which has arisen through a condensation of innumerable, similar processes. It is primarily a precipitate or deposit, and therefore a typical basic form of a certain ever-recurring psychic experience. As a mythological motive, therefore, it is a constantly effective and continuall ̣ recurring expression which is either awakened, or appropriately formulated, by certain psychic experiences.' (Jung, C.G. *Psychological Types,* tr. by Baynes, H.G., Harcourt, Brace, New York and London, 1923)

Also known as *archetype.* See *image.*

'The most immediate primordial image is the mother, for she is in every way the nearest and most powerful experience; and the one, moreover, that occurs in the most impressionable period of a man's life. Since the conscious is as yet only weakly developed in childhood, one cannot speak of an "individual" experience at all. The mother, however, is an arche-typal experience; she is known by the more or less unconscious child not as a definite, individual feminine personality, but as the mother, an archetype loaded with significant possibilities. As life proceeds the primordial image fades, and is replaced by a conscious, relatively individual image, which is assumed to be the only mother-image we have.' (Jung, C.G. *Contributions to Analytical Psychology,* tr. by Baynes, H.G. and C.F., Kegan Paul, Trench, Trubner, London, 1928)

imagery, eidetic The general meaning of this term applies to a psychological phenomenon which is intermediate between the ordinary visual memory-image and the after-image. This phenomenon attains its significance for constitutional medicine from the observation of E.R. Jaensch that although it occurs in 60 per cent of children under 12, it persists after adolescence only in two types, the *Basedow* type and the *tetany* type, or, as they are usually called, the B type and the T type.

The eidetic image differs from the ordinary memory-image by the following details: (1) it possesses a pseudo-perceptual quality; (2) it is superior in clearness and richness of detail, and this clearness is less dependent upon the organization of its content; (3) it is more accurate (mimetic) in its reproduction of detail; (4) it is more brilliant in coloration; (5) it requires more rigid fixation for its arousal; and (6) it shows a greater degree of coherence with the projection ground. It differs from the after-image by the following characteristics: (1) it may be aroused by a more complicated and detailed object; (2) it is superior in clearness and continues longer in the visual field; (3) it is subject to voluntary recall, even after the lapse of considerable time, as well as to voluntary control; (4) it requires a shorter length of exposure and less rigid fixation for its arousal; and (5) it is more dependent upon factors of interest.

The B type is nearer to the memory-image and has been observed only in persons with Basedow's disease or the tendency to it. The T type, in which the imagery approaches the after-image, has been found in individuals whose blood calcium and potassium show either definite evidence of tetany or changes in the direction of it. These differences in imagery, referable to the different biochemical conditions in Basedow's disease and tetany, are thought to be symptomatic of two contrasting types of mind, the integrated and the disintegrated, respectively. According to the studies of W. Jaensch, characteristic capillary loops of the nail beds are an additional item of difference in these two distinctive psychosomatic types.

imagery, hypnagogic (hip-nà-goj'ik) Imagery, occurring during the stage between wakefulness and sleep, that is, just before sleep has set in. 'Silberer demonstrates this [i.e. symbolic representation in images] also by means of hypnagogic visions. On one occasion in a state of sleep-intoxication he wished to develop an idea, but instead of getting on with it, he became constantly more entangled; he then saw before him a curtain rising, but slipping back repeatedly on the roller.' (Storch, A. *The Primitive Archaic Forms in Schizophrenia,* tr. by Willard, C. Nervous and Mental Disease Publishing Company, New York and Washington, 1924)

imagery, hypnopompic (hip-nō-pom'pik) The visions or mental pictures that occur just after the sleeping state and before full wakefulness. The phenomenon is analogous to hypnagogic imagery, save for the time at which the images occur.

imagery, spontaneous Augusta Jellinek's term for visual images which can be produced at will when the eyes are closed. Spontaneous imagery is not a pathological phenomenon and is seen more commonly in children, probably because most children have a positive eidetic disposition. Spontaneous imagery is sometimes misinterpreted as visual hallucinations.

image, secondary visual Speaking of hypnosis, Morton Prince says: 'As the subject's eyes had been clouded in hypnosis, and, in any event, as she could not have seen her own face, there were at the time no *visual* perceptions of herself smoking a cigarette, and therefore the vision could not have been simply a reproduction of a visual experience. There were, however, factual, gustatory, and other perceptions and ideas of self and environment, and these perceptions and ideas of course possessed *secondary visual images.*' (Prince, M. *The Unconscious,* Macmillan, New York, 1916)

image, social Burrow's term for an affective impression representing crystallized opinions, beliefs, and prejudices which are deeply ingrained in the individual and in society but for which there is no objective, demonstrable correspondence in actuality. These emotionally toned impressions have no direct relation to the object or situation upon which they are projected. The social image is wishfully determined and is not based upon demonstrable reality. See *affect; partitive; 'I'-persona; semiopathic.* (Burrow, T. 'Social Images Versus Reality,' *The Journal of Abnormal and Social Psychology, XIX,* 230–35, 1924)

image, unconscious See *memory unconscious.*

imaginarii (ē-mä-gē-nä'rē-ī) One of Linnaeus's three subdivisions of mental disorders, characterized by disturbances of the sensory faculties.

imagination, creative The terms *creative imagination* or *creative work* designate the process in which dormant, unrelated contents of the unconscious become associated with the organized labor of consciousness and accomplish something new.

imago See *image.*

imbalance, intellectual Among social workers this means 'the state of an individual with special abilities or disabilities, markedly competent in some respects and deficient in others, but not well integrated or compensated.' (Hamilton, G. *A Medical Social Terminology,* Presbyterian Hospital, New York, 1930)

imbalance, sibling A social service term for the situation in which 'the number or distribution of children in a family contributes to a problem of spoiling, or economic insufficiency; e.g., only boy in female setting, hyper-large family, etc.' (Hamilton, G. *A Medical Social Terminology,* Presbyterian Hospital, New York, 1930)

imbecile (im'be-sil) See *amentia, degree of; deficiency, mental.*

imbecility, moral (im-be-sil'i-tē) See *insanity, moral.*

imbecillitas (ēm-bā-kēl'lē-tàs) Weakness, feebleness, imbecility. 'It is often taken for a disease, but generally means a debilitated state of the habit, and sometimes the word *arrhostia* is made use of to express imbecility.' (Motherby, G. *A New Medical Dictionary,* 5th ed., for J. Johnson, St. Paul's Church-Yard, etc., London, 1801)

imitation In sociology, 'the tendency,

under the influence of copies socially presented, to build up mechanisms of habits, sentiments, ideals, and patterns of life.' (Park, R.E., and Burgess, E.W. *Introduction to the Science of Sociology*, University of Chicago Press, Chicago, 1921)

imitation, hysterical A psychiatric term which denotes the ability of a hysterical patient to imitate all the symptoms that impress him when they occur in others. The psychological mechanism at work in hysterical imitation is identification: the patient (unconsciously) identifies himself with a person who has the same unconscious needs as he, who is 'just like' him. As a result, the patient reproduces the symptom shown by the person with whom he identifies. Through this hysterical imitation 'patients are enabled to express in their symptoms not merely their own experiences, but the experiences of quite a number of other persons; they can suffer, as it were, for a whole mass of people, and fill all the parts of a drama with their own personalities.' For example, one girl in a school may react to a love letter with a fainting spell. Some of the other girls then may also get fainting spells. Unconsciously the other girls also wanted love letters, and having had the same unconscious wish they had to suffer the same consequence—they, too, had fainting spells through hysterical identification. (Freud, S. *The Interpretation of Dreams* in *The Basic Writings of Sigmund Freud*, Modern Library, Random House, New York, 1938)

immobilization-paralysis See *paralysis, immobilization.*

immorality, maniacal An older term for the preponderance of overt and uncontrollable sexuality in cases of simple mania. (Clouston, T.S.)

immortality This concept is encountered with great frequency in psychiatric patients. It is expressed directly by certain schizophrenic individuals, who believe that they have always existed and always will. The belief is intimately associated with delusions of omnipotence, omniscience, timelessness, and ubiquity. Other patients, notably those with a psychoneurosis, express the same God-like qualities but in a highly symbolized manner. The concept gains frequent expression in dream form.

Jones believes that wish-fulfillment plays

an important role in this belief. He holds that 'salvation betokens a joyful reunion with the parents against whom the unconscious sinful thoughts were directed.' (Jones, E. *Papers on Psycho-Analysis,* 4th ed., Wood, Baltimore, 1938)

imperative, authoritative The pressing directives emanating from the superego which subconsciously direct the individual's behavior; the commanding voice of parental or social rule in the individual's subconscious mind. According to Stekel, a compulsion is always a substitute for an imperative. The current (adult) imperative is always a resonance of infantile imperatives. 'One may say that neurotics run after their infantile imperatives. The imperative apparently leads to an action which, however, in reality consists only of an inhibition.' (Stekel, W. *Compulsion and Doubt,* Liveright, New York, 1949)

imperative, categorical The expression *categorical imperative,* a psychoanalytic concept in psychiatry, is the equivalent of *blanket demand.* The superego, for instance, is said to exercise its duties by the rigid 'yes' or 'no' rule, by the 'all or none' law.

imperative, ethical The inexorable disciplinary power of moral principles exerted upon the individual's mental life and behavior. It represents 'the wish of the moral self, the endeavor of the nobler side of man leading the ego to higher and better things in life.' One may also speak in terms of 'the upward aspiration of man,' which in fact constitutes the admonitions of the moral consciousness in the life of an individual. (Stekel, W. *The Interpretation of Dreams,* Liveright, New York, 1943)

imperative, immoral The antisocial unconscious impulses that compel the individual to desire the occurrence of events, or the performance of actions, considered unethical or antimoral. This mental mechanism is often observed in the compulsive-neurotic. It is a compulsion to act against the rules of society, an impulsive subconscious rebellion against moral principles. The destructive aims of the immoral imperative are, most of the time, orientated against religious principles, precisely because religion is one of the most powerful barriers controlling man's instinctual life. (Stekel, W. *Compulsion and Doubt,* Liveright, New York, 1949)

impetus (im'pe-tus) (L. 'attack, onset, violent impulse or motion') From the psychoanalytic point of view the impetus of an instinct is 'its motor element, the amount of force or the measure of the demand upon energy which it represents. The characteristic of impulsion is common to all instincts, is in fact the very essence of them. Every instinct is a form of activity; if we speak loosely of passive instincts, we can only mean those whose aim is passive.' (Freud, S. *Collected Papers,* vol. 4, tr. by Riviere, J., Leonard and Virginia Woolf and The Institute of Psychoanalysis, London, 1924–25)

implant, dynamic Introduction or instillation of a significant idea into consciousness. The term is used mainly in connection with *psychic driving* (q.v.), one of whose values is said to be long-lasting action on the part of the patient as a result of one or more dynamic implants. The latter bring the patient to focus on specific behavior or action tendencies; this usually leads to intensified activity in the form of tension and anxiety and thus to greater efforts to free himself of such intensification. As a result, the patient tends to ruminate over and to reorganize his reactions to the material in question. This would appear to be a mechanistic description of one type of insight.

impostor A type of pathological liar who seeks to gain some advantage by means of imposing on others fabrications of his attainments, position, or worldly possessions. Phyllis Greenacre (*Psychoanalytic Quarterly 27:* 359–82, 1958) has noted the compulsive, pressured aspect to the impostor's urge to seek the limelight and 'put something over' on his audience. This writer outlines the following features which appear to be of psychodynamic significance: the typically ambivalent and over-possessive mother creates so intense a maternal attachment in the child that he is unable to develop a full sense of separate identity. At the same time his ability to assume an uncontested supersedence over the father as far as the mother is concerned intensifies infantile narcissism and favors a reliance on omnipotent phantasy to the exclusion of reality testing. Imposture is an outgrowth of the oedipal conflict and represents an attempt to kill the father and/or to rob him of his more adequate penis. Success of this mechanism as evidenced by belief in the impostor by his audience (the mother) furnishes a powerful incentive for endless repetition of the fraudulent behavior.

impotence, impotency (im'pō-tens, -tensē) In psychiatry the term usually means a male individual's inability to perform sexual intercourse. Impotence may occur under a variety of conditions. It may manifest itself only with regard to certain women, while the individual may be potent with others. Or he may be potent at the beginning of the act and become impotent during it.

The mentioned manifestations of impotence are associated with psychic causes. 'The disorder is in fact due to the inhibiting influence of certain complexes in the mind that are withdrawn from the knowledge of the person in question. As the most universal feature of the pathogenic material an incestuous fixation on mother and sister which has not been surmounted stands out.' (Freud, S. *Collected Papers,* vol. 4, tr. by Riviere, J., Leonard and Virginia Woolf and The Institute of Psychoanalysis, London, 1924–25) Freud mentions also 'accidental impressions of a painful kind connected with infantile sexuality' as a cause of impotence. There are many other causes, among which may be mentioned the castration complex that gives rise to the adoption of a passive feminine role, so clearly depicted among certain schizophrenic individuals.

The corresponding condition in a woman is called *frigidity.*

impotence, anal A term describing certain types of constipation in which the analogy to cases of neurotic genital sexual impotence in males is emphasized. In this type of constipation, anxiety concerning the injurious or filthy aspect of the fecal mass to be ejected or parted with is of central importance. This is analogous to the anxiety of many orgastically impotent men concerning the poisonous or sullying effect of the seminal ejaculation. Thus, constipation in the anorectal area is the result of inhibitions against *offending,* but they result in emissive and ejaculatory impotence in the seminal vesical or prostatic areas.

At military induction centers it is a frequent experience that many candidates cannot void (produce a urine specimen) in the presence of others. This is also commonly seen in boys' camps where certain boys find it impossible both to urinate and to defecate unless they have absolute privacy. Fundamentally such symptoms stem back to the early infantile developmental conflicts concerning soiling and toilet training. These symptoms can be thought of as the adult neurotic residues of conflicts between desires for cooperative regularity, giving, and cleanliness, on the one hand, and desire for the maintenance of continued stubborn autonomy, spite, defiance, soiling, and direct stool pleasure on the other. (Weiss, E., and English, O.S. *Psychosomatic Medicine*, 2nd ed., Saunders, Philadelphia and London, 1949)

impotence, cerebral Magnus Hirschfeld postulates four types of impotence: (1) cerebral, due to cerebral causes; (2) spinal, associated with difficulties of erection and ejaculation, of spinal origin; (3) genital, connected with genital defects; and (4) germinal. (Hirschfeld, M. *Sexual Pathology*, tr. by Gibbs, J., Emerson, New York, 1939)

impotence, genital (jen′i-tal) See *impotence, cerebral*.

impotence, germinal (jẽr′mi-nal) See *impotence, cerebral*.

impotence, orgastic (awr-gas′tik) The incapacity for achieving the orgasm or acme of satisfaction in the sexual act. Neurotics cannot achieve adequate discharge of their sexual energy through the sexual act. This orgastic impotence operates in all types of sexual behavior shown by neurotics. For example, the neurotic 'may attempt to achieve satisfaction by persistent repetitions of the sexual act.' Although he thus gives the impression of being very vigorous genitally, in reality he never achieves genuine satisfaction and cannot lose his desire. Also, as a result of their inability to attain genuine end-pleasure, many neurotics lay more stress on the fore-pleasure mechanisms.

'In other cases the physiological course of the sexual act may seem to be normal; but if a person whose sexuality actually has remained infantile tries to ward off a contradicting anxiety by ungenuinely performing acts of adult sexuality these acts can never bring full gratification.' The sexual behavior is rigid and, although a certain narcissistic functional pleasure is felt, this is not the complete relaxation of a full orgasm. In this 'pseudo-sexuality,' narcissistic aims are disturbing the true sexuality.

Finally, in the neurotic there may be a diminution of conscious sexual interest.

This reflects his constant struggle with his repressed sexuality which 'diminishes his disposable sexual energy.' In some cases, however, the amount lacking is rather small, so that the patient's sexual life appears superficially undisturbed and he feels subjectively as if his sexuality were satisfactory.

According to Fenichel, an important concomitant of orgastic impotence is that these patients are incapable of love. Their need for self-love, for self-esteem, overshadows their capacity for object love. In further elucidating the mechanism of orgastic impotence, Fenichel quotes Reich's analysis of the course of sexual excitement. According to Reich, in order to obtain an 'economically sufficient discharge in orgasm, the full development of the latter part or "second phase" of sexual excitement in which there are involuntary convulsions of the muscles of the floor of the pelvis is necessary. The climax of pleasure occurs at the climax of sexual excitement in this second phase and coincides with a loss of ego. In orgastically impotent egos this climax of pleasure does not occur. Indeed it is at this very point that the pleasure turns into anxiety and loss of ego control.' (Fenichel, O. *The Psychoanalytic Theory of Neurosis*, Norton, New York, 1945)

impotence, psychic (sī′kik) The functional inability of the male to perform sexual intercourse in spite of sexual desire and the presence of intact genital organs. There may be erective impotence (inability to get an erection), ejaculatory impotence or psychogenic *aspermia* (inability to expel seminal fluid), or orgastic impotence (inability to attain full orgasm). Premature ejaculation, *ejaculation retardata, postcoitum triste* (depression following the sexual act), etc., are all types of psychic impotence.

impotence, spinal (spī′nal) See *impotence, cerebral*.

impotency, spiritual Impotence due to psychic causes. Also called psychic impotence; see *impotence*. 'Antifetishistic idiosyncrasy plays an important role as the case of spiritual impotency.' (Hirschfeld, M. *Sexual Pathology*, tr. by Gibbs, J., Emerson Books, New York, 1939)

impotentia coeundi (ēm-pô-ten′tē-à kô-e-oon′dē) Inability to cohabit.

improvement, transference Amelioration

of neurotic symptoms on the basis of the transference relationship. The physician is perceived unconsciously as a reincarnation of the parents, and as such he is thought of as providing love and protection, or as threatening with punishments. So-called 'flight into health' is an instance of transference improvement.

impuberism (im-pū′bĕr-iz′m) The state of not having reached the age or stage of puberty. While, strictly speaking, the term denotes the life-period before puberty and thus embraces the stages of infantilism and childhood, generally it means, nevertheless, that the mental and physical characteristics of childhood or occasionally of infancy run into and continue during the chronologically later and distinct adolescent or even adult life. For example, infantilism, that is, the carrying over of infantile anatomy and physiology into adulthood, is a case in point.

Impuberism may appear also in the psyche. Certain patients, adult in age, are children in behavior, feeling, and thought.

impulse From the psychic standpoint an impulse is a stimulus that sets the mind in action. The stimulus may originate in (1) the objective world, or (2) the subject himself: (a) his soma—within or any part of the body; (b) his psyche—its conscious or its unconscious part. In psychoanalysis the term impulse most commonly refers to the instincts; a basic impulse is an instinct, the source of which is a 'somatic process in an organ or part of the body.' (Freud, S. *Collected Papers*, vol. 4, tr. by Riviere, J., Leonard and Virginia Woolf and The Institute of Psychoanalysis, London, 1924–25)

Jones says: 'The ego defends itself against external danger by repressing the genital impulses directed towards the love-object.' (Jones, E. *Papers on Psycho-Analysis,* 4th ed., Wood, Baltimore, 1938)

'Besides this we have a number of strivings which become effective even without any external cause. Among these we may mention the impulse to live, the activity impulse, the self-assertion impulse, the impulse for knowledge, hunger, and the sex impulse.' (Bleuler, E. *Textbook of Psychiatry,* tr. by Brill, A.A., Macmillan, New York, 1930.) See *instinct.*

impulse, component A psychoanalytic term. According to Freud, the sexual instinct is broken up, during the period of infancy, into several component or partial

impulses, each of which strives for independent action. Freud uses the term *sexual* in a very broad sense; to him sexual satisfaction means the relief of somatic irritability.

During the infancy period some of the component impulses are expressed in sucking, biting, touching, defecating, urinating, looking (voyeurism), showing (exhibitionism), sadism, masochism, etc. Later, curiosity in one form or another becomes important as a component impulse and still later the many derivatives of those impulses just mentioned come under the same heading. See *component-instinct.*

impulse, cross Kraepelin often uses this term for an impulse that crosses the path of another impulse and in so doing checks the further development of the latter.

'The side impulses which at first bring about only flourishes in action may gradually become cross impulses which lead to complete derailment of volition.' (Kraepelin, E. *Manic-Depressive Insanity and Paranoia,* tr. by Barclay, R.M., Livingstone, Edinburgh, 1921)

impulse-disorder, hyperkinetic (hī-pĕr-ki-net′ik) A type of childhood behavior disorder, believed to be due to diencephalic dysfunction, characterized by hyperactivity, short attention span, poor concentration, and irritability.

impulse-disorders A varied group of personality disorders with the following characteristics: (1) the impulse or symptom is ego-syntonic; (2) there is a pleasurable component; (3) there is minimal distortion of the original impulse, and (4) the impulse possesses a quality of irresistibility.

Frosch and Wortis (*American Journal of Psychiatry 3:* 132–138, 1954) differentiate two groups of impulse-disorders, the discrete symptom type (including what others call the impulse neuroses, perversions, and catathymic crises) and the diffuse character type, with low frustration tolerance and a tendency to explosive reactions to deprivation.

Some of these patients show rather typical epileptoid records on encephalography, often with indications of pathologic discharge in the temporal lobe.

impulse, epistemophilic (ē-pis-tē-mō-fil′ik) The impulse toward knowledge; learning; an impulsion to inquire into things. Jones

defines it as the *instinct of curiosity*. See
epistemophilia.

impulse, fundamental social A psychiatric
term used for designating the fundamental
social impulse to check the sprouting
manifestations of evil. Influenced by
Jung's investigations, Baynes thinks that
this impulse expresses itself in various
social rituals (such as coronation, marriage, ordination of priests, and other
forms of social rites) brought into being
by this single fundamental necessity, all
of them merely elaborations of the same
pattern, their symbolic elements remaining
relatively constant with both savage and
civilized people all over the world.
(Baynes, H.G. *Mythology of the Soul*,
Williams and Wilkins, Baltimore, 1940)

impulse, irresistible Weihofen says: 'A
large minority [of states], however, hold
that this test, i.e., right and wrong is not
sufficient in all cases, and that a person
who knew he was committing an act
which was morally wrong and prohibited
by law may nevertheless be excused from
responsibility, if he lacked the power of
conscious volition and inhibition (freedom
of will) to resist the impulse to commit
it.' (Weihofen, H. *Insanity as a Defense
in Criminal Law*, Commonwealth Fund,
Oxford University Press, New York, 1933)

'Some persons are assailed by most urgent desires, which they abominate, repel,
and resist, to do things which are criminal,
and which they abhor. They are constantly
urged by, some internal irrational compulsion, to steal, to injure themselves or other
people, to set things on fire, and to do
other criminal acts.' (Mercier, C.A. *A
Text-Book of Insanity*, George Allen and
Unwin, London, 1914)

impulse-life In psychoanalysis this term
refers to the instinctual life of the individual. See *impulse*.

impulse, sexual component The psychoanalytical conception of the nature of the
sexual instinct constitutes the frame of
reference in which this term has meaning
in psychiatry. This conception is described
by Jones as follows: 'The sexual instinct
is not at first a unit. It consists of various
components, emanating from manifold
organic sources. These components at first
function quite independently of one another, each as it were blindly seeking for
organic pleasure and satisfaction, and it
is only later that they combine in the

function of reproduction. They at first
begin in conjunction with the activity of
ego instincts, for instance hunger, with
which they have a common source, aim
and object, and only gradually do they
emancipate themselves from this association to achieve an existence of their own.
An infant sucks its food before it sucks its
thumb and long before it uses its lips for
kissing.' (Jones, E.J. *Papers on Psycho-
Analysis*, Williams and Wilkins, Baltimore,
1949)

This same conception of the nature of
the sexual instinct is expressed by Fenichel: 'The small child is an instinctual
creature full of polymorphous perverse
sexual drives or, to put it more correctly,
full of a still undifferentiated total sexuality which contains all the later "partial
instincts" in one. Reality seems to be
judged at first only as to whether it is
compatible with instinct satisfaction. Reality, as conceived of by the primitive
ego, is colored by the status of its sexual
aims. Every kind of excitation in the
child can become a source of sexual excitement: mechanical and muscular stimuli, affects, intellectual activity, and even
pain. In infantile sexuality excitement
and satisfaction are not sharply differentiated, although there are already orgasm-
like phenomena, that is, pleasureful sensations that bring relaxation and the end
of sexual excitation. In time, however, the
genitals begin to function as a special discharge apparatus, which concentrates all
excitation upon itself and discharges it
no matter in which erogenous zone it
originated.

'It is called genital primacy when this
function of the genitals has become dominant over the extragenital erogenous
zones, and all sexual excitations become
finally genitally oriented and climactically
discharged.' (Fenichel, O. *The Psychoanalytic Theory of Neurosis*, Norton, New
York, 1945)

impulse, side An impulse that exists by the
side of another impulse. Kraepelin says
that the condition is common in dementia
praecox (schizophrenia). Often the side
or secondary impulse interrupts the primary one, producing irrelevant action or
speech.

impulse, thought According to Freud certain forms of psychic activity of the waking stage are carried over into the stage
of sleep, in which they may be incor-

porated in dreams. For example, wish-impulses, constituting conscious wishes may instigate dream-formation. Likewise, thought-impulses, 'which are not wishes' may provoke dreams.

'Unsolved problems, harassing cares, overwhelming impressions, continue the activity of our thought even during sleep, maintaining psychic processes in the system which we have termed the preconscious. The thought-impulses continued into sleep may be divided into the following groups. . . .' (Freud, S. *The Interpretation of Dreams*, 3rd ed., tr. by Brill, A.A., Macmillan, New York, 1933)

impulse, wandering Drapetomania; dromomania; ecdemomania; *wanderlust* (q.v.).

impulse, wish See *wish-impulse*.

impulsion (im-pul'shun) L. Bender and P. Schilder use this term to describe the particular type of infantile urge characterized by the fact that the inner impulses or drives approved and openly followed by the child are in the foreground of the mental picture. Furthermore, they state that such an urge is 'in close relation to the obsession and compulsion neurosis of adolescence.' In children, the existence of impulsion is due to the fact that 'interpersonal relations and the super-ego have not led to an organized defense' against the blind obedience to the internal drives. In adults with obsessive neurosis, there is a continuous change in the relationship between the internal and external drives, and in such cases one may observe impulsion when the organization of a defensive reaction is weak. In these circumstances the impulsion may be a symbolic expression of a deeper wish: the individuals may be misers, hoarders, cruel moralizers, and so on, but they consider their impulses right and follow them openly. It can be readily understood that in adults the impulsion is much more symbolic than in children. (Schilder, P. *Psychotherapy*, Norton, New York, 1938)

impulsive Relating to, characterized by, impulse. In psychoanalysis, *impulsive* and *instinctive* are generally used interchangeably as equivalent terms. In general psychiatry, impulsive usually applies to swift action without forethought or conscious judgment.

'In most cases this word refers to the impulses for actions, which are accom-plished unexpectedly, without real reflection, or with inconsistent reflection, or without the assent of the whole personality.' (Bleuler, E. *Textbook of Psychiatry*, tr. by Brill, A.A., Macmillan, New York, 1930)

impulsiveness See *impulsive*.

Imu A psychoreactive phenomenon seen among the Ainu, consisting of hyperkinesia, catalepsy, echolalia, echopraxia, and command automatism. Imu occurs almost exclusively in adult females.

inadequacy, constitutional An expression implying an anatomical and physiological imbalance between two or more of the systems (physical and mental) of the body. In general it is based upon studies relating to the biological growth of organs or organic systems. It includes, for instance, such topics as are associated with Godin's law, namely, that in normal growth, phases of growth in width alternate with phases of growth in length; or with the law of Viola: 'The ponderal (weight) evolution, or increase of mass, and the morphological evolution, or change of proportion, are in inverse proportion to each other. The more an organ evolves ponderally the less does it evolve morphologically; the less it evolves ponderally the more does it evolve morphologically.' (Pende, N. *Constitutional Inadequacies*, tr. by Naccarati, S., Lea & Febiger, Philadelphia, 1928)

These, and the many other concepts identified with the school of constitutional medicine, throw considerable light upon many essential factors in psychiatry. Closely associated with constitutional inadequacy is constitutional anomaly.

inadequacy, intellectual See *deficiency, mental*.

inadequacy, psychical (sī'ki-kal) An expression used by Freud to denote the incapacity of the psyche to master sexual excitation. In describing the etiology of anxiety-neurosis he states: 'The psyche develops the affect of anxiety when it feels itself incapable of dealing (by an adequate reaction) with a task (danger) approaching it externally; it develops the neurosis of anxiety when it feels itself unequal to the task of mastering (sexual) excitation arising endogenously.' (Freud, S. *Collected Papers*, vol. 1, tr. by Riviere, J., Leonard and Virginia Woolf and The Institute of Psychoanalysis, London, 1924–25) inadequate personality See *personality pattern disturbance.*

inappetence (in-ap'ē-tens) Absence of appetite or desire.

inattention, selective Inattention to or disregard of by choice, contingent on keeping out of the sphere of a child's awareness (during the development of his self-system) the attributes which, for the time being, are neither 'good' nor 'bad' in the eyes of the significant people in a child's milieu.

According to Sullivan, the self is finally formed out of a great number of potentialities. The child tends to develop and enhance those of his traits that are pleasing or acceptable to the significant adults, and to block out of awareness and disassociate those attributes that meet with their disapproval. Obviously there are some attributes that are neutral in the estimation of the significant people. Since no special attention is paid to these attributes, the child may or may not be aware of them, and it may be said that 'selective inattention' has been at work. Unlike disassociated material, disavowed because it has been disapproved by the significant adults, the material on which selective inattention acts can, without great difficulty, be incorporated into the *self-system* (q.v.) if such behavioral attributes should later become important in the eyes of others. The difference between selective inattention and disassociation is not clear cut, however, and is merely one of degree.

in-between A literal translation of Hirschfeld's *Zwischenstufe,* meaning an in-between stage or homosexualist.

inbred Produced by inbreeding. Pertaining to the origin and qualities of animals which originate from the breeding from types of the same parentage, or in the more general sense of human genetics, relating to the descent and biological conditions of individuals descended from common ancestors, that is, from ancestors who frequently or persistently intermarried among themselves, thus creating a particular population group (see *intermarriage*).

inbreeding In genetics, this means the special form of reproductive conditions which prevail in a rather isolated and relatively homogeneous group of individuals, exclusively and persistently selecting their marriage partners from their own group. Such selective process of reproduction gradually leads to the formation of more or less pure-bred stocks and counteracts the normal effects of propagation, consisting of the continuous creation of new combinations of hereditary or non-hereditary differences (see *variation*).

In the reproduction of a species in which *hybridization,* or even *panmixia,* has been the rule, the results of *inbreeding* are almost invariably disadvantageous. The worst effects are caused by the increased production of homozygotic carriers of *recessive* traits, which under normal reproductive conditions would appear only rarely.

Another disadvantage of inbreeding is that, for unknown reasons, inbreeding weakens the offspring and reduces the capacity for reproduction. This weakening always progresses until, sooner or later, a stable minimum is attained. 'The vital efficiency of the offspring decreases at first rapidly generation after generation, but eventually the decrease slackens, and in the end a condition is reached wherein further inbreeding does no more harm. The minimal efficiency thus reached varies greatly from one organism to another.' (Baur, E., Fischer, E. and Lenz, F. *Human Heredity,* Macmillan, New York, 1931)

A doubtful kind of dysgenic inbreeding effect may be due to the fact that inbreeding, when of a marked degree, tends to make mutations more frequent. It must be taken into consideration, however, that the majority of mutations are recessive, so that inbreeding may only facilitate their easier discovery.

incendiarism (in-sen'di-à-riz'm) *Pyromania* (q.v.).

incest From the psychiatric point of view, sexual congress between male and female who are blood related. The condition, when occurring, generally takes place between mother and son, father and daughter, brother and sister, and among cousins. However, as a real act, incest is comparatively rare among psychiatric patients, although the impulse toward it is extremely common. Indeed, there are but few well-defined psychiatric states in which incestuous tendencies do not enter as one of the central themes.

'Boys wander at night to mother's and girls to father's bed. Noctambulism is frequent among brothers and sisters, and I have had cases under observation where lengthy incestuous relations took place, and where the recollection of the events occurring during the night was completely absent in the morning.' (Stekel, W. *Encyclopaedia Sexualis,* edited by Robinson, V., Dingwall-Rock, New York, 1936)

When incest appears in a psychiatric condition it constitutes an incest complex.

Jung believes that incestuous phantasies really do not center at those related by blood; to him they are merely symbols for ethical ideals.

incest-barrier See *barrier, incest.*

incidence (in'si-dens) In epidemiology, incidence is the number of cases occurring in a given population in a given period of time (in psychiatric diseases, usually one year). See *rate; prevalance.*

incoherence (in-kō-hēr'ens) In the second half of the 19th century A. Pritchard (1804–82) used this term in a diagnostic sense, equating it with dementia of psychic origin; it is synonymous with *ataxophemia.*

incompetence, incompetency (in-kom'petens, -ten-sē) A legal term of psychiatric significance in cases where an individual's mental competence is in question. Incompetence refers primarily to defects in intellectual functioning such that comprehension of the nature of a transaction is interfered with or otherwise inadequate. The term, thus, refers to intellectual capacity and takes no note of temperament, emotions, or the like which may also interfere with an individual's capacity to function. Ordinarily, incompetence implies an interference with thinking which gives rise to defects in judgment and leads to behavioral abnormalities such as squandering, hoarding, or gullibility. Competence bears little or no relationship to underlying psychiatric diagnosis and will vary in degree according to the magnitude or significance of the action under consideration. Thus an individual of low intelligence might be considered competent to handle and manage a weekly allowance of twenty dollars, but he might be considered incompetent to manage a trust fund of $20,000.

inco-ordination (in-kō-or-di-nā'shun) Ataxia.

incorporation (in-kor-por-ā'shun) *Introjection* (q.v.). Many authors use the terms incorporation, introjection, and identification synonymously. Incorpora-

tion is the earliest instinctual aim directed toward objects and the most primitive method of recognizing external reality. Everything that is pleasurable is something to swallow and becomes ego; thus incorporation is the prototype of instinctual satisfaction, and all sexual aims are derivatives of incorporation aims. Incorporation is also the prototype of regaining the omnipotence previously projected onto adults. But what is incorporated and taken in is also destroyed, so that the ego later uses incorporation in a hostile way to execute destructive impulses. Any instinctual aim may regress to incorporation or introjection.

incubus (in'kū-bus) (L. nightmare) *Obs.* Nightmare. See *succubus.*

incubus, family In social work, a term for 'a person who, because of mental or physical incapacity or difficult personality creates a problem distinctly burdensome or depressing to others.' (Hamilton, G. *A Medical Social Terminology,* Presbyterian Hospital, New York, 1930)

index-case A term used in genetics to refer to a person disclosing clinical evidence of the trait under investigation.

index, cephalic (se-fal'ik) A measure of head size obtained by dividing the maximal breadth of the head by its maximal length and multiplying by 100. Medium heads (mesocephaly) have an index number from 76.0 to 80.9. Long heads (dolichocephaly) have an index below 76.0; broad or short heads (brachycephaly) have an index of 81.0 or over.

index, homeostatic (hō-mē-ō-sta'tik) Any measure of the capacity to resist alteration of the status quo; the higher the homeostatic index, the more rapidly will an organism 'recover' from any disturbing situation and return to normal balance.

index, hyperglycemic (hī-pēr-glī-sē'mik) Often abbreviated H.I. The hyperglycemic index is a measurement used by McGowan as a prognostic indicator in various psychoses.

The index is computed as follows:

$$\text{H.I.} = \frac{\text{2-hour blood sugar level—FBS}}{\text{maximal blood sugar level—FBS}} \times 100$$

A high index is considered unfavorable and is seen in melancholia, and in catatonic and depressive stupors, but is usually low in mania. McGowan considers the hyperglycemic index to be a measure of the emotional tension under which a patient labors.

index of body build See *body build, index of.*

index of sexuality An index proposed by Linhares and De Oliveira:

$$\text{I.S.} = \frac{\text{urine 17 ketosteroids (in mg.)} \times 10}{\text{urine phenol-steroids (in microgm.)}}$$

Normal values are 2.6 to 4.3 for men, 0.6 to 1.0 for women. The index is low in hypogenital men and high in climacteric women.

index, skelic (ske'lik) A measurement used in anthropometry; the ratio between the length of the legs and the length of the trunk.

indicator, complex Any stimulus that arouses an emotion because it has touched off some unconscious complex is termed complex indicator. 'In group therapy . . . despite subject matter, which is probably quite involved for the average patient, it is significant how often "complex indicators" are uncovered concerning which the patients will evidence far more comprehension than they might be credited with.' (Klapman, J.W. *Group Psychotherapy,* Grune and Stratton, New York, 1946)

indigestion, nervous A diagnostic term combining both descriptive and etiological factors, referring specifically to symptoms of gastrointestinal dyspepsia, the origin of which is assumed to be psychological (emotional). The syndrome usually constitutes a combination of varied abdominal, colonic, and gastric complaints. Optimally, the diagnostic validation of the basic cause for the symptoms is arrived at through the combination of two medical approaches: (1) the personality inventory, study, and investigation; and (2) the exclusion of 'organic' disease by the full employment of the diagnostic skills and armamentarium of physical medicine.

The symptoms of nervous indigestion are the overt result of the dysfunction or malfunctioning of the gastrointestinal viscera. This malfunctioning has the hidden significance of expressing (in archaic organ language) the repressed emotional conflicts between adult and infantile goals and aims of the personality.

indirect method of therapy See *therapy, indirect method of.*

individual Jung defines the psychological individual as 'unique-being.' 'The psychological individual is characterized by its peculiar, and in certain respects, unique psychology. The peculiar character of the individual psyche appears less in its elements then in its complex formations.' (Jung, C.G. *Psychological Types,* tr. by Baynes, H.G., Harcourt, Brace, New York and London, 1923)

'The psychological individual, or individuality has an *a priori* unconscious existence, but it exists consciously only in so far as a consciousness of its peculiar nature is present, i.e. in so far as there exists a conscious distinctiveness from other individuals.' (ibid.)

He adds: 'Everything is individual that is not collective, everything in fact that pertains only to one and not to a larger group of individuals. Individuality can hardly be described as belonging to the psychological elements, but rather to their peculiar and unique grouping and combination.' (ibid.)

individual psychology See *psychology, individual.*

individuation (in-di-vij-ū-ā'shun) Jung says: 'The concept of individuation plays no small role in our psychology. In general, it is the process of forming and specializing the individual nature; in particular, it is the development of the psychological individual as a differentiated being from the general, collective psychology. Individuation, therefore, is a *process of differentiation,* having for its goal the development of the individual personality.' (Jung, C.G. *Psychological Types,* tr. by Baynes, H.G., Harcourt, Brace, New York and London, 1923)

Individuation is often used to refer to therapy by the methods of Jungian psychology.

induction, dream A psychiatric term denoting the production of a dream through hypnotic stimulation. Such dreams may be 'artificially stimulated on command during hypnosis or they may be posthypnotically suggested, to appear later during spontaneous sleep.' Both the induction and the interpretation of this type of dream play an important part in the technique of hypnoanalysis. (Wolberg, L.R., *Hypnoanalysis,* Grune and Stratton, New York, 1945)

induction, psychological (in-duk'shun, sī-kō-loj'i-kal) A psychological charging; psychological irradiation.

inefficiency, family In social work, a term for 'the state of a "shiftless" family chronically without financial margin or unable to manage its own affairs without assistance.' (Hamilton, G. *A Medical Social Terminology,* Presbyterian Hospital, New York, 1930)

inefficiency, general In social work, a term for 'a broken-down state, physical, mental or both; an enfeebled condition; decay; not necessarily due to old age but to wasting diseases, infections, overwork, etc.' (Hamilton, G. *A Medical Social Terminology,* Presbyterian Hospital, New York, 1930)

inertia, psychic (in-ẽr'shà, sī'kik) Jung says that a peculiar psychic inertia which opposes any change and progress is a basic condition of a neurosis. Freud holds that 'this inertia is in fact most peculiar; it is not a general one, but is highly specialized; it is not even all-powerful within its own scope, but fights against tendencies towards progress and reconstruction which remain active even after the formation of neurotic symptoms.' He adds: 'This specialized "psychic inertia" is only a different term, though hardly a better one, for what in psycho-analysis we are accustomed to call a *fixation*.' (Freud, S. *Collected Papers,* vol. 2, tr. by Riviere, J., Leonard and Virginia Woolf and The Institute of Psychoanalysis, London, 1924–25)

infancy From the psychiatric point of view the period of infancy normally extends from birth until the beginning of the sixth year. It is believed, however, that the period should not be restricted too carefully; rather, it should be stated that the upper limit of the period of infancy should be expressed at approximately the fifth or sixth year. According to psychoanalysts, there is a gradual transition from the infantile to the latency period.

'This period of life, during which a certain degree of directly sexual pleasure is produced by the stimulation of various cutaneous areas (erotogenic zones), by the activity of certain biological impulses and as an accompanying excitation during many affective states, is designated by an expression introduced by Havelock Ellis as the period of auto-erotism.' (Freud, S. *Collected Papers,* vol. 2, tr. by Riviere, J.,

Leonard and Virginia Woolf and The Institute of Psychoanalysis, London, 1924–25)

infanticide (in-fan'ti-sīd) The killing of an infant or child. See *euthanasia.*

infantile (in'fan-til) Of or belonging to the period of *infancy* (q.v.). The term is used particularly in reference to those who are adults chronologically but whose behavior, or psychic organization, betrays more of its childhood background than is ordinarily accepted as 'normal.' See *infantilism.*

infantile paralysis Poliomyelitis (q.v.).

infantilism (in-fan'ti-liz'm) In psychoanalysis, the state of infancy.

'With the extension of the concept of the Ucs [unconscious], infantilism is still regarded as one of the main characteristics of this system, and the term now seems to refer not only to the content, but also to the unconscious mode of functioning.' (Healy, W., Bronner, A.F., and Bowers, A.M. *The Structure and Meaning of Psychoanalysis,* Knopf, New York, 1930)

In constitutional medicine, the term means anomalous type of hypoevolute constitution characterized by the persistence of certain constitutional (psychological, physiological, morphological) features of childhood up to an age which is no longer infantile. This anomaly may concern the body mass as well as the proportions, the soma as well as the psyche (although in different degrees) and cause the individual who has either reached or passed the puberal crisis to be left in the psychosomatic condition of an infant or child.

It is still open to question whether the concept of infantilism should be limited to cases of equal and uniform developmental inhibition of the whole body or whether it should include also those cases in which the inhibition is universal or inharmonious. Other disputed points are whether a pure extraglandular and a glandular infantilism are to be distinguished, and whether or not a universal and uniform type of infantilism may be referable to the endocrine system.

According to Pende, the ordinary form of infantilism is to be differentiated from such other forms of *hypoevolutism* as *microsomia, hypogenitalism, juvenilism,* and *persistent puberism.*

infantilistic (in-fan-ti-lis'tik) Referring to

or characterized by *infantilism* or a particular form of *dwarfism* (q.v.).

infantilization (in-fan-ti-li-zā'shun) 'The performance of activities in the case of a child beyond the time when such activities usually occur.' (Levy, D. 'Maternal Overprotection,' *Psychiatry 2*, 99, 1939)

infection, familial mental Seguin's term for psychosis of association. See *association, psychosis of.*

infection, psychic (sī'kik) The 'induction' of a mental syndrome upon another person. 'It happens that paranoid or paranoiac and rarely hypomanic patients not only can make those with whom they live close together believe in their delusions, by they so infect them that the latter under conditions themselves continue to build on the delusions.' (Bleuler, E. *Textbook of Psychiatry*, tr. by Brill, A.A., Macmillan, New York, 1930.) See *folie à deux; association, psychosis of.*

infectious disease, psychosis with Acute diseases such as influenza, pneumonia, acute rheumatic fever, typhoid fever, etc. may give rise primarily and predominantly to psychosis, especially during the febrile period. The psychosis is characterized by delirium, with or without motor excitement or hallucinations. Frequent shifts in the levels of consciousness may be observed and the attacks may be followed by amnesia for the period. The mental picture usually improves with improvement in the physical disease. Such psychoses are today classified as acute brain syndrome associated with systemic infection, if there is complete recovery.

inferiority (in-fē-ri-or'i-tē) A common term in psychiatry. It refers in general to the existence of types of emotional adaptation that are of a lower order than is normally expected. It is characteristic of psychiatric states that they represent regressive forms of adjustment. For example, schizophrenia is a type of biological adaptation at some level below what is normally expected of the individual. The schizophrenic patient with a paranoid syndrome exhibits inferiority in his inability to grow up emotionally beyond the latency period, specifically beyond that of homosexuality. The catatonic and hebephrenic patients are inferior in the sense that they are instinctually fixated in the narcissistic and auto-erotic zones. The patient with conversion hysteria has never

successfully handled the issues of the early Oedipus complex.

Psychiatrists have found that the instincts are subject to the general laws of growth that apply to organic matter. In general it may be stated that the psyche, including, of course, its energic system, may lag behind in development, may progress normally or may advance too quickly. The indicated types of growth may involve the entire psyche, or any part of it.

Adler is known chiefly for the stress he places upon feelings of inferiority. He believes that everyone is born with an inferiority—organic or psychical—and that the manner in which the inferiority is handled determines the 'style of life' led by the individual. He believes that psychiatric states are the result of faulty management of the inferiority characterizing the individual.

'Ideas concerning innate inferiority, predisposition, and constitutional weakness may be found in the very beginnings of scientific medicine.' (Adler, A. *The Neurotic Constitution*, tr. by Glueck, B. and Lind, J.E., Moffat, Yard, New York, 1917)

From the psychoanalytic point of view perhaps the most important contribution to what is called the *inferiority complex* stems from the early Oedipus situation. 'The irreconcilability of these [Oedipus] wishes with reality and the inadequacy of the childhood stage of development lead to a narcistic scar that constitutes the basis of the inferiority feeling.' (Healy, W., Bronner, A.F., and Bowers, A.M. *The Structure and Meaning of Psychoanalysis*, Knopf, New York, 1930)

inferiority, constitutional psychopathic (sī-kō-path'ik) Psychopathic inferiority; psychopathy; psychopathic state. The term is rarely used today.

inferiority, feeling of By this term Adler indicates that through the whole period of development, the child possesses a feeling of inadequacy in its relation both to parents and the world at large.

Adler states: 'Because of the immaturity of his organs, his uncertainty and lack of independence, because of his need for dependence upon stronger natures and his frequent and painful feeling of subordination to others, a sensation of inadequacy develops that betrays itself throughout life.' (Adler, A. *The Practice and Theory of Individual Psychology*, tr. by

Radin, P., Kegan Paul, Trench, Trubner, London, 1924)

inferiority, functional Adler includes this term as a sub-group of organ inferiority. He states: 'Its [functional inferiority's] characteristic quality is, briefly stated, a quantity or quality of work insufficient to satisfy a standard of required effectiveness.' (Adler, A. *Study of Organ Inferiority and its Psychical Compensation,* tr. by Jelliffe, S.E., Nervous & Mental Disease Publishing Company, New York, 1917)

inferiority, general In social work, the term for 'a lack of efficiency rather than a wasting process. This phrase refers to one who constitutionally does not have average physical or mental equipment or energy.' (Hamilton, G. *A Medical Social Terminology,* Presbyterian Hospital, New York, 1930)

inferiority, morphologic (mor-fō-loj'ik) This term as used by Adler describes a sub-group of organ inferiority. Morphologic inferiority connotes a deficiency in the shape of an organ, or in its size, its individual portions of tissue, its individual cell complexes, of the whole apparatus or of limited parts of it.

inferiority, organ In connection with the study of the urinary apparatus, Adler concluded: 'All pathological changes whether functional or morphological were associated with an hereditary inferiority of the organ and the nerve superstructures. This inferiority frequently remained latent and the resulting deficiency was compensated for in some way. Very often the inferiority disclosed itself at one point of the organism and dominated the whole picture of the disease.' (Adler, A. *The Practice and Theory of Individual Psychology,* tr. by Radin, P., Kegan Paul, Trench, Trubner, London, 1924)

Adler maintained that 'inherited inferiorities' of gland or organs, if they made themselves felt psychically, were conducive to a neurotic disposition, i.e., they caused a child with some 'inherited stigma' to feel a sense of inferiority in relation to his environment. This feeling of humiliation and inferiority induced by some constitutional or organ defect produces psychic compensatory and hypercompensatory strivings in the individual.

inferiority, psychic constitutional (sī'kik) This expression, used by Healy, refers to a state of permanent abnormal social and mental reaction to the usual conditions of living on the part of those who are called borderline cases.

inferiority, psychopathic (sī-ko-pa'thik) This obsolescent expression used to be synonymous with *constitutional psychopathic inferiority.* It was later replaced by the term *psychopathic personality.*

inferiority, simultaneous co-ordinate Adler thus indicates simultaneous manifold inferiority of organs due to reciprocal embryonic influence, or embryonic connection of many organs. As an example, he cites gastro-intestinal affections in diseases of the lungs, in emphysema, and particularly in tuberculosis. He does not feel that these gastro-intestinal affections are dependent upon a primary lung disease, but are due to simultaneous inferiority of both systems.

inhalation, carbon dioxide See *therapy, carbon dioxide inhalation.*

inheritable (in-her'it-à-b'l) Capable of being transmitted from parents to offspring—as applied to a physical or mental trait. *Genet.* The English term most closely approximating the German term *erbfest,* 'fixed in heredity' and contrasting the hereditary qualities of an individual with those which are acquired by the phenotype during its own lifetime and do not become transmissible by heredity. See *Mendelism.*

inheritance This specifically genetic term has two meanings: (1) the *process* of transmission of inheritable attributes from parent to offspring—being then equivalent to *hereditary transmission;* (2) more commonly, the *trait* transmitted. In the second sense it is frequently modified by an adjective or phrase, as *Mendelian* inheritance, *cytoplasmic* inheritance, inheritance of *acquired characters.*

inheritance, archaic This psychological term relates to the realization of racial influences operating in the development of the individual psyche (see *phylogenesis*). It is used by analytical psychologists and psychoanalysts metaphorically as a mere analogy to biological mechanisms in the sphere of the psyche, and that the biological process of inheritance is confined to physical or mental characters, based on Mendelian gene units. See *Mendelism.*

As a figurative concept, archaic inheritance rests upon the old theory that 'morbid mental conditions presenting them-

Inhibit [385] Inhibition, Occupational

selves as a reflection of a disease of the organism, are rendered more comprehensible, if we look upon them as the reappearance of a peculiar form of life which is normal for a lower level of organic development.' On this theory, propounded by Carus early in the 19th century, Jung based and built his doctrines of the 'racial unconscious' and 'archetypes,' but he makes it clear that the archetypes, too, are *literally* inherited.

Dreams are believed to give best evidence of the primitive elements in the individual minds of modern man. According to Freud, they 'preserve for us an example of the manner in which the primitive apparatus worked, a mode that has now been abandoned as useless.' Nietsche expressed the same idea in saying: 'The dream carries us back to a condition of human culture far removed from the present and furnishes us with the means of a better understanding of that former condition.'

Other evidence of the operation of archaic inheritance comes from ethnology, archaeology, and anthropology as indicated in the following quotations:

'The extension of the field of individual psychology into that of racial psychology, the psychological analysis of the myths, fairy tales, and magic practices of primitive peoples and early societies, opened up to the clinician a surprising perspective and gave rise to a multitude of new and stimulating problems.' (Storch, A. *The Primitive Archaic Forms in Schizophrenia,* tr. by Willard, C., Nervous and Mental Disease Publishing Company, New York and Washington, 1924)

'Primitive man is known to us by the stages of development through which he has passed: that is, through the inanimate monuments and implements which he has left behind for us, through our knowledge of his art, his religion and his attitude towards life, which we have received either directly or through the medium of legends, myths and fairy tales; and through the remnants of his ways of thinking that survive in our own manners and customs.' (Freud, S. *Totem and Taboo,* tr. by Brill, A.A., New Republic, New York, 1931)

inhibit To restrain, curb, check.

inhibition (in-hi-bish'un) As conceived in current psychiatry, inhibition is described principally in psychoanalysis. It is an unconscious confining, hemming in, check-

ing, or restraining of an instinctual impulse or some manifestation of it, originating in the id part of the unconscious and striving to gain access to the particular motor apparatus that should serve as its vehicle of expression into reality.

However its transit into the field of the conscious involves the preliminary traversing of a path through the domain of the over-severe and over-moral superego. The force of the superego inhibits the impulse, prevents it from crossing the boundary-line between the id and the superego. 'All manifestations of neurotic *inhibition* rest upon the schematic procedure of the super-ego.' (Alexander, F.)

Accordingly, inhibition serves to obviate, prevent possible conflicts between ego and id—conflicts for which the remedy or cure is *repression* (q.v.), and as the saying goes, 'prevention is better than cure.'

The two processes may be illustrated in a homely way: the locking up (inhibition) of the most rabid or fire-spitting leaders in times of extreme civil strife, in order to anticipate, forestall or prevent bloodshed and mob violence that will have to be combated (repression) by armed forces a day or two later.

Inhibition partly enters also 'in the service of self-punishment.' (Freud, S.)

Inhibition is not a symptom. According to Freud 'these do not flourish on the same soil.' A symptom is an indication of a disease process, while inhibition does not necessarily indicate something pathological. Nevertheless, both serve a similar purpose in that they keep the ego from getting into dangerous situations.

In Pavlovian conditioned-reflex psychology, inhibition refers to the active restraining of response by the experimental subject during the latent period of delayed reaction. Inhibition can itself be inhibited by any extraneous stimulus administered during the latent period, and the result will be a release of the response from its original inhibition.

inhibition-formation See *formation, inhibition.*

inhibition, occupational An inhibition in the field of the work or vocation of a patient. The concept 'inhibition' relates specifically to the function and means a restriction or reduction of some particular function. Thus, an occupational inhibition would be a restriction or reduction in the patient's functioning in his occupation.

This could be 'evidenced in diminished pleasure in work, or in its poor execution or in such reactive manifestations as fatigue (vertigo, vomiting) if the subject forces himself to go on working.'

In general, inhibitions 'represent a limitation and restriction of ego functions, either precautionary or resulting from an impoverishment of energy.' Thus, the occupational inhibition may arise for either reason. In some cases, there has been a widespread impoverishment of energy, a general inhibition in all the ego functions, of which occupation is only one. This occurs when the ego must use all of its energy for some particularly difficult task such as mourning, the suppression of rage, etc. As a result of concentrating all its energies on this particular task the ego is unable to perform many of its other usual functions such as the sexual function, eating, work.

In other cases of occupational inhibition, we have to deal with a specific inhibition, that is, a precautionary limitation of the work function. The inhibition is carried out in order to prevent a conflict with the superego. The strict superego has forbidden that any advantage or success accrue to the patient. Thus the patient must insure inadequate functioning in the work area, i.e. he inhibits his behavior in this area. In Freud's words, occupational inhibitions 'subserve a desire for self-punishment.' (Freud, S. *The Problem of Anxiety*, Norton, New York, 1936)

inhibition, prenefarious (prē-nē-fâ′ri-us) An expression used by Jones for the first stage in the development of the guilt reaction. 'With guilt there is first what we have termed the *prenefarious inhibition,* the function of which is to assist the early fear reaction and which in effect is hardly to be distinguished from it, and, secondly, the stage of guilt proper, the function of which is to protect against the external dangers.' (Jones, E. *Papers on Psycho-Analysis,* 4th ed., Wood, Baltimore, 1938)

inhibition, specific This psychiatric term denotes an inhibition in some particular function of the ego. Inhibitions may be divided into two main categories, the specific and the general inhibitions. A specific inhibition is a restriction or reduction of some particular function of the ego, e.g. of eating, of sexual function, of locomotion, etc. An inhibition of eating would most frequently be expressed as anorexia; sexual inhibition as various forms of impotency or frigidity; inhibitions of locomotion as an antipathy to and weakness in walking. These specific inhibitions (e.g. of writing) are renunciations of functions which if exercised would give rise to severe anxiety or guilt. Under analysis this type of inhibition—that is, of functions involving the use of the fingers—reveals an excessive erotization of the fingers. Writing acquires the significance of a sexual activity; and allowing fluid to flow out from a tube upon a piece of white paper might have the symbolic meaning of coitus.

On the other hand, the mechanism known as a general inhibition is a widespread impoverishment of the energy available to the ego for the execution of its various functions. This occurs when the ego is forced to use all of its energy for some 'psychic task of special difficulty, as for example . . . mourning, a wholesale suppression of affect, or . . . the necessity for holding constantly mounting sexual fantasies in check.' Thus there is left no energy available to execute many of the usual special functions of the ego and many special functions such as sexual activity, eating, work, etc. will be inhibited at the same time. (Freud, S. *The Problem of Anxiety,* Norton, New York, 1936)

initiation, individual and collective An individual initiation is a ritual that takes place 'under the command of heaven.' It indicates a dedication to an individual goal that demands the utmost intensity of purpose and unreserved lifelong devotion. In such cases the libido is transformed from its original objective into a cultural one, usually in the framework of a religious idea. The coronation of a king and the ordination of a priest illustrate such an initiation. Initiation also takes place in some ethnic groups in a collective way, where, for instance, adolescents are initiated into manhood with appropriate ceremonies. The purpose of these ceremonies is to direct the infantile libido into mature objectives. (Baynes, H.G. *Mythology of the Soul,* Williams and Wilkins, Baltimore, 1940)

innervation, antagonistic inversion of the (in-ēr-vā′shun) In his general remarks on hysterical attacks, Freud states: 'A particularly effective form of distortion is *antagonistic inversion of the innervation,* which is analogous to the very usual changing of an element into its opposite by dream-work. For instance, in an hysterical attack an embrace may be represented by the arms being drawn back convulsively until the hands meet above the spinal column. Possibly the well-known *arc de cercle* of major hysterical attacks is nothing but an energetic disavowal of this kind, by antagonistic innervation of the position suitable for sexual intercourse.' (Freud, S. *Collected Papers*, vol. 2, tr. by Riviere, J., Leonard and Virginia Woolf and The Institute of Psychoanalysis, London, 1924–25)

innervation, expressive This psychiatric term denotes the starting of nervous energy or of nerve stimulus for affecting specific or 'express' emotional activities: a type of behavior exemplified by laughter, weeping, blushing, usually directed toward relieving 'express' specific emotional tensions. Sexual phenomena are also considered as belonging in this category. According to Alexander, these emotional expressions are not motivated by utilitarian goals, which are present in voluntary behavior. The expressive innervations are involuntary, even though they can be influenced, up to a point, by volition. (Alexander, F., and French, T.M. *Studies in Psychosomatic Medicine,* Ronald Press, New York, 1948)

insane Of, or one who is of, unsound mind. This term has been losing currency in American psychiatry during the past quarter of a century. Today psychiatrists employ it only when called upon to describe psychiatric conditions from the standpoint of law, which still uses the expression.

In current psychiatry the term *psychiatric* or less frequently *psychopathic* is substituted for *insane*.

insania cadiva (ēn-sä-nē-à kà-dē'và) *Obs.* Epilepsy.

insania gravidarum (grà-vē-dä'room) *Obs.* Insanity of pregnancy or gestation.

insania lactantium (làk-tàn'tē-oom) (L. 'insanity of those giving the breast') Lactational insanity.

insania lupina (loo-pē'nà) (L. 'wolfish insanity') Lycanthropia.

insania post partum (pôst pàr'toom) (L. 'after-birth insanity') Post-partum psychosis.

insania puerperarum (poo-er-pe-rä'room) (L. 'insanity of women in childbirth') Puerperal psychosis.

insaniola (in-sà-ni-ō'là) Eccentricity.

insanities of reproduction C.A. Mercier used this diagnostic title for psychiatric states associated with childbearing. He subdivided them into *insanity of pregnancy, puerperal insanity* and *insanity of lactation.* (Mercier, C.A., *A Text-Book of Insanity,* George Allen & Unwin, London, 1914)

insanity (in-san'i-tē) Weihofen says: 'For a branch of learning which consists largely of definition the law is strangely lax in the use of the word "insanity." Unfortunately, the word has no technical meaning either in law or in medicine, and it is used by courts and legislators indiscriminately to convey either of two meanings: (1) any type or degree of mental defect or disease, or (2) such a degree of mental defect or disease as to entail legal consequences (i.e., as to require commitment to an insane institution, or the appointment of a guardian, or to avoid a contract or relieve from responsibility for crime).' (Weihofen, H. *Insanity as a Defense in Criminal Law,* Commonwealth Fund, New York, 1933)

'The test of insanity as laid down in the law centers about three matters; namely, the knowledge of right and wrong, the existence of delusion, and the presence of an irresistible impulse. . . . Insanity is purely a legal concept and means irresponsibility, or incapacity for making a will, or for entering into a contractual relationship, or for executing a conveyance or what not as the case may be. The tests are essentially medical in character.' (White, W.A. *Insanity and the Criminal Law,* Macmillan, New York, 1923)

Singer and Krohn define insanity as 'a disorder of the mind due to disease, characterized by more or less prolonged departure from the individual's usual method of thinking, feeling or acting.' (Singer, H.D. and Krohn, W.O. *Insanity and Law,* Blakiston, Philadelphia, 1924)

insanity, adolescent (ad-ō-les'ent) An older term for *hebephrenia.*

'This great predisposition of *youth* led Hecker to the name *hebephrenia,* "insanity of youth," for the group delimited by him.' (Kraepelin, E. *Dementia Praecox and Paraphrenia,* tr. by Barclay, R.M., Livingstone, Edinburgh, 1919)

insanity, affective *Psychosis, affective* (q.v.).

insanity, alternating See *mania.*

insanity, amenorrhoeal (ā-men-o-rē'al) ('due to absence of the menses') See *insanity, uterine.*

insanity, apathetic (ap-à-thet'ik) *Obs.* 'A form of insanity simulating dementia, but in which the memory is not wholly impaired, and the mind is in a state of torpor.' (Tuke, D.H. *A Dictionary of Psychological Medicine,* vols. 1–2, Blakiston, Philadelphia, 1892)

insanity, atheromatous (ath-ĕr-om'à-tus) *Obs.* Psychosis with cerebral arteriosclerosis.

insanity, attonic (a-ton'ik) *Obs.* Catatonia.

insanity, choreic (ko-rē'ik) This is an obsolete term and concept. 'There is no form of mental disorder that can truly be called "choreic insanity," but every patient suffering from chorea exhibits some symptoms of mental disturbance.' (Craig, M., and Beaton, T. *Psychological Medicine,* 4th ed., Churchill, London, 1926)

insanity, circular See *mania.*

insanity, climacteric (klī-mak-tĕr'ik) Insanity due to menopause.

insanity, collective Ireland's term for psychosis of association. See *association, psychosis of.*

insanity, communicated See *folie à deux; association, psychosis of.*

insanity, constitutional An early 19th-century psychiatric term referring specifically to a concept of etiology or causation of certain mental disorders. To the observers of that time it appeared that these disorders were of an inborn nature, predetermined by congenital, hereditary, or 'constitutional' peculiarities, defects, or deviant trends. In our newer terminology the old term 'constitutional insanity' would be equated with mental disorders with outstanding phylogenetic or genotypic hereditary etiological factors, in contrast to the ontogenetic, postnatal, environmental, experiential causes.

In 1941 M.B. Sampson wrote: 'This, I consider, might with propriety be made the foundation for a division of lunatics into two great classes—those who are in-

sane from original constitution, and never were otherwise—and those who have been insane at some period of life from diseased action of the brain, either permanent or intermittent.' (Quoted from Hunt, J.McV., *Personality and the Behavior Disorders,* vol. 2, Ronald Press, New York, 1944)

insanity, criminal sexual The state of Michigan has recognized a condition of insanity termed criminal sexual insanity. The statute states: 'Any person who is suffering from a mental disorder and who is not insane or feebleminded, which mental disorder has existed for not less than one year and is coupled with criminal propensities to the commission of sex offenses is hereby declared to be a sexual psychopathic person.' (*Michigan State Annotations XXV, XXVIII,* 967 (2) (3) (4) (5) (6) (7), 1942.) (Abrahamsen, D. *Crime and the Human Mind,* Columbia University Press, New York, 1944)

insanity, cyanotic (sī-à-not'ik) Clouston wrote that he was 'in the habit of speaking loosely of "cyanotic delirium" and "cyanotic insanity" from the non-oxygenation of the blood in bronchitic and cardiac disease.' (Clouston, T.S. *Clinical Lectures on Mental Diseases,* 6th ed., Churchill, London, 1904)

insanity, cyclic (sī'klik, sik'lik) See *mania.*

insanity, delusional A rarely used term for 'acute conditions in which delusions and hallucinations or even only one of the two symptoms dominate the picture. . . .' (Bleuler, E. *Textbook of Psychiatry,* tr. by Brill, A.A., Macmillan, New York, 1930)

insanity, deuteropathic (dū-tĕr-ō-path'ik) This was one of the large subdivisions of insanity under the classification arranged by Bucknill and Tuke. (Bucknill, J.C., and Tuke, D.H. *Manual of Psychological Medicine,* 3rd ed., Churchill, London, 1874.) It comprised "Insanity caused by Disorder of, or Developmental Changes occurring in other Organs than the Encephalic Centres' and included such classifications as pubescent insanity, masturbatic insanity, uterine and ovarian insanity, tubercular insanity, syphilitic insanity, etc.

insanity, dissolute Dissolute insanity, or the insanity of dissolution, includes those forms of psychiatric syndromes characterized by regression and the symptoms thereof. The terms are not in common use today.

insanity, double Tuke's term for folie à deux. See *association, psychosis of.*

insanity, gestational (jes-tā'shun-al) *Obs.* A mental state occurring during pregnancy.

insanity, hysterical (his-tĕr'i-kal) An infrequently used general term for 'severe' forms of hysteria.

'It is possible that sometimes through a certain treatment the affective relation to the environment may resemble an insanity.' (Bleuler, E. *Textbook of Psychiatry,* tr. by Brill, A.A., Macmillan, New York, 1930)

insanity, ideal ('pertaining to ideas') In 1782 Arnold divided insanity into three classes: *ideal, notional,* and *pathetic.*

insanity, idiopathic (id-i-ō-path'ik) See *insanity, symptomatic.*

insanity, impulsive An older term for those psychiatric states in which 'in addition to the ordinary symptoms of nervous fatigue, abnormal impulses, phobias, and various other psychical disturbances form part of the clinical picture.' (Patton, S. *Psychiatry,* Lippincott, Philadelphia and London, 1905)

insanity, induced See *folie à deux; association, psychosis of.*

insanity, infectious Ideler's term for psychosis of association. See *association, psychosis of.*

insanity, intellectual Prichard's term, now obsolete, for the forms of insanity known in the 19th century as monomania, mania, and dementia.

insanity, intelligential (in-tel-i-jen'shal) Noble and Mones (19th century) used this term for the large class of mental disorders known today as *organic dementias.*

insanity, intermittent Manic-depressive psychosis.

insanity, interpretational See *interpretation, delirium of.*

insanity, involute (in'vō-lūt) 'Insanity of underdevelopment' (Mercier, C.A. *A Text-Book of Insanity,* George Allen & Unwin, London, 1914); feeblemindedness.

insanity, masturbational (mas-tĕr-bā'-shun-al) This is an old expression and an old concept. It is not believed today that the habit of masturbation 'acquires a power that is dominative and destructive to body and mind.' (Clouston, T.S. *Clinical Lectures on Mental Diseases,* 6th ed., Churchill, London, 1904) Nor is it thought today that there is such a state as insanity induced by masturbation.

insanity, melancholic (mel-an-kol'ik) See *melancholia, paranoid.*

insanity, moral This is infrequently used in current psychiatry, perhaps because of the many interpretations given to the term moral. Bleuler suggests to reserve the expression for the condition of those individuals 'in whom the feeling tone of all ideas concerned in the weals and woes of others is stunted (*moral imbeciles*) or is entirely absent (*moral idiots*); both groups together would be designated as *moral oligophrenics.* Sympathy with others, instinctive feelings of the rights of others (not one's own) is absent, or is inadequately developed. At the same time the other kinds of emotional feelings can be perfectly retained. . . .' (Bleuler, E. *Textbook of Psychiatry,* tr. by Brill, A.A., Macmillan, New York, 1930)

Prichard stated that patients of this group showed 'uncontrollable violence and depravity of the instincts and emotions, without any impairment of the intellectual faculties.'

Henderson and Gillespie say: 'His (Prichard's) "moral insanity" was what would now be called in England "moral imbecility," and priority is claimed for his description of it.' (Henderson, D.K. and Gillespie, R.D. *A Text-Book of Psychiatry,* 4th ed., Oxford University Press, London, 1936)

insanity, normal ' "Normal insanity" begins [writes Carl Jung, whose term it is] when the emotions are aroused. In these days we have ample opportunity to observe this process on a grand scale. We can see every form of mental contagion, from the crudest sentimentalism to the most subtle, secret poisoning of reason, and this among the so-called normal people—the average individuals who largely make up a nation or a state. Their amazing defenselessness against suggestions, even against the wildest social and political ideas and ideals, is not exactly a proof of the strength of consciousness and reason. But since there must be strength somewhere, it is presumably in that which overcomes reason—in the *irrational and emotional factors.*' (*The Integration of the Personality*, Farrar and Rinehart, New York, 1939) For Jung the difference between insanity and what he terms 'normal insanity' is in degree—that is, the extent to which unconscious autonomy has overcome and supplanted conscious autonomy. Jung states that 'the lunatic is an individual completely overcome by the unconscious. The same condition may exist to a less degree in the case of a person whom we cannot characterize as lunatic. We then have to deal with a man who is only partially overcome by his unconscious. He is not entirely "beside himself," but only partially or metaphorically. Or, the condition may be temporary. Such a case can be a matter of ordinary panic or some other emotional upset. In such a state of violent emotion one says or does things out of proportion, things one regrets afterward when reason is restored. Even the most normal individual is not proof against this danger. Under suitable conditions he will "jump out of his skin" and temporarily imitate the insane, with more or less success. Not much is needed; love, hatred, joy, or sadness is often strong enough to reverse the relation between the ego and the unconscious.

'On such occasions, strange ideas may seize upon otherwise sound individuals. Groups and societies, even whole peoples may have seizures of a similar kind; these are mental epidemics. In such a case only malevolent critics speak of a psychosis, while others speak of an "ism." The ordinary lunatic is generally a harmless, isolated case; since everyone sees that something is wrong with him, he is quickly taken care of. But the unconscious infections of groups of so-called normal people are more subtle and far more dangerous, although they derive from the autonomy of unconscious processes just as much as does insanity.' (ibid.)

insanity, notional A 19th century diagnostic division of mental disorders, suggested by Noble and Mones; it included roughly what today is known as the schizophrenias and the psychoneuroses.

insanity of childhood An older diagnostic term for any type of mental disorder occurring before the age of puberty.

insanity of negation Psychosis with nihilistic delusions. See *Cotard's syndrome.*

insanity of pregnancy See *psychosis, puerperal.*

insanity, old maid's Clouston used this term synonymously with what was then called *ovarian insanity* by Skae. Both expressions had doubtful validity. Clouston said: 'There is really no definite proof that the ovaries are either disturbed in function or diseased in structure in those cases, but it consists no doubt of a morbid transformation of the normal affectiveness of women toward the opposite sex.' (Clouston, T.S. *Clinical Lectures on Mental Diseases,* 6th ed., Churchill, London, 1904)

insanity, ovarian (ō-vā'ri-an) See *insanity, old maid's.*

insanity-panic, neurotic (nū-rot'ik) Severe anxiety arising from the fear of becoming insane.

insanity, partial This expression, usually of medico-legal import, is sometimes synonymous with *monomania;* it was so regarded in the M'Naghten case. It is also defined as a borderline type of mental unsoundness.

Weihofen says that partial insanity 'means a mental impairment which is not so complete as to render its victim irresponsible for his criminal acts.' The law speaks of 'limited responsibility.' 'There are, as we have seen, two types of cases in which this concept of "limited responsibility" may be called into play: (1) cases in which, though there is evidence of mental disorder which probably was a contributing cause in the criminal conduct, the disorder is not of such a type as to come within the legal test, so as to render the person irresponsible; (2) cases in which, by reason of mental disorder, the person was incapable of deliberation, premeditation, malice, or other mental state usually made a requisite for first degree offenses, and in which, therefore, a lesser offense than that charged was in fact committed.' (Weihofen, H. *Insanity as a Defense in Criminal Law,* Commonwealth Fund, Oxford University Press, New York, 1933)

insanity, periodic Manic-depressive psychosis.

insanity, presenile (prē-sē'nīl) See *senium praecox.*

insanity, primary delusional An old term, synonymous with *folie systématisée* and with *paranoia.*

insanity, primary traumatic (traw-ma'tik) The symptomatology, such as delirium, coma, stupor, insomnia, somnolence, headache, dizziness, etc. which is directly the consequence of injury, is called primary traumatic insanity.

insanity, progressive systematized An older expression, formed by Magnan, as synonymous with *paranoia*.

insanity, protopathic (prō-tō-path'ik) Bucknill and Tuke speak of protopathic insanity as 'Insanity or Mental Deficiency caused by Primary Disease or Defective Development of the Encephalic Centres.' They subsumed *congenital or infantile deficiency, traumatic insanity, general paresis, paralytic insanity, epileptic insanity,* and *senile insanity* as protopathic forms. (Bucknill, J.C. and Tuke, D.H. *Manual of Psychological Medicine,* 3rd ed., Churchill, London, 1874)

insanity, psychic, psychocerebral (sī'kik, sī-kō-ser'ē-bral) Tuke proposed to classify mental disorders into two great classes: those affecting the intellect and will (emotional and volitional insanity) and those connected with the soma. He said: 'Under the first division . . . we ought to recognize a number of important cases which arise from excessive action or otherwise of the mental functions themselves, the brain being injured thereby. We might, perhaps, comprise this class in the general term "psycho-cerebral insanity," or psychic insanity.' (Bucknill, J.C. and Tuke, D.H. *Manual of Psychological Medicine,* 3rd ed., Churchill, London, 1874)

insanity, pubescent (pū-bes'ent) ('reaching puberty') An older term for *hebephrenia.*

insanity, reasoning This is an older expression, not in common use today. 'The exaltation is commonly very pure brain exaltation, often with hyperaesthesia and exaltation of many of the nervous functions, with much reasoning power left but little self-control or common-sense, the lower qualities in morals being elevated, the higher depressed, the condition described by the French as *folie raisonnante* or J.C. Prichard's (1786–1848) moral insanity, being well marked in the early stage.' (Clouston T.S. *Clinical Lectures on Mental Diseases,* 6th ed., Churchill, London, 1904)

insanity, reciprocal Parsons' term for psychosis of association. See *association, psychosis of.*

insanity, saturnine (sat'ēr-nīn) A neuropsychiatric condition brought about by lead poisoning. 'This condition, pointed out by Tanquerel, and confirmed as well as described by Delasiauve, was for some time regarded as true progressive paralysis from lead, especially by Devouges, until Régis, who was able to follow some cases and verify complete recovery, distinguished it from true progressive paralysis, terming it *saturnine pseudo-general paralysis.*' (Bianchi, L. *A Text-Book of Psychiatry,* tr. by MacDonald, J.H., Baillière, Tindall & Cox, London, 1906)

insanity, secondary An old concept and an old term, denoting the schizophrenic syndrome which allegedly follows a phase of acute mental excitement. In current psychiatry the two states are considered slightly different phenomena of the same syndrome, namely, schizophrenia.

insanity, secondary traumatic (traw-ma'-tik) When a mental syndrome, resembling one of the formal mental disorders, such as schizophrenia, manic-depressive disorder, neurasthenia, hysteria, etc. is superimposed upon an injury, it is known as secondary traumatic insanity.

insanity, sequelar (sē-kwel'ēr, -kwē'lēr) Insanity ensuing as a result. When a psychiatric syndrome follows an acute infectious disorder, C.A. Mercier suggests that it be termed *sequelar insanity.*
'The second direct stress that leaves insanity behind it as a sequel is the poison of specific fever.' (Mercier, C.A., *A Text-Book of Insanity,* George Allen & Unwin, London, 1914)

insanity, stuporous (stū'pēr-us) Old term for *anergic stupor.*

insanity, sympathetic *Obs.* Insanity for which the primary cause or seat was believed to be in an organic part of the body (as, e.g., the large intestine) biologically unconnected with the cerebrum.

insanity, symptomatic (simp-tō-mat'ik) This is an older term, used by Mercier, to refer to those psychiatric states that are known to be associated with an organic disease or disorder; today it is called *organic psychosis* in contradistinction to those psychiatric syndromes, termed *idiopathic insanity* by Mercier, which are not to be identified with an organic substratum and which are called psychogenic disorders.

insanity, syphilitic (si-fi-li'tik) Obsolete term for chronic brain syndrome associated with central nervous system syphilis.

insanity, toxic (tok'sik) Bucknill and Tuke classified insanity into three great groups: (1) protopathic; (2) deuteropathic; and (3) toxic, as examples of which they included alcoholic insanity, pellagrous insanity, and cretinism. (Bucknill, J.C. and Tuke, D.H. *Manual of Psychological Medicine,* 3rd ed., Churchill, London, 1874)

insanity, traumatic (traw-ma'tik) See *psychosis, traumatic.*

insanity, uterine (ū'tĕr-in) The terms uterine or amenorrhoeal insanity are no longer in use. Clouston expressed the feeling that 'insanity in some few cases actually results *de novo* from this [amenorrhoea] as an exciting or predisposing cause. . . Most of them, two-thirds at least, are melancholic in character, the mental symptoms following the amenorrhoea and passing away when regular menstruation occurs.' (Clouston, T.S. *Clinical Lectures on Mental Diseases,* 6th ed., Churchill, London, 1904)

insanity, volitional (vō-lish'un-al) An older term synonymous with the present compulsive-obsessive form of psychoneurosis.

insanorum paralysis generalis (ēn-sä-nō'-room pà-rà'lē-zēs ge-ne-rä'lēs) (L. general paralysis of the insane.) General paresis.

insecurity Insecurity, more commonly, emotional insecurity, is a feeling of unprotectedness and helplessness against manifold anxieties arising from a sort of all-encompassing uncertainty about oneself: uncertainty regarding one's goals and ideals, one's abilities, one's relations to others, and the attitude one should take toward them. The insecure person does not or dares not have friendly feelings in what seems to him an unfriendly world. He lives in an atmosphere of anticipated disapproval. He has no confidence today in yesterday's belief, no faith tomorrow in today's truth.

Almost without exception, the emotionally insecure adult was an emotionally insecure child. For it is in early childhood,

in the home, that the foundations for the development of a secure personality must be laid. If this most important aspect of growth is neglected, the usual result is that the child will be seriously handicapped, probably throughout his life. For the emotionally insecure person there can be no effective living, no real happiness. The development of emotional security in the child is dependent upon the gratification of three specific needs: according to Preston's formulation, security rests on the three pillars of affection, approval, and consistency. (Preston, G.H. *The Substance of Mental Health,* Farrar and Rinehart, New York, 1943)

'Genuine parental *affection* is as much a fundamental prerequisite of wholesome development as is the need for food and shelter. Personality development is governed basically by the amount, genuineness, and kind of affection which an infant receives. Its presence or absence spells the difference between security and insecurity. There are no substitutes for affection.

'Affection includes full *acceptance.* An affectionate parent accepts the child for what he *is,* regardless of whether or not he approves of any one particular thing he *does.*

'Children are unable to form the certainties which arise from *consistent* patterns, if they experience unpredictable fluctuations in which there is no cohesion. Frequent changes of residence and schools break constantly into any attempt at forming friendships, belonging to a neighborhood group, cementing the concept of "home," getting accustomed to a method of instruction. The child's need of *consistency* rests chiefly for its gratification on parental attitudes and parental behavior. If you can predict what you can do tomorrow from what you have been permitted to do through a series of yesterdays, you acquire confidence in foresight and faith in your ability to "get along." If what you are permitted to do today depends, not on what you were permitted to do yesterday, but on parental indigestion, the stock market, the number of last night's highballs, or the latest article on child training published in the Sunday paper, then, as long as you live, you may never know where you stand in relation to any other human being.' (Kanner, L. *Child Psychiatry,* Thomas, Springfield, Ill., 1948) insemination (in-sem-i-nā'shun) *Biol. Obs.* The act of impregnating or fertilizing.

The technical expression for *artificial insemination* is *eutelegenesis* (q.v.).

insight In psychiatry this term means the patient's knowledge that the symptoms of his illness are recognized as abnormalities or morbid phenomena. For example, when a patient who fears crowds realizes that the fear is a symptom of abnormality within his own mind but is unfounded in reality, he is said to have insight. When, on the other hand, a patient affirms that his body is composed of many other human beings, that God, Napoleon, Mithras, and others are actually within his organs, he is described as having no insight.

Insight is further defined from the standpoint of knowledge of the factors operating to produce the symptoms. When a patient says he understands the explanation regarding the origin and development of his symptoms, it is said that he possesses insight.

'With perfect insight there is recognition of the abnormality through which the patient has passed.' (MacCurdy, J.T. *The Psychology of Emotion,* Harcourt, Brace, New York, 1925)

insight, derivative Insight arrived at by the patient himself without interpretation by the therapist—characteristic of activity therapy groups.

insight, imaginative See *empathy*.

insipientia (ĕn-sē-pē-en'tē-ȧ) *Obs.* Dementia.

insolation (in-sō-lā'shun) Sunstroke.

insomnia (in-som'ni-ȧ) (L. 'sleeplessness') Sleeplessness.

instance Freud uses the word in a special sense. 'The term "instance," in German "Instanz," was originally a legal term, *cf.* "court of first instance," and is used in psycho-analysis, as in law, in the sense of one of a hierarchy of functions or authorities.' (The quotation, written by John Rickmann, appears in Ferenczi, S. *Further Contributions to the Theory and Technique of Psycho-Analysis,* tr. by Suttie, J.I., Leonard and Virginia Woolf and The Institute of Psychoanalysis, London, 1926)

instigator (in'sti-gā-tĕr) A term used to describe any member in a therapy group who stimulates others toward activity or verbalization. See *catalytic agent; isolate; neutralizer.*

instinct Unreasoning impulse. In modern psychiatry the most commonly accepted concept of instinct is derived from the psychoanalysis of Freud. From the generic point of view it is usually agreed that an instinct is 'an organized and relatively complex mode of response, characteristic of a given species, that has been phylogenetically adapted to a specific type of environmental situation.' (Warren, H.C. *Dictionary of Psychology,* Houghton Mifflin, Boston, 1934)

McDougall says: 'Every instinctive process has the three aspects of all mental processes, the cognitive, the affective, and the conative. Now, the innate psychophysical disposition, which is an instinct, may be regarded as consisting of three corresponding parts, an afferent, a central, and a motor or efferent part, whose activities are the cognitive, the affective, and the conative features respectively of the total instinctive process.' (McDougall, W. *An Introduction to Social Psychology,* 15th ed., Luce, 1923) McDougall says that the primary emotions, such as anger, fear, and disgust are instinctive, while what he calls secondary emotions, such as jealousy, hatred, and admiration, that is, those compounded of two or more primary emotions, are not.

For all practical purposes the psychiatrist of today may be said to accept the psychological point of view known as voluntarism, in contrast to sensationism, mechanism, and behaviorism. The basic concept of voluntarism is constructed out of the thought that the activities of men constitute a purposive striving toward ends or goals. That is the fundamental principle underlying the formulations of Freud, Jung, Meyer, and Adler.

An instinct, according to Freud, is a primal trend or urge that cannot be further resolved. Jealousy can be resolved into love and hate; therefore, it is not an instinct; it is a 'part-instinct' or an 'instinct-component.' From the Freudian standpoint there are two primal instincts, those of *life* and of *death*.

The two instincts are constant psychic forces, arising from the organism itself; their sources are in the soma and represent the biological needs of the body. Somatic processes create the need, which acts through the psyche in order to secure specific forms of motor discharge for the relief of the 'tension' set up in the original source. Successful gratification of the instinctual needs can be attained only through contact with the outer world.

The two primal instincts are (1) Eros or life instinct, the function of which is to maintain life; its aim is constructive. It is composed of three principal manifestations; (a) the uninhibited sexual or organ-gratifying impulses; (b) sublimated impulses derived from those originally associated with organ-satisfaction; and (c) self-preservative impulses, which strive to protect and preserve the body and the mind.

(2) The second primal instinct is Thanatos, the death or destruction instinct. Freud says that the tendency of the instinct is 'to re-establish a state of things which was disturbed by the emergence of life.' The death instinct is said to be composed of (a) impulses that tend toward regression, that is, toward a reinstatement of an earlier level of personality development; (b) impulses that aim to injure or destroy the individual, and (c) those that possess the aim of (b) with regard, however, to objects outside of oneself. Freud has emphasized that the death instinct does not exist literally as such in the unconscious; rather it is expressed as complete passivity toward which the organism instinctively strives.

One of the basic theses upon which psychoanalysis rests assumes that the process of life is a conflict and a compromise between the two primal instincts.

Jung says that 'the collective unconscious consists of the sum of the instincts and their correlates, the archetypes.'

instinct, aggressive See *instinct, death.*

instinct, aim of In all cases, the aim of an instinct is the reestablishment of that state of relative total organismal balance which existed before the instinct was aroused, through either external or internal stimulation. The state of instinct arousal in an organism is a state of tension or unpleasure in that organism 'driving' the organism, as a whole, in the direction of 'finding' and 'applying' the appropriate means for relieving the arousal tension—or dissatisfaction through gratification. The Boston physiologist Cannon coined the phrase 'homeostatic equilibrium' for this state of relative harmony and balance, and used the term 'homeostasis' for the multiplicity of forces that interact within the organism and react to internal or external stimulation in the directional trend of equilibrium.

The *aim* of an instinct must be sharply discriminated from the *object* of that instinct. Water is the object of the instinct of thirst, while the aim of thirst is gratified through the imbibition and absorption of water by the tissues—namely, the disappearance of the unpleasurable state of thirstiness or 'thirst.' The process of gratifying the instinctual aims is heralded in consciousness by the sensation of pleasure. (Sterba, R. *Introduction to the Psycho-analytic Theory of the Libido,* Nervous and Mental Disease Monographs, No. 68, New York, 1942)

instinct, antipathic sexual (an-ti-path'ik sek'shoo-al) Krafft-Ebing thus denotes 'great diminution or complete absence of sexual feeling for the opposite sex, with substitution of sexual feeling and instinct for the same sex (homosexuality, or antipathic sexual instinct).' (Krafft-Ebing, R.v. *Psychopathia Sexualis,* Login, New York, 1908)

instinct, complementary The tendency of all infantile sexual instincts with an active aim to be integrally associated with, or accompanied by, the antithetical instinct drive with a passive aim. In infancy and childhood, the separation or *defusion* (q.v.) of these equal and opposite active and passive instinctual aims is marked. On the other hand, in adult life, with the achievement of emotional maturity at the so-called genital level, this persistence of antagonistic instinctual trends toward the same object tends to drop out or disappear. In childhood, side by side with the wish to beat, there exists the wish to be beaten; the wish to eat co-exists with the wish to be eaten, etc. In adult life one frequently finds, as an infantile remnant, the wish to be loved by a person and, simultaneously, the wish to love that person. See *ambivalence.*

instinct-component (-kom-pō'nent) *Part-instinct* (q.v.). See also *component-instinct.*

instinct, conscience S. Radó says: 'It seems advisable to designate as the "conscience-instinct" the dynamic expression of the institution of conscience. According to Freud's discovery this instinct represents the phylogenetically most recent differentiation in human instinctual life and is mainly determined by its topographical position.' (*International Journal of Psychoanalysis VII*, 406, 1926)

instinct, curiosity See *impulse, epistemophilic.*

instinct, death The destructive or aggressive or ego instinct(s). In psychoanalytic psychology, two basic instincts or drives are recognized: those under the control of the pleasure-unpleasure principle (the life instincts, the sexual instincts, Eros); and those instincts under the control of the repetition-compulsion principle (the death instincts, destructive instincts, ego instincts, aggressive instincts, destrudo, Thanatos).

It was not until 1920, in *Beyond the Pleasure Principle,* that Freud first recognized the death instincts as an independent drive. During the earlier years of psychoanalysis Freud occupied himself largely with the libidinal or erotic instinct and later conceived of an aggressive or destructive instinct which in its primary form he considered to be non-sexual. He came to believe that not all mental processes were subject to the pleasure-pain (pleasure-unpleasure) principle, and that there was a phylogenetically older principle, the repetition-compulsion principle. The latter operates to restore a previous condition of pleasure and harmony, whenever noxious stimuli cannot adequately be handled by the pleasure-pain principle. Since the repetition-compulsion tends to restore the status quo, Freud reasoned that it must ultimately tend to return the organism to the earliest state of all, namely that of inanimate existence; thus the manifestations of the repetition-compulsion principle were called the death instinct, and it was presumed that deflection of the death instinct onto objects in the external world constituted the aggressive instinct.

Because Freud's consideration of the death or destructive drives came relatively late in the development of his psychology, the term *libido,* which technically refers only to the energy of the sexual instinct, is often used as a general term to refer also to the energy of the death instinct. The term *destrudo* was suggested for the energy of the death instinct, but this has not been widely accepted.

The death instinct strives for a state of complete and eternal rest, is averse to new experiences, seeks to return to the past, and is essentially conservative in nature. As a rule, neither the life nor the death instinct is seen in pure and completely independent form; rather, there is fusion of the two. The death instinct goes through approximately the same ontogenetic development as does the sexual instinct, but the death instinct is not as intimately related to the erogenous body zones as is the sexual. It is not known if the discharge of destructive or aggressive drives brings pleasure; Freud believed that it did not, but many contemporary psychoanalytic writers believe that it does.

The death instinct is a biological tendency to self-destruction which, although always operative, is ordinarily deeply hidden; in its earliest developmental stage it is known as *primal masochism.* By union with the narcissistic libido (that part of the sexual libido which has the ego as its object, as is seen in purest form in the narcissistic phase of development, when the libido has not yet come to know or cathect objects in the external world) the death instinct acquires an erotic tinge and becomes pleasurable; it is then known as *actual masochism.* The aggressive or death instinct aims at destroying the outside world which is the source of disturbing stimuli; but disturbing stimuli may also come from within by means of an increase in (sexual) libido. As the sexual instincts develop, this increase in libido is accompanied by a transformation of narcissistic libido into object libido. The primal masochism, directed originally against the narcissistic libido, is now projected onto the objects of the libido in the outside world as *sadism.*

Just as the genital is the executive organ of the sexual instinct, so is the musculature (both striated and smooth) the executive organ of the death instinct.

The death instinct operates in the oral phase, which thus is often termed the cannibalistic stage; for gratification of hunger also destroys the object. In the anal phase, the destructive instinct appears as soiling, retention, and other means of defiant rejection of the disturbing external world. In the phallic phase, phantasies of piercing, penetration, or dissolution of the object betray the operation of the destructive instinct. Genital sadism appears in the form of hatred, which normally is restricted by love and persists only as the activity involved in taking possession of the love object. In the genital phase, there is fusion of the destructive instinct with the sexual instinct, and the destructive instincts, if not completely paralyzed by the sexual instincts, are at least restrained by them. In certain psychiatric conditions, however, there is a greater or lesser defusion of the instincts; this is seen particularly in depressive psychoses and in certain forms of schizophrenia.

instinct, destruction See *instinct, death.*

instinct-eruption See *thrust.*

instinct, herd From the psychoanalytic point of view this is not an instinct; rather, social and group phenomena are explained as results of *identification,* the origin of which is to be found in the jealousy and hostility of childhood. It is said that the first child is jealous of his successors and desires to get rid of them. He realizes, however, that his animosity cannot be maintained without injury to himself. If the jealousy is maintained he will lose the admiration and love of his parents. He is eventually compelled to unite (to identify himself) with his brothers and sisters.

It is generally agreed by psychoanalysts that identification serves the purpose of escaping conflicts with those in authority. (Alexander, F.) Ferenczi expresses a corollary when he says that identification is one of the methods of making oneself independent of an object.

When identification takes place it is followed by reaction-formation, that is, sympathy with the rival replaces hostility. The herd instinct (called group feeling or group-formation by psychoanalysts) in adulthood is explained on the same basis. Identification with the leader is of the same order as the earlier identification with the father. The leader is a new ego-ideal.

MacCurdy says: 'It is possible and convenient to group instincts (or interests) under three great headings, ego-activities (self-preservation and aggrandizement), sexual proclivities (mating and parenthood) and herd or social functions.' (MacCurdy, J.T. *The Psychology of Emotion,* Harcourt, Brace, New York, 1925)

instinct, mastery According to Fenichel, 'mastery means the ability to handle outer demands and inner drives, to postpone gratification when necessary, to assure satisfaction even against hindrances.' There

exists, however, no instinct bent on mastering. Mastery 'is a general aim of every organism, but not of a specific instinct.'

Although there is no instinctual satisfaction associated with mastery, there are pleasurable feelings in mastering, that is, in enjoying one's own abilities. These pleasurable feelings are seen clearly in the growing infant. They arise in the infant, because through mastery he has ended certain overwhelming anxieties: he had felt these anxieties because he had been unable to exercise particular functions or control particular situations. When the infant finds that he can now exercise these functions or overcome these situations without experiencing the previous overwhelming anxiety, he experiences a certain kind of pleasure. Also, when the anxiety arising out of the inability to master a particular excitation is relieved, an erogenous pleasure in the excitation is now possible. For example, a child tossed into the air will have a fear of falling. If he has confidence in the tossing person and the height is not too great, he will overcome this fear. Then the child will have pleasure at the relief of anxiety, and he will also be able to enjoy the pleasurable sensation of the equilibratory and cutaneous perceptions arising out of being tossed into the air. (Fenichel, O. *The Psychoanalytic Theory of Neurosis,* Norton, New York, 1945) See *mastery, oral.*

instinct-need See *need.*

instinct, passive When Freud speaks of a passive instinct, he refers to the aim of the instinct and not to its state of activity or inactivity. 'Every instinct is a form of activity; if we speak loosely of passive instincts, we can only mean those whose aim is passive.' (Freud, S. *Collected Papers,* vol. 4, tr. by Riviere, J., Leonard and Virginia Woolf and The Institute of Psychoanalysis, London, 1924–25) For example, an instinct may be reversed into its opposite; an active instinct (e.g., sadism) may be reversed and appear as a passive one (e.g., masochism).

It appears that the *aim* of a passive instinct is the same as that of an active one. The difference rests in the object. When oneself is the object, the instinct is passive, while it is active when the instinct is directed away from oneself.

instinct, possessive In the psychoanalytic sense, this term denotes the drive for power, the individual's primitive urge to conquer and retain the love-object. In the infant, the possessive instinct manifests itself in the acts of sucking and swallowing, and in the stubbornness with which the child holds on to the nipple of the mother. It is also shown in the capacity to control the anal sphincter and thus retain the feces. The possessive instinct is partly responsible for the child's excessive need of having exclusively for himself the parent's undivided love. Later the infant's crude possessive urge is transformed into a more socialized form; it becomes, one may say, 'civilized,' in order to be approved by the community and accepted by the individual himself. In this more socialized form, the possessive instinct may express itself in stinginess, punctuality, the habit of collecting things, even the search for intellectual knowledge, and in many other character traits. In the adult, the crude possessive urge is sublimated under the constant exigencies of the superego (a code of moral behavior) and acquires a constructive quality, a proper intensity, and an acceptable direction toward admissible goals. (Schilder, P. *Psychotherapy,* Norton, New York, 1938)

instinct-presentation The mode by which an instinct is expressed is called an *instinct-presentation* (Freud). For example, a patient dreads cancer; cancer is the instinct-presentation. Another patient must always first read the obituary column in a newspaper; the obituary column is the object that conveys the instinct; it is an instinct-presentation.

instinct-ridden Wilhelm Reich uses this term to convey the idea that the personalities of certain groups of individuals, notably criminals, are 'infested,' so to speak, with instinctual qualities.

instinct, self-preservative See *Eros.*

institution An institution, according to Sumner, 'consists of a concept (idea, notion, doctrine, interest) and a structure [which] is a framework, or apparatus, or perhaps only a number of functionaries [and which] holds the concept and furnishes instrumentalities for bringing it into the world of facts and action in a way to serve the interests of men in a society.' (Sumner, W.G. *Folkways,* Ginn, New York, 1906)

McIver defines institutions more specifically as 'the established forms or conditions of procedure characteristic of group activity.' (McIver, R.M. *Society, Its Structure and Changes,* Macmillan of Canada, Toronto, 1931)

Typical social institutions in the broader sense are the family, the school, the church, the economic system, and the state. Each institution has its particular function to play in its service to its members and to society.

instrumentalism (in-stroo-men'tal-iz'm) In social work, this term means 'an extreme form of *Self-Extension* in which one makes use of people for pleasure or profit; exploitation of others.' (Hamilton, G. *A Medical Social Terminology.* Presbyterian Hospital, New York, 1930)

insufficiency, apperceptive (ap-ẽr-sep'tiv) In his studies of the vitally important psychic process of symbolism (the indirect representation of objects or ideas by means of symbols), Silberer originated this term for the essential cause of symbolism—an incapacity of the apperceptive faculty of the mind. Because of this incapacity the mind cannot truly and correctly apperceive the nature of some hitherto unencountered object by appraising the attributes of this object *sui generis,* so to speak, but only by appraising similarities and/or dissimilarities of the new object in association with some old (known) object. The new object then becomes synonymous with the old object and is given the same name. One is the other: the other is the one. Silberer stated (as translated by Jones): 'In agreement with the majority of writers, I see the chief and most general condition of symbol-formation—valid with the phenomena of health and disease, in the individual and in the race—in an *inadequacy* of the apprehensive faculty in regard to its object, or, as one might also say, in an *apperceptive insufficiency.*' (Jones, E.J. *Papers on Psycho-Analysis,* Williams and Wilkins, Baltimore, 1949)

Silberer recognizes two types of apperceptive insufficiency: (1) of purely intellectual origin; (2) of affective origin. In the first type apperception is insufficient by reason of mental incapacity inherent in the organism (or by reason of a capacity *as yet undeveloped*), or by mental incapacity of functional nature, i.e. as induced by sleep, fatigue, drugs, etc. In the second type apperception is insufficient because of psychopathology existing in the interplay of affective (emotional) components attaching to the apperceiver or to that which is to be apperceived.

insufficiency, segmental (seg-men'tal) Adler uses this term to establish the meaning of external stigmata as signs of the inferiority of the related organ.

He states: 'There are a great number of external stigmata in which perhaps the acceptance of an inferiority of the organ to which they belong, the skin, might be proved but which, however, unquestionably show a closer relation to their segmentally related internal organs, so that their presence shows an inferiority of the segment, a segmental insufficiency.' (Adler, A. *Study of Organ Inferiority and Its Psychical Compensation,* tr. by Jelliffe, S.E., Nervous and Mental Disease Publishing Company, New York, 1917)

In the external stigmata, Adler includes nevi of all types, angiomas of the skin, externally visible telangiectasis, and neurofibromas.

insularity, psychological The quality or state of being narrowminded or circumscribed in outlook, mentality, and character. 'The most important value to character formation of group experiences is the modification or elimination of egocentricity and psychological insularity.' (Slavson, S.R. *An Introduction to Group Therapy.* The Commonwealth Fund, Oxford University Press, New York, 1943)

insular sclerosis See *sclerosis, multiple.*

insulin treatment See *treatment, insulin.*

insurance, narcissistic (när-si-sis'tik) S. Radó writes: 'It is the narcissistic satisfaction derived from the fulfilling of an ideal which benumbs the critical judgment of the ego, and secures gratification of the forbidden aggressive tendencies. This economic mechanism may be described as a kind of *narcissistic insurance.*' (*International Journal of Psychoanalysis IX,* 222, 1928)

integration (in-te-grā'shun) Act of bringing together the parts into an integral whole. In early infancy the components of the mind operate independently, as separate entities. One component does not influence another by any so-called combination of forces. The singleness of individual parts remains a characteristic of the mind during the greater part of the infantile period. From the psychoanalytic point of view, for example, oral, anal, and genital factors remain essentially discrete

for a considerable period; gradually, however, through various mechanisms the individual parts begin to act in co-operation with one another; it is the harmonizing of separate parts that is called integration.

During the infantile period, extending approximately through the fifth year of life, integration is relatively simple, being manifested chiefly in the form of knowledge on the part of the child that its body and mind are distinct from the environment. The integration at this stage of development is called *primary.* Subsequent integration that co-ordinates individual components into unified and socialized action is termed *secondary integration.*

'The integration is a product of individual evolution from a stage in which one function might exceed another in development or operate in relative independence of others. The integration is established together with consciousness. Now the little child cannot be said to have consciousness in the adult sense of the word; it has a mass of poorly combined, and relatively independent, reaction tendencies.' (MacCurdy, J.T. *The Psychology of Emotion,* Harcourt, Brace, New York, 1925)

When integration, having once been established, breaks down into its component parts, that is, when there is a reversal of the processes of integration, the condition is known as *disintegration.* Disintegration is a common phenomenon in psychiatric states. It is manifest, for example, in manic-depressive psychosis and schizophrenia, in which conditions the elementary components of the psyche acquire independent activity.

When disintegration is followed by a reorganization of the individual parts into a harmonious whole, the process is called *reintegration.* Hence, it is said that a manic-depressive patient is disintegrated during the illness and reintegrated following it.

integration (in psychoanalysis) A recent development in the outlook of psychoanalytic practice with a view of combining or integrating the sundry achievements of psychiatry and general medicine, because in the course of a half a century or so, each of the two branches worked almost entirely in its own field with scant regard for the sister science.

The integrative viewpoint emphasizes the study of the total reactions of the organism in contrast to the study of isolated organs. Furthermore, it tries to integrate the physiological functions of the organism with the motives of behavior of the total personality. For some time in the past, medicine became more and more a laboratory science, concerned mainly with the functions of isolated organs of the body. On the other hand psychoanalysis took the point of view of studying the whole organism and especially the motives for its behavior. That these two approaches should be integrated into one is a consummation devoutly to be wished. (Alexander, F., and French, T.M. *Studies in Psychosomatic Medicine,* Ronald Press, New York, 1948)

integration, primary See *integration.*

integration, secondary See *integration.*

intellect (in´te-lekt) From the standpoint of Jung (analytical psychology) intellect is 'directed thinking.' He adds: 'The faculty of passive, or undirected, thinking, I term *intellectual intuition.* Furthermore, I describe directed thinking or intellect as the *rational* function, since it arranges the representations under concepts in accordance with the presuppositions of my conscious rational norm. Undirected thinking, or intellectual intuition, on the contrary, is, in my view, an *irrational function,* since it criticizes and arranges the representations according to norms that are unconscious to me and consequently not appreciated as reasonable.' (Jung, C.G. *Psychological Types,* tr. by Baynes, H.G., Harcourt Brace, New York and London, 1923)

intellectual inadequacy See *deficiency, mental.*

intellectualization (in-te-lek-chū-al-i-zā´-shun) See *brooding.*

intelligence (in-tel´i-jens) According to Thorndike, there are three distinctive types of intelligence: *abstract, mechanical,* and *social.*

The capacity to understand and manage abstract ideas and symbols constitutes abstract intelligence; the ability to understand, invent, and manage mechanisms comprises mechanical intelligence; and the capacity to act reasonably and wisely as regards human relations and social affairs constitutes social intelligence.

Tolman's pragmatic viewpoint regards intelligence as the interrelated capacities of an organism (a) to perceive its environment through its various sensory modali-

ties ('discriminanda'); (b) to integrate these sensations into total configurations ('Gestalt apperceptions'); (c) to attribute meaning and personal reference ('symbolization' and 'value') to them in terms of retained past experiences ('memory'), and (d) to respond to such differentiated apperceptions by internal and external reactions of various degrees of finesse, versatility, and efficiency ('manipulanda' capacities).

Spearman's 'g' is an overall index of general intelligence, made up of: 'p' (perseveration factor); 'f' (fluency factor); 'w' (will factor); and 'is' (speed factor).

intelligence quotient See *quotient, intelligence.*

intelligence, subconscious Morton Prince asks whether 'a subconscious process can perform the same functions as are ordinarily performed by conscious *intelligence* (as we commonly understand that term); that is to say memory, perception, reasoning, imagination, volition, affectivity, etc.?' He cites clinical material at great length, concluding that 'in the quality of the functions performed they [i.e. subconscious processes] frequently exhibit that which is characteristic of *intelligence.*' (Prince, M. *The Unconscious,* Macmillan, New York, 1916)

intensity, displacement of psychic According to Freud, in order to avoid the censorship, the affects associated with an idea or impulse are frequently shifted onto ideas or impulses that seem inconsequential.

'This product, the dream, has above all to be withdrawn from the censorship, and to this end the dream-work makes use of the *displacement of psychic intensities,* even to the transvaluation of all psychic processes; thoughts must be exclusively or predominantly reproduced in the material of visual and acoustic memory-traces, and from this requirement there proceeds the *regard of the dream-work for representability,* which it satisfies by fresh displacements.' (Freud, S. *The Interpretation of Dreams,* 3rd ed., tr. by Brill, A.A., Macmillan, New York, 1933) See *condensation; displacement.*

intent, criminal Singer and Krohn state: 'The best short definition [of criminal intent] we can frame is: Criminal intent is a knowing disregard of criminal law (bearing in mind that ignorance of a law is no defense as knowledge of the law itself is presumed). Any person manifesting this disregard is an outlaw, that is to say, he is a criminal in the eyes of the law.' The authors add: 'Intent is often wrongly confused with motive; motive is merely that which impels.' (Singer, H.D. and Krohn, W.O. *Insanity and Law,* Blakiston, Philadelphia, 1924) Years ago Sir FitzJames Stephen wrote that 'intention is the result of deliberation upon motives, and is the object aimed at by the action caused or accompanied by the act of volition. Though this appears to me to be the proper and accurate meaning of the word it is frequently used and understood as being synonymous with motives.'

intention 'An impulse for action which has already found approbation, but whose execution is postponed for a suitable occasion.' Freud stresses the forgetting of intentions, saying that they can 'invariably be traced to some interference of unknown and unadmitted motives—or, as may be said, they [are] due to a *counter-will.*' (Freud, S. *The Basic Writings of Sigmund Freud,* tr. by Brill, A.A., Random House, New York, 1938)

inter-cortical (in-tĕr-kor'ti-kal) A term applied by Burrow to the interrelationship among individuals by means of the sign, word, or symbol. In man's inter-cortical functioning only the restricted, cortical segment of one individual is brought into contact with the cortical segment of another. Contrasted with intra-se, intra-organismic. Synonymous: inter-individual, inter-se, social, symbolic, semiotic, linguistic. (Burrow, T. *The Biology of Human Conflict,* Macmillan, New York, 1937, pp. 219–20)

intercourse, buccal (buk'al) Act of applying the mouth to the genitals.

interego (in-tĕr-ē'gō) Stekel's proposed substitute for the Freudian term superego. According to Stekel, the Freudian *superego* (q.v.) should be considered not as a simple 'watchman' (the vigilant moral part of the ego), but rather as an intermediary between our inner crude impulses and the final conscious aims of those impulses. For this reason Stekel prefers to call the superego an interego—a structure functioning as a compromiser between crude subconscious trends and the moral principles. (Stekel, W. *The Interpretation of Dreams,* Liveright, New York, 1943)

interest To interest is to attract and hold the attention, to occupy and engage a patient's concern to the extent of employing his time. This is one of the basic principles upon which occupational therapy is applied.

interest, stimulation See *occupation, stimulating.*

intermarriage In genetics, marriage between two blood-relations, especially in the sense of a *cousin marriage,* or the union between two individuals belonging to different racial groups of a mixed population.

Cousin marriages are of particular genetic significance in the case of *recessive* Mendelian inheritance (see *recessiveness*).

intermediate In genetics this term generally applies to the type of Mendelian inheritance characterized by the fact that the expressivity of a dominant character is not always complete, but is to a certain extent modifiable by the recessive member of a given pair of contrasting characters. The term denotes both this 'blended' kind of inheritance and the particular hybrids who resemble neither parent exactly, but are *intermediate* in several respects between the original characteristics of the two parent types. For instance, pink hybrids would be intermediate when they have one red and one white parent. See *dominance.*

Within the intermediate mode of heredity, many cases are known in which one and the same genetic factor has a dominant effect on one set of characters, but a recessive effect on others.

Another modification is constituted by those cases in which each member of a contrasting pair of factors produces its own effect independently, so that the heterozygote is neither a blend nor an intermediate, but a *mosaic.*

intermission When a psychiatric syndrome ends in a disappearance of symptoms for a temporary period, only to reappear at a subsequent time, the interval between attacks is called an *intermission.* When after an attack it is not known that the symptoms will reappear, the term *remission* (q.v.) is used. A patient in a state of remission may never have another attack.

internal capsule See *basal ganglia.*

interpenetration (in-tĕr-pen-e-trā'shun) A speech or writing defect in which the intensity of the patient's preoccupations reduces his ability to respond directly to questioning and instead every now and then will be interjected a few fragments of the topic suggested by the question. Interpenetration is also used to refer to intrusion of the patient's complexes and preoccupations into any direct response he may give to a question. Interpenetration is seen frequently in the schizophrenias but occurs in other disorders as well; it is, therefore, considered an accessory schizophrenic symptom.

interpretation (in-tĕr-pre-tā′shun) The description or formulation of the meaning or significance of a patient's productions and, particularly, the translation into a form meaningful for the patient of his resistances and symbols and character defenses. 'Interpretation consists of seeing beyond the façade of manifest thinking, feeling and behavior, into less obvious meanings and motivations. Involved in interpretative activities are different degrees of directiveness. The lowest degree consists of waiting for the patient to interpret things for himself, giving him as few cues as possible. Next, the patient is enjoined to attempt the interpretation of representative experiences. Of greater degree, is a piecing together of items of information, and of seemingly unrelated bits, so that certain conclusions become apparent to the patient. Leading questions are asked to guide the patient to meaningful answers. More directive is the making of interpretations in a tentative way, so that the patient feels privileged to accept or reject them as he chooses. Finally, the therapist gives the patient strong authoritative interpretations, couched in challenging, positive terms.' (Wolberg, L.R. *The Technique of Psychotherapy*. Grune & Stratton, New York, 1954)

interpretation, action S.R. Slavson defines this as 'the non-verbal reaction of the therapist of the group to the statements or acts of the patient. Action interpretation is employed almost exclusively in activity group psychotherapy.'

interpretation, allegoric (al-ē-gor′ik) 'A view which interprets the symbolic expression as an intentional transcription or transformation of a known thing is *allegoric*.' (Jung, C.G. *Psychological Types*, tr. by Baynes, H.G., Harcourt, Brace, New York and London, 1923) See *semiotic*.

interpretation, anagogic (an-à-goj′ik) This is an expression used by H. Silberer to denote a form of dream interpretation. He says that every dream is capable of two different interpretations. The first he calls the *psychoanalytic*, referring particularly to interpretations from the standpoint of infantile sexuality; the second, the *anagogic*, 'reveals the more serious and often profound thoughts which the dream-work has used as its material. . . . The majority of dreams require no overinterpretation, and are especially insusceptible of an anagogic interpretation.' (Freud, S. *The Interpretation of Dreams*, 3rd ed., tr. by Brill, A.A., Macmillan, New York, 1933)

interpretation, delirium of (dē-lir′i-um) Sérieux and Capgras suggest that there are but two forms of paranoia; one is the *delirium of interpretction*, characterized by delusions of persecution; the other is the *delirium of revindication*, the central theme of which has to do with a delusional organization based upon the urgency to gain justice for alleged offenses perpetrated against the patient. The term *delirium* in this sense signifies a delusional, not a delirious state.

interpretation-delusion See *delusion, interpretation*.

interpretation, serial This term applies to the elucidation of a consecutive number of dreams taken as a group. The interpretation of a series of dreams taken as a group gives the analyst important psychic material which no study of a single, individual dream can bring forward. In other words, when the patient describes a dream, the analyst should not confine himself to the interpretation of the individual dream, but should rather consider this dream in relation to previous dreams and also wait for the occurrence of further dreams before he reaches a conclusion. This is the only way to elucidate very repressed material which expresses itself only in part in sundry dreams. After such a serial study the analyst can reconstruct the jigsaw puzzle of the whole conflict with the aid of the various pieces. 'Serial interpretation is of great advantage. Should a symbol whose meaning seems inexplicable turn up, we can tranquilly await its reappearance in later dreams. It will recur often, until its meaning grows plain.' (Stekel, W. *The Interpretation of Dreams*, Liveright, New York, 1943)

inter-psychology (in-tĕr-sī-kol'ō-jē) A term used by Tarde, Janet, and others for interpersonal relationships.

intersex (in'tĕr-seks) In biology this term means a sexually intermediate individual that has developed as a male (or female) up to a certain point in its life-history and thereafter has continued its development as a female (or male).

Owing to the supersession of one type of sex tendency by the other, intersexes usually show a mixture of male and female parts and are almost invariably sterile. They are *not* gynandromorphs, because their structures are not definitely and clearly male or female.

In cattle, an intersex which 'is made so by action of a hormone of the opposite sex' is called a *freemartin*. According to Shull, all these freemartins are modified females.

intersexuality This biological term signifies the condition of incomplete sex reversal which leads to the production of individuals intermediate between the sexes, as the final result of a competition between two opposed male and female tendencies, in which supremacy is gained at the 'turning point' by the formerly less developed tendency. The time at which this switch-over takes place determines the degree of intersexuality. Intersexuality is thought to be of common occurrence, even if it may not yet be exactly recognizable.

A special form of intersexuality, occurring in man as well as in domesticated mammals, is probably caused by delayed or deficient hormone production and results in modifications of both internal and external sex organs and secondary characteristics.

interstimulation (in-tĕr-stim-ū-lā'shun) A psychiatric term denoting the modification of behavior in response to the presence of others. In the case of a child, for instance, his general conduct is altered by the presence of one or more other children. Interest is stimulated or diminished, activity is intensified or decreased, and anxiety is heightened.

interview, Amytal (am'i-tal) See *narcotherapy.*

intoxication, alcoholic Alcohol poisoning; the state resulting from excessive ingestion of alcohol. Psychiatrically, alcoholic intoxication generally refers to an acute brain syndrome which develops as a result of overdose of alcohol. This syndrome may be of two varieties: (1) acute intoxication, or (2) pathologic intoxication (also known as mania à potu).

Acute intoxication: Alcohol is a physiological depressant, but the release of higher control as a result of this depression leads to an initial heightening of physical and mental activities and to a greater psychomotor speed; during this initial period, organic tremors may be decreased. With increasing depression, however, there soon appear generalized muscular weakness, impairment of intellectual functions, and, because the cerebellar system is attacked early, ataxia, reeling gait, and coarse inco-ordination of the upper extremities. The marked loss of inhibition typically gives rise to many medico-legal problems. Walking a chalk line, repeating certain paradigmata, and chemical analysis of the breath, urine, and blood have all been used to determine the degree of intoxication, but none of these is completely valid because of the adaptation of the central nervous system to alcohol. Tolerance to alcohol varies greatly; the epileptic, the hysteric, many schizophrenics, and some psychopaths have a low tolerance, as do patients following a head injury.

Pathologic intoxication, or mania à potu: This occurs predominantly in people with a low tolerance to alcohol. Usually the syndrome lasts several hours, although it may continue for a whole day. It is characterized by extreme excitement ('alcoholic fury') with aggressive, dangerous, and even homicidal reactions. Persecutory ideas are common. The condition terminates with the patient falling into a deep sleep; there is usually complete amnesia for the episode.

intoxication, hypnagogic (hip-nȧ-goj'ik) Bleuler says that hypnagogic intoxication '. . . may occur during awakening in people who seem perfectly well, but more frequently it follows a rough waking, which generates a dream, and induces motility before the dream disappears. In rare cases something clumsy is then performed, indeed, under the influence of terrifying ideas an attack or murder may be perpetrated.' (Bleuler, E. *Textbook of Psychiatry,* tr. by Brill, A.A., Macmillan, New York, 1930)

intoxication, pathological See *intoxication, alcoholic.*

intoxication, senseless *Rare.* Bleuler thus designates a form of alcoholism in which there are no 'qualitatively unusual symptoms.'

intracranial tumor See *tumor, intracranial.*

intralaminar system See *system, intralaminar.*

intrapsychic, intrapsychical (in-trà-sī'kik, -sī'ki-kal) Situated, originating, or taking place within the psyche. Modern concepts of the psyche are built around a working hypothesis which assumes that the mind or psyche is an organ of the individual's body (analogously to the kidneys, liver, brain or heart) and like them has its own special structure and autonomous correlative functions, and is made up of phylogenetic and ontogenetic ideas, feelings, and modes of action.

On the basis of this hypothesis any one of the component parts or materials (such as delusions, fears, obsessions and compulsions) is believed to have its origin 'within the psyche,' i.e. to be intrapsychic. Thus the superego of Freud, the collective unconscious of Jung, and the goal-idea of Adler are regarded as intrapsychic structures.

intrauterine (-ū'tĕr-in) From the psychiatric point of view the uterus plays a significant role. Patients express impulses toward the uterus in a variety of ways, the most common of which is a tendency to return to the phase of intrauterine existence. The impulse is most directly and vividly expressed by the schizophrenic patient, who may openly assert that he is 'back in my mother's body, as I used to be.' It represents a return to the stage of complete inertia and passivity. Often the patients act out the impulse by assuming the posture of universal flexion; while at the same time they say they are in the mother.

The intrauterine theme is common among psychoneurotic patients, but in them it is expressed in highly symbolic form. For example, a patient thought of suicide as a means of 'rejoining mother earth' or they have a desire to remain in dark rooms.

Freud, more than anyone else, has developed the theme at great length, particularly through studies of dream life. The rebirth phantasy is often represented in dreams in which the dreamer is floating peacefully on water.

'Thus the caul was the veil which hid him from the world and hid the world from him. The complaint that he made was in reality a fulfilled wish-phantasy; it exhibited him as back once more in the womb and was, in fact, a wish-phantasy of flight from the world.' (Freud, S. *Collected Papers,* vol. 3, tr. by Strachey, A. and J., Leonard and Virginia Woolf and The Institute for Psychoanalysis, London, 1925)

intrinsic factor See *sclerosis, posterolateral.*

introitus (in-trō'i-tus) The entrance into a canal or hollow organ. In psychiatry the term denotes the act of sexual penetration.

introject (in-trō-jekt') To withdraw psychic energy (libido) from an object and direct it upon the mental image of the object.

introjection (in-trō-jek'shun) The act of introjecting or state of being introjected. When an individual incorporates into his ego system the picture of an object as he conceives the object to be, the process is known as introjection. Libido is then transferred from the object in the environment to the mental picture of the object. For example, when an individual becomes depressed due to the loss of a loved one, his feelings are directed to the mental image he possesses of the loved one. He acts toward the image as if it were the loved one in reality.

Introjection appears to be identical with *secondary identification* and perhaps also with *secondary narcissism.* 'The replacement of object-cathexis by identification brings about a profound change in the libidinal situation. The image thus incorporated into the (super-) ego serves itself as an object to the libidinal impulses proceeding from the id, so that more of them are directed towards the ego as a whole than previously; this constitutes what Freud terms "secondary narcissism." ' (Jones, E. *Papers on Psycho-Analysis* 4th ed., Wood, Baltimore, 1938)

'The objects presenting themselves, are absorbed by the ego into itself, "introjected" (according to an expression coined by Ferenczi).' (Freud, S. *Collected Papers,* vol. 4, tr. by Riviere, J., Leonard and Virginia Woolf and The Institute of Psychoanalysis, London, 1924–25)

From the point of view of analytical psychology, introjection is 'psychologically . . . a process of assimilation, while projection is a process of dissimilation. Introjection signifies an adjustment of the object to the subject, while projection involves a discrimination of the object from the subject, by means of a subjective content transveyed into the object.' (Jung, C.G. *Psychological Types,* tr. by Baynes, H.G., Harcourt, Brace, New York and London, 1923)

'A *passive* and an *active* introjection may be discriminated: to the former belong the transference-processes in the treatment of the neuroses and, in general, all cases in which the object exercises an unconditional attraction upon the subject; while *"feeling-into,"* regarded as a process of adaptation, should belong to the latter form.' (ibid) See *identification; incorporation.*

intropunitive (-pū'ni-tiv) Having the quality of turning anger against the self, as in the self-pejorative, demeaning, and belittling trend of the depressed patient. This is in contrast to extra-punitive, which refers to externally directed anger.

introversion (-vēr'shun) From the standpoint of instinctual psychology, the turning of the instincts inwardly upon oneself. 'The libido in introversion is directed toward the inner world, the world of representation, instead of the world of reality. With object-love there is a desire for motor discharge, a going out toward the object, but with introversion there is no desire for motor expression: satisfaction is found in imagined response, in dwelling on phantasied activities in connection with images and ideas of external objects.' (Healy, W., Bronner, A.F., and Bowers, A.M. *The Structure and Meaning of Psychoanalysis,* Knopf, New York, 1930)

Introversion is often used synonymously with *phantasy-cathexis.* Both imply a loss of contact with reality and because of it, they differ from *narcissism,* which does not imply such loss.

Freud's definition of introversion differs from Jung's. Freud says that introversion does not mean that erotic relation with reality has been severed but that the individual 'has ceased to direct his motor activities to the attainment of his aims in connection with real objects.' (Freud, S. *Collected Papers,* vol. 4, tr. by Riviere, J., Leonard and Virginia Woolf and The Institute of Psychoanalysis, London, 1924–25) 'Introversion means a turning inwards of the libido, whereby a negative

relation of subject to object is expressed. Interest does not move towards the object, but recedes towards the subject. Everyone whose attitude is introverted thinks, feels, and acts in a way that clearly demonstrates that the subject is the chief factor of motivation while the object at most receives only a secondary value.' (Jung, C.G. *Psychological Types,* tr. by Baynes, H.G., Harcourt, Brace, New York and London, 1923)

introversion, active Jung states: 'Introversion is *active,* when the subject *wills* a certain seclusion in face of the object; it is *passive* when the subject is unable to restore again to the object the libido which is streaming back from it.' (Jung, C.G. *Psychological Types,* tr. by Baynes, H.G., Harcourt, Brace, New York and London, 1923, p. 567)

introversion, passive See *introversion, active.*

introvert (in'trō-vērt) One whose psychic energy (libido) is turned inwardly upon himself.

introverted (in-trō-vēr'ted) Turned inwardly upon the subject himself.

intuition (in-tū-ish'un) A literary and psychological term with no exact scientific definition or connotation. It refers specifically to a special method of perceiving and evaluating objective reality. Intuition differs from foresight and conscious perception and judgment in that it relies heavily on unconscious memory traces of past and forgotten experiences and judgments. In this way, a storehouse of unconscious wisdom which had been accumulated (in unconscious memory) in the past is used in the present.

Intuition is characterized by accurate 'predictability' in the engineering and mathematical sense. It is also characterized by the fact that people will feel and say 'I don't know just how I know that, but I know it's correct,' and it often is. The wisdom of the sum total of all past experiences, which have registered in some way or another in the individual, albeit these past experiences may be unremembered, is the generally accepted concept of what is meant by intuition.

E.F. Sharpe (*Collected Papers on Psycho-analysis,* Hogarth Press, Ltd., and The Institute of Psychoanalysis, London, 1950) states: '. . . the scientist who understands without having to learn to understand is working with and not against intuitive powers in the same way as the artist. He projects intuition which, when it works in reality to the discovery of real facts, must be initially based upon his own real bodily and psychical experiences.'

intuition, intellectual See *intellect*.

invalidism (in'vȧ-lid-iz'm) Condition of being a chronic invalid. From the standpoint of the social worker: 'the habit of preoccupation with one's health not justified by one's actual condition.' (Hamilton, G. *A Medical Social Terminology*, Presbyterian Hospital, New York, 1930).

invalidism, psychological (sī-kō-loj'i-kal) A psychiatric term describing the mental state of a patient who, though he has been cured of his physical illness, refuses to accept this fact. He repudiates the idea of getting well and gives a thousand reasons why he should continue to live as he was compelled to live during the height of his physical illness.

Through this unrealistic attitude toward a physical illness, the patient 'accepts all the restrictions placed upon him; so much so that as he starts to recover, he resists any attempt to remove them.' Such an attitude is observed particularly among children. 'The child will not hear any encouragement to the effect that he is better and can do more now. Instead of recovering, he becomes a chronic invalid. When the situation is studied, it is found that he has learned that there are many benefits from being an invalid—extra attention, marked concern by his parents, extra food and toys, and frequent excuse from duties.' The mechanism is largely an unconscious one, however; most children who suffer from chronic invalidism are not aware that they are using their disability as a means of gaining benefits. (Pearson, G.H.J. *Emotional Disorders of Children*, Norton, New York, 1940)

invalid, nervous An unscientific term used by the laity to designate an individual who is mentally upset or emotionally disturbed, yet in ordinary parlance is not regarded as a 'mental' case.

inversion (in-vẽr'shun, -ver'zhun) See *inversion, sexual*.

inversion, absolute Freud speaks of those who are 'absolutely inverted; i.e., their sexual object must always be of the same sex, while the opposite sex can never be to them an object of sexual longing, but

leaves them indifferent or . . . may even evoke sexual repugnance.' (Freud, S. *The Basic Writings of Sigmund Freud*, tr. by Brill, A.A., Random House, New York, 1938)

inversion, amphigenous (am-fij'e-nus) Certain individuals are 'amphigenously inverted (psychosexually hermaphroditic); i.e. their sexual object may belong indifferently to either the same or to the other sex. The inversion lacks here the character of exclusiveness.' (Freud, S. *The Basic Writings of Sigmund Freud*, tr. by Brill, A.A., Random House, New York, 1938)

inversion, occasional At times, 'chiefly when the normal sexual object is inaccessible, or through imitation, they [i.e. introverts] are able to take as the sexual object a person of the same sex and thus find sexual gratification.' (Freud, S. *The Basic Writings of Sigmund Freud*, tr. by Brill, A.A., Random House, New York, 1938) Occasional inversion is also known as accidental homosexuality, or homosexuality faute de mieux.

inversion, sexo-esthetic (sek-sō-es-thet'ik) A term used by Havelock Ellis for 'the tendency to adopt the mental attitude and habits and costume of the opposite sex.' Eonism. ('The Synthesis of Dreams: A Study of a Series of One Hundred Dreams,' *Psychoanalytic Review 13:* 56, 1926)

inversion, sexual Homosexuality. The expression *sexual inversion* is used today in psychiatry in its psychoanalytic sense. 'The popular theory of the sexual instinct corresponds closely to the poetic fable of dividing the person into two halves—man and woman—who strive to become reunited through love. It is, therefore, very surprising to find that there are men for whom the sexual object is not woman but man, and that there are women for whom it is not man but woman. Such *persons* are designated as contrary sexuals, or better, inverts, and the situation of such a relationship is called inversion.' (Freud, S. *The Basic Writings of Sigmund Freud*, tr. by Brill, A.A., Random House, New York, 1938) Freud distinguished three types of sexual inversion: *absolute, amphigenous*, and *occasional* (qq.v.).

inversion, sleep Somnolence by day and insomnia at night.

invert (in'vẽrt) In psychiatry today the

term *invert,* usually modified by *sexual,* is synonymous with *homosexualist.*

invest From the point of view of psychoanalysis to invest an object is *to charge* it with affect, *to connect* affect with it. The idea *to charge* is, however, more dynamic. An electric battery is charged with electricity; an idea is charged with affect. A patient invests intense affect in the thought of dying. Invest is synonymous with *cathect* (q.v.).

investment From the psychoanalytic point of view investment refers to the affective charge given to an idea or object. For example, a patient has a morbid dread of thunder; thunder is the idea or object, in which dread is invested or cathected.

involutional psychotic reaction See *psychosis, involutional.*

iophobia (ī-ō-fō′bi-à) Fear of poison.

'I'-persona (ī-pẽr-sō′nà) By this term Burrow denotes the identity- or personality-constellation that synthesizes man's socially interfunctioning symbol-exchange. The 'I'-persona represents the systematized sum of the organism's cortical, partitive, or symbolic processes, but not the primary co-ordination of functions motivating the organism as a whole in its total bionomic adaptation. With man's attempt, by means of the cephalic segment, to symbolize or project feelings and sensations that are intrinsic to the organism as a whole, there has resulted the artificial conversion of these total sensations into partitive and divisive 'feelings' or affects. It is through this mechanism that the 'I'-persona has become a purely partitive, affective identity throughout man's interrelations. Contrasted with organic persona. Synonyms: Social substantive 'I,' pseudo-persona. (Burrow, T. *The Biology of Human Conflict,* Macmillan, New York, 1937, p. 390)

ipsation (ip-sā′shun) An infrequent term in English psychiatric literature, the equivalent of *autoerotism* as used by Freud. It was coined by the Polish physician Kurkiewicz and is used extensively by Hirschfeld.

The self-interest may be expressed through various parts of *ipse,* and the word *ipsation* is then combined with the adjective applying to the particular zone of the body: anal ipsation, mammary ipsation, etc. The aim of the pleasure is sexual.

ipsation, anal See *ipsation.*

ipsation, mammary (mam′à-rē) See *ipsation.*

I.Q. Abbreviation of intelligence quotient. See *quotient, intelligence.*

iridoplegia (ir-i-dō-plē′gi-à) Paralysis of the iris muscle; failure of the pupil to react to light. The Argyll Robertson pupil is a special form of reflex iridoplegia. Reflex iridoplegia may be caused by optic nerve lesions, optic tract lesions, lesions in the upper part of the midbrain, and lesions in the motor path (oculomotor nerve). The condition is occasionally seen in alcoholic polyneuritis and in diabetes.

irradiation, psychological (i-rā-di-ā′shun, sī-kō-loj′i-kal) Janet uses this expression in connection with the theory of 'discharge.' He explains that 'the discharge may not be simply a loss of energy; for it may also be a putting into circulation of forces in a way which favours a new distribution, and, in especial, favours the transformation of part of the energy into tension.' He had previously said that '. . . the tension necessitated by the action has induced a general condition of tension which has persisted for a considerable time. We may speak of this as "psychological induction" or a "psychological irradiation," and we may contrast it with the phenomenon of derivation which we have studied in connexion with depression.' (Janet, P. *Psychological Healing,* vols. 1–2, tr. by Paul, E. and C., Macmillan, New York, 1925)

irradiation, ultrasonic (ul-tra-so′nik) Ultrasonic irradiation of the prefrontal areas of the brain has been used as a substitute for lobotomy; it is said to cause less variable and less severe cerebral damage than the surgical procedure, to entail minimal risk, and to give comparable results. Irradiation is applied through bilateral trephine openings, using a frequency of 1000 kc. per second and an average intensity of 7 watts per sq. cm. for 4 to 14 minutes.

irrational (ir-rash′un-al) Though commonly this term means unreasonable, Jung says: 'As I make use of this term it does not denote something contrary to *reason,* but something outside the province of reason, whose essence, therefore, is not established by reason.'

'Elementary facts belong to this category, e.g., that the earth has a moon, that chlorine is an element, that the greatest density of water is found at 4.0 centigrade. . . . Both thinking and feeling as *directed functions* are rational,' while sensation and intuition are irrational. (Jung, C.G. *Psychological Types,* tr. by Baynes, H.G., Harcourt, Brace, New York and London, 1923) See *rational.*

irregular Social workers' expression 'covering unlegalized unions, unconventional love affairs, and adultery.' (Hamilton, G. *A Medical Social Terminology,* Presbyterian Hospital, New York, 1930)

irresistibility (ir-re-sist-i-bil′i-tē) See *impulse, irresistible.*

irresponsibility (ir-rē-spon-si-bil′i-tē) Weihofen says: 'What the test for irresponsibility should be is a question upon which authorities differ.

'The law in this country (except in New Hampshire) can be summarized as follows:

'A person is not criminally responsible for an offense if at the time it is committed he is so mentally unsound as to lack

'1. Knowledge that the act is wrong, or

'2. (In seventeen states) will power enough to resist the impulse to commit it.

'The first part of this rule states the so-called "right and wrong test." This part of the rule is law everywhere; and it is the *sole* test of irresponsibility in England and in twenty-nine American states. The wording of the rule varies considerably; in fully half the cases it is stated that to be excused, a defendant must be so disordered as not to know the "nature and quality" (sometimes "nature and character," "consequences," etc.) of the act, or if he did know it, that he did not know that it was wrong.

'The second part states the "irresistible impulse test," which is added as a second test of responsibility in seventeen states and in the District of Columbia. In these jurisdictions, a person is excused if he is incapable of knowing the wrongfulness of the act, or, even though he does know that it is wrong, if he is incapable of controlling the impulse to commit it.' (Weihofen, H. *Insanity as a Defense in Criminal Law,* Commonwealth Fund, Oxford University Press, New York, 1933)

irritability, acoustic (ir-i-tà-bil′i-tē, à-kōōs′tik) Auditory hypersensitivity. A generalized, diffuse irritability is one of the common characteristics of the traumatic neurosis. 'From the point of view of distribution, irritability is present in every case of traumatic neurosis. It chiefly concerns auditory stimuli, but in some instances there may be abnormal sensitivity to temperature, pain, or sudden tactile stimuli. From the physiologic point of view there exists a lowering of the threshold of stimulation; from the psychologic point of view—a state of readiness for fright reactions. This is intimately connected with the general hypertensity of these cases. Auditory hypersensitivity is the most common symptom, being occasioned by the most widely distributed sudden stimulus, perceived by the oldest sense organ which establishes contact with its environment, and the most intimately connected with fright.' (Kardiner, A., and Spiegel, L. *War Stress and Neurotic Illness,* Hoeber, New York, 1947)

irrumation (i-rōō-mā′shun) Fellatio.

I.S. *Index of sexuality* (q.v.).

ischnophonia (isk-nō-fō′ni-à) Stammering.

ischophonia (is-kō-fō′ni-à) Stammering.

iscortex (ī-sō-kor′teks) The most commonly found type of cortex of the cerebral hemispheres, composed of 6 layers of cells which have their embryologic origin in the mass of gray matter surrounding the ventricles—the outermost molecular layer, external granular layer, external pyramidal layer, internal granular layer, ganglionic layer, and the innermost fusiform layer. The isocortex is also known as the neocortex.

'I,' social substantive See *'I'-persona.*

isogamous (ī-sog′à-mus) *Genet.* Pertaining to or characterized by gametes which are equal in size and similar in structure in both sexes (see *syngamy*).

isolate (ī′sō-lāt, is′ō-) A term suggested to describe, in the therapy group, any one of the individuals who do not participate in group activities or make contact with other members of the group. They usually indulge in what is described as isolating activity. See *instigator; neutralizer.*

isolate (is′ō-, ī′sō-lāt) From the psychoanalytic point of view, 'to separate experiences or memories from their affect.'

isolation (is-ō-, ī-sō-lā′shun) In psychoanalysis, this term means the separation of an idea or memory from its affective cathexis or charge, 'so that what remains in consciousness is nothing but an ideational content which is perfectly colorless and is judged to be unimportant.' (Freud, S. *Inhibitions, Symptoms and Anxiety*, tr. by Strachey, A., Leonard and Virginia Woolf and The Institute of Psychoanalysis, London, 1936.) For example, a patient remembered the many occasions on which he made ineffectual attempts to murder his father. The recollections were entirely without affect.

Isolation may also be observed in the motor sphere. There is a pause 'in which nothing is to happen, no perception is made, no action carried out.' (Freud, S. *Inhibitions, Symptoms and Anxiety*, tr. by Strachey, A., Leonard and Virginia Woolf and The Institute of Psychoanalysis, London, 1936)

Freud distinguishes between *isolation* and *undoing*. Isolation implies a kind of foresight that tries to check the appearance of something unpleasant; it is a rational process, according to Freud, whereas *undoing* is 'irrational or magical in nature.'

As a therapeutic regimen *isolation* has been practiced for centuries. P. Janet writes: 'The chief difficulties in life arise in connection with social relationships, and it has long been felt that social activities are more exhausting than any other kind. On this recognition has been based a method of treatment which is often associated with the rest cure of nervous diseases, namely, treatment by isolation.' (Janet, P. *Psychological Healing*, vols. 1–2, tr. by Paul, E. and C., Macmillan, New York, 1925)

In 1895 Déjérine inaugurated a particularly strict plan of isolation. He kept his patients continuously in a bed completely surrounded by white curtains.

In sociology isolation is the separation of the person or group from social contacts. 'Isolation means a limitation of the opportunity for stimulus and response.' (Young, K. *An Introductory Sociology*, American Book Company, New York, 1934)

'By reason of poverty, geographical isolation, caste, feeling, or "pathos," individuals, communities, and races may be excluded from some of the stimulations and copies which enter into a high grade mind. The savage, the Negro, the peasant, the slum dweller, and the white woman are notable sufferers by, isolation.'

(Thomas, W.I. 'Race Psychology,' *American Journal of Sociology* XVII, 744, 1911–12)

isolation, action in With this expression P. Janet designates independent initiative. He spoke of one of his patients, Lydia, who tried to conceal her distress when she was separated from her sister. 'Now the art of living alone, of taking the initiative in isolation, is an art of a very special kind, one which stands at a high level, one which has developed slowly, and which has played an important psychological part by becoming the starting-point of ideas of unity and freedom.' (Janet, P. *Psychological Healing*, vols. 1–2, tr. by Paul, E. and C., Macmillan, New York, 1925)

isolation, perceptual (per-sep'chu-al) See *deprivation, sensory*.

isolation, psychic (si'kik) Carl Jung's term for the sense of estrangement from one's fellows which is immediately felt upon experiencing material communicated from one's collective unconscious. Under certain conditions material from this area of the psyche irrupts into consciousness. 'Such irruptions are uncanny, because they are irrational and inexplicable to the individual concerned. They signify a momentous alteration of the personality in that they immediately constitute a painful, personal secret that estranges the human being from his environment and isolates him from it. It is something that "you can tell to no one," except under fear of being accused of mental abnormality, and with some justification, for something quite similar befalls the insane. It is still a long way from an intuitively sensed irruption to pathological overthrow; but a layman does not know this.

'The result of the *psychic isolation* through a secret is, as a rule, the vivifying of the psychic atmosphere as a surrogate for the lost contact with the individual's fellow beings.' (Jung, C.G. *The Integration of the Personality*, Farrar and Rinehart, New York, 1939) Emphasizing and explaining the comparative rarity of such revelations of the unconscious, Jung writes: 'The resistance of consciousness to the unconscious, as well as the underestimation of the latter, is a historic necessity of human psychic development, for otherwise consciousness could never have differentiated itself from the unconscious at all points. The consciousness of modern man, however, has withdrawn somewhat too far from the reality of the unconscious. We have forgotten that the psyche does not correspond to our conscious intention, but is for the most part autonomous and unconscious. For this reason, the approach of the unconscious arouses a panic fear in civilized man, not least of all because of the threatening analogy to insanity. There is nothing questionable to the intellect in describing the unconscious as a passive object; on the contrary, such an activity would correspond to rational expectations. But to let the unconscious happen and to experience it as a reality—this exceeds the courage as well as the powers of the average Occidental. He prefers simply not to understand this problem. It is also better so for the weak in spirit, since this thing is not without its danger. The experiencing of the unconscious is a personal secret communicable only to the very few, and that with difficulty. *It isolates the individual to whom it happens.* But isolation effects a compensatory animation of the psychic atmosphere, and this is uncanny.' (ibid.)

isolation, psychological (sī-kō-loj'i-kal) A psychiatric term that denotes an individual's disinclination, aversion to, or fear of making contact with another member of the group. 'In group therapy . . . it may reasonably be believed that a patient, who has thus formed a relationship with another individual in the class, has taken the first step in breaking his own psychological isolation.' (Klapman, J.W. *Group Psychotherapy*, Grune and Stratton, New York, 1946)

isolation, sensory (sen'sor-ē) See *deprivation, sensory*.

isophilic (ī-sō-fil'ik) H.S. Sullivan's term for affection or liking for others of the same sex, such affection lacking the genital element characteristic of homosexuality. Isophilic is approximately synonymous with homoerotism.

it The same as *id*.

itching See *craving, autonomic-affective*.

J

Jacksonian epilepsy See *epilepsy, Jacksonian.*

Jackson, John Hughlings (1834–1911) British neurologist.

Jackson's syndrome A bulbar syndrome due to involvement of the vagus, spinal accessory, and hypoglossal nerves. Symptoms are: homolateral paralysis of the soft palate, pharynx, and larynx; homolateral paralysis of the sternocleidomastoid and trapezius muscles; and homolateral paralysis and atrophy of the tongue.

Jack the Clipper The designation given to any individual possessed of the morbid propensity to clip hair or braids of girls; the name was first used in reference to a man in Chicago who for several years carried on the practice.

Jack the Ripper A London physician, an epileptic, who over a period of years committed brutal murders.

jactatio capitis nocturna (yȧk-tä′tē-ō kȧ′-pi-tis nôk-toor-nȧ) (L. 'nocturnal head-tossing or head-shaking') A disturbance of sleep sometimes observed in children: it consists in rhythmical rolling of the head from side to side—which hinders normal sleep. See *head-rolling.*

jactation (jak-tä′shun) See *jactitation.*

jactitation (jak-ti-tä′shun) Extreme restlessness or tossing about.

James-Lange theory See *theory, James-Lange.*

James, William (1842–1910) American philosopher and psychologist.

Janet's disease (Pierre Janet, French psychiatrist, 1859–1947) Psychasthenia.

jargon, organ (jär′gon) Adler applies this term to the 'somatic language' (symptoms) which the neurotic uses to express a masculine protest. According to Adler, the child's ego-consciousness is in contrast with the facts of his environment. Thus, he wishes to be big and powerful but actually he is small and weak. The child therefore constructs all its aggressive attitudes into one of masculine protest against all symptoms of weakness (femininity) such as tenderness, subordinacy, and, most important, manifestations of organ inferiority. The neurotically predisposed child, however, endeavors further to gain an

effective weapon by associating with his organ inferiority such character-traits as originate in his ego-consciousness—i.e. obstinacy, need of affection, exaggerated cleanliness, pedantry, covetousness, ambition, etc. Thus, in order to gain attention and affection a psychogenic epileptic managed so that most of his 'attacks' were preceded by obstipation, thereby worrying his family—all this to offset his degradation. In this way the masculine protest makes use of a 'somatic language' or organ-jargon to gain expression. As one of Adler's patients expressed it in a dream, 'my disease has its origin in my feeling of inferiority.' (Adler, A. *The Neurotic Constitution,* tr. by Glueck, B. and Lind, E., Moffat, Yard, New York, 1917)

Jaspers, Karl Th. (1883–   ) (yäs′pērs) German psychiatrist.

jaw-jerk A deep reflex. The patient opens his mouth so that the lower jaw hangs a little; the examiner places his finger on the side of the lower jaw, and strikes it with a percussion hammer; this results in contraction of the masseter muscle and raising of the jaw.

jealousy According to Freud, normal jealousy is compounded of (1) grief, which is the pain caused by the thought of losing the loved object; this being associated with (2) narcissistic injury, i.e. a loss of self-esteem; (3) feelings of enmity against the successful rival; and, finally (4), self-criticism which blames the person himself for his loss. This reaction is not completely rational, for it is disproportionate to the real circumstances, not completely under the control of the conscious ego, and not derived from the actual situation. Rather it is rooted deep down in the unconscious, originating in the individual's Oedipus complex. Frequently jealousy is experienced also bisexually: for example, a man will feel both 'the suffering in regard to the loved woman and the hatred against the male rival,' and 'grief in regard to the unconsciously loved man and hatred of the woman as a rival.' (Freud, S. *Certain Neurotic Mechanisms in Jealousy. Paranoia and Homosexuality* in *Collected Papers,* vol. 22, Hogarth Press, London, 1924)

jealousy, projected The type of jealousy

that is derived from the person's own actual unfaithfulness or from repressed impulses toward it. In this type of jealousy, the individual who is being tempted in the direction of infidelity alleviates his guilt by projecting his own impulses onto the partner to whom he owes fidelity. Now, social conventions permit a certain amount of latitude to the married woman's desire to attract, and the married man's desire to possess, members of the opposite sex. Through these social flirtations the individual exercises his tendency to unfaithfulness and the desire now awakened is gratified by a turning back to the marital partner. The jealous person, however, does not recognize these conventions of tolerance: having projected onto his partner his own impulses toward infidelity, he will interpret as actual infidelity this behavior that covers such unconscious impulses in his partner. (Freud, S. *Certain Neurotic Mechanisms in Jealousy. Paranoia and Homosexuality* in *Collected Papers,* vol. 2, Hogarth Press, London, 1924)

Jelliffe, Smith Ely (1866–   ) American psychiatrist and neurologist.

Jendrassik reinforcement (yen'drà-sĕk) (Ernest Jendrassik, 1858–1922, Slovakian physician) A weak response of the knee-jerk may often be reinforced, that is, strengthened, by having the patient grasp his own hands and pull vigorously on them.

jerk, elbow See *reflex, triceps.*

jerk, knee Patellar reflex; the leg is flexed at the knee joint and the quadriceps tendon is tapped just below the patella; this results in extension of the leg with visible and palpable contraction of the quadriceps muscle. The femoral nerve contains both the afferent and the efferent pathways for the patellar reflex, whose spinal center is at L_{2-4}.

jerk, patellar Knee-jerk.

jerk, pendular knee When tapping the patellar tendon, several oscillations of the leg occur before it comes to a stop; observed in disease of the cerebellum.

joint, Charcot See *arthropathy.*

Jones, Ernest (1879–1958) British psychoanalyst; one of the original group who gathered around Freud in the early days of psychoanalysis; first to introduce psychoanalysis into English-speaking world

(England, 1906); one of the founders of American Psychoanalytic Association (1911) and British Psychoanalytic Society (1913); honorary life-president of International Psychoanalytic Association; 3-volume biography of Freud.

judgment Of the many definitions of judgment, the one most commonly used in psychiatry has to do with the ability to recognize the true relations of ideas. This involves what is called *critical judgment.* 'But if we speak in psychiatry and jurisprudence of the capacity to judge, we mean the ability to form judgments, that is, the capacity to draw correct conclusions from the material acquired by experience.' (Bleuler, E. *Textbook of Psychiatry,* tr. by Brill, A.A., Macmillan, New York, 1930)

Some authorities distinguish between *critical* and *automatic* judgment, meaning by the latter the performance of action as a reflex. When a patient with good vision walks directly into a wall, instead of stopping or turning, it is said that his automatic judgment is impaired.

jumps See *epilepsy, myoclonic.*

junctim (junk'tim) Adler defines this term as a 'purposive connection of two thoughts and affect-complexes that have in reality little or nothing to do with one another, in order to strengthen the affect. For example, a patient with agoraphobia, in order, by a complicated mechanism, to raise his prestige at home and force his environment into his service and to prevent himself likewise from losing, while on the street or in open places, the "resonance" so fervently desired, unites unconsciously and emotionally into a "junktim," the thought of being alone, of strange people, of purchases, search for the theatre, society, etc., and the phantasy of an apoplectic stroke, a confinement on the street, disease infection through germs on the street.' (Adler, A. *The Practice and Theory of Individual Psychology,* tr. by Radin, P., Kegan Paul, Trench, Trubner, London, 1924)

Jung, association test See *association.*

Jung, Carl Gustav (1875–   ) (yoong) Swiss psychiatrist; originally associated with Freud, later founded own school of *analytic psychology* (q.v.).

jus primae noctis (ūs' prē'mē nôk'tēs) (L. 'right to the first night') The 'right to the first night' or 'right of the lord' (*droit du seigneur*) is usually described as 'a lascivious tribute levied by feudal lords upon their vassals, in accordance with which the lord enjoyed the first embrace of the vassal's bride.' (From Putnam's translation of Paolo Mantegazza's *Gli amori degli uomini*.) It was also called *virginal tribute*. Among certain primitive tribes the 'right to the first night' belonged to the father of the bride and was supposedly symbolical of his authority.

juvenile (jōō′vē-nīl) From the standpoint of psychiatry the juvenile period extends from the beginning of the phase of puberty to the end of the stage of adolescence; that is, juvenilism includes the phases of puberty and adolescence.

juvenile general paresis See *paresis, juvenile general*.

juvenile tabes See *tabes, juvenile*.

juvenilism (jōō′vē-ni-liz'm) A constitutional condition characterized by a persistently youthful appearance of the body in a mature individual exhibiting all the signs of having passed the puberal crisis.

K

Kahlbaum, Karl Ludwig (1828–99) (käl'-boum) German psychiatrist; catatonia.

kainophobia (kī-nō-fō'bi-à) See *neophobia; kainotophobia.*

kainotophobia (kī-no-tō-fo'bi-à) Fear of change or novelty.

kakergasia (kak-ĕr-gas'i-à) See *merergasia.*

kakidrosis (kak-i-drō'sis) Perspiration with disagreeable odor. 'Perspiration is diminished and sometimes transformed in character, so as to give a peculiar and often extremely disagreeable odor (kakidrosis).' (Church, A. and Peterson, F. *Nervous and Mental Diseases,* 8th ed., Saunders, Philadelphia and London, 1916)

kakorrhaphiophobia (kà-kō-raf-i-ō-fō'-bi-à) Fear of failure.

Kalinowsky, Lothar B. (1899–   ) German-born neuropsychiatrist; in U.S. since 1940; electroconvulsive and other somatic treatments.

Kallmann, Franz J. (1897–   ) German-born psychoanalyst and geneticist; genetics of human behavior, especially schizophrenia, manic-depressive psychosis.

Kandinsky-Clérambault complex See *complex, Clérambault-Kandinsky.*

katalepsia (kat-à-lep'si-à) *Obs.* Same as *catalepsy.*

katasexual (ka-ta-seks'ū-al) Necrophiliac.

katatonia See *catatonia.*

kathisophobia (kà-this-ō-fō'bi-à) Fear of sitting down.

Kayser-Fleischer ring (Berhard Kayser, German ophthalmologist, 1869–   , and Richard Fleischer, Munich physician, 1848–1909) See *degeneration, hepatolenticular.*

Keeler polygraph Lie detector.

kenophobia, cenophobia (ken-ō-fō'bi-à, sen-ō-fō'bi-à) Fear of barren or empty space, of void.

keraunoneurosis (kē-raw-nō-nū-rō'sis) This term, introduced by H. Oppenheim, refers to traumatic neuroses associated with electric shocks.

keraunophobia Keraunophobia or the fear of lightning is common among psychoneurotic subjects. It is related to the fear of strong and superior forces and as such it appears to stem from the fear of the father, arising during the stage of phallic primacy. It is, therefore, closely allied with the fear of castration.

kernicterus, kernikterus (kĕr-nik'ter-us) See *icterus gravis neonatorum.*

key-concept Arnold Gesell and his co-workers at the Yale Clinic of Child Development have formulated the idea that in all psychological studies of the pre-school child the interpretation of individual differences should be governed by one key-concept: that a child's abilities are all relative to one inclusive ability, his ability to grow. 'Growth, therefore, becomes a *key-concept* for the interpretation of individual differences. There are laws of sequence and of maturation, which account for the general similarities and basic trends of child development. But no two children grow up in exactly the same way.' (Gesell, A., *et al. The First Five Years of Life,* Harper, New York, 1940)

The tempo and style of growth is different in every child and is characteristic of its individuality. Gesell holds that 'mental growth is a patterning process: a progressive morphogenesis of patterns of behavior,' and that 'envisagement of the mind as a growing system puts us in a better position to observe and comprehend the determinants of the child's behavior.'

kinesalgia (kin-es-al'ji-à) Pain induced by movement. A common phenomenon when organic lesions are present. Very vivid pain of psychical origin (psychalgia) may also be experienced in the absence of organic pathology. This is especially true among hysterical individuals and is regarded as a conversion symptom, i.e. due to the conversion or expression of psychical pain in terms of physical manifestations.

kinesis (ki-nē'sis) Generic term for motion.

kinesitherapy (ki-nēs-i-ther'a-pē) See *therapy, physical.*

kinesophobia (ki-nē-sō-fō'bi-à) Fear of motion.

kinesthesia (kin-es-thē'zhi-à) Perception

of one's own movement; proprioception. The receptors for kinesthesia are located in the muscles, tendons, and joints. The cell bodies of these peripheral sensory neurons are in the spinal root ganglia. The central processes pass via the dorsal roots into the spinal cord and brain-stem and, uncrossed in the posterior columns of the spinal cord, ascend to the gracilis and cuneate nuclei. Here they make synaptic connections with their second-order neurons, which cross and enter the medial lemniscus of the opposite side and thence pass to the thalamus. Synaptic connections are made here with third-order neurons, which ascend to the sensory projection center in the postcentral gyrus of the cortex (areas 3,1,2 of Brodmann).

kinetic (ki-net′ik) Relating to movement.

kinship *Genet.* The blood-relationship among individuals belonging to the same stock by common descent. See *consanguinity*.

Kirchhoff, Theodor (1853–1922) (kirK′-hôf) German psychiatrist; historian of psychiatry.

Kirkbride, Thomas Story (1809–83) American psychiatrist.

Klebedenken (klä′be-den-ken) Adhesive, sticky, perseverative thinking. Klebedenken is one of the associational disturbances seen in the schizophrenias.

Klebenbleiben (klä′ben-blī-ben) A type of language disturbance occurring in schizophrenic patients in which the speaker remains glued to the same topic; he restates the topic in different words, elaborates it, qualifies it, explains it, but cannot leave it.

Kleine-Levin syndrome See *syndrome, Kleine-Levin.*

kleptolagnia (klep-tō-lag′ni-à) A morbid desire to steal. A psychiatric term devised by J. C. Kiernan to designate 'theft associated with sexual excitement'—on the analogy of 'algolagnia.' In 1896 La Cassague (and others later) had stressed that sex and kleptomania were often associated, but the prevailing view that 'cleptomania was a syndrome of irresistible and motiveless impulses to theft based on constitutional "degeneration"' persisted. 'In 1908, Stekel observed that irresistible and apparently motiveless thefts were substitutive forms of sexual gratification [consequent to sexual deprivation

or repression]. Ellis's concept of kleptolagnia represented the theft as a means of generating fear and anxiety to "reinforce" the "feeble sexual impulse" in its drive for gratification. Lacking understanding of the psychodynamics which comes from clinical training and experience, Ellis could not appreciate that the states of anxiety which to him appeared to "overflow into the sexual sphere" are in actuality, as in the theft itself, a form of defense of the ego against sexual impulses which threaten to overwhelm it. Ellis separated his concept of kleptolagnia from essentially similar cases of other investigators and the fundamental conclusions of Stekel. But his observations were influential in ending the obscurantism regarding cleptomania. The understanding of pyromania, for which Ellis in a footnote proposed "pyrolagnia," following Kiernan, must also have been indirectly furthered by this study, although not comparably with observations by Stekel on the subject.' (Freedman, B. 'The Contributions of Havelock Ellis to Sexology,' *Psychoanalytic Quarterly 11*, 416–17, 1942)

kleptomania (klep-tō-mā′ni-à) Morbid impulse to steal. It is also known as pathological stealing. From the psychoanalytic standpoint it is believed that obsessive stealing stems from the period of infantile sexuality. The individual steals objects that possess libidinal value to him (or should we say 'her,' for stealing is regarded by Staub as essentially a female problem). It is held that stealing is rooted in a definite repressed wish, associated with penis-envy. When one steals from those in superior position, it is said that the theft traces back to original penis-envy and active castration of the superior (father).

Abraham and Alexander believe that the motive for stealing arises at the suckling stage, when the mother refuses to give the child the breast. Abraham further maintains that obsessive stealers are those who were emotionally starved during the infancy period; they become anti-social, because they were not loved. The narcissistic injury gives rise to revenge.

Adler says: 'Lies, thefts and other crimes committed by children are manifestly attempts to extend the limits of power in this way' [i.e. toward superiority]. (Adler, A. *The Neurotic Constitution,* tr. by Glueck, B. and Lind, J.E., Moffat, Yard, New York, 1917)

kleptophobia (klep-tō-fō'bi-à) Fear of stealing or becoming a thief.

Klippel-Feil syndrome See *syndrome, Klippel-Feil.*

klon See *clone.*

klopemania (klō-pē-mā'ni-à) *Obs.* Kleptomania.

Klumpke-Déjerine syndrome See *syndrome, Klumpke-Déjerine.*

Klüver-Bucy syndrome See *syndrome, Klüver-Bucy.*

knowledge-test See *rule, M'Naghten.*

knowledge, unconscious See *unconscious.*

Kohler, Wolfgang (1887–   ), German psychologist.

Kohnstamm maneuver See *test, Kohnstamm.*

koinotropy (koi-not'rō-pē) The state of being identified with the common interests of others or the public (Adolf Meyer).

kolyphrenia (ko-li-frē'ni-à) Cortical inhibitability.

kolytic (kō-lit'ik) Inhibitory. J.R. Hunt

has used this term in a way which is approximately equivalent to 'schizoid.'

kopophobia (kō-pō-fō'bi-à) Fear of fatigue.

Korsakoff psychosis See *psychosis, Korsakoff.*

Krabbe's disease (Korud H. Krabbe, contemporary Copenhagen neurologist) See *sclerosis, diffuse.*

Kraepelin, Emil (1856–1926) (krā'pe-lin) German psychiatrist; psychiatric nosology and systematization; attempted to sort out definite disease entities and differentiated between manic-depressive psychosis and dementia praecox (schizophrenia), and between endogenous and exogenous psychoses; prognostic approach, by correlating basic symptoms with course of illness.

Krafft-Ebing, Richard (1840–1903) (kräft'-ā'bing) German sexologist.

Kretschmer, Ernst (1888–   ) (krech'-mēr) German psychiatrist.

Kronfeld, Arthur (1886–   ) (krōn'-felt) German psychiatrist; psychotherapy.

Kuf's disease See *amaurotic family idiocy.*

L

la belle indifference (la bel äN-dē-fā-räNs) See *hysteria*.

labile (lāb'il) Characterized by free and usually uncontrolled expression of the emotions. See *lability*.

lability (la-bil'i-tē) The quality of being labile or unstable. In psychiatry it generally refers to the emotions. When the expression emotional lability is used, it means that the emotions are inordinately mobile and hence not under adequate control. Emotional lability is seen most commonly in the acute and chronic brain syndromes (i.e. the organic psychoses) and in the early stages of schizophrenia.

labyrinthine (lab-ē-rin'thēn) A term used often to describe a type of schizophrenic speech based upon association defects. Labyrinthine speech wanders aimlessly, from one topic to another, without obvious connection between the various topics. Certain topics may be elaborated tangentially, others appear to be an outgrowth of circumstantiality; the overall effect on the listener is to produce a massive, vague, hazy maze of words, made all the more remarkable by the fact that typically the patient is able to return to the initial topic of conversation and appears to think that his incomprehensible ramifications have been appropriately related to that topic.

laceration, cerebral (la-ser-ā'shun, ser'e-bral) A cerebral contusion of sufficient severity to cause a visible breach in the continuity of the brain substance. This may occur either directly below the site of the blow to the head, or by contre-coup on the opposite side of the brain. See *contusion, brain*.

lachschlag-anfall (läK'shläK än'fàl) (G. 'attack of short loss of consciousness due to laughter') A condition described by Herman Oppenheim (German neurologist, 1858–1919) in which the patient falls unconscious in violent laughing.

Laehr, Henrich (1820–1905) (lâr') German psychiatrist; bibliography.

lagneia furor (làg-nā'à foo'rôr) Mason Good's expression for erotomania.

lagnesis (lag-nē'sis) *Obs.* Erotomania.

lagneuomania (lag-nū-ō-mā'ni-à) Sadism expressed by the male.

-lagnia (-lag'ni-à) Combining form meaning lust, from Gr. *lagneía,* act of coition, salaciousness, lust.

lagnosis (lag-nō'sis) Satyriasis.

lagophthalmos, lagophthalmus (làg-of-thal'mus) A condition in which the upper lid fails to move down when the patient attempts to close the eye. It is one of the signs of affection of the seventh, or facial nerve.

Laignel-Lavastine, Maxine (1875–) (lā-ñel'-là-và-stēn') French psychiatrist.

-lalia (-lā-li'à) combining form meaning talk(ing) from Gr. *laliá,* talk(ing), chat, loquacity.

laliophobia (lā-li-ō-fō'bi-à) Fear of talking (and possibly stuttering).

lallation, lalling (la-lā'shun, lal'ing) Unintelligible speech, such as infantile babbling; often used more specifically to refer to substitution of *l* for more difficult consonants such as *r*.

lalo- (lal'ō-) Combining form meaning talk(ing), from Gr. *lálos,* talkative, babbling, loquacious.

laloneurosis (lal-ō-nū-rō'sis) Nervous speech-disorder.

laloneurosis, spasmodic (spaz-mod'ik) Stammering.

lalopathy (là-lop'à-thē) Any form of speech disorder.

lalophobia (lal-ō-fō'bi-à) Fear of speaking.

laloplegia (-plē'gi-à) Inability to speak because of paralysis of speech muscles other than the tongue muscles.

lalorrhea (-rē'à) See *tachylogia*.

lambitus (lam'bi-tus) Cunnilinction. 'Such men, besides cohabitation or instead of it, usually undertake still other acts. The first of these is active and passive oral genital action, lambitus, to which such people are often almost forced.' (Hirschfeld, M. *Sexual Pathology,* tr. by Gibbs, J., Emerson Books, New York, 1939)

Landry's paralysis (Jean Baptiste Octave Landry, French physician, 1826–1865) Acute ascending paralysis; a disorder of unknown etiology (?infectious; ?toxic) consisting of flaccid paralysis beginning in the lower limbs and spreading upward to the bulbar and respiratory muscles. Males account for 80 per cent of cases, and most cases occur during the third decade of life. Between 50 per cent and 80 per cent die by the fifteenth day; in the remainder, recovery is usually complete within three months.

Lange, Carl Georg (1834–1900) (läng'ē) Danish pathologist.

Lange's colloidal gold reaction (Carl Lange, German physician, 1883–   ) A diagnostic test whose theoretical basis is only incompletely understood; it depends upon the fact that cerebrospinal fluid in certain diseases is able to precipitate a preparation of colloidal gold. The test is performed using 10 test tubes, each with the same amount of gold solution but with progressively smaller concentrations of cerebrospinal fluid. The unchanged gold solution is cherry red in color; the changes caused by precipitation are expressed numerically, 0 signifying no change and the figures 1 to 5 denoting progressive degrees of alteration. Normal fluids cause no precipitation; the normal curve is thus reported as 0000000000. The 'paretic' curve (seen in general paralysis, meningo-vascular syphilis, tabes, and in about half of multiple sclerosis cases) is 5555321000. The 'luetic' or 'tabetic' curve (seen in tabes and meningovascular syphilis) is 1233210000. The 'meningitic' curve (seen usually in meningitis) is 0012344310.

language, artificial Bleuler speaks of the artificial language of schizophrenic individuals, meaning neologistic language.

language, gestural-postural A method or form of communication between persons by means of gestures and/or postures without resorting to the use of words. Communication of this kind is better known by the more inclusive expression 'communication by means of non-verbal language,' and gestural-postural language is but one form of this. See *language, nonverbal*.

language, hypochondriac (hī-pō-kon'dri-ak) See *speech, organ*.

language, irrelevant Words, phrases, utterances that have meaning only for the speaker and for *no other person*. In listening to schizophrenic patients, the psychiatrist commonly encounters instances of irrelevant language. In the course of an otherwise wholly intelligible utterance, the patient has said a word, phrase, or even a sentence which conveys or communicates nothing to the psychiatrist. The patient has a clear understanding of what his utterance means *to himself*, for it is his own creation—he has made it up. According to Kanner, instances of irrelevant language occur in 'the language of schizophrenia and early infantile autism.' He points out that the irrelevant utterances, 'though peculiar and out of place in ordinary conversation, were far from meaningless. Some words or phrases were metaphoric substitutions.' Kanner cites the following example where an irrelevant utterance of an autistic child was traced to an earlier source: 'Jay S., not quite four years old, referred to himself as "Blum," whenever his veracity was questioned by his parents. This was explained when Jay, who could read fluently, once pointed to the advertisement of a furniture firm which said in large letters: "Blum tells the truth." Since Jay had told the truth, he *was* Blum.' (Kanner, L. *Child Psychiatry,* Thomas, Springfield, Ill., 1948)

language, metaphoric (met-à-for'ik) The term metaphoric language is used in psychiatry in a sense rather different from the one it has in rhetoric and, for that matter, in ordinary speech. *Metaphor* means the use of a word (or phrase) literally denoting one kind of object (or idea), instead of another word (or phrase), through suggested likeness. In the case of a psychiatric patient's metaphoric language, that other object (or idea) (by which the metaphor has suggested itself to the speaker through likeness or similarity) remains an unrevealed entity and *eo ipso* makes the metaphor incomprehensible to the listener, though perfectly logical and legitimate for the speaker. Hence, the term *irrelevant* for the language of psychiatric patients—often framed in this kind of 'meaningless metaphoric configuration.'

language, nonverbal Nonverbal language is not expressed in words, but consists of gestures, sounds, facial expressions, posturings, and so forth. In psychiatry, especially in child psychiatry, communication between doctor and patient by way of nonverbal language often tells more than any words that may be spoken. For example, in an initial interview between a child psychiatrist and his young patient, the latter's attitude with regard to the psychiatrist may be established before the doctor has spoken a word.

language, primitive psychosomatic (sī-kō-sō-mat'ik) A phrase used by L.E. Hinsie to characterize the expression of feelings or thoughts by means of bodily movements rather than by words. This mode of expression is very primitive and, indeed, 'primitive language was very extensively developed in terms of body movements.'

This primitive psychosomatic language can be easily observed in schizophrenics and in latent schizophrenics. Children who later in life develop catatonia often exhibit rather early a 'tendency to stubbornness manifested through postures, gestures, immobility or exaggerated movements of the body. These children speak more with their muscles than with their mouths.' For example, when they do not want to see anything they shut their eyes tightly, or they close the lips tightly when they do not want to talk. In advanced schizophrenics body movements often express specific beliefs or delusions. A patient may sway to and fro in the belief that this movement is necessary to keep the universe going or may drop his outstretched hand repeatedly in the belief that he thus destroys the universe. (Hinsie, L.E. *Understandable Psychiatry,* Macmillan, New York, 1948)

lapse Same as *petit mal.*

lapsus calami (lăp'soos kà'là-mī) A very common phenomenon, usually understood in psychiatry from the point of view of psychoanalysis.

'A lady once told me that an old friend in writing to her had closed the letter with the curious sentence, "I hope you are well and *un*happy." He had formerly entertained hopes of marrying her himself, and the slip of the pen was evidently determined by his dislike at the thought of her being happy with some one else. She had recently married.' (Jones, E. *Papers on Psycho-Analysis,* 4th ed., Wood, Baltimore, 1938) See *act, symptomatic.*

lapsus linguae (lin'gwē) Slip of the tongue. See *act, symptomatic.*

lapsus memoriae (me-mô'rē-ē) Lapse or slip of the memory. See *act, symptomatic.*

lascivia (làs-kē'vē-à) (L. 'jollity, wantonness, lewdness) Nymphomania.

lasciviency (la-siv'i-en-sē) Lasciviousness; lewdness. 'Still another group of symbolism is constituted by those anomalies represented essentially by certain lasciviencies —that is, acts of a voluptuous nature

which, however, do not go so far that they may be looked upon as physiologic substitutes for coitus, as is, for instance, masturbation.' (Jacoby, G.W. *The Unsound Mind and the Law,* Funk & Wagnalls, New York and London, 1918)

lascivus (làs-kē'voos) (L. 'wanton, frisky, lewd, lustful, lascivious') Paracelsus' term in describing chorea, to denote the unrestrained character of the motor symptoms.

Lasègue sign (la-sâg') (Ernest Charles Lasègue, French physician, 1816-83) The Lasègue sign is significant of disease of the sciatic nerve. Pain and resistance are caused by extending the leg on the thigh and flexing the thigh at the hip joint.

lata, latah, lattah (là-tà) A behavioral pattern seen among the Malays, usually precipitated by sudden fright or tickling, consisting of imitative behavior (echopraxia), automatic obedience, and coprolalia. It is seen more often in women and usually in middle or older age; it does not occur before late adolescence. Some authorities consider latah and related states, such as the miryachit or olonism of Siberian tribes, the inu of the Ainu, and the Jumpers of New England (a nineteenth century Shaker sect), as acute forms of schizophrenia. Others classify latah as a hysterical reaction or a startle pattern, and among the Malays themselves it is considered as a behavioral quirk rather than a disease.

'It has been traditional in much of the medical literature to treat *maladie des tics* as though it were identical with latah and its cognate disorders. This is almost certainly incorrect. Tics, the earliest and often the most striking manifestation of Gilles de la Tourette's disease, are unknown in latah, whereas the imitation phenomena, which are the core of latah reactions, are often totally lacking in *maladie des tics.* The coprolalia in latah always follows provocation and is never preservative. Latah reactions (with the significant exception of "jumping") are far more common in females, *maladie des tics* in males.' (L. Eisenberg, E. Ascher, and L. Kanner. *American Journal of Psychiatry 115:* 715–723, 1959)

latency The expression *latency period,* used principally in psychoanalysis, refers to the psychic period of one's life extending from the end of the infantile to the beginning of the adolescent stage. In point of years it normally begins at about the age of five and terminates at about the age of puberty.

During the latency period there is normally a relinquishment of sexual expressions characteristic of the infantile phase in favor of activities and interests that take on the qualities of sublimations and reaction-formations. For example, in the latency period cleanliness takes the place of dirtiness; display of knowledge replaces display of body; interest in sex is transformed into prudery.

lateropulsion (lat-ĕr-ō-pul'shun) Rapid running sidewise with short steps, in paralysis agitans.

laughter, compulsive This expression applies principally to patients with the hebephrenic form of schizophrenia. They often engage in hearty laughter when there is no occasion known to them or to others for laughing. They usually say that they do not know that they are laughing and they seldom, if ever, give any reason for it.

'Among the affective disturbances [in schizophrenia] compulsive laughter is especially frequent; it rarely has the character of the hysterical laughing fit, but that of a soulless mimic utterance behind which no feeling is noticeable. It may often be provoked by allusion to a complex. Sometimes the patients feel only the movements of the facial muscles (the "drawn laughter").' (Bleuler, E. *Textbook of Psychiatry,* tr. by Brill, A.A., Macmillan, New York, 1930)

laughter, drawn See *laughter, compulsive.*

laughter, obsessive See *laughter, compulsive.*

Laurence-Moon-Biedl syndrome See *syndrome, Laurence-Moon-Biedl.*

law, autonomic-affective According to Kempf, 'all the autonomic-affective cravings, whether they compel an acquisitive or an avertive course of behavior or attitude toward the environment, follow the same two laws:

1. When an autonomic-affective craving is aroused, either to compensate for the deficiencies due to metabolism (as in hunger) or through the influence of an exogenous stimulus (as in fear), it compels the projicient (striped muscle) apparatus to shift the exteroceptors about in the environment so that they will acquire such stimuli as are necessary to counterstimulate and neutralize the autonomic derange-

ment so that the segment will assume comfortable tensions.

2. The projicient apparatus that shifts the receptors about so as to expose them to appropriate stimuli is organized and coordinated so as to bring a *maximum of affective gratification with a minimum expenditure of energy.*' (Kempf, E.J. *Psychopathology,* Mosby, St. Louis, 1921)

law, biogenetic mental (bī-ō-jen-e'tik men'tal) According to the biogenetic law of the mind, 'the history of the development of the species repeats itself in the embryonic development of the individual. Thus to a certain degree in his embryonic life man passes through the anatomical forms of primordial times. The same law is valid for the mental development of mankind. Accordingly, the child develops out of an originally unconscious and animal-like condition to consciousness; first to a primitive, and then slowly to a civilized consciousness.' (Jung, C.G. *Contributions to Analytical Psychology,* tr. by Baynes, H.G. and C.F., Kegan Paul, Trench, Trubner, London, 1928)

law, Briggs' A law of Massachusetts named after L. Vernon Briggs providing for routine examination before trial. Among its provisions is the following paragraph:

Whenever a person is indicted by a grand jury for a capital offense or whenever a person, who is known to have been indicted for any other offense more than once or to have been previously convicted of a felony, is indicted by the grand jury or bound over for trial in the superior court, the clerk of the court in which the indictment is returned, or the clerk of the district court or the trial justice, as the case may be, shall give notice to the department of mental diseases, and the department shall cause such person to be examined with a view to determine his mental condition and the existence of any mental disease or defect which would affect his criminal responsibility. Whenever the probation officer of such court has in his possession or whenever the inquiry which he is required to make by section eighty-five of chapter two hundred and seventy-six discloses facts which if known to the clerk would require notice as aforesaid such probation officer shall forthwith communicate the same to the clerk who shall thereupon give such notice unless already given. The department shall file a report of its investigation with the clerk of the court in which the trial is to be held, and the report shall be accessible to the court, the probation officer thereof, the district attorney, and to the attorney for the accused.

law, Mendelian (men-dē'li-an) The Mendelian law relating to the mechanism of inheritance, accounts for the results of Mendel's breeding experiments in terms of the segregation, independent assortment, and recombination of the individual gene factors, which he postulated as existing in the gametes as independent units for every inherited character. This system consists of at least two different principles.

First, segregation, or clear separation of genetic factors during the formation of the gametes: the various characters of hybridized organisms are transmitted separately and distributed to the reproductive cells independently of each other so that they may form every possible combination. Every known hereditary trait operates in accordance with segregation, and this principle is to be regarded as the basic aspect of the Mendelian system of heredity. Although it was evolved from examples with both dominant and recessive characters, dominance is not an essential feature of Mendelian inheritance, as is demonstrated by many intermediate hybrids. While dominance alone does not necessarily presuppose the existence of unit characters, this element is essential to the law of segregation.

Second, the *independent* assortment of the genetic factors and their recombination. It is demonstrated by the $9:3:3:1$ ratio in the redistribution of the four gene factors involved in the crosses with two different pairs of allolomorphic characters (see *Mendelism*). According to the same principle, the ratio $27:9:9:9:3:3:3:1$ results, on the average, in the F_2 generation of a 'trihybrid' mating, that is, one involving three pairs of allolomorphs, one member of each pair being dominant.

The simplest formulation of the entire Mendelian law seems to be as follows: When we cross two organisms unlike with respect to any character, the offspring of the first generation will be apparently like one of the parents in regard to the character in question. The parent who impresses a trait upon the offspring in this manner is called *dominant,* while the one who fails to be visibly represented is *re-*

cessive. When, however, the hybrids of this first generation are in turn crossed with each other, they will produce a variety of offspring. One fourth of them will be like the dominant grandparent, one fourth like the recessive one, and the remaining half like the parents who resembled the dominant grandparent, yet failed to breed true to it. See *dominance; recessiveness.*

law of avalanche Law of the distribution of energy in the nervous system as framed by Cajal. Sensory stimuli reaching the central nervous system normally gain release through a number of paths of discharge, which take the form of reflex arcs. When some of these reflex arcs are closed, so to speak, as avenues of release for nervous energy, the energy is forced to flow through the remaining arcs. It is possible, as, for instance, in epilepsy, that, when discharged, the dammed-up energy produces a condition likened by Cajal to an avalanche.

'Such a conception would apply equally well to the "idiopathic" or "genuine epilepsy" with Ammon's horn gliosis and the typical character traits, and to the epilepsies associated with marked developmental defects (idiocy) in which it may be conceived that the wider paths for avalanche discharge have not been laid down.' (Jelliffe, S.E. and White, W.A. *Diseases of the Nervous System,* 6th ed., Lea & Febiger, Philadelphia, 1935)

law of retrogenesis See *retrogenesis.*

lay analyst See *psychiatrist.*

layers, cortical See *isocortex.*

leadership Leadership 'may be broadly defined as the relation between an individual and a group built around some common interest and behaving in a manner directed or determined by him.' (Schmidt, R. *Leadership; Encyclopaedia of the Social Sciences,* vol. 9, Macmillan, New York, 1933, p. 282)

Two types of leadership are 'representative or symbolic and dynamic or creative.' (ibid.) Max Weber has emphasized the importance of the *charismatic* form of leadership, where the leader is thought to have divinely instilled or at least extraordinary qualities. (Weber, M. *Wirtschaft und Geselschaft,* Tübingen, 1925)

leadership, dual See *psychotherapy, multiple.*

lead pipe rigidity See *rigidity, lead pipe.*

leaping ague See *ague, leaping.*

Leber's disease See *disease, Leber's.*

lecanomancy (lek'à-nō-man-sē) 'A method of divination by means of a suitable person looking into a bowl half-filled with water, on the surface of which the indefinite images of candle flames are reflected . . .' Herbert Silberer used free association to find the meanings of the visions reported. This showed 'how the divination[s] are merely the results of the medium's own complexes' and the close relation between the visions and dreams was well brought out. (*Psychoanalytic Review I,* 348, 1913–14, reporting Herbert Silberer's 'Lekanomantische Versuche,' pp. 566–87, *Zentralblatt für Psychoanalyse II,* 10–11, Wiesbaden, 1912)

lécheur (lā-shēr') One who applies the mouth to the genitals of others, that is, practices fellatio; cunnilingus.

left-handedness See *dextrality-sinistrality.*

leipolalia (līp-ō-lā'li-à) Elision; ellipsis.

lengthening reaction See *rigidity, decerebrate.*

-lepsia (-lep'si-à) Combining form meaning seizure, attack, from Gr. *-lēpsía,* as in *epilepsía, epílepsis,* epilepsy.

leptomeninges (lep-tō-men-in'jez) See *meninges.*

leptomeningitis (-men-in-jī'tis) See *meningitis.*

leptoprosopia (-pros-ō'pi-à) In anthropology and constitutional medicine, a condition characterized by a narrow face and an elongated cranium.

leptosomal, leptosomic (-sō'mal, -sō'mik) Identical with *asthenic* (q.v.). In coining the term Kretschmer wanted to describe the main structural characteristics of the anthropological type in question rather than a secondary and not universal property of the type.

leptosome (lep'tō-sōm) This term is used in constitutional medicine to classify an individual as *leptosomic,* or *asthenic* (q.v.).

lerema, leresis (le-rē'mà, -'sìs) *Obs.* Garrulity; childish speech observed in patients with senile dementia.

lesbianism (lez'bi-an-iz'm) *Sapphism,* lesbian love. Aristophanes (*Frogs,* 1308) uses the word *lesbiázein,* 'to do like the Lesbian women,' translated in the Greek dictionary

by L. *fellare.* See *homosexuality, female.*

leschenoma (les-kē-nō'mà) Garrulity; see *leresis.*

lethal (lē'thal) Deadly, fatal. This describes a hereditary character which in its homozygous condition produces an extreme modification that is *fatal* to the organism affected.

Lethal factors occur quite frequently in all kinds of animals and plants and are always recognizable by their drastic effect only in the form of homozygosity. 'In the heterozygous condition they may be carried with impunity by perfectly normal individuals, but that portion of the offspring of such individuals in which segregation has brought two lethals together is killed.' (Sinnott, E.W. and Dunn, L.D. *Principles of Genetics,* 3rd ed., McGraw-Hill, New York and London, 1939)

lethe (lē'thē) *Obs.* Total loss of memory.

letheomania (lē-thē-ō-mā'ni-à) Morbid longing for narcotic drugs.

leucomoria (lū-kō-mō'ri-à) *Obs.* Agitated melancholia.

leucotomy; leucotomy, frontal (lū-kot'ō-mē) See *lobotomy, prefrontal.*

leukodystrophy (lū-kō-dis'trō-fē) See *sclerosis, diffuse.*

leuko-encephalopathia myeloclastica primitiva (lū-kō-en-sef-à-lō-pà'thi-à mē-ē-lō-klas'tē-kà prē-mē-tē'và) See *sclerosis, diffuse.*

level, hedonic (hē-don'ik) See *psychodynamics, adaptational.*

level, maintenance The dosage of therapeutic agent which must be repeated at stated intervals in order to sustain the desired effect. In subacute combined degeneration of the spinal cord, for example, maintenance level of vitamin B_{12} is commonly 40 micrograms weekly for 6 months; in various psychiatric patients, maintenance level of chlorpromazine hydrochloride may be 200 mg. per day for an indefinite period of time.

level of confidence See *confidence level.*

level of risk *Confidence level* (q.v.).

levels, mental From the standpoint of analytical psychology (Jung) there are three mental levels: '(1) consciousness; (2) the personal unconscious; (3) the collective unconscious. The personal unconscious consists of all those contents that have become unconscious, either because, their intensity being lost, they were forgotten, or because consciousness has withdrawn from them, i.e., so-called repression. Finally, this layer contains those elements —partly sense perceptions—which on account of too little intensity have never reached consciousness, and yet in some way have gained access into the psyche. The collective unconscious, being an inheritance of the possibilities of ideas, is not individual but generally human, even generally animal, and represents the real foundations of the individual.' (Jung, C.G. *Contributions to Analytical Psychology,* tr. by Baynes, H.G. and C.F., Kegan Paul, Trench, Trubner, London, 1928)

levophobia (lē-vō-fō'bi-à) Fear of objects to the left; opposite of *dextrophobia.*

Lewis, Nolan D.C. (1889–   ) American psychiatrist; research in schizophrenia, history of psychiatry; Director, New York State Psychiatric Institute, 1936–1953.

lex talionis (leks' tà-lē-ō'nēs) (L. 'law of retaliation, retribution') See *talion.*

liar, pathological (path-ō-loj'i-kal) The pathological liars and swindlers are often grouped under the category of 'psychopathic personality.' 'The pathological liars and swindlers are among the most interesting examples of the "charming scamps." They are extremely imaginative and champion tellers of "tall tales," in which they invariably play the leading role. They make social contacts easily and build up their stories by proper accessories, such as accents, uniforms, forged documentary evidence, and other items. From time to time newspapers report the exposure of a bogus nobleman, officer, diplomatic agent, or some other impostor. Their activity sometimes takes the form of sexual conquests, and they may obtain money under false pretenses, either on the promise of marriage or after a bigamous marriage.' (Lowrey, L.G. *Psychiatry for Social Workers,* Columbia University Press, New York, 1946)

libidinal, libidinous (li-bid'i-nal, -nus) (1) Relating to psychic energy; (2) relating to the erotic instinct.

libidinal-cathexis (-kà-thek'sis) See *cathexis.*

libidinization (li-bi-di-ni-za'shun) See *erotization.*

libidinize (li-bid'i-nīz) See *eroticize.*

libido (li-bēd'ō) In the early years of psychoanalysis, when studies revolved principally around sexual issues, the energy associated with the issues was termed *libido.* As other concepts developed and the same instinctual forces were ascribed to them the expression *libido* was applied also to them.

Instincts are endowed with energy. The energy is called libido. From the psychoanalytic point of view it does not seem possible to separate the two, save in the sense that there are two fundamentally different kinds of instincts, the sexual or erotic and the aggressive or death instincts. It seems that the energy is the instinct. 'An instinct may be described as having a source, an object and an aim. The source is a state of excitation within the body, and its aim is to remove that excitation; in the course of its path from its source to the attainment of its aim the instinct becomes operative mentally. We picture it as a certain sum of energy forcing its way in a certain direction.' (Freud, S. *New Introductory Lectures on Psycho-Analysis,* tr. by Sprott, W.J.H., Norton, New York, 1933)

Freud says that 'one can either drop the term "libido" altogether, or use it as meaning the same as psychic energy in general.' When used in this sense libido may be combined with Eros (erotic libido) or with Thanatos (destructive or death libido). Because of the psychoanalytic history of the word *libido,* that is, because it was originally identified with erotic components for a number of years before the concept *death instinct* was introduced, *libido* is used by many synonymously with *Eros.*

Healy, Bronner, and Bowers say: 'He (Freud) feels justified from the scientific point of view of his researches, he says, in viewing as "sexual," or "love," or "libido," or "Eros," not only desires for sexual union but much else.' (Healy, W., Bronner, A.F., and Bowers, A.M. *The Structure and Meaning of Psychoanalysis,* Knopf, New York, 1930)

It does not seem that *libido* can be the same as *instinct* and *Eros.* Eros is one of the instincts; the other is Thanatos. 'And now the instincts in which we believe separate themselves into two groups; the erotic instincts, which are always trying to collect living substance together into ever larger unities, and the death instincts which act against that tendency and try to bring living matter back into an inorganic condition.' (Freud, S. *New Introductory Lectures on Psycho-Analysis,* tr. by Sprott, W.J.H., Norton, New York, 1933) It seems that *libido* means psychic energy.

'I have advocated calling the energy concept used in analytical psychology by the name "libido." ' (Jung, C.G.)

Libido is 'a psychoanalytic term for sexual appetite; it stands to sexual instinct in the same relation as hunger does to nutritional instinct.' (MacCurdy, J.T. *The Psychology of Emotion,* Harcourt, Brace, New York, 1925)

To Jones libido is 'sexual hunger; the love energy of the instincts.'

McDougall suggests the term *hormê* for libido. He adds that it is the equivalent of Bergson's *élan vital.*

libido, asexual 'If we go back to the earliest possible manifestations of libido, we must admit that they probably have very early beginnings in the unicellular animal, and that as such, the libido is in itself asexual, and it may be that we shall have to come to the conclusion that the libido is always asexual, and that it only becomes sexual because it flows through sexual channels.

'After considering all these points we are led to wonder whether the libido really can be designated masculine or feminine in any circumstances.' (Bousfield, P. 'Freud's Complex of the Overestimation of the Male,' *Psychoanalytic Review 12,* 142–3, 1925)

libido-binding See *activity, immobilizing.*

libido deficiens (lē-bē′dō dā-fē′kē-ens) (L. 'failing libido') Lack of sexual urge.

libido, displaceability of A psychoanalytic concept pertaining to one aspect of the 'libido theory' of sexual development from infancy to childhood. In order of their appearance and development, the libidinal phases are usually considered as: (1) the oral, (2) the anal, (3) the masochistic, (4) the phallic, (5) the primary oedipal, (6) the latency, (7) the pubertal or secondary oedipal, (8) the genital.

Sexual excitations and gratifications are specifically related to the erogenous zones, characteristic of each specific phase of libidinal development, and have been called 'partial' impulses, since they tend to form or contribute partial components to the total final pattern of fully achieved adult sexuality. These partial impulses are usually discernible in adult sexual life, in what we call 'foreplay' or fore-pleasure activities or perversion traits.

In the individual's development these partial impulses can substitute for and replace one another in both excitation and gratification. Dissatisfaction at one zone may make for earlier or later increased activity at another zone. This gives the metaphorical impression that the total sexual instinct energy, or libido, is fluid in nature, subject to metaphorical hydrostatic and hydrodynamic forces. From this impression are derived such psychoanalytic terms as 'block,' 'recanalization,' 'displacement,' implying the shunting of excitation and gratification from one area of outlet to another. (Sterba, R. *Introduction to the Psychoanalytic Theory of the Libido,* Nervous and Mental Disease Monographs No. 68, New York, 1942)

libido-fixation See *fixation, libido.*

libido, mobility of The libidinal energy's characteristic ease of transfer from one object to another. Freud defines the libido as the total energy available to the love instinct, Eros. This instinct is one of the two sources of all human activity and it aims at the satisfaction of its need, which is 'to establish ever greater unities and to preserve them thus—in short, to bind together.' The other instinct, which likewise aims at the satisfaction of its need, is the death instinct, whose final aim is to destroy, 'to reduce living things to an inorganic state.' Basically the two instincts (both of somatic origin) represent the physiological demands of the human organism. The 'interaction of the two basic instincts with and against each other gives rise to the whole variegation of the phenomena of life.' For example, the biological function of eating both destroys the object and unites with it by incorporation.

Initially, all libido is stored up in the ego 'and serves to neutralize the destructive instincts which are simultaneously present.' This is the state of primary narcissism. Later, as the infant begins to discern an outside world, he begins to invest the objects of the outside world with libidinous energy, with the energy of the love instinct. He 'begins to cathect the presentation of objects with libido—to change narcissistic libido into object libido.' The aim of uniting is directed toward objects. Throughout life, moreover, libidinous energy can be sent out toward different objects and withdrawn with ease. This ease with which libidinous energy can be shifted from one object to another is termed 'mobility of libido.' Freud contrasts the mobility of libido with the fixation of libido, in which the libido attaches itself to particular objects and often the attachment persists through life. (Freud, S. *An Outline of Psychoanalysis,* Norton, New York, 1949)

libido, object See *libido; ego; object.*

libido, plasticity of That specific quality of the libido which makes for the adaptability of the sexual instincts (or the partial impulses of the libido) to modified discharge of tensions through indirect rather than direct avenues of gratification.

The general fate of instinctual energy that cannot be overtly or directly discharged in instinct gratification has been described under the general term of 'the vicissitudes of the instinct.' The four major vicissitudes, or indirect avenues for partial gratification and discharge of instinct, are: (1) repression with subsequent symptom and dream formation; (2) sublimation; (3) transformation of the instinct aim into its opposite; (4) transformation of the direction of the instinctual aim from an external object onto the self. R. Sterba (*Introduction to the Psycho-analytic Theory of the Libido,* Nervous and Mental Disease Monographs No. 68, New York, 1942) states: 'We owe our culture to the plasticity of the sexual instinct, which is manifested in its vicissitudes.' See *libido.*

libido, primal See *force, central.*

libido-quantum (-kwon′tum) See *ego-libido.*

libido-theory See *theory, libido.*

libido, traumatization of the (traw-mȧ-ti-zā′shun) Injury of instinctual energy. 'The author contends that any depletion of the heterosexual constituent of the libidinous urge by virtue of psychic trauma in the moral sphere, or traumatization must divert the libido's energy so as to augment the other components; homosexuality, narcism and the perversions are enlarged, at the expense of heterosexuality . . . The word "trauma" is applicable to material injury, the ultimate result of action. In the neologism "traumatization" action

takes place, but it is not final: it continues in a state of metamorphosis.' (London, L.S. *Libido and Delusion,* 2nd ed. enlgd., Mental Therapy Publications, Washington, D.C., 1946)

libido, viscosity of (vis-kos′i-tē) A psychiatric term carrying still further the metaphorical idea concerning the fluidity of the libido. The concept of the libido's viscosity is apt because of the following two characteristics of the libido: first, the slow pace of emotional growth from infancy to maturity; second, the tendency of the libido to remain fixed at or return, at slight provocation, to earlier phases of infantile sexual gratification.

The forward movement of libidinal development is apparently more oscillatory than direct, with many strong reactionary expressions of a kind of stubborn inertia, as well as a tendency toward the maintenance and reactivation of old or earlier phases of libidinal development. This makes for an instability and undependability of the newer or more recently acquired phases of developmental maturity. See *libido, displacement of.* (Sterba, R. *Introduction to the Psycho-analytic Theory of the Libido,* Nervous and Mental Disease Monographs No. 68, New York, 1942)

libido-wish See *wish, libido.*

Liebeault, Ambroise-August (1823–1904) (lē-bō′) French psychiatrist; hypnotism.

lie detector See *detector, lie.*

lie, life Adler uses this term for the tendency of the neurotic individual to include in his life-plan the idea that he will fail because of the fault of others or owing to events beyond his control.

'It is a categorical command of his life-plan that he should fail either through the guilt of others and thus be freed from personal responsibility, or that some fatal trifle should prevent his triumph.' (Adler, A. *The Practice and Theory of Individual Psychology,* tr. by Radin, P., Kegan Paul, Trench, Trubner, London, 1924)

lie, white Lying is one of the conscious defense mechanisms that help the individual out of difficulties. We have a double standard for lying, differentiating a white lie, which is harmless and condonable, from the lie that is told with malicious intent or habitually, just for the sake of lying. That white lies are just another mode of self-expression is borne out by the fact that primitive people invariably lie when they wish to get out of some difficulty, and the same is true of children. Such a tendency among children is not considered pathological: it simply indicates an immature mentality which has not yet acquired all the necessary ethical habits and, therefore, follows its impulses. (Brill, A.A. *Basic Principles of Psychoanalysis,* Doubleday, New York, 1949)

life Just as death often has a special meaning to certain psychiatric patients, so does the term life. Oliver Wendell Holmes defined life as 'the state of an organized being, in which it maintains, or is capable of maintaining, its structural integrity by the constant interchange of elements with the surrounding media.' (*Old Vol. of Life,* p. 201)

Many psychiatric patients, of whose ailment schizophrenia may be taken as the prototype, withdraw more or less completely from their natural environments; indeed, they do not look upon their bodies as such, but rather regard their bodies as a part of their 'environment.' Since they deny the existence of environment, as we understand it, they also believe that their bodies do not exist.

The schizophrenic individual conceives himself only in the light of his psychology. Moreover, his psychology is that of cosmic identification, in which there is no distinction between the 'I' and the 'not I.' Thus, it may be said that the schizophrenic patient does not believe that he possesses any structural or spiritual unity or integrity. What we call life does not exist to him. For him there is neither life nor death. He lives eternally, not as himself, but as the universe. There is no embodied vitality.

This concept of life is often, in principle, observed among other groups of psychiatric patients; in fact, it is not without its parallel among the members of sects or cults that do not bear the imprint of formal psychiatric classification.

life-course See *closure, law of and lifecourse.*

life-cycle, evolutionary The living being at any one moment of its history must be regarded merely as a phase of a life cycle. The whole life cycle of an individual is indissolubly linked with previous life cycles, because of his ancestors, and the activities of the organism can be understood only in the light of an individual as a link in the evolutionary life cycle. The unconscious of a person contains material which goes back through the previous life cycles of his ancestors to the very beginning of time. (Baynes, H.G. *Mythology of the Soul,* Williams and Wilkins, Baltimore, 1940)

life-goal See *goal, life.*

life-lie See *lie, life.*

life, mental See *mentality.*

life, noon of A figure of speech denoting the dividing line between the first and second halves of an individual's life: used by Jacobi in his book on the psychology of Jung. Referring to Jung's 'functional' and 'attitudinal' types he writes: 'This opposition of the functions and of the conscious and unconscious attitude intensifies itself into a conflict in the individual, as a rule, only toward the second half of life; indeed, it is just that problem which indicates an alteration of his psychological situation in that portion of life. Often it is precisely the capable persons, well adjusted to the environment, who, once past their forties, suddenly find that they are, in spite of their "brilliant mind," perhaps not equal to domestic difficulties or are, for example, insufficiently suited to their professional position. If this phenomenon is correctly understood, it must be taken as a sign and warning that the inferior function, too, now demands its rights and that a confrontation with it has become a necessity. The latter, therefore, plays in such cases the greatest role at the beginning of an analysis.

'Just as the differentiation and isolation of that function which is constitutionally destined in the individual to enable him most surely to find food and meet the demands of the external world is the most important psychic task in youth, the differentiation of the other functions can only be taken up after the successful accomplishment of this task. For before the individual has firmly anchored his consciousness in reality—and that occurs only in adulthood, often only after a certain amount of experience in later life—the way into the unconscious cannot and should not be ventured upon unless absolutely necessary. It is the same with the attitudinal habitus. The constitutionally given habitus must take the lead in the first half of life, because the individual can in all likelihood best find his place in the world with the help of his naturally given attitude. The task of letting the opposite habitus come into its own only emerges during the second half of life. That it will be easier for the born extravert than for the born introvert to accomplish the external adjustment that the first half of life above all requires needs no further explanation. Perhaps one may then venture the assertion: the born extravert gets along in the world more easily in the first, the born introvert in the second half of his life; with which justice is done at least approximately. The danger threatening both types is one-sidedness. An efficient person can be so far driven into the world by his extraversion that he never finds his "way home." His most personal, inner being has grown strange to him. He is continually in flight from it, until one day he can go no farther. Or he may have relied too much upon his reason, have exercised and strengthened only his intellectual function, and now he perceives that he has estranged himself from his own living core. No feeling reaches from him even to the nearest of his fellow-men. Not only for him who is open to the world, but also for the introvert difficulties arise in the course of life from his one-sided orientation. The neglected functions and the unlived attitude revolt—as it were, demand their place in the sun—to be seized by means of a neurosis if not otherwise. For the goal is always totally—the ideal solution, in which all four psychological functions and both forms of attitudinal reactions are at the individual's command in as nearly the same degree of consciousness and disposability as possible. And once, at least, must a certain approximation to this ideal be attempted. If it does not make itself felt earlier as a demand, then the *noon of life* signifies the last summons to attain it now or never and thereby to "round out" the psyche, so that it may not go toward life's evening unfinished and incomplete.' (Jacobi, J. *The Psychology of C.G. Jung,* Kegan Paul, Trench, Trubner, London, 1942)

life-organization See *organization, life.*

life-plan See *plan, life.*

Lilliputian (lil-i-pū′shan) (From *Lilliput,* an imaginary kingdom of 6 inch pygmies in Jonathan Swift's (1667–1745) *Gulliver's Travels.*) Lilliputian concepts are not uncommon in psychiatry. Patients often hallucinate people in miniature form.

'In Lilliputian or microptic hallucinations, the objects seen appear much reduced in scale.' (Henderson, D.K. and Gillespie, R.D. *A Text-Book of Psychiatry,* 4th ed., Oxford University Press, London, 1936) See *micropsia.*

Lilliputian hallucinations have been reported in intoxication from alcohol, chloral, ether, trichlorethylene, cholera, typhoid, scarlet fever, and cocainism.

limb, phantom The feeling that an extremity which has been lost is really present. Fenichel points out that phantom extremity phenomena are closely associated with what is termed the *body image* (q.v.). In its development the infant is first able to discern self from non-self because its own body can be distinguished from all other parts of the universe, or the rest of the world, by the fact that the body is perceived through two types of sensation simultaneously: external tactile sensations and internal sensations of depth sensibility. Thus the first idea of self consists of the sum total of the mental representations of the body and its organs, the so-called body image. The nucleus of the ego is this body image. 'Freud stated that the ego is primarily a bodily thing, that is, the perception of one's own body.'

In phantom extremity phenomena, the basic importance of the body image is underlined. For, indeed, the patient finds great difficulty in correlating with his body image the objective fact of the absence of the extremity. In the body image, which is the basic mental representation of the body, and the nucleus of the ego, the extremities are of the greatest importance. Thus a phantom extremity can be included in the body image. (Fenichel, O. *The Psychoanalytic Theory of Neurosis,* Norton, New York, 1945)

limbus See *rhinencephalon.*

limitation, sex See *sex-limitation.*

limophoitas (lī-mō-foi′tas) Psychosis induced by starvation.

limophthisis (lim-of′thi-sis) Emaciation from insufficient nourishment.

limosis (lī-mō′sis) Mason Good's term to designate the mental disorders associated with abnormal appetites.

Lindau's disease (Arvid Lindau, contemporary Swedish pathologist) Angioma of the brain occurring in connection with angiomatosis of the retina, occasionally familial and hereditary.

line, pure This biological term was introduced by the Danish botanist Johannsen, to characterize the identical *genotypical* equipment of an autogamous stock of organisms descended from a common ancestor by self-fertilization. According to the pure line theory, these organisms will continue to breed true regardless of environmental differences, forming lines genetically pure for all their characters. Whenever such genetic purity has been attained, all differences except newly occurring mutations must be caused by environmental influences and, therefore, cannot be hereditarily transmitted.

lingula (lin′gū-là) See *cerebellum.*

linkage Act of linking, or state of being linked. This is an important exception to the Mendelian principle of independent assortment and is the foundation of the modern chromosome theory of inheritance as formulated by Morgan, in 1910, from his famous Drosophila experiments. It is characterized by the tendency of genes located in the same chromosome to remain in their original combinations and to be inherited as a 'block,' rather than independently of one another.

Apart from the assumption that *linked* genes must be located in the same chromosome, in order to permit such a *coupling*—the mechanism of linkage has been partly explained by the discovery that 'the gametes of a plant or animal which is heterozygous for two linked traits are not formed in equal numbers, but that the gametes with the parental combinations of genes are always more numerous than the gametes with the new combination of genes.' (Sinnott, E.W. and Dunn, L D. *Principles of Genetics,* 3rd ed., McGraw-Hill, New York and London, 1939)

Because of the frequent occurrence of *crossing over* (q v.), most of the known instances of linkage are *incomplete.* Although it is theoretically possible that two linked genes may never separate, because they are so close together in the chromosome that a break cannot occur between them, actual cases of *complete* linkage are exceedingly rare.

linkage, sex See *sex-linkage.*

linonophobia (li-nō-nō-fō′bi-à) Fear of string.

lip-pursing See *schnautzkrampf.*

liquidation, mental (lik-wi-dā′shun) (liter. 'settling of accounts, adjustment') P. Janet thus denotes freedom from painful psychological situations. He speaks of 'liquidating the complicated intrigues of WKV' [one of his patients]. 'This was not an easy matter, because the poor girl begged me not to breathe a word to her parents. She recovered tranquility as soon as she was out of the toils. I grieve to say that no less than eight times I have had to help in the breaking off of engagements to marry.' (Janet, P. *Psychological Healing,* vols. 1–2, tr. by Paul, E. and C., Macmillan, New York, 1925)

lisping A type of defective articulation in which the sounds 's' and 'z' (sibilants) are not pronounced perfectly, by pressing the tip and next narrow part of the blade of the tongue to the alveoli (the sockets where upper front teeth are rooted), but are pronounced by carelessly pushing the tip of the tongue forward and touching the edges of the upper front teeth as when uttering the sound of 'th.' Like all speech disorders, lisping is more common in boys than in girls. Lisping may be based on any or all of the following etiological factors: (1) local conditions, secondary to congenital or acquired organic defects; (2) mental retardation; (3) faulty training, especially as a result of parental ignorance or carelessness and the use of 'baby talk.' It is this last factor that is the most important and the most common, and when it is operative lisping is often found to be a behavior reaction acquired in the interest of some personal or social goal. Treatment is directed to the removal or correction of organic defects and to re-education of parents and child. Speech classes are usually helpful in removing the defect.

Lissauer's dementia paralytica (dā-men′-tē-à pà-rà-lē′tē-kà) (Heinrich Lissauer, German neurologist, 1861–91) An atypical syndrome of general paresis characterized by (1) unusually well-retained intellectual functions and (2) severe focal symptoms, such as apoplectiform attacks, hemiplegia, aphasia, etc.

lithiasis, hysterical (li-thī′à-sis, his-ter′i-kal) In the nine cases (eight of whom were women) of the disturbance labeled hysterical lithiasis in the Mayo Clinic's report, the 'hysterical lithiasis' was neither *hysterical* nor *lithiasis,* but simply a disease picture faked for a definite purpose. These patients made use of foreign bodies that would appear as kidney stones. One patient placed a bag of pebbles in the kidney region at the time of the x-ray exposure. Another patient manufactured a renal colic to obtain morphine, to which she was addicted. (Dunbar, F. *Emotions and Bodily Changes,* Columbia University Press, New York, 1946)

lithic diathesis See *diathesis, lithic.*

Litten's sign (Moritz Litten, German physician, 1845–1907) In paralysis of the diaphragm—non-projection of shadow by the diaphragm x-rayed during respiration.

Little Hans See *Hans.*

Little's disease (William John Little, 1810–94, English surgeon) Congenital diplegia; cerebral palsy; atrophic lobar sclerosis; congenital spastic paralysis; spastic diplegia. A congenital disorder, probably due to in utero degeneration, consisting of a bilateral symmetrical atrophy of the nerve cells and gliosis, mainly of the pyramidal tracts. As a result the limbs (particularly the lower) become weak and spastic. Other symptoms include involuntary movements and ataxia and, usually, some degree of mental deficiency. Predominant symptoms are spastic in 65 per cent of cases, athetoid in 25 per cent, and ataxic in 10 per cent. Few cases survive beyond the early adult years.

load, case In psychiatric social work, a term for the number of 'clients,' as well as for the intensity of service being given.

lobar sclerosis, atrophic (lō'bĕr sklē-rō'sis, at-rō'fik) *Little's disease* (q.v.).

lobectomy, prefrontal (lō-bek'tō-mē, prē-frun'tal) A psychosurgical procedure consisting of bilateral symmetrical excision of the prefrontal areas of the frontal lobes. This procedure is much like prefrontal lobotomy, with the following major differences: (1) prefrontal lobectomy is an open procedure; (2) prefrontal lobectomy destroys more cortex. Also called frontal lobectomy. See *lobotomy, prefrontal.*

lobe, flocculonodular (flok-ū-lō-nod'ū-lĕr) See *cerebellum.*

lobe, frontal That portion of the cerebral hemisphere which lies in front of the central sulcus and above the lateral fissure. The principal areas of the frontal lobe, as designated by Brodmann, are: area 4 (precentral gyrus; principal motor area); immediately in front of 4 is area 6 (pre-

motor area; a part of the extrapyramidal tract circuit); in front of this, area 8 (which is concerned with eye movements and pupillary changes); and in front of this, at the frontal pole and continuing along the inferior surface of the frontal lobe, areas 9, 10, 11, and 12 (which are frontal association areas).

Cells of the precentral gyrus (Betz cells) control voluntary movements of skeletal muscle on the opposite side of the body via the pyramidal tracts; irritative lesions in this area may give convulsive seizures (Jacksonian epilepsy). Destructive lesions in area 4 produce flaccid paralysis; spasticity will occur if area 6 and intermediate cortex are also involved. Forced grasping is often seen following destructive lesions of area 6. Destruction of the frontal association areas (9, 10, 11, and 12) may produce facetiousness (Witzelsucht), change in moral and social behavior, loss of interest, intellectual deterioration, and distractibility.

lobe, limbic (lim'bik) See *rhinencephalon.*

lobe, occipital (ok-sip'i-tal) The posterior lobe of the cerebral hemisphere; it is pyramidal in shape and lies behind the parieto-occipital fissure. Visual function is localized in the occipital lobe, primarily in the calcarine cortex (area striata, area 17 of Brodmann). Neurons from the retina project to the external geniculate body, whence 2nd-order neurons project to the calcarine cortex. Fibers from the nasal half of each retina cross in the optic chiasm and so are projected onto the visual cortex of the opposite side; fibers from the temporal half of the retina remain uncrossed. The posterior occipital poles are mainly concerned with macular (central) vision; the more anterior parts of the calcarine area are concerned with peripheral vision. The human loses both object vision and light perception when the calcarine cortex is removed.

The calcarine cortex (area 17) projects to area 18 (parastriate lobule), which in turn projects to area 19 (preoccipital area). Areas 18 and 19 are visual association areas; lesions here cause disturbances in spatial orientation and word-blindness (alexia). Area 19 receives projections from all parts of the cortex and then coordinates visual with other reflexes.

lobe, parietal (pȧ-rī'e-tal) That portion of the cerebral hemisphere which extends from the central sulcus to the parieto-occipital fissure and laterally to the level of the Sylvian fissure. The postcentral gyrus (areas 3-1-2, the somesthetic area), the supramarginal gyrus, and the angular gyrus are portions of the parietal lobe. The postcentral gyrus receives projections from the relay nuclei of the thalamus; the latter receive the great ascending somatosensory tracts of the spinal cord and the trigeminal lemniscus. Areas 5 and 7, which make up the posterior parietal lobule, are sensory association areas. Experimental studies indicate that the body surface is projected dermatome by dermatome on the postcentral gyrus. It appears that taste is also a function of the sensorimotor area and is localized at the inferior end of the lobe, possibly on the opercular surface of the Sylvian fissure.

lobe, temporal That portion of the cerebral hemisphere which lies below the Sylvian fissure and extends back to the level of the parieto-occipital fissure. The temporal lobe receives auditory projections from the medial geniculate body, and ablation of the temporal lobe in man results in partial deafness, contralateral disturbance in auditory localization, and disturbance in memory for auditory impressions. The temporal lobe also receives vertibular projections, but the source of these is unknown.

Symptoms of temporal lobe tumors include visual field defects, auditory and speech defects, and minor seizures known as dreamy states (see *states, dreamy*). If the uncus is implicated, there may be hallucinations of smell and taste (uncinate seizures).

lobotomy, Grantham Lobotomy performed by means of electrocoagulation of the ventromedial quadrant of the prefrontal lobe of the brain.

lobotomy, prefrontal (lō-bot'ō-mē) A psychosurgical procedure consisting of ablation of the prefrontal area of the frontal lobe. The prefrontal area is that portion of the frontal lobe anterior to Brodmann's area 6, the premotor area. As a psychosurgical procedure, the operation is ordinarily performed bilaterally. In contrast to frontal lobectomy, which is an open procedure in which tissue is excised and, therefore, more direct cortical damage is caused, the lobotomy procedure is 'blind.' A hole is drilled through the skull and a leukotome is inserted to cut white nerve fibers connecting the frontal lobe with the

thalamus. Thus, in lobotomy, there is less cortical damage than in lobectomy. This procedure interrupts frontothalamic and thalamafrontal fibers and also the association systems of the frontal lobe.

Prefrontal lobotomy was among the first psychosurgical procedures used in the United States. It seems to reduce anxiety feelings and introspective activities; and feelings of inadequacy and self-consciousness are thereby lessened. Lobotomy reduces the emotional tension associated with hallucinations and does away with the catatonic state. Because nearly all psychosurgical procedures have undesirable side effects, they are ordinarily resorted to only after all other methods have failed. The less disorganized the personality of the patient, the more obvious are post-operative side effects. For this reason, bilateral prefrontal lobotomy is employed more commonly in schizophrenia than in any other disorder. Prefrontal lobotomy is of value in the following disorders, listed in a descending scale of good results: affective disorders, obsessive-compulsive states, chronic anxiety states and other non-schizophrenic conditions, paranoid schizophrenia, undetermined or mixed types of schizophrenia, catatonic schizophrenia, and hebephrenic and simple schizophrenia. Good results are obtained in about 40 per cent of cases, fair results in some 35 per cent, and poor results in 25 per cent or thereabouts. The mortality rate probably does not exceed 3 per cent. Greatest improvement is seen in patients whose premorbid personalities were 'normal,' cyclothymic, or obsessive-compulsive; in patients with superior intelligence and good education; in psychoses with sudden onset and a clinical picture of affective symptoms of depression or anxiety, and with behavioristic changes such as refusal of food, overactivity, and delusional ideas of a paranoid nature.

Convulsive seizures are reported as sequelae of prefrontal lobotomy in 5 to 10 per cent of cases. Such seizures are ordinarily well controlled with the usual anticonvulsive drugs. Post-operative blunting of the personality, apathy, and irresponsibility are the rule rather than the exception. Other side effects include distractibility, childishness, facetiousness, lack of tact or discipline, and post-operative incontinence.

Prefrontal lobotomy has also been used

successfully to control pain secondary to organic lesions. In this case, the tendency has been to employ unilateral lobotomy, because of the evidence that a lobotomy extensive enough to relieve psychotic symptoms is not required to control pain.

Since the introduction of prefrontal lobotomy and prefrontal lobectomy various other psychosurgical procedures have been initiated—transorbital lobotomy, thalamotomy, cortical undercutting, and topectomy. The present trend is toward selective operation, the particular procedure being chosen on the basis of the nature of the disease, its duration and extent, the patient's age, etc. Also called *frontal lobotomy; prefrontal leukotomy; frontal leukotomy.*

lobotomy, transorbital (trans-or′bi-tal) A psychosurgical procedure consisting of partial ablation of the prefrontal area. The approach is through the superior conjunctival sac, and the operation is usually performed bilaterally. The plane of section corresponds roughly to that of *topectomy* but, like prefrontal lobotomy, the procedure is a 'blind' one and white matter rather than gray matter is destroyed. The incision interrupts the fronto-thalamic and thalamofrontal radiations and also the frontal lobe association fibers. Some surgeons prefer the transorbital approach to classical prefrontal lobotomy, because they feel that incontinence, apathy, and other undesirable side effects are less frequent. See *lobotomy, prefrontal.*

locomotor ataxia (lō-kō-mō′ter à-tak′si-à) See *tabes.*

Loewenfeld, Leopold (1847–1924) (lě′venfelt) German psychiatrist and sexologist.

logagnosia (log-ag-nō′zhi-à) Sensory aphasia.

logamnesia (log-am-nē′zhia) Forgetting of words; nominal or amnestic aphasia.

-logia, -logy (-lō′ji-à, -′lō-jē) Combining form meaning (1) speaking, speech; (2) science, doctrine, theory, from Gr. *-logía* (in composition), from *lógos,* word, speech, discourse.

logoclonia (log-ō-klō′ni-à) Logospasm.

logodiarrhea (-dī-à-rē′à) See *tachylogia.*

logomania (-mā′ni-à) See *tachylogia.*

logomonomania (-mon-ō-mā′ni-à) The term, coined by Guislain, and no longer in use, refers to an abnormal mental state characterized only by great loquacity. It is difficult today to name a psychiatric state of which volubility is the only symptom.

logoneurosis (-nū-rō′sis) *Obs.* Any neurosis associated with a speech defect.

logopathy (lō-gop′à-thē) A general term for any type of speech disorder.

logopedics (log-ō-pē′diks) The study of speech and its disorders.

logophasia (-fā′zhi-à) A form of aphasia, characterized by loss of ability to use articulate language correctly.

logoplegia (-plē′ji-à) (*Obsnt*) *Aphasia.*

logorrhea (-rē′à) See *tachylogia.*

logospasm (log′ō-spaz′m) Explosive speech; stuttering.

Lombroso, Cesare (1836–1909) Italian criminologist and psychopathologist.

longeval (lon-jē′val) *Rare.* Longevous.

longevity (lon-jev′i-tē) Length of life. In its medical and statistical sense, this term refers to the phenomenon of a long duration, or great length, of life, and hence to a biological concept with important implications in medical statistics as well as in constitutional medicine and genetics.

The existence of *genetic* factors operating in human longevity has been conclusively demonstrated by a number of family studies, although the details of the genetic mechanism involved have not yet been elucidated. Certain experiments of Pearl have shown *longlivedness* to be dominant over *shortlivedness* in Drosophila. A number of cases of short lifespan may thus be accounted for by single-recessive mechanisms. There is also the possibility of *lethal* (q.v.) genes which merits consideration as a factor influencing life-span, although the present evidence is to the effect that the significant role of lethal genes is in the fairly early (prenatal) stages.

According to Pearl's theories, it is 'the total genetic constitution of the individual, rather than any particular genes lethal or other, that is most important as a factor in determining length of life.' (*Human Biology,* volume 3) However, Scheinfeld advances as a speculative opinion the notion that if there are genes producing a fatal breakdown at early stages of life, there might also be genes 'timed' to bring death at later periods. On this theory rests the belief that there may be sets of genes, collectively inherited in given families, which in a general way make some of them potentially long-lived and others short-lived. (Scheinfeld, A. *You and Heredity*, Book of the Month Club, New York, 1939)

Concerning the constitutional aspect of longevity it has been shown by Pearl that the long-lived are more asthenic and the short-lived more pyknic, that women have a decided biological advantage over men, and that in youth all individuals below average height have a greater mortality, while overweight means greater mortality in individuals over 40 years of age.

Studies on the factor of *marital status* in longevity have demonstrated an advantage for the married over the unmarried in general, but this is mainly due to selective factors rather than to environmental benefits conveyed by marriage. Longevity is also positively correlated with a favorable *social* and *economic* status, and with professional work as opposed to manual occupations, although the question of the relative influence of genetic factors determining simultaneously low grade occupation and a poor constitution on the one hand, and the environmental disadvantages of manual occupations on the other has not been carefully worked out.

As regards the *physico-chemical* basis of longevity there is Meggendorfer's interesting hypothesis that it is not duration of life as such that is hereditarily determined, but only longevity in the sense of a definite quantity of life energy. Environmental influences such as temperature and light may affect longevity by altering the speed of metabolic processes and hence the rate of consumption of the fixed available supply of energy.

longevous (lon-jē'vus) Living a long time or being of great age.

longilineal (lon-ji-lin'ē-al) In constitutional medicine, this term refers to one of the two constitutional types distinguished by Manouvrier on the basis of the configuration of the body as a whole. Persons of this type are built on lines that tend to be long rather than broad, and are to be contrasted with the *brevilineal* (q.v.) type.

The *longilineal* type corresponds roughly to the *asthenic* (q.v.) type of Kretschmer, and the *dolichomorphic* type of Pende.

longitypical (-tip'i-kal) Identical with *longilineal* and *dolichomorphic*.

look, metallic See *gloss, metallic*.

look, paranoid (par'à-noid) The facial appearance of a paranoid schizophrenic when he thinks about certain of his complexes. 'In a few patients, this phenomenon can be evoked or made to disappear again momentarily by changing the subject of conversation. I do not know on what it is based. Often it remains perfectly recognizable even if a mask leaves nothing but the eyes visible.' (Bleuler, E. *Dementia Praecox or the Group of Schizophrenias*, International Universities Press, New York, 1950)

love In psychiatry the most commonly accepted definition of *love* is contained in the word *pleasure*, particularly as it applies to gratifying experiences between members of the opposite sex. The manifestations of love are almost legion, ranging from those of the infantile period up to those of sublimated maturity.

Love is pleasure; when the pleasure is directed to oneself it is self-love; the word is annexed by a hyphen to the particular part of oneself that pleases; it may be oral, anal, genital, muscular, dermal, psychic (with all its subdivisions). When love is directed away from oneself it becomes object-love, which has as many manifestations as self-love.

In general it may be said to correspond to *Eros* and *libido*. Freud defines libido as 'the energy . . . of those instincts which have to do with all that may be comprised under the word "love." '

According to Freud the choice of a love-object may be based upon (1) the narcissistic type, with four possibilities: one may love (a) a person like himself; (b) a person resembling him as he once was; (c) a person who meets the requirements of being what one would like to be; and (d) someone who was once part of himself.

The love-object, (2) patterned after the anaclitic type, may be: (a) the woman who tends or (b) the man who protects.

love, anal-sadistic Each of the three principal erotogenic zones (the oral, anal, and genital) is said to be associated with gratification during the infancy period. The child wishes to perpetuate the pleasures. Alimentary activities give rise to oral pleasures; the premium paid to the child for exemplary anal habits is associated with pleasure; the same holds true for good urinary behavior.

According to Abraham, there are two anal stages, the one aiming to control and exploit the object, the other associated with its destruction. When at a later age love centers around one of the two or both aims, it is called anal-sadistic love.

love, Dorian (dō′ri-an) Love for boys. Stekel refers to the works of the philologist E. Bethe: 'The author proves that boy love in Hellas was introduced by the Dorians. Although traces of the custom are found also among the Ionians, boy love, like knighthood, became fashionable in Greece through the Dorians.' (Stekel, W. *The Homosexual Neurosis,* tr. by van Teslaar, J.S., Badger, Boston, 1922)

love, genital (jen′i-tal) The type of object love characteristic of the genital or adult stage; adult, mature, non-ambivalent object love.

love, monkey A literal translation of the German term *Affenliebe.* It refers to inordinate maternal love in which the mother caters unqualifiedly to all the wishes and whims of the child.

love, mother The feeling of affection, devotion, possessiveness, and the need of protecting the child born to a woman. 'Mother love is frequently called an instinct, a proclivity that appears in a woman, because she becomes a mother and for no other reason. There may be something to this idea, but . . . "instinct" is not all that is involved. In general, people love those for whom they have to make sacrifices, and babies demand sacrifices. Not only "instinct" but many other types of pressures—social mores, the expectancy of the family for her to act in a motherly way, her husband's pride in her motherhood, pity for the helpless infant— are also involved in setting up the pattern of feeling and action we recognize as mother love.' (Lemkau, P.V. *Mental Hygiene in Public Health,* McGraw-Hill, New York, 1949)

love-object See *object-love.*

love, partial From the psychoanalytic standpoint 'love' begins to express itself early in the pregenital phase. Thus, there are the many manifestations of oral and anal 'love,' which give way in part to later phallic, and still later genital love. The manifestations of love, being focal-

ized, so to speak, upon particular parts of an individual (the mother) and not upon the total individual, are termed *partial love.*

love, passive object See *narcissism.*

love, phallic (fa′lik) The type of object love characteristic of the phallic period.

love, pregenital (prē-jen′i-tal) Abraham thus terms the behavior of the child toward the mother in particular, during the pregenital phase. Although the infant is relatively, if not completely, indifferent to the welfare of the object in the early suckling phase, it shows the first signs of caring for the mother during the biting stage. 'We may also regard such a care, incomplete as it is, as the first beginnings of object-love in a stricter sense since it implies that the individual has begun to conquer his narcissism.' (Abraham, K. *Selected Papers,* tr. by Bryan, D. and Strachey, A., Leonard and Virginia Woolf, Hogarth Press, London, 1927)

love, smother A phrase sometimes applied to the mother who overprotects her child so that he has little opportunity to develop independence, overindulges him so that he becomes unable to tolerate frustrations, dominates and controls his every action, and ultimately engenders multiple fears in him and doubts about his own adequacy and ability. Smother love predisposes to passive dependent types of mastery and is seen often in obsessive or phobic mothers.

L.P. Lumbar puncture. See *puncture, lumbar.*

LSD See *psychotomimetic.*

lucidity From the legal point of view 'a lucid interval is not a perfect restoration to reason, but a restoration so far as to be able, beyond doubt, to comprehend and do the act with such perception, memory and judgment as to make it a legal act.' (Frazer *v.* Frazer, 2 Del.Chi., 263)

ludic (lū′dik) Unreal, play-like, quasi, pseudo. See *activity, ludic.*

lues (lū′ēz) Originally, plague or pestilence; in current usage, syphilis.

lues deifica (loo′es de-ē′fe-kà) (L. 'sacred plague,' epilepsy) *Obs.* Epilepsy.

lues divina (dē-vē′nà) (L. 'divine plague') *Obs.* Epilepsy.

luetic curve (lū-e′tik) See *Lange's colloidal gold reaction.*

lumbar puncture See *puncture, lumbar.*

lunacy (lū'na-sē) This term is almost entirely obsolete in psychiatric literature. It prevails in forensic psychiatry, because it is incorporated in organic law; it refers to mental abnormality of such degree as to render the patient incompetent and bring him under the guardianship of the state.

lunacy commission A committee, usually of qualified psychiatrists, appointed by judicial order to determine the mental state of an individual whose case the court has under consideration.

lunacy, moral An old psychiatric term emphasizing social and moralistic attitudes toward symptomatic behavior disorders, for which the present-day synonyms are (1) psychopathic personality; (2) constitutional psychopathic inferiority; (3) the impulse neuroses and perversions.

In the contrast between the old and new terms, we thus see the trend toward change from the moralistic, demoniacal, and punitive attitudes of the past to the objective, scientific, personality-determined understanding of the present. (Hunt, J.McV. *Personality and the Behavior Disorders,* vol. 2. Ronald Press, New York, 1944.) See *depravity, insanity and.*

lunatic (lū'nà-tik) One possessing a mental disorder.

lunatismus (loō-nà-tēz'moos) (G. 'somnambulism') An old expression given to those somnambulists who only walk about at the time the moon shines.' (Tuke, D.H. *A Dictionary of Psychological Medicine,* vols. 1–2, Blakiston, Philadelphia, 1892)

lune (lūn) *Obs.* A fit of insanity.

Luys, body of (Jules Bernard Luys, French physician, 1828–98) See *subthalamus.*

lycanthropy (lī-kan'thrō-pē) Some patients believe that they are able to change themselves or others into a wolf or some other animal. The belief is called lycanthropy. It is not uncommon among schizophrenic patients.

'The *delirium of metamorphosis* or transformation into some form of animal (lycanthropy) . . . is met with much more rarely today than in past centuries, including even the first half of the nineteenth century.' (Bianchi, L. *A Text-Book of Psychiatry,* tr. by MacDonald, J.H., Baillière, Tindall & Cox, London, 1906)

lycomania (lī-kō-mā'ni-à) Lycanthropy.

lycorexia (lī-kō-rek'si-à) Bulimia.

lygophilia (lī-gō-fil'i-à, lig-ō-) Longing for dark or gloomy places.

lying, pathological (pa-thō-loj'i-kal) 'Pathological lying is falsification entirely disproportionate to any discernible end in view, engaged in by a person who, at the time of observation, cannot be definitely declared insane, feebleminded or epileptic. Such lying rarely, if ever, centers about a single event; although exhibited in very occasional cases for a short time, it manifests itself most frequently by far over a period of years, or even a lifetime. It represents a trait rather than an episode.' (Healy, W. and Healy, M.T. *Pathological Lying, Accusation, and Swindling.* Little, Brown, Boston, 1915) Pathological lying is also known as mythomania or pseudologia fantastica.

lypemania (lip-ē-mā'ni-à; lī-pē) Esquirol, the pupil of Pinel, divided mental disorders into five classes:

1. Lypemania or melancholia.
2. Monomania, in which 'the disorder of the faculties is limited to one or a small number of objects, with excitement and predominance of a gay and expansive passion.'
3. Mania, characterized by 'delirium' extending 'to all kinds of objects' and accompanied by excitement.
4. Dementia, 'in which the insensate utter folly, because the organs of thought have lost their energy and the strength requisite for their functions.'
5. Imbecility or idiocy, 'in which the conformation of the organs has never been such that those who are thus afflicted can reason justly.'

lypothymia (lī-pō-thī'mi-à, -thim'i-à; lip-ō) Melancholy.

lysatotherapy (lī-sa-tō-ther'à-pē) A form of treatment for clinical depression reported by Timopheyev which uses a lysate of the anterior hypophysis. Lysatotherapy is based on the assumption that hypophyseal hypofunction is of etiologic significance in the pathogenesis of pure depression or cyclothymia.

lysergic acid diethylamide (lī-ser'jik a'sid dī'eth-il-am-id) See *psychotomimetic.*

lyssa (lis'à) *Obs.* Insanity.

lyssophobia (lis-ō-fō'bi-à) Fear of becoming insane.

M

M Rorschach scoring symbol for human movement response.

m Rorschach scoring symbol for motion response.

machlaenomania (mak-lē-nō-mā′ni-à) Masochism in women.

machlosyne (mak-lōs′i-nē) Nymphomania.

macro- (mak′rō-) Combining form meaning large, enlarged, extended, from Gr. *makrós,* long, large.

macrobiotic (mak-rō-bī-ot′ik) Longevous.

macrocephaly (-sef′à-lē) Abnormally large size of the head.

macrogenitosomia (-jen-it-ō-sō′mi-à) This is a syndrome occurring in children before the age of puberty, due to tumors of the pineal gland. The condition is also known as *pubertas praecox* (precocious puberty) and consists of precocious development of the body and mind. The sexual development is precocious with early ejaculation or menstruation and the growth of prematurely large genitals. The secondary sex characters occur early with gruff voice, facial, pubic, and axillary hairs, and mammary gland development.

macrogenitosomia, precocious Pellizzi introduced this term for a particular form of *gigantism* (q.v.) occurring in children and characterized by premature, rapid, and exaggerated development of the entire organism, including the sexual organs. In addition to the overgrowth of stature and body mass, which may reach the dimensions of the adult in a few years, there are frequently dissociations and partial hypoevolutisms of the sexual characteristics, and also adiposity and a certain degree of mental deficiency.

This syndrome is caused either by tumors of the adrenal cortex, the testicle, or the pineal gland, or in rare cases by dyspituitarism and, in female children, sometimes by constitutional hypothyroidism.

macrology (mak-rol′ō-jē) Long speech with little reasoning.

macromania (mak-rō-mā′ni-à) *Obs.* 'That form of insanity in which the insane person conceives things, especially parts of his own body, to be larger than they in reality are.' (Tuke, D.H. *A Dictionary of Psychological Medicine,* vols. 1–2, Blakiston, Philadelphia, 1892)

macromimia (-mim′i-à) Exaggerated mimicry.

macropsia, macropsy (mak-rop′si-à, mak′rop-sē) When objects appear larger than they really are, the condition is known as macropsia. The phenomenon is sometimes observed in psychiatric patients, particularly in those with hysteria. Charcot said that when objects are held close to the affected eye they seem to the patient to be enormously magnified. The expression *macropsia hysterica,* or hysterical macropsy, was formerly used to denote the condition.

mactation (mak-tā′shun) Murder of a sacrificial victim, a concept occasionally observed among psychotic patients.

madbrain A popular expression denoting rashness, ungovernability.

madcap A popular term for a rash, wild, reckless person.

madman A popular expression for one mentally unbalanced.

madness A popular term for mental disorder.

maenad (mē′nad) *Obs.* A mentally sick woman.

maenas (mē′nas) *Obs.* Mania.

magic In psychiatry magic plays a particularly significant role. Magical thinking and acting are common to almost all psychiatric states. They are seen in their most vivid forms in the schizophrenias, in which the mere act of thinking or of gesticulation or posturing is assumed by the patient to accomplish the fulfillment, the wish or impulse. A patient stands erect; by so doing he corrects all the evils of the universe; another thinks of the death of an alleged enemy; his thought is sufficient to cause the death.

'Now we know that the schizophrenic overestimates the scope of his thoughts and wishes and ascribes to them an efficacy which they do not possess. . . . While he remains passive and inactive, perhaps in a semi-stuporous state, he believes that he is carrying on the most wonderful and magnificent works in the cosmos.' (Storch, A. *The Primitive Archaic*

Forms in Schizophrenia, tr. by Willard, C., Nervous and Mental Disease Publishing Company, New York and Washington, 1924) Freud speaks of 'the all-powerfulness of his thought.'

'The more primitive the man is, the more firmly he holds fast to the belief that he can attain anything by willing.' (Scheler, M.)

Magna Mater (mag'nå mā'tĕr, måg'nå mä'ter) (L. '(the) Great Mother') Cybele, whose cult as a goddess originated in Asia Minor (Phrygia), later known to the Romans most commonly as the Great Mother of the Gods, the symbol of universal motherhood, the parent of gods and every living being, particularly wild creatures. In her reputed nocturnal wanderings over wooded mountains, the religious retinue of semi-demonic Corybantes attended her with noisy music and armed dances. Her festivities were celebrated by eunuch priests (wearing women's attire), the Galli, headed by the chief Archigallus, together with the priestesses, amid rites of raving excitement and dancing (to the tunes of wild music), until they collapsed in utter exhaustion. The term designates one of Jung's archetypes. See *archetype; archetype, mother.*

magnetism Magnetism is an obsolete concept, because formerly it was felt that some force was transmitted from man to man (animal magnetism) like the force sent out by the magnet. Magnetism was supposedly the principal factor in hypnotism or Braidism.

magnus morbus (måg-noos môr'boos) (L. 'great disease,' epilepsy) *Obs.* Epilepsy.

magrums (ma'grumz) P.R. Vessie says: 'The old English dialect word "magrums," meaning mad-staggers and fidgets, was also applied to the adult type of chorea. It is still used by residents of lower New England.' ('Hereditary Chorea: St. Anthony's Dance and Witchcraft in Colonial Connecticut,' *Journal of the Connecticut State Medical Society, 3,* 598, 1939)

maid *Obs.* A virgin man, one who has not had sexual intercourse.

maieusiomania (mā-ū-si-ō-mā'ni-å) *Obs.* Puerperal psychosis.

maieusiophobia (mā-ū-si-ō-fō'bi-å) Fear of childbirth.

mainliner A slang expression for addicts who take narcotics by intravenous injection.

maintenance, ego The drive for self-preservation, by maintaining or supporting one's ego.

maintenance-level See *level, maintenance.*

maitre de plaisir (mâtr' dĕ plâ-zēr') (F. 'master of pleasure') One who derives satisfaction from arranging for the sexual pleasures of others.

make-up, mental By the expression *mental make-up,* psychiatrists usually refer to the constitution of the mind prior to the onset of a psychiatric condition. It is a loosely employed phrase, often synonymous with *personality make-up.*

make-up, personality The constitution of the personality; see *constitution, personality.*

makroskelic (mak-rō-skel'ik) Manouvrier's system of constitutional types. This term refers to a type which is characterized by an excessive length of the legs and corresponds roughly to Kretschmer's *asthenic* type.

maladaptation, common See *psychodynamics, adaptational.*

maladie des tics (må-là-dĕ' dā tĕk') *Gilles de la Tourette syndrome* (q.v.).

maladie du pays (må-là-dĕ' dü pā-ē') (F. 'homesickness') Nostalgia.

maladjustment From the psychoanalytic point of view, maladjustment is the result of conflict between instinctual drives and social requirements. Blanton defines it as the insubordination of the wishes, desires, needs of the individual to those of the group. 'It is only by the most delicate type of adjustment that we may live in comfort in the present group arrangement. The child is born without knowledge of how to make this adjustment. It is often assumed that he has an inherent knowledge of how to develop his own ego; instead, it must be painfully learned.' (Blanton, S. and M. *Child Guidance,* Century, New York, 1927, p. 165)

Neuroses in children are more frequently expressed in the form of maladjustment than is the case with adults. 'Though the symptoms of neuroses are usually subjective disturbances, in some adults and more frequently in children, they are acted out in the environment. The reason is probably that with less developed emotional control in children, emotional conflicts are more likely to be solved by disguise of the act than by its complete curtailment. In some adult neurotics, for example, one can trace the same neurotic symptom as acted out in childhood and as a subjective symptom in later years.' (Levy, D.M. 'On the Problem of Delinquency,' *American Journal of Orthopsychiatry II,* 197–211, 1932)

maladjustment, simple adult Adult situational reaction. See *transient situational personality disorders.*

malady, English *Obs.* Hypochondriasis.

mal d'orient (màl′ dô-ryäN′) (F. 'oriental evil') Homosexuality used to be known as the Oriental 'evil.' It is said that the practice spread to Europe through the influence of the Crusaders. In some countries a homosexualist is called a Turk or a Bulgar; hence, the French term *bougre* and the English *bugger,* both denoting a homosexualist. (Hirschfeld, M.)

malinger (mà-ling′gẽr) To feign or protract one's illness; to simulate, with intent to deceive.

malingering Simulation of symptoms of illness or injury with intent to deceive. Malingering occurs, usually, in one of the following situations: (1) in criminal cases, when psychosis or mental deficiency is advanced as a defense; (2) in personal injury actions and compensation cases; and (3) in military service or similar special situations where nervous or mental disease might afford an escape from hazardous or arduous duty. The diseases most likely to be malingered are amnesiae, psychoses, psychoneuroses, and mental deficiency. Detection in the latter case is relatively simple with available psychometric tests.

malleation (mal-ē-ā′shun) A symptom characterized by convulsive movements of the hands, as if in the act of hammering.

malum caducum (mà′loom kà-dōō′koom) (L. 'falling evil or sickness') *Obs.* Epilepsy.

malum minus (mē′noos) (L. 'minor evil') Petit mal form of epilepsy.

mammalingus (mam-à-lin′gus) One who apposes his mouth to the woman's breast. A term suggested by Jones to refer to the psychoanalytic meaning of practicing fellatio toward a woman.

'The fellatio conception of coitus, in fact, would seem to be only one-half of the story. One finds also the complementary idea that the father not only gives to the mother, but receives from her; that in short she suckles him. And it is here that the direct rivalry with the father is so strong, for the mother is giving him just what the girl wants (nipple and milk).... When this "mammalingus" conception, as it may be called, gets sadistically cathected, then we have the familiar feminist idea of the man who "uses" the woman, exhausts her, drains her, exploits her, and so on.' (Jones, E. *Papers on Psycho-Analysis,* 4th ed., Wood, Baltimore, 1938)

man, effeminated (e-fem′i-nāt-id) Passive homosexual male. In homosexual intercourse effeminated men feel themselves in the act always as a woman.' (Krafft-Ebing, R.v. *Psychopathia Sexualis,* Login, New York, 1908)

mania (mā′ni-à) The term is commonly used today in conjunction with *melancholia,* since the two states are regarded as manifestations of a single disorder called manic-depressive psychosis. The principal characteristics of mania are expressed in three fields; of ideas, feelings, and motility. Each of the three shows pronounced exaggeration, in the sense that ideas are voluminous, feelings are intensely elevated, and there is marked psychomotor overactivity.

The main disturbances in the ideational sphere are: *overproductivity, flight of ideas,* that is, a rapid shifting from one topic to another; of which *distractibility* is a part, the patient changing from topic to topic in accordance with the stimuli from without and from within; the shifting may be occasioned by what is called *clang association*—stimulation of a new train of thought by some external sound; *leveling of ideas,* that is, essentially all topics have about the same value to the patient; *ideas of importance, grandiose ideas,* the patient expressing delusions of greatness perhaps in all fields; the feelings of well-being are expressed also in the sphere of *physical excellence.* Often the ideas are reproductions of those relating to *infantile sexuality.*

The principal modifications in the emotional field are: exaggerated feelings of gaiety, well-being, extreme happiness—in consonance with the ideas expressed.

The expression *psycho-motor overactivity* refers to physical overactivity. In extreme states it is incessant throughout the waking hours; the patient attempts to motorize, that is, to put into physical execution all the ideas that occur to him; this tendency, therefore, leads to a shifting of physical activity paralleling that in the mental sphere.

Depending upon the degree of mania, there are three types: *hypomania,* which is a less intense form; *mania,* which is presumably the common or usual type; *hypermania,* or a more intense expression of the manic reaction.

Some authors use the term *acute mania* synonymously with *mania,* and *hypermania* is often referred to as *delirious mania, Bell's mania, typhomania, delirium grave,* or *collapse delirium,* with partial or complete disorientation as the rule.

When a patient has a succession of manic attacks the condition is known as *recurrent* or *periodic mania.* When manic and depressive episodes alternate, the condition is called *alternating* or *circular psychosis* or *insanity.*

Periodic mania is to be distinguished from *chronic mania,* a form described by Schott in 1904 in which manic symptoms continue uninterruptedly for an indefinite number of years (in Schott's series, for 30, 25, 21, and 17 years). In all such cases which have been reported, the particular episode which becomes chronic has begun after the age of 40.

A patient in a manic phase may not talk; his state is then known as *unproductive* or *stuporous mania;* he is said to be in a condition of *manic stupor.*

When a patient presents the symptoms of mania, but does not move, his condition is called *akinetic mania.* Follow-up studies reveal that akinetic mania and manic stupor and all of Kraepelin's 'mixed' or 'intermediate' states are really schizophrenic.

'The psychoanalytic point is one which several analytic investigators have already formulated in so many words, namely, that the content of mania is no different from that of melancholia, that both the disorders are wrestling with the same "complex," and that in melancholia the ego has succumbed to it, whereas in mania it has mastered the complex or thrust it aside.' (Freud, S. *Collected Papers,* vol. 4, tr. by Riviere, J., Leonard and Virginia Woolf and The Institute of Psychoanalysis, London, 1924–25) In mania, the ego for a time has thrown off the yoke of the superego and protests, 'I don't need con-

trol any more.' The removal of inhibition allows all those impulses (mainly oral) which had been kept down to come to the fore. But the freedom from the superego is not a real one, and the ego must deny its fear of the superego by overcompensation. The cramped nature of the symptoms is due to the fact that they are of a reaction-formation type and deny opposite attitudes. Mania is not a genuine freedom from depression but rather a cramped denial of dependencies.

mania, absorbed See *stupor.*

mania, acute See *mania.*

mania, akinetic (ak-i-net′ik) See *mania.*

mania, ambitious Delirium grandiosum; megalomania; folie ambitieuse.

mania, anxious This is a mixed form of manic-depressive psychosis. 'If in the picture depression takes the place of cheerful mood, a morbid state arises, which is composed of flight of ideas, excitement, and anxiety. The patients are distractible, absent-minded, enter into whatever goes on round them, take themselves up with everything, catch up words and continue spinning out the ideas stirred up by these. . . .' (Kraepelin, E. *Manic-Depressive Insanity and Paranoia,* tr. by Barclay, R.M., Livingstone, Edinburgh, 1921)

mania a potu (mà′nē-à à pō′tōō) (L. 'madness from drink(ing)') A state, produced by alcohol, characterized by extreme excitement and sometimes leading to homicidal attacks. The attack is usually brought on, in a susceptible individual, by the ingestion of comparatively small amounts of alcohol. See *alcoholism.*

mania, Bell's (Luther V. Bell, American physician, 1806–62) Delirious mania; see *mania.*

mania, brooding Morbid impulse to meditate long and anxiously.

'We have already mentioned the important part played by the sadistic instinctual components in the genesis of obsessional neuroses. Where the epistemophilic instinct is a preponderating feature in the constitution of an obsessional patient, brooding becomes the principal symptom of the neurosis.' (Freud, S. *Collected Papers,* vol. 3, tr. by Strachey, A. and J., Leonard and Virginia Woolf and The Institute of Psychoanalysis, London, 1925)

mania, Caesar This is an infrequently used term. Bleuler defines this uncommon term as 'a feeling of being absolute master of life and death among savages.' (Bleuler, E. *Textbook of Psychiatry*, tr. by Brill, A.A., Macmillan, New York, 1930)

mania, chattering *Obs.* Uncontrollable urge to talk gibberish.

mania, choreic Synonym for choreic insanity. See *insanity, choreic.*

mania, chronic Term first used by Schott for the manic type of reaction that is more or less permanent.

mania, chronic intellectual *Obs.* 'A general disturbance of the intellect characterized by the existence of varying unsystematized delusions, accompanied by periods of mental excitement or depression, with more or less incoherence and mental weakness.' (Foster, F.P. *Medical Dictionary*, Appleton, New York, 1892–94)

mania, classification of See *depression, classification of.*

mania(co)comium (mā-ni-à-[kō]-kō'mi-um) Psychiatric hospital.

mania, collecting The morbid impulse to collect is commonly observed in psychiatric practice. It is seen in one of its most vivid forms in patients with schizophrenia, who often collect all sorts of articles, most of them useless; they stuff their clothing with trash. The collecting mania is often clearly representative of anal erotism.

mania concionabunda (mà'nē-à kôn-kē-ô-nà-boon'dà) *Obs.* Mania for addressing the public. (*Lancet,* 1176, 1886)

mania, depressive *Anxious mania* (q.v.).

mania, doubting An obsessive doubting in which the patient finds it necessary to say 'no' to everything. This patient will raise objections to whatever comes into his mind from within or without. For example, the names of people known intimately for years may become uncertain to the patient. He may realize intellectually that what he objects to is correct, but his emotions deny the fact. Usually, under analysis, it emerges that unconscious instinctual demands are being denied through the doubting-mania. (Hinsie, L.E. *Understandable Psychiatry*, Macmillan, New York, 1948)

mania, drinking Bleuler says: 'Theoretically alcoholism and drinking mania should be distinguished. He who cannot abstain from spirituous drinks even when he realizes that it would be better not to drink, he who habitually oversteps the measure which he himself considers proper, is a drinking maniac; he who shows other psychic results of drinking or physical alcoholic signs, is an alcoholic.' (Bleuler, E. *Textbook of Psychiatry*, tr. by Brill, A.A., Macmillan, New York, 1930)

mania, ephemeral (e-fem'ēr-al) See *mania transitoria.*

mania errabunda (mà'nē-à er-rà-boon'dà) *Obs.* An impulsive form of insanity, in which the patient wanders from home apparently without aim.

mania, flagellation (mā'ni-à) *Obs.* Malleation.

mania, grumbling 'If in these cases the excitement is moderated, the *grumbling* forms of mania perhaps arise, to the slightest phases of which Hecker has specially drawn attention. The patients, indeed, display exalted self-consciousness, are pretentious and high-flown, but by no means of cheerful mood; they rather appear dissatisfied, insufferable, perhaps even a little anxious. They have something to find fault with in everything, feel themselves on every occasion badly treated, get wretched food, cannot hold out in the dreadful surroundings, cannot sleep in the miserable beds, cannot have social intercourse with the other patients.' (Kraepelin, E. *Manic-Depressive Insanity and Paranoia,* tr. by Barclay, R.M., Livingstone, Edinburgh, 1921)

mania, histrionic (his-tri-on'ik) *Obs.* The syndrome in which the patient assumes the part of an actor.

mania, homicidal; homicidomania 'In popular, and sometimes in medical phraseology, "homicidal mania" means any kind of mental disease where there is an attempt or desire on the part of a patient to kill. But, as you have seen, the homicidal desire may occur in melancholia, and is often associated with the suicidal feeling. As we shall see, it may occur as an uncomplicated impulse, not accompanied by depression or exaltation of mind, and it then stands as one of the varieties of impulsive insanity.' (Clouston, T.S. *Clinical Lectures on Mental Diseases,* 6th ed., Churchill, London, 1904)

mania, hysterical *Obs.* A manic syndrome in a hysterical individual.

mania, incendiary Pyromania.

mania, inhibited This expression, used by

Kraepelin, refers to the clinical state characterized by flight of ideas, cheerful mood, and psychomotor inhibition. 'The patients of this kind are of more exultant mood, occasionally somewhat irritable, distractible, inclined to jokes; when addressed they easily fall into chattering talk with flight of ideas and numerous clang associations, but remain in outward behaviour conspicuously quiet, lie still in bed, only now and then throw out a remark or laugh to themselves. It appears, however, as if a great inward tension, as a rule, existed, as the patients may suddenly become very violent. Formerly I classified this "inhibited mania" with manic stupor; I think, however, that it may be separated from that on the ground of the flight of ideas which here appears distinctly.' (Kraepelin, E. *Manic-Depressive Insanity and Paranoia*, tr. by Barclay, R.M., Livingstone, Edinburgh, 1921)

mania, metaphysical *Obs.* Folie du doute; insanity of doubt.

mania mitis (mȧ′nē-ȧ mē′tēs) (L. 'mild madness') This is an older term, designating what is today called *hypomania.* 'The slightest forms of manic excitement are usually called "hypomania," mania mitis, mitissima, also, but inappropriately, *mania sine delirio.*' (Kraepelin, E. *Manic-Depressive Insanity and Paranoia*, tr. by Barclay, R.M., Livingstone, Edinburgh, 1921)

mania, muscular (mā′ni-ȧ) This expression is now obsolete. 'That was an extreme and pure sample of a symptom which we see commonly enough in mania, viz., automatic coördinated movements that are ordinarily voluntary, but result evidently from morbid exaltation of function in the highest motor centres in the convolutions. It is a *muscular mania,* the intellectual and volitional power being comparatively intact, but the highest ideo-motor centres being paralysed.' (Clouston, T.S. *Clinical Lectures on Mental Diseases*, 6th ed., Churchill, London, 1904) He refers to exaggerated motor activity.

mania, periodic See *mania.*

maniaphobia (mā-ni-ȧ-fō′bi-ȧ) Fear of insanity.

mania postmenstrualis (mȧ′nē-ȧ pôst-men-stroo-a-lēs) *Obs.* Post-menstrual insanity of a maniacal form.

mania, puerperal (mā′ni-ȧ) 'People very often speak of "puerperal mania" in the sense of a particular form of insanity produced exclusively by the puerperium, but this view can only be maintained today within very narrow limits. Where mania really appears in the puerperal state, it is, like every other kind of mania, only a link in the chain of attacks of maniacal-depressive insanity. The puerperium cannot therefore be regarded as the cause, but only as the last impulse to the outbreak of the disease.' (Kraepelin, E. *Lectures on Clinical Psychiatry*, 3rd ed., revised and edited by Johnstone, T.H., Ballière, Tindall & Cox, London, 1913) A variety of *puerperal psychosis.*

mania, reactive Bleuler says that there is no condition known as *reactive mania,* though a milder state akin to it, *reactive exaltation,* is described. The latter state, resembling that of *hypomania,* is induced by some external cause and ceases when the cause is removed.

mania, reasoning See *insanity, reasoning.*

mania, recurrent See *mania.*

mania, religious See *paranoia, amorous.*

mania senilis (mȧ′nē-ȧ se-nē′lēs) (L. 'old-age madness') See *melancholia senilis.*

mania sine delirio (mȧ′nē-ȧ sē′ne dā-lē′rē-ō) (L. 'mania without delirium') Mania mitis.

mania, stuporous See *mania.*

mania transitoria (mȧ′nē-ȧ trȧn-zē-tō′-rē-ȧ) (L. 'passing, temporary madness') 'This term is used to describe a somewhat rare form of maniacal exaltation, which comes on suddenly, is usually sharp in its character, and is accompanied by incoherence, partial or complete unconsciousness of familiar surroundings, and sleeplessness. An attack may last from an hour up to a few days.' (Clouston, T.S. *Clinical Lectures on Mental Diseases*, 6th ed., Churchill, London, 1904) It was also called *ephemeral mania.*

mania, tropical (mā′ni-ȧ) A general term for a variety of psychiatric disorders occurring in the tropics; save in specific instances, such as heat stroke, it is not known what role, if any, heat plays in the disorders.

mania, wandering See *wanderlust; impulse, wandering.*

manic-depressive See *psychosis, manic-depressive.*

manie de perfection (mȧ-nē′ dē per-fek-syawN') (F. 'perfection mania') The compulsive tendencies of certain individuals to achieve perfection in everything they do, or in anything that is done for them. Everything in the life of these individuals has to be 100 per cent moral, 100 per cent good, 100 per cent clean, 100 per cent efficient, 100 per cent perfect. This constant preoccupation haunts the individual in every aspect of his life. According to Stekel the manie de perfection 'is a direct consequence of the patient's desire to strengthen his supposedly insecure position in life.' (Stekel, W. *Compulsion and Doubt,* Liveright, New York, 1949)

manie de rumination (rü-mē-na-syawN') (F. 'rumination mania') This term was introduced in psychiatry by Dr. Pierre Janet to describe the morbid tendency to recall to mind and consider past events again and again. One may say that in the neurotic the events constantly resuscitated in the mind are, in general, adverse or painful experiences. It seems that there is a quality of remorse in the repeated rememoration of the past. The patient seems to tell himself: 'If I had done this instead of that, things would have been much better.' (Stekel, W. *Compulsion and Doubt,* Liveright, New York, 1949)

manie raisonnante (re-zo-nant') (F. 'reasoning mania') See *insanity, reasoning.*

maniodes (man-i-ō'dēz) *Obs.* Maniacal; ferine, brutal, beastly.

manipulanda (mà-nē-poo-làn'dà) See *intelligence.*

mannerism A gesture or other form of expression usually peculiar to a given individual. It gains significance in psychiatry when it acquires the value of a symptom. Mannerisms are particularly common among psychiatric patients. Thus, a psychoneurotic individual has to perform every act six times; another must never look at the one to whom he is speaking. Patients with schizophrenia exhibit a variety of mannerisms. One patient must constantly describe a rotatory movement about the abdomen with his hands; another must take one short step for every three average paces; a third patient must always sway three times before he begins an act.

Some authorities believe that 'a mannerism differs from a stereotypy in that it is not so monotonously repeated, and is more in keeping with the personality.' (Hender-

son, D.K. and Gillespie, R.D. *A Text-Book of Psychiatry,* 4th ed., Oxford University Press, London, 1936)

manustupration (man-ū-stū-prā'shun) An older term for *masturbation* (q.v.).

MAO *Monoamine oxidase* (q.v.).

marasmus nervosus (mà-ràz'moos nervō'zoos) (Neo L. 'nervous emaciation') *Obs.* Neurasthenia.

Marburg, Otto (1874–) (màr'boork) Austrian neurologist.

marche à petits pas (màrsh á pē-tē-pà') (F. 'short-step walking') This is a disturbance in gait in which the patient takes very short steps. The condition may be observed in cerebral arteriosclerosis and striatal rigidity.

Marchiafava-Bignami disease A rare neuropsychiatric syndrome associated with alcoholism; the essential pathology is central necrosis of the corpus callosum and sometimes of the anterior commissure. This syndrome appears most typically in chronic alcoholics who are addicted to Italian red wine; when the central necrosis begins, the patient develops an acute psychotic picture consisting of excitement, ataxia or apraxia, disorientation, and confusion. With progression (and presumably due to spread of the process to the cingulate gyri), the clinical picture changes markedly: the patient becomes totally apathetic, aboulic, quiet, and completely inattentive; he appears devoid of all conation, shows akinetic mutism, and may develop hemiplegia or hemiparesis. Once this stage is reached, death is the usual end-result. It is generally believed that alcohol per se is not the cause of this syndrome, but rather that it is due to metallic impurities found in wine as a result of processing.

Marcuse, Max (1877–) (màr-kōō'ze) German sexologist.

Marcus Gunn sign (Marcus Gunn, contemporary British surgeon.) The raising of a ptosed lid on opening the mouth and moving the jaw to the opposite side.

margin, conscious See *fringe.*

Marie's ataxia See *ataxia, Marie's hereditary cerebellar.*

Marie's disease (Pierre Marie, French physician, 1853–1940) See *acromegaly.*

marihuana, marijuana (mä-rē-hwä'nä) A variety of cannabis indica obtained from the flowering tops of the Indian hemp plant, which grows freely in all parts of the United States and Mexico; also known as hashish and bhang. Marihuana is most commonly taken in the form of 'reefers'— shorter and thicker than the usual cigarette and wrapped in brown paper. Smoking two or three reefers gives the desired effect: a dreamy state of partial consciousness in which ideas are disconnected, uncontrollable, and plentiful; at times, euphoria and an excited joyousness, at other times a moody reverie or panic and fear of death; imagination runs riot, and perception is crowded and disturbed; a peculiar distortion of time, so that minutes seem to be hours, and of space, which is broadened so that near objects seem far away; vivid, pleasant hallucinations, often with a sexual coloring; loss of discriminatory ability so that a three-piece honky-tonk band may seem like a symphony orchestra. Under the influence of marihuana behavior is impulsive, mood is elevated, and random ideas are quickly translated into action. Prolonged use in those with a psychopathic personality may result in a certain degree of mental deterioration, but no positive relationship between violent crime and the use of the drug has ever been demonstrated. Marihuana, as also cocaine and peyote, does not produce physical dependence; hence there is not the great drive to get these drugs as is seen with opiates. These drugs, like alcohol, merely release inhibitions and thereby expose the basic inadequate personality of the habitual user. Treatment consists of abrupt withdrawal.

Marin Amat syndrome See *syndrome, Marin Amat.*

marriage, psychiatric aspects of Nearly one-half of the United States have laws whose interest is to prevent persons with mental disorder to marry. In some cases, issuance of a license is interdicted; in others, performance of the ceremony is forbidden. Most states afford no means of enforcing such laws, however, and the question of legality of marriage typically arises only when one of the parties concerned seeks annulment of the marriage contract. The validity of the marriage can be questioned by the 'incompetent' spouse on the ground that he was incapable of understanding what he was doing. By statute in England, and in most of the United States, marriage may be voided on the ground of mental unsoundness. Similarly, England and more than half of the United States consider 'incurable insanity' as grounds for divorce.

marriage, therapeutic (ther-à-pū'tik) As an adjunct to their treatment certain probably well-intentioned, but misguided, physicians actually advise marriage for their patients. Generally, this is rationalized in the following fashion: it functions as an impetus or catalyzer for the patient, forcing the emergence of emotional maturity. As a rule, these patients have presented themselves for treatment for the symptomatic physical expression of disorders of neurotic psychogenic origin, usually centering around various forms of psychogenic impotence in the male, and frigidity and sexual aversion in the female. When such individuals, upon the well-meant advice of physicians, actively carry out the counsel to marry, the specific character-testing intimacies of the marital situation, particularly in the sexual sphere, soon precipitate the symptoms of their characterological emotional inadequacies. As a therapeutic medium the advice 'to marry' is commonly either contraindicated or unnecessary.

The best guarantee for the development of marital problems is for two immature personalities to 'fall in love' and marry. Contrariwise, when two mature people find each other attractive and marry there is the best chance for marital happiness. One of the criteria of minimal maturity for marriage is for people to assume the responsibility of their own choice, and to marry 'under their own steam.' (Weiss, E., and English, O.S. *Psychosomatic Medicine*, 2nd ed., Saunders, Philadelphia and London, 1949)

masculine attitude in female neurotics Adler uses this term to indicate the masculine protest against feminine or apparently feminine stirrings and sensations occurring in the female neurotic individual. She manifests unconscious tendencies to play the masculine (domineering, active, cruel) role with the use of all available means.

masculine protest See *protest, masculine.*

masculinity While *maleness* primarily relates to the proper sex chromosome structure of XY individuals, *masculinity* is preferably understood as an attribute of a male individual exhibiting the typical and well-developed *secondary* sex characteristics of a man (see *sex determination*).

mask Stekel uses this term to mean disguise: 'Less known are other masks of homosexuality which I now mention. The love of old women (gerontophilia) and passion for children often covers a homosexual tendency.' (Stekel, W. *Bi-Sexual Love,* tr. by van Teslaar, J.S., Badger, Boston, 1922) See *persona.*

masked hysteria See *hysteria, masked.*

masochism (maz′ok-iz'm) (From Leopold von Sacher Masoch (1836–95), an Austrian novelist, whose characters indulge in all kinds of sex perversions deriving sexual pleasure from being cruelly treated) When sexual satisfaction depends upon the subject himself 'suffering pain, ill-treatment and humiliation' (Freud), the condition is known as masochism.

Krafft-Ebing defined masochism as 'a peculiar perversion of the psychical *vita sexualis* in which the individual affected, in sexual feeling and thought, is controlled by the idea of being completely and unconditionally subject to the will of a person of the opposite sex, of being treated by this person as by a master, humiliated and abused. This idea is colored by sexual feeling; the masochist lives in fancies in which he creates situations of this kind, and he often attempts to realize them.' (Krafft-Ebing, R.v. *Psychopathia Sexualis,* Login, New York, 1908, p. 115)

Havelock Ellis notes that Stefanowsky termed it *passivism.*

Freud originally believed that masochism was always secondary and represented a turning of sadism against the ego under the influence of guilt. Later, however, applying his theories of Thanatos or the Nirvana principle, he differentiated three types of masochism:

1. *erotogenic* or *primary masochism,* when masochism is a requisite condition for sexual gratification. The self-destructive tendencies arising from the death instinct are to a large extent disposed of early in life by displacement onto objects in the outer world; this is the origin of mastery, the will to power, and true sadism. The part which is not so disposed of remains as the original erotogenic masochism, elements of which can be traced through all the developmental stages of the libido: oral (fear of being devoured), anal (desire to be beaten by the father),

phallic (castration phantasies), and genital (in situations characteristic of womanhood, the passive part in coitus and the act of giving birth).

2. *feminine masochism,* as an expression of feminine nature.

3. *moral masochism,* when there is a need for punishment arising from unconscious needs relating to re-sexualization of the parental introjects and reactivation of the Oedipus complex. The basic desire is to have intercourse with the father passively, and through regressive distortion this becomes a desire to be beaten by the father. The moral masochist must act against his own interests, even to the point of destroying himself, in order to provoke punishment from authority figures. Asceticism is related to moral masochism, for the mortification is sexualized and the act of mortifying becomes a distorted expression of the blocked sexuality.

Wilhelm Reich agreed that behind the masochist's behavior lay a desire to provoke authority figures, but he disagreed that this was in order to bribe the superego or to execute a dreaded punishment. Rather, he maintained, this grandiose provocation represented a defense against punishment and anxiety by substituting a milder punishment and by placing the provoked authority figure in such a light as to justify the masochist's reproach, 'See how badly you treat me.' Behind such a provocation is a deep disappointment in love, a disappointment of the masochist's excessive demand for love based on the fear of being left alone.

More recently, B. Berliner has emphasized the role of the infantile love object in the genesis of masochism; he regards the masochistic attitude as a bid for the affection of a hating love object. 'Masochistic suffering represents in the unconscious the original personal love object that once gave suffering. Masochism is the sadism of the love object fused with the libido of the subject.' ('The Role of Object Relations in Moral Masochism,' *Psychoanalytic Quarterly* 27: 38–56, 1958)

masochism, actual See *instinct, death.*

masochism, erotogenic (ē-rō-tō-jen′ik) Of the three types of masochism described by Freud, erotogenic masochism is 'the lust of pain.' It is the form commonly implied by the term masochism. See *masochism.*

masochism, feminine Freud says that masochism 'comes under our observation in three shapes: as a condition under which sexual excitation may be roused; as an expression of feminine nature; and as a norm of behavior. According to this one may distinguish an *erotogenic*, a *feminine*, and a *moral* type of masochism.' (Freud, S. *Collected Papers*, vol. 2, tr. by Riviere, J., Leonard and Virginia Woolf and The Institute of Psychoanalysis, London, 1924–25) See *masochism*.

masochism, ideal ('mental, psychic.') Usually the term refers to injury to oneself from the physical point of view. When, however, the injury is psychical, Freud speaks of *ideal masochism*.

'Such people are called "ideal" masochists if they seek pleasure not in the bodily pain which may be inflicted upon them, but in humiliation and psychic chastisement.' (Freud, S. *The Interpretation of Dreams*, 3rd ed., tr. by Brill, A.A., Macmillan, New York, 1933) Some use the term *moral masochism* in the same sense.

masochism, mass By this term Reik denotes 'the mixture of (a) renunciation of one's own power and (b) enjoyment of its being used by proxy,' such as may be seen in the enthusiasm and devotion shown by the masses to a dictator, who completely dominates the will of the individual. In such cases the 'masses are partially exercising their will by impersonating it in that of a single man,' their hero. At the same time, the tyrannical will of such a cruel dictator demands hardships and sacrifices of the masses, which they would be unable to bear if they did not consider him to be their own idealized image. (Reik, T. *Masochism in Modern Man*, Farrar and Rinehart, New York, 1941)

masochism, mental See *masochism, ideal*.

masochism, moral Moral masochism, 'a norm of behavior' is 'in certain respects the most important form in which masochism appears.' (Freud, S. *Collected Papers*, vol. 2, tr. by Riviere, J., Leonard and Virginia Woolf and The Institute of Psychoanalysis, London, 1924–25) See *masochism*.

masochism, primal See *instinct, death*.

masochism, psychic (sī'kik) See *masochism, ideal*.

masochism, secondary During growth the main part of sadism or the death-instinct is directed outwardly; the portion that remains in the individual is called primary sadism or (now being directed inward upon the subject himself) masochism. Under given conditions, for example, in states of deep depression the objectivated sadism is withdrawn from objects, returning to the individual; that is, it is introjected. This involves the process of regression to its earlier condition. 'It then provides that secondary masochism which supplements the original one.' (Freud, S. *Collected Papers*, vol. 2, tr. by Riviere, J., Leonard and Virginia Woolf and The Institute of Psychoanalysis, London, 1924–25) See *masochism*.

masochism, social This term is employed to denote a characteristic subordinate attitude toward life, forcing the individual to a submissive and passive behavior, which enables him to stand defeats, privations, and misfortune. Such a situation can be described as a 'giving up' attitude. (Reik, T. *Masochism in Modern Man*, Farrar and Rinehart, New York, 1941)

masochism, verbal A psychiatric situation in which the masochistic individual who craves to hear insulting or humiliating words derives sexual excitement by imagining himself abused or insulted verbally. A certain choice, succession, or emphasis of words and sentences seems important for the sexual excitement. Dialogues during the masochistic phantasy are quite frequent. These imagined situations 'are frequently maintained for years with little or no change, and yet remain exciting. Alterations are usually restricted to trifling displacements and substitutions of persons, times and places, while the main theme, if it may be called so, is adhered to.' (Reik, T. *Masochism in Modern Man*, Farrar and Rinehart, New York, 1941)

massa intermedia (mȧs'ȧ ĕn-tẽr-mād'ē-ȧ) See *thalamus*.

massotherapy (mas-ō-ther'ȧ-pē) Treatment by massage.

mastery, oral Mastery in which the mouth is the organ utilized in implementing the mastery. Mastery is a technique which the infant utilizes in adapting itself to its environment when seeking to control (master) it. 'In the fourth month of life the mastery technique consists of seeing an object, grasping it, and directing it to the mouth. This may be called the phase of oral mastery.' (Kardiner, A., and Spiegel,

L. *War Stress and Neurotic Illness,* Hoeber, New York, 1947) See *instinct, mastery.*

mastigophobia (mas-ti-gō-fō′bi-à) Fear of flogging.

mastodynia (mas-tō-din′i-à) A type of intercostal neuralgia in which there is pain and tenderness of the breast and often hyperesthesia of the nipples.

masturbation (mas-tĕr-bā′shun) The original meaning of manual friction of the genitals (penis or clitoris) for purposes of experiencing pleasurable sensations still persists. It is recognized, however, that genital excitation by oneself may be achieved by any number of intermediary agents which all serve the same end. The expression *psychic masturbation* is sometimes used to refer to solitary genital excitation (with ejaculation), stimulated by the mind.

'It is recognized that all children masturbate during the infantile period, most do during adolescence, and some do during the latency period. Masturbation, then, can be considered psychologically normal during childhood, and is a major avenue for the discharge of instinctual tension. Under present cultural conditions, masturbation can also be considered psychologically normal during adolescence, and to some extent even in adulthood when gratification of a physical and emotional relationship with a member of the opposite sex is not possible.

'Kinsey finds that masturbation occurs in 92 per cent of American males, and these figures are in line with other surveys and estimates both in this country and in Europe.

'Those adolescents who do not masturbate during puberty show regularly in analysis an especially deep repression of infantile masturbation, threats about which have overwhelmed them with guilt and fear; such patients, incidentally, have a poor prognosis in psychotherapy.

'Certainly sexual gratification is important to the individual, yet the healthy person can tolerate a temporary lack within certain limits and can find substitute gratification along the line of sublimation; it is only the disturbed, neurotic patient who is unable to tolerate any diminution in or postponement of gratification without becoming depressed, and such patients use masturbation to prevent potential depression and to remove already existing depression. The conflicts which the adolescent has over his masturbatory activity are often solved by reaction formations; if he is successful, these contribute to the formation of valuable character traits; if unsuccessful, he must find substitutes for masturbation, or the masturbation itself becomes a neurotic symptom. Thus the control and inhibition of instinctual impulses, at least within certain limits, may well be salutary for the development of character and personality.

'Probably the most important consequence of masturbation is the guilt which typically accompanies it, and the struggle to defend oneself against it which may last for years and adsorb onto itself all the energy of the psychic system. And it is surprising to note how very incompletely the adolescent can be reassured about the dangers of masturbation, to which he ascribes almost every conceivable ill— pimples, insanity, stooped shoulders, weakness, loss of manly vigor, weak eyes, ulcers, impotence, feeblemindedness, cancer, to name only a few. Freud tended to the view that neurasthenia could follow upon excessive masturbation; it is nowadays felt that it would be more correct to say that neurasthenia is an outcome of insufficient orgasm—that is, if anxieties and guilt disturb the satisfactory character of the masturbation.

'It appears, then, that harmful physical consequences may possibly follow masturbation, but that these effects and the likelihood of their occurrence have been greatly exaggerated, and that the chief harmful consequence is in the psychic sphere and pertains to the feeling of guilt over masturbation. When one deals with the adolescent in conflict about the practice, however, he is soon aware that the young boy is unable to accept this benign approach. Instead, he has a deep need to believe that masturbation is a terrible thing and he strongly resists enlightenment about its harmlessness. This is because the conscious masturbatory phantasies are distorted derivatives of unconscious Oedipus phantasies, and if the adolescent did indeed believe that masturbation is harmless he would have to resurrect these phantasies and would have to face the Oedipal desires which are responsible for the guilt.' (Campbell, R.J. 'Sexual Development and Pathology in the Second Decade,' *Proceedings,* 2nd Institute for Clergy on Problems in Pastoral

Psychology, Fordham University, New York, 1957)

masturbation, compulsive An ill-defined term used with various meanings by different authors. Some use it synonymously with habitual masturbation or pathological masturbation, i.e. when masturbation is preferred to sexual intercourse or when masturbation is used, not occasionally to relieve sexual tension, but so frequently as to indicate a disturbed capacity for sexual satisfaction. Others apply the term to the constant impulse to masturbate which is seen in some children, who stimulate their genitals frequently, without regard to their environment, and usually without accompanying sexual erotic phantasies. More properly, the term is confined to repetitive masturbatory activity performed without adequate sexual feelings or without any accompanying sexual feelings. 'Symptoms that were created for the purpose of warding off masturbation, through penetration by the warded-off forces, eventually may be replaced by masturbation. A masturbation of this kind does not bring pleasure. The lack of satisfaction increases the striving for satisfaction. The protection-forgiveness of the gods, which would make a relaxing satisfaction possible, may be sought with the same aggressive fury by masturbating, with which it is sought by the gambler in his gambling. And like gambling, masturbation also may be performed for the purpose of punishment, being thought of as an equivalent of castration. The ego demonstrates its self-destruction equivalent to its superego, asking for forgiveness by ingratiation and by stubbornness. And the superego behaves as the gods did who punished King Midas' greediness by ruining him through the fulfillment of his wishes. The sexuality the ego wanted is granted, but in a painful and devastating manner. . . . Instinctual behavior of this kind may also represent a desperate and inadequate attempt to discharge, in a sexual way, tensions of any kind. The act is carried out not only to obtain pleasure or to achieve punishment but also to get rid of an unbearable painful tension and to be relieved of a state of depression. In the same way that the drug may become insufficient in addictions and an ever increasing amount of the drug is needed, so the orgastic impotence in such cases may require more and more of the pseudo-

sexual acts. In severe cases of "sexual addictions," sexuality loses its specific function and becomes an unsuccessful nonspecific protection against stimuli.' (Fenichel, O. *The Psychoanalytic Theory of Neurosis,* Norton, New York, 1945)

Used in a more general sense as synonymous with habitual, pathological, or overfrequent masturbation, or masturbatory pseudo-sexuality, the term compulsive masturbation implies a disturbance in the capacity for satisfaction. Such cases are often based on: (1) conflicts over hostility and aggressiveness, especially in those who are afraid to manifest overt defiance; or (2) conflicts over the expectation of punishment, for which masturbation may represent a substitute; or (3) conflicts over 'perverse' sexual impulses, where masturbation is felt to afford a higher pleasure than can be achieved in reality; or (4) attempts to forestall threatened depression or to remove existing depression, which typically is related to unsatisfied yearnings for love and narcissistic supplies; or (5) use of masturbation to withdraw from reality in those who are neurotically inhibited, shy and afraid of interpersonal relationships. (Campbell, R.J. 'Habitual Masturbation,' *Proceedings,* 2nd Inst. for the Clergy on Problems in Pastoral Psychology, Fordham University, New York, 1957)

masturbation, habitual See *masturbation, compulsive.*

masturbation, insanity of See *insanity, masturbational.*

masturbation, larval See *onanism, larval.*

masturbation, normal The rubbing or manipulation of the genitals by the hand for the purpose of obtaining pleasurable sensations. In a more general sense, masturbation includes 'any stimulation of any part of the person's own body for the purpose of obtaining pleasurable sensations.' This widespread practice, common among children and adolescents, is said to be more prevalent among boys than among girls. When deprived of a satisfactory sexual life, many adults masturbate; married couples separated for long periods and persons prohibited from sexual contact are often driven to masturbation. (Pearson, G.H.J. *Emotional Disorders of Children,* Norton, New York, 1949)

masturbation, passive An older expression for fellatio.

'. . . in other cases, passive masturbation, or *ejaculatio viri dilecti in ore.*' (Krafft-Ebing, R.v. *Psychopathia Sexualis,* Login, New York, 1908)

masturbation, pathological (pa-thō-loj'i-kal) See *masturbation, compulsive.*

masturbation, psychic (sī'kik) When an individual's genital excitement results in an orgasm without the intervention of any physical agents, but only by psychic stimuli arising from the individual himself or herself, the phenomenon is known as psychic masturbation.

masturbation, repressed A psychoanalytic term referring to the almost universal fate of early primary infantile masturbation activity. These urges become repressed under the censorious and critical forces of external parental admonitions, coupled with the intrapsychic erection of analogous forces (parent images, 'superego,' or conscience) within the child. The pleasure-seeking masturbatory urges succumb to repression by the desire for 'goodness,' 'cleanness,' parental love, and approval. The repression of early infantile masturbation can remain the prototype for a guilt-ridden attitude toward all subsequent pleasure-seekings of a more adult nature. The guilt-feeling concerning enjoyment and the need to justify one's right to pleasure often stem from these early masturbatory conflicts.

masturbation, symbolic The displacement of thinly disguised masturbatory activity upon bodily parts and organs which function as symbolic objects substituting for the phallus-clitoris, or penis, even if they give no direct orgastic gratification. Such symbolic masturbation can consist of nail-biting, playing with hangnails, pulling the cuticle, twisting the coat sleeve or handkerchief corners, pulling at buttons, twisting and plucking hairs or hair strands, fingering nose, ear-lobe, or inserting of finger into nose, mouth, or ear. These symbolic substitutive masturbatory activities are frequently the foci for analytic interest and for interpretation as they appear in the course of a psychoanalysis. They also appear as symptomatic behavior in the psychopathology of everyday ('normal') life.

materialization, hysterical (mà-tēr-i-al-i-zā'shun, his-ter'i-kal) A term used by Ferenczi to characterize the process through which hysterical individuals convert their repressed phantasies into alterations of physical functions.

One of the prerequisites for the development of conversions is the turning from reality to phantasy, 'a replacement of real sexual objects by the phantasy representatives of infantile objects.' Thus the daydreams of hysterical individuals are frequently connected with repressed instinctual impulses. Sometimes when the daydreams come too close to the repressed instinctual impulses which they satisfy, they, too, must be repressed. In the final step, the repressed phantasies return in a distorted form as conversion symptoms. Thus the repressed thoughts undergo a 'hysterical materialization,' finding 'their substitute expression in a material change of physical functions.' The particular alterations occurring in physical functions symbolize certain specific memories and phantasies, determined by the patient's history and centering around the repressed instinctual demands and the anxieties they cause. Sometimes the conversions can be analyzed in the same way as dreams and the underlying phantasies uncovered, for often the same distortion mechanisms are used. (Fenichel, O. *The Psychoanalytic Theory of Neurosis,* Norton, New York, 1945)

matronism, precocious In constitutional medicine, this term refers to a dysgenital syndrome in young girls, which owes its name to the physical and sexual forms of a mature woman (matron's body) occurring in them at such a very early age. The particular characteristics of this condition apply to the size and form of the pendulous breasts, the breadth of the shoulders, pelvis and thighs, and the adiposity of the legs and ankles. The face also has an adult expression, the menstruation appears prematurely, and the temperament is vivacious and irritable.

The morphological basis of this anomaly probably consists of a pluriglandular imbalance, in which follicular hyperovarism and cortical hyperadrenalism predominate.

mattoid (mat'oid) A person of erratic mind, a compound of genius and fool. Eugenio Tanzi used the term for that subgroup of paranoia characterized by abstract delusions, garrulousness, and feelings of persecution. These patients have no hallucinations, but are erotic and ambitious types. G. Lombroso used the term mattoid for cranks, eccentrics, etc. who are not overtly psychotic but are rather on the borderline of a psychosis.

maturation (mach-ū-rā'shun) In genetics, the term denotes the cell process (in sexual reproduction) which leads to the formation of gametes in the gonads.

Following the multiplication of the reproductive cells by repeated cell division of the ordinary duplicating type, some of these cells cease to divide by ordinary division and become the *primary spermatocytes* and *primary oöcytes* in the respective sexes. When these cells mature, they grow in size, and the homologous chromosomes pair in them.

Two cell divisions follow to complete maturation: (1) the *equation* division in which the chromosomes are duplicated as in ordinary cell division, (2) the *reduction* division, in which the chromosomes are merely separated so that the number of chromosomes per cell is reduced to half (see *meiosis*).

maturation, anticipatory, principle of Carmichael uses this term in proposing a tentative generalization that almost all functions in a wide variety of organisms can be elicited by experimental means at some time prior to the spontaneous appearance of the function in the normal life cycle of the organism. This principle intimates that such functions are fully developed before they are needed by the organism.

mature *Genet.* The term describes the reproductive cells which have undergone the process of *maturation* or *meiosis.*

McDougall, William (1871–1938) American psychologist and psychiatrist.

McNaughton See *rule, M'Naghten.*

mean Arithmetic average.

mechanism (mek'ä-niz'm) In psychiatry this term designates the mode of action performed by a psychic structure. For instance, repression is called a mental mechanism; it refers to functions of psychic structures and to the forces that give rise to them. One of the functions of the ego is to repress unconscious elements that are unwanted in consciousness. The various activities involved in the repression, from the time that the unwanted impulse makes itself felt or known in consciousness until the ego represses, constitute a mechanism.

Healy, Bronner, and Bowers list 17 dynamisms or mechanisms: displacement, transference, symbolization, condensation, unconscious phantasy, repression, reaction-formation (reversal-formation), projection, isolation, undoing, conversion, introjection, identification, sublimation, rationalization, idealization, and dream-work.

'The fundamental regulating mechanisms of mental processes are the tendencies to seek pleasure by bringing about a relief from psychical tension, and to avoid pain by preventing accumulation of psychical energy.' (Jones, E. *Papers on Psycho-Analysis,* 4th ed., Wood, Baltimore, 1938)

The term mechanism is also used in a less specialized sense to refer to the way in which any machine or system operates; it is also used to refer to the philosophical doctrine that human behavior is wholly explicable in terms of the laws of physical mechanics.

mechanism, compensatory 'These persons [psychoneurotics] who are intolerant of themselves often develop a compensatory attitude of intolerance of others. It is very common to find that persons who are overbearing, over-certain, almost offensive in manner, are underneath shy, sensitive, and fearful of their own inadequacies. Frequently they will criticize harshly in others the very faults which they themselves display.' (Kraines, S.H. *The Therapy of the Neuroses and Psychoses,* Lea & Febiger, Philadelphia, 1948)

mechanism, flight The ego's (or psychic structure's) mode of procedure to escape from unbearable suffering. 'I pointed out one or two other methods by which the ego attempts to escape from the sufferings connected with the depressive position, namely either the flight to internal good objects (which may lead to severe psychosis) or the flight to external good objects (with the possible outcome of neurosis).' (Klein, M. *Contributions to Psycho-analysis,* 1921–1945, The Hogarth Press, London, 1948)

mechanism, homogenic (hō-mō-jen'ik) A mechanism described by Burrow in which *part-impressions* of an object are substituted for the actual contact with the object itself, and *part-feelings* or *affects* are substituted for the total feelings with which the organism natively responds to the object as a whole. This mechanism has to do with the picture-forming processes associated with inter-individual affects. Contrasted with central constant, orthogenic mechanism. Synonyms: graphogenic system, graphonomic system, index-system. (Burrow, T. *The Biology of Human Conflict,* Macmillan, New York, 1937, p. 297)

mechanism, mote-beam Ichheiser's term for that distortion of social perception wherein the individual is exaggeratedly aware of the presence of an undesirable trait in a minority group although oblivious to its presence in himself.

mechanism, orthogenic (or-thō-jen'ik) As described by Burrow this mechanism refers to the organism's total co-ordinative function. It preserves the balance of the organism as a whole in its relation to the total environment. Contrasted with homogenic mechanism. (Burrow, T. *The Biology of Human Conflict,* Macmillan, New York, 1937, pp. 296–7)

mechanism, scapegoat A term used to denote the mental state of a patient who has strong antisocial feelings and looks for incidents on which he can displace, project, and rationalize his hostilities. (Burton, A., and Harris, R.E., eds. *Case Histories in Clinical and Abnormal Psychology,* Harper, New York, 1947)

mechanophobia (mek-à-nō-fō'bi-à) Fear of machinery.

median (mē'di-an) If all items constituting a series with respect to any measurable character are arrayed from smallest to largest, in order, the median is that value which will divide the total frequency in half, with just as many below as there will be above.

Example: Five individuals are aged 15, 20, 22, 25, and 26 years, respectively. The median age is 22, since 2 are younger and 2 are older.

medicine, constitutional That branch of medical science which occupies itself with the study of the heredito-constitutional elements governing the biological equilibrium of human organisms and controlling their resistance or susceptibility to disease (see *constitution*).

Its aim is a most comprehensive and synthetic conception of the natural history of Man, while its research procedure consists mainly of devising methods for classifying human beings according to both their disease potentialities and capacities for adaption, and of establishing correlations between types of human morphology and the success or failure of these types in the struggle for existence. 'The evidence

of the outcome of this reaction between individual and environment is expressed in terms of health, physical disease, insanity, criminality, and other less sharply defined inadequacies both physical and mental.' (Draper, G. *Disease and the Man,* Macmillan, New York, 1930)

Another definition of the main purpose of constitutional medicine is that of Pende, stressing the evaluation of *correlational principles,* 'according to which the various combinations of organs and organic fluids and the special relationship or anatomical and functional correlations between the parts of the body, which determine the different physical and mental constitutions, *vary* according to the characteristics that are dominant in the interorganic equilibrium.' (Pende, N. *Constitutional Inadequacies,* tr. by Naccarati, S., Lea & Febiger, Philadelphia, 1928)

The four basic categories or 'panels,' which are distinguished by Draper as the primary objects of constitutional investigation, are 'the hereditary unit characters found in the domains of anatomy, physiology, psychology, and immunity.' See *panels, personality.*

medicine, physical See *physical medicine.*

medulla oblongata (me-doo'là ob-lon-gà'-tà) The pyramid-shaped portion of the brain-stem lying between the spinal cord and the pons. The ventral portion contains the pyramidal decussation; the lateral portion contains the olive; the dorsal portion contains the funiculus gracilis and the funiculus cuneatus. The medulla also contains the nucleus of the hypoglossal nerve, the nucleus ambiguus (somatic motor nucleus of glossopharyngeal, vagus, and spinal accessory nerves), the dorsal motor nucleus, and the sensory nucleus of the vagus nerve, and the dorsal and ventral cochlear nuclei. The medulla oblongata is sometimes called the bulb; syndromes resulting from lesions of the medulla are therefore known as bulbal syndromes, whose characteristic symptoms are due to involvement of the various tracts passing through the medulla and particularly to involvement of the nuclei of cranial nerves IX, X, XI, and XII.

megalo- (meg'à-lō-) combining form meaning big, large, great, from Gr. *mégas, -álon,* big, great, akin to L. *magnus.*

megalomania (meg-à-lō-mā'ni-à) A type of delusion in which the subject considers himself possessed of greatness. He may believe himself to be Christ, God, Napoleon, etc. He may think that he is everybody and everything. He is lawyer, physician, clergyman, merchant, prince, generalissimo, ace athlete in all divisions of sports, etc.

'The question arises: What is the fate of the libido when withdrawn from external objects in schizophrenia? The megalomania characteristic of these conditions affords a clue here. It has doubtless come into being at the expense of the object-libido. The libido withdrawn from the outer world has been directed on to the ego, giving rise to a state which we may call narcissism.' (Freud, S. *Collected Papers,* vol. 4, tr. by Riviere, J., Leonard and Virginia Woolf and The Institute of Psychoanalysis, London, 1924–25)

'Apparently as a compensation to his very modest existence he was seized with megalomania and believed himself to be the Savior.' (Jung, C.G. *Contributions to Analytical Psychology,* tr. by Baynes, H.G. and C.F., Kegan Paul, Trench, Trubner, London, 1928)

The ideas in megalomania are called *delusions of grandeur.*

megalophobia (-fō′bi-à) Fear of large objects.

megalopia hysterica (me-gà′lô′pē-à histe′rē-kà) See *macropsia.*

megalosplanchnic (meg-à-lō-splangk′nik) According to Viola's classification of the constitutional forms of body build, this term refers to the type which has the abdominal portion of the body relatively large in proportion to the thoracic, owing to the large size of the abdominal viscera. This type is further characterized by a predominance of the trunk over the extremities.

megrim (mē′grim) *Obs.* Migraine.

meiosis (mī-ō′sis) See *miosis.*

meiotic (mī-ot′ik) Relating to or manifesting miosis.

melancholia, melancholy (mel-an-kō′li-à, mel′an-kol-i) A morbid mental state characterized by depression. It may be a manifestation of any one of a large variety of psychiatric nosologic states, although it is usually considered today as chiefly one of the phases of the manic-depressive psychosis.

The most exhaustive psychodynamic

concepts on melancholia are derived from psychoanalysis. 'The distinguishing mental features of melancholia are a profoundly painful dejection, abrogation of interest in the outside world, loss of the capacity to love, inhibition of all activity, and a lowering of the self-regarding feelings to a degree that finds utterance in self-reproaches and self-revilings, and culminates in a delusional expectation of punishment. This picture becomes a little more intelligible when we consider that, with one exception, the same traits are met with in grief.' (Freud, S. *Collected Papers,* vol. 4, tr. by Riviere, J., Leonard and Virginia Woolf and The Institute of Psychoanalysis, London, 1924–25) The one exception is the loss of self-esteem, which is not seen in grief or normal mourning.

According to Freud, normal mourning is to melancholia as normal fear is to morbid anxiety. Briefly stated, the loss of a love-object leads to withdrawal of libido from reality and the introjection of the libido upon the mental picture of the lost love-object. The self-reproaches of the melancholic patient are understood to be directed toward the lost love-object. Abraham has shown that in these states libido regresses to the oral stage.

When the melancholic state is mild, it is known as *simple retardation.* When it is 'average' it is called *acute depression;* when it is severe it may reach the stage of *stuporous depression.*

A depressed or melancholic patient may show psycho-motor overactivity; the patient is then said to show *agitated depression.* Or the depressed patient may have a great volume of ideas that shift rapidly as they do in the state of mania; when that is so, the term *depressive mania* is used; the ideas are of a depressive character. Most cases of depressive mania are seen on follow-up to be schizophrenic.

melancholia, abdominal A rarely used term for depressions (mainly the agitated, involutional type) characterized by a delusional fixation on the gastro-intestinal tract, with vociferous complaints of dyspepsia, eructation, flatulence, constipation, etc.

melancholia activa (me-làn-kô′lē-à àk-tē′và) (L. 'active melancholy') *Melancholia agitata* (q.v.).

melancholia, acute (mel-an-kō′li-à) Melancholia of sudden onset.

melancholia agitata (me-làn-kô′lē-à à-gē-tä′tà) (L. 'agitated melancholy') This expression, not common in the sense in which it was employed in the latter half of the 19th century, referred to what is now known as the excitement phase of the catatonic form of schizophrenia. When using the Anglicized term *agitated melancholia,* psychiatrists generally imply that the condition is associated with manic-depressive psychosis or with involutional melancholia.

melancholia, alcoholic (mel-an-kō′li-à) Bleuler says: 'Not very rarely alcoholics suffer from depressive conditions which cannot be distinguished symptomatologically from a melancholia of manic-depressive insanity, even though the delusions remain merely rudimentary. But they do not last long, only about two weeks.' (Bleuler, E. *Textbook of Psychiatry,* tr. by Brill, A.A., Macmillan, New York, 1930)

melancholia, amenorrhoeal (ä-men-o-rē′-al) 'Melancholia associated with the organic disturbances that have produced amenorrhoea, and that is erroneously attributed to the latter.' (Quain, R., ed. *A Dictionary of Medicine,* Appleton, New York, 1899)

melancholia anglica (me-làn-kô′lē-à ang′-glē-kà) *Obs.* English melancholy, or suicidal insanity.

melancholia attonita (me-làn-kō′lē-à àt-tô′nē-tà) The term describes the morbid state, common in the catatonic form of schizophrenia, characterized by immobility and muscular rigidity.

melancholia canina (kà-nē′nà) (L. 'canine, doggish melancholy') *Obs.* Lycanthropy.

melancholia, cataleptic (mel-an-kō′li-à, kat-à-lep′tik) A form of stuporous melancholia, in which there are cataleptic manifestations.

melancholia, chronic 'Many patients remain permanently quiet, depressed, uninterested, stand about in corners with dejected or anxious appearance, fold their hands, lament in a low voice, when questioned give hesitating, monosyllabic, but sensible and usually appropriate answers. They are inactive, irresolute, timid, have to be forced to everything, resist energetically when much interfered with. Frequently also the residua of depressive delusions still persist; the patients call

themselves the devil, ask for forgiveness, for a mild punishment, are afraid they will be sent away, that they will have to remain there forever.' (Kraepelin, E. *Manic-Depressive Insanity and Paranoia,* tr. by Barclay, R.M., Livingstone, Edinburgh, 1921)

melancholia, climacteric (klī-mak-ter′ik) Melancholia developing at the climacteric period of life.

melancholia complacens (me-làn-kô′lē-à kôm-plà′kens) (L. 'complacent melancholy') Melancholy with complacency.

melancholia, convulsive (mel-an-kō′li-à) *Obs.* Melancholia associated with Jacksonian epilepsy.

melancholia, excited Clouston's term, who says: 'This, like other varieties of the disease, may be one stage in the complete clinical history of a case, or may be the type from beginning to end. . . . The patients rush about, are violent to those about them, wander ceaselessly, walk up and down like tigers in a cage, or roll about on the floor, bite their fingernails, or wring their hands, or shout, or groan, or moan, or weep loudly, or tear their clothes, and in all their attitudes and motions express strongly their mental pain.' (Clouston, T.S. *Clinical Lectures on Mental Diseases,* 6th ed., Churchill, London, 1904) The condition formerly was also known as *motor melancholia.*

melancholia, fantastic 'A further, fairly comprehensive group of cases is distinguished by a still greater development of *delusions.* We may perhaps call it "fantastic melancholia." Abundant *hallucinations* appear. The patients see evil spirits, death, heads of animals, smoke in the house, black men on the roofs, crowds of monsters, lions' cubs, a grey head with sharp teeth, angels, saints, dead relatives, the Trinity in the firmament, a head rising in the air.' (Kraepelin, E. *Manic-Depressive Insanity and Paranoia,* tr. by Barclay, R.M., Livingstone, Edinburgh, 1921)

melancholia flatuosa (me-làn-kô′lē-à flà-too-ō′zà) (L. 'flatuous melancholy') *Obs.* Hypochondriasis.

melancholia gravis (grà′vēs) (L. 'severe melancholy') Kraepelin's term for the depressive syndrome in which 'the patients see figures, spirits, the corpses of their relatives; something is falsely represented to them, "all sorts of devil's work." Green rags fall from the walls; a coloured spot on the wall is a snapping mouth which bites the heads off children; everything looks black. The patients hear abusive language ("lazy pig," "wicked creature," "deceiver," "you are guilty, you are guilty"), voices which invite them to suicide; they feel sand, sulphur vapour in their mouth, electric currents in the walls.' (Kraepelin, E. *Manic-Depressive Insanity and Paranoia,* tr. by Barclay, R.M., Livingstone, Edinburgh, 1921)

melancholia, homicidal (mel-an-kō'li-à) See *mania, homicidal.*

melancholia, hypochondriacal (hī-pō-kon-drī'à-kal) A symptom complex consisting of depressive affect, inhibition of thinking and acting, and hypochondriacal delusions. When not organic, this symptom complex is almost always schizophrenic in nature. Monoideism, in contrast to the simple melancholias, may here be almost absolute. For long periods there seem to be no thoughts other than the constantly repeated wishes, complaints, or maledictions. Even though the affect seems to dominate the entire personality, it is typically stiff, superficial, and exaggerated. In this condition, ideas of grandeur may co-exist with appalling fears and terrors in spite of logical contradictions involved.

melancholia, intermittent (in-tēr-mit'ent) Recurrent melancholia.

melancholia, involutional (in-vō-lū'shun-al) See *psychosis, involutional.*

melancholia, motor *Obs.* See *melancholia, excited.*

melancholia nervea (me-làn-kô'lē-à ner'-ve-à) (Mod L. 'nervous melancholia') *Obs.* Hypochondriasis.

melancholia, neurasthenic (mel-an-kō'li-à, nū-ras-then'ik) This uncommon term was coined by Friedmann for melancholia with pronounced neurasthenic symptoms. In current psychiatry the clinical syndrome is usually classified with the manic-depressive disorder.

melancholia, nostalgic Melancholia caused by homesickness.

melancholia, organic Melancholia that accompanies some gross organic lesion of the brain.

melancholia, panphobic (pan-fō'bik) *Obs.* Melancholia in which there is dread of everything.

melancholia, paranoid (par'à-noid) 'The depressive attack [of manic-depressive disorder], also, because of the increase of the hallucinations or the thought disturbance, may assume a paranoid or delirious appearance (*melancholic insanity*).' (Bleuler, E. *Textbook of Psychiatry,* tr. by Brill, A.A., Macmillan, New York, 1930)

melancholia, paretic (pa-ret'ik) Melancholia that may be the prodrome or concomitant of paresis.

melancholia, passive *Obs.* 'Melancholia that develops slowly with a gradual failure of physical health, restless worry or jealousy being the first objective sign.' (Quain, R., ed. *A Dictionary of Medicine,* Appleton, New York, 1899)

melancholia, periodic See *neurasthenia, periodic.*

melancholia, puerperal (pū-ēr'pēr-al) Melancholia that appears after and apparently as a result of childbirth.

melancholia, recurrent *Obs.* 'Melancholia in which the patient recovers from the disease but relapses at a longer or shorter interval, especially if placed in the environment in which the first attack occurred.' (Quain, R., ed. *A Dictionary of Medicine,* Appleton, New York, 1899) This term is approximately synonymous with 'manic-depressive psychosis, recurrent depression' as used by other writers.

melancholia, religious *Obs.* Melancholia with delusions of a religious nature.

melancholia, resistive *Obs.* Melancholia with unreasoning active or passive resistance as its characteristic feature.

melancholia senilis (me-làn-kô'lē-à se-nē'lēs) L. 'senile melancholy') 'The mild affective displacements which are frequent in old age can give rise to melancholic and manic conditions, of which the first are very frequent, the second rather rare (*senile melancholia and mania*).' (Bleuler, E. *Textbook of Psychiatry,* tr. by Brill, A.A., Macmillan, New York, 1930)

melancholia, sexual (mel-an-kō'li-à) *Obs.* Melancholia as a result of believing oneself impotent.

melancholia simplex (me-làn-kô'lē-à sēm'pleks) (L. 'simple melancholy') Simple depression, according to Kraepelin.

melancholia, sympathetic (mel-an-kō'li-à) *Obs.* Melancholia that arises from some organic disturbance other than that of the brain.

melancholia vera (me-lăn-kô′lē-à vā′rà) (L. 'true melancholy') See *anxietas prae-senilis.*

melancholia zoanthropia (zō-àn-thrō′pē-à) (L. 'zooanthropic melancholy') Lycanthropy.

melancholy (mel′an-kol-ē) In current psychiatry the term is synonymous with *melancholia.* In the literature of the 19th century melancholy was distinguished from melancholia 'in that there are no morbid sense perversions, no irrationality of conduct, no morbid loss of self-control, no sudden or determined impulse towards suicide or homicide, and where surrounding events and occurrences still afford a certain amount of interest, though lessened in degree, and where the power of application to ordinary duties is still present.' (Tuke, D.H. *A Dictionary of Psychological Medicine,* vols. 1–2, Blakiston, Philadelphia, 1892)

melissophobia (me-lis-ō-fō′bi-à) Fear of bees.

Melkersson-Rosenthal syndrome See *syndrome, Melkersson-Rosenthal.*

melomania (mel-ō-mā′ni-à) *Obs.* Psychosis characterized by incessant singing.

mem-element (mem′-el′ē-ment) See *system.*

memory For the psychoanalytic conception of memory see *system.*

memory, abreaction of See *abreaction.*

memory, automatic It is said that an experience of emotional value 'excites one or more of the emotional instincts of anger, fear, disgust, etc. . . . The instincts then become organized about one or more of the ideas to form a sentiment (Shand) and the whole is incorporated in a complex which then acquires an affective character.' The quotation is from Prince, who adds: 'Given such an emotional complex nearly anything associated with some detail of the experience may, by the loss of association, automatically or involuntarily revive it, or the emotional reaction with a greater or lesser number of its associated memories.' (Prince, M. *The Unconscious,* Macmillan, New York, 1916)

memory, biological A supposedly inherited knowledge of how to react. Eugenio Rig-nano believes that instincts result from such biological memories or inherited engrams. The collective unconscious of Jung probably springs from biological memories in that the motives and images which he includes in the term collective unconscious are not dependent upon the acquisitions of personal existence, but originate in the inherited brain structures.

memory, cover See *memory, screen.*

memory, dislocation of Holland's term for complete but temporary forgetfulness or amnesia.

memory-hallucination See *hallucination, memory.*

memory, hyperesthetic (hī-pēr-es-thet′ik) Oversensitive memory. In the communication *On the Psychical Mechanism of Hysterical Phenomena,* Breuer and Freud, referring to the onset of hysterical attacks, said that they may 'arise spontaneously, as memories commonly do; but they may also be provoked, just as any memory may be aroused according to the laws of association. Provocation of an attack occurs either by stimulation of an hysterogenic zone or by a new experience resembling the pathogenic experience. We hope to be able to show that no essential difference exists between the two conditions, apparently so distinct; that in both cases a hyperaesthetic memory has been stirred.'

memory, liquidation by This phrase used by P. Janet, means release of painful memories. 'A situation has not been satisfactorily liquidated, has not been fully assimilated, until we have achieved, not merely an outward reaction through our movements, but also an inward reaction through the words we address to ourselves, through the organization of the recital of the event to others and to ourselves, and through the putting of this recital in its place as one of the chapters in our personal history.' (Janet, P. *Psychological Healing,* vols. 1–2, tr. by Paul, E. and C., Macmillan, New York, 1925, p. 662)

memory, physiological (fiz-i-ō-loj′i-kal) 'Memory as commonly regarded and known to psychology is a *conscious* manifestation, but, plainly, if we regard it, as we have thus far, as a process, then, logically, we are entitled to regard any process which consists of the three factors, registration, conservation, and reproduction of experiences, as memory, whether the final result be the reproduction of a conscious experience, or one to which no consciousness was ever attached. In other words, theoretically it is quite possible that acquired physiological body-experiences may be reproduced by exactly the same process as conscious experiences, and their reproduction would be entitled to be regarded as memory quite as much as if the experience were one of consciousness.' (Prince, M. *The Unconscious,* Macmillan, New York, 1916) See *memory, psycho-physiological.*

memory, psycho-physiological (sī-kō-fiz-i-ō-loj'i-kal) 'Still another variety of memory is *psycho-physiological.* This type is characterized by a combination of psychological and physiological elements and is important . . . because of the conspicuous part which such memories play in pathological conditions. Certain bodily reactions which are purely physiological, such as vaso-motor, cardiac, respiratory, intestinal, digestive, etc., disturbances, become, as a result of certain experiences, linked with one or another psychical element (sensations, perceptions, thoughts), and, this linking becoming conserved as a "disposition," the physiological reaction is reproduced whenever the psychical element is introduced into consciousness.' (Prince, M. *The Unconscious,* Macmillan, New York, 1916) See *memory, physiological.*

memory, racial The part of the individual's mental life which he brings with him at birth, the archaic heritage of fragments of phylogenetic origin. This archaic inheritance consists, first of all, of the ability and tendency of all human organisms 'to follow a certain direction of development and to react in a particular way to certain excitations, impressions, and stimuli.' The differences among individuals in this respect are the constitutional element in the individual.

Freud states, however, that ideational contents, memory traces of the experiences of former generations, as well as these dispositions to react in the particular ways mentioned above, are included in the archaic heritage. The existence of this type of racial memory has been indicated by analytic research. The study of the reactions to early traumata has shown that these reactions 'do not keep strictly to what the individual himself has experienced, but deviate from this in a way that would accord much better with their be-

ing reactions to genetic events and in general can be explained only through such an influence. The behavior of a neurotic child to his parents when under the influence of the Oedipus and castration complex is very rich in such reactions which seem unreasonable in the individual and can be understood only phylogenetically, in relation to the experiences of earlier generations.' Analytic research has yielded another result, the universality of speech symbolism, which seems readily explicable as the inheritance of memories of ancestral experiences from the time when speech was first developing. The use of symbols appears naturally in children. However, 'we cannot trace the way in which they learned it and must admit that in many cases to learn it would be impossible.' Moreover, symbolism seems to have no connection with difference in languages, the same symbols being current with many different peoples. Freud states that, in the case of symbols, an alternative explanation might be that symbols represent thought-connections (between ideas) which were formed when speech first developed in the distant past yet have to be repeated every time the individual passes through such a development. In that case, what is inherited with respect to symbols is a thought-disposition rather than a memory-trace.

A particular memory becomes part of the racial memory when the experience is either important enough or repeated often enough or both. Such a memory will become conscious again (though in an altered and distorted form) when an actual repetition of the remembered event has recently occurred. The obsessive character of religious phenomena in particular demonstrates the altered and distorted return (to consciousness) of memory-traces of experiences that had occurred in the distant past and remained in the racial memory. (Freud, S. *Moses and Monotheism,* Hogarth Press, London, 1939)

memory, replacement The substitution of one memory for another.

'Of especial interest is the fact that the repressed complex, which was responsible for the forgetting, betrayed itself in the replacement-memory, which was, as is always the case, a compromise-formation.' (Jones, E. *Papers on Psycho-Analysis,* 4th ed., Wood, Baltimore, 1938)

memory-romance See *romance, memory.*

memory, screen When a memory, a real thought, not a phantasied one, is used as a shield to conceal an allied memory, it is called a screen-memory. Thus, when a patient recalls playing in the basement, but does not remember the nature of the play, he is said to be providing a screen-memory.

memory, subconscious 'Almost any conserved experience under certain conditions can function as a subconscious memory and become translated into, i.e., produce sensory and motor automatic phenomena such as hallucinations, writing, speech, etc.' (Prince, M. *The Unconscious,* Macmillan, New York, 1916)

memory-symbol See *symbol, memory.*

memory-system See *system.*

memory-trace See *trace, memory.*

memory, unconscious A term used to denote the retention of mental impressions of an event, even though, in ordinary circumstances, they are not subject to recall into consciousness. Freud first applied the concept to his studies of hysteria. He found that certain events, usually sexual, occurred to the patient, but were so unbearable that they were actively put out of consciousness by being repressed. In the process of *repression* (q.v.), the ideational content as well as its affective component is relegated to the unconscious and kept there as an unconscious memory or unconscious image. 'At puberty, when the sexual drive is stronger, this unconscious mental impression, under certain conditions, is reactivated. Because of the increased capacity for sexual feeling, the repressed memory acquires new force. It now produces the same result as an actual event in the present, an effect which the original experience itself lacked. Such a memory is not conscious. When, at puberty, it is reawakened, there is a liberation of affect, although the ideas associated with it remain repressed.' (Thompson, C. *Psychoanalysis, Evolution and Development,* Hermitage House, New York, 1950) In such instances, the goal of therapy is to bring back into consciousness the unconscious ideational content as well as the associated affect.

mendacity As used in psychiatry, pathologic lying.

Mendel, Abbot Johann Gregor (1822– 84), an Augustinian monk (and later abbot) at Brünn, published in 1865 his *Experiments on Plant Hybrids,* the result of his experiments on peas and honeybees in the monastery garden. In 1910 his findings and theories were rediscovered simultaneously by Correns, von Tschermak, and De Vries, and thus *Mendelism* (q.v.) became the new science of *genetics* (q.v.).

Mendelian law See *law, Mendelian.*

Mendelism (men'del-iz'm) The term designates the biological phenomena underlying the distributive mechanism of organic inheritance as discovered by Mendel.

The problem of how true-breeding varieties within a species are related was attacked by him from its simplest side by concentrating his attention upon the genetic mode of inheritance of sharply contrasted pairs of characters: he crossed round peas with wrinkled ones, or a yellow species with a green one, and was thus able to determine that all hybrids of the first filial generation (F_1) resembled each other, but exhibited only one of the two alternative characters distinguishing the parents. In the crosses of round and wrinkled peas all the offspring were round, and this 'prevailing' member of a pair of individual characters was called *dominant,* while the other member which was 're-pressed' was called *recessive.*

If the round F_1 plants were allowed to become self-fertilized and the seeds were harvested separately and sown separately, producing the second filial generation (F_2), the wrinkled form reappeared in this generation in the proportion of one wrinkled to three round. By inbreeding, in turn, the wrinkled F_2 individuals it was found that they constantly produced wrinkled peas while the round form completely failed to reappear; genetically speaking, every individual exhibiting the recessive character bred true. Of the auto-fertilized round (*dominant*) individuals one-third likewise produced only round offspring. The remaining two-thirds propagated themselves in the same proportion as the uniform first generation, one-quarter wrinkled to three-quarters round, and similarly in all the subsequent generations.

These phenomena are explained by Mendel's theory that the hybrid does not produce any hybrid gametes, but merely pure gametes of various kinds, some of which bear dominant and others recessive characters. The hybrids of the first filial generation with round seeds contain the factor for wrinkled as well as the factor for round, but the former is hidden and suppressed by the latter. Since the recessive character reappears in the next generation, the dominant and the recessive characteristics must necessarily separate at the moment when the hybrid forms its gametes. See *law, Mendelian.*

mendicancy, pathological (men'di-kan-sē, path-ō-loj'i-kal) A syndrome characterized by the necessity on the part of the patient to beg, regardless of whether or not he has any real financial need. This type of individual is happy only when carrying on the activity of begging. Accounts in the daily newspapers testify to the frequency with which beggars, on their deaths, are discovered to have left fortunes behind them. According to Nielsen and Thompson, the mechanism of this bizarre trait is obscure. (Nielsen, J.M., and Thompson, G.N. *The Engrammes of Psychiatry,* Thomas, Springfield, Ill., 1947) See *beggar, emotional.*

meninges (men-in'jēz) The membranous coverings of the brain and spinal cord. The outermost meninx is the dura mater; the middle one is the arachnoid; the innermost is the pia mater. The dura mater is known as the pachymeninx; fibrous processes of the dura mater form the falx cerebri (which separates the two cerebral hemispheres), the tentorium cerebelli (which forms a partition between the posterior and middle fossae of the skull), the falx cerebelli (which separates the cerebellar hemispheres) and the diaphragma sellae (which forms a roof to the sella turcica and through which passes the infundibulum). The arachnoid and pia mater are known as the leptomeninges; the space between them is the subarachnoid space, which contains the cerebrospinal fluid.

meningismus (men-in-jiz'mus) Meningeal manifestations closely simulating those of meningitis, but in which no actual inflammation of the meninges is present.

meningitic curve See *Lange's colloidal gold reaction.*

meningitis (men-in-jī'tis) This is a condition in which the meningococcus, pneumococcus, or other pyogenic microorganisms infect the cerebrospinal leptomeninges, producing mental symptoms of

the organic reaction type, in its acute form, with severe headache, delirium, somnolence, or stupor. Localized or generalized convulsions, generalized rigidity, twitchings, and monoplegia or hemiplegia may also occur.

meningitis, serous (sēr'us) See *pseudotumor cerebri.*

meningitis, tuberculous A condition in which the tubercle bacillus infects the meninges of the central nervous system and produces mental symptoms of the organic reaction type. The disease is always secondary to a tuberculous focus elsewhere in the body, and the course is usually slowly progressive toward a fatal termination. Headache, delirium, stupor, and convulsions occur. The neck is rigid; often the tubercle bacillus can be demonstrated in the spinal fluid.

meningitophobia (men-in-ji-tō-fō'bi-à) A hysterical presentation of meningeal symptoms; morbid dread of brain disease.

meningocele (me-ning'gō-sēl) A developmental anomaly in which there is a protrusion of the membranes of the brain or spinal cord through a defect in the skull or spinal column respectively.

menses (men'sēz) Flow of blood, normally recurring every month, from a woman's uterus.

mens rea (mens' rē'à) (L. 'criminal mind') 'Every crime becomes a mental problem, inasmuch as it involves vicious conduct, expressed by action or inaction, and a criminal intent or *mens rea.*' (East, W.N. *An Introduction to Forensic Psychiatry in the Criminal Courts,* London, 1927, p. 24)

'It is a general principle of our [English] law that there must be as an essential ingredient in a criminal offense some blameworthy condition of mind. Sometimes it is negligence, sometimes malice, sometimes guilty knowledge, but as a general rule there must be something of that kind which is designated by the expression *mens rea.*' (Cave, J.: Chisholm *v.* Doulton (1889) 22 Q.B.D. 736)

mensuration (men-shoo-rā'shun) In the field of psychiatry the term refers particularly to the act of measuring areas and distances on the surface of the body. 'Mensuration has been used rather more extensively within the past few years, though limited rather sharply to the matter of total height vs. span and trunk-extremity relationship.' (Draper, G. *Disease and the Man,* Macmillan, New York, 1930)

mental aberration See *aberration, mental.*

mental deficiency See *deficiency, mental.*

mental disorders, classification of See *nomenclature, 1952 revision.*

mentales (men-tä′lās) Linnaeus, in 1763, divided mental disorders (*mentales*) into three classes: *ideales, imaginarii,* and *pathetici.*

mentalia (men-tä′li-à; L. -tä′lē-à) Psychalia.

mentalism (men′tal-iz′m) The primitive tendency to personify, in spirit form, the forces of nature and the motions of things on the earth and in the heavens; the endowment of inert matter with the quality of 'soul'—thus synonymous with *animism* (q.v.). This philosophical concept implies the existence of spiritual or mental forces completely different from the somatic structures, and denotes the subjective, mental, or mind approach to psychiatry in contrast to the behavioristic approach, which stresses objective physiological activities.

mentality (men-tal′i-tē) Mental action or power—the psyche in action. In psychiatry mentality is considered from two points of view: (1) of intellectuality and (2) of the instincts. The former refers to the intellectual capacity, such as superior, average, or inferior intelligence.

The second (instinctual) aspect of mentality forms the basis of personality structure and function. Since the introduction of the formulations of Freud the mind or psyche has been conceived in the light of an organ of the body, with its own structures and functions, and with its correlative action with other body organs and with the environment.

According to authoritative schools of thought today, the psyche is the central organ that expresses mentality from the instinctual point of view, while the brain occupies an analogous position with regard to the intellectual aspects of mentality.

mental make-up See *make-up, mental.*

mental science Psychology.

mental status The psychological and be-

havioral appearance of an individual; in clinical psychiatry this term is commonly used to refer to the results of the mental examination of a patient. The written report of the mental status usually contains specific references to the following areas (adapted from N.D C. Lewis. *Outlines for Psychiatric Examinations,* State Hospitals Press, Utica, New York, 1943):

I. Attitude and General Behavior
  A. General health and appearance (?weak ?prematurely aged ?immature)
  B. General habits of dress (?overmeticulous ?slovenly)
  C. Personal habits (toilet and eating habits)
  D. General mood (elation, excitement, calm, apathy, dejection)
  E. Use of leisure time
  F. Degree of sociability
  G. Speech (productivity; disorders of speech such as stuttering; topics of conversation)
II. Attitude and Behavior During Interview
  A. Co-operativeness
  B. Poise (?stilted ?poised ?boisterous ?uncontrolled)
  C. Facial expression (pain, grief, anxiety, distrust, bewilderment, anger, defiance, contempt, exaltation, preoccupation, apathy)
  D. Motor activity (gestures, co-ordination, retardation, or acceleration)
  E. Mental activity (flow of speech; flow of thought; loss of continuity or alterations of language and speech structure)
  F. Emotional reactions (appropriateness, harmony)
  G. Trend of thought (persecutory, hypochondriacal, unreality, nihilism, dejection, grandiosity, hallucinations, delusions, illusions, obsessions, compulsions, fears)
III. Sensorium, Mental Grasp, and Capacity
  A. Orientation
  B. Memory and retention
  C. School and general knowledge
  D. Estimate of intelligence
  E. Abstraction ability
  F. Tests of absurdity, interpretation of proverbs
  G. Judgment

mente capti (men′te kàp′tē) (L. 'out of

their senses, out of mind, mad') See *furiosi*.

menticide (men'ti-sīd) 'An organized system of psychological intervention and judicial perversion, in which a powerful tyrant synthetically injects his own thoughts and words into the minds and mouths of the victims he plans to destroy by mock trial, may well be called menticide. Menticide is a growing threat to mankind—a threat far worse than genocide. Genocide as defined by the United Nations is the direct physical destruction of another racial or national group. Menticide is an attack on man's very mind, on his sovereign will and conviction. It destroys free thought and makes servile, mechanical instruments of his inviolate thought processes.

'In the hands of dictators and secret police, menticide is more deadly than lethal weapons, yet is still unrecognized as an official institution for the suppression of political opposition. Psychological attacks involving planned mental torture are, however, more than the human being can withstand. Menticide changes normal human wishes into pathological cravings. . . . Thus, at some point, capitulation in the form of false confession, rather than continued resistance, serves the need for infantile self-preservation.' (Meerlo, J.A.M. 'The Crime of Menticide,' *American Journal of Psychiatry CVII*, No. 8, Feb. 1951, pp. 594ff.)

Menticide is popularly known as 'brainwashing.'

mentiferous (men-tif'ẽr-us) Telepathic.

mentism (men'tiz'm) *Rare*. Mental derangement.

Mercier, Charles Arthur (1852–1919) British psychiatrist; forensic psychiatry.

mere-, -mere (mẽr') Combining form meaning part, portion, partial, from Gr. *méros*, part, share.

merergasia (mer-ẽr-gas'i-à) Partial ability to work, function. Term used by Adolf Meyer to designate a clinical psychiatric syndrome that causes only a partial disorganization of the personality. In general it may be stated that the psychoneuroses and neuroses constitute the merergastic reactions.

mergent, partial (mẽr'jent) Burrow thus denotes the inter-verbal conditioning that

occurs reflexly among individuals and is socially systematized within groups or communities. By virtue of this reflex community-reaction coincident with the employment of words or symbols, two phenomena which are completely disparate and unrelated outside the organism may become united or merged socially (inter-cortically) into a common motivation or 'meaning' within the organism. Through this mechanism the organism's primary total feelings have been socially replaced by mere reflex partial affects. The partial mergent represents a false mergent in contrast to the organism's total or true mergent. Contrasted with total mergent. (Burrow, T. *The Biology of Human Conflict,* Macmillan, New York, 1937)

mergent, total Burrow's term for the organism's response as a whole to the total environmental situation. Contrasted with partial mergent. (Burrow, T. *The Biology of Human Conflict,* Macmillan, New York, 1937)

merogony (me-rog'ō-nē) This genetic term designates the process in which the egg cytoplasm comes from one parent and the nucleus, through the sperm, from the other, thus making possible a comparison of their effects. Boveri fertilized enucleated eggs of one species with sperm from a markedly different one. The merogonous embryos resembled the species from which the sperm was derived.

Thus development seems to be controlled by the nucleus, even if it is surrounded by cytoplasm from a very different source. However, since there is evidence that the nuclear material may not have been removed from the egg entirely, the resemblance to the male parent may be explained on other genetic grounds (see *nucleus*), and the question is still open.

merycism (mer'i-siz'm) 'Merycism is a voluntary regurgitation, moderate in degree and slow, but rather pleasant, of food from the stomach to the mouth, in which it is masticated and tasted a second time, as in rumination. This remarkable habit is special to certain idiots and dements of a very low type.' (Tanzi, E. *A Text-Book of Mental Diseases,* tr. by Robertson, W.F. and Mackenzie, T.C., Rebman, New York, 1909)

mescaline (mes'ka-lēn) The active principle of the cactus from which peyote is obtained. See *peyotism*.

Mescaline is used today as one of the two chief agents to produce an experimental or model psychosis (the other agent is lysergic acid). The major effects are personality disturbances and an increase in sympathetic tension in the experimental subject; the former include visual (and sometimes auditory) hallucinations, illusions, distortions of the body image, altered time sense, thought-language changes, and an increase in self-observation sometimes to the point of complete withdrawal and feelings of unreality and detachment.

The mode of action of mescaline is not fully understood. It is a powerful synaptic inhibitor, and its sympathomimetic effects may be due to inhibition of the opposing parasympathetic system. It seems more likely, howover, that its effects are due to stimulation of the sympathetic system by reason of imitation of norepinephrine at the latter's receptor sites, this leading to arousal, sympathetic outflow, increased psychomotor activity, and enhancement of sensitivity to external stimuli. It has also been suggested that the mescaline psychosis is due to formation of a protein-bound mescaline compound in the liver, which then acts as a toxic agent to sensitive areas in the brain.

mesencephalon (mes-en-sef′à-lon) *Midbrain* (q.v.).

mesenchyme, mesenchyma (mes′eng-kīm, -′ki-mà) Although this term was introduced in embryology by O. and R. Hertwig to denote that part of the *mesoderm* (q.v.) which separates from the original mesothelium as a loose mass of anastomosing cells to form the connective tissues, it has lost some of its precise meaning. It is now generally assumed that the mesenchymal tissue, occupying practically all the intervals between the epithelial layers, does not arise from the middle germ layer alone, but probably from certain parts of the *entoderm* and *ectoderm* also (qq.v.), and that it forms not only the various forms of connective tissue, but also the skeletal system, the smooth muscular tissue, the stroma of the iris and the ciliary body, the cartilages and ligaments of the larynx, and, especially, the blood and blood vessels.

In constitutional medicine, the *mesenchyme* has been steadily acquiring greater

physiological importance as the tissue designed for the *vegetative* functions of the organism. Viola's ontogenetic law contrasts *ponderal* evolution, or increase of mass due to the mesenchyme with *morphological* evolution, or change of proportion due to the *parenchyme* (q.v.), and holds that these two evolutionary types are in inverse proportion to one another. It is believed by Viola that, when there is evolutionary disharmony, one system preponderates over the other, giving rise to the two great antithetic types of deviation from the average human constitution, namely, the *megalosplanchnic* and the *microsplanchnic* (qq.v.).

Godin's *law of alternations* is a corollary to Viola's. It also identifies the mesenchyme with mass, and the parenchyme with morphological differentiation, and stresses the fact that, in normal growth, phases of growth in width alternate with phases of growth in length.

Mesmer, Franz (or **Friedrich**) **Anton** (1733–1815) An Austrian who first gave a demonstration of hypnotism (animal magnetism) in Vienna about 1775.

mesmerism (mez′mẽr-iz′m) Hypnotism; animal magnetism.

mesmeromania (-ō-mā′ni-à) *Obs.* Misguided faith in the power of mesmerism.

meso- (mes′ō-) Combining form meaning middle, intermediate, from Gr. *mésos*, middle.

mesocephaly (mes-ō-sef′a-lē) See *index, cephalic.*

mesoderm (-dẽrm) The middle or third germ layer which is developed in the tridermic stage of the embryo called *notogenesis* (q.v.), or the fundamental tissues subsequently derived from this layer.

The *medial* portions of the original mesoderm, the paraxial or segmental mesoderm, become subdivided into blocks of tissue, the mesodermic segments or *somites*, while the *lateral* plates develop a split-like cavity, the *celom*. The connections between somites and lateral plates are collectively known as the *intermediate cell mass*, the primordium of the urogenital system.

The main tissue derivatives developed from the primitive middle germ layer include all muscular, connective, and vascular tissues, with blood and lymph vessels and all lymphoid organs; the cortex of the suprarenal gland and the sex cells; the epithelium of uriniferous tubules, renal pelves, and ureters, of the seminiferous tubules and the associated excretory ducts of the testis; of oviduct and uterus; and of pleurae, pericardium, and peritoneum.

mesomorphic (-mor′fïk) In W.H. Sheldon's system of constitutional types this term describes the type characterized by a predominance of its third component (bulk), that is, the structures of the body that are developed from the *mesodermal* layer of the embryo (q.v.). Persons of this type are contrasted with the *ectomorphic* or *endomorphic* (qq.v.) types and correspond roughly to Kretschmer's *athletic* (q.v.) type.

mesontomorph (mes-on′tō-morf) According to Beau's system of constitutional medicine, this general constitutional type is to be distinguished from the *hyperontomorph,* characterized by broad, stocky body with long intestines. See *type, pyknic.*

mesoskelic (mes-ō-skel′ik) Possessing legs of normal length.

In Manouvrier's system of constitutional types this describes a type which is intermediate between the *brachyskelic* and the *macroskelic* types (qq.v.). See *type, athletic.*

meta- (met′à-), **met-** (before vowels) Prefix meaning change, transformation; after, next; trans-, beyond, over, from Gr. *metá-,* together with, after, behind, change.

metabolism (me-tab′ō-liz′m) The biophysiological processes by which the living cells and tissue systems of an organism undergo continuous chemical changes in order to build up new living matter and to supply the energy necessary for the life of an individual.

The morphological effect of *metabolism* can be *anabolic* or *catabolic* (qq.v.), according to whether it is of a constructive or destructive nature.

metabolism, destructive Catabolism; see *metabolism.*

metabolism, mental 'An increase in "mental metabolism" ' was the phrase used by Abraham to describe the condition characteristic of mania in which the patient is continuously 'hungry for new objects.' In general, manic phenomena arise out of an immense increase in self-esteem or, what is the same thing, a decrease in conscience. There are no longer any inhibitions: all the impulses formerly inhibited now seek discharge, and the energies themselves, formerly used to restrain these impulses, are now released. Henceforth, these energies as well as the now uninhibited impulses 'flow out, using any available discharge.' As a result the patient is 'hungry for objects' in order 'to get rid of the now uninhibited impulses that seek discharge.'

Fenichel notes that most of these uninhibited impulses are oral in nature. The manic's object relationships aim unconsciously at incorporation of the object. Accordingly, it is particularly appropriate to describe this condition as an increase in mental metabolism since the manic, in effect, continually consumes new objects in order to discharge his intensified uninhibited oral instinctual impulses. (Fenichel, O. *The Psychoanalytic Theory of Neurosis,* Norton, New York, 1945)

metaerotism (met-à-er′ō-tiz′m) S. Radó stresses the idea that intoxicants [e.g. morphine] effect changes principally 'in the abode of the libido.' He says: 'The whole peripheral sexual apparatus is left on the one side as in a "short circuit" and the exciting stimuli are enabled to operate directly on the central organ. I propose to term this phenomenon, which deserves to be distinguished by a special name, "metaerotism." ' He adds in a footnote that he prefers 'to use this term rather than the obvious "paraerotism," which I think should be reserved for the less questionable scientific designation of the perversions.' (*International Journal of Psychoanalysis VII,* 402, 1926)

metallophobia (mē-tal-ō-fō′bi-à) Fear of metals.

metalloscopia (-skō′pi-à) An obsolete method of treatment in hysteria by the application of metals to anesthetic areas.

metals, psychosis due to Individuals with prolonged exposure to metallic poisoning, such as lead, mercury, and arsenic, may show psychotic reactions. Early symptoms may include gastro-intestinal disturbances and peripheral nerve toxic symptoms, followed possibly by delirium with marked prostration. There may be recovery from these mental symptoms or the patient may present a residual intellectual and emotional defect, based on the neurological changes associated with these toxins. The clinical picture occasionally resembles the

Korsakoff syndrome. According to the 1952 revision of psychiatric nomenclature, these psychoses are classified as acute or chronic brain syndromes due to poisons.

metamorphosis, delirium of See *lycanthropy.*

metamorphosis sexualis paranoica (metá-môr-fō′zēs sek-soo-ä′lēs pà-rà-nô′ē-ka) *Rare.* Delusion, often seen in paranoid patients, that their sexuality has been changed into that of the opposite sex.

metaphase (met′à-fāz) *Biol.* The second stage of the division of a cell by mitosis. (See *division, cell.*)

metaphrenia (-frē′ni-à) Staercke attempts to draw parallelisms between the basic phenomena of paraphrenia and of metaphrenia. The latter is a condition characterized by compulsions regarding time and money.

'Metaphrenia then consists of: (1) The remainder of the earlier phases (orthophrenia), (2) An obsessional neurosis (products compulsion), (3) A narcissistic neurosis (idealism), (4) An anxiety hysteria (over-developed hygiene, etc.), (5) Transference neurosis of the second group (domestication, formation of the State, etc.).' (*International Journal of Psychoanalysis II,* 393, 1921) He later (ibid., *X,* 189, 1929) defined metaphrenia as 'the mental condition of the individual in the modern State.' He adds that the 'mental condition of the individual who is part of a family or horde' is called orthophrenia.

metapsychoanalysis (met-à-sī-kō-à-nal′i-sis) Otto Rank's term to denote an analysis beyond psychoanalysis.

metapsychology (-sī-kol′ō-jē) Philosophical speculation regarding the mind, its origin, structure, function, physiology, pathology, etc.—speculation that cannot be verified by direct experience.

metempsychosis (met-em-sī-kō′sis) Migration of the soul or rational spirit at death into another body; the doctrine of metempsychosis is part of the Hindu religion, which further teaches that the soul carries with it the memories of former existences for a thousand years. It then induces forgetfulness by drinking of Lethe and begins all over again.

metencephalon (met-en-sef′à-lon) See *hindbrain.*

meteorophobia (mē-tē-or-ō-fō′bi-à) Fear of meteors.

methilepsia (meth-i-lep′si-à) Morbid impulse for intoxicants.

method, concentric (kon-sen′trik) A concept of stratification of the personality employed by Laignel-Lavastine. Five concentric (i.e. having a common center) zones of personality are recognized: psychic, nervous, endocrine, visceral, and morbific. Personality difficulties and psychiatric symptomatology result from abnormalities in any zone, or in any combination of zones.

method, co-twin control A method of study developed by Gesell and Thompson for use in medical genetics. In this method, observational twin data are obtained from a few selected one-egg pairs, whose aptitudes or adjustments under different life conditions are then compared.

method, cross-cultural Comparison of different cultures or societies to determine the effect of a particular variable on behavior.

method, need-press A technique of analysis of the TAT used by Murray (one of the originators of the test); in this method, each sentence of the subject's story is analyzed as to the needs of the hero and the press (environmental forces) he is exposed to. Each need and press is given a weighted score and a rank-order system of the needs and press is then tabulated. The method is not widely used clinically because it is too time-consuming to be practical.

method, pedigree Study of the family history to determine the frequency with which a familial trait occurs in the members of an affected family. This method does not ordinarily afford conclusive proof of heredity and is largely restricted to rare pathological traits which are fairly constant in penetrance and expressivity.

method, projective As distinguished from the direct, question-and-answer method in psychiatric examination, the projective method seeks to gain information indirectly, through the use of certain test techniques specifically designed to provide opportunity for self-expression without direct verbal accounting. Kanner says: 'It has been known for a long time that personality can reveal itself in more, and sometimes better, ways than through verbal self-evaluation. The Binet test expects the average 10-year-old to be able to answer the question: "Why should we judge a person more by his actions than by his words?" A plus score is given, if a child recognizes that a person's actions tell more about him, "speak louder," than his words. Are there then, performances which could be used clinically to elicit material which a patient will not or cannot disclose in ordinary conversation? Can he be helped to "project" his feelings and inner experiences on some sort of screen at a time when embarrassment, guilt, confusion, or unawareness renders verbal accounting relatively useless? . . . A variety of performances has been tried, and some were found to be helpful beyond expectation.' (Kanner, L. *Child Psychiatry,* Thomas, Springfield, Ill., 1948) Frank compared the role of these methods to that of the x-ray in the biologic sciences: 'In similar fashion we may approach the personality and induce the individual to reveal his way of organizing experience by giving him a field (objects, materials, experiences) with relatively little structure and cultural patterning so that the personality can project upon that plastic field his way of seeing life, his meanings, significances, patterns, and especially his feelings. Thus we elicit a projection of the individual personality's *private world,* because he has to organize the field, interpret the material, and react effectively to it.' (Frank, L. K. 'Projective Methods for the Study of Personality,' *Journal of Psychology 8,* 389–413, 1939) *Play therapy* (q.v.) in child psychiatry and the Rorschach Test represent outstanding examples of the projective method in psychiatric examination.

method, sibship (sib'ship) A method devised by Weinberg for use in psychiatric genetics. In this method, the blood relatives of a statistically representative number of probands or index cases are studied to determine whether or not a particular trait occurs more frequently in them than it does in the general population (or in a group of persons not related to the carriers by blood).

method, Turkish-bath A type of treatment based on transference relationship in which the therapist applies threats and reassurances one after the other—one day hot, the next day cold.

method, twin-study One of the two principal methods used in psychiatric genetics for differentiation between genetic and environmental influences in relation to specific forms of adjustment or maladjustment. In this method, the dissimilarities of one-egg twins, genotypically identical individuals, are compared with the behavioral variations seen in ordinary sibs or two-egg twins.

methomania (meth-ō-mā'ni-à) *Methilepsia* (q.v.).

metonymy (me-ton'ō-mē) A disturbance of language seen most commonly in the schizophrenias in which an approximate but related term is used in place of the more precise, definite, or idiomatic term which would ordinarily be used. A young schizophrenic patient, for example, spoke in a labyrinthine, circumstantial manner for many minutes during a psychotherapy session, but suddenly became blocked. He recovered spontaneously after 5–10 seconds, and said: 'Now let's see. What was I saying? I seem to have lost the piece of string of the conversation.' The phrase, piece of string, would be considered a metonymic substitution for the idiom, to lose the thread of conversation.

Metrazol (met'rà-zol) Cardiazol. See *treatment, Metrazol.*

metromania 1. Mania for incessant writing of verses. 2. *Obs.* Nymphomania.

Meyer, Adolf (1866–1950) American psychiatrist; 'the mind in action,' psychobiology.

Meynert, Theodore (1833–92) (mī'nẽrt) German neurologist and psychiatrist.

micro- (mī'krō-) Combining form meaning small, minute, diminished, from Gr. *mikrós,* small, little.

microbiophobia (mī-krō-bī-ō-fō'bi-à) *Microphobia* (q.v.).

microcephaly (-sef'à-lē) Smallness of the head; a condition in which there is defective development of the whole brain and premature ossification of the skull.

microcosm (mī'kro-koz'm) See *words, microcosm of.*

microglia (mi-krog'li-à) See *neuroglia.*

micromania (mī-krō-mā'ni-à) An obsolete term, denoting 'the form of insanity in which the patient imagines that his body or some part of it has become small. Delusion of belittlement.' (Tuke, D.H. *A Dictionary of Psychological Medicine,*

vols. 1–2, Blakiston, Philadelphia, 1892)
The concept prevails today, though it does
not have the value of a clinical entity;
rather it is regarded as a symptom. Thus,
in psychoanalysis the 'small penis' complex is an example of what was formerly
known as micromania. See *délire d'énormité.*

microphobia (-fō'bi-à) Fear of small
objects.

microphonia (-fō'ni-à) Weakness of the
voice.

micropsia, micropsy (mī-krop'si-à, mī-
krop'sē) Perception of objects as smaller
than they really are. This may be occasioned by organic or psychic causes. When
the latter prevail the condition may also
be known as Lilliputian hallucination (see
hallucination, Lilliputian). Micropsia is
not uncommon in hysteria and genuine or
ideopathic epilepsy. In the psychiatry of
the 19th century the state of *hysterical
micropsy* was defined as 'the visual defect
found in hysterical subjects, in which objects at a certain distance appear smaller
than they really are, associated as a rule
with functional monocular polyopia and
hysterical macropsy.' (Tuke, D.H. *A Dictionary of Psychological Medicine,* vols.
1–2, Blakiston, Philadelphia, 1892)

micropsychia (mī-krō-sī'ki-à) *Obs.* Feeblemindedness.

micropsychosis (mī-krō-sī-kō'sis)   See
schizophrenia, pseudoneurotic.

micropsy, hysterical See *micropsia.*

microscopy, mental (mī-kros'kō-pē) See
psychoscopy.

microsome, microsoma (mī'krō-sōm, -sō'-
mà) In biology, one of the minute granules found in vegetable protoplasm; this
should not be confused with the concept
of *microsomia* used in constitutional medicine.

microsomia (mī-krō-sō'mi-à) See *dwarfism.*

microsplanchnic (-splangk'nik) According
to Viola's classification of the constitutional forms of body build, this term refers
to the type which has the abdominal portion of the body relatively small in proportion to the thoracic portion, owing to the
small size of the abdominal viscera. It is
further characterized by the overdevelopment of the vertical diameters of the body
in comparison with the horizontal diame-

ters, so that the body presents an elongated
appearance.

This *microsplanchnic* type corresponds
to the *hypovegetative* biotype of Pende,
the *asthenic* (q.v.) type of Kretschmer.

Midas punishment See *masturbation, compulsive.*

midbrain Mesencephalon; that portion of
the brain lying between the pons and the
cerebral hemispheres, containing the *corpora quadrigemina* (q.v.), the cerebral
peduncles and the aqueduct of Sylvius.
The base of each peduncle contains the
homolateral corticospinal, corticobulbar,
and corticopontile tracts. The substantia
nigra is a broad layer of pigmented gray
substance occupying the central portion
of the peduncle. The roof or dorsal portion of the base is the tegmentum, which
contains: lateral and medial lemnisci,
median longitudinal fasciculus, red nucleus, spinothalamic and spinotectal tracts,
superior cerebellar peduncle, the nuclei of
the trochlear and oculomotor nerves, and
the nucleus of the mesencephalic root of
the trigeminal nerve.

Lesions of the corpora quadrigemina
cause paralysis of upward eye movements;
of the cerebral peduncle, spastic contralateral paralysis; of the red nucleus, substantia nigra, or reticular substance, involuntary movements and rigidity. In cats,
destruction of portions of the tegmentum
produces cataleptic manifestations similar
to cerea flexibilitas.

migraine (mī'grān) A syndrome of periodic, unilateral headache with photophobia, vomiting, nausea, and various prodromata such as scotomata, occasional
paresthesiae, and speech difficulties. After
the attack there is often a marked sensation of well-being. Between 50 and 80 per
cent of patients have a directly homologous heredity; the mother to daughter
transmission is the most common, mother
to son is next common. There is a close
relation between migraine and epilepsy,
and they may be clinical manifestations
of the same disorder; 60 per cent of epileptic patients have a migrainous heredity,
but only 17 per cent of normal individuals.
Epilepsy occurs more frequently in migraine patients, and migraine more frequently in epileptics, than in the general
population. The same patient may have
alternate periods of epileptic attacks and
migraine attacks, one affliction replacing
the other for a considerable time. Puberty

is the most usual time of onset, and 50 per cent of cases begin before the thirtieth year. It affects females two and a half times more frequently than males. Individual attacks may be precipitated by a variety of conditions; mental and emotional excitement are common precipitants.

The headaches usually appear at irregular intervals; several attacks a month are common. The headache has a crescendo type of intensity; it may be dull, boring, pressing, throbbing, vise-like, lancinating, or hammering in character. It may begin at any point on the head and spread to involve the entire side. Because of the frequency of associated gastro-intestinal symptoms, migraine is often called sick headache or bilious headache. The headache rarely lasts longer than 12 to 24 hours. The present-day conception is that migraine is a result of functional disturbances in the carotid cranial vascular tree; these occur in response to various etiologic agents which apparently vary greatly in different cases.

Migraine is usually considered to be a psychosomatic (psychophysiologic autonomic) disorder. Psychodynamically, destructive and hostile impulses are the important feature, and migraine in a sense is a hostile attack. Alexander considers migraine the result of inhibition of the phase of psychological preparation for an aggressive attack. See *hypertension, essential.*

migrateur (mē-gra-tēr') (F. 'migratory, migrant') One suffering from an obsession to wander.

milieu (mē-lyē') Environment; surroundings. In psychiatry, the *social setting,* emphasis being placed upon the setting from the emotional point of view. To a psychiatrist a most important milieu is the home. From the psychoanalytic standpoint it is the most significant. Other environments—scholastic, recreational, industrial, religious, etc.—play a leading role in the growth of the personality.

'Freud compares the inheritance of the neuroses with that of tuberculosis. Just as in inherited tuberculosis a thorough examination often shows that one has to deal with an infection acquired in childhood from a diseased environment and not merely the congenital organic weakness; in the same way, in the case of children of neurotic parents, we must, along with heredity, attribute great importance also to the abnormal mental impressions to which they have been exposed since early childhood.' (Ferenczi, S. *Further Contributions to the Theory and Technique of Psycho-Analysis,* tr. by Suttie, J.I., Leonard and Virginia Woolf and The Institute of Psychoanalysis, London, 1926)

'We obtain this knowledge through the thorough investigation of the psychic life-history of the child, taken both from himself and from his milieu.' (Jung, C.G. *Contributions to Analytical Psychology,* tr. by Baynes, H.G. and C.F., Kegan Paul, Trench, Trubner, London, 1928)

Millard-Gubler syndrome (August L.J. Millard, French physician, 1830–1915, and Adolphe Gubler, French physician, 1821–79) Paralysis of the external rectus on one side and supranuclear paralysis of the bulbar muscles and limbs on the opposite side.

Milligan annihilation method A type of regressive electroshock therapy (REST) in which 3 treatments are administered the first day, and 2 treatments are given daily thereafter until the desired regression is obtained.

-mimesis (-mi-mē'sis) Combining form meaning imitation, mimicry, from Gr. *mímēsis,* imitation, from *mimeīsthai,* to mimic, imitate.

-mimia (-mim'i-à) Combining form meaning imitation, mimicry, gesture, from Gr. *mimía,* imitation.

mind *Psyche* (q.v.).

mind, miniature A term used by Lindberg to describe the stunted mind of a person afflicted with psycho-infantilism. It has been defined 'as a symmetrical retardation in all aspects of mental life, in contradistinction to mental deficiency. The psycho-infantile person is regarded as one with a *miniature mind,* a mental midget.' (Lindberg, B.J. *Psycho-Infantilism,* Ejnar Munksgaard, Copenhagen, 1950) See *psycho-infantilism.*

mind-reading See *telepathy.*

mind-stuff See *psychology, atomistic.*

mineralo-corticoid (min-er-a-lō-kor'ti-koid) See *syndrome, general adaptation.*

miolecithal (mī-ō-les'i-thal) Referring to the human type of *cleavage* (q.v.) in the development of an embryo.

miopragia (mī-ō-prā'ji-à) In constitutional medicine, diminished functional activity of an organ. For example, individuals with the asthenic habitus may possess a small, immature, and functionally diminished cardiovascular apparatus. Thus, Lewis, in *Constitutional Factors in Dementia Praecox* reported, among other things, a hypoplastic heart with lessened functional capacity.

miosis (mī-ō′sis) A. Contraction of the pupil. B. The genetic term *miosis* refers to that particular kind of cell division in sexual reproduction which occurs in the sex glands immediately preceding gametic formation and results in a *reduction* of the chromosomes from the double or *diploid* number, characteristic of all somatic cells, to the halved or *haploid* number characteristic of gametes. This 'reduction division' leads to the separation of the two elements of each chromosome pair and provides the necessary basis for the segregation of genetic factors. Miotic divisions are thus genetically *segregation divisions*.

According to A.F. Shull, the following features of miosis are most essential to the processes of heredity:

1. The pairing of the homologous maternal and paternal chromosomes;

2. The separation of these paired chromosomes and their passage to different cells in the reduction division;

3. The consequent separation of the genes of each pair to different germ cells;

4. The independence of the several pairs of chromosomes in this separation;

5. The resultant assembling of various combinations of maternal and paternal chromosomes in the different mature germ cells;

6. The variety of combinations of genes thus produced in the different germ cells;

7. The reduction of the number of chromosomes in the mature germ cells to half that found in the reproductive cells before maturation.

miriasha (mē-ryä′shà) A person affected with *miryachit* (q.v.).

mirror-imaging In genetics, reversed *asymmetry*, quite frequent in twins, with respect to handedness, hair whorl, dental irregularities, fingerprints, and other symmetrical characters including certain morbid traits based on heredity. The presence of *mirror-imaging* is confirmatory evidence of *monozygotic* twins, though monozygosity is not excluded by its absence (see *twin*).

mirror sign See *sign, mirror*.

miryachit (mē-ryä′chēt) 'This is the term applied in Russia and Eastern Siberia to a morbid condition, which, however, is met with under different names in various parts of the world. The term itself is part of a verb meaning "to fool" or "play the fool," and the victim of the disease, if he may be so named, has a desire, apparently irresistible, to imitate whatever action is carried out in his presence, and also to repeat whatever is said to him or in his hearing.' (*A Dictionary of Medicine*, ed. by Quain, R. Appleton, New York, 1899) See *echolalia; echopraxia; lata*.

misanthropy (mis-an′thrō-pē, miz-an′-) Hatred of, or aversion to, mankind. A profound morbid distrust of human beings individually and collectively.

misidentification, amnesic (am-nē′zik) The inability of an individual to identify the person confronting him. The misidentification is due to the impairment of the memory or to clouding of consciousness.

misidentification, delusional A failure to recognize well-known objects as such, due to the delusion that the objects have been transformed; e.g. a patient may believe that a woman has been transformed into a man; or that a young person has been changed into an old one; or a new coat into a shabby one, etc.

misidentification, hyperbolic (hī-per-bol′-ik) A condition sometimes found in manic states in which an individual flippantly calls a person by someone else's name. This misidentification is rarely clung to with conviction.

miso- (mis′ō-)Combining form meaning hate, hatred, from Gr. *misos,* hate, hatred.

misocainia (-kī′ni-à) The hatred of anything new or strange is not uncommon among psychiatric patients. Its form is very vivid in patients with involutional melancholia, who get into a severe panic whenever they must move from their accustomed surroundings.

misogamy (mi-sog′à-mē) Hatred of marriage. Among psychiatric patients the hatred of wedlock almost invariably stems from childhood experiences associated with the parents. It is said by psychoanalysts to be one of the consequences of an unresolved Oedipus complex. Misogamy is especially common in patients with schizophrenia, who overtly avoid any situation that might possibly lead to marriage. To them marriage is equated with incest and misogamy is their defense against it.

misogyny (mi-soj′i-nē) Hatred of women. When the hate of women is part of a morbid mental state, it may be associated with a wide variety of nosologic entities. The most common explanation for the condition has to do with the events of childhood, particularly those relating to the parents (see *complex, Oedipus*).

Abhorrence of women is expressed alike by women and men. It is not infrequently a reflection of a homosexual conflict. A hysterical woman detested all women and all things effeminate; she had always wanted to be a male; indeed, throughout her childhood her father chided her because she was female; since early childhood she detested effeminacy and did as much as possible to become masculine.

Passive homosexual male individuals may hold women in severe contempt, as a reaction to their disappointment with their own masculinity. A paranoid, homosexual patient killed a woman in order to gain her femaleness. Thereafter he denied that he had any attributes, physical or mental, of masculinity.

misologia, misology (mis-ō-lō′ji-à, mi-sol′ō-jē) Hatred of speaking or arguing. Some patients hate to converse. A psychoneurotic individual was sure that if she uttered any word, no matter how innocuous, it could only provoke an argument as a consequence of which someone would be injured or might even die. A patient with the catatonic form of schizophrenia remained mute lest the world should be destroyed through her speaking.

misomania *Obs.* Mania of hatred. The syndrome characterized by delusions of persecution.

misoneism (mis-ō-nē′iz′m) Hatred of innovation, *misocainia* (q.v.).

misopedia (-pē′di-a) Morbid hatred of children. A patient had an obsession to kill all children, because they were produced through the intervention of the male sex. He devoted his life to the Doctrine of Immaculate Conception.

Behind the hatred of children is often the idea of incest, the parent unconsciously acting on the impulse that the child is the consequence of incestuous relations.

misopsychia (-sī′ki-à) *Obs.* Hatred or

weariness of living; synonymous with the obsolete terms *misozoeticus* and *misozoia*.

Mitchell, S(ilas) Weir (1829–1914) American neurologist and psychiatrist.

mitissima (mē-tēs′sē-mà) Mania mitis; paraphrosyne.

mitosis (mi-tō′sis) Originally meaning the division of the *nucleus* of a cell, the term is now often used for the entire process of cell division, involving all radical changes in the structure of a cell which are of utmost significance in inheritance (see *division, cell*).

mixoscopia (mik-sō-skō′pi-à) A form of sexual perversion, deriving pleasure from watching the act of coition between the desired one and another person. Jones defines it as 'excitement at witnessing a sexual act.'

mixovariation (-và-ri-ā′shun) This genetic term is synonymous with *combination*, signifying hereditary variations between related individuals, due to the sorting out and recombining of separate factors in the generations following crosses of mates with unlike hereditary equipment (see *combination*).

mixture, Cloetta's (Max Cloetta, Swiss pharmacologist, 1868–1940) A combination of paraldehyde, amylene hydrate, chloral hydrate, alcohol, barbituric acid, digitalin and ephedrine hydrochloride which is usually administered per rectum in continuous sleep treatment. (See *treatment, continuous sleep*).

M'Naghten rule See *rule, M'Naghten*.

mneme (nē′mē) A term coined by Richard Semon to denote a form of memory that all body-cells are believed to possess.

mneme, phylogenetic (fī-lō-jē-net′ik) The racial ancestral memory present in the deep unconscious of the individual.

mnemic (nē′mik) Pertaining to or characterized by memory.

mnemism (nē′miz′m) Mnemic hypothesis that cells possess memory. See *mneme*.

-mnesia, -mnesis (-[m]nē′z[h]i-à, -[m]nē′-sis) Combining form meaning memory, recollection, from Gr. *mnēsi-* only in composition, from unrecorded Gr. *mnēsis,* memory, from *mnāsthai,* to remember.

mob 'A highly excited form of the crowd.' (Bernard, L.L. *Mob; Encyclopaedia of the*

Social Sciences, vol. 10, Macmillan, New York, 1933, p. 552)

The mob is 'the crowd that acts.' (Thrasher, F.M. *The Gang,* University of Chicago Press, Chicago, 1927)

Examples of mob behavior are riots, lynchings, and mutinies.

mobility (mō-bil′i-tē) 'A change of movement in response to a new stimulus or situation.' (Park, R.E. and Burgess, E.W. *The City,* University of Chicago Press, Chicago, 1925)

Mobility 'measures not merely the social contacts that one gains from travel and exploration, but the stimulation and suggestions that come to us through the medium of communication, by which sentiments and ideas are put in social circulation.' (Park, R.E. and Burgess, E.W. *Introduction to the Science of Sociology,* University of Chicago Press, Chicago, 1921)

mobility, social The free interactions among, and the changing roles and status of, members in a group. This term is used in contrast to social fixity. (See *fixity, social.*)

mobilization, psychological (mō-bi-li-zā′-shun, sī-kō-loj′i-kal) P. Janet places the concept of psychological mobilization 'under the patronage of William James, for it has been inspired by his interesting essay, *The Energies of Men.* There can be no doubt that, in the activities of daily life, human beings do not expend all the energies they possess, for they keep a large amount of energy in reserve. Under the pressure of unforseen happenings, not only the normal individual, but even an extremely depressed patient, will be found capable of a quite unexpected activity. He is able to call up his reserves.' Janet adds that certain patients 'have considerable reserves; but these reserves are not fluid, and for practical purposes at the particular time when the patients come under our observation the amount of their available energies is insufficient, for the bulk of their forces cannot be mobilised at this particular moment.' (Janet, P. *Psychological Healing,* vols. 1–2, tr. by Paul, E. and C., Macmillan, New York, 1925)

mode The value in a frequency curve at which the height of the curve is greatest; i.e. the most frequently recurring score in a distribution. The mode is a very unstable measure.

modification In genetics, the term is limited to variations in the phenotype which are caused by environmental influences and modify the individual appearance without affecting the idioplasm. Drastic effects of the environment of living beings may lead to profoundly modified developments, but it is safe to assume that they cannot become inheritable.

Even phenotypical impairment due to poisons, alcohol, or domestication are apparently not transmitted *as such* to descendants. 'The few experiments leading to the opposite conclusion are of doubtful validity and do not in any case amount to proof.' (Sinnott, E.W. and Dunn, L.D. *Principles of Genetics,* 3rd ed., McGraw-Hill, New York and London, 1939)

Of the modifying factors which interact to produce a human phenotype, the physiological effects of nutrition, light, and climate seem just as important as social, cultural, and psychological influences. These various environmental modifications can be best observed in identical co-twins reared apart under different life conditions (see *variation*).

modifier In accordance with the genetic principle that of the several hereditary factors which interact to produce a given phenotype, some contribute a greater share than others to the total effect, this term is used to denote those factors which appear merely to modify the effect of another factor, having little or no effect when the main factor is not present.

A modifier is called *specific* when its effects are produced only upon a specific genotype. See *variation.*

Moebius, Paul Julius (1853–1907) (mē′-bi-oos) German neuropathologist and sexologist.

mogigraphia (moj-i-graf′i-à) Writer's cramp. See *neurasthenia, professional.*

mogilalia (moj-i-lā′li-à) Hesitancy or difficulty in speaking. A phenomenon particularly common among psychiatric patients; when psychically determined it is regarded as a manifestation of resistance.

Moira (moi′rà) Moira in Greek mythology was the goddess of fate and was sometimes identified with the supreme power *anánkē* to which even the gods were subject, the destiny which even they could not escape. (Baynes, H.G. *Mythology of the Soul,* Williams and Wilkins, Baltimore, 1940)

molilalia (mol-i-lā'li-à) *Mogilalia* (q.v.).

molimina, premenstrual (mo-lim'i-na, prē-men'stroo-al) Premenstrual tension; the term includes both physical and psychic symptoms referable to the premenstrual period.

molysmophobia (mol-iz-mō-fō'bi-à) Fear of contamination.

mongol One belonging to the Mongolian race. One who presents the clinical syndrome of mental deficiency called *mongolism* (q.v.).

mongolism (mong'gol-iz'm) Mongolian idiocy; variously called the Mongolian, Kalmuck, Khirghiz, or Tartar type of mental deficiency. Affected children are usually born of a mother near the close of the reproductive period, i.e. over 40 years of age. Mongolism occurs in more than one member of the same fraternity more often than would be expected by chance. It has been reported in both monozygotic twins and in both dizygotic twins (but not in twins of different sex); whether this is indicative of a primary genetic basis or of environmental factors operating at or soon after fertilization is still an unsolved problem.

Pathologically, the brain is small, and there are widespread defects in the cortical cell layers and in the number of ganglion cells. Whole gyri may be faulty in development. The process apparently is stationary, for regressive changes are not seen. There are many signs characteristic of mongolism, but not all are seen in each case. In one reported series, the signs appeared with the following frequencies: slanting of the palpebral fissures (88%), hyperextensible joints (88%), flabby hands (84%), brachycephalic skull with flat occiput (82%), ear anomalies or small lobules (80%), diastasis recti (76%), high-arched palate (74%), irregular alignment of teeth (68%), flat nipples (56%), epicanthus (50%), speckling of the iris (30%), heart murmurs (28%), double-zoned iris (22%), and pathologically open fontanels (16%). (Levinson, A., Freidman, A., and Stamps, F. 'Variability of Mongolism,' *Pediatrics 16:* 43–54, 1955)

Mentally, the mongoloid is usually docile and tractable and may give an appearance of higher mental capacity than is really present because of imitativeness. The majority have a mental age of 4 to 7 years, although there are variations from moronity to pronounced idiocy. A few are hyperactive and sometimes destructive.

Because of associated defects, probably less than 60 per cent live more than five years.

Moniz, Egas (1874–1955) Pen name for Antonio Caetano deAbreu Freire, Portugese neurologist; development of cerebral angiography and of frontal leukotomy (the first psychosurgical procedure), for which he received the Nobel Prize for medicine in 1949.

mono- (mon'ō-) Combining form meaning one, only, single, from Gr. *mónos,* alone, only, single, unique.

monoamine oxidase (mon-ō-am'ēn oks'i-dās) Also known as MAO; an enzyme, discovered by Hare in 1928, which has since been shown to be able to oxidize (and thus inactivate) various amines, including serotonin, the catecholamines and their methoxy derivatives. Of interest clinically is that fact that inhibitors of monoamine oxidase seem to be psychic energizers.

monobulia (mon-ō-bū'li-à) 'Between not wishing anything at all and wishing one thing only—that is to say, between abulia and *monobulia*—the difference may seem very small, but often it is very considerable. Indeed, in the term "monobulia" there may be included two somewhat different varieties of psychical state. There is a static or continued monobulia, which consists in the presence of a permanent and overmastering volition that inhibits and eliminates every other mental phenomenon. There is also a dynamic or discontinuous form of monobulia, which consists in a repeated and relentless return of the same volitional tendency.' (Tanzi, E. *A Text-Book of Mental Diseases,* tr. by Robertson, W.F. and Mackenzie, T.C., Rebman, New York, 1909)

monobulia, obsessive Tanzi thus denotes what is today known as an obsession as it appears in the psychoneuroses.

'The morbid origin of these true *obsessions* is evidenced by the characteristic circumstance that the patient feels himself to be invaded and dominated by a will that is foreign to his psychical personality. It causes him annoyance, displeasure, horror, fear, or despair, according to the representational content of the obsession.' (Tanzi, E. *A Text-Book of Mental Diseases,* tr. by Robertson, W.F.

and Mackenzie, T.C., Rebman, New York, 1909)

monoecism (mō-nē'siz'm) See *hermaphroditism.*

monohybrid Differing with respect to only *one* hereditary character (in a hybrid individual). Similarly *schizophrenia* is a monohybrid trait. See *hybrid.*

monohybridity, monohybridism (mon-ō-hī-brid'i-tē, -hī'brid-iz'm) The state of a hybrid whose parents differ in a single character, or the character of belonging to a type of individual heterozygous for a single pair of genes.

monoideism (mon-ō-ī'dē-iz'm) 'The theory according to which an idea detached from other ideas will exercise an unusually powerful force in the mind. This notion was formulated long ago both by Descartes and by Condillac. The magnetisers were well aware that suggestion was more powerful when the subjects were "isolated," that is to say when they were apparently unable to perceive any phenomena except the personality of the magnetiser and his utterances.' (Janet, P. *Psychological Healing,* vols. 1–2, tr. by Paul, E. and C., Macmillan, New York, 1925)
'In suggestion all other objects disappear; a suggestion is as detached from surroundings as are the images of an ordinary dream.' (Delboeuf, *Révue Philosophique,* 1887)
The term also means a patient's monoideism—harping on one idea. Monoideism is seen most frequently in the senile group and in the schizophrenias.

monomania This rare term was defined by D.H. Tuke as 'partial insanity. Those who have logically maintained its existence hold that the morbid mental state is restricted to one subject, the patient being of sound judgment and healthy feelings on all others. Employed in this sense it must be discarded as untrue to clinical experience. . . .' (Tuke, D.H. *A Dictionary of Psychological Medicine,* vols. 1–2, Blakiston, Philadelphia, 1892)
In older psychiatry there were such expressions as *intellectual monomania* (e.g. paranoia); *affective monomania,* which corresponded with *manie raisonnante,* characterized by emotional deviation; *instinctive monomania,* which in general is the equivalent of the com-

pulsive-obsessive syndrome of modern psychiatry.
When monomania or partial insanity was associated with depressive states, Esquirol suggested that the term *lypemania* be used, to distinguish the monomania with exaltation of mood.

monomania, affective An obsolete expression, used by Esquirol, most likely equivalent of the manic phase of manic-depressive psychosis.

monomania, homicidal (hom-i-sīd'al) *Obs.* Once thought to be a clinical entity, but now regarded as a symptom which may occur in a variety of psychiatric conditions.

monomania, instinctive See *monomania.*

monomania, intellectual See *monomania.*

monomania, reasoning *Obs.* Paranoia sine delirio.

monomanie boulimique (mô-nô-mȧ-nē' boo-lē-mēk') (F. 'bulimic impulse') Bulimia.

monomanie du vol (dü vôl') (F. 'impulse to steal') Kleptomania.

monomanie érotique (ā-rô-tēk') (F. 'erotic obsession') Erotomania.

monomanie expansive (ek-späN-sēv') (F. 'cheerful obsession') Amenomania.

monomanie incendiaire (eN-säN-dē-âr') (F. 'incendiary impulse') Pyromania.

monomanie meurtrière (mēr-trē-âr') (F. 'murderous impulse') Morbid impulse to kill.

monomanie orgueilleuse (or-gē-yēz') (F. 'obsession of haughtiness') Megalomania.

monomoria (mon-ō-mō'ri-ȧ) *Obs.* Melancholia.

mononoea (-ne'ȧ) Concentration on a single subject, as in monomania.

monopagia (-pā'ji-ȧ) Clavus hystericus.

monopathophobia (-path-ō-fō'bi-ȧ) Fear of a single, specific organic disease.

monophobia Fear of being alone.

monoplegia (mon-o-plē'ji-ȧ) Paralysis of one limb or single part of the body, such as one arm, one leg, or the face alone, or only the fingers.

monopsychosis (-sī-kō'sis) *Obs.* Term, coined by Clouston, synonymous with *monomania.*

monosex The term monosex has been

losing more and more in definiteness with advances in the biological sciences. 'It is exceedingly difficult to define sex from a biologic viewpoint, and according to Lillie, there is no such entity, but rather a dimorphism into contrasting characters whether they be biological, psychological, etc.' (Young, H.H. *Genital Abnormalities, Hermaphroditism and Related Adrenal Diseases,* Williams and Wilkins, Baltimore, 1937)

Psychiatrists experience the same difficulties in this respect, because it is not yet possible to describe all the character traits of an individual as either masculine or feminine.

Monosex may be used only in a relative sense: an individual may be preponderantly masculine or feminine.

monosymptomatic (mon-ō-simp-tō-mat′-ik) Manifested by a single symptom. When a disorder is presented in the form of a single symptom it is said to be monosymptomatic.

'Hysterias in children without marked change of character are mostly monosymptomatic.' (Bleuler, E. *Textbook of Psychiatry,* tr. by Brill, A.A., Macmillan, New York, 1930)

monozygosity, monozygocity (-zi-, zigos′i-tē) Both terms are used in genetics with reference to the origin from one egg of *monozygotic* or *identical* twins.

monozygote (-zī′gōt) One of the *monozygotic* (identical) co-twins.

monozygotic (-zī-got′ik) This genetic term describes the sets of twins developed from a single egg and exhibiting extreme resemblances because of their identical genotypes. These *monozygotic,* or *identical,* or *one-egg* twin pairs are to be distinguished from the *dizygotic, fraternal,* or *non-identical* twin pairs produced by two eggs. See *twin.*

moodcyclic disorders See *psychodynamics, adaptational.*

mood, manic (man′ik) See *disposition, constitutional manic.*

mood, melancholic (mel-an-kol′ik) See *disposition, constitutional depressive.*

mood-swings The oscillation between periods of the feeling of well-being and those of depression or 'blueness.' All individuals have mood-swings, and normal individuals may have blue hours or blue days. Mood-swings are somewhat more marked in the neurotic than in the normal individual. In the manic-depressive patient, the swings are of much greater intensity and much longer duration.

moonstruck A popular term, meaning insane.

morale (mō-räl′) 'Group persistence in the pursuit of collective purposes.' (Lasswell, H.D. *Morale; Encyclopaedia of the Social Sciences,* vol. 10, Macmillan, New York, 1933, p. 640)

'Morale can be thought of as giving persistency and determination to a movement; its test is whether solidarity can be maintained in the face of adversity.' (Blumer, H.E. in Park, R.E. *Principles of Sociology,* Barnes & Noble, New York, 1939)

morality, sphincter (sfingk′tēr) The expression is a psychoanalytic concept. The term *sphincter* literally refers to the circular muscles, which through relaxation and contraction cause an orifice to open and close respectively. There are two sphincter zones of the body to which psychoanalysts ascribe great significance from the standpoint of the instincts. They are the oral and the anal zones. Certain children are 'over-successfully' trained as regards oral and anal habits; in instances of this kind Ferenczi speaks of 'a severe sphincter-morality.' Abraham holds that some children are forced to 'good' oral and anal habits before they are psychically prepared for them; this often leads to an attitude of fear, rather than of love, toward objects. It is the opinion of psychoanalysts that excessive indulgence, just as drastic intimidation, plays an influential role in later character-formation.

moralization, medical 'This method [medical moralization] appeals to man's intelligence, to his reason, to his moral and religious sentiments, relying on these influences to bring about the restoration of health. It is an old method. . . . Still, if we think of widespread practice rather than of theory, it will be proper to regard Paul Dubois of Berne, a famous Swiss doctor, as the pioneer of this therapeutic method.' (Janet, P. *Psychological Healing,* vols. 1–2, tr. by Paul, E. and C., Macmillan, New York, 1925, p. 98)

moramentia (mor-à-men′shi-à) *Obs.* Absolute amorality.

morbus astralis (môr′boos às-trä′lēs) (L.

'disease pertaining to the stars') *Obs.* Epilepsy.

morbus attonitus Celsi (àt-tô'nē-toos kel'sē) (L. 'Celsus's disease,' from Aurelius Cornelius Celsus, a Roman compiler of a medical encyclopedia, about 25 A.D.) *Obs.* Catalepsy.

morbus comitialis (kô-mē-tē-ä'lēs) (L. 'disease, pertaining to the comitia or elections,' as its occurrence on the day of the comitia was an ill omen and postponed the elections) *Obs.* Epilepsy.

morbus eruditorum (ā-roo-dē-tô'room) (L. 'disease of the learned') Hypochondriasis.

morbus foedus (foy'doos) (L. 'foul, loathsome disease') Epilepsy.

morbus hypnoticus (hip-nô'tē-koos) (L. 'hypnotic disease') Drosdow introduced this term for a form of narcolepsy resembling the hypnotic state.

morbus infantilis (ēn-fàn'tē-lēs) (L. 'infantile disease') Epilepsy.

morbus interlunis (ēn-ter-lōō'nēs) (L. 'new-moon disease') Epilepsy.

morbus mirachialis (mē-rà-kē-ä'lēs) (L. 'abdominal disease') *Obs.* Hypochondriasis.

morbus popularis (pô-poo-lä'rēs) (L. 'people's disease') Epilepsy.

morbus publicus (poob'lē-koos) (L. 'public, common, disease') Epilepsy.

morbus puerilis (poo-e'rē-lēs) (L. 'disease of childhood') Epilepsy.

morbus resiccatorius (rā-sēk-kà-tō'rē-oos) (L. 'drying, exhausting disease') Hypochondriasis.

morbus sacer (sà'ker) (L. 'sacred disease') Epilepsy.

morbus Sancti Joannis (sangk'tē yô-àn'-nēs) (L. 'Saint John's disease') Epilepsy.

morbus Sancti Valentini (và-len-tē'nē) (L. 'Saint Valentine's disease') Epilepsy.

morbus scelestus (ske-les'toos) (L. 'wicked, infamous disease') Epilepsy.

morbus sonticus (sôn'tē-koos) (L. 'dangerous, critical, disease') Epilepsy.

mores (mō'rēz) 'The popular habits and traditions, when they include a judgment that they are conducive to a societal welfare, and when they exert a co-ercion on the individual to conform to them, although they are not co-ordinated by any authority.' (Sumner, W.G. and Keller, A.G. *The Science of Society*, Yale University Press, New Haven, 1927–28)

'When the conviction arises that certain folkways are indispensable to the welfare of society, that they are the only "right" ways and that departure from them will involve calamity, i.e., when philosophical and ethical generalizations are developed about them, they are called mores.' (Davis, M.R. *Folkways; Encyclopaedia of the Social Sciences*, vol. 6, Macmillan, New York, 1931, p. 294)

mores, social Codes of manners and morals imposed by tacit authority (of 'unwritten' law) upon the individual to guide his social behavior in a given society, culture, or ethnical group and varying with the shift from one group, society, or culture to another.

moria (mō'ri-à) A morbid impulse to joke.

'More rarely we notice a stupid euphoria with a mania for joking (moria).' (Bleuler, E. *Textbook of Psychiatry*, tr. by Brill, A.A., Macmillan, New York, 1930)

moron (mor'on) A mentally, that is, intellectually defective person having a mental age between 84 and 143 months; or a child with an I.Q. between 50 and 74. In England the individuals of this group are called *dullards*.

morosis (mō-rō'sis) *Obs.* Fatuity; also idiotism.

-morph (-morf) Combining form meaning one endowed with (specific) form or shape. From this are further formed *-morphic, -morphous, -morphy.*

morphinism (mor'fin-iz'm) Morphinomania.

morphinomania, morphiomania (mor-fi-nō-mā'ni-à, -ō-mā'ni-à) Morbid craving for morphine.

mort douce (mawr' doos') (F. 'sweet death') Some authorities (e.g. Hirschfeld) use this expression to refer to the 'sweet death' accompanying the termination of the sexual act. Psychoanalysts liken the phenomena attendant upon the completion of the sexual act to those of 'sweet death.'

Other authorities make the phrase synonymous with *euthanasia.*

mortido (mor-tid'ō) Federn's term for

the destructive instinct. Same as *destrudo* (q.v.).

morula (mor'oo-là, -ū-là) The embryological stage of a human organism, comprising the segmenting process of *cleavage* of a fertilized egg up to the 32-cell stage and the formation of the *blastula*.

Morvan's disease (Augustin Marie de Lannitis Morvan, French physician, 1819–97) See *syringomyelia*.

mosaic (mō-zā'ik) See *intermediate*.

mother-fixation See *fixation, mother*.

mother, great See *Magna Mater*.

mother-hypnosis (-hip-nō'sis) See *hypnosis, father*.

mother-image See *image*.

mother, phallic The phantasy, which occurs early in the male's psychic development, that the mother has a phallus. In the course of his development, the male child reaches a stage in which his interest is concentrated on his genitals. Because this organ is so valuable and important to him, he believes that it is also present in other persons. Having seen no other type of genital formation, he will perforce assume that women also possess genitals like his. As part of the erotic activity developing around his genitals, the child manifests an intense desire to see the genitals of other persons, probably in order to compare them with his own. This erotic desire is very strong with regard to his mother, on whom his most intense feelings are concentrated at this age. He wishes to see the penis which he believes his mother possesses, and thus is developed the phantasy of the phallic mother in the male child.

This phantasy or belief may leave ineradicable traces in the child's subsequent psychic life. When he finds later that women, indeed, have no penis, his longing to see his mother's penis 'often becomes transformed into its opposite and gives place to disgust which in the years of puberty may become the cause of psychic impotence, of misogyny, and of lasting homosexuality.' And in fetishism the object which the patient reveres is 'a substitutive symbol for the once revered and since then missed member of the woman.' In mythology, too, 'this revered and very early fancied bodily formation of the mother' is retained. It is personified in those maternal deities appearing in many cultures in which the goddess is represented as having, in addition to breasts, a phallus. (Freud, S. *Leonardo da Vinci*, Kegan Paul, French, Trubner, London, 1922)

mother-substitute See *surrogate, mother*.

mother-surrogate See *surrogate, mother*.

motility, unconscious This psychiatric term designates the motility or movements that are of an unconscious character. Unconscious motility is most clearly observed in hysterical motor disturbances such as muscular spasms, hysterical convulsions, and in the hysterical conversion symptom of sleep-walking. All these syndromes show movements that are dissociated from the conscious mind, for conversions are the unconscious and distorted physical expression of repressed instinctual demands.

Unconscious motility may also, however, be understood in a broader sense. All living organisms carry out the basic functions of perception and motility. 'This is true even before there is any differentiation of the ego. . . . Before a systematic conception of reality can be developed there must of necessity exist a certain unsystematic perception.' And consciousness only 'comes into being at some point in the process of systematization,' which 'depends on the ability to utilize memories.' Thus motility is clearly a basic function of the living organism, even before the development of consciousness. (Fenichel, O. *The Psychoanalytic Theory of Neurosis*, Norton, New York, 1945)

motivation, unconscious The term describing the aim or goal (not recognized consciously by the individual) which lies at the basis of a symptom, a slip of the tongue, or a dream. This is a psychoanalytic concept which refers to the fact that dreams, symptoms, slips of the tongue, etc. are often determined by unfulfilled aims and desires which operate outside the field of conscious awareness. Thus hysterical vomiting in a pregnant woman may be determined by a desire to rid herself of the fetus, a desire of which she is not consciously aware.

Freud's early work with hypnosis in hysterical patients led him to the conclusion that the symptoms afford a release of excitation in response to certain events, usually sexual, which are so unbearable to the individual that they are actively put out of consciousness and relegated into the unconscious portion of the psychic structure. But even though there is no longer any conscious awareness of these events, it does not mean that they cease to affect the individual: they nonetheless produce excitation which seeks for discharge, yet cannot operate within the field of awareness, and, therefore, finds *abnormal* discharge in symptoms, slips of the tongue, and dreams.

motive, lay See *tendency, final.*

motor cortex (kor'teks) That area of the cerebral hemisphere which controls movement; sometimes used synonymously with *precentral convolution,* although this is inaccurate, since movements can be excited from other areas as well.

motorium (mō-tor'i-um) 1. The motor cortex. 2. That faculty of the mind which has to do with volition (as the function of the sensorium is perception and of the intellect, thinking).

motor-neurosis See *neurosis, motor.*

Mott, Frederick Walker, Sir (1859–1926) British neurologist.

mourning Freud says that 'a correlation of melancholia and mourning seems justified by the general picture of the two conditions. Moreover, wherever it is possible to discern the external influences in life which have brought each of them about, this exciting cause proves to be the same in both.' (Freud, S. *Collected Papers,* vol. 4, tr. by Riviere, J., Leonard and Virginia Woolf and The Institute of Psychoanalysis, London, 1924–25) It appears that mourning is used as the equivalent of grief. See *melancholia.*

mourning, belated Grief 'for the loss of a love object only after failure to escape trouble and grief.' (Wittels, F. *Psychoanalytic Quarterly VIII,* 1939)

movements, hypermetamorphotic (hī-pēr-met-à-mor-fot'ik) Wernicke's term for 'touching.'

Much-Holzmann reaction (Hans Much; W. Holzmann, German physicians) The alleged property of the serum from a person with schizophrenia or manic-depressive psychosis to inhibit hemolysis by cobra venom.

multiple sclerosis See *sclerosis, multiple.*

multiplication of personality See *personality, multiplication of.*

multiplicity, target A term suggested by S.R. Slavson to indicate the multiple possibilities existing in a group for projecting or displacing hostility on other patients, who replace the therapist as the target.

multipolarity (mul'ti-pō-lar'i-tē) A term introduced by S.R. Slavson to stress the fact that in group psychotherapy transference is directed toward more than the one person of the therapist. The interpatient (sibling and identification) transference produces a state of multipolarity in transference.

Münsterberg, Hugo (1863–1916) (mün'-stēr-berk) American psychologist and psychotherapist.

musicomania (mū-zi-kō-mā'ni-à) *Obs.* 'A variety of insanity in which the passion for music has been fostered to such an extent as to derange the mental faculties.' (Tuke, D.H. *A Dictionary of Psychological Medicine,* vols. 1–2, Blakiston, Philadelphia, 1892)

musicotherapy (-ther'à-pē) Treatment of nervous and mental disorders by means of music.

musomania (mū-zō-mā'ni-à) See *musicomania.*

musophobia (mū-sō-fō'bi-à) Fear of mice.

mussitate (mus'i-tāt) To mutter.

mussitation Movement of the tongue or lips as if in speech, without the production of articulate sounds.

mutant, mutational, mutated Pertaining to new hereditary characters originated by mutation.

mutation (mū-tā'shun) In genetics, the term refers to that kind of a *variation,* in the biological make-up of individual members of a species, which is the outcome of a permanent change in their idioplasmic equipment. Whether these mutational variations are minor or more conspicuous, it is their clear distinction from the parental type and their ability to reproduce the new type which distinguish them from other forms of variation.

Mutant characters arise suddenly, breed true from the beginning, and give rise to a new and distinct race. They seem to occur in each species, usually with irregular frequency and more or less 'spontaneously.' This means that very little is known about the real cause, although it has been possible experimentally to produce various mutations by such external influences as high temperatures, radium, or chemicals.

In human beings we find most frequently the so-called *factor mutations* brought about by a change in one of the chromomeres. These mutated genes produce more or less *pathological* types which often have a restricted viability (lethal factors). It may be assumed that the majority of hereditary malformations are caused by such factor mutations. Other kinds of mutation arise from changes in the chromosome equipment or in the position of genes.

Although all present evidence indicates that mutations are relatively common in nature and probably the starting point for every form of evolutionary development, it is clear that more differences among individuals are derived from combination than from changes of genes. As soon as a multiplicity of unlike genes have originated by mutation, the genes are brought together in ever new combinations as rapidly as crosses are effected between individuals differing with respect to them. In the last analysis, however, mutations must underlie the origin of each new stock, race, or species.

mutinus, mutunus (moo-tē′noos, moo-too′noos) Priapus; penis.

mutism (mūt′iz'm) The state of being mute, dumb, silent; voicelessness without structural alterations and with psychic causes. It is silence due to disinclination to talk, as the 'vows of silence' in anchorites or monastics of various religious creeds or individuals who would not tell the reason for their mutism: they can, but they will not, speak.

Mutism is not uncommonly observed among psychiatric patients as a result of psychogenic causes. It is common among patients in a stage of stupor; indeed, the term *stupor* is (in use, at least) often a synonym for *mutism*. The condition is frequently observed in the catatonic form of schizophrenia, in the stupor of melancholia, and in states of hysterical stupor.

'They (patients with catatonic stupor) characteristically often refuse to speak at all. This mutism is a manifestation of the negativism.' (Jelliffe, S.E. and White, W.A. *Diseases of the Nervous System,* 6th ed., Lea & Febiger, Philadelphia, 1935)

'Dora had a very large number of attacks of coughing accompanied by loss of voice. Could it be that the presence or absence of the man she loved had had an influence upon the appearance and disappearance of the symptoms of her illness? . . . I asked her what the average length of these attacks had been. "From three to six weeks, perhaps." How long had Herr K's absences lasted? "Three to six weeks, too," she was obliged to admit.' (Freud, S. *Collected Papers,* vol. 3, tr. by Strachey, A. and J., Leonard and Virginia Woolf and The Institute of Psychoanalysis, London, 1925)

myasthenia (mī-as-thē′ni-à) This term appears frequently in neurological literature: it has come into the field of psychiatry principally through the school of constitutional medicine. There are constitutional anomalies of muscles. The individual, possessing the asthenic physique in general, may have a structural and functional immaturity of the muscular system, giving rise to myasthenia or weak muscles.

'It is probable that the marked muscular asthenia that we find in certain endocrine temperaments depends upon special anomalies of structure of the muscular tissue. . . .' (Pende, N. *Constitutional Inadequacies,* tr. by Naccarati, S., Lea & Febiger, Philadelphia, 1928)

In schizophrenia, particularly in its simple type, myasthenia is a frequent symptom: the patient complains of rapid muscular fatigue. The complaint is frequent also among depressed patients.

myasthenia gravis (grā′vis) A chronic disorder of conduction at the myoneural junction, due possibly to a toxic factor from the thymus gland which interferes with transmission at this site. The disorder shows a marked tendency to remissions and exacerbations; females are more commonly affected than males; and onset is usually between the ages of 20 and 50 years. The characteristic symptom is muscular fatigability; this begins in the ocular muscles (producing ptosis and diplopia) and eventually leads to the other common disturbances: snarling smile, nasal speech, difficulty in swallowing and articulation, etc. The upper limbs are more affected than the lower. Sooner or later, permanent paralysis of the affected muscles develops.

Prostigmin, which rapidly abolishes the muscular weakness, is of value in diagnosis and treatment, and cortisone appears also to be of value. Anticholinesterase compounds such as DFP may be helpful; thymectomy is indicated in severe cases.

myelasthenia (mī-el-as-thē'ni-à) *Obs.* Neurasthenia of the spinal region.

myelencephalon (mī-el-en-sef'à-lon) See *hindbrain.*

myelinoclasis, acute perivascular (mī-el-in-ok'la-sis, à-kūt per-i-vas'kū-lar) See *encephalomyelitis, acute disseminated.*

myelitis (mī-e-lī'tis) Inflammation of the spinal cord.

myelo- (mī'el-ō-) Combining form meaning marrow; spinal cord, from Gr. *myelós,* marrow.

myelocystocele (mī-el-ō-sis'tō-sēl) Spinal cord substance contained in a spina bifida.

myelodysplasia (-dis-plā'zhi-à) See *inferiority, organ.*

myelogram An X-ray of the spine following injection of a suitable contrast medium (usually Pantopaque®) into the spinal subarachnoid space by means of spinal puncture. Myelography is most commonly used to demonstrate herniations of the intervertebral discs.

myelomeningocele (mī-el-ō-me-ning'gō-sēl) Spina bifida with protrusion of both the cord and its membranes.

myo- (mī'ō-) Combining form meaning muscle, from Gr. *mys,* gen. *myós,* mouse, muscle.

myoclonia (mī-ō-klō'ni-à) Any disorder characterized by spasmodic muscular contractions, as in *infectious myoclonia,* or *chorea.*

myoclonic epilepsy A type of petit mal epilepsy. See *epilepsy.*

myoclonus (mī-ō-klō'nus) A sudden, regular or irregular contraction of a muscle which does not usually produce movement of the part supplied by the muscle; it occurs oftenest in the limbs, but may be seen in the body and face.

myoclonus epilepsy See *epilepsy, myoclonus.*

myodynia, hysterical (mī-ō-din'i-à) Muscular tenderness, usually over the ovarian region, observed occasionally in hysteria.

myo-edema (-e-dē'mà) Swelling of muscle; on tapping a muscle with a percussion hammer, a localized swelling appears and persists for a few moments; a sign of hyperirritability of atrophic muscles.

myokymia (-kim'i-à) A transient quiver of a muscle, occurring in weak, anemic individuals.

myoneurasthenia (-nū-ras-thē'ni-à) Muscular weakness associated with neurasthenia.

myopsychopathy (-sī-kop'à-thē) A tremor, paralysis, or other muscular disorder associated with the presence of mental weakness or change.

myopsychosis (-sī-kō'sis) See *myopsychopathy.*

myotonia atrophica (-tō'ni-à a-trof'i-kà) *Dystrophia myotonica* (q.v.).

mysophilia (mī-sō-fil'i-à) A psychiatric term denoting a pathologic interest in, and desire for, filth or dirt; the desire to become unclean or polluted by contact with dirty or filthy objects—the opposite of *mysophobia* (q.v.). Mysophilia is commonly associated with *coprophilia* and *urophilia* and related to *paraphilias* (q.v.). Mysophilia is demonstrated in the following statement of a patient: 'I get more sex thrill from the idea of a dirty wench than I do from a clean one.'

mysophobia Fear of contamination. It is commonly observed in the form of incessant handwashing. Some patients spend the greater part of their waking hours washing their hands. They may exhibit the dread of uncleanliness by many other actions. Some refuse to touch anything unless they wear gloves; others must constantly wash everything in their surroundings.

'In the case of *mysophobia* the *compulsion* to wash the hands was the compensation for the fear of being "contaminated" by dirt, germs, feces, etc. The fear of fecal contamination, however, was based upon the craving or love for anal-autoerotic fancies and sensations.' (Kempf, E.J. *Psychopathology,* Mosby, St. Louis, 1921)

mystical participation See *participation, law of.*

mystic union See *union, mystic.*

mythomania (mith-ō-mā′ni-à) Mania for lies. A morbid interest in myths and propensity for incredible stories and fabrications, a condition sometimes seen in psychiatric patients.

mythophobia Fear of stories or myths.

myxoneurosis (mik-sō-nū-rō′sis) A neurosis affecting the mucous membranes, marked by an excessive secretion; a mucous discharge from the respiratory or intestinal mucous membrane, unaccompanied by signs of active inflammation.

N

Nachmansohn, D. (Contemporary neuro-physiologist) See *process, elementary.*

N-allylnormorphine (en-al-il-nor-mor'-fēn) See *psychotomimetic.*

naming A disturbance in association, peculiar to schizophrenia, in which the only recognizable association to external stimuli consists in naming them. Thus, in a word-association test, even though the patient understands its purpose, his only responses may be an enumeration of the furniture in the examining room. This 'naming' does not appear only in response to visual impressions. When asked to do something, the patient may name the act: 'Now he is sitting down.' Such patients appear to be completely dependent upon, and at the mercy of, external impressions. This seems to be related to the lack of a goal-concept, to the lack of directives and aims.

nanism (nā'niz'm, nan'iz'm) Paltauf's term for a special form of *dwarfism* (q.v.), which is of dysglandular origin and may best be classified as partial hypo-evolutism affecting especially the skeletal growth. A conspicuous exception to this underdeveloped skeleton is a very large skull, with which a normal development of brain and intelligence may be associated, although the face (saddle-nose) usually takes on a cretinoid aspect. Since the genitals also may be sufficiently developed, these dwarfs can procreate others of the same type.

According to Pende, Paltauf's nanism is closely connected 'on the one side with Hansemann's primordial nanosomia and on the other side with the various infantilistic nanisms of endocrine origin, which assume different clinical forms according to the glands principally attacked by dysfunction.' (Pende, N. *Constitutional Inadequacies,* tr. by Naccarati, S., Lea & Febiger, Philadelphia, 1928)

nanism, senile See *progeria.*

nanosomia (nā-nō-sō'mi-à, nan-ō-) See *dwarfism.*

nanosomia, primordial Hansemann's term for a rare form of *dwarfism* (q.v.) with regular physical proportions of the dwarfed body and normal mental development. It seems to be hereditary, is more common in the male sex and is transmitted from the father. Although small from birth, these dwarfs accomplish their pubertal crisis regularly and are able to reproduce.

This *nanosomic* group of Hansemann is practically identical with the other special forms of *microsomia* called *pygmeism* by the French school and *heredo-familial essential microsomia* (q.v.) by E. Lévi.

narce (när'sē) Hippocratic term for mental torpor.

narcema (när-sē'mà) *Obs.* Narcosis.

narcism (när'siz'm) A shortened form of *narcissism.*

narcissism (när-sis'iz'm) This term was first used by Näcke to indicate the form of auto-erotism characterized by self-love, often without genitality as an object. Not infrequently, however, narcissism is associated with genital excitation: Krafft-Ebing cited the instance of a man who masturbated before a mirror.

In psychoanalytic psychology, narcissism is a stage in the development of object relationships in which the child's estimation of his capacities is heightened to the degree of omnipotence. At the narcissistic stage, which follows the auto-erotic or somatogenic stage, the infant is still in the primary undifferentiated phase of consciousness; he is ignorant of any sources of pleasure other than himself and does not differentiate between the breast (or other objects) and the self. The breast is thought of as a part of his own body, and since his slightest gestures are followed by satisfaction of his instinctual nutritional needs, he develops the 'autarchic fiction of false omnipotence.' This is the stage of *primary narcissism.* The ego believes itself to be omnipotent, but this is disproved by experience and frustration; the infant then comes to believe that the parents are the omnipotent ones, and he partakes of their omnipotence by introjection (the 'primary identification'). Even though reality has destroyed the feeling of omnipotence, the longing for this primary narcissism remains—the narcissistic needs—and self-esteem is the awareness of how close the individual is to the original omnipotence. The desire to partake of the parental omnipotence, even though it arose originally from the basic desire for the satisfaction of hunger, soon becomes differentiated from the hunger itself, and the child craves affection in a passive way ('passive object-love'); he is even willing to renounce other satisfactions if rewards of affection are promised. Thus the narcissistic needs are developed in relation to the ego and superego (and the term *secondary narcissism* refers to such love of the ego by the superego); the sexual needs, on the other hand, are developed in relation to the object.

When applied to the adult, the term narcissism implies a hypercathexis of the self and/or a hypocathexis of objects in the environment and/or a pathologically immature relationship to objects in the environment. Because the concept of narcissism was developed before Freud had formulated his last theory of the instincts (i.e. the dual-instinct theory of the sexual and aggressive instincts), it is not clear how Freud would have incorporated the aggressive instinct into his formulation of narcissism as described above; the formulation given refers only to the sexual drive.

narcissism, disease Ferenczi used this expression to describe narcissism associated with an organic disease, in a soldier 'whose lower jaw had been almost entirely blown away by a shell. His face was horribly deformed by the injury. The only striking thing about his behaviour, however, was his naive narcissism. He requested that the nursing sister should manicure him thoroughly every day; he would not eat the hospital food, since much finer fare was due to him, and he reiterated these and similar requests unceasingly, after the fashion of querulants —a case, therefore, of true "disease-narcissism." ' (Ferenczi, S. *Further Contributions to the Theory and Technique of Psycho-Analysis,* tr. by Suttie, J.I., Leonard and Virginia Woolf and The Institute of Psychoanalysis, London, 1926)

narcissism, negative Negative narcissism, a psychoanalytic expression, is defined by Abraham as an exaggerated underestimation of oneself. It is particularly expressed in states of melancholia, characterized by ideas of inadequacy, unreality, and self-accusation.

narcissism, primary Primary narcissism refers to the original energy embodied in the ego. It is the 'original libidinal ego-cathexis, part of which normally persists while the rest is gradually transferred to objects.' (Healy, W., Bronner, A.F., and Bowers, A.M. *The Structure and Meaning of Psychoanalysis,* Knopf, New York, 1930)

'The primary narcissism of the child assumed by us, which forms one of the hypotheses in our theories of the libido, is less easy to grasp by direct observation than to confirm by deduction from another consideration. If we look at the attitude of fond parents towards their children, we cannot but perceive it as a revival and reproduction of their own, long since abandoned narcissism. . . . Parental love, which is so touching and at bottom so childish, is nothing but parental narcissism born again, and transformed though it be into object-love, it reveals its former character infallibly.' (Freud, S. *Collected Papers,* vol. 4, tr. by Riviere, J., Leonard and Virginia Woolf and The Institute of Psychoanalysis, London, 1924–25)

'It will be remembered that the original (primal) narcissism of the infant becomes in the course of development distributed in four directions, the actual proportion in each of these varying enormously with different individuals. *One* portion remains in an unaltered state attached to the real ego. . . .' This portion, of course, remains primary narcissism. A *second* portion, as Jones says, 'becomes attached to the idea of the parent, leading to adoration, devotion, and general over-estimation'; a *third* is transferred to an ego-ideal and 'the *fourth* is transformed into object-love.' (Jones, E. *Papers on Psycho-Analysis,* 4th ed., Wood, Baltimore, 1938) The last three are manifestations of secondary narcissism.

narcissism, secondary The narcissism once attached to external objects but now withdrawn from those objects and placed in the service of the ego (and not to objects in phantasy) is called secondary narcissism. This means that object-libido is transformed into ego-libido. 'The narcissism which arises when libidinal cathexes are called in away from external objects must be conceived of as a secondary form, superimposed upon a primary one that is obscured by manifold influences.' (Freud, S. *Collected Papers,* vol. 4, tr. by Riviere, J., Leonard and Virginia Woolf and The

Institute of Psychoanalysis, London, 1924–25) For example, when a schizophrenic patient regresses, he withdraws libido from reality. The libido becomes attached, for instance, to ideas of grandeur and is called secondary narcissism. It is closely related, as Freud says, to infantile manifestations of megalomania.

Secondary narcissism is not introversion, as Freud describes the latter. In introversion libido goes into the service of phantasies of real objects.

narcissistic, narcistic (när-si-sis'tik, när-sis'tik) Relating to self-love or narcissism.

narcoanalysis (när-kō-à-nal'i-sis) See *narcotherapy.*

narcocatharsis (-kà-thär'sis) See *narcotherapy.*

narcolepsy (när'kō-lep-sē) Narcolepsy or Friedmann's disease is usually discussed in conjunction with epilepsy. Kraepelin classifies it as a hysterical disorder. It is a disorder characterized by short spells of sleepiness. Jelliffe and White say: 'Sudden attacks of sleepiness are usually psychogenic in origin and will often be found to disguise auto-erotic phantasying and to be compulsive in character.' Some authorities believe narcolepsy and petit mal attacks of epilepsy to be the same disorder.

'Narcolepsy is characterized by attacks of sleep or trance-like states which often come on suddenly without apparent cause. The patient has practically no control over these attacks. He may fall asleep while talking or engaged in manual activity. He can be aroused, but falls to sleep again until the attack is over, a period lasting from several minutes to a few hours.' (Henry, G.W. *Essentials of Psychiatry,* 3rd ed., Williams and Wilkins, Baltimore, 1938)

narcolepsy, idiopathic (id-i-ō-path'ik) A disorder characterized by narcolepsy and cataplectic attacks; it is also known as the Gélineau syndrome.

narcomania A morbid desire to gain relief from painful stimuli usually through medicinal agencies (morphine, opium, etc.), but also occasionally through psychic measures (for example, hypnosis).

narcosis, continuous (när-kō'sis) See *treatment, continuous sleep.*

narcosuggestion (när'kō-su(g)-jes'chun) See *narcotherapy.*

narcosynthesis See *narcotherapy.*

narcotherapy A form of treatment used extensively in the war neuroses of World War II. As a general group term it includes narcosuggestion, narcocatharsis, narcoanalysis, narcosynthesis, amytal interview, pentothal interview, 'truth serum.' The treatment consists of injecting a barbiturate drug intravenously, either sodium amytal or sodium pentothal. When slowly injected intravenously in a 5 to 10 per cent solution in doses of from 0.2 to 0.5 gram, either of these two drugs induces a state of complete relaxation and a feeling of well-being and serenity, with a desire to communicate thoughts and a capacity to verbalize easily. Previously repressed memories, affects, and conflicts are expressed and the therapist then guides the patient along the lines of narcosuggestion, narcoanalysis, or narcosynthesis.

Narcosuggestion implies the active utilization of suggestion and reassurance while the patient is in a state of complete relaxation in the process of receiving sodium amytal or sodium pentothal intravenously. Narcocatharsis or narcoanalysis (the two words are used interchangeably) implies either free association or direct questions by the therapist to uncover repressed memories and affects while the patient is under the effects of sodium amytal or sodium pentothal given intravenously. At the end of the narcoanalysis, after the effects of the drug have worn off, the therapist explains to the patient the significance of what he recalled. Narcosynthesis uses free association, dreams, and transference material obtained during the amytal or pentothal interview, but a day or so later the material is discussed with the patient, who is guided by the therapist to conative and emotional reintegration, behavioral adjustments, and social rehabilitation. Although this method is also known as 'truth serum' treatment, a patient who does not wish to tell the truth cannot be made to do so by the intravenous injection of amytal or pentothal. Consequently, this method is of limited value in medico-legal work.

narcotism (när'kō-tiz'm) The state of being under the influence of narcotic drugs. As commonly used, the term refers to the condition in which the drug is present in amounts great enough to be toxic, or, in any event, sufficient to alter behavior.

nationality Nationality is defined as 'a type of community sentiment, a sense of belonging together, created by historical circumstances and supported by common spiritual possessions of such an extent and so strong that those who feel it desire to have a common government peculiarly or exclusively their own.' (McIver, R.M. *Society, Its Structure and Changes,* Macmillan of Canada, Toronto, 1931)

naturalia (nä-tōō-rä'lē-à) The sexual organs.

nature, experiment of A term frequently used in the field of objective psychobiology. Adolf Meyer emphasizes the study and treatment of stressful situations and the ways in which an individual reacts to such stresses. He refers to 'experiment of nature,' meaning the individual's reaction to real environmental situations.

nature, first A term denoting 'the undiluted and unmodified instincts.' In the beginning, the infant has energy 'affiliated with a variety of primitive drives or impulses, called instincts.' These instinctual impulses are ingrained in the organs of the body, the bodily tissues. Soon, however, these impulses leave their points of origin and are distributed over the whole body, and some instinctual energy is also taken up by the mind. The state of the instincts before this process takes place is what is termed first nature. (Hinsie, L.E. *Understandable Psychiatry,* Macmillan, New York, 1948)

nature, second A term that describes the inner conscience or superego of the child. The instinctual energies that invest the body regions of the child are necessarily supervised by the parents in their management of the child's activities. Since they are directed by the parents, these instinctual energies of the child will acquire a large quantity of parental coloring. Also the first ideas and thoughts created in the mind of the child 'are not of the body's own making, but are definitely those of its parents.' These 'mental images which the child develops of its body and mind, together with the incorporation of parental disciplines, constitute the *super-ego,* sometimes also known as the *inner conscience* or *second nature.*'

(Hinsie, L.E. *Understandable Psychiatry,* Macmillan, New York, 1948)

nautomania (naw-tō-mā'ni-à) Seaman's mania. Not infrequently sailors are affected by a morbid fear of a ship or water.

-nea (-nē'à) Same as *-noea;* see *-noia.*

necro- (nek'rō-) Combining form, meaning dead (body), from Gr. *nekrós,* dead.

necromania (nek-rō-mā'ni-à) Morbid desire for a dead body, the interest in the corpse usually being of a sexual character. A patient could have satisfactory sexual congress only when his partner kept repeating the phrase that she was dead.

necromimesis (-mi-mē'sis) The delusion in which the patient believes himself to be dead and acts as though he were.

necrophilia (-fil'i-à) The desire to possess the dead body (of a woman) for purposes of sexual intercourse. Krafft-Ebing, Hirschfeld, and others have described many patients with such desire. It is said that the impulse stems from a primitive custom and is associated with other similar customs, such as necrophagia.

necrophilism (ne-krof'i-liz'm) 1. A morbid desire to be in the presence of dead bodies.

2. A sexual perversion in relation to corpses.

necrophobia (nek-rō-fō'bi-à) Fear of a corpse.

need According to Freud, stimuli of instinctual origin arise from the organism itself and not from the outside world. 'A better term for a stimulus of instinctual origin is a "need." (Freud, S. *Collected Papers,* vol. 4, tr. by Riviere, J., Leonard and Virginia Woolf and The Institute of Psychoanalysis, London, 1924–25)

need, aboriginal See *psychodynamics, adaptational.*

need, acculturated (a-kul'chēr-à-ted) See *psychodynamics, adaptational.*

need, delusional Kraepelin devised this expression to denote the so-called inner, that is, unconscious need for delusions. Bleuler says: 'There are no other needs than the affective. Delusions, therefore, always follow a definite direction corresponding to the patient's affects, and in the vast majority of cases cannot be corrected by new experience or instruction, as long as the condition which gave origin to them continues.' (Bleuler, E. *Textbook of Psychiatry,* tr. by Brill, A.A., Macmillan, New York, 1930)

need for punishment See *criminal from sense of guilt.*

needle-spray See *spray, needle.*

need-press See *method, need-press.*

needs, narcissistic (när-sis-is'tik) See *narcissism.*

negation (ne-gā'shun) Negation or denial includes the concept repulsion or aversion. It is a widespread symptom in psychiatric patients, being manifested in overt form, for example, in the patient with the catatonic form of schizophrenia. In this syndrome the patient is averse to the whole of reality; in every possible way he shuts off stimuli from without and does not communicate in any manner with the environment.

Negation or denial may also take place between the conscious ego and components of the unconscious. It is frequently manifested in the form of *resistance.*

The negation may become so pronounced that the patient denies the existence of externality or of himself or both. This syndrome is known as a delusion of negation. It is often associated with depersonalization.

negation, delusion of See *negation.*

negation, insanity of An older term introduced by J. Cotard as *délire dés negations* for the syndrome known as depersonalization.

negativism (neg'à-tiv-iz'm) Negative attitude or behavior. In psychiatry *negativism* is equivalent to *resistance.* It means that the individual, aware of stimuli from without, actively or passively opposes conformation with the stimuli. It is sometimes called contrasuggestibility or contrariety, though the latter terms are used more frequently in psychology than in psychiatry. It is also called command negativism.

Negativism is said to be active when the subject does the opposite of what he is asked to do. For example, when a catatonic patient closes his fists tightly upon being requested to open his hands, he presents active negativism. The phenomenon is not uncommon in the catatonic form of schizophrenia. When, for instance, an attempt is made to bend the arm at the elbow, the patient strenuously resists the efforts; he closes the lids tightly, when asked to open them.

He is said to exhibit passive negativism when, without prompting, he does not do things he is expected to do. He remains passive to his physiological urges; he does not get out of bed in the morning, nor dress, nor eat. Bleuler calls this *inner negativism.*

Some authorities use the expression intellectual *negativism* when an individual always expresses an opposite to a thought. Thus, a patient thought: 'I must go; I must not go. I am a man; no, I am a woman. I will tell him; I will not tell him.'

negativism, active See *negativism.*

negativism, command See *negativism.*

negativism, inner See *negativism.*

negativism, intellectual See *negativism.*

negativism, passive See *negativism.*

negativism, sexual Hirschfeld thus denotes absence of sexual interests, due, he believes, to deficiency 'in the sexual glands.' Synonymous with *anerotism.*

negrophilia (nē-grō-fil'i-à) Love for the Negro.

negrophobia Fear of the Negro.

neighborhood The 'first grouping beyond the family which has social significance and which is conscious of some local unity [as the result of factors] such as topography and original vegetation, nationality bonds, religious purpose, the migration from a common place of residence and economic and social purposes.' (Kolb, J.H. *Rural Primary Groups,* Research Bulletin 51, Agricultural Experiment Station, University of Wisconsin)

The neighborhood is not only to be found in rural districts, but also 'in towns and cities, especially in residential areas which are not overdensely settled and which possess a population for the most part homogeneous and exhibiting a low rate of mobility.' (Carpenter, N. *Neighborhood; Encyclopaedia of the Social Sciences,* vol. 11, Macmillan, New York, 1933, p. 356)

neo- (nē'ō-) Combining form meaning new, recent, from Gr. *néos,* new, novel.

neoatavism (nē-ō-at'à-viz'm) The recurrence, in a descendant, of characters or traits of a near or immediate ancestor. See *paleoatavism.*

neocortex (-kor'teks) See *isocortex*.

neographism (nē-og'ra-fiz'm) The graphic equivalent of neologism.

neography (nē-og'ra-fē) Neologistic writing.

neolalia (nē-ō-lā'li-a) Neologistic speech; frequent use of neologisms in patient's speech.

neologism (nē-ol'ō-jiz'm) From the psychiatric point of view, the patient's (coinage of) new words or phrases or bestowing new meanings upon words and phrases in common use. Neologisms occur with great frequency among psychiatric patients, notably in schizophrenia. A patient said: 'So as to get the branch there without the man being dead in London.' (Hinsie, L.E. *The Treatment of Schizophrenia,* Williams and Wilkins, Baltimore, 1930) The phrase contained many condensations, displacements, etc., having the essential qualities of dreams.

'*Neologisms* are words of the patient's own making, often portmanteau condensations of several other words, and having originally had a special meaning for the patients.' (Henderson, D.K. and Gillespie, R.D. *A Text-Book of Psychiatry,* 4th ed., Oxford University Press, London, 1936)

'A paranoid female "is a Billy-goat," i.e., she is united with her beloved minister: minister=Christ=lamb=billy-goat.' (Bleuler, E. *Textbook of Psychiatry,* tr. by Brill, A.A., Macmillan, New York, 1930)

'In another dream the same patient imagined she was called "Hokerring," a neologism produced by fusing the two words "smoked herring". . . . The term smoked herring reminded her of bloater, and of a rather vulgar word in her native language meaning nude, pronounced bloat.'* (Jones, E. *Papers on Psycho-Analysis,* 4th ed., Wood, Baltimore, 1938)

* In Dutch *bloot* means 'bare, naked'; cf. G. *bloss,* bare, naked, mere, and Scotch *blate,* bare, naked.

neomnesis (nē-om-nē'sis) Memory for the recent past.

neophasia, polyglot (nē-ō-fā'zhi-a) A type of neologism formation in which one or more languages are devised by the patient, sometimes with full vocabulary, grammar, and syntax. Polyglot neophasia is rarely seen except in expansive paranoiacs and, to a lesser extent, in manic states.

neophobia Fear of anything new or unfamiliar.

neophrenia (nē-ō-frē'ni-a) In 1863 Kahlbaum classified psychiatric conditions (then called insanity) in accordance with the patient's age: neophrenia (the insanity of childhood), hebephrenia (the insanity of adolescence) and presbyophrenia (the insanity of old age).

neopsychic (-sī'kik) Of recent psychic development.

neostriatum (nē-ō-strē'a-toom) See *basal ganglia*.

nephelopsychosis (nef-e-lō-sī-kō'sis) Intense interest in clouds.

'Nephelopsychoses, if such a word may be coined, are distinctly more prominent and numerous among girls than boys, and as the female organism is more conservative this of itself suggests *rapport* with phylogeny.' (Hall, G.S. *Adolescence,* vol. 1, Appleton, New York, 1908, p. 181)

nerve, abducens (ab-du'senz) The sixth cranial nerve. The abducens nerve arises in the lower portion of the pons and supplies the external rectus muscle of the eye. For symptoms of abducens nerve lesions, see *nerve, oculomotor*.

nerve, acoustic The eighth cranial nerve. The acoustic nerve is a sensory nerve with two separate portions, the cochlear or auditory nerve (hearing) and the vestibular nerve (orientation in space). First-order neurons pass from the receptor cells in the spiral organ of Corti to the cochlear nuclei; from here, second-order neurons proceed through the trapezoid body and lateral lemnisci to the medial geniculate bodies. From here, auditory radiations are projected to the auditory cortex. First-order neurons of the vestibular nerve pass from the receptor cells in the vestibular ganglion (Scarpa's ganglion) to the vestibular nuclei, and thence to the cerebellum.

Symptoms of cochlear nerve involvement include tinnitus, deafness, and, in the case of supranuclear disorders, auditory aphasia or word-deafness. Symptoms of vestibular nerve involvement include vertigo and nystagmus.

nerve, cochlear (kok'lē-ēr) See *nerve, acoustic*.

nerve, facial The seventh cranial nerve. The facial nerve is primarily a motor nerve which originates in the posterior pons and supplies the stapedius muscle of the middle ear and the superficial musculature of the face and scalp. Parasympathetic fibers supply the glands and mucous membranes of the pharynx, palate, and nasal cavity. The facial nerve also has some sensory fibers which carry taste from the anterior tongue. Lesions of the facial nerve may be peripheral (Bell's palsy or prosoplegia), nuclear, or supranuclear. In peripheral facial paralysis, the following signs will be seen on the affected side: drooping mouth, inability to whistle or wink or wrinkle forehead, tearing of eye, loss of deep facial sensation; food collects between cheek and gum, paralysis is of the flaccid (lower motor neuron) type. In the nuclear type of facial palsy, the above signs are also seen and, in addition, contralateral hemiplegia due to pyramidal involvement. In the supranuclear type of facial palsy, the paralysis is of the spastic (upper motor neuron) type, the frontalis muscle is spared because of its bilateral cortical innervation, and reflexes and emotional responses are retained. Supranuclear facial paralysis is often associated with homolateral hemiplegia or monoplegia.

nerve, glossopharyngeal (glos-sō-far-in′-gē-al) The ninth cranial nerve. The glossopharyngeal nerve is motor to the stylopharyngeus muscle and sensory to the pharynx, soft palate, posterior tongue, and to the carotid body (for reflex control of respiration, blood pressure, and heart rate). The glossopharyngeal nerve also supplies taste buds in the posterior third of the tongue. Symptoms associated with lesions of this nerve include loss of gag reflex, loss of taste in posterior tongue, and deviation of uvula to the unaffected side.

nerve, hypoglossal (hī-pō-glos′sal) The twelfth cranial nerve. The hypoglossal nerve is motor to the muscles of the tongue. Peripheral paralysis results in homolateral flaccidity, paralysis, and atrophy, and the tongue deviates to the side of the lesion. Supranuclear paralysis results in contralateral hemiplegia, contralateral spastic paralysis of the tongue, and deviation of the tongue to the side opposite the lesion.

nerve, oculomotor (ok-ū-lō-mō′tĕr) The third cranial nerve. The oculomotor nerve arises at the level of the superior colliculus and is the motor nerve to the following eye muscles: internal rectus, superior rectus, inferior rectus, inferior oblique, and levator palpebrae. Parasympathetic fibers originate in the Edinger-Westphal nucleus and proceed via the nasociliary branch of the oculomotor nerve to the ciliary ganglion, whence the short ciliary nerves pass to the sphincter muscle of the iris.

The other muscles of the eye are supplied by the trochlear and abducens nerves, which functionally are considered together with the oculomotor nerve. Symptoms of involvement of these three cranial nerves include: lid drop (ptosis), nystagmus, double vision (diplopia), squint (strabismus), and conjugate deviation, in which both eyes are turned to the same side. Strabismus may be internal, in which case the visual axes cross each other, or external, in which case the visual axes diverge from each other.

J.G. Chusid and J.J. McDonald (*Correlative Neuroanatomy and Functional Neurology,* 8th ed., Lange, Los Altos, California, 1956) suggest the following classification of disorders of these three cranial nerves:

A. Opthalmoplegias (paralyses)
　1. Oculomotor paralysis
　　a. external ophthalmoplegia—divergent strabismus, diplopia, ptosis
　　b. internal ophthalmoplegia—dilated pupil, loss of light and accommodation reflexes
　　　(Total ophthalmoplegia refers to a combination of external and internal ophthalmoplegia.)
　　c. Argyll Robertson pupil—miosis with loss of light and cilio-spinal reflexes, and preservation of accommodation reflex (pretectal lesion)
　　d. Paralysis of convergence (central lesion)
　2. Trochlear paralysis (rare)—slight convergent strabismus and diplopia on downward gaze
　3. Abducens paralysis (most common) —convergent strabismus and diplopia
　4. Chronic progressive ophthalmoplegia (Graefe's disease)—usually involves all three nerves
B. Myasthenic States
C. Spasmodic Ocular Disorders (supranuclear lesions)
　1. Conjugate deviation spasm

2. Lateral or ventral association spasm
3. Central nystagmus: rhythmic (vestibular origin) or undulating (cerebral or cerebellar origin)

nerve, olfactory (ol-fak'to-rē) The first cranial nerve. The olfactory nerve is structurally a fiber tract of the brain; it is a sensory nerve which transmits olfactory (smell) stimuli. Symptoms due to olfactory nerve lesions include: anosmia (loss of sense of smell), hyperosmia, parosmia (perverted sense of smell), cacosmia (sensation of unpleasant odors), and olfactory hallucinations. The Foster Kennedy syndrome, caused by tumors at the base of the frontal lobe, includes anosmia with atrophy of the optic and olfactory nerves, blindness, and contralateral papilledema.

nerve, optic (op'tik) The second cranial nerve. The optic nerve is structurally a fiber tract of the brain; it is a sensory nerve which transmits visual stimuli. The rods and cones of the retina of the eye are the first-order neurons; they connect with the bipolar cells of the retina, which in turn connect with the ganglion cells. These form the optic nerve-fibers, which proceed to the optic chiasma, form the optic tracts, and then pass to the lateral geniculate bodies, the superior colliculi, and the pretectal region. From the geniculate bodies, fibers pass (as the geniculocalcarine tract) to the occipital cortex. Fibers from the superior colliculi pass to various cranial and spinal nuclei (for involuntary oculoskeletal reflexes); fibers from the pretectal region pass to the Edinger-Westphal nuclei (for the simple and consensual light reflexes).

Visual defects include scotomata (abnormal blind spots in the visual fields), amblyopia (reduction of visual acuity), amaurosis (complete blindness), *field-defects* (q.v.), hemeralopia (day blindness), nyctalopia (night blindness), color blindness, and optic agnosia or word blindness.

nerves A colloquialism, meaning general excitability, uneasiness and fearfulness; it is often said that one 'has a bad case of nerves,' that one is 'jittery' or has the 'jitters.'

nerve, spinal accessory The eleventh cranial nerve. The spinal accessory nerve is motor to the trapezius and sternocleidomastoid muscles. Unilateral paralysis results in inability to rotate head to unaffected side, atrophy of sternocleidomastoid, inability to shrug affected shoulder, and drooping of affected shoulder. Bilateral paralysis results in difficulty in rotating head or lifting chin, and in a dropping forward of the head.

nerve, trigeminal (trī-gem'in-al) The fifth cranial nerve. The trigeminal nerve has both motor and sensory components. Motor fibers arise from the motor nucleus in the pons and supply the muscles of mastication (masseter, temporal, internal and external pterygoids). Sensory fibers are in three divisions: the ophthalmic division supplies the forehead, eyes, nose, temples, and meninges; the maxillary division supplies the upper jaw and hard palate; the mandibular division supplies the lower jaw and tongue. Symptoms of trigeminal nerve lesions include: pain, loss of sensation, paralysis of muscles of mastication with deviation of the jaw to the affected side, loss of jaw jerk, sneeze, lid reflex, conjunctival reflex and corneal reflex, and various trophic changes in the nose, face, and jaw.

nerve, trochlear (trok'lē-ēr) The fourth cranial nerve. The trochlear nerve arises at the level of the inferior colliculus and is the motor nerve to the superior oblique muscle of the eye. For symptoms of trochlear nerve lesions, see *nerve, oculomotor.*

nerve, vagus (vā'gus) The tenth cranial nerve. The vagus nerve is motor to the muscles of the soft palate and pharynx, sends parasympathetic fibers to the thoracic and abdominal viscera, and is sensory to the pharynx, larynx, trachea, esophagus, and the thoracic and abdominal viscera. Symptoms of vagus nerve lesions include: aphonia, dysphagia, paralysis of the soft palate with loss of the gag reflex, cough, bradycardia (with irritative lesions), or tachycardia (with vagus palsies).

nerve, vestibular (ves-tib'ū-lēr) See *nerve, acoustic.*

nervosism (nēr'vō-siz'm) An old doctrine which maintained that all morbid mental phenomena were due to variations in nerve force.

nervosismus (nēr-vô-ziz'moos) *Obs.* Neurasthenia.

nervosity (nēr-vos'i-tē) Kraepelin uses

Nervous [484] Neurasthenia

this term in about the same sense that *nervousness* is used today. It includes a wide variety of psychic manifestations that do not substantially handicap an individual in his daily activities, but which stamp him as temperamentally unstable, nervous, eccentric, etc. In his reactions he stands between mental health and the more formal psychiatric states. See *nervousness*.

nervous (nĕr'vus) 1. Relating to a nerve or the nerves.
2. Easily excited or agitated; suffering from instability or weakness of nerve action.

nervousness A popular term, generally referring to a mild mental indisposition, not having the significance of a mental 'disease.' See *neurosis; character, neurotic.*

nervous system, autonomic See *autonomic nervous system.*

nervous system, parasympathetic See *autonomic nervous system.*

nervous system, sympathetic See *autonomic nervous system.*

nervous system, third See *third nervous system.*

nervous system, vegetative See *autonomic nervous system.*

net fertility See *fertility, net.*

networks, psychological 'Psychological networks are formed when certain parts of social atoms link themselves with parts of other social atoms and these again with parts of other social atoms, thus forming complex chains of interrelations. On the other hand, numerous parts of social atoms remain isolated or buried between individuals.

'Some individuals comprising certain links of a network are unacquainted with those in more distant links, but can exert influence by indirection. The older and wider the network as it spreads the less significant becomes the individual position within it. The function of the networks is to shape social tradition and public opinion.

'The changing psychological currents in a network tend to maintain a natural level as long as they are made up by spontaneous determinants only, or, the feelings and ideas which arise solely from the individuals themselves. Through the use of modern technological methods for the dissemination of propaganda artificial or

mechanical determinants enter into the development of psychological currents. They denaturalize their spontaneous unfoldment and degenerate, by retroaction, the feelings of the individuals themselves. One of the chief objectives of sociometric techniques has been the control of network formations.' (Moreno, J.L. *Sociometry 1,* 213, 1937)

neuradynamia (nū-rad-i-nā'mi-à) Neurasthenia.

neuralgia, Fothergill's (nū-ral'ji-à) See *Fothergill's neuralgia; tic douloureux.*

neuralgia, hallucinatory (ha-lū'si-nà-tō-rē) A cerebral impression of local pain occurring without any actual peripheral nerve pain.

neuralgia, reminiscent In a hypersensitive person, a cerebral impression of pain persisting after the actual attack of neuralgia has passed away.

neuralgia, trifacial (trī-fā'shal) See *tic douloureux.*

neuralgia, trigeminal (trī-gem'in-al) See *tic douloureux.*

neural plate (tube) (nū'ral) See *cephalogenesis.*

neurämie (noi-rā-mē') *Neurasthenia* (q.v.).

neurasthenia (nū-ras-thē'ni-à) Nervous debility. The concept *neurasthenia* was introduced in America in 1869 by G.M. Beard; it had been outlined by Bouchut as *nervosisme* in 1860. During the second half of the 19th century it was more of a generic than a nosologic term. In Tuke's *Dictionary of Psychological Medicine,* Arndt said that neurasthenia 'represents to a certain degree the starting point of all the more severe nervous disorders, and the soil from which they grow.' (Vols. 1–2, Blakiston, Philadelphia, 1892). Thus it was the forerunner to hysteria, epilepsy, locomotor ataxia, general paralysis, etc. For a number of years neurasthenia was regarded as a syndrome associated with a more fundamental disorder.

Until modern times the expression *neurasthenia* was taken literally to mean weakness or exhaustion of the nervous system. Bleuler says: 'A general decline of strength is no neurosis. People who toil hardest, who with a few hours of sleep and at that frequently interrupted through attention to the children, regularly do a day's work of 16 or more hours, year in and year out, only exceptionally become neurasthenic.' (Bleuler, E. *Textbook of Psychiatry*, tr. by Brill, A.A., Macmillan, New York, 1930)

The clinical syndrome is characterized by a wide variety of symptoms, including easy fatigability, feeling of physical and mental weakness, aches, pains, paresthesias, and a number of other pathological physical sensations; inadequate functioning of any organ or organic system of the body; insomnia, etc. While some individuals run the gamut of symptoms, usually complaints center upon some particular organ or system.

Bleuler generally speaks of the so-called neurasthenia syndrome. He says that '*neurasthenia is usually a pseudoneurasthenia, and only that name should be used for it, if it were not too long.*'

The general idea prevails today that neurasthenia may be best understood in terms of the psyche. 'What usually produces the so-called neurasthenia are affective difficulties.'

Freud has treated the topic at some length. He says: 'The aetiology of neurasthenia proper as well as of anxiety-neurosis can now be brought within the compass of this conception of the sexual process. Neurasthenia arises whenever a less adequate relief (activity) takes the place of the adequate one, thus, when masturbation or spontaneous emission replaces normal coitus under the most favorable conditions.' (Freud, S. *Collected Papers*, vol. 1, tr. by Riviere, J., Leonard and Virginia Woolf and The Institute of Psychoanalysis, London, 1924–25) The foregoing was written in 1894. Four years later he said that neurasthenia was looked upon by him as an *actual neurosis*. 'Psychoneuroses appear under two kinds of conditions, either independently or in the wake of actual neuroses (neurasthenia and anxiety-neurosis).' (ibid.)

'If we separate out from the cases of illness hitherto designated as neurasthenia everything that should be relegated to other, more natural nosological classifications, there remain behind a well-characterized group in which there predominate, pressure in the head, spinal irritation, constipation, paraesthesias, diminished potency, and from the effect of these conditions, a depression of the spirits.' (Ferenczi, S. *Further Contributions to the Theory and Technique of Psycho-Analy-*

sis, tr. by Suttie, J.I., Leonard and Virginia Woolf and The Institute of Psychoanalysis, London, 1926)

neurasthenia, abdominal A term applied to cases of neurasthenia in which symptoms relating to the gastro-intestinal tract dominate the clinical picture. (Taylor, A.S. 'Abdominal Neurasthenia,' *Archives of Neurology and Psychiatry 4*, 638–44, 1920)

neurasthenia, aviator's This term defines 'a chronic functional nervous and psychic disorder occurring in aviators and characterized by gastric distress, nervous irritabilities, minor psychic disorders, fatigue of the higher voluntary mental centers, insomnia, and increased motor activity.' The principal exciting etiological factor is emotional stress. This condition is also known as *aëroneurosis* (q.v.), *staleness*, and *flying sickness*. (Sladen, F.J. (ed.). *Psychiatry and the War*, Thomas, Springfield, Ill., 1943)

neurasthenia, periodic 'Many cases which on superficial examination would be regarded as ordinary (neurasthenic) hypochondria belong to this group of obsessional affects; so-called "periodic neurasthenia" or "periodic melancholia" in particular appears to be reducible with unexpected frequency to obsessional affects and obsessional ideas—a recognition that is therapeutically by no means unimportant.' (Freud, S. *Collected Papers*, vol. 1, tr. by Riviere, J., Leonard and Virginia Woolf and The Institute of Psychoanalysis, London, 1924–25)

neurasthenia, professional Nervous prostration manifested principally in the patient's total or almost total inability to use the organ(s) habitually employed in the course of his profession or occupation.

'Writing for a long time causes fatigue of the nervous mechanism specialized for this function. In such a case, every time the subject prepares to write he is seized, even from the very start or after he has written a few lines, by a painful feeling of fatigue in the arm, or by a spasm that prevents him continuing (mogigraphia).' (Bianchi, L. *A Text-Book of Psychiatry*, tr. by MacDonald, J.H., Baillière, Tindall & Cox, London, 1906)

neurasthenia, traumatic (traw-mat'ik) A neurasthenic reaction pattern which develops in response to physical trauma, such as those caused by automotive or industrial accidents. Trauma is here considered to have precipitated an acute exacerbation of an underlying neurotic potentiality. See *neurasthenia.*

neurasthenia, tropical A diagnosis made on soldiers invalided in the tropics who manifested low blood pressure, peripheral congestion, dizziness, marked weakness, fainting, even shock. It is doubtful whether this constitutes a true entity. Removal to a temperate climate relieved all symptoms. See *mania, tropical.*

neurasthenia, war A more recent and simpler psychiatric term for neurocirculatory asthenia as observed in soldiers in time of war. Neurocirculatory asthenia, or effort-syndrome, is a frequently observed disorder in civilian neuropsychiatry. When the disorder was met with and recorded in military neuropsychiatric casualties, its name took on a military flavor. Neurocirculatory asthenia became war neurasthenia, and effort-syndrome became soldier's heart.

As for the condition itself, however, most observers agree that neither of these names is really suitable. Weiss and English state that 'medicine would be better off without the term neurocirculatory asthenia, which concentrates attention on a part when the disorder is of the total personality. In other words, neurocirculatory asthenia is psychoneurosis with cardiac manifestations and, while it may have special coloring in military life, it is still primarily a neurosis and should be looked upon and treated as such. If special evidences of vasomotor instability are present, they are only another phase of the disordered constitution and do not invalidate the principle that the neurotic element is the more important from the standpoint of management.' (Weiss, E., and English, O.S. *Psychosomatic Medicine,* W.B. Saunders, Philadelphia, 1943) See *asthenia, neurocirculatory.*

neurasthenic, arrived Déjérine and Gauckler speak of 'neurasthenics who have arrived.' In them 'the intellectual fatigue is real, and in direct proportion to the emaciation and weakness of the subject, who may at the same time be physically as well as morally depressed. In these patients a very curious phenomenon sometimes occurs which resembles a periodic psychosis. It is not at all rare among such subjects to find that for short periods of time intellectual work becomes

almost too easy for them.' (Déjérine, J. and Gauckler, E. *The Psychoneuroses and Their Treatment by Psychotherapy,* 2nd ed., tr. by Jelliffe, S.E., Lippincott, Philadelphia and London, 1915)

neurasthenics, dyspepsia of (dis-pep'shà) A general term, denoting the existence of gastric disorders of a psychogenic nature.

neurasthenoid (nū-ras'then-oid) Resembling neurasthenia.

neuremia (nū-rē'mi-à) Laycock's term for functional disorders of the nervous system.

neuriatry, neuriatria (nū-rī'à-trē, -ri-at'-ri-à) Treatment of nervous diseases.

neurinomatosis (nū-rin-ō-mà-tō'sis) See *diathesis, glial.*

neuritis, optic (nū-rī'tis, op'tik) An inflammatory process affecting the head of the optic nerve, or that part within the bulb of the eye. The condition is usually bilateral, and early loss of vision is characteristic. Ophthalmoscopically, there is blurring of the margins of the disk with congestion, dilatation of the veins, and narrowing of the arteries. The retina may show hemorrhages, pigment deposits, exudates, connective tissue changes, and atrophic spots. Optic neuritis may occur in severe renal disease, syphilis, leukemia, carbon monoxide poisoning, diabetes, anemia, and other constitutional diseases.

neuro- (nū'rō-) Combining form meaning nerve, from Gr. *neŭron,* nerve.

neuroarthritism (nū-rō-är'thri-tiz'm) A condition with a predisposition to nervous and rheumatoid or gouty disorders.

neuro-central See *constant, central.*

neurofibromatosis (-fi-brō-ma-tō'sis) Neurofibroblastomatosis; von Recklinghausen's disease. A congenital, hereditary disorder, transmitted as a Mendelian dominant, consisting of café-au-lait pigmentation of the skin and the formation of tumors in various tissues (e.g. cutaneous fibromas or mollusca fibrosa, and perineural fibroblastomas of the peripheral and cranial nerves). The tumors are often associated with overgrowth of the skin and subcutaneous tissues. Of the cranial nerves, the eighth nerve is the most commonly involved. The disorder is sometimes progressive, but it does not always shorten life. Treatment is palliative; the painful tumors may be excised or irradiated with X-ray.

neurogenic (-jen'ik) Caused or produced by, born of, springing from, or engendered by nerves or a nerve.

neuroglia (nū-rog'li-à) A fine web of supporting tissue in the nervous system, composed of modified ectodermal elements in which are enclosed the neuroglia (or glia) cells: astrocytes, oligodendroglia, and microglia.

neurogram (nū'rō-gram) 'Whatever may be the exact nature of the theoretical alterations left in the brain by life's experiences they have received various generic terms; more commonly "brain residual," and "brain dispositions." I have been in the habit of using the term *neurograms* to characterize these brain records. Just as telegram, Marconigram, and phonogram precisely characterize the form in which the physical phenomena which correspond to our (verbally or scripturally) thoughts, are recorded and conserved, so neurogram precisely characterizes my conception of the form in which a system of brain processes corresponding to thoughts and other mental experiences is recorded and conserved.' (Prince, M. *The Unconscious*, Macmillan, New York, 1916)

neurohumor A chemical substance which transmits the nerve impulse at the synapse. See *process, elementary; epinephrine; serotonin*.

neurohypnology (nū-rō-hip-nol'ō-jē) The study of 'magnetic sleep.' (Braid)

neurohypnosis (-hip-nō'sis) Braid's original term (now obsolete) which means literally sleep of the nervous system; later Braid dropped the first part of the word, and used hypnosis instead, 'for the sake of brevity.'

neuroinduction (-in-duk'shun) Suggestion.

neurokym (nū'rō-kim) Psychokym.

neuroleptica (nū-rō-lep'ti-ka) See *tranquillizer*.

neurology (nū-rol'ō-jē) The branch of medicine that devotes itself to the study of the organization and function of the nervous tissue. The diseases of the peripheral nerves of the spinal cord and the brain, as far as they are based on organic pathology, are in the realm of neurology.

(Hinsie, L.E. *Understandable Psychiatry*, Macmillan, New York, 1948)

neurometadrasis (nū-rō-met-à-drā'sis) *Obs.* Animal magnetism or the influence of one body upon another.

neuromimesis (-mi-mē'sis) *Obs.* Mimicry of disease or disorder of a mental or nervous character.

neuromyelitis optica (-mē-e-lē'tis op'tĕ-ka) *Devic's disease* (q.v.).

neuropathic (-path'ik) Pertaining to organic symptoms rooted in the mind.

neuropathy (nū-rop'à-thē) *Rare.* This term was used in much the same sense that one now uses the term psychogenesis.

neuropsychiatry (nū-rō-sī-kī'à-trē) Combined neurology and psychiatry, the specialty dealing with diseases of both mind and nervous system.

neuropsychology (sī-kol'ō-jē) The science dealing with the relationships obtaining between the psyche and the nervous systems.

neuropsychopathy (-sī-kop'à-thē) A neurosis accompanied by mental symptoms.

neuropsychosis (-sī-kō'sis) *Obs.* This term used to mean what *psychosis* means today. It is not interchangeable with *psychoneurosis*.

neuro-psychosis, defense One of Freud's earliest communications, published in 1894, is captioned *The Defense Neuro-Psychoses*. In this paper he referred to defense-neuroses and defense-psychoses. The terms are infrequently used today, save from the standpoint of historical interest.

'The simultaneous appearance of phobias and hysterical symptoms, observed so often in practice, is one of those factors which render it difficult to distinguish hysteria in a clear-cut manner from other neuroses, and make it necessary to set up the category of "mixed neuroses." To be sure, hallucinatory confusion is not often compatible with a continuance of hysteria, nor of obsessions as a rule. On the other hand, it is not rare for a defense psychosis to break out episodically in the course of an hysterical or mixed neurosis.' (Freud, S. *Collected Papers*, vol. 1, tr. by Riviere, J., Leonard and Virginia Woolf and The Institute of Psychoanalysis, London, 1924–25)

Two years later (in 1896) Freud wrote

that 'in a short paper published in 1894 I included hysteria, obsessions, and certain cases of acute hallucinatory confusion under one heading as "Defense Neuro-Psychoses." I did this because one point of view showed itself as applying in common to all these affections: their symptoms arise through the psychical mechanism of (unconscious) defense, that is, through an attempt to repress an intolerable idea which was in painful opposition to the patient's ego.' (ibid.)

neurosal (nū-rō'sal) Pertaining to neurosis.

neuroses, class differences in Neuroses are considered by many authorities as consequences of the specific social and economic circumstances of a particular class. For example, some have felt that poverty and social misery are the chief conditions for the development of neurosis. Others, on the contrary, have said that only the idle and privileged classes have had the time to develop neuroses and that the hard-working lower classes are protected from neuroses by their all-absorbing preoccupation with keeping fed and sheltered.

Fenichel denies both views, pointing out that neuroses are equally widespread in all socio-economic groups. Further, he remarks on the negligible differences between types of neuroses prevalent in different classes. This 'illustrates the fact that morality is not too different in different classes of the same society,' for the particular type of neurosis found within a society or group depends on the specific repressions that society imposes upon biological instinctual demands—in other words, on the society's morality. (Fenichel, O. *The Psychoanalytic Theory of Neurosis,* Norton, New York, 1945)

neurosis (nū-rō'sis) As used today, this term is interchangeable with the term *psychoneurosis* (q.v.). At one time it was used to refer to any somatic disorder of the nerves (the present-day term for this meaning is neuropathy) or to any disorder of nerve function. In psychoanalytic terminology, neurosis often is used more broadly to include all psychical disorders; thus Freud spoke of actual neuroses (neurasthenia, including hypochondriasis, and anxiety-neurosis); transference or psychoneuroses (anxiety-hysteria, conversion-hysteria, obsessional and compulsive neurosis; and Fenichel adds to this group

organ neuroses, pregenital conversions, perversions, and impulse neuroses); narcissistic neuroses (the schizophrenias and manic-depressive psychoses); and traumatic neuroses.

Using the term in its more restricted sense, as being synonymous with psychoneurosis, the following may be said about neurosis and neurositic phenomena:

The distinctions between neurosis and psychosis are symptomatic, psychopathological, and therapeutic. In the neuroses, only a part of the personality is affected (Meyer's 'part-reaction'), and reality is not changed qualitatively although its value may be altered quantitatively (i.e. diminished). The neurotic acts as if reality had the same kind of meaning for him as the rest of the community. Psychopathologically, the psychotic change in reality is partly expressed as projection, and of a type which does not occur in the neuroses. In the neuroses, language as such is never disturbed, while in the psychoses language is distorted and the unconscious may come to direct verbal expression. In the neuroses, the unconscious never attains more than symbolic expression, and regression to primitive levels (e.g. soiling and wetting) is not found in the presence of clear consciousness. Symptoms of neurosis include sensory, motor, or visceral disturbances and mental disturbances such as anxieties, specific fears and avoidances, memory disturbances, trance-states, somnambulisms, troublesome thoughts, and the like.

Charcot was the first to make a systematic study of the neuroses; he formulated a group of clinical pictures which he called hysteria, which was considered to be an outcome of hereditarily determined degeneration. Pierre Janet was the first to attempt a grouping of neuroses on the basis of their dynamics. He theorized that there are two kinds of psychological operations—easy ones, requiring the co-operation of only a few elements; and difficult ones, requiring the systematization of an infinite number of elements, involving a very new and intricate synthesis in each operation. When the 'nervous tension' or psychological force is lowered (by puberty, disease, fatigue, emotion, etc.) there is a general lowering of the mental level and only the simpler acts can be performed. Psychasthenia (including obsessions, compulsions, fears, and feelings of fatigue) results from a generalized lowering of the mental level; in hysteria, the lowering is localized in one particular function, which disappears (is dissociated) in consequence from the rest of the conscious personality.

Since Janet, there have been many other attempts at dynamic formulation of the neuroses, but Freud's concepts are probably the most widely accepted and the most complete explanations at the present time. They developed out of his clinical experience with hysteria, where Freud and Breuer found that hysterical symptoms disappear when the patient recalls, under hypnosis, previous experiences which have been forgotten. These experiences were found to be traumatic and sexual in nature, and this led Freud to pursue an investigation of sexuality. He described the various stages of development, from auto-erotism to object-love, and he noted that the various erotogenic zones, which originally are autonomous, are finally subordinated to the primacy of the genitals and reproduction. Not all of the instinctual energy associated with these various zones is useful for procreation, however, and normality as defined by our culture is achieved when these component instincts are repressed and diverted into sublimation. There are three stages in cultural development which correspond with this development of the sexual instinct: a stage in which the sexual impulse is allowed free rein regardless of its usefulness in procreation; a stage in which the whole of the sexual impulse is repressed except for that portion which subserves procreation; and a third stage in which procreation itself is limited by various factors. It is this latter which is our current civilized sexual morality. But constitutionally, not all people are capable even of the second stage and there thus arise two forms of deviation from normal sexuality—the perversions and the inversions (homosexuality). In the perversions, there has been fixation on an infantile aim; in the inversions, the sexual aim has been deflected from its normal object onto one of like sex. In both cases, those tendencies which conflict with the cultural norms may be completely repressed, but such repression requires all of the energy which would otherwise be used in cultural activities. If such repression is not achieved, the individual may remain in conflict with his culture (the overt perversions), or re-

pression may be only partially successful. In the latter case, the inhibited sexual impulses (and the painful memory of infantile sex experiences) are not expressed as such but reappear in a disguised form (symptoms of neurosis). Thus the neuroses are seen to be the negative of the perversions. If this disguise takes the form of somatic symptoms, the clinical picture is that of conversion hysteria; if conversion is not achieved, the conflict between the repressed material and the ego leads to conscious fear which is bound to some specific and apparently indifferent content, and the clinical picture is that of anxiety hysteria; if the material is allowed to remain in consciousness but is deprived of its affective cathexis, the clinical picture is that of obsessive-compulsive neurosis.

The above represents Freud's earlier theory of neurosis. He later came to recognize that aggression as well as the sexual instinct is important in the etiology of the neuroses, and he elaborated his theory of the death instinct (Thanatos or Nirvana principle). At the present time, it is believed that the neurotic conflict is essentially between the id (sexual and/or aggressive instincts) and the ego, with the superego taking either side. The external world may represent temptation or punishment so that the conflict may appear to be between the world and the ego. The ego attempts to defend itself against the instinctual impulses and does so successfully in the case of sublimation; but if the defense is unsuccessful, the warding-off process must be maintained at a high level of counter-cathexis. To escape the defenses, the impulses attempt indirect discharge through substitute impulses—the 'derivative.' The defensive system requires a damming up of tension and an inhibition of impulses; what then happens is that the original impulse manages to break through, in which case a symptom will be formed, or intensification of the defense will in itself constitute a symptom, or both of these may occur and the impulse will find a substitute outlet which helps to ward off the remainder of the impulse. Thus, three main types of precipitating factors can be recognized in the neuroses: (1) an increase in the warded-off drive; (2) a decrease in the warding-off forces; and (3) an increase in the warding-off forces. An increase in the instinctual energy may be absolute, as in puberty and the climacteric; or relative, as in the case of exposure to temptation, or devaluation of other drives whose energy is then displaced onto the warded-off drive, or blocking of instinctual satisfaction which has hitherto been obtainable, or blocking of any activity which has supplanted instinctual satisfaction. A decrease in the warding-off forces is seen in fatigue, intoxication, and when the ego is strengthened at one point and in its false confidence allows some of its censorial activities to lapse. An increase in warding-off forces is found in instances of increase in anxiety or guilt feelings, when any means of support or reassurance are lost, and, finally, a reactive increase is ordinarily seen after any temporary diminution.

The type of defense mechanism (i.e. the choice of neurosis) depends on the nature of the warded-off impulse, the age of the patient when the decisive conflict was experienced, the intensity and nature of the frustrating factors, the availability of substitute gratifications at the time of the frustration, and, particularly, the specific historical situation, which forces certain types of reaction.

General symptoms of the neurotic conflict include: (1) specific avoidances; (2) inhibitions of partial instincts (such as smoking and eating), of aggressiveness, of sexualized functions, and of emotions; (3) sexual disturbances such as impotence, premature ejaculation, and frigidity; (4) lack of interest in the environment and general impoverishment of the personality due to the constant drain of energy necessary to maintain countercathexes, and awareness of this impoverishment gives rise to inferiority feelings; (5) use of emergency discharges for the relief of tension, and (6) sleep disturbances, because of the many dreams and because of the fear of the ego to relax its guard during sleep.

neurosis, actual In Freud's terminology, a true neurosis, i.e. symptoms which develop as a result of actual, true, or real disturbances of the sexual economy. Forced abstinence, frustrated sexual excitement, incomplete or interrupted coitus, sexual efforts which exceed the psychical capacity, sexual outlet rendered inadequate by guilt-feelings or other conflicts, the need to revert to more primitive and/or less satisfactory means of sexual

expression—these are the common 'present-day' disturbances of sexuality which give rise to actual neurosis. Psychoneurosis, on the other hand, is determined by infantile and childhood experiences, and present-day occurrences are significant only in that they represent or repeat earlier events. Freud considered neurasthenia (a form of which is hypochondriasis) and anxiety-neurosis as true or actual neuroses.

neurosis, alternation of This is an older expression 'calling attention to the fact that nervous disorders are frequently relieved by acute bodily disease, so that persons suffering from insanity may be temporarily or even permanently cured by the occurrence of some acute bodily ailment. . . .' (Tuke, D.H. *A Dictionary of Psychological Medicine,* vols. 1–2, Blakiston, Philadelphia, 1892) The more usual present-day term for this phenomenon is *pathocure* (q.v.).

neurosis, analytic (an-à-lit'ik) A neurosis that develops subsequently to, and as a result of, interminable analysis. Stekel is of the opinion that after a too lengthy analysis, conducted over a period of many years, the patient, even if cured of his neurotic symptoms, 'loses his natural attitude toward life, and what should have cured him becomes his illness.' In this manner, after maintaining an emotional dependency for several years the patient develops toward analysis and analysts a special attitude which is called analytic neurosis. Similarly, the harmful effects upon psychic life produced by an analysis that is carried out without the necessary skill are also known as analytic, or post-analytic, neurosis. (Stekel, W. *Compulsion and Doubt,* Liveright, New York, 1949)

neurosis, anxiety See *anxiety-neurosis.*

neurosis, arrangement of the This term is used by Adler to indicate that the neurotic individual utilizes an unconscious 'arrangement' of character-traits, affect-preparations, and symptoms to safeguard himself; and also for the purpose of keeping these factors within the life-line, thus employing them both as a means to an end and as an artifice of the neurosis.

neurosis, artificial See *neurosis, experimental.*

neurosis, association See *psychosis, association.*

neurosis, benign Kempf thus characterizes the syndromes with a 'tendency to accept the personal source of the wishes or cravings which cause the distress or psychosis.' (Kempf, E.J. *Psychopathology*, Mosby, St. Louis, 1921)

neurosis, cardiovascular (kar-di-ō-vas'kū-lĕr) A neurosis characterized by symptoms and signs of cardiovascular disorder without any evidence of pathological changes in the structure of the cardiovascular apparatus.

neurosis, character The expression *neurotic character* is used by most authorities to refer to the individual who shows abnormalities in the sphere of personality. The abnormalities may be mild or severe.

'The result of such an investigation of the neurotic character should furnish proof of the value and utility of our method of comparative, individualistic psychology in the problems of mental life.' (Adler, A. *The Neurotic Constitution*, tr. by Glueck, B. and Lind, J.E., Moffat, Yard, New York, 1917)

In psychoanalysis the expression has acquired a nosologic implication. A neurotic character is one which in point of mental deviation occupies a position between the healthy and the clear-cut neurotic personality. Apparently the difference is largely one of degree. Alexander says that the neurotic character is one who suffers 'from no very definite symptoms of illness, but whose behavior in life is in the highest degree impulsive and frequently even compulsive.' Jones claims that the neurotic character exhibits 'manifestations intermediate between normal character traits and neurotic symptoms.' (Jones, E. *Papers on Psycho-Analysis*, 4th ed., Wood, Baltimore, 1938)

The neurosis is, as Jones expresses it, 'built into the character'; character traits acquire the significance of symptoms. Hence, the neurotic character is said to have a *character neurosis*. For example, an individual, presenting no formal symptoms, but excessively pedantic, meticulous, and cruel in an intellectual way, is said to be a neurotic character and to exhibit a character neurosis.

neurosis, choice of See *compliance, somatic.*

neurosis, circulatory See *neurosis, cardiovascular.*

neurosis, combat See *shell-shock.*

neurosis, compensation (1) Kempf classifies as a *compensation neurosis* one in which there is 'persistent striving to develop potent functions and win social esteem initiated by fear of impotence or loss of control of asocial cravings.' (Kempf, E.J. *Psychopathology*, Mosby, St. Louis, 1921)

(2) A form of traumatic neurosis induced by desire of monetary recompense.

It is believed that certain individuals after sustaining an injury may develop a neurosis in the hope of gaining financially (and otherwise) as a result of the injury. See *neurosis, indemnity.*

Compensation neurosis has been defined as 'a state of mind, born out of fear, kept alive by avarice, stimulated by lawyers, and cured by verdict.' The degree and duration of the neurosis are often inversely proportional to the extent of injury.

neurosis, compulsion A mental disorder, characterized by an irresistible impulse to perform a morbid act or an act considered morbid by the subject. See *obsession.*

In every compulsion-neurotic, Adler states, 'there inheres the function of withdrawing from external compulsion, so that he may obey only his own compulsion. In other words, the compulsion-neurotic struggles so definitely against the will of another and against every foreign influence, that, in his fight against these, he comes to the point of positing his own will as sacred and irresistible.' (Adler, A. *The Practice and Theory of Individual Psychology*, tr. by Radin, P., Kegan Paul, Trench, Trubner, London, 1924)

neurosis, compulsive-obsessive See *neurosis, compulsion; neurosis, obsessional.*

neurosis, contagiousness of The alleged but generally disputed capacity of a person's neurosis to affect another through contagion. In cases of hysteria there is a tendency for the patient to pick up additional symptoms from other patients who may be in the same ward. This occurs only occasionally. The term does not have the same significance as bacterial contagion and is used merely as a figure of speech.

neurosis, contagiousness of traumatic The psychoanalytic concept that the symptomatology of chronic traumatic neurosis can be acquired through suggestion and that the disorder is therefore 'contagious.'

Of this concept Kardiner writes: 'Some authors have emphasized too much the fact that these symptoms were acquired in hospitals as a result of suggestion, that is, from seeing other patients in the same condition. This cannot be, for in almost every persistent case of this type the condition is kept alive eight years or more after the traumatic event by a distinct group of dynamic forces which no suggestion can set in motion. Furthermore, parts of the original traumatic experience are attached to or become a part of the symptom itself. The fact that the symptoms of a traumatic neurosis make their appearance sometime after the traumatic experience can be verified without question. For this reason, attributing them to the contagiousness of the condition in hospital wards is somewhat exaggerated.' (Kardiner, A., and Spiegel, L. *War Stress and Neurotic Illness,* Hoeber, New York, 1947)

neurosis, covetous Compensation neurosis.
'Inordinate desire for gain is stressed as a psychogenic character, whether or not it [i.e. traumatic neurosis] is marked by structural molecular changes.' (Huddleson, J.H. *Accidents, Neuroses and Compensation,* Williams and Wilkins, Baltimore, 1932)

neurosis, dissociation Kempf says that in this neurosis 'the uncontrollable cravings dominate the personality despite efforts of the ego to prevent it.' The symptomatology constitutes 'distressing visceral tensions, with or without functional distortions, with or without eccentric defenses or compensations.' (Kempf, E.J. *Psychopathology,* Mosby, St. Louis, 1921)

neurosis, ego A term used by many authorities to designate a traumatic neurosis. This neurosis 'differs in mental content from the non-traumatic psychoneuroses in that the conscious ego is more vividly disordered than are the unconscious parts of the mind.' There may be, for example, disturbances of orientation and memory, even delirious states and extreme fatigue and weakness, throwing out of gear almost all of the ego. For that reason the traumatic neurosis has been termed an egoneurosis. (Hinsie, L.E. *Understandable Psychiatry,* Macmillan, New York, 1948)

neurosis, esophageal (ē-sō-fa-jē′al) Psychogenic disturbances of the swallowing functions of the esophagus, usually manifested by choking on food, inability to 'get it down,' or the sensation of a foreign body in the upper region of the esophagus, the globus hystericus. The major unconscious emotional basis for the symptom is the rejection of, or defense against, the process of 'incorporation.' To these individuals, incorporation represents a guilty oral aggressive (castrative) wish.
A patient prone to cunnilingus, associated with phantasies of oral castration (eating off the female phallus, i.e. clitoris), developed frequent severe choking spells while voraciously eating symbolic foods such as asparagus or melon at meals, following such sexual activity. 'Kronfeld, on the basis of a systematic psychiatric study, distinguished two forms of esophageal neurosis, a sensory hyperalgetic and a reflectory spastic form.' (Alexander, F. *Psychosomatic Medicine,* Norton, New York, 1950)

neurosis, expectation As Bleuler says an expectation neurosis is really not a neurosis; it is a symptom that is not uncommon to a number of nosologic entities. Sometimes, however, it is a major symptom or it may have what Bleuler calls 'monosymptomatic circumscription.' When an individual develops an anxiety regarding the anticipated performance of an act, he is said to exhibit an *expectation neurosis.*

neurosis, experimental Disorganized behavior which appears in the experimental subject in response to inability to master the experimental situation. Such behavior was noted by Pavlov in his dogs; when the animals were unable to discriminate between sounds of similar pitch or test objects of similar shape, they 'went to pieces.' Experimental neuroses have been induced in other animals as well—monkeys, chimpanzees, cats, goats, pigs, etc.
Neurotic symptoms are based on insufficiencies of the normal control apparatus and can be understood as involuntary emergency discharges which supplant the normal ones. The insufficiency may be brought about in two ways (which are not mutually exclusive)—too much excitation may be presented so that it cannot be mastered, as in traumatic neurosis; or a previous blocking or inadequacy of discharge may lead to an accumulation of tensions within the organism so that previously innocuous stimuli may release

them and thus operate as though they were traumatic. The experimental neurosis is an example of this second type. 'Some stimulus which had represented pleasant instinctual experiences or which had served as a signal that some action would now procure gratification is suddenly connected by the experimenter with frustrating or threatening experiences, or the experimenter decreases the difference between stimuli which the animal had been trained to associate with instinct gratification and threat respectively; the animal then gets into a state of irritation which is very similar to that of a traumatic neurosis. He feels contradictory impulses; the conflict makes it impossible for him to give in to the impulses in the accustomed way; the discharge is blocked, and this decrease in discharge works in the same way as an increase in influx: it brings the organism into a state of tension and calls for emergency discharges.' (Fenichel, O. *The Psychoanalytic Theory of Neurosis*, Norton, New York, 1945)

neurosis, fate Failure in one's career as a result of unconscious need for punishment; a type of moral masochism. See *masochism*.

neurosis, fear 'Complexes consisting entirely of the physiological manifestations of emotions without conscious emotion undoubtedly occur. A long time ago [1898] I described such a neurosis under the name of Fear Neurosis in distinction from psychosis.' (Prince, M. *The Unconscious*, Macmillan, New York, 1916)

neurosis, fright This infrequent term designates an intense but qualitatively normal reaction to a real, external frightful situation, such as an earthquake, dangerous fire, accident of any type, etc., in an individual not essentially predisposed. The symptoms vary with each individual, but fright or terror forms the nucleus of the reaction.

neurosis, holiday See *neurosis, Sunday*.

neurosis, housewife's This expression defines a compulsion-neurosis characterized by the individual's constant preoccupation with cleaning, washing, and dusting the house. Though justified by the patient, who explains that these exaggerated domestic activities are necessary in view of the danger inherent in the lack of hygiene in the place where she lives, in reality they constitute an external disguise for obsessive ideas concealed by the patient. According to Stekel, the inner 'compulsions are covered up for many years until the decrease of the patient's working capacity, or the danger of complete isolation force the patient to confess her illness to other people.' (Stekel, W. *Compulsion and Doubt*, Liveright, New York, 1949) See *psychosis, housewife's*.

neurosis, iatrogenic (ī-a-trō-jen'ik) See *iatrogeny*.

neurosis, indemnity A neurotic craving for or lust of indemnity. Levy-Bruhl's term for compensation neurosis.

neurosis, infantile The neurosis that is to become manifest in the adult and is already present in the infant. Thus, whether the psychiatrist speaks of the adult neurosis or the infantile neurosis he speaks of the same neurosis. The infantile neurosis usually differs from the neurosis as it will appear later in adult life in not showing any symptoms at that (i.e. infantile) period, and if it does, the symptoms are so mild that they go unnoticed.

The basic structure of the neurosis is already present, however, and is hence termed infantile neurosis, although it will not *necessarily* manifest itself as a full-blown neurosis when adulthood is reached; but if the adult *does* exhibit neurosis it is *this* neurosis which will have overtaken him. In every case of adult neurosis it can be shown that the foundation upon which it rests is already formed in the infancy period, but the converse is not true any more than in a proposition in geometry.

neurosis, infinity Neurotic preoccupation with the infinity of space and time, usually encountered in youth entering upon adulthood. 'But it would almost seem from our returns that every well-endowed youth, before or very soon after the age of twenty has an infinity neurosis concerning space and time, which is more or less specific and is often at first perhaps chiefly automatic and instinctive, but unique and heretofore little known.' (Hall, G.S. *Adolescence*, vol. 2, Appleton, New York, 1908, p. 159)

neurosis insana (nev-rô'sēs ēn-sä'nà) (L. 'insane neurosis') *Obs.* Psychoneurosis.

neurosism (nū'rō-siz'm) Nervousness, neurasthenia, neuroticism; a condition of perverted or irritable nervous action.

neurosis, malignant A neurosis in which the symptomatology continues to progress, that is, become more and more severe. This is in contradistinction both to a stationary neurosis, in which the defenses against instinctual urges operate successfully without further increase in anxiety or other symptomatology, and to a neurosis in which for several reasons there may be a spontaneous improvement or even temporary cure.

In the malignant neurosis, the increase in instinctual demands becomes so great that the neurotic symptomatology standing on guard against these urges may sum up completely all the behavior or adaptation of the patient. For example, his phobias may become so all-embracing that he is unable to carry out any activity. He may become a prisoner in his own room or even in his own bed, unable to care for his simplest needs. Or compulsive symptoms may become so widespread that the patient may not be able to make the slightest decision concerning work, social activities, etc. (Fenichel, O. *The Psychoanalytic Theory of Neurosis,* Norton, New York, 1945)

neurosis, military War neurosis.

neurosis, mimic-cramp 'The frequency with which these stereotypies are associated with insane ideas referring to movements of defense suggested to Bressler that this symptom-complex was a neurosis of self-protection due to an exaggerated excitability of the psychomotor centres. He proposed the name "mimic-cramp neurosis," basing his theory on the observations of Breuer and Freud in cases of hysteria where the movements were thought to be largely imitative.' (Paton, S. *Psychiatry,* Lippincott, Philadelphia and London, 1905)

neurosis, mixed In Freud's earliest psychoanalytic communications this (now infrequent) term denoted a neurosis that contained phenomena of two or more subdivisions of the neuroses. It is now recognized that many of these more properly belong in the schizophrenic group, and particularly to the subtype described by Hoch and Polatin, the 'pseudoneurotic' schizophrenias.

neurosis, monosymptomatic See *monosymptomatic.*

neurosis, motor This term is sometimes applied to the neuroses that are characterized principally by disorders of movement, e.g. the various tics.

neurosismus (nū-rō-siz'mus) This term was coined by Dubois to include such subdivisions as neurasthenia, hysteria, hystero-neurasthenia, hypochondria, melancholia, and borderline psychoses.

neurosis, obsessional See *obsessive-compulsive, psychoneurosis.*

neurosis, occlusal (o-klōo'sal) This is 'a grinding, pounding, or setting of the teeth, when the mouth is empty; that is, entirely apart from the perfectly normal activity of mastication.' Bruxism is an occlusal neurosis occurring during the night. (Frohman, B.S. 'Occlusal Neurosis,' *Psychoanalytic Review 19, 298, 1932)*

neurosis, occupational It is the general opinion of psychiatrists that there are no occupations in and of themselves that cause a neurosis. Bleuler states that *'overexertion and exhaustion certainly are only rarely causes of neuroses, and never of psychoses. . . .'* Occupation may set free a psychiatric condition, that is, it may act as a precipitating agent, but one must look elsewhere for the basic causative factors. (Bleuler, E. *Textbook of Psychiatry,* tr. by Brill, A.A., Macmillan, New York, 1930)

Dana spoke of occupational neuroses as 'the nervous troubles which affect people engaged in skilled manual occupations, and [which] are due to the neuromuscular work itself. . . .' He classified them into occupational pains and symptomatic cramps, occupational neuritis and atrophy, acroparesthesias, and true occupational or professional cramps. (Dana, C.L. 'Occupational Neuroses,' *Medical Record 81,* 451, 1912)

neurosis, organ See *psychosomatic.*

neurosis, parent as carrier of The essence of this term is found in the word 'carrier,' used here as in bacteriology and immunology: the term relates to the etiology or causation of neurosis and emphasizes the etiological factor of neurosis, especially character neurosis, in parents, as a dynamic and powerful force seriously marring the healthy character development of children and influencing them in the direction of the development of childhood and adult neuroses and psychoses.

In the parents, neurotic character traits may be latent and subtle in their expression and manifestation. By the un-discerning and the more superficial observers these parents are often accepted as so-called model, socially adjusted, socially admirable adults. Their character defects, however, have a fatal, distorting, and scarring effect in their impact on the plastic and impressionable dependent personalities of their children.

E. Weiss and O.S. English (*Psychosomatic Medicine,* 2nd ed., Saunders, Philadelphia and London, 1949) state that 'the most common types of such parental carriers of neurosis to the children are: (a) The "cold" parents, who cannot give the warmth and love the children need; (b) the over-indulgent parents, who cannot expose their children to the disciplines and reality frustrations necessary to the child's development of adult survival traits; (c) the sexually frustrated parents, who displace their sexual needs onto the establishment of an over-intense emotional bond to their children as a substitute love-object; (d) the unconsciously hating parent, who visits repressed and denied aggression and hostility on his child, expressing repressed and denied jealousy and rivalry.'

neurosis, pension A form of compensation neurosis.

neurosis, performance From the standpoint of psychodramatics a performance-neurosis is a mental disturbance which may take place in the course of any performance whose normal execution requires any degree of spontaneity. An illustration is an attack of trembling overcoming a violinist while playing. This trembling attack may be caused by a maladjustment to the violin and/or maladjustment to the musical conserve. These factors are linked to a peculiar development of the musician's creative ego. A surplus of motor images, which would find an easy outlet in spontaneity work, does not find an easy outlet in the playing of a musical conserve.

'A performance-neurosis may become manifest in the performance of any role which is accompanied by a loss of spontaneity and in the living of any relationship which is accompanied by a loss of tele.' (Moreno, J.L., *Sociometry 2, 3,* 1939)

neurosis, perhaps A psychiatric term denoting a very common mental mechanism in certain neurotic patients who are in the grip of the following formula: '*If* I

had done this instead of that, *perhaps* my sister would still be alive.'

Certain authors have called this compromising formula of 'if' and 'perhaps,' which the patient uses as a vain attempt to elude his guilt, the 'perhaps neurosis.' (Stekel, W. *Compulsion and Doubt,* Liveright, New York, 1949)

neurosis, pernicious According to Kempf's mechanistic classification, a neurosis is pernicious when there is a tendency on the part of the patient 'to oppose or refuse to accept the personal source of the wish or craving, to hate those who would attribute a personal source, to blame an external or impersonal cause.' (Kempf, E.J. *Psychopathology,* Mosby, St. Louis, 1921)

neurosis, population A collective or group-neurosis prevailing in the populace of a locality or region. 'The neuroses of a group are not simply the sum total of the neuroses among the individual members thereof. There is an interaction between individual members of a group so that there results a community type of response which has characteristics all of its own. The community, also, may show symptoms of tension and of symbolism as a mass reaction.' (Kraines, S.H. *The Therapy of Neuroses and Psychoses,* Lea & Febiger, Philadelphia, 1948)

neurosis, postconcussion A form of traumatic neurosis following cerebral concussion; a postconcussion neurosis, according to Osnato, is symptomatic of traumatic encephalopathy. On the other hand, C.S. Mullin (*U.S. Armed Forces Medical Journal 4:* 1748–52, 1953) feels that 'blast concussion' bears a closer relationship to neurosis than to cerebral trauma.

neurosis, post-traumatic (post-traw-ma'-tik) Traumatic neurosis.

neurosis, prison See *chronophobia.*

neurosis, progredient (prō-grē'di-ent) A neurosis that takes a progressive course, with increasing severity of symptoms. The clinical course which a neurosis may follow is variable. It may remain stationary or even improve spontaneously. On the other hand, it may run a malignant course, with increasingly severe symptoms. These types are called progredient neuroses. At times, neuroses that have been stationary or improving may become progredient.

In progredient neurosis, the damming-up of instincts increases more and more. Because there is neither adequate discharge nor adequate defense, the neurosis becomes increasingly severe. For example, in a phobic patient conditions assume an ever-increasing scope. At first, the patient may not be able to walk across a particular square. Later on he cannot go out of doors, and finally, perhaps, not even out of his room. In the case of the compulsion-neurotic, 'ambivalences and doubts increase, until no decision whatsoever can be made.' Eventually there will be a full paralysis of the conscious will.

Another type of progression may occur when neuroses that have been stationary for a time suddenly become progredient again. A compulsive equilibrium may change into uncontrollable vegetative attacks, or a rigid character neurosis into a symptom neurosis with anxiety attacks, depressions, or other symptoms. (Fenichel, O. *The Psychoanalytic Theory of Neurosis,* Norton, New York, 1945)

neurosis, regression According to Kempf's classification of neuroses, this subdivision is characterized by 'failure to compensate but regression to a preceding, more comfortable, irresponsible level, permitting wish-fulfilling fancies, postures and indulgences.' The symptoms are built around 'distressing visceral tensions, rare, but persistent maintenance of characteristic affective attitudes of the prenatal, infantile or preadolescent stage.' (Kempf, E.J. *Psychopathology,* Mosby, St. Louis, 1921)

neurosis, repression Kempf uses this term for a neurosis in which there is 'vague consciousness to total unconsciousness of the nature and influence of the ungratifiable affective cravings.' The symptoms are the same as those in the suppression neurosis 'plus functional distortions of the projicient apparatus and changes in reactivity to the sense organs.' (Kempf, E.J. *Psychopathology,* Mosby, St. Louis, 1921)

neurosis, social Burrow's term for the common condition of disorder and conflict which exists throughout society's structure, though generally unrecognized by it. It is expressed symptomatically in the nervous and mental disorder of the individual, and also in man's so-called normal interrelations—in his peaceful social institutions, in economic conflict, crime,

and war. Viewed phylobiologically, this general social condition is the primary and essential disorder of which the individual manifestation of neurosis is an arbitrarily isolated expression. (Burrow, T. 'An Ethnic Aspect of Consciousness,' *Sociological Review XIX,* 74–5, 1927; also Burrow, T. *The Social Basis of Consciousness,* Harcourt, Brace, New York and London, 1927)

neurosis, space See *neurosis, infinity.*

neurosis, spinal *Obs.* Hysteria referable to the spinal region.

neurosis, structural traumatic 'Trauma often causes neurologic syndromes that are not neuroses, and a clear differentiation between neurotic and non-neurotic effects is occasionally almost or quite impossible.' (Huddleson, J.H. *Accidents, Neuroses and Compensation,* Williams and Wilkins, Baltimore, 1932) When the neurosis is more or less definitely attributable to structural, somatic pathology, it is known as structural traumatic neurosis.

neurosis, substitution When repressed, affects 'tend to flow in any direction open' to them, 'whether this is a physical (conversion-hysteria) or mental one (substitution neurosis, obsessions).' (Jones, E. *Papers on Psycho-Analysis,* 4th ed., Wood, Baltimore, 1938)

neurosis, Sunday Ferenczi speaks of neuroses 'the oscillation of whose symptoms were dependent on the particular day of the week.' He says he has treated 'several neurotics the history of whose illness, recounted spontaneously or reproduced during the analysis, contained the information that certain nervous conditions had developed—mostly in youth—on a certain day of the week, and had then regularly recurred. . . . Most of them experienced these periodical returns of the disturbances on *Sundays.*' (Ferenczi, S. *Further Contributions to the Theory and Technique of Psycho-Analysis,* tr. by Suttie, J.I., Leonard and Virginia Woolf and The Institute of Psychoanalysis, London, 1926)

neurosis, suppression From the standpoint of Kempf's psychopathology, in a *suppression-neurosis* there is 'clear to vague consciousness of the nature and effect of the ungratifiable affective cravings.' The symptoms are said to be due to 'distressing hypertensions or hypotensions of autonomic (visceral) segments (mild to severe).' (Kempf, E.J. *Psychopathology,* Mosby, St. Louis, 1921)

neurosis, transference A transference-neurosis, a 'new artificial neurosis,' occurs only during psychoanalytic treatment. It is the reappearance of the early infantile Oedipus situation. The analyst represents one or both parents as a love-object, as if he were really the original parent in the original infantile setting of the patient. The patient also lives out all his old ego attitudes and incest prohibitions.

Transference-neurosis represents 'a stage where the history of the patient's development, leading up to the infantile neurosis, is re-enacted in the analytic room—the patient plays the part of actor-manager, pressing into service (like the child in the nursery) all the stage property that the analytical room contains, first and foremost, the analyst himself.' (Glover, E.)

neurosis, traumatic (traw-ma'tik) 'A traumatic neurosis may be defined most simply as a psychogenic or nonstructural nervous disorder, shortly following a physical injury, and complicated or not by structural changes in the central nervous system or elsewhere.' (Huddleson, J.H. *Accidents, Neuroses and Compensation,* Williams and Wilkins, Baltimore, 1932) The nature of the disorder often helps in the determination of the diagnosis. Many classifications have been suggested. Huddleson says that 'the symptomatology of traumatic is that of nontraumatic anxiety neuroses, neurasthenias, hypochondriases, and conversion hysterias, plus more or less of the wound-of-the-head syndrome. Ego-neuroses are more characteristic of the group as a whole than are psychosexual conflicts.

'Many symptom complexes are so superficial as scarcely to merit the designation of neuroses, particularly when monetary compensation is involved. Some exaggeration is the rule, and a preponderance of simulated over nonsimulated symptoms is not uncommon.' (ibid.) Psychotic, neurotic, or behavioral reactions consequent upon trauma to the brain are classified as brain syndromes (organic reaction types); it is only those reactions to injury of the head and other parts of the body which are not dependent upon physical or structural alteration of brain functioning which are properly termed traumatic neuroses. In the 1952 revision

of psychiatric nomenclature, such neuroses are to be classified within the psychoneurotic type whose symptoms they present (such as phobic reaction or dissociative reaction) and are not given a separate listing as traumatic reaction.

While a traumatic experience can precipitate any of the well-known types of neurotic or psychotic disorders, the most common conditions seen in combat are hysteria, anxiety-states, and exhaustion conditions. The essential features of traumatic neurosis are: (1) fixation on the trauma with amnesia for the traumatic situation which may be total or partial; (2) typical dream-life (dreams of annihilation, aggression dreams where the patient is the aggressor but is defeated, frustration or Sisyphus dreams, and occupational dreams in which it is the means of livelihood rather than the body-ego which is annihilated); (3) contraction of the general level of functioning, with constant fear of the environment, disorganized behavior, lowered efficiency, lack of co-ordinated goal activities, and profoundly altered functioning in the autonomic, motor, and sensory nervous system; (4) general irritability; and (5) a proclivity to explosive aggressive reactions. A malignant type of traumatic neurosis, *psychorrhexis* (q.v.), is seen in 2 to 3 per cent of war neuroses.

neurosis, traumatic psychosexual (traw-ma'tik sī-kō-sek'shoo-al) Kardiner speaks of 'true' traumatic neuroses, which develop along lines of ego reactions. He affirms that 'traumatic neurosis is not devoid of libidinal components but most of the symptomatology refers to egoistic disturbance.' ('Anxiety and Fright,' *Archives of Neurology and Psychiatry, XXI,* 714, 1929)

Other traumatic neuroses show the psychosexual type of regression that is said to characterize the psychoneuroses; the expression psychosexual traumatic neurosis is applied to this condition.

neurosis, vagabond See *drapetomania; dromomania.*

neurosis, vagus (vā'gus) An uncommonly used term for anxiety state.

neurosis, vascular (vas'kū-lĕr) See *neurosis, cardiovascular.*

neurosis, vasomotor (vas-ō-mō'tĕr) See *constitution, post-traumatic.*

neurosis, vegetative The expression of

emotion, or unconscious emotional conflict, by disturbed functioning of the internal visceral organs. The term is usually employed in contradistinction to conversion-hysteria: whereas conversion hysteria takes place in the voluntary neuromuscular, or sensory perceptive systems, the vegetative neurosis has its site in the internal visceral organs.

It is found that chronic repressed, suppressed, and denied resentment and anger are an invariable factor in the personality reactions of individuals with essential hypertension (high blood pressure). Similarly, individuals developing duodenal ulcer seem to suffer from long-standing, chronic conflict between independency-aggressive strivings and dependency-submissive trends. 'A vegetative neurosis is not an attempt to express an emotion, but is the physiological response of the vegetative organs to constant, or to periodically returning, emotional states.' (Alexander, F. *Psychosomatic Medicine,* Norton, New York, 1950)

The term vegetative neurosis is sometimes also used synonymously with *acrodynia* (q.v.).

neurosis, wish Bing thus denotes a traumatic neurosis in which the wish to be afflicted seems to constitute the essential etiology; traumatic hysteria.

neurosity (nū-ros′i-tē) *Obs.* Nerve-force.

neuro-social See *constant, extrinsic.*

neurosthenia (nū-rō-sthē′ni-à) Excessive quantity of so-called nervous energy.

neurosyphilis (-sif′i-lis) Neurosyphilis is a generic term for all forms of involvement of the nervous system by the spirochaeta pallida.

neurosyphilis, asymptomatic (à-simp-tō-mat′ik) Neurosyphilis without clinical symptoms but with physical signs and laboratory findings of syphilitic involvement of the nervous system. An example would be asymptomatic general paresis. Here mental symptoms are absent, although clinical signs and laboratory findings indicate general paresis.

neurosyphilis, ectodermogenic (ek-tō-dĕr-mō-jen′ik) Since the cerebrospinal axis proper, that is, the brain, spinal cord, and nerves, are derived from the ectodermal embryonal layer, the predominant involvement of these structures in the syphilitic process is generically termed ectodermogenic neurosyphilis.

neurosyphilis, interstitial (in-tĕr-stish′al) A general term, not commonly employed, for the pathological changes occurring in the meninges and blood vessels of the nervous system in persons affected with syphilis.

neurosyphilis, meningeal (men-in-jē′al) Meningeal neurosyphilis is a disease of the nervous system occurring in individuals affected with syphilis. The pathologic lesions are observed mainly in the leptomeninges (the pia mater and arachnoid considered as one membrane). A clinical example is syphilitic meningitis (pachy- and leptomeningitis) which is included in the generic term of cerebral syphilis.

neurosyphilis, meningo-encephalitic (men-in-gō-en-sef-a-lit′ik) The pathological designation of the clinical picture named general paresis.

neurosyphilis, meningo-vascular (men-in-gō-vas′kū-lĕr) A disease of the nervous system occurring in individuals affected with syphilis. The pathologic process primarily and predominantly involves the meninges and blood vessels rather than the parenchyma of the nervous system. A clinical example is cerebral syphilis.

neurosyphilis, mesodermogenic (mes-ō-dĕr-mō-jen′ik) Since the meninges, blood vessels, and nerve sheaths are derived from the mesodermal embryonal layers, the predominant involvement of these structures in the syphilitic process attacking the nervous system is generically termed mesodermogenic neurosyphilis.

neurosyphilis, parenchymatous (par-eng-kīm′à-tus) A general term designating degenerative, less often inflammatory, processes mainly of the substance of the brain and spinal cord. Clinical examples are general paresis, tabes, taboparesis, and juvenile general paresis.

neurosyphilis, vascular (vas′kū-lĕr) A disease of the nervous system occurring in individuals affected with syphilis. The pathologic lesions are observed mainly in the blood vessels of the nervous system, especially the arteries. A clinical example is syphilitic endarteritis of the nervous system, which is included in the generic term of cerebral syphilis.

neurotherapeutics, neurotherapy (-ther-à-pū'tiks, -ther'á-pē) The treatment of nervous disorders.

neurotic (nū-rot'ik) Relating to or affected by neurosis. See *neurosis*.

In Burrow's usage this term takes on a broader significance than that ordinarily attaching to it. Neurotic behavior is not looked upon as characteristic of the clinically aberrant individual only. From a phylobiological viewpoint the affective behavior of the average 'normal' individual is as deviate and unco-ordinated as are the socially phantastic and extravagant reactions of the psychoneurotic patient. See *partitive; semiopathic; image, social.* (Burrow, T. *The Biology of Human Conflict,* Macmillan, New York, 1937, pp. 125–6; 133–4)

neuroticism (nū-rot'i-siz'm) A neurotic condition; state of neurosis. Ferenczi states that 'functional psychoses and psychoneuroses are distinguished from normal mental activity only by a matter of degree.' (Ferenczi, S. *Further Contributions to the Theory and Technique of Psycho-Analysis,* tr. by Suttie, J.I., Leonard and Virginia Woolf and The Institute of Psychoanalysis, London, 1926.) Jones says: 'The deviation [of the neurotic] from the so-called normal is throughout quantitative, not qualitative.' (Jones, E. *Papers on Psycho-Analysis,* 4th ed., Wood, Baltimore, 1938)

neurotigenic (nū-rot-i-jen'ik) Producing or favoring the induction of a neurosis.

neurotization (nū-rot-i-zā'shun) Direct implantation of nerve into a paralyzed muscle.

neurotoidism (nū-rot'oid-iz'm) Certain mental states that develop from injury; Norbert Bromberg felt that they are not to be regarded as neuroses, though they closely resemble them. (*American Journal of Psychiatry, 103,* 31, 1946–7)

neurotrophasthenia (nū-rō-trof-as-thē'-ni-á) Defective nutrition of the nervous system.

neurypnology (nū-rip-nol'ō-jē) Braid's term for the science of hypnosis.

neuter, social A member of a group who has very little effect upon its structure and behavior because of his weakness, ineffectualness, or indifference. See *instigator; isolate; neutralizer.*

neutrality The role of therapist in activity group psychotherapy; here he is not only passive and permissive, but neither has nor applies criteria of right and wrong, proper and improper behavior on the part of the patient. According to Slavson, who introduced this concept, neutrality of therapist means 'that each patient can utilize him in accordance with his own particular needs. It is as though the therapist were a screen of neutral tone like that in a movie on which different colors are projected. Each member of the group projects on the therapist his unconscious attitudes toward adults. Neutrality on the part of the therapist makes this possible.' (Slavson, S.R. *An Introduction to Group Therapy,* The Commonwealth Fund, Oxford University Press, New York, 1943, p. 33)

neutrality, sexual Krafft-Ebing says: 'The sexual instinct and desire, save for indistinct feelings and impulses, remain latent until the period of development of the sexual organs. The child is *generis neutrius*.' (Krafft-Ebing, R.v. *Psychopathia Sexualis,* Login, New York, 1908)

neutralization In psychoanalysis, neutralization is a general term which includes both *desexualization* (q.v.) and *desaggressivization* (q.v.). 'The term neutralization implies that an activity of the individual which originally afforded drive satisfaction through discharge of cathexis ceases to do so and comes to be in the service of the ego, apparently nearly or quite independent of the need for gratification or discharge of cathexis in anything which even approaches its original instinctual form.' (Brenner, C. *An Elementary Textbook of Psychoanalysis,* International Universities Press, New York, 1955) From the standpoint of Kempf's psychopathology, it is said that 'this autonomic-affective craving compels the organism to acquire such stimuli as have the especial capacity to relieve the craving, and, as a *counter-irritant,* cause the gastric muscle [for example] to resume comfortable tensions and movements, *neutralizing the craving.*' (Kempf, E.J. *Psychopathology,* Mosby, St. Louis, 1921)

neutralizer A member of a therapy group who neutralizes, i.e. counteracts and controls, the aggressivity, impulsiveness, and destructiveness of other members of the group. See *instigator; isolate.*

névrospasmie (nā-vrô-spás-mē') *Obs.* Neurasthenia.

nexus (nek′sus) See *thought-nexus.*

night-eating See *syndrome, night-eating.*

nightmare A fright reaction during sleep. 'In the nightmare (ephialtes, incubus) the child awakens in terror from a dream usually characterized by a feeling of suffocation and helplessness. He can ordinarily relate his bad dream; he is well oriented, can recognize people about him, and can be calmed readily. Nightmares are often very vivid and the memory of them, accompanied by a sense of dread, sometimes recurs the following day when the child is awake. They are not uncommon and generally take place within an hour or two after going to bed.' (Bakwin and Bakwin. *Clinical Management of Behavior Disorders in Children,* Saunders, Philadelphia, 1953)

night-phantasy See *phantasy, night.*

night-psychosis See *psychosis, night.*

nightshade poisoning See *poisoning, deadly nightshade.*

night-terror See *terror, night.*

nihilism (nē′[h]il-iz'm) In psychiatry *nihilism* denotes the delusion of non-existence. The delusion may be widespread in the sense that it includes everything—the patient himself and the entire world. Such an extensive delusion may be encountered in patients in a deep, depressive stuporous reaction. The delusion may be selective, so to speak, in that it refers only to some part of oneself or one's environment. Some depressive patients believe, though it is not so, that all the members of their family are dead. It is commonplace for a schizophrenic patient to believe that he has been dead for some time.

'Indeed, in some cases, instead of a feeling of well-being and euphoria, a state of intense depression is present, even amounting to stupor with mutism. The feature of the depression is the frequency with which absurd nihilistic ideas are expressed. Patients claim that they are dead, that their blood has ceased to circulate, that they have no pulse, that their bodies are utterly destroyed.' (Henderson, D.K. and Gillespie, R.D. *A Text-Book of Psychiatry,* 4th ed., Oxford University Press, London, 1936)

Nirvana (nir-vä′nà) Psychiatrists place much emphasis upon what is called mental tension, which means the charge of psychic energy in various psychic structures. The tendency of mental life is to keep psychic tension at the lowest possible ebb, in a relatively tensionless state.

While discussing the psychology of the stupor reaction, representing deep regression, MacCurdy says: 'Viewed from the adult standpoint, the emptiness of this early mental state must seem like the Nirvana of death. At least death is the only simple term we can use to represent such a complete loss of our habitual mental functions.' (MacCurdy, J.T. *The Psychology of Emotion,* Harcourt, Brace, New York, 1925)

In psychoanalysis the expression *nirvana-principle* (suggested by Barbara Low) refers to a manifestation of the action of the death instinct, 'the aim of which is to lead our throbbing existence into the stability of an inorganic state.' Freud maintains that 'the *Nirvana*-principle expresses the tendency of the death-instinct, the *pleasure*-principle represents the claims of the libido, and that modification of it, the *reality*-principle, the influence of the outer world.' (Freud, S. *Collected Papers,* vol. 2, tr. by Riviere, J., Leonard and Virginia Woolf and The Institute of Psychoanalysis, London, 1924–25)

noasthenia (nō-as-thē′ni-à) *Obs.* Mental debility.

nocar (nō′kĕr) *Obs.* Lethargy.

noctambulation (nok-tam-bū-lā′shun) Night-walking; sleep-walking.

noctambulism (nok-tam′bū-liz'm) *Rare.* The term is synonymous with somnambulism in psychiatric import, but is more specific as regards the time of the day when the sleep-walking occurs.

'In this connection should be mentioned sleep-walking (noctambulism). This manifests itself chiefly in childhood, but frequently in adults as well.' (Stekel, W. *Encyclopaedia Sexualis,* ed. by Robinson, V., Dingwall-Rock, New York, 1936)

noctiphobia (nok-ti-fō′bi-à) See *nyctophobia.*

nodal behavior See *behavior, nodal.*

-noea (-nē′à) Variant of *-noia.*

noematic (nō-ē-mat′ik) Relating to the mental processes.

-noia (-noi′à) Combining form meaning

mind, mental state, from Gr. (pará)*noia,* from *nóos, noũs,* mind.

nomad, extravertive This term is applied to a certain type of individual who joins the air forces as a result of a strong unconscious desire to roam from place to place. (See *nomadism*) These are individuals who go out to meet reality and enjoy the exhilaration of flying, satisfying in this manner both their introversion (by being alone in the plane) and their nomadism by constantly going from place to place. (Sladen, F.J. *Psychiatry and the War,* Thomas, Springfield, Ill., 1943)

nomadism A pathological tendency to roam from place to place, which is so strong that it gives rise to serious social maladjustment. 'Occasional and episodic nomadism apparently arises on the basis of a mental mechanism similar to that underlying resorting to alcohol or drugs. It is often associated with mental deficiency, epilepsy, and psychotic disease. It is not infrequently seen in children as residuals of epidemic encephalitis and may be part of the clinical picture of the residuals of cerebral birth trauma.' (Selling, L.S. *Synopsis of Neuropsychiatry,* Mosby, St. Louis, 1947) See *wanderlust; dromomania.*

nomenclature, 1952 revision The following table is adapted from the 1952 revision of psychiatric nomenclature adopted as the officially supported nomenclature of the American Psychiatric Association.

Disorder	New Code No.	Standard Nomenclature No.
Acute Brain Syndrome, associated with		
infection	01	(009-100; 000-100)
intoxication	02	(000-3..)
trauma	03	(000-4..)
circulatory disturbance	04	(000-5..)
convulsive disorder	05	(000-550)
metabolic disturbance	06	(000-7..)
intracranial neoplasm	07	(000-8..)
disease of unknown or uncertain cause	08	(000-900)
acute brain syndrome of unknown cause	09	(000-xx0)
Chronic Brain Syndrome, associated with		
prenatal (constitutional) conditions	10	(009-0..)
central nervous system syphilis	11	(009-147)
other intercranial infection	12	(009-163)
intoxication	13	(009-3..)
trauma	14	(009-050; 009-4..)
circulatory disturbance	15	(009-5..)

Disorder	New Code No.	Standard Nomenclature No.
convulsive disorder	16	(009-550)
disturbance of metabolism, growth, nutrition	17	(009-7..)
new growth	18	(009-8..)
unknown or uncertain cause	19	(009-9..; 009-xx0)
Psychotic Disorders		
involutional psychotic reaction	20	(009-796)
affective reactions (manic-depressive reactions, psychotic depressive reaction)	21	(000-x10)
schizophrenic reactions	22	(000-x20)
paranoid reactions	23	(000-x30)
Psychophysiologic Autonomic and Visceral Disorders	30-39	(00.-580)
Psychoneurotic Disorders	40	(000-x0.)
Personality Disorders		
personality pattern disturbance	50	(000-x4.)
personality trait disturbance	51	(000-x5.)
sociopathic personality disturbance	52	(000-x6.)
special symptom reaction	53	(000-x7.)
transient situational personality disturbance	54	(000-x8.)
Mental Deficiencies		
familial or hereditary	60	(000-x90)
idiopathic	61	(000-y90)

nonaria (nō-nä′rē-à) (L. 'public prostitute') Occasional synonym for a prostitute: in ancient Rome a prostitute could not appear in the streets before the ninth hour (*nonus,* ninth).

non compos mentis (nōn kôm′pôs men′tēs) (L. 'not of a sane mind, not in possession of his mind') Not of sound mind, mentally incapable of managing one's affairs.

non-directive therapy See *therapy, client-centered.*

non-reporting See *psychodynamics, adaptational.*

non-restraint Management of the psychotic patient without the use of the strait-jacket or other forms of restraint.

nonsense-syndrome See *syndrome, nonsense.*

nonsense-witticism See *wit, nonsense in.*

noöklopia (nō-ō-klō′pi-à) N.D.C. Lewis defines the term as *thought theft obsessions.*

'I have offered the term noöklopia or, with apologies to etymology, one might call it castrophrenia to include the clinical manifestations of a group of phenomena occasionally encountered as part of the schizophrenic content, and as I believe constituting a very definite trend based on the castration complex as such.' ('The Psychobiology of the Castration Reaction,' *Psychoanalytic Review XV*, 77, 1928) Lewis adds: 'The extremely heterogeneous elements of this phenomenon are cemented together by the morbid cenesthetic idea inducing a person to believe that his thoughts are being sucked out of his brain by some sinister personal magnetism, a purposely constructed machine. . . .' (ibid.)

noölogy (nō-ol'ō-jē) The doctrine of the mind; the science of the understanding.

noöpsyche (nō-ō-sī'kē) Stransky coined this term with the idea that there are two separate psychic factors: (1) the *noöpsyche*, comprising all purely intellectual processes, and (2) the *thymopsyche*, made up of affective processes. In his opinion, intrapsychic ataxia, which results in marked incongruity between ideas and emotions, is a consequence of the more or less independent activities of the two psychic factors.

noösphales (nō-os'fal-ēz) *Obs.* Mentally deranged.

noösteresis (nō-ō-stē-rē'sis) *Obs.* Dementia.

noradrenalin (nor-ad-ren'à-lin) Norepinephrine; see *epinephrine*.

norepinephrine (nor-e-pin-e'frin) See *epinephrine*.

normosplanchnic (nor-mō-splangk'nik) In Viola's system of constitutional forms of body build, this term denotes the type which has a normal or average relationship between thoracic and abdominal size, owing to medium size of the abdominal and thoracic viscera. This type is further characterized by a proportionality between vertical and horizontal diameters, resulting in a harmonious physique.

Persons of this type correspond roughly to Kretschmer's *athletic* (q.v.) type.

normotonic (-ton'ik) In Tandler's system of constitutional types, this term describes a type characterized by normal or average tone of the voluntary muscles, in contrast to the *hypotonic* and *hypertonic* types.

normotype (nor'mō-tĭp) In constitutional medicine a term for the structurally or morphologically average individual. It is synonymous with eumorph.

normotypical (nor-mō-tip'i-kal) In constitutional medicine three types of body build are recognized: (1) dolichomorphic or longitypical; (2) brachymorphic or brachytypical; (3) eumorphic or normotypical or normosplanchnic.

norm, psychic (sī'kik) From the psychiatric point of view, a psychically normal person is one who is in harmony with himself and with his environment. He conforms with the cultural requirements or injunctions of his community. He may possess organic deviation or disease, but as long as this does not impair his reasoning, judgment, intellectual capacity and ability to make harmonious personal and social adaptation he may be regarded as psychically sound or normal.

From the standpoint of instinctual psychology (i.e. psychoanalysis) Freud said (1905) that 'it appeared that normality developed as the result of repression of certain component-instincts and components of the infantile disposition, and of a subordination of the remainder under the primacy of the genital zone in the service of the reproductive function.' (Freud, S. *Collected Papers*, vol. 1, tr. by Riviere, J., Leonard and Virginia Woolf and The Institute of Psychoanalysis, London, 1924–25) This means harmonious relationship of the forces of the id, superego, and ego. 'The original urges are not unhealthily inhibited, but rather are domesticated in the service of the individual and society.' (Healy, W., Bronner, A.F., and Bowers, A.M. *The Structure and Meaning of Psychoanalysis,* Knopf, New York, 1930) The same authors say that 'the normal character is defined by E. Glover as an organized series of behavior reactions which secure equilibrium between Id tendencies and surrender to reality.'

'The "average normal" is a theoretical being possessing an average of the characteristics of a great variety of more or less stable individuals.' (Henry, G.W. *Essentials of Psychiatry*, 3rd ed., Williams and Wilkins, Baltimore, 1938)

'The term norm is closely related to the terms criterion and standard. Criterion applies, however, more definitely to the process of judgment; it is the rule or mode of control as employed to assist judgment in making proper discriminations. . . . The standard is the principle used to measure value, and to lay off a scale of values.' (Baldwin, J.M., ed. *Dic-*

tionary of Philosophy and Psychology, vol. 2, Macmillan, New York, 1928, p. 182)

nos(o)- (nos'[ō]-) Combining form meaning disease, from Gr. *nósos,* sickness, disease.

nosogenesis, nosogeny (nos-ō-jen'e-sis, nō-soj'ē-nē) Synonymous with *pathogenesis.*

nosography nō-sog'rȧ-fē) The description of diseases.

nosology (nō-sol'ō-jē) The study of diseases and, particularly, of the classification of diseases.

nosomania (nos-ō-mā'ni-ȧ) Hypochondriasis advanced to the point of insanity.

nosophobia Fear of disease; a condition common in hypochondriacal individuals. It implies a morbid dread, usually associated with no discoverable organic illness, or if the latter is present, the fear is grossly exaggerated and has been superimposed upon natural concern about the illness.

nostalgia Longing to return home or to one's native land; homesickness. This is explained by psychoanalysts as intense yearning for the members of one's family or for some particular member of the family. It is related to the dread of being alone, which is but another way of saying that the individual feels at ease when he is with someone to whom he is emotionally bound.

The analysis of nostalgia patients reveals that it is not the home itself to which one desires to return, but to somebody, in the home, dear or emotionally bound to the individual. In one patient it was distinctly associated with the relinquishment of adult activities in favor of the resumption of puerile relations connected with his own home. Hence, a latent meaning of nostalgia is a return to some earlier and more pleasant form of adaptation.

nostomania (nos-tō-mā'ni-ȧ) An intense form of nostalgia; an irresistible impulse to return home. The concept home may, as a symbolic expression, mean the fatherland (or motherland), the city of one's birth, or one's parental house. See *nostalgia.*

nostras(s)ia (nos-tras'i-ȧ) *Obs.* Nostalgia.

nothingness, mental 'Finally we must consider the meaning of the deep stupor where no mentation of any kind can be proven and where none but vegetative functions seem to be operating. This state is either one of organic coma, in which case it marks the appearance of a physical factor not evidenced in the milder stages, or else it is the acme of this regression by withdrawal of interest. As has been stated, back of the period of primitive childish ideas there lies a hypothetical state of mental nothingness. If we accept the principle of regression, we find an analogue, to what is apparently the mental state of deep stupor, in the earliest phases of infancy.' (MacCurdy, J.T. *The Psychology of Emotion,* Harcourt, Brace, New York, 1925)

Nothnagel, Carl Wilhelm Hermann (not'-nä-gel) (1841–1905) Austrian neurologist.

notogenesis (nō-tō-jen'e-sis) The later stages of *gastrulation* (q.v.), in which the *notochord,* or embryonic backbone, is formed. This period is associated with the appearance and development of the third germ layer, the *mesoderm* (q.v.), and thus implies a tridermic condition of the embryo.

Subsequently, at a stage overlapping the next salient step of development, *cephalogenesis,* the plates of the mesoderm become differentiated into a more robust *medial* portion, and a thinner *lateral* portion, the two connected by a constricted plate of the original mesoderm.

noumenal (nōō'mē-nal) Intellectually, not sensuously, intuitional; relating to the object of pure thought divorced from all concepts of time or space.

noxa (nôk'sȧ) Any injurious agent, mental or physical.

noxious (nok'shus) Injurious; hurtful.

nuclear (nū'klē-ēr) Pertaining to, or having the character of, a nucleus.

nucleus (nū'klē-us) (L. 'a nut, kernel') In the minute structure of a typical cell, the *nucleus* is a denser body in the midst of its protoplasm, usually rounded in form and representing the directive center of most cellular activities. As it governs the mitotic process of cell division, it plays a decisive role in the chromosomal mechanism of hereditary transmission.

The actual seat of the genetic elements in the nucleus is a fine reticulum of various protein substances which stain very readily and are collectively called the *chromatin*. In addition to this chromatin network, the nucleus contains not only a liquid in which the chromatin floats, but frequently also one or more dense, rounded bodies, the *nucleoli*.

In a resting cell, the nucleus is surrounded by a thin membrane, the tension of which tends to keep the nucleus round. All cytoplasmic substances entering the nucleus must pass through this membrane.

nucleus, caudate (kaw'dāt) See *basal ganglia*.

nucleus, dentate (den'tāt) See *cerebellum*.

nucleus, Edinger-Westphal See *accommodation*.

nucleus, emboliform (em-bol'i-form) See *cerebellum*.

nucleus fastigius (noo-klā-oos fas-tig'ē-oos) See *cerebellum*.

nucleus globosus (glō-bō'soos) See *cerebellum*.

nucleus pulposus (pul-pō'soos) See *disk, herniated lumbar intervertebral*.

nucleus ruber (roo'ber) Red nucleus. See *midbrain*.

nyctalopia (nik-ta-lō'pi-à) Night-blindness; inability to see well at night or in dim light; sometimes due to vitamin A deficiency. See *hermalopia*.

nyctiplanctus (nik-ti-plangk'tus) *Obs.* Somnambulistic agitation.

nyctobadia, nyctobatia (nik-tō-bad'i-à, -bat'i-à) *Obs.* Somnambulism.

nyctophobia Fear of night (or darkness).

nyctophonia (nik-tō-fō'ni-à) Night voice. The term denotes the ability to speak at night and implies the loss of the voice during daylight hours. It is not a common symptom in any formal sense of the word, being, perhaps, more generally encountered among those without psychiatric classification. Some who address public audiences—orators, lecturers, actors, etc.—are insistent that their addresses be given at night. When they have to perform their task during the daytime they become quite temperamental.

nympholepsy (nim'fō-lep-sē) *Obs.* Demoniac frenzy.

nymphomania (nim-fō-mā'ni-à) A mor-

bid, insatiable impulse to heterosexuality in women.

nymphomania, active See *nymphomania, grave*.

nymphomania, grave The French use this expression to denote nymphomania severe in extent in contrast with what they call *slight* or *lesser nymphomania*.

Thoinot and Weyese further subdivide nymphomaniacs into an *active* and *platonic* type. 'The latter does not manifest her morbid desires outwardly; she is the equivalent of the *platonic* sadist and fetichist. Her desires are no less keen than those of the great [or grave] nymphomaniac, but she is mistress of them and knows how to content herself—apart from legitimate relations, which merely deceive her needs for a moment—by the enjoyment she experiences, with or without the aid of solitary masturbation at the sight or mental image of a man.' (Thoinot, L. and Weyese, A.W. *Medico-Legal Aspects of Moral Offenses*, Davis, Philadelphia, 1927)

nymphomania, heterosexual Inordinate sexual desire of women for men.

nymphomania, homosexual See *nymphomania, inverted*.

nymphomania, inverted A woman's excessive sexual desire for women; homosexual nymphomania. 'We shall have finished with the symptoms of nymphomania when we have spoken of *inverted* nymphomania. There is, in fact, beside heterosexual nymphomania, a homosexual nymphomania, just as beside heterosexual fetichism there is homosexual fetichism.' (Thoinot, L. and Weyese, A.W. *Medico-Legal Aspects of Moral Offenses*, Davis, Philadelphia, 1927)

nymphomania, lesser See *nymphomania, grave*.

nymphomania, platonic See *nymphomania, grave*.

nystagmus (nis-tag'mus) An involuntary to-and-fro movement of the eyeballs induced when the patient looks upward or laterally. It is usually a pathological sign.

Nystagmus may be *horizontal*, the most common form, when the oscillations of the eyeballs are from side to side; or *vertical*, when the movements are up and down; or *rotatory*, when the oscillations are in a circular direction.

O

oaf An old term for an idiot. According to Brewer (*A Dictionary of Phrase and Fable*), the idea was held that 'idiots were changelings left by fairies in the place of the stolen ones.' (Quoted from Tuke, D.H. *A Dictionary of Psychological Medicine*, vols. 1–2, Blakiston, Philadelphia, 1892)

obedience, automatic Many patients, particularly those with the catatonic form of schizophrenia, carry out the orders of others through blind obedience, that is, without critical or automatic judgment. 'The impulse for an action carried out sometimes consciously, and sometimes compulsively, can also come from without, as, for instance, in automatic obedience, that is, the compulsive-like or also automatic obedience to requests for simple actions of all kinds. The patients carry out any commands whatsoever, even if it is against their will, as for example, putting out their tongue when they know a pin will be stuck into it. . . .' (Bleuler, E. *Textbook of Psychiatry*, tr. by Brill, A.A., Macmillan, New York, 1930)

obedience, deferred According to Freud, a prohibition, command, or threat received early in life may be repressed and the effect deferred for many years until a neurotic illness occurs and the original prohibition or command is obeyed.

In spite of his father's opposition, a man became a painter. 'His incapacity to paint after the father's death would then . . . be an expression of the familiar "deferred obedience."' (Freud, S. *Collected Papers*, vol. 4, tr. by Riviere, J., Leonard and Virginia Woolf and The Institute of Psychoanalysis, London, 1924–25)

obesity, psychogenic Corpulence or the state of being overweight as a result of emotional factors which lead to overeating. Overeating may be a nonspecific response to emotional tension, a substitute gratification in intolerable life situations, a specific symptom of emotional illness such as hysteria or depression, or a type of addiction. Bruch has claimed that there is a characteristic psychologic constellation in psychogenic obesity in children, consisting of maternal ambivalence, hostility, and compensatory overprotec-

tion. Most other investigators have failed to confirm these claims.

object From the instinctual point of view, 'the *object* of an instinct is that in or through which it can achieve its aim. It is the most variable thing about an instinct and is not originally connected with it, but becomes attached to it only in consequence of being fitted to provide satisfaction. The object is not necessarily an extraneous one; it may be part of the subject's own body.' (Freud, S. *Collected Papers*, vol. 4, tr. by Riviere, J., Leonard and Virginia Woolf and The Institute of Psychoanalysis, London, 1924–25)

Freud points out that the object of an instinct may, and usually does, change from time to time throughout life; moreover, 'the same object may serve for the satisfaction of several instincts simultaneously.'

object-addiction See *addict, object.*

object, bad A psychoanalytic concept that is part of the dichotomous formulation '*good object* versus *bad object*.' 'Good' and 'bad' as used in this connotation refer essentially to moral, conscience (superego) evaluation: 'good' stands for nonsexual (clean), while 'bad' stands for sexual (dirty). In the unconscious the ultimate good object is equated with God, while the bad object means the Devil.

object-cathexis See *cathexis.*

object-choice See *choice, object.*

object-finding See *finding, object.*

object, good A psychoanalytic term for one half of the dichotomous concept 'good object versus bad object.' See *object, bad.*

object, homoerotic See *homosexuality, male.*

object-identification See *identification.*

object-ill A term applied by Stekel to describe the compulsive-neurotic who expresses his own mental conflict in the form of symbolization of objects pertaining to the outer world (i.e. outside his body) and also through symbolization of 'the function of his everyday life such as washing, dressing, eating, defecating. . . . In compulsive diseases it is the patient's relationship to an object (usually a close member of the family) that is disturbed.'

In opposition to the object-ill patient, Stekel calls 'subject-ill' the individual suffering from phobias. In the phobic or 'subject-ill' patient, the individual uses his own body to symbolize his emotions. 'The patient shows an ambivalent emotional attitude toward this object, that is, the polar tension between the extremes of love and hate with regard to this object is also extreme. . . .

'The "object-ill" is conscious of his abilities; he fails, because of his bipolar family fixations which create defiance, aggression and self-punishment; while the "subject-ill" feels that he has failed in his relations with the outer world and feels inferior to the demands of life. . . . The "object-ill" is introverted and makes no attempts at extraversion; the "subject-ill," however, makes efforts to extravert himself in order to adjust himself to the world.' (Stekel, W. *Compulsion and Doubt,* Liveright, New York, 1949) See *subject-ill.*

objectivation A type of projection in which one's own unrecognized impulses or feelings are quickly detected and recognized in others. Objectivation may lead to overemphasis of the importance or significance of such impulses in others and, when present in the analyst, may produce troublesome counter-transference manifestations.

object, libidinal (li-bid′i-nal) The object of one's psychic energy. It may be outside of or within oneself.

object-libido (-li-bēd′ō) See *ego-libido.*

object-love Impulses or instincts arising from the id are more or less fixed entities, but the objects to which the instincts become attached are various and multitudinous. The number of objects that may be peculiarly fitted to provide satisfaction for an instinctual quality is almost unlimited. At different levels of libidinal evolution in the individual the object changes (unless there is fixation) to meet the cultural needs of the environment, though the original aim remains unchanged.

Instincts arise from the id, which is blind and ruthless in its demands for satisfaction; it seeks somatic pleasure only, striving to gain it without regard for reality. With the organization of the ego, however, the choice of a suitable object

is delegated to the ego, occupying a position between the id and reality.

'To objects we have grown to like through use, or because of their aesthetic value, we obviously have a personal relationship which is quite analogous to sexual attraction. There are many different degrees of this kind of object-love. Many persons have almost no needs in this respect, while others are completely under the domination of their passion for certain objects.' (Abraham, K. *Selected Papers,* tr. by Bryan, D. and Strachey, A., Leonard and Virginia Woolf and The Institute for Psychoanalysis, London, 1927)

The expression *love-object* means, of course, the object of love, the object of the instincts. 'During the *Latency Period* though, the libido normally continues to be directed toward the parental love-object. . . .' (Healy, W., Bronner, A.F., and Bowers, A.M. *The Structure and Meaning of Psychoanalysis,* Knopf, New York, 1930)

object-love, passive See *narcissism.*

oblativity (ob-la-tiv′i-tē) 'The individual fails to develop the capacity to give up the mother or her substitute; he does not learn to tolerate this or any other similar situation in which he encounters frustration, and he remains arrested, more or less completely according to the individual case, on the anal-sadistic level of libidinal development. Consequently the capacity for renunciation, barred by the dread of castration, is only imperfectly developed, and it is this defect which, as I want to show, dogs the psyche and spoils its whole efficiency. I would suggest that we call this defect a deficiency in oblativity, meaning by oblativity that competence which the psyche attains through the satisfactorily accomplished weaning of the child's libido from the mother or mother-substitute.' (Laforgue, R. *International Journal of Psychoanalysis VIII,* 475, 1927)

obnubilation (ob-nū-bi-la′shun) Clouding of consciousness, stupor.

obscenity Compulsive and uncontrollable use of coprophrasia.

observation, delusion of See *delusion of observation.*

observer, participant In psychoanalysis, this term is used to describe the analyst as he is viewed by those who feel that he must be something more than an authoritarian sounding board or a mirror in which the patient's problems are reflected. Although the therapist must be objective, he also takes active part in the interpersonal process of therapy. The so-called cultural interpersonal school of psychoanalysis particularly emphasizes the participant role of the analyst. See *process, interpersonal.*

obsessed Beset with irresistible ideas or feelings, or with both—as is generally the case.

obsession An idea or an emotion (an impulse) that persists in the mind of an individual and cannot be gotten rid of by any conscious processes. From the standpoint of the conscious mind the obsession is uninfluenced by logic or reasoning and is distinctly unwanted.

Obsessions may be experienced by normal and abnormal individuals. An obsession may be regarded as normal when it does not interfere in any substantial way with the adequate performance of one's mental functions. This means that it is not long-lasting, that it only partially modifies sound thinking, and that its influence may be minimized or nullified after a varying length of time by concentration of interests upon other topics.

Morbid obsessions are those that essentially control the conscious realm. They plague the individual more or less constantly, compelling him to act in such a way as to minimize their effects as much as possible.

Obsessions usually appear in the form of *ideas* (strongly charged with emotions). Thus, there are (1) the so-called intellectual obsessions, such as constant preoccupation with a metaphysical question. For example, an individual may be compelled to keep asking himself why he was born, why he is living and where he will go after this life. This type of obsession usually leads to incessant activity in an effort to gain an answer. There are (2) inhibiting obsessions, made up, for instance, of doubts, scruples, or fears. The multiple phobias (e.g. acro-, agora-, algo-, neo-, toxophobia) belong to this class; they are so called, because they tend to inhibit action. Another type is known as (3) impulsive obsessions, because they are generally associated with morbid gratification in action. They are made up of the

so-called *manias* (e.g. arithmo-, dipso-, klepto-, onomatomania).

Obsessions may appear as *feelings,* without any clear-cut ideas. Anxiety is an outstanding example; feelings of inadequacy, unreality, and depersonalization are other examples.

Some authorities classify the various *tics* as obsessions; the latter then appear in the form of involuntary and irresistible muscular activity.

The most commonly accepted explanation today for obsessions is concerned with activity of the unconscious. Freud believes that obsessions are the consequence of the release of repressed instinctual qualities from their unconscious representation; the released instincts are transferred to the sphere of consciousness, existing therein apparently alone (as in certain anxiety states), but usually in conjunction with some idea or set of ideas (constellation) which have no presumptive relationship (from the standpoint of the patient) to the unconscious impulse. The patient cannot understand why he should be obsessed by the thought that obsesses him.

Freud's principal emphasis regarding a compulsion rests upon concepts associated with infantile sexuality; Jung stresses the role of the collective unconscious; Adler relates it to feelings of inferiority.

Obsessions 'may be arranged by gradations in types in which they appear:

A, as purely physical disturbances;

B, as physical disturbances plus conscious emotion;

C, as physical disturbances plus conscious emotion plus a specific idea of the object of the emotion, but *without* logical meaning;

D, as physical disturbances plus emotion plus idea plus meaning.' (Prince, M. *The Unconscious,* Macmillan, New York, 1916)

obsession, masked A psychiatric term applied to an obsession which appears in the disguised (masked) form of other symptoms. One of the most interesting forms is the obsessive idea which disguises itself in the form of pain. 'The patients complain of pain, state that it drives them to suicide, yet they remain attached to the pain which—on closer scrutiny—may prove to represent pleasurable though tabooed memories. . . Such pain (for which usually no organic cause can be found) then appears as a mask of the obsessive idea. The real idea is hidden behind the pain, so that the patients, instead of complaining of obsessions, complain of pain. It is diagnostically important that the usual sedatives are always ineffective in these cases or, if forced upon the patient, may lead to narcotomania.' (Stekel, W. *Compulsion and Doubt,* Liveright, New York, 1949.) See *narcomania.*

obsession, somatic (sō-mat'ik) This psychiatric term denotes the patient's morbid preoccupation with his body or an individual organ. 'Usually these obsessions concerning the body or individual organs are connected with [the] patient's feeling of guilt and inferiority. The somatic obsessions are mostly monosymptomatic, though they are always parts of a more complicated neurotic system. A person who has an obsession centered on his nose, not only is forced to think constantly of his nose, but also operates with a "nose-currency," so to speak, that is, in looking at people he sees only their noses and compares them with his own. No other human problem appears to be worthy of his attention.' (Stekel, W. *Compulsion and Doubt,* Liveright, New York, 1949)

obsession, temptation In *Obsessions and Phobias: Their Psychical Mechanisms and Their Aetiology* Freud cites examples of temptation-obsessions: 'They were women who, not being at all satisfied in marriage, had to struggle against the desires and voluptuous ideas that haunted them in the presence of men.'

obsession, traumatic (traw-mat'ik) 'As regards classification of the subject, I propose to exclude a group of intense obsessions which are nothing but memories, unaltered images of important experiences. As an example, I will cite Pascal's obsession: he always thought he saw an abyss on his left hand "after he had nearly been thrown into the Seine in his coach." These obsessions and phobias, which might be called *traumatic,* are allied to the symptoms of hysteria.' (Freud, S. *Collected Papers,* vol. 1, tr. by Riviere, J., Leonard and Virginia Woolf and The Institute of Psychoanalysis, London, 1924–25)

obsession, visual In *A Mythological Parallel to a Visual Obsession (Collected Papers,* vol. 4, tr. by Riviere, J., Leonard and Virginia Woolf and The Institute of Psychoanalysis, London, 1924–25) Freud

says: 'In a patient of about twenty-one years of age the unconscious mental activity expressed itself consciously not only in obsessive thoughts but also in obsessive visual images. The two could accompany each other or appear independently of each other. At one particular time, whenever he saw his father coming into the room, there came into his mind in close connection with each other an obsessive word and an obsessive picture.'

obsessive-compulsive (psycho)neurosis Obsessive-compulsive reaction; a type of psychoneurosis characterized by disturbing, unwanted, anxiety-provoking, intruding thoughts or ideas, and repetitive impulses to perform acts (ceremonials, counting, hand-washing, etc.) which may be considered abnormal, undesirable, or distasteful to the patient. The 'psychasthenia' of earlier writers usually included obsessive-compulsive psychoneurosis.

Psychoanalytically, obsessive-compulsive psychoneurosis is interpreted as a defense against aggressive and/or sexual impulses, particularly in relation to the Oedipus complex. The initial defense is by regression to the anal-sadistic level, but the impulses at this level are also intolerable and must be warded off—by reaction-formation, isolation, and undoing. Because the use of these defenses renders superfluous the use of repression proper, the offensive impulses can exist in consciousness although when they do they are divorced from their affective significance and so remain meaningless to the patient. See *obsession; compulsion.*

obsessive-ruminative tension state A general pattern of personality reaction, so named by Adolf Meyer; it is equivalent to what is more commonly known today as the compulsive-obsessive form of psychoneurosis of Freud.

obstipation (ob-sti-pā'shun) This medical term denotes extreme or intractable constipation. In psychotherapy the symptom of obstipation is frequently of a psychogenic nature. According to Fenichel, somatic changes of a psychogenic nature fall into two main categories: the conversion and the organ-neurosis. Obstipation can appear either as a conversion or as an organ-neurosis.

Like all conversions, obstipation, as a conversion, is the somatic expression of a specific, repressed, unconscious sexual phantasy. Usually obstipation expresses retentive tendencies connected with pregnancy wishes or incorporation phantasies. This is 'in accordance with the equation child = penis = feces.'

As an organ-neurosis, obstipation is a physiological change in organic function, resulting from an unconscious attitude or affect. In the particular case of obstipation, the unconscious attitude is a chronically frustrated retentive pressure. The retentive pressure may exist for several reasons. It may represent an anal erotic fixation, a desire for anal retentive pleasure; or, the feces may represent introjected objects as in the case of the conversion. Again, in some other instances, the retentive pressure, with its resulting obstipation, might be associated with a continuous and repressed aggressiveness. (Fenichel, O. *The Psychoanalytic Theory of Neurosis*, Norton, New York, 1945)

obstipatio paradoxa (ob-stē-pà'tē-ō pà-rà-dok'sà) Soiling associated with constipation. 'The child retains the stools, which become very hard and can be felt through the abdominal wall. Small pieces of firm stool are passed from time to time and are retained between the buttocks, macerating the perianal skin.' (Bakwin and Bakwin. *Clinical Management of Behavior Disorders in Children*, Saunders, Philadelphia, 1953) See *obstipation*.

obstruction The term *obstruction* is generally confined to the group of psychiatric disorders called dementia praecox or schizophrenia. Bleuler says: 'Among the formal disturbances of the mental stream [of thought] the *obstructions* (deprivation of thought) are the most striking and when they occur too readily or too often or become too general and too persistent, they are positively pathognomonic of schizophrenia.' (Bleuler, E. *Textbook of Psychiatry*, tr. by Brill, A.A., Macmillan, New York, 1930)

Thought-deprivation or sudden cessation of thought may last for variable periods of time.

A schizophrenic patient, talking incessantly, covered a wide variety of apparently unrelated topics. It appeared that each new idea was suddenly obstructed, cut off, and was promptly followed by a fresh topic.

The phenomenon known as *blocking* is of a somewhat similar order, save that when the thought is obstructed, the patient may have difficulty in finding a new

theme or topic. Some authorities believe that *obstruction* and *blocking* are one and the same phenomenon.

obstupescentia (ôbs-stoo-pes-ken'tē-à) *Obs.* Stupor.

occupational therapy See *therapy, occupational*.

occupation, prescribed In occupational therapy, an activity which has been prescribed or recommended by the physician for a particular patient.

occupation, sedative (sed'à-tiv) In occupational therapy this term refers to a form of activity characterized by repetitions, uniform movements which, because of their monotonous recurrence, have a soothing and quieting effect. It is usually prescribed for overactive patients. An example of sedative occupation is simple weaving.

occupation, stimulating In occupational therapy an occupation is regarded as stimulating when its processes are so varied that the lack of monotony and repetition tends to arouse and awaken to activity the slow, retarded, and depressed patient. For instance, the various activities associated with photography constitute a type of stimulating occupation.

ochlophobia (ok-lō-fō'bi-à) Fear of crowds.

odaxesmus (ō-dak-sez'mus) Marshall Hall (English physician, 1790–1857), used this term to refer to the biting of tongue, cheek, or lip during an epileptic seizure.

odontophobia (ō-don-tō-fō'bi-à) Fear of teeth.

-odynia (-ō-din'i-à) Combining suffix meaning grief, pain, from Gr. *odýnē*, pain of body or mind, sorrow.

odynophobia Fear of pain.

oedipal (ed'i-pàl) Pertaining to Oedipus. This adjective is occasionally encountered, though as a rule the noun *Oedipus* is used unchanged as an adjective, as: Oedipus complex.

'In short, we gain the conviction that one cannot understand women, unless one estimates this *pre-oedipal attachment to the mother* at its proper value.' (Freud, S. *New Introductory Lectures on Psycho-Analysis*, tr. by Sprott, W.J.H., Norton, New York, 1933)

oedipism *Rare.* Self-inflicted injury to the eyes.

Oedipus, complete Freud states that, in all instances of neuroses, it is desirable to assume the existence of what he calls the *complete Oedipus*. The expression refers to the simultaneous presence of both a positive and a negative (or inverted) Oedipus situation; the child displays mother object-love and father identification, and father object-love and mother identification. The quantity of cathexis (or emotional charge) given to each of these four conditions is a reflection in part of the strength of innate bisexuality, and in part of experiential factors.

Oedipus complex See *complex, Oedipus.*

Oedipus, inverted Same as *Oedipus, negative* (q.v.).

Oedipus, negative According to Lampl-DeGroot, the *negative Oedipus phase* is one of the stages through which the female child normally passes. She believes that libidinal development in both the boy and the girl is similar up to the phallic stage—in both the mother is the love-object. When the girl becomes aware of the differences between her genitals and those of the boy, her narcissism is wounded; she feels obliged to renounce her yearning for the mother, because she does not have to fear castration as the boy does: it is already an accomplished fact. Hence, the girl identifies herself with her mother and takes the father as a love-object, for it is through the father that she can have a baby, that is, the equivalent of the penis. Lampl-DeGroot says that the castration complex in girls is a secondary formation, derived from the preceding negative Oedipus phase. The latter is therefore the Oedipus stage prior to the development of the castration complex.

oenomania (ē-nō-mā′ni-à) Oinomania.

oestromania, estromania (es-trō-mā′ni-à) Nymphomania.

-oid Suffix meaning like, resembling, having the form of, from Gr. *oeidês* from *eîdos,* form, shape, figure.

oikiomania (oi-ki-ō-mā′ni-à) See *ecomania.*

oikiophobia (oi-ki-ō-fō′bi-à) See *oikophobia.*

oikofugic (oi-kō-fū′jik) Pertaining to the or swayed by the impulse to wander or travel.

oikophobia (oi-kō-fō′bi-à) Bianchi says: 'If an individual has suffered from terror, or something extremely disagreeable in his own house, he will have a horror of that house that is sometimes invincible (*oikophobia* of Verga, Salemi-Pace, and others).' (Bianchi, L. *A Text-Book of Psychiatry,* tr. by MacDonald, J.H., Baillière, Tindall & Cox, London, 1906)

oikotropic (-trōp′ik) Homesick.

oinomania (oi-nō-mā′ni-à) Dipsomania; craving for alcoholic liquor; delirium tremens.

olfaction (ol-fak′shun) See *rhinencephalon.*

olfactophobia (ol-fak-tō-fō′bi-à) Fear of odors.

oligergasia (ol-i-gĕr-gas′i-à) Adolf Meyer's term synonymous with intellectual deficiency or feeble-mindedness.

olig(o)- (ol′i-gō-) Combining form meaning little, few, scanty, from Gr. *olígos,* small, pl. *few.*

oligodendroglia (ol-i-gō-den-drog′li-à) See *neuroglia.*

oligomania (ol-i-gō-mā′ni-à) Insanity on a few subjects. Old term for monomania, but differing from it in that monomania itself is made up of a few symptoms and only seldom, if ever, of one symptom or impulse.

oligomania, abulic (à-bū′lik) *Obs.* Abulomania.

oligomania, affective *Obs.* See *mania sine delirio.*

oligomania, agoraphobic (ag-ō-rà-fō′bik) *Obs.* Agoraphobia.

oligomania, claustrophobic (klaws-trō-fō′bik) *Obs.* Claustrophobia.

oligomania, intellectual *Obs.* Intellectual monomania. See *monomania.*

oligomania, mysophobic (mī-sō-fō′bik) *Obs.* Mysophobia.

oligophrenia (ol-i-gō-frē′ni-à) Mental deficiency.

oligophrenia, moral See *insanity, moral.*

oligophrenia, phenylpyruvic (fē-nil-pī-rōō′vik) A constitutional type of mental deficiency characterized by the combination of mental deficiency and an inherited biochemical alteration in the body. 'A certain type of defective is found to excrete in the urine an aromatic compound, phenylpyruvic acid. The great majority of these patients are low grade defectives. Stature and general physical development are within normal limits, the blond type predominates, being more than 90% of the cases and coexisting generally with blue eyes and pale, delicate skin. In addition to constitutional traits, neurological signs are generally found, consisting of hypertonicity of muscles, increase of deep reflexes, hyperkinetic manifestations such as tremor, athetosis, tics. In a small percentage of cases marked psychotic trends may be observed. . . . The disease is characterized biochemically by an inhibition in the metabolism of phenylalanine at the stage of phenylpyruvic acid, the subject being unable to oxidize this keto acid at a normal rate.' (Jervis, G. *Archives of Neurology 38,* 944, 1937)

oligopsychia (ol-i-gō-sī′ki-à) *Obs.* Mental deficiency.

oligoria (ol-i-gor′i-à) In certain forms of melancholia, an abnormal indifference toward or dislike of persons or things.

oligosthenic (ol-i-gō-sthen′ik) Kretschmer's variety of *asthenic* (q.v.) type characterized by moderate strength and intermediate between the *phthinoid* and the *eusthenic* (qq.v.).

oligothymia (-thī-mi-à) Poverty of affectivity; a term suggested by Davidson for the syndrome of psychopathy.

oliguresis, hysterical (ol-i-gū-rē′sis) Scanty or abnormally diminished urination, which usually appears as a conversion symptom. All conversion symptoms are the distorted physical expression of repressed instinctual impulses which have taken the form of sexual and/or aggressive phantasies. These phantasies usually relate to the Oedipus complex. The conversion symptom, which is a change in physical function, can be analyzed in the same way as dreams, and the repressed phantasies can thus be cleared up. The symptom of oliguresis lends itself to the expression of sexual phantasies because it is rooted in a period of infantile sexuality, when urination is 'still in the service of pleasure-seeking.' In particular, oliguresis may express 'retention tendencies connected with pregnancy wishes or incorporation phantasies.' According to Fenichel, the equation is 'child = penis = feces.' (Fenichel, O. *The Psychoan-*

alytic Theory of Neurosis, Norton, New York, 1945)

-oma (-ō′mà) Noun-forming suffix meaning affected or diseased state, from Gr. *-ōma.*

ombrophobia (om-brō-fō′bi-à) Fear of rain-(storm).

-ome (-ōm) Combining form from F. *-ome,* equivalent of *-oma.*

omega melancholium (ō′me-gà me-làn-kô′lē-oom) (L.L. 'melancholy omega') A wrinkle (between the eyebrows) in the shape of the last letter of the Greek alphabet, the omega (ω), assumed to indicate a state of melancholy.

ommatophobia (om-à-tō-fō′bi-à) Fear of eyes.

omnipotence (om-nip′ō-tens) Feelings of omnipotence and self-esteem undergo extensive development and change, concomitant with the development of the ego. There is a feeling of omnipotence from the very beginning, even before the conception of objects exists. The outside world is perceived by the organism as part of it (the organism), within itself, though there is as yet no non-ego. Similar phenomena are observed in mental patients when they lose contact with reality and relapse to a child-like level of emotional behavior: the person loses the distinction between his personality (ego) and the environment (reality). Such a person is in a state of primitive all-powerfulness, believes that he is omniscient and omnipotent, and has phantasies which know no bounds. To attain such a state of primitive all-powerfulness the patient usually passes through a phase of rebirth. He believes that he has gone back into his mother's womb: he acts the part, curls up in a fetal position, and behaves like a small infant. In such a state of omnipotence the patient can express ideas that he is able to move the universe, to create war and peace, to give birth to millions of children, etc. In delusional adults the symptom is more commonly called *megalomania.* (Hinsie, L.E. *Understandable Psychiatry,* Macmillan, New York, 1948)

This feeling of unlimited omnipotence, often termed the 'oceanic feeling,' becomes limited as the ego and sense of reality develop: this occurs when the infant experiences tensions he cannot master, which in turn lead to unco-ordinated discharge movements. 'Something outside' becomes necessary to quiet the infant's tension and, through recognizing this 'something outside,' the infant makes his first distinction between ego and object. Also he develops a new concept of omnipotence. When his movements are understood by the environment to be a signal calling for a quieting of his tension, the child experiences this train of events as an 'omnipotence of movements.' However, he still longs for his original 'oceanic feeling.' His earliest reaction to objects is to swallow them; he tries to 'swallow' or incorporate all pleasurable sensations and, through introjection, to make parts of the external world flow, like tributaries, into his ego. Unpleasurable sensations are perceived as being non-ego and are 'spat out.' Thus, through introjection, anything pleasurable becomes part of the ego and, through projection, anything unpleasant becomes non-ego.

These efforts to re-establish the 'oceanic feeling' of primary narcissism and also the 'omnipotence of movements' are doomed to failure, however, since, through his experiences, the child realizes he is not omnipotent. The adult is now considered omnipotent and, by reuniting with this omnipotent force in the external world, the child tries to share this omnipotence: either he incorporates parts of this world or has the phantasy of being incorporated by it. The latter type of omnipotence is at work in religious ecstasy and patriotism. Mass political movements may also attest the participation of the powerless followers in the omnipotence of their leaders. The feeling of having been reunited with the omnipotent force is known as secondary narcissism. The longing for the omnipotence of primary narcissism is the 'narcissistic need' which all people experience. ' "Self-esteem" is the awareness of how close the individual is to the original omnipotence.' Originally, the longing for omnipotence was a longing for the removal of instinctual tension, which would restore the objectless narcissistic state: self-esteem was restored by getting rid of an unpleasant stimulus. This was done through nourishment. Thus the first regulation of self-esteem and satisfaction of narcissistic need was through food. After the infant relinquishes its feeling of omnipotence, however, and tends to participate in the adult's omnipotence, his self-esteem is regulated by tokens of love from the adults. The child gains self-esteem when he gains affection and loses self-esteem when he loses affection: through the promise of these and the threats of withholding or withdrawing them, the child becomes ready to obey authority and forego other satisfactions. 'This is what makes children educable.'

In later development, needs for self-esteem, the narcissistic needs, are all-important: they develop in the relationship between ego and superego. Guilt-feeling lowers self-esteem and fulfillment of ideals raises it. But even in the relationship to objects in which the sexual needs develop, part of the relationship remains governed by the needs of self-esteem. In persons fixated at this level the dominant need from objects is narcissistic. These individuals may attempt to maintain their self-esteem either through aggressive or submissive behavior toward their objects or through both methods simultaneously. (Fenichel, O. *The Psychoanalytic Theory of Neurosis,* Norton, New York, 1945)

omnipotence, magic See *identification, cosmic.*

onanism (ō'nan-iz'm) Strictly speaking *onanism* is sexual intercourse interrupted before ejaculation.

Havelock Ellis says: 'Onan's device was not auto-erotic, but an early example of withdrawal before emission, or *coitus interruptus.*'

Some writers use the term *onanism* interchangeably with masturbation.

onanism, buccal Fellatio.

onanism, larval (lär'val) Masked undercover masturbation. 'I take this opportunity of saying something further about larval and vicarious onanist activities. There are many otherwise not neurotic people, especially many neurasthenics, who are, so to say, almost life-long onanists unconsciously. If they are men they keep their hands in their trouser pockets all day, and it is noticeable, from the movements of their hands and fingers, that in doing this they pull, squeeze, or rub the penis.' (Ferenczi, S. *Further Contributions to the Theory and Technique of Psycho-Analysis,* tr. by Suttie, J.I., Leonard and Virginia Woolf and The Institute of Psychoanalysis, London, 1926)

onanism, primary Ferenczi thus denotes

masturbation in an infant—'of a purely local genital excitement without the involvement of the rest of the psyche.' (Ferenczi, S. *Further Contributions to the Theory and Technique of Psycho-Analysis,* tr. by Suttie, J.I., Leonard and Virginia Woolf and The Institute of Psychoanalysis, London, 1926)

onanism, psychic (sī'kik) See *masturbation, psychic.*

oneirism (on'ī-riz'm) Dream-state while one is awake.

oneir(o)- (ō-nī-r[ō]-) Combining form meaning dream, from Gr. *óneiros, dream.*

oneiro-delirium (ō-nī-rō-dē-lir'i-um) Literally, this term means dream delirium. Certain French psychiatrists apply the term oneiro-deliria to that group of psychoses which is marked by delirium. Delirium tremens is the prototype of this group and is considered to be essentially a prolonged dream. Fever deliria are also part of this group, because they are so closely related to dreams. Although it is true that hallucinations can be interpreted in the same way as dreams, this does not mean that deliria, schizophrenic hallucinations, and dreams are etiologically the same, as this term would imply.

oneirodynia (-din'i-à) This is an old term, constituting one of the four great divisions of insanity as recognized by Cullen. The four were amentia, melancholia, mania, and oneirodynia (somnambulism and nightmare).

oneirogonorrhea (-gon-ō-re'à) Nocturnal emission of semen.

oneirogonos (ō-nī-rog'ō-nos) Oneironosus.

oneirology (ō-nī-rol'ō-jē) The science of dreams.

oneironosus (-nō'sus) Morbid dreaming.

oneirophrenia (-frē'ni-à) A term suggested by Meduna and McCulloch for a schizophrenoid psychosis which, like schizophrenia, shows disturbances in associations and in affectivity but, unlike schizophrenia, shows in addition clouding of the sensorium. Onset is usually acute, during the episode the patient is in a dream-like condition, and prognosis is usually good.

By others, oneirophrenia is considered to be an acute form of *schizophrenia* (q.v.).

oneiroscopy (ō-nī-ros'kō-pē) Dream-analysis, diagnosis of the mental state by a study of the person's dreams.

oniomania (ō-ni-ō-mā'ni-à) Irresistible impulse to buy, extending inordinately beyond the needs of the individual. Women, in whom the symptom is said to predominate, carry out the act of purchasing without judgment of the consequences.

'They do not even feel the impulse, but they act out of their nature like a caterpillar devouring leaves.' (Bleuler, E. *Textbook of Psychiatry,* tr. by Brill, A.A., Macmillan, New York, 1930, p. 540)

onirism (on'ī-riz'm) A term suggested by Régis for a state of prolonged dreaming.

onology (ō-nol'ō-jē) *Rare.* Asinine talk.

onomatomania (on-ō-ma-tō-mā'ni-à) A type of obsessive thinking in which certain words or sentences obtrude themselves into the patient's thoughts. A patient with an obsessive-compulsive psychoneurosis was beset with anxiety, because a man's name was incessantly forcing itself upon him. It was the surname of a man, with whose wife the patient had had intercourse; the anxiety was occasioned by the fear of being attacked by the husband, though the patient knew that he need have no fear of attack in the usual sense.

onomatophobia Fear of hearing a certain name.

onomatopoiesis, onomatopoësis (-poi-ē'sis, -pō-ē'sis) The formation of an echoic word, i.e. in imitation of the sound associated with the thing or action. The words, *hiss, swish, crash, hush, whizz, hum, buzz, thump, click, tick, tap, cackle, yap (chug), boom, bing, hoepoe, whippoorwill, chickadee* closely resemble the sound. In psychiatry the phenomenon is often observed in morbid form among patients with schizophrenia, who create a number of neologisms on the basis of sound association.

ontogenesis, ontogeny (on-tō-jen'ē-sis, on-toj'ē-nē) In biology, the development of the individual organism as compared with the evolutionary or *phylogenetic* development of the species. This fundamental distinction was clarified by Haeckel, when in 1867 he formulated his famous 'biogenetic law' that 'ontogeny recapitulates phylogeny' (*Natürliche Schöpfungsgeschichte*). If the histories of the genealogical and of the individual development are distinguished in accordance with this law, it follows that 'the organism in its development is to a great extent an epitome of the form-modifications undergone by the successive ancestors of the species in the course of their historic evolution.'

In other fields of science one finds the term ontogenesis or *ontogeny* applied in a more limited and specialized sense. With bacteriologists it means the evolution of the individual germ. According to certain psychologists, ontogeny refers to factors in the life of human beings after their birth, as the psyche is believed to have its special form of development, its own embryology, physiology, structural evolution, and pathology (see *phylogenesis*).

onychophagia (on-i-kō-fā'ji-à) Nail-biting. This is given by Kanner as one of the habitual manipulations of the body encountered in neurotic children and considered by him as one of the several forms of motor discharges of inner tension. 'Tension is especially apt to express itself in the form of nail-biting if the pattern has been furnished by older members of the family. The intensity varies with the degree of tension and with the occasion.' (Kanner, L. *Child Psychiatry*, Thomas, Springfield, Ill., 1935)

oö- (ō'ō-) Combining form meaning egg, from Gr. *ō(i)on*, egg.

oöcyte (ō'ō-sīt) In sexual reproduction, the female germ cells or *oögonia* divide into two unequal daughter cells, the larger of which is called the *primary* or *secondary oöcyte*, according to whether it is produced by the first or second meiotic division. See *egg*.

oögonia (-gō'ni-à) In sexual reproduction, the *oögonia* represent the first stage in the development of mature reproductive cells in the female. See *egg*.

oöphorectomy (-fō-rek'tō-mē) See *ovariotomy*.

oöphorepilepsy (-fō-rep'i-lep-sē) *Obs.* Epilepsy originating in the ovaries.

oöphoria (-fō'ri-à) Dr. Barnes's term for hysteria, which he thought to be caused by the condition of the ovaries.

oöphoromania (-fō-rō-mā'ni-à) *Obs.* Psychosis due to ovarian disease.

oöthecomania (-thē-kō-mā'ni-à) Mental disorder associated with ovarian disease.

open-door policy Approximately equivalent to *community, therapeutic* (q.v.). The term open-door emphasizes the growing trend in psychiatric hospitals to minimize or even eliminate completely any form of restraint or enforced confinement ('locked doors').

ophidiophilia (ō-fid'i-ō-fil'i-à) A morbid fascination with snakes.

ophidiophobia (ō-fid'i-ō-fō'bi-à) Fear of snakes.

ophthalmoplegia (of-thal-mō-plē'ji-à) See *nerve, oculomotor*.

-opia, -opy (-ō'pi-à, -ō-pē) Combining form meaning defect of sight, from Gr. *ōps, ōpós*, eye.

opinion, public 'A composite opinion formed out of several opinions that are held in the public; or better, as the central tendency set by the striving among these separate opinions and consequently as being shaped by the relative strength and play of opposition among them.' (Blumer, H.E., in Park, R.E. *Principles of Sociology*, Barnes & Noble, New York, 1939)

opiomania (ō-pi-ō-mā'ni-à) Addiction to the use of opium or any of its derivatives.

opisthotonos (op-is-thot'ō-nos) See *arc de cercle*.

opotherapy (op-ō-ther'à-pē) See *endocrinotherapy*.

Oppenheimer treatment (Issac Oppenheimer, a New York physician.) A secret method of treatment of alcoholism and drug addiction.

Oppenheim reflex See *reflex, Oppenheim*.

Oppenheim's dystonia musculorum deformans (dis-tō'nē-à mus-koo-lō'room dā-for'mans) (Hermann Oppenheim, Berlin neurologist, 1858–1919) See *dystonia, torsion*.

opposite, reversal into the Reversal into the opposite is one of the major defensive processes of a psychological nature by which the ego handles, or defends itself from, the sexual (or aggressive) instinct which impinges upon it while seeking direct gratification. The specific nature of this process consists of the transformation of the aim of an instinct into its opposite, and the substitution of the instinct itself for the external object. This process is called into play when the aim of the instinct has been blocked from direct object gratification by internal intrapsychic or external environmental prohibition and restriction. In the process of reversal into the opposite, the active aim usually becomes a passive one. See *libido, plasticity of.*

R. Sterba (*Introduction to the Psychoanalytic Theory of the Libido,* Nervous and Mental Disease Monographs No. 68, New York, 1942) states: 'A simple example will demonstrate this process. It is very much easier for a child to achieve his desire to be beaten, through being naughty, than to satisfy his desire to beat somebody; he has only to be troublesome and naughty in order to attain his goal.'

-opsia (-op'si-à) See *-opia.*

opsomania (op-sō-mā'ni-à) 'Either a craving for some particular aliment to the extent of insanity, or a morbid craving for dainties.' (Tuke, D.H. *A Dictionary of Psychological Medicine,* vols. 1–2, Blakiston, Philadelphia, 1892)

optimism, oral A psychiatric term used to denote the optimism appearing as an oral character trait. Oral eroticism is extremely important for the formation of character. At the time when oral eroticism occurs in infantile development, children 'become acquainted with objects and learn to assume relationships with them.' Consequently, the way in which this happens 'remains basic in determining the whole subsequent relationship to reality.' Thus all positive or negative attitudes to taking and receiving have an oral origin. In particular, whenever there is unusually pronounced oral satisfaction in infancy, the results are a self-assurance and optimism which may persist throughout life. Fenichel remarks, however, that if frustration has followed this satisfaction, there may be created a state of 'vengefulness coupled with continuous demanding.' (Fenichel, O. *The Psychoanalytic Theory of Neurosis,* Norton, New York, 1945)

oral-aggressive See *defense, character*

orality (ō-ral'i-tē) A general term referring to the oral components of sexuality, to manifestations of instinctual conflict centering about the oral stage of sexual development, to manifestations which indicate fixation at the oral stage of development, to manifestations of oral erogeneity. Orality is prominent in manic-depressive psychosis and addictions. A driving ambition in the field of

oratory or speech-making is often based on oral conflicts. Excessive generosity in a person often has the following significance: 'As I shower you with love, in the same way do I want to be showered with love'; this mechanism is typical of the oral receptive individual. The oral-sadistic person often shows extreme niggardliness: 'You must make up for the love denied me.' Volubility, restlessness, haste, and a tendency to obstinate silence are also indicative of extreme orality. Dr. Edmund Bergler ('A Short Genetic Survey of Psychic Impotence,' *Psychiatric Quarterly 19,* 412, 657, 1945) believes that the mechanism of orality is as follows: (1) through his behavior the individual provokes disappointment, thus identifying the outer world with the refusing, pre-oedipal mother; (2) the individual becomes aggressive, seemingly in self-defense; (3) the individual indulges in self-pity, a manifestation of his psychic masochism. See *character, oral.*

orchestromania (or-kes-trō-mā'ni-à) Chorea; St. Vitus's dance.

Orestes (ō-res'tēz) A famous figure of Greek mythology, Orestes illustrates how the forces of unreason often appear inappeasable in the schizophrenic's fate. The Furies demanded the blood of Orestes. Athena confronted these creatures of chaos with divine reasoning, but her persuasive powers were of no avail and she was unable to accomplish anything. In schizophrenics, the antithesis between the rational and irrational is very often irreconcilable. The unconscious forces do not listen to reason. (Baynes, H.G. *Mythology of the Soul,* Williams and Wilkins, Baltimore, 1940)

-orexia (-ō-rek'si-à) Combining form meaning appetite, desire, from Gr. *órexis,* appetite, desire, longing.

organ-erotic Relating to or characterized by the attachment of the erotic instinctual component to an organ of the body.

'Bearing these facts in mind it will be easy to understand that the child's first sexual feelings have reference to its own body, more particularly to parts, segments, of its body; it is organ-erotic.' (Jelliffe, S.E. and White, W.A. *Diseases of the Nervous System,* 6th ed., Lea & Febiger, Philadelphia, 1935)

organ-erotism Libido or erotism situated in an organ.

organ, executive The organ that is used for the execution of responses to stimuli. 'In the infant the technique of mastery has two chief executive organs, the hand and the mouth, the eye being the leading auxiliary organ.' (Kardiner, A. and Spiegel, H.X. *War Stress and Neurotic Illness,* Hoeber, New York, 1947) Thus it will be seen that when hunger is the stimulus, response to it is executed by way of the mouth; when the stimulus is the desire to grasp at an object, response to it is executed by means of the hand.

organic driveness See *driveness, organic.*

organicism (or-gan′i-siz'm) The theory that refers all disease to material lesions of organs. Disordered physiology may give rise to symptoms, yet there may be no demonstrable lesions.

Today the term means more commonly the theory that all symptoms are organically determined.

There is a third meaning, appearing in constitutional medicine—'the theory that the various organs of the body have each their own special constitution.' (Pende, N. *Constitutional Inadequacies,* tr. by Naccarati, S., Lea & Febiger, Philadelphia, 1928)

organicist One who believes in the *organicism* theory. One who regards all psychical and physical activity as a reflection of the material organs of the body is called an organicist. This point of view stands in strong contrast with that of the psychogeneticist, who believes that there is also a psyche. To the latter the psyche is the equivalent of an organ of the body with its own special growth, structure, and constitution.

organic reaction See *syndrome, organic.*

organismic (or-gan-iz′mik) In phylobiology this term implies a wholeness that is phyletic as well as individual. From this organismic frame of reference the species man is regarded as an organically interrelated whole. Contrasted with partitive. (Burrow, T. *The Biology of Human Conflict,* Macmillan, New York, 1937, p. 320)

organization, libido (li-bēd′ō) See *zone, primacy.*

organization, life The life-organization of a person is 'a set of rules for definite situations [such as] moral principles, legal

prescriptions, economic forms, religious rites, social customs.' (Thomas, W.I. and Znaniecki, F. *The Polish Peasant in Europe and America,* Knopf, New York, 1927)

'The concept of individual life-organization may be used to indicate the existence, within the sphere of experience of an individual, of a limited number of selected and organized groups of social values which play a preponderant part in his life.' (ibid.)

organization, pregenital (prē-jen′i-tal) An expression used by psychoanalysts to denote the arrangement of the libido in the stages prior to that of infantile genitality.

'As a result of numerous impressions, and in particular of one specially cogent analytical experience, I came to the conclusion a few years later that in the development of the libido in man the phase of genital primacy must be preceded by a "pregenital organization" in which sadism and anal erotism play the leading parts.' (Freud, S. *Collected Papers,* vol. 2, tr. by Riviere, J., Leonard and Virginia Woolf and The Institute of Psychoanalysis, London, 1924–25)

organization, social Social organization consists of 'socially systematized schemes of behavior imposed as rules upon individuals.' (Thomas, W.I. and Znaniecki, F. *The Polish Peasant in Europe and America,* Knopf, New York, 1927)

It is the 'differentiated unity of mental or social life, present in the simplest intercourse, but capable of infinite growth and adaptation.' (Cooley, C.H. *Social Organization,* Scribner, New York, 1912)

'Social organization is the process or complex of activities through which relationships are developed, groups or institutions or whole cultures are built up.' (Queen, S.A., Bodenhofer, W.B., and Harper, E.B. *Social Organization and Disorganization,* Crowell, New York, 1935)

'Every human group is organized; its individual components do not behave independently of one another, but are linked by bonds, the nature of which determines the types of social unit. Kinship, sex, age, co-residence, matrimonial status, community of religious or social interests, are among the unifying agencies; and in stratified societies members of the same level form a definite class.' (Lowie, R.H. "Social Organization," *Encyclopaedia of the So-*

cial Sciences, vol. 14, Macmillan, New York, 1934, p. 141)

organ-jargon See *jargon, organ.*

organ-libido (-li-bēd'ō) See *organ-erotism.*

organ-neurosis See *psychosomatic.*

organogenesis (-jen'ē-sis) Somatogenesis.

organogenic, organogenetic (or-gan-ō-jen'ik, -ō-jē-net'ik) Synonymous with *somatogenic.*

organotherapy (-ō-ther'à-pē) Treatment with preparations or substances as they are found naturally in the body. In general it is called 'replacement' therapy, because usually the object is to restore to the body in sufficient quantity to maintain health something that is lacking in the body. Thus, thyroid products are given to those whose thyroid gland does not provide sufficient thyroid substances. Endocrinotherapy is one form of organotherapy.

organ-pleasure Freud says that the sexual instincts first express themselves in the service of self-preservation. They attach themselves to various parts of the body, with special emphasis on the erotogenic zones—oral, anal, and early genital. While gaining strong cathexis to these zones during the period of infantile sexuality, the sexual instincts are simply laying the groundwork, so to speak, for race-preservation, which will operate practically, beginning with early adolescence. It is obvious, therefore, that, when Freud refers to sexual instincts of the infantile period, he means that the instincts, designed eventually to serve the race-preservative element, must first prepare the individual for his later destiny.

The sexual instincts condition special body areas in preparation for object-love leading to the gratification of the race-preservative component. 'An attempt to formulate the general characteristics of the sexual instincts would run as follows: they are numerous, emanate from manifold organic sources, act in the first instance independently of one another and only at a late stage achieve a more or less complete synthesis. The aim which each strives to attain is "organ-pleasure"; only when the synthesis is complete do they enter the service of the function of reproduction becoming thereby generally recognizable as sexual instincts.' (Freud, S. *Collected Papers,* vol. 4, tr. by Riviere,

J., Leonard and Virginia Woolf and The Institute of Psychoanalysis, London, 1924–25)

organ speech See *speech, organ.*

organ, target See *syndrome, general adaptation.*

orgasm (or'gaz'm) Orgasm means a state of excitement in an organ. As used today the term generally refers to the acme of sexual excitation in the genital zone. 'What can be asserted without fear of contradiction is that a very considerable number of women never experience any pleasurable sensation whatever, that a much larger number experience it only in a slight degree and without ever knowing in their own life what an orgasm means, and that with only the minority of women is the capacity for full sensation and orgasm properly developed.' (Jones, E. *Papers on Psycho-Analysis,* 4th ed., Wood, Baltimore, 1938)

'In co!tus the orgasm tends to occur more slowly in women than in men.' (Ellis, H.)

The non-genital physiological accompaniments (rapid pulse, increased breathing, etc.) of an orgasm often occur symbolically without the individual recognizing that sexuality is the cause. In this instance the sexuality is unconsciously determined and is to all appearances desexualized.

Other individuals, notably those with schizophrenia, may transfer feelings normally belonging to the genital area to other organs (i.e. to the head, lungs, stomach, etc.). According to the patient, these substituted organs go through the process of excitement, which the psychiatrist, not the patient, recognizes as an orgasm. This peculiar mental mechanism is often observed among those who show latent homosexuality or in whom a strong Oedipus impulse may be demonstrated.

While speaking of latent homosexuality in prostitutes, Stekel says: 'For there are prostitutes who are attached to their lover (cadet), and who experience orgasm only during intercourse with him, while the embraces of other men leave them unaffected.' (Stekel, W. *Frigidity in Woman,* vols. 1–2, tr. by van Teslaar, J.S., Boni & Liveright, New York, 1926)

Havelock Ellis says: 'In man the process of tumescence and detumescence is simple. In women it is complex. In man we have the more or less spontaneously erectile penis, which needs but very simple conditions to secure the ejaculation which brings relief. In women we have in the clitoris a corresponding apparatus on a small scale, but behind this has developed a much more extensive mechanism, which also demands satisfaction, and requires for that satisfaction the presence of various conditions that are almost antagonistic.' (Ellis, H. *Studies in the Psychology of Sex,* vol. 1, Davis, Philadelphia, 1919)

It is generally agreed that very prolonged intercourse gives the greatest amount of pleasure and relief to women. According to Jaeger, that is why some women prefer intercourse with men castrated after puberty, for these are capable of prolonged erections.

orgasm, alimentary (al-i-men'tȧ-rē) In psychoanalysis the gastro-intestinal tract plays an important role from the standpoint of emotional or libidinal investment and action. Rado, speaking of 'alimentary orgasm,' refers to a stage of comfortable alimentary satisfaction following the appeasement of hunger. The condition is believed to be pronounced in the early years of life. (Rado, S. *Internationale Zeitschrift für Psychoanalyse,* vol. XII, p. 540)

orgasmus deficiens (ôr-gȧz'moos dā-fē'kē-ens) (L. 'failing, deficient orgasm') Lack of sexual pleasure.

orgone (or'gōn) Wilhelm Reich's term for the life energy, which he believed to be specific and identifiable.

orient To orient oneself is to know one's temporal, personal, and spatial relationships.

orientation In psychiatry orientation refers to the knowledge of one's own temporal, personal, and spatial relationships. An individual has intact orientation when he relates himself correctly to his surroundings, including the concept of time.

Bleuler refers also to 'orientation as to the patient's own situation,' an expression synonymous with *insight* (q.v.).

orientation, autopsychic This denotes the appreciation of oneself, of one's own personality, one's psychic self. When an individual is aware that changes take place in his personality he is said to possess intact autopsychic orientation. For example, the patient with a manic-depressive

disorder usually has full knowledge of the changes that have appeared in his personality. The patient with schizophrenia, however, ordinarily denies that he has changed in any way. He is autopsychically disoriented.

The expression *autopsychic orientation* is seemingly synonymous with *insight.*

orientation, delusion of See *orientation, double.*

orientation, double Bleuler thus terms the condition in which a patient expresses a delusion about time, place, or person, while at the same time he also knows in a purely intellectual sense the actual relationship existing between him and time, place, and person. The delusions take precedence over the real facts. Thus, a patient with schizophrenia acts, feels, and thinks as if he were a new-born babe, giving the current date as his date of birth, though he also gives the correct current date. He earnestly believes that he is at home with his mother, though he correctly names the hospital in which he has been a patient for years. Moreover, he identifies the nurse as his mother, though he calls her by her correct name.

orientation, illusion of Misinterpretation of something real in the environment, owing to an unclear sensorium. The phenomenon is not uncommon in confusional states associated with toxicity (e.g. typhoid delirium). The patient sees something in his hospital room which reminds him of his own home, whereupon he believes that he is at his own home. Or he hears the voice of a nurse, which he mistakes for that of his wife.

orientation, oral In psychiatry, this term denotes the oral awareness or knowledge of a given situation. The oral orientation of the primitive ego arises from the fact that among the earliest primitive reactions to objects which the infant shows is the desire to put them into his mouth.

The recognition of the outside world, i.e. objects, grew out of the infant's hunger and other stimuli which disturbed his sleep. These disturbing stimuli brought about a state of tension and the resulting tendency to get rid of the tension. This state of tension disappeared with satiation. As the infant grew and became aware that something was done by the outside world to alleviate his stimuli, he developed his first longing for objects.

When the infant began to long for something already familiar to him, absent at the moment, but with the ability to gratify his needs, he became aware of an object for the first time. When the object appeared, the longing for it disappeared and sleep followed. Thus hunger compelled the awareness of objects, i.e. the recognition of the outside world.

Next, the experience of satiation which first banished the hunger that had disturbed sleep became 'the model for the mastery of external stimuli in general.' That is, the taking of objects into his mouth was one of the first reactions to objects on the part of the infant. Thus the first recognition of reality on the part of the infant is for him to judge whether he should swallow an object or spit it out. In the way described above, the reaction to recognition of the outside world, that is, to the perception of objects on the part of the primitive ego, is taking-into-the-mouth: oral introjection. 'This incorporation which is the first reaction to objects in general and the precursor of the later sexual and destructive attitudes in a psychological sense destroys the existence of the object. The attitude that the object exists only for the ego's satisfaction and may disappear once satisfaction is achieved can still be observed in some childish types of love.' Fenichel emphasizes, however, that the aim to incorporate objects does not necessarily reflect subjective destructive tendencies toward those objects. The fact that in incorporation the object disappears, i.e. is destroyed, is an incidental consequence and shows merely that oral incorporation is an urge to get satisfaction without any further thought of the object. Rather, this primary oral attitude of incorporation is the attitude out of which love and destructive hate grow at a later stage of development. (Fenichel, O. *The Psychoanalytic Theory of Neurosis,* Norton, New York, 1945)

orientation, reversed A state in which a person when walking in a certain direction feels that he is walking in the opposite direction. The condition is purely subjective; the person orients himself correctly by reasoning.

ornithophobia (or-ni-thō-fō′bi-à) Fear of birds.

orthergasia (orth-ĕr-gas′i-à) See *euergasia.*

ortho- (or′thō-) Combining form meaning straight, right, correct, sound, from Gr. *orthós.*

orthopathic (or-thō-pa′thik) Burrow's term for feeling that is primary, direct, whole. Contrasted with autopathic.

orthophrenia (-frē′ni-à) Soundness of mind; also: the curing of a disordered mind.

orthopsychiatry (-sī-kī′à-trē) A subdivision of psychiatry which deals with the study and treatment of mental deviations that are known in general as borderline states; it also includes the study of methods of preventing mental disorders. The term is approximately equivalent to *mental hygiene.*

orthostatic epileptoid See *epileptoid, orthostatic.*

orthovagotonia (-vā-gō-tō′ni-à) Exaggerated functioning of the vagotonic or parasympathetic nervous system, but only when this exaggerated functioning is in harmony with that of the sympathetic nervous system.

orthriogenesis (or-thri-ō-jen′e-sis) Federn's term for the recapitulation by the ego of its whole development, which he felt occurs at the moment of awakening when the ego, which has been without cathexis in deep sleep, suddenly has its cathexis restored.

-osis (-ō′sis) Noun-forming suffix meaning action, state, condition, process, from Gr. *-ōsis,* as in (metamórph)*ōsis.*

-osmia (-oz′mi-à) Combining form meaning smell, odor, from Gr. *osmé,* smell, odor.

osmophobia (oz-mō-fō′bi-à) Fear of odors.

osphresia, osphresis (os-frē′zhi-à, os-frē′-sis) The sense of smell.

osphresiolagnia (os-frē-zhi-ō-lag′ni-à) The sense of smell often gains much significance in psychiatric patients in whom it has close association with matters of infantile sexuality. Some patients believe that their body sends out an odor that is remarkably disagreeable and hurtful to others. They think that the odor makes others sick or insane. Indeed, the obsession or delusion, whichever it may be, is one of the ways by which the sadistic impulse toward others is expressed. When the allegedly lewd odor is smelled by the patient who produces it, the sadistic impulse is turned inwardly upon himself; he considers his own body is deteriorating.

The schizophrenic patient, particularly the one with delusions of persecution, often projects the idea of bad odors upon others, coming to the delusion then that others force evil body odors upon him, the patient.

One who possesses a morbid idea regarding body odors is called an osphresiolagniac or a renifleur.

'It turned out that our patient, besides all his other characteristics, was a renifleur (or osphresiolagniac). By his own account, when he was a child he had recognized every one by their smell, like a dog; and even when he was grown up he was more susceptible to sensations of smell than most people.' (Freud, S. Collected Papers, vol. 3, tr. by Strachey, A. and J., Leonard and Virginia Woolf and The Institute of Psychoanalysis, London, 1925)

Freud says that he has 'come to recognize that a tendency to osphresiolagnia, which has become extinct since childhood, may play a part in the genesis of neurosis.' (Freud, S., ibid.)

osphresiophilia Love of odors or smells. This gains psychiatric importance when morbidly expressed. A patient with a compulsive-obsessive neurosis collected and stored his feces, from which he derived intense gratification from the standpoint of smell.

ophresiophobia Fear of odors. Some patients are morbidly afraid of odors, believing that they would be contaminated by these odors. This is the negative counterpart of *osphresiophilia* (q.v.), for the unconscious impulse toward odors may become consciously expressed as a fear of them.

ossification (os-i-fi-ka'shun) Lewin's term for the relative rigidity of behavior patterns which have become second nature or autonomous because of frequent repetitions.

O.T. Occupational therapy. See *therapy, occupational.*

otiumosis (ō-shi-um-ō'sis) An alternative term suggested by E. Bergler for *alysosis* (q.v.).

otohemineurasthenia (ō-tō-hem-i-nū-ras-thē'ni-à) Functional deafness affecting one ear.

otoneurasthenia (-nū-ras-thē'ni-à) Functional deafness.

ovariomania (ō-vâr-i-ō-mā'ni-à) *Obs.* Mania due to ovarian disorder.

ovariotomy (ō-vâr-i-ot'ō-mē) This is the name of the operation by which one or both ovaries of a woman are removed. Bilateral ovariotomy is required for the castration of a female and usually leads, if performed before puberty, to such a marked disturbance in the sex balance as to produce a eunuchoid symptomatology with secondary male sex characteristics (see *castration*). Also called *oöphorectomy.*

over activity, psychomotor See *mania.*

overcompensation The term has been made popular by Alfred Adler. When the feeling of inferiority is so great that the individual fears he will never be able to compensate for his weakness, his striving for power and dominance is exaggerated and intensified to a pathological degree.

Such individuals endeavor to secure their position in life by extraordinary efforts, by greater haste and impatience, by more violent impulses, and without consideration for anyone else. Their attitudes are apt to have a certain grandiose quality.

Briefly then, according to Adler, overcompensation is the counterpose of an overwhelming feeling of inferiority which is profusely neutralized by steps toward a towering goal of dominance.

overconsciousness According to Schilder, this term describes an exaggerated development of self-consciousness as the result of 'over-socialization with leveling of the object relations.' The term applies to parents who first identify themselves too strongly with their children as love-objects, and then perform acts ostensibly of 'self-sacrificing love,' which, in psychiatric terms, are mere expressions of an increased narcissism on the part of the parents. Overconsciousness, it may be said, is a narcissistic attitude developed as a result of object relations of a special intensity and character. (Schilder, P. *Mind, Perception and Thought,* Columbia University Press, New York, 1942)

overdependence, social See *psychodynamics, adaptational.*

overdetermination 'As a rule neuroses are *overdetermined;* that is to say, several factors in their etiology operate together.' (Freud, S. *Collected Papers,* vol. 1, tr. by Riviere, J., Leonard and Virginia Woolf and The Institute of Psychoanalysis, London, 1924–25)

over-interpretation See *dream-interpretation.*

overprotection, maternal Overprotection of the growing infant by the mother can result in difficulties for the individual in later life. Overindulged and overprotected at an early age, the infant has not learned to bear frustrations. As a result, at a later period of development, little frustrations that a less spoiled individual could tolerate will have the effect of a severe frustration. That is, the infant will refuse to go further in development, but will demand the withheld gratification associated with the particular little frustrations. Thus there will be fixations of the individual at the level of development at which the frustrations occur. These fixations resulting from overprotection produce personality difficulties such as various neurotic defense symptoms, or character attitudes, and primitive types of love.

Specifically, Fenichel discusses maternal overprotection from the point of view of its effect on the Oedipus complex. In general, 'the particular form of the Oedipus complex will determine the specific nature of the subsequent disturbances in object relationships. The resultant character disturbances possible are as manifold as the infantile experiences.' These character disturbances are reflected in misjudgments and dissatisfactions in all types of social relationships and, in particular, in the characteristics of the love life. Now, an overprotecting mother predisposes the individual in question to passive, dependent types of mastery. As a result, he will be unable to adapt himself objectively, but his passive dependent needs will color all his activities and relationships, causing the inevitable illusions and disappointments. (Fenichel, O. *The Psychoanalytic Theory of Neurosis,* Norton, New York, 1945)

over-reactive disorders See *psychodynamics, adaptational.*

over-repression An expression used by Alexander in psychoanalysis for the exaggerated and often unnecessary repression by the superego.

'Thus an over-severe Super-ego may exclude from consciousness "and therefore from access to the motor apparatus" many forms of outlet which would be by no means ego-dystonic, namely unacceptable to the Ego.' (Healy, W., Bronner, A.F., and Bowers, A.M. *The Structure and Meaning of Psychoanalysis,* Knopf, New York, 1930)

overtone, psychic (sī′kik) One of the many faintly perceived associated impressions grouped about a mental image.

ovum (ō′vum) (L. 'an egg') See *egg.*

oxycephaly (ok-sē-sef′a-lē) Tower-head; turrecephaly. A congenital anomaly in which there is premature closure (carniosynostosis) of the coronal and lambdoid sutures, resulting in an upward elongation of the head, which thus appears dome-shaped. The anomaly does not affect mentality or length of life, but in order to preserve vision the King corrective operation must be performed early in life.

P

P Rorschach scoring symbol for a popular response, i.e. a response which occurs frequently.

pachymeningitis (pak-ē-men-in-jī'tis) See *meningitis.*

pachymeninx (pak-ē-men'ingks) See *meninges.*

pack In psychiatric nursing, the application of sheets to the patient's body. The pack may be wet or dry, hot or cold. In each case the patient is wrapped in several sheets. When a *cold pack* is used the sheets are immersed in water at a temperature of 60° F.; the temperature of the water in case of a *hot pack* is 130° to 145° F.

Dry packs are sometimes used to induce increase of body temperature by lessening heat elimination.

paederastia (ped-ē-ras'ti-à) Pederasty.

paedicatio (pī-dē-kä'tē-ō) Pederasty. 'The significance of this added fragment will be evident when I mention that the patient, who had frequently indulged in paedicatio, was a pronounced *voyeur.*' (Jones, E. *Papers on Psycho-Analysis,* 4th ed., Wood, Baltimore, 1938)

paedicatio mulierum (pī-dē-kä'tē-ō mōō-lē'e-room) (L. 'women's pederasty') The act of pederasty with girls as the passive agent.

paed(o)- See *ped(o)-.*

paedophilia erotica (pī-dō-fē'lē-à e-rō'tē-kà) (Mod.L. 'erotic love of children') A term coined by Krafft-Ebing denoting the same clinical condition as *pederosis* (q.v.).

paidicatio (pī-dē-kä-tē-ō) Pederasty; sodomy.

pain, ecstatic 'The *hunger for excitement* of some people comes about in this manner. There are people who must always be doing something; it matters little whether the situation is of a pleasurable or painful nature. Sometimes a decided preference is shown for the latter; they experience "ecstatic pain," martyrlike pleasure, and forever consider themselves unfairly treated.' (Bleuler, E. *Textbook of Psychiatry,* tr. by Brill, A.A., Macmillan, New York, 1930)

pain, psychic (sī'kik) Same as *psychalgia.*

pain, referred Irradiation of pain sensation, with or without hyperalgesia, into an area of skin when a viscus or muscle is the site of the lesion. Although the basis for referral of pain must be excitation of common pathways, it is uncertain whether the brain, the spinal cord, or the peripheral nerves are involved.

painting, finger Direct manipulation of the paint with the fingers and hands to achieve a graphic effect. In psychology, finger-painting is used as a projective technique, the assumption being that finger-painting is a form of expressive behavior, the analysis of which reveals significant characteristics of the individual. Finger-painting was developed by Miss Ruth F. Shaw (1934) as one of her various educational techniques, and it has since been used as a diagnostic projective technique, as a means for stimulating free associations, as a part of psychotherapy and play therapy, and by occupational therapists in rehabilitation of spastic patients, the deaf, and the blind.

pal(a)eo- (pā'lē-ō-, pal'ē-ō-) Combining form meaning old, ancient, from Gr. *palaiós,* old, ancient.

pal(a)eophrenia (pā-lē-ō-frē'ni-à, pal-ē-) This psychoanalytical term, meaning literally ancient or primitive mentality, was suggested by Oliver J. Osborne to be used instead of schizophrenia to emphasize the regression to a primitive type of thinking which is often seen in schizophrenics. (O'Connor, W.A. *Psychiatry: A Short Treatise,* Williams and Wilkins, Baltimore, 1948)

paleoatavism (-at'à-viz'm) Among ethnological psychologists the opinion prevails that, from the psychic as well as the somatic point of view, ontogeny repeats phylogeny. The history of the mind from ancient times is relived in each individual.

'Assuming the bionomic law, infant growth means being loaded with paleoatavistic qualities in a manner more conformable to Weismannism, embryonic growth being yet purer, while the pubescent increment is relatively neoatavistic.' (Hall, G.S. *Adolescence,* vol. 1, Appleton, New York, 1908, p. 50)

paleologic (-loj'ik) Archaic or ancient

logic; with this term, Arieti refers to the same method of thinking which has been variously designated as pre-Aristotelian, prelogical (Levy-Bruhl) or paralogical (Von Domarus). Paleologic is seen most clearly in schizophrenic thinking disorders. See *mind, pre-logical.*

paleomnesis (pā-lē-om-nē′sis) Memory for the remote past in the life of the individual.

paleopsychic (pā-lē-ō-sī′kik) Pertaining to or possessing primitive mentality.

paleopsychology (-sī-kol′ō-jē) The study of paleopsychic phenomena; it is believed by Freud, Jung, and many others that remote ancestral modes of mental activity reside in the unconscious of modern man.

paleosensation The term of the Dutch school of neurologists (Brouwer, Kappers) for the protopathic sensations as vital, in contradistinction to the epicritic and deep, which they call *gnostic* or new sensation.

paleosymbol A private symbol, which is highly individualistic, fleeting, flexible and mutable and which is evolved and maintained without regard for socialization or interpersonal relationships. Paleosymbols are seen as a form of *paleologic* (q.v.) and are characteristic of immediately prehuman races although they probably exist also in apes in rudimentary form.

pali- (pal′i-) Combining form meaning morbid or obsessive repetition or reiteration, from Gr. *pálin,* backward, again.

paligraphia (-graf′i-à) The morbid or obsessive repetition of something (letters, words, phrases, etc.) in writing.

palilalia (-lā-li-à) A rare speech disorder in which a phrase is repeated with increasing rapidity. The most common causes of palilalia are encephalitis or other conditions producing Parkinsonism and pseudo-bulbar palsy due to vascular lesions.

palilexia (-lek′si-à) The morbid rereading of words or phrases.

palilogia (-lō′ji-à) Morbid or obsessive repetition of something spoken.

palingraphia (pā-lin-graf′i-à) Mirror-writing.

palinlexia (pā-lin-leks′i-à) Backward reading.

paliphrasia (pā-li-frā′zhi-à) The morbid repetition of phrases in speaking.

pallesthesia (pal-es-thē′zhi-à) The vibratory sensation felt when the foot of a vibrating tuning-fork is placed over subcutaneous bony surfaces.

pallidum (pà-li′-doom) See *basal ganglia.*

palmesthesia (pal-mes-thē′zhi-à) *Pallesthesia* (q.v.).

palsy Paralysis.

palsy, cerebral *Little's disease* (q.v.).

palsy, progressive bulbar See *sclerosis, amyotrophic lateral.*

palsy, pseudobulbar (sū-dō-bul′bēr) See *sclerosis, amyotrophic lateral.*

palsy, shaking Paralysis agitans; Parkinson's disease.

pamphobia (pam-fō′bi-à) *Obs.* Panophobia.

pamplegia, panplegia (pam-plē′ji-à, pan-) *Obs.* General paralysis (not the clinical entity).

pan-, pam- (pan-, pam-) Combining form meaning all, total, from Gr. *pãn,* neut. sing. of *pãs, pantós,* all, whole.

pan-anxiety See *schizophrenia, pseudoneurotic.*

panels, personality The concept of a four-panel Japanese screen, across which is painted a complete picture, moved Draper to introduce into the vocabulary of constitutional medicine the term panels of personality for the four main divisions of the human individuality representing themselves for systematic investigation.

These panels relate to the anatomical, physiological, psychological, and immunological elements of an individual, each of which 'may be considered to occupy one panel of the great screen across which Man's personality is drawn.' (Draper, G. *Human Constitution,* Saunders, Philadelphia and London, 1924)

'The direct observation and correlation of these characters of anatomy, physiology, psychology, and immunity offers a wider scope to the physician for the exercise of his powers of observation, and thus inevitably leads to a deeper understanding of the personality of his patient.' (ibid.)

panglossia (pan-glos′i-à) Garrulity, especially psychotic.

panic An attack of overwhelming anxiety. See *anxiety.*

panic, homosexual An acute schizophrenic episode characterized by intense fear, marked excitement, and paranoid ideas, usually of short duration, occurring in individuals whose homosexuality is unconscious; sometimes called Kempf's disease.

panmixia (pan-mik'si-à) In genetic population studies this term indicates equal and unrestricted mating conditions of individuals with different racial characteristics in a mixed population group. See *homogamy.*

pan-neurosis (-nū-rō'sis) See *schizophrenia, pseudoneurotic.*

panphobia, panophobia, pantophobia (pan-fō'bi-à, pan-ō-, pan-tō-) Fear of everything.

pansexualism The doctrine that all human behavior stems from sex. There is no school of psychiatric medicine today whose leaders profess such a doctrine. Freud has frankly disavowed any connection between pansexualism and psychoanalysis.

pantaphobia (pan-ta-fō'bi-à) *Obs.* Absolute fearlessness.

Papez' circle See *emotion, Papez' theory of.*

papilledema (pap-i-lē-dē'mà) Papilledema or choked disk is a condition in which the optic nerve is literally choked at the optic foramen by increased intracranial, and especially intraventricular, pressure, leading to an increase in the intra-ocular tension. The condition is usually bilateral, although there may be differences in the degree of choking on the two sides. Ophthalmoscoptically, the disk is raised, at times to five or six or more diopters; the margins of the disk are blurred; the veins are tortuous and full, the arteries thin; and hemorrhages may occur. Papilledema is most commonly caused by tumor of the brain. Other conditions producing choked disk may be fracture of the skull, hydrocephalus, abscess of the brain, subarachnoid hemorrhage, sinus thrombosis, meningitis, encephalitis, and possibly multiple sclerosis and anemia.

para-, par- (par'à) Prefix meaning beside, past, aside, beyond, i.e. perverted, amiss, wrong, faulty, irregular, disordered, abnormal, *mis-*, from Gr. *pará*, from (the side), beside, near, beyond, against.

parabulia (par-a-bū'li-à) Perversion of volition or will. When an impulse is partly or completely checked and is then replaced by another impulse, the condition is known as parabulia. The phenomenon occurs with much frequency and clarity in patients with schizophrenia. A patient had the impulse to strike his physician; he advanced toward the physician for that purpose, but suddenly stopped 'to regulate the universal voices.' See *will, disturbances of.*

paracenesthesia (-sen-es-thē'zhi-à) Any abnormality of the general sense of well-being.

parachromatopsia, parachromopsia (-kroma-top'si-à, -kro-mop'si-à) Partial color blindness, such as red-green color blindness.

paracope (par-ak'ō-pē) An obsolete term, by which Hippocrates denoted delirium accompanying fever; later synonymous with *insanity.*

paracousia, paracusia (-à-kōō'z[h]i-à, -kū'-si-à) Auditory illusion.

paracusis imaginaria (pà-rà-kōō'sēs ē-mà-gē-nä'rē-à) (Mod.L. 'imaginary paracusia') Auditory hallucination.

paradementia (pa-ra-de-men'shi-à) Brugias' term for dementia praecox (schizophrenia).

paradise A place of bliss. 'This age of childhood, in which the sense of shame is unknown, seems a paradise when we look back upon it later, and paradise itself is nothing but the mass-phantasy of the childhood of the individual. This is why in paradise men are naked and unashamed, until the moment arrives when shame and fear awaken; expulsion follows, and sexual life and cultural development begin.' (Freud, S. *The Interpretation of Dreams,* 3rd ed., tr. by Brill, A.A., Macmillan, New York, 1933)

paradoxia sexualis (pà-rà-dôk'sē-à sek-soo-ä'lēs) Sexual impulses contrary to the physiological age, whether in the old, or children. For example, masturbation in children, prior to the development of physiological sexuality, is a sexual paradox. This is what Krafft-Ebing meant in speaking of the 'sexual instinct manifesting itself independently of physiological processes.' (Krafft-Ebing, R.v. *Psychopathia Sexualis,* Login, New York, 1908)

paradox, neurotic (nū-rot'ik) This term indicates that neurotic behavior often persists indefinitely despite the fact that it is seriously self-defeating and even inimical to the individual. Freud attempted to explain this paradox by assuming that it was due to the retention of an oversevere superego, evolved from too zealous childhood training. This explanation, however, is contrary to all learning theory, which says that learning tends to undergo extinction unless periodically reinforced. It is more likely that the paradox results from infantile ego resistance to socializing forces, so that the basic values and attitudes of society are faultily assimilated into the personality. It may also be that the neurotic behavior represents a means to an end that is unconsciously determined, the desire for which overcomes the wish to conform.

paraerotism See *metaerotism.*

paraflocculi (pà-rà-flō-kōō-lē) See *cerebellum.*

parageusia (par-à-gū'si-à) Perverted sense of taste.

paragnomen (par-ag-nō'men) An unexpected action, not understandable for the subject's environment or by reason of his usual conduct or behavior, which at the moment it is performed is considered to be consciously performed and adequate to the situation but which later appears inexplicable even to the subject. Paragnomens are seen frequently in schizophrenic patients.

paragrammatism (pa-ra-gram'à-tiz'm) Perverted grammar in word; pun. Bleuler applies the term to the neologisms so frequently used by schizophrenic patients. 'At times grammar fails them (*paragrammatism*). Many words are used incorrectly, thus, e.g., frequently the word "murder" that designates all the tortures that the patients suffer.' (Bleuler, E. *Textbook of Psychiatry,* tr. by Brill, A.A., Macmillan, New York, 1930)

paragraphia (-graf'i-à) Perverted writing. Ordinarily, however, it does not refer to alterations in the handwriting itself, such as are manifested by tremors, rigid writing, flourishes and abnormalities in the size of the script; rather, it has to do with such errors as the omission and transposi-

tion of letters or words, or the substitution of a wrong letter or word. Errors of this kind are usually due to cerebral injury.

Paragraphia may be occasioned by psychic disorders. For example, many schizophrenic patients write words and sentences that are definitely of a neologistic character. See *neologism.*

parahypnosis (-hip-nō'sis) Abnormal sleep as in hypnotism or somnambulism.

parakinesia (-ki-nē'si-à) Bizarre and clumsily executed movement.

paralalia (-lā'li-à) Any speech defect, especially the habitual substitution of one letter for another.

paralalia literalis (pà-rà-lā'lē-à lē-te-rä'-lēs) (Mod.L. 'literal paralalia') Perversion in uttering certain sounds; usually combined with stammering.

paraleresis (par-à-lē-rē'sis) Mild delirium.

paralexia (-lek'si-à) Misreading of printed or written words, other meaningless words being substituted for them.

paralipophobia (-lī-pō-fō'bi-à) Fear of neglecting duty.

paralogia (-lō'ji-à) Perverted logic or reasoning in speaking. 'Evasion or *paralogia* consists in this, that the idea which is next in the chain of thought is suppressed and replaced by another which is related to it.' (Kraepelin, E. *Dementia Praecox and Paraphrenia,* tr. by Barclay, R.M., Livingstone, Edinburgh, 1919)

paralogia, derailment, displacement See *akataphasia.*

paralogia, metaphoric (met-à-for'ik) See *by-idea.*

paralogia, thematic (thē-mat'ik) Perverted reasoning in relation chiefly to one theme or subject, upon which the mind dwells insistently.

paralysis (pà-ral'i-sis) Loss of power of voluntary movement in a muscle due to injury or disease of its nerve supply.

paralysis, acute ascending *Landry's paralysis* (q.v.).

paralysis agitans (pà-rà-lē'sēs à'gē-tàns) (L. 'shaking palsy') Paralysis agitans (Parkinson's disease, Parkinsonism) is a chronic, progressive disease of the central nervous system, occuring more commonly in males than females, oftenest between the ages of 50 and 70, and characterized by a rhythmical tremor of various muscle groups, propulsion in walking, mask-like facies, loss of associated movements of the arms, rigidity of body musculature, dysarthric speech, etc.

With encephalitis so widespread and paralysis agitans as a frequent sequel, the syndrome may be observed in individuals of all ages, including very young children.

Mental symptoms may or may not be associated with paralysis agitans. If mental disturbances arise, they may include anxiety, depression, suicidal ideas, euphoria, scornfulness, sarcasm, pessimism, or paranoid delusions.

In the senile and arteriosclerotic cases, the globus pallidus and ansa lenticularis are mainly the loci of degeneration. In the post-encephalitic cases, the substantia nigra may also be involved.

paralysis, congenital spastic *Little's disease* (q.v.).

paralysis, divers' Same as *disease, caisson* (q.v.).

paralysis, familial periodic A hereditary disorder consisting of abrupt, periodic attacks of flaccid paralysis which may last anywhere from hours to three or four days. The illness, which appears to be based on an abnormal demand for potassium, usually begins during adolescence. Prodromata such as hunger, thirst, or sweating are common, and the attacks themselves tend to occur in the early morning. The paralysis is at its height an hour after onset; the proximal limb is affected more than the distal portion and during the attack deep reflexes are abolished, but there is no loss of consciousness. Attacks may occur every few days, or only once every few years. They tend to be precipitated by exposure to the cold, excess sugar intake, fasting, or overexertion. Potassium chloride is used in the treatment of individual attacks and prophylactically when attacks occur frequently.

paralysis, hysterical A paralysis that has a hysterical origin, i.e. a psychogenic etiology, in contradistinction to a paralysis of organic origin. Freud points out the characteristic features of a hysterical paralysis. In the first place, it is 'much more dissociated and systematized' than an organic paralysis. The aphasia will be total, the paralysis of a limb complete. Or one segment of a limb may be completely paralyzed, while other portions remain entirely normal. Or on the same side of the body, one limb may be paralyzed and not the other, or both limbs may be involved but not the remainder of that side. Secondly, the symptoms are produced 'in the severest degree.' The organic paralyses are never so complete as the hysterical paralyses. The hysterically paralyzed limb will be absolutely inert; the hysterical aphasic is completely mute. Thus, hysterical paralysis shows both 'an exact delimitation and an excessive intensity.' These two characteristics of hysterical paralysis also demonstrate the underlying fact that the hysterical lesion is entirely independent of the anatomy of the nervous system. 'Hysteria behaves in its paralyses and other manifestations as if anatomy were nonexistent, or as if it had no knowledge of it.' (Freud, S. *Some Points in a Comparative Study of Organic and Hysterical Paralysis* in *Collected Papers*, vol. 2, The International Psycho-analytical Press, London, 1924)

paralysis, immobilization 'In wound-cases where there had been immobilization of a limb in splints for some time, the immobilization sometimes persisted long after the splints were removed—the so-called "immobilization-paralysis." The patient had "failed to realize when he had become well." The hysterical purpose was the same as in the unwounded cases of functional paralysis. The same phenomenon is encountered in the "traumatic," of peace time.' (Henderson, D.K. and Gillespie, R.D. *A Text-Book of Psychiatry*, 4th ed., Oxford University Press, London, 1936)

paralysis, infantile *Poliomyelitis* (q.v.).

paralysis, Landry's See *Landry's paralysis.*

paralysis, periodic See *paralysis, familial periodic.*

paralysis, progressive *Obsnt.* General paralysis.

paralysis, pseudo-general *Obs.* Partial cerebral paralysis associated with mental deterioration. The term general paralysis was applied to cases of a more general and progressive mental and physical deterioration.

paralysis, psychogenic (si-kō-jen'ik) Paralyses may occur as a result of unconscious conflicts without any discoverable organic pathology and represent conversion phenomena. They are often called *hysterical paralyses.* Neither the paralysis nor the anesthesia fits into a peripheral or segmental type of lesion. There is no loss of tone or of deep reflexes, little or no atrophy, few or no trophic disturbances, and no impairment of electrical reactions.

paralysis, saturnine pseudo-general See *insanity, saturnine.*

paramimia (par-à-mim′i-à) Perversion of sense for gestures or mimetic movements leading to incongruities between feeling and means of expression.

paramnesia (par-am-ne′zhi-à) Perversion of memory in which real facts and phantasies are confused. Thus, a patient was unable to tell whether he had dreamed or actually experienced that of which he was giving an account. Paramnesia is a common phenomenon in dreams, and in the schizophrenias where it often appears as false recognition such as déjà fait, déjà vu, etc. Such paramnesiae may also occur in the normal individual.

paranee (par-à-ne′) A term introduced by Dr. Richard M. Brickner to designate the victim of a paranoid patient. (*American Journal of Orthopsychiatry, 13,* 405, 1943) By projection the ruthless, driving, *paranoiac* superior psychogenically traumatizes his helpless, passive, subordinate victim (the *paranee*), whom he blames for his own failure, and 'takes it out,' as it were, on his downtrodden scapegoat. (Rosen, H. and Kiene, H.E. 'The Paranoiac Officer and the Officer Paranee,' *American Journal of Psychiatry, 103,* 614, 1946–47)

paranoia, paranoea (par-à-noi′à, -ne′à) 'Perhaps no term in psychiatry has undergone wider variations of meaning than the term paranoia. In its earliest days, in the Greek period, it meant little more than just craziness, although perhaps it may have been used somewhat more specifically in some instances, and later on, well into the Middle Ages, it was still a term that was not infrequently used to include the whole group of the so-called insanities.' (Jelliffe, S.E. and White, W.A. *Diseases of the Nervous System,* 6th ed., Lea & Febiger, Philadelphia, 1935)

Although paranoia in the sense of mental derangement, delirium, occurs in Aeschylus (Theb. 756), Euripides (Orestes 822), Plato (Laws 928E and elsewhere), i.e. the term is even pre-Hippocratic, credit is generally given to Vogel

for having introduced or reintroduced the term in medicine in 1764.

'The general concept of paranoia which has been prevalent for many years is that of a psychosis presenting delusions of persecution of a pretty clearly defined type, well supported and defended by the patient, in other words, systematized. These delusions generally involve a more or less circumscribed portion of the mentality, although they tend to spread out slowly and involve more and more. With this state of mind there is no marked tendency toward deterioration, the disease having essentially a chronic course and remaining unchanged for years. Associated with the delusions and harmonized with them in content are frequently auditory hallucinations—voices.' (Jelliffe, S.E. and White, W.A., ibid.)

From the psychodynamic point of view, the concepts of Freud prevail today: 'We should be inclined to say that what was characteristically paranoiac about the illness was the fact that the patient, as a means of warding off a homosexual wish-phantasy, reacted precisely with delusions of persecution of this kind.' (Freud, S. *Collected Papers,* vol. 3, tr. by Strachey, A. and J., Leonard and Virginia Woolf and The Institute of Psychoanalysis, London, 1925)

On the basis of his analysis of the Schreber case, Freud concluded that the core of the conflict in paranoia (at least in males) is a homosexual wish-phantasy of loving a man. The forms of paranoia represent the contradictions of the proposition: I, a man, love him, a man. This proposition is contradicted (a) in the subject, by delusions of jealousy: 'It is not I who love the man, it is she'; (b) in the predicate, by delusions of persecution: 'I do not love him, I hate him, and because of this he hates me and persecutes me'; (c) in the object, by erotomania: 'I do not love him, I love her, because she loves me'; and (d) by complete denial in megalomania: 'I do not love anyone else at all, but only myself.'

paranoia, abortive At times paranoia may 'spontaneously' be 'cured,' that is, the syndrome may disappear entirely. Bleuler, however, would reserve the term *paranoia* for incurable states. 'Some of the abortive and "milder" paranoias (*Friedmann*) are probably mild manic-depressive delusional forms. The "periodic" paranoia belongs partly to our schizophrenia, to a less extent to manic-depressive insanity.' (Bleuler, E. *Textbook of Psychiatry*, tr. by Brill, A.A., Macmillan, New York, 1930)

paranoia, acquired Krafft-Ebing described two principal forms of paranoia: (1) *original paranoia*, developing before or at puberty—always hereditary; (2) *acquired paranoia*, developing late in life, particularly at the involutional period.

paranoia, acute *Obs.* 'Paranoia coming on without prodromes and characterized by a delusion of vague persecutions without persecutors.' (Foster, F.P. *Medical Dictionary*, Appleton, New York, 1892–94).

paranoia, acute hallucinatory (ha-lū'si-nà-tō-rē) Coined by Ziehen, this term denotes what he considered a separate syndrome, characterized by delusions and hallucinations resembling paranoia, but regarded in current psychiatry as a phase of schizophrenia.

paranoia, alcoholic (al-kō-hol'ik) Delusions originating in jealousy are not uncommon in states of alcoholism. As a rule, however, unless a predisposition has been released by alcohol and continues upon the cessation of imbibition, the paranoid reaction does not last long. At other times a clinical syndrome not at all dissimilar symptomatically from paranoia may be associated with alcoholism, though more commonly the paranoid syndrome is more closely identified with schizophrenia.

paranoia, ambitious *Obs.* Paranoia in which the syndrome is associated with delusions of omnipotence.

paranoia, amorous 'The condition of acute excitement with many hallucinations, general restlessness and abnormal motor activity constitutes, when coloured by religious ideas, what used to be called religious mania. The disorder where the patient shows an emotional excitement which is bound up with some sentiment, and is continually agitating for some wild social scheme, is similar to the manic phase of manic-depressive psychosis. These two varieties constitute the so-called "eccentric paranoia," while the paranoid jealous reaction of the erotic patient is the so-called "amorous paranoia."' (Craig, M. and Beaton, T. *Psychological Medicine*, 4th ed., Churchill, London, 1926) The patient with amorous

paranoia develops delusions of marital infidelity in relation to his spouse. According to Freud's analysis of the Schreber case, such delusions are based on a denial of unconscious homosexuality: 'It is not I who love the man, it is she.'

paranoia completa (pà-rà-noi'à kôm-plā'tà) (Mod.L. 'complete, perfect, paranoia') A term coined by Magnan (*délire chronique à évolution systématique*) equivalent to present conceptions of the paranoid form of schizophrenia.

paranoia, degenerative (par-à-noi'à) *Obs.* A form of paranoia in which the degenerative defects are not profound and do not reduce the patients to the last degree of the scale of degenerates.' (Foster, F.P. *Medical Dictionary*, Appleton, New York, 1892–94.)

paranoia dissociativa (pà-rà-noi'à dēs-sô-kē-à-tē'và) (Mod.L. 'dissociative paranoia') An expression coined by Ziehen to designate states of acute confusion (amentia) with paranoid elements.

paranoia, eccentric (par-à-noi'à) See *paranoia, amorous.*

paranoia hallucinatoria (pà-rà-noi'à hàl-lōō-kē-nà-to'rē-à) *Obs.* Paranoia with hallucinations.

paranoia hallucinatoria acuta (à-kōō'tà) (Mod.L. 'acute hallucinatory paranoia') *Obs.* 'Paranoia characterized by sudden hallucinations, especially of hearing, accompanied by ideas of grandeur. There may be insane impulses or complete dejection.' (Foster, F.P. *Medical Dictionary*, Appleton, New York, 1892–94)

paranoia hallucinatoria chronica (krô'nē-kà) (Mod.L. 'chronic hallucinatory paranoia') *Obs.* 'Paranoia having a slow beginning and a remitting course. Hallucinations and delusions of persecution appear first, and at the end of a certain time the ideas of grandeur become prominent.' (Foster, F.P. *Medical Dictionary*, Appleton, New York, 1892–94)

paranoia hypochondriaca (hē-pô-kôn-drē'à-kà) (Mod.L. 'hypochondriacal paranoia') *Obs.* 'The troubles of general sensibility form the foundation of the delusions of persecution accompanied by illusions and hallucinations.' (Foster, F.P. *Medical Dictionary*, Appleton, New York, 1892–94)

paranoia, idiopathic (par-à-noi'à id-i-ō-path'ik) *Obs.* Sandler thus denotes syndromes of paranoia that begin in early childhood.

paranoia, intermediate *Obs.* Paranoia in which there are no delusions, but a tendency to quibbling or quarreling.

paranoia, involutional By this term Kleist refers to a paranoid syndrome not uncommonly set free during the involutional period.

paranoia, latent This infrequently used expression refers to the paranoid condition presumably inactive or hidden from others but not necessarily from the patient. Its presence is more surmised than proven and the implication appears to have support when the patient experiences clearcut paranoid reactions in the form of episodes.

paranoia, litigious (li-ti′jus) Same as *paranoia querulans* (q.v.).

paranoia, mystic Pike's term for psychosis of association. See *association, psychosis of.*

paranoia, negative Paranoia in which the false beliefs of the person have to do with matters *favorable* to him rather than with those *unfavorable*. The delusionary material is characterized by praise, protection, and defense instead of persecution, accusation, destruction, and the like. Dr. Lewin introduced the term negative paranoia in referring to a patient who falsely believed that 'everyone was organized to do him good.' (*Bulletin of the American Psychoanalytic Association,* December 1950, p. 45) It is obvious that *good* instead of *evil* is the negation of the latter, and this suggested to Dr. Lewin the term negative paranoia.

paranoia, original See *paranoia, acquired.*

paranoia originaria (pà-rà-noi′à ô-rē-gē-nä′rē-à) (L. 'original paranoia') Sanders coined this rarely used expression to denote a paranoid state originating in childhood.

paranoia, periodic (par-à-noi′à) See *paranoia, abortive.*

paranoia persecutoria (pà-rà-noi′à per-se-kōō-tō′rē-à) (L. 'persecutory paranoia') *Obs.* Paranoia in which the delusions of persecution are especially prominent.

paranoia querulans (kwe′rōō-làns) (Mod. L. 'complaining paranoia') A form of paranoia characterized by more or less incessant quarrelsomeness due to alleged

persecution. Often starting from a factual injustice, the patient weaves a delusional trend about it and then seeks redress at the hands of the law.

paranoia, reformatory (par-à-noi′à) (that aims at reforms) 'That host of unbalanced dreamers who are frequently known as "cranks," and who may be further classified on the basis of the content of their delusional system into *inventive, reformatory, religious* and *erotic* varieties. These patients have made some wonderful invention, are destined to carry on great reforms, are the viceregent of God, or believe themselves beloved by some royal person.' (White, W.A. *Outlines of Psychiatry,* 12th ed., Nervous & Mental Disease Publishing Company, Washington, D.C., 1929)

paranoia religiosa (pà-rà-noi′à re-lē-gē-ō′zà) (L. 'religious paranoia') *Obs.* Paranoia characterized by religious delusions.

paranoia, rudimentary (par-à-noi′à) 'What distinguished the delusions of these patients from those of pronounced paranoia was their *vagueness* and the *absence of systematic working up.* Their fears and hopes were of a more indefinite kind, were brought forward as indications and conjectures, or they consisted in a strong personal valuation of actual events, which was not too far removed from the onesidedness of normal individuals. As far as could be known, no internal connection of the individual component parts of the delusion with a paranoiac view of life had taken place. . . . At present the assumption appears to me to be well founded, that cases of undeveloped, "rudimentary" paranoia would not only fit in with our view of the character of the disease, but also come actually under observation.' (Kraepelin, E. *Manic-Depressive Insanity and Paranoia,* tr. by Barclay, R.M., Livingstone, Edinburgh, 1921) The expression was coined by Morselli.

paranoia, secondary An older expression, often synonymous with *dementia, secondary.*

paranoia senilis (pà-rà-noi′à se-nē′lēs) (L. 'senile paranoia') A paranoid syndrome appearing during the senile period. 'The forms showing a clear sensorium with delusional formation and eventually hallucinations are designated as *senile paranoia* (or paranoid forms of dementia senilis); they are not frequent. Such people think they are spied on by neighbors, teased, robbed especially by those living in the same house; everywhere they find references to themselves, and confirmation of their ideas in voices, etc.' (Blueler, E. *Textbook of Psychiatry,* tr. by Brill, A.A., Macmillan, New York, 1930)

paranoia simplex (sĕm′pleks) (L. 'simple paranoia') *Obs.* 'Acute or chronic paranoia in which there are bodily as well as mental disturbances. The latter are characterized by the existence of some one of the many monomanias.' (Foster, F.P. *Medical Dictionary,* Appleton, New York, 1892–94)

paranoia sine delirio (sē′ne dā-lē′rē-ō) (L. 'paranoia without delirium') *Obsnt.* Reasoning monomania.

paranoia somatica (sō-mat′i-kà) This term apparently applies to the close link between paranoid delusions and hypochondriacal complaints. Very frequently in clinical psychiatry a patient with paranoid symptoms also has many somatic complaints. This is probably an attempt on the part of the ego to establish causality. It is as if the patient were saying: 'if I am being followed and if they are focusing a machine on me to influence me then I have terrible aches and pains and burning sensations wherever the machines strike me.' (Tausk, V. 'On the Origin of the "Influencing Machine" in Schizophrenia,' *Psychoanalytic Quarterly 2,* 522, 1933) See *personification.*

paranoia, true (par-à-noi′à) Same as *paranoia, idiopathic.*

paranoid, paranoidal (par′à-noid, -noi′-dal) Relating to or resembling paranoia. Psychiatrists today speak of *paranoid conditions,* usually referring to clinical states that occupy a position between paranoia and the paranoid form of schizophrenia. In the eighth edition of his textbook Kraepelin uses the term *paraphrenia* to designate this group. He divided the group into four parts: (a) *paraphrenia systematica,* the equivalent perhaps of what today is known as paranoia; (b) *paraphrenia expansiva,* seen only in women and characterized by ideas of grandeur with exaltation; (c) *paraphrenia confabulans,* characterized by delusions of persecution and grandeur based upon falsification of memory; (d) *paraphrenia phantastica,* with auditory hallucinations, un-

systematized delusions, and phantastic accounts of adventures.

paranoid dementia gravis (dē-men′shi-à grà′vis) See *dementia paranoides gravis.*

paranoid dementia mitis (mī′tis) See *dementia paranoides gravis.*

paranoid personality See *personality pattern disturbance.*

paranoid schizophrenia See *schizophrenia, paranoid.*

paranormal (par-à-nor′mal) Alongside or beyond the normal, as in paranormal cognition (telepathy). See *perception, extrasensory; telepathy.*

paranosic (-nō′sik) Relating to the primary advantage derived from an illness or paranosis.

parapathic proviso See *proviso, parapathic.*

parapathy (pà-rap′à-thē) Stekel's term for neurosis; he objects to the word neurosis because connotatively it indicates a functional nervous disorder. Parapathy, on the other hand, indicates that psychiatrists deal with emotions, not with nerves.

paraphasia (par-à-fā′zhi-à) Perversion of the power of speech, practically a partial or milder form of aphasia. Accordingly paraphasia is caused by some pathological lesion in the brain and its various manifestations may repeat those of the aphasias only in less severe form.

paraphemia (-fē′mi-à) *Rare.* Distorted speech (occasionally manifesting neurotic lisping).

paraphia (par-af′i-à) Perverted sense of touch. Common in organic and psychic conditions. Impairment of tactile sensibility is often observed in hysteria.

paraphilia (par-à-fil′i-à) Sexual perversion; see *perversion.*

paraphobia The term mild fear or phobia designates a degree of fear which is under fairly good control, though the task of controlling it irks the individual.

paraphora (par-af′ō-rà) A mild state of mental disorder.

paraphrasia (par-à-frā′zhi-à) Perverted sense or faculty of constructing a phrase; a speech disorder of a less severe nature than aphrasia from which it differs in degree, but not in kind. The difficulties of *aphrasia* (q.v.) and, consequently, of paraphrasia are of mental origin and are not due to cerebral injury as in aphasia. The phenomenon is especially common in psychiatry, being observed in vivid form, for example, in the schizophrenias. Thus, a patient, wishing to refer to a certain person, says 'Saturday' instead; it was on a Saturday that a particularly intense emotional reaction took place between the patient and the person in question.

'We shall have to keep apart two chief forms of paraphrasic disorders; firstly, *derailments in finding words,* secondly, *disorders in connected speech.*' (Kraepelin, E. *Dementia Praecox and Paraphrenia,* tr. by Barclay, R.M., Livingstone, Edinburgh, 1919)

paraphrasia, thematic (thē-mat′ik) This expression was used by Arndt to denote incoherent speech 'wandering' from the theme or subject.

paraphrasia vesana (pà-rà-frà′zē-à vā-sä′nà) (L. 'insane paraphrasia') '. . . if the formation of ideas and of thought is disturbed in its whole extent, so that it is only with difficulty that a single proper judgment can be expressed, and if new words are coined to express the imperfect and strange thoughts, such neologisms being but maimed fragments of regular words, veritable heaps of syllables, then we have *paraphrasia vesana,* an effect of profound psychic decadence.' (Bianchi, L. *A Text-Book of Psychiatry,* tr. by MacDonald, J.H., Baillière, Tindall & Cox, London, 1906)

paraphrenesis (par-à-frē-nē′sis) *Obs.* Delirium.

paraphrenia (par-à-frē′ni-à) Kraepelin uses the term in a special sense; see *paranoid.* Freud uses the expression to refer to dementia praecox or schizophrenia. (Freud, S. *Collected Papers,* vol. 4, tr. by Riviere, J., Leonard and Virginia Woolf and The Institute of Psychoanalysis, London, 1924–25)

In the early part of the 19th century Guislain used this term synonymously with that of the clinical syndrome then known as *folly* (q.v.).

The most common usage of the term today is to denote a disorder characterized by phantastic, absurd, paralogical delusions without deterioration, dementia, or loss of contact with reality except in the area of the delusional system. In paranoid schizophrenia, on the other

hand, there is deterioration and splitting off of many of the psychic functions, while in paranoia the delusions are so logical, at least on the surface, as to appear to be little more than an extension of the premorbid personality.

paraphrenia confabulans (pà-rà-fre′nē-à kôn-fä′boo-làns) (Mod.L. 'confabulation paraphrenia') See *paranoid.*

paraphrenia expansiva (eks-pàn-sē′và) (Mod.L. 'expansive paraphrenia') See *paranoid.*

paraphrenia, involutional (par-à-frē′ni-à) It is generally recognized that there are two principal psychiatric syndromes associated with the period of involution: one closely resembles manic-depressive psychosis; the other, schizophrenia. Lerko calls the latter *involutional paraphrenia.*

paraphrenia phantastica (pà-rà-fre′nē-à fàn-tàs′tē-kà) (Mod.L. 'phantastic paraphrenia') See *paranoid.*

paraphrenia, pre-senile (par-à-frē′ni-à) Among the many psychiatric syndromes having their onset after the involutional and before the senile phase of life, there is a schizophrenic form which Albrecht calls pre-senile paraphrenia.

paraphrenia systematica (pà-rà-fre′nē-à sēs-tä-mà′tē-kà) (Mod. L. 'systematic paraphrenia') See *paranoid.*

paraphrenitis (par-à-frē-nī′tis) *Obs.* Mental derangement in general.

paraphrosyne (pà-rà-fros′i-nē) *Obs.* 'It is a transitory insanity without a fever. A *delirium.* A symptomatic madness.' (Motherby, G. *A New Medical Dictionary,* 5th ed., for J. Johnson, St. Paul's Church-Yard, etc., London, 1801)

paraplegia (par-à-plē′ji-à) Paralysis of the musculature of the lower extremities and of the torso, the latter to a lesser extent; when the upper extremities are paralyzed, the condition is called *superior paraplegia.*

paraplegia, ataxic (a-tak′sik) Unsteadiness of station and gait in association with paraplegia.

paraplegia, hereditary spastic (spas′tik) A familial disorder, usually affecting several siblings and occurring more frequently in males, which begins between the ages of 3 and 15 years with progressive destruction of the pyramidal tracts of the spinal cord, beginning in the lower limbs. To a lesser degree, there is also destruction of the posterior columns and of the cells of the precentral cortex. The disease is slowly progressive with a fatal termination after many years. Mentality is usually normal.

parapraxis (par-à-prak'sis) Misaction. Freud applies this term to symptomatic acts such as slips of the tongue, mislaying of objects, etc.

parapsychology (-sī-kol'ō-jē) The branch of psychology which deals with paranormal behavior and events such as telepathy, precognition, and clairvoyance, which are not explicable by present-day 'natural' laws. See *perception, extra-sensory.*

parapsychosis (-sī-kō'sis) See *apsychosis.*

para-reaction Meyer refers to the reactions 'characterized by essentially formally correct, but short-circuited, reasoning, amounting to delusion formation. The tenacity of the false beliefs, and their growth and systematization are the earmarks of the insatiable need which is the affective investment of the complex material at work.' (Muncie, W. *Psychobiology and Psychiatry,* Mosby, St. Louis, 1939) It includes such reactions as paranoia and paranoid states.

parasexuality Perverted sexuality, comprising such practices as pederasty, voyeurism, pedophilia, sodomy, sadism, masochism, etc.

'The various kinds of parasexuality are usually connected with a *premature appearance of the sex impulse* and hence can become known very early, at the age of three or four.' (Bleuler, E. *Textbook of Psychiatry,* tr. by Brill, A.A., Macmillan, New York, 1930)

parasitophobia (par-à-sī-tō-fō'bi-à) Fear of parasites.

parasomnia (par-à-som'ni-à) Perverted or disordered sleep; a term coined to denote a sleep disturbance associated with lesion(s) of the nervous system.

'Sleep is essentially a complex vegetative phenomenon, and the governing mechanism, I believe, is not the cortex but rather diencephalic and mesencephalic centers in which there are concentrated so many other vegetative functions. . . . Until recently we have had **very** little insight as to how such a mechanism, situated in the diencephalon

and mesencephalon, can bring about sleep. Perhaps a clue is afforded by the work recently done on cerebral concussion. The unconsciousness brought about by brain injury has some points of resemblance to sleep. In fact, Geoffrey Jefferson, the English neurosurgeon, would like to speak of traumatic unconsciousness as "parasomnia." Jefferson also stresses the part played by lesions in the region "extending caudally from the upper half of the fourth ventricle to the hypothalamus cephalad," in causing parasomnia.' (Brook, S., discussing Davison, C., and DeMuth, E.L., 'Disturbances in Sleep Mechanism' [A Clinicopathologic Study], in *Journal of Nervous and Mental Disease 100,* 305, 1944)

parastriate lobule (par-à-strī'āt lob'ūl) See *lobe, occipital.*

parasympathetic nervous system (par-à-sim-pa-the'tik) See *autonomic nervous system.*

parasympathicotonia (par-à-sim-path-i-kō-tō'ni-à) Originally, in constitutional medicine this term denoted a particular hyperirritability of the whole parasympathetic system; now it has become identical with *vagotonia* since the latter's meaning is stretched to cover the entire parasympathetic system.

parateresiomania (-tē-rē-si-ō-mā'ni-à) Morbid impulse to observe; peepingmania.

parathymia (-thim'i-à, -thī'mi-à) Perversion of mood. When a condition or occasion that should produce a certain mood evokes the opposite of the expected reaction, the phenomenon is called parathymia. A patient, having asked for a new suit so that he might enjoy a coming party, was enraged when he received it.

'Parathymias are often indissolubly connected with *alteration of the impulses.*' (Bleuler, E. *Textbook of Psychiatry,* tr. by Brill, A.A., Macmillan, New York, 1930) Parathymia is one of the affect disturbances seen in the schizophrenias.

parathyroidism (-thī'roid-iz'm) Excessive functioning of the parathyroid gland.

paratonia progressiva (pà-rà-tō'nē-à prō-gre-sē'và) Bernstein's term for dementia praecox (schizophrenia).

paratype (par'à-tīp) The sum of all external, or *peristatic,* factors acting upon the phenotypical development of an organism or bringing about the individual manifestation of a genetic character. See *biotype*.

paravariation (par-à-vâr-i-ā'shun) In genetics, synonym of *modification* (q.v.).

parenchyma, parenchyme (pà-reng'ki-mà, -'kīm) This term is used especially in constitutional medicine to contrast the tissues which are peculiar to the individual organs and serve to distinguish one organ from another, with the tissues derived from the *mesenchyme* (q.v.).

According to the theories of Godin and Viola, the *parenchyme* has to do with morphological differentiation and morphological evolution, and the mesenchyme with mass and ponderal evolution. In normal growth, phases of growth in width alternate with phases of growth in length. When there is evolutionary disharmony through the preponderance of one system over the other, the normal or average human constitution deviates into either the *megalosplanchnic* or the *microsplanchnic* type.

parents, dethronement of The process termed the dethronement of the parents begins in the so-called latency period, when the child sets up a new ideal, as it were, on the throne hitherto occupied by the reigning ideals—his parents. In the earliest stage, the young child develops as part of his personality or character certain ideals and values: the parents serve as the child's model and he identifies himself with them, making their standards and ideals his own. As the child grows, however, he begins to form relationships with other individuals, new models and new ideals come into his consciousness, and he makes further identifications. In Fenichel's words, 'it is rather characteristic for normal development that ideals and values become more independent of the infantile models when the libidinal ties to the family are abandoned.' (Fenichel, O. *The Psychoanalytic Theory of Neurosis*, Norton, New York, 1945)

parents, problem The term refers to parents who, because of their own unresolved unconscious conflicts, manifest unhealthy attitudes toward their children, who, in turn, become problem children. Consequently, the problems of children may in part be merely a reflection of the problems of the parent or parents. The morbid attitudes of parents, such as perfectionis-

tic, overconscientious, overly critical, overindulgent, over-ambitious, over-anxious, and rejecting attitudes, may play a major role in setting up sequences which later cause symptoms in their child.

parent-surrogate See *surrogate*.

parepithymia (par-ep-i-thim'i-à, -thī-mi-à) Perverted desire or craving.

parerethisis (par-ē-reth'i-sis) *Obs.* Perverted excitement.

parergasia (par-ēr-gas'i-à) Perverted functioning; mismatched action. In the eighth German edition of his *Text-book of Psychiatry*, Kraepelin uses the term to refer to a form of parabulia in which the impulse to carry out an act is interrupted before the patient takes the first step toward performing the act. The interruption is occasioned by what he calls cross impulses, that is, by impulses which cross the path of the first impulse and thus check its further course. The process is also known as *derailment of volition*. For example, the patient, who has the impulse to reach for a cup at the table, suddenly brushes his hair. 'The patient who is to show his tongue, opens his eyes widely instead; he flings the cup away instead of putting it to his mouth.' (Kraepelin, E. *Dementia Praecox and Paraphrenia*, tr. by Barclay, R.M., Livingstone, Edinburgh, 1919)

This is a psychiatric reaction-type characterized usually by deep regression, abandonment of reality, and reconstruction of the conception of the self, and by delusions and hallucinations; in other words, this term, as used by Adolf Meyer, refers to schizophrenia and to schizophrenoid syndromes.

parerosia (par-ē-rō'si-à) *Rare.* Sexual perversion.

paresis (pà-rē'sis, par'ē-sis) Partial paralysis.

paresis, alcoholic See *pseudo-paresis, alcoholic*.

paresis, general General paresis (general paralysis of the insane, dementia paralytica, Bayle's disease) is a psychiatric disorder characterized by mental and physical symptoms. It is always due to syphilis of the central nervous system. It is, as a rule, a gradually progressive, chronic disease occurring five to twenty years or longer after the appearance of the chancre. It may occur in an asymptomatic form in which no mental symptoms are observed but where physical signs and laboratory findings indicate paresis. A hereditary type may occasionally be observed in the form of juvenile general paresis. Pathologically, the disease is characterized by an inflammation of the meninges, particularly of the brain, and of a diffuse inflammation and degeneration of the parenchyma of the cerebral cortex. At times the cranial nerves and often the pathways for the pupillary reflexes are involved in the pathologic process. The symptoms may include mild or severe paralytic attacks, slurring speech, ataxia, Argyll Robertson pupils, coarse tremors, intellectual disorders, emotional instability, and psychiatric syndrome of the schizophrenic or manic-depressive order.

The blood and spinal fluid Wassermann reactions are positive, the number of lymphocytes in the spinal fluid is increased, and there is a typical 'paretic' gold curve.

paresis, juvenile Juvenile general paresis is the result of 'inherited' syphilis and does not differ essentially from the adult form. The disease is usually observed in children twelve to fourteen years of age. The early symptoms may be motor for the most part, such as stumbling and clumsiness in walking. With this is associated an incipient disturbance of speech with a freshly budding dullness in school. Then occurs a progressive mental deterioration, school knowledge is finally absolutely lost, and the dementia becomes profound. The motor symptoms steadily progress in severity, contractures of the extremities develop quite early, and the patient becomes absolutely helpless.

paresis, Lissauer type (Heinrich Lissauer, German neurologist, 1861–91) An atypical syndrome of general paresis characterized by (1) unusually well-retained intellectual functions and (2) severe focal symptoms, such as apoplectiform attacks, hemiplegia, aphasia, etc.

paresthesia (par-es-thē'zhi-à) Perverted sense of touch. Unpleasant sensation, such as tingling, burning, tickling, etc. caused by a tactile stimulus.

paretic (pà-ret'ik, -rē'tik) Relating to or suffering from paresis.

paretic curve See *Lange's colloidal gold reaction.*

Parkinsonism (James Parkinson, English physician, 1775–1824) See *paralysis agitans.*

parole A system of supervision of a patient who is away from the hospital or any of its adjuncts—such as colonies—prior to his legal discharge. While on parole, a patient is considered as still on the books of the hospital, and may, if necessary, be returned to the hospital without the necessity for formal court action.

paroniria (par-ō-nī'ri-à) Morbid dreaming; sleep disturbance. See *ecphronia.*

paroniria ambulans (pà-rô-nē'rē-à àm'boo-làns) (Mod.L. 'walking paroniria') *Obs.* Somnambulism.

parorexia (par-ō-rek'si-à) Perverted appetite.

parosmia (par-oz'mi-à) Perversion of the sense of smell. It may be occasioned by organic or by psychic causes.

From the psychic point of view it enters prominently into many psychiatric conditions, being particularly important in many psychoneurotic states (see *osphresiolagnia; osphresiophilia*). It gains significance in the paranoid type of schizophrenia in the form of olfactory hallucinations.

parosphresis (par-os-frē'sis) *Parosmia* (q.v.).

paroxysmal cerebral dysrhythmia (paroks'mal ser'e-bral dis-rith'mi-à) *Epilepsy* (q.v.).

Parry-Romberg's syndrome See *hemiatrophy, facial.*

pars pro toto (pàrs' prō tō'tō) (L. 'part for the whole') This expression is used in psychiatry to describe a special form of psychic displacement. When a part of an object or a person stands for the whole object or person, the process is known as *pars pro toto.* A voice, a gesture, some physical trait, a bit of wearing apparel—each may be substituted for the total individual.

part-brain See *third nervous system.*

parthenogenesis (pär-thē-nō-jen'e-sis) Virgin reproduction. *Biol.* The uniparental mode of sexual reproduction, in which an egg develops into a new individual without having first been fertilized by a spermatozoön. Although organisms produced in this way have only one parent, they originate sexually, as they undergo a process similar to that of typical maturation. See *reproduction*.

The best known example of parthenogenetic origin is supplied by the honey bee, in which the haploid egg, if unfertilized, develops into a male individual (drone).

parthenophobia Fear of girls.

partialism (pär′shal-iz′m) A form of sexual perversion in which the subject seeks gratification of the sexual impulse from a certain part of the partner's body, as the leg, thigh, buttock, and so on. Partialism must be differentiated from fetishism, in which the partner is eliminated and displaced by an object symbolic of the genitals.

partiality, sexual A rarely used synonym for fetishism; sexual idolatry.

participation, law of The law of participation, formulated by Lévy-Bruhl, accounts for the fact that it is possible for primitive peoples to believe that they are certain definite individuals, yet at the same time they are others. The phenomenon is commonly observed in schizophrenic patients.

'This simultaneous participation in several individuals is described by our patients as taking place in a peculiarly diffuse and complex manner. Thus the teacher . . . who felt himself in sexual union with a girl who was at a distance, said that the girl for him was Eve, while he himself was Adam; but he was also the serpent; he had found this out, because "things were always going around in circles and convolutions."' (Storch, A. *The Primitive Archaic Forms in Schizophrenia,* tr. by Willard, C., Nervous and Mental Disease Publishing Company, New York and Washington, 1924)

participation, mystical See *participation, law of.*

part-instinct By this expression Freud denotes a secondary representation of the two principal innate instincts. Thus, most of the impulses clinically demonstrable are part-instincts or instinct-components. What one actually experiences is not the instinct itself, but the instinct as it is combined with a wish, urge, or striving. The term is generally restricted to instinctual manifestations of the infantile period.

partitive (pär′ti-tiv) In Burrow's usage the term refers to behavior-processes whose interaction socially has become independent of and at variance with the primary motivation of man's organism as a whole. Partitive are the processes mediated by the organism's part-functions restricted to the cephalic segment and making contact only with the part-features (symbols) of outer objects. Partitive behavior is a function of the socio-cortical or symbolic segment with the development of language or of an inter-symbolic nexus of communication; this segment tends to supersede and dominate the behavior of man's organism in its phylo-autonomic primacy. The term partitive applies to those feeling-reactions which have ceased to issue as a direct expression of the organism as a totality but which have been secondarily displaced into the symbolic segment and now issue in mere images of feeling, or in affects. In accordance with investigations in phylobiology the artificial supremacy of this partitive (affecto-symbolic) mode of behavior over the primary motivation of the organism as a whole constitutes the basis of both individual and social neurosis. Contrasted with total, organismic. Synonyms: affective, inter-cortical, symbolic. (Burrow, T. *The Biology of Human Conflict,* Macmillan, New York, 1937)

passio hypochondriaca (pà′sē-ō hē-pō-kon-drē-à′kà) *Obs.* Hypochondriasis.

passive-aggressive personality See *personality trait disturbance.*

passivism (pas′iv-iz′m) A form of sexual perversion in which the subject, usually male, is submissive to the will of the partner in the unnatural sexual practices.

passivity (pa-siv′i-tē) One of the several modalities of adaptation. For example, it is possible for the organism to adapt itself to its environment by going either forward to meet it or backward to escape it. The first procedure would be termed the modality of activity in adaptive maneuver, while the latter would be termed the modality of passivity.

In transference neurosis the consequences of inhibition of the modality of activity may find the organism simply abandoning this modality and falling back upon the modality of passivity. In traumatic neurosis, however, the modality of passivity cannot be resorted to when activity is inhibited, since it is impossible for the organism to remain completely passive to the outer world. One can retreat from an inhibiting *person*, but complete retreat from the inhibiting *forces* of the outer world is impossible—short of death.

past-pointing See *pointing*.

pathema (på-thē′må) *Obs.* Disease; often mental disease.

pathematology (på-the-ma-tol′ō-jē) A general term for pathology, although it is ordinarily used to denote mental pathology. It has been replaced by the term psychopathology.

pathergasia (path-ēr-gas′i-å) Adolf Meyer's term for personality maladjustment in association with organic, functional, or structural changes. It is approximately equivalent to Ferenczi's *pathoneurosis*.

pathetism (path′ē-tiz′m) *Obs.* Synonym of mesmerism and hypnotism.

pathic (path′ik) Pertaining to or affected by disease or disorder.

pathic *Obs.* A male passive partner who submits to unnatural sexual practices; apparently pederasty. See *catamite; passivism*.

patho-, path- (path′o-) Combining form meaning suffering, passion, disease, from Gr. *páthos,* suffering, disease.

pathobiology (path-o-bi-ol′ō-jē) A general term referring to the study of diseased or disordered conditions arising from a biological source.

pathocratia, pathocratoria (-krat′i-å, krat-ō′ri-å) *Obs.* Self-restraint.

pathoctonus (på-thok′tō-nus) *Obs.* Killing of passion; self-restraint.

pathocure (path′ō-kūr) The disappearance of a neurosis upon the outbreak of an organic disease. Pathocure is seen in moral masochists whose neurosis is first of all, unconsciously, a suffering that pacifies the superego: the neurosis becomes superfluous as soon as it is replaced by another kind of suffering. Pathocure is the opposite of pathoneurosis, which is a neurosis developing as a result of somatic disease.

A pathocure was observed in a masochist who developed pulmonary tuberculosis. The patient had been a chronic failure in everything he undertook. Under analysis, he began to gain some insight into the masochistic nature of his character defenses. Analysis was interrupted by the tuberculous process, and after the patient's release from the hospital he went back to work. He functioned well on his job and previous symptomatology did not reappear. The disease in this instance was one especially suitable for the character type of the patient—it was chronic, it necessitated definite limitations of activity, and the likelihood of recurrence was ever present. Other pathocures of a more temporary nature have been observed when the organic disease was short-lived and required no permanent or long-term changes in the patient's way of living. In such cases, neurotic symptoms tend to reappear with the disappearance of the organic condition.

pathoformic (path-ō-for′mik) This term refers to the beginning of pathological states; to the symptoms occurring in the transitional stage between health and disease or disorder proper.

pathogenesis, pathogenesy, pathogeny (path-ō-jen′e-sis, -jen′e-sē, på-thoj′e-nē) The way in which a disease or disorder originated or developed; also called nosogenesis.

For example, from the psychoanalytic point of view it is possible 'to trace back the predisposition to neurosis to its source in the developmental history of the libido, and to reveal the factors operative in this predisposition as inborn varieties of sexual constitution and the effects of external experiences in early childhood.' (Freud, S. *Collected Papers,* vol. 2, tr. by Riviere, J., Leonard and Virginia Woolf and The Institute of Psychoanalysis, London, 1924–25) Freud lists some of the causes, as (a) *frustration, due to* alteration in *the external world;* 'the patient falls ill from an event'; 'reality denies gratification to the libido'; (b) *frustration* derived *from* certain trends within *the ego;* reality offers the individual gratification; 'he falls ill of the attempt to adapt himself to reality and to fulfil the *requisitions of reality,* for in doing so he is confronted with insurmountable inward obstacles'; (c) *inhibition of development,* which is an exaggeration of (b), namely a 'succumbing before the requisitions of reality'; 'the libido has never forsaken its infantile fixations'; (d) *damming-up of libido:* 'as a result of reaching a certain period of life, and in accordance with regular biological processes, the *quantity* of libido in their mental economy has increased to an extent which by itself suffices to upset the balance of health and establish the conditions for neurosis.' (Freud, S. *Collected Papers*, vol. 2, tr. by Riviere, J., Leonard and Virginia Woolf and The Institute of Psychoanalysis, London, 1924–25)

pathognomonic, pathognomic (pà-thog-nō-mon'ik, path-og-nom'ik) Typical or thoroughly characteristic of a disease; diagnostic.

pathognomy (pà-thog'nō-mē) The science of recognizing or diagnosing a disease or pathological condition.

pathognostic (pà-thog-nos'tik) Pathognom(on)ic.

pathography (pà-thog'rà-fē) Description of a disease.

patho-hysteria 'Organic illness can result not only in a narcissistic, but eventually, preserving the libidinal object-relation, in a "transference-neurotic" (hysterical) disturbance of the libido. I should call this condition patho-hysteria (disease-hysteria), as contrasted with Freud's sexual neurosis, in which the disturbance of libido is the primary, the organic disturbance of function the secondary thing (hysterical blindness, nervous asthma).' (Ferenczi, S. *Further Contributions to the Theory and Technique of Psycho-Analysis*, tr. by Suttie, J.I., Leonard and Virginia Woolf and The Institute of Psychoanalysis, London, 1926)

patholesia (path-ō-lē'z[h]i-à) *Rare.* Any impairment or abnormality of the will. See *will, disturbances of.*

pathology (pà-thol'ō-jē) The science of the nature of diseases.

pathology, semantic This term is used in relation to the various anatomo-pathological disturbances that may affect the function of speech. Such lesions may be found on the tongue itself, in the hypoglossal nerve, in the motor cortex, in the cortico-bulbar tracts, or elsewhere in the central nervous system. Destruction of neural tissue in the so-called quadrilateral space of Marie may seriously impair the function of speech without alterations of the tongue itself or its muscular mechanism. Other lesions, centrally located in the brain, may impair not only speech but also the capacity to understand the meaning of words. (Seliger, R.V., *et al.*

Contemporary Criminal Hygiene, Oakridge Press, Baltimore, 1946) See *speech disorders.*

pathomania *Obs.* Mania without delirium; it was synonymous with *moral insanity.*

pathomimesis, pathomimicry (path-o-mimē'sis, -mim'ik-rē) The mimicry of a disease or disorder; not uncommon in hysteria and hysteroid conditions.

pathomorphism (-mor'fiz'm) Abnormal morphology. For example, extremes of bodily build, such as are observed among certain individuals with an asthenic, pyknic, or dysplastic habitus, are said to be pathomorphic.

pathoneurosis (-nū-rō'sis) Whenever there is an organic disease a varying quantum of emotions is directed to the sick organ or to a mental image of the sick organ as conceived by the patient. The well-adjusted individual gives adequate care (including emotions) to his illness, while he, who is so disposed, gives an inordinate quantity of feelings. An entire psychiatric syndrome may be invested in a sick organ. For example, the patient, with symptoms of appendicitis, may give expression to an underlying psychoneurosis, the type of psychoneurosis varying with the disposition of the individual. This condition is called pathoneurosis.

Ferenczi regarded pathoneurosis as a special form of narcissistic neurosis 'which can result as a consequence of falling ill or from injury to the bodily parts or organs, especially of the erogenous zones, which are most important for life, or highly prized by the ego. The conception of the *Pathoneuroses* culminates in the idea that quantities of libido can be stored up not only within the ego in general, but in sick organs themselves (or in their psychical representations). . . .' (Hallos, S. and Ferenczi, S. *Psychoanalysis and the Psychic Disorder of General Paresis,* tr. by Barnes and Keil, Nervous and Mental Disease Publishing Company, New York, 1925)

pathopatridalgia (-pat-ri-dal'ji-à) *Obs.* Homesickness or nostalgia.

pathophobia *Obs.* Fear of disease; synonymous with *hypochondriasis.*

pathophrenesis (-fren'e-sis) A nonspecific term for disturbance in the intelligence, regardless of its basis.

pathoplasty (path'ō-plas-tē) Birnbaum thus refers to the *form* of a disease, in contradistinction to the term pathogenesis, which relates to the *cause.*

pathopoeesia, pathopoiesis (path-ō-pē-ē'si-à, -poi-ē'sis) *Obs.* Synonymous with *pathogenesis.*

pathopsychology (-sī-kol'ō-jē) Wilhelm Specht suggested this term for the study of abnormal psychic data from the point of view of general psychology. He proposed to restrict the expression *psychopathology* to the study of the same data from the standpoint of medical psychology.

pathopsychosis (-sī-kō'sis) When an organic process, such as brain tumor, general paresis, etc. gives rise to a psychotic condition, the syndrome is known as a pathopsychosis. See *pathoneurosis.*

pathosis, attitudinal (pa-thō'sis) Thorne's term for a type of personality disorder, seen frequently in compensation and post-accident cases, in which the patient's attitude and self-righteous belief that because he was injured he cannot work or deserves special consideration forms a central core in all his thinking about the effects of his injury. Kamman distinguishes this reaction from traumatic neurosis (which term he would reserve for latent psychoneurosis precipitated by accident) and from compensation neurosis (where, although it is usually unconscious, the basic motive is the desire for cash compensation), mainly because of the conscious volitional element in attitudinal pathosis. This disorder is presumed to fall somewhere between psychopathic personality and traumatic neurosis. See *neurosis, compensation.*

patient, person in the A term expressing the basic key-concept of the psychosomatic medical approach to the patient and emphasizing the patient's personality or character as a factor in the production of physical symptoms and complaints. Whereas the organic, or physical, approach tends to exclude awareness and interest in emotional, personality, and character factors as causative agents to be investigated and treated, the psychosomatic approach, conversely, tends to include these factors and give them central importance. It must be borne in mind, however, that the psychosomatic approach does not in any way exclude the usual physical and organic avenues of investigation.

The investigation into the personality of the patient requires a more inclusive, time-consuming history of the individual's psychosexual emotional development, as well as an understanding of his habits and habitual attitudes. A comprehensive grasp of the patient's character development, from infancy through childhood into adult life, is a basic necessity in this approach. E. Weiss and O.S. English (*Psychosomatic Medicine,* 2nd ed., Saunders, Philadelphia and London, 1949) state: '. . . people look upon the physician as an authoritarian figure who will "do something" about their illness and they are usually quite unprepared to have to do something for themselves, in other words, discuss themselves as persons as well as "medical cases." We must look for the person in the patient.'

patient-government Patient participation in the ward administration of a psychiatric hospital; one of the ways of implementing the concept of the psychiatric hospital as a therapeutic community.

patroiophobia (pat-roi-ō-fō'bi-à) Fear of heredity.

pattern, constitutional From the psychiatric point of view the psyche, in its early manifestations, is not something that arises *de novo* at birth. It has its own *anlage,* just as any organ of the body has. It is an organ of the body that has been reproduced as many times as the heart, liver, lungs, kidneys, muscles, nerves, etc. As a consequence of innumerable reproductions certain patterns have developed. There is a phylogenetic division of the mind, as well as an ontogenetic. Those patterns which are the outcome of, or the repetition of phylogeny, are called *constitutional patterns.*

For example, feelings of inferiority comprise one of the constitutional patterns for Adler; the collective unconscious is of the same order for Jung; Freud's Eros is a constitutional pattern.

pattern, expressive See *psychodynamics, adaptational.*

pattern, specific dynamic Franz Alexander's term for the specific nuclear conflict or dynamic configuration which is unique to a particular psychosomatic disorder or organ-neurosis. See *psychosomatic.*

Pavloff's theory of schizophrenia (Ivan Petrovich Pavloff, Russian physiologist, 1849–1936) A theory propounded by Pavloff, who held that the symptoms of schizophrenia are the result of a state of inhibition of the cerebral cortex.

pavor diurnus (pà'vôr dē-oor'noos) (L. 'daytime terror') Fear reactions which occur in the young child during the afternoon nap, similar to night terrors but not so frequently taking place as the latter.

pavor nocturnus (nok-toor'noos) A rare type of sleep disturbance which differs from the nightmare '. . . in that the child does not waken fully and has no recollection of the incident. He is usually found sitting up in bed or standing or running about, greatly agitated and screaming. Often there are hallucinations of strange people or animals in the room. The child is disoriented and does not recognize persons about him. The attacks subside after several minutes, the child dropping off to sleep without remembering the episode. It may be necessary to waken the youngster in order to terminate the attack.' (Bakwin, H., and Bakwin, R.M. *Clinical Management of Behavior Disorders in Children,* Saunders, Philadelphia, 1953) In contrast to this definition, which is generally accepted by American workers, Ernest Jones considers pavor nocturnus to be a wider term than nightmare, which he believes to be a very rare and special condition.

pcpt Abbreviation of *perception*.
'This system, there [i.e. *The Interpretation of Dreams*] called Pcpt. (perception), we now identify with the system Cs. [conscious]' (Freud, S. *Collected Papers,* vol. 4, tr. by Riviere, J., Leonard and Virginia Woolf and The Institute of Psychoanalysis, London, 1924–25)

Pcs Abbreviation of *pre-conscious*.

PEAQ *Personal Experience and Attitude Questionnaire* (q.v.).

peccatiphobia (pe-kā-ti-fō'bi-à) Fear of sinning.

pecunia olet (pā-kōō'nē-à ô'let) (L. 'money smells') In a communication with this title Ferenczi cites instances to show that money and odors are intimately related. In conclusion he says: 'The Latin proverb which, in an alternative wording, I chose for the title of this article appears in a new light after the above explanation. The sentence, money does *not smell,* is a euphemistic reversal. In the unconscious it is certainly: *pecunia olet,* that is money = filth.' (Ferenczi, S. *Further Contributions to the Theory and Technique of Psycho-Analysis,* tr. by Suttie, J.I., Leonard and Virginia Woolf and The Institute of Psychoanalysis, London, 1926) The idea is already found in Plautus (Aulularia II, 2,39): aurum huic olet, 'he smells the gold,' literally: 'the gold (=-money) rouses his sense of smell.'

pedantry, stool This expression, suggested by Ferenczi, refers to 'exaggerated promptitude and punctuality' which are overcompensations 'for the infantile anal-erotic tendency to hold back the stool as long as possible.' (Ferenczi, S. *Further Contributions to the Theory and Technique of Psycho-Analysis,* tr. by Suttie, J.I., Leonard and Virginia Woolf and The Institute of Psychoanalysis, London, 1926)

pederasty (ped'er-as-tē) The meaning of pederasty varies among different authors, though it is most commonly defined as *coitus per anum* practiced on boys. It is not considered synonymous with *sodomy* (q.v.), though at times confused with it.

pederosis (ped-ē-rō'sis) Auguste Forel coined this term in 1905 and defined it as 'sexual passion for children.' It is not uncommon among certain types of psycopathic individuals, especially those who from a nosological point of view are termed *psychopathic personalities;* however, it appears to be no less frequent in psychoneurotic patients.

pedication (ped-i-ka'shun) See *pederasty; sodomy.*

pedigree See *method, pedigree.*

pediophobia (ped-i-ō-fō'bi-à) Fear of dolls. Bianchi cites the instance of a boy of fourteen who had 'an extraordinary fear of dolls. . . . The sight of a doll inspired him with very great fear. When he walked through the streets of the city he would leave his friends, who were on the pavement, and go along the middle of the street, lest he should pass near shops with dolls in the windows. . . . If I were fond of giving names to phobias that have not yet been described I might call this one "pediophobia," but it is not worth while.' (Bianchi, L. *A Text-Book* *of Psychiatry,* tr. by MacDonald, J.H., Baillière, Tindall & Cox, London, 1906)

pedologia (pē-dō-lō′ji-a) Infantile or childish speech, which omits all but the principal words and substitutes easily pronounced sounds for more difficult ones; baby talk.

pedophilia Love of children. This term implies the love of children by an adult for sexual purposes. It is not uncommon among the group of individuals termed *psychopathic personalities.*

Forel called it *pederosis;* Krafft-Ebing termed it *paedophilia erotica.*

A patient impotent with women was capable of sexual excitation only with young boys, with whom he frequently engaged in the acts of pederasty and fellatio.

peduncle, cerebral (ped′un-k′l) See *midbrain.*

peeping See *voyeurism.*

peeping Tom (From the name of the Coventry tailor who peeped at naked lady Godiva riding through the city's streets by order of her husband, lord of Coventry) Voyeur.

P-element See *system.*

Pelizaeus-Merzbacher's disease (Friedrich Pelizaeus, German neurologist, 1850– , and Ludwig Merzbacher, in Argentina, 1875–) See *sclerosis, diffuse.*

pellagra (pe-lā′grà; -lag′rà) Erythema endemicum; Lombardy leprosy; elephantiasis italica; dermatagra; maidism; psychoneurosis maidica; an affection characterized by gastro-intestinal disturbances, erythema followed by desquamation, and nervous and mental disorders; it was formerly believed to be an intoxication caused by eating diseased maize, but now recognized as a vitamin deficiency disease; mental disturbances include deliria or confused states similar to other toxic-organic reactions.

pendulum, psychic (sī′kik) This term denotes the swing between two opposite tendencies, between good and bad, love and hate, aggression and submission. When using this term, Stekel gives it a rather limited meaning, restricting its significance to the oscillation between ambition and sexuality. In a more general sense, this expression is broader and applies to all the doubts, oscillation, and vacillation between two final goals, or

two opposite trends. (Stekel, W. *Compulsion and Doubt,* Liveright, New York, 1949.) See *mood-swings.*

penetrance, penetrancy (pen′e-trans, pen′e-tran-sē) Synonymous with *expressivity,* this term denotes the important biological principle that the phenotypical expression of any hereditary factor is not only capable of *variation,* but, under certain conditions, is also able to remain incomplete or to be inhibited entirely. The manifestation of the given character is always the result of complex interactions within a variety of genetic factors constituting the individual genotype of the organism in question. See *variation.*

penial (pē′ni-al) Penile.

peniaphobia (pē-ni-à-fō′bi-à) Fear of poverty.

penile (pē′nil) Relating to the penis.

penilingus Fellatio.

penis (pē′nis) The male organ of copulation. In psychoanalysis it refers to the organ after the boy has reached the stage of genital love. See *phallus.*

penis captivus (kap′tē-voos) *Vaginismus* (q.v.) occurring during sexual intercourse so that withdrawal of the erect penis is impossible. The condition is the subject of many anecdotes, but the paucity of clinical reports indicates that such anecdotes are based more on male castration fears and female active castration tendencies than on real occurrences.

penis-envy See *envy, penis.*

penis, female A term in psychoanalysis indicating the unconscious fear that the neurotic male has of being castrated. Accordingly, he must constantly reassure himself that everyone, male and female alike, has a penis. This often leads to polymorphous perverse sexual activities, especially voyeuristic and exhibitionistic tendencies, and, more particularly, to the compulsive need of performing cunnilingus. It is as if the patient were forever saying: 'It is not true that a woman has no penis. I ascertain that she has one by playing with it and sucking it, and so I do not have to fear losing my own.' (Lorand, S. *Technique of Psychoanalytic Therapy,* International Universities Press, New York, 1946) See *penis, women with.*

penis, women with A childhood theory (that every woman has a penis) or idea, stemming from a universal, albeit usually forgotten, experience in the psychosexual development of all boys and girls. It generally appears between the ages of two and five as a consequence of the child's discovering the crucial anatomical difference between males and females, i.e. the absence of the penis in females. On finding the supposed organic deficiency or inferiority, most little girls react to their discovery with varying degrees of shock. In boys the same discovery tends to make their dread of castration more real for them, since it confronts them with the actuality of 'the missing organ.' This dread of castration (castration anxiety) is a universal sequela of guilt and fear stemming from indulgence in masturbation and its accompanying incestuous phantasy.

The idea that a woman once possessed or possesses a penis functions as a protective defensive denial of the 'horrible' psychic reality, by which the child has theoretically explained to itself the observed absence of the penis in females. R. Sterba (*Introduction to the Psychoanalytic Theory of the Libido,* Nervous and Mental Disease Monographs, No. 68, New York, 1942) states: 'In the small boy's phantasies of this period and as the corresponding basis of subsequent neurotic symptoms, the idea that the woman possesses a penis like the man plays an important part and is often obstinately retained, because it gives protection against the thought of the possibility of the loss of his own penis.'

pentothal interview (pen'tō-thal) See *narcotherapy.*

peotillomania (pē-ō-til-ō-mā'ni-à) False masturbation, pseudo-masturbation; a nervous tic consisting in constant pulling at the penis.

percentile See *rank, percentile.*

percept (pēr'sept) The thing perceived; the complete mental image (formed by the process of perception) of an object present in space.

percept-image Storch quotes Shelling to the effect that 'the oldest languages of the world contained nothing more than sensory images for ideas.'

'It seems,' adds Storch, 'that the formation of images instead of ideas by discriminative analysis of phenomena is also a characteristic of earlier ontogenetic intellectual levels.

'In this connection the so-called percept-images must be mentioned, for our knowledge of which the Marburg school under the guidance of Jaensch has done so much in late years. These are certain concrete images of hallucinatory clearness which may appear as phantasy or memory images. . . . This class of experiences, namely, the percept-images, which in general have been lost to adults, represents, according to the researches of Jaensch, a primitive level of intellectual life.' (Storch, A. *The Primitive Archaic Forms in Schizophrenia,* tr. by Willard, C., Nervous and Mental Disease Publishing Company, New York and Washington, 1924) The phenomenon is common among schizophrenic patients.

perception (pēr-sep'shun) The mental process by which the nature of an object is recognized through the association of a memory of its other qualities with the special sense, sight, taste, etc., bringing it at the time to consciousness.

perception, extra-sensory In psychiatry, a still sparingly used term to denote cognition which is paranormal, or a response to an external event which has not presented itself to any of the five known senses. Telepathy and clairvoyance are two modalities of this single surmised basic function—extra-sensory perception—and they differ only in the targets, thoughts, or objects upon which they operate: clairvoyance is the extra-sensory perception of objective events; telepathy is the extra-sensory perception of the mental activities of another person. Abbreviated as E.S.P.

perception-hallucination See *hallucination of perception.*

perception, identity of See *process, primary.*

perception, subconscious Perceptions of the environment which never even entered the fringe of the personal consciousness, i.e. of which the individual was never even dimly aware. (Prince, M. *The Unconscious,* Macmillan, New York, 1916)

perceptivity (per-sep-tiv'i-tē) The power of perception; the character of being perceptive.

perceptorium (-tō'ri-um) Sensorium.

perceptualization (per-sep-choo-al-i-zā'-shun) The act or process of representing reality as it appears to the senses rather than to the intellect, such as is seen in dreams and hallucinations. The term is also used to refer to regressive loss of higher conceptualization processes such as is seen in many schizophrenics whose ideas become more and more related to specific instances and less and less related to classes, groups, or categories. This is one of the expressions of *paleologic* (q.v.) and leads, among other things, to *concretism* (q.v.).

percipient (per-sip'i-ent) In parapsychology, the receiver of telepathically transmitted messages.

periblepsis (per-i-blep'sis) The wild stare of a delirious person.

perichareia (-kȧ-rī'ȧ) Delirious rejoicing.

period, Oedipus The period beginning at about the age of three during the phallic stage of development and reaching its height at four to five years. Psychoanalysts believe that the *Oedipus complex* is characteristic of all individuals, the boy, normally, becoming sexually attached to his mother, the girl to her father. In the phallic period, sexual interest at first is autoerotic: (1) the boy identifies himself with the penis but soon merges his sexual interest into the sexuality of the mother; (2) the girl's clitoris sexuality leads to penis-envy and the belief that the mother has been the castrator, and the girl turns to the father as a sexual object. In the *male,* the Oedipus period *ends because of castration anxiety,* for the oedipal object can be achieved only at the risk of losing the penis. In the *female,* on the other hand, the Oedipus situation *is brought about by castration anxiety.* Thus the Oedipus period is likely to be prolonged in the female; it has been suggested that its disappearance is due to the fact that the child is not mature enough to understand the full significance of the sexual organs. The fate of the Oedipus complex in the female is still unclear to psychiatry. See *complex, Oedipus.*

period, refractory See *refractory.*

peristasis (pē-ris'tȧ-sis) Some geneticists prefer this term to *environment* to indicate that the environment of a certain genetic factor includes all the biophysiological processes which take place in the organism itself and are essential to the phenotypical development of the given genotype. According to modern physiological genetics, every inherited character necessarily becomes subject to the individual *peristatic* conditions.

permissiveness See *environment, permissive.*

pernoctation (pĕr-nok-tā'shun) *Obs.* Insomnia.

peroneal muscular atrophy See *atrophy, peroneal muscular.*

perplexity, vague A symptom seen most commonly in the organic psychoses, especially in the acute brain syndromes associated with systemic infection as part of the beginning of a toxic delirium. The patient feels 'mixed-up in the head,' shows a deficient grasp of the total situation, drowsiness, torpor, and disturbances of the associations, memory, attention, and will.

persécuteurs persécutés (pâr-sā-kü-tēr' pâr-sā-kü-tē') (F. 'persecuted persecutors') Some paranoid persecuted patients also become persecutors, in an effort, as they believe, to defend themselves against their persecutors. They are referred to as *persécuteurs persécutés.*

perseveration (pĕr-sev-ĕr-ā'shun) Persistent repetition of an activity, as in stereotypy of speech or gesture. Perseveration may be seen as an association disturbance in the schizophrenias (see *verbigeration*), and it may also appear with forced grasping and groping and associated reactions that follow lesions of the premotor area (6a) of the brain.

persona (pĕr-sō'nȧ) With this term Jung denotes the disguised or masked attitude assumed by an individual, in contrast to the more deeply rooted personality components. 'Through his more or less complete identification with the attitude of the moment, he at least deceives others, and also often himself, as to his real character. He puts on a *mask,* which he knows corresponds with his conscious intentions, while it also meets with the requirements and opinions of his environment, so that first one motive then the other is in the ascendant. This mask, viz. the *ad hoc* adopted attitude, I have called the *persona,* which was the designation given to the mask worn by the actors of antiquity. A man who is identified with this mask I would call "personal" (as opposed to "individual").' (Jung, C.G. *Psychological Types,* tr. by Baynes, H.G., Harcourt, Brace, New York and London, 1923)

personal See *persona.*

personal equation See *equation, personal.*

Personal Experience and Attitude Questionnaire A screening questionnaire which is said to be a highly significant discriminator of psychopathic behavior. The test contains 150 items covering criminalism, emotional instability, inadequate personality, sexual psychopathy, nomadism, and other psychopathic traits.

personalism Personalism means the character of being personal, as distinguished from the impersonal. In medicine it refers to those factors, within the individual, that are the result of his own development, in contrast with those that come from the environment. 'Now, however, we have reached a point of such out-and-out *individualism* or *personalism* that it is difficult for the well-balanced mind to hold an exact eclectic course between the late *exogenism* and the modern *exogenism.*' (Pende, N. *Constitutional Inadequacies,* tr. by Naccarati, S., Lea & Febiger, Philadelphia, 1928)

personalities, inmate The classification of the personalities of inmates of penal institutions has had many radical modifications under the influence of modern psychiatry. It differs from institution to institution, and is also affected by the particular laws of each state. In any case, there are two main groups: the administrative and the psychiatric. We give here, as a guide, a sample of each:

ADMINISTRATIVE CLASSIFICATION
1. Colony Group
   (a) Extensive privilege
   (b) Limited privilege
2. Restricted Group
   (a) Temporary restricted
   (b) Prolonged tractable
   (c) Prolonged intractable
3. Psychiatric Group
   (a) Ambulatory
   (b) Observation
4. Hospital Group
5. Defective Delinquent
6. Insane

PSYCHIATRIC CLASSIFICATION
1. Normal
   (a) Without significant deviation
   (b) With moderate personality deviation
   (c) With pronounced personality deviation
   (d) With intellectual inferiorities
2. Feebleminded
3. Neuropathic
   (a) Psychopathic
   (b) Psychoneurotic
   (c) Epileptic
   (d) Drug Addict
   (e) Alcoholic
   (f) Post-encephalitic
   (g) Other brain abnormalities with psychoses
4. Psychotic
5. Potentially Psychotic
   (Seliger, R.V. *et al. Contemporary Criminal Hygiene,* Oakridge Press, Baltimore, 1946)

personality Among psychiatrists the term personality is used almost in its literal sense, of the mask worn on the stage by actors in ancient Rome. The personality is like a mask in the sense that it is made up of patterns of behavior through which the individual expresses his inner interests. Healy, Bronner, and Bowers describe personality as 'the habitual patterns of behavior of the individual in terms of physical and mental activities and attitudes, particularly as these have social connotations.' (Healy, W., Bronner, A.F., and Bowers, A.M. *The Structure and Meaning of Psychoanalysis,* Knopf, New York, 1930)

Psychiatrists agree in general with the foregoing definition as to what constitutes the personality. Disagreement arises over the dynamic forces that operate to produce the elements of personality. Psychoanalysts believe that personality is largely the resultant of the interaction of the instincts and the environment. Jung emphasizes the same forces, and adds the collective unconscious. Adler believes that personality is formed out of original feelings of inferiority.

personality, alternating Many consider this expression as synonymous with *personality, split* (q.v.), for the splitting of consciousness implies that the individual lives alternatingly now as one person and then as another (as in the familiar case of Dr. Jekyl and Mr. Hyde), but never as two persons simultaneously.

'A special type of disturbance of personality is the *alternating personality*, also known as *dual consciousness*.' (Bleuler, E. *Textbook of Psychiatry*, tr. by Brill, A.A., Macmillan, New York, 1930)

personality, amputation of Sladen uses this term to define the gradual fading away of the potential personality of schoolboys during their passage from kindergarten to senior high school. In Sladen's opinion, 'If one allows himself to recognize the contrast between the potential wealth of personality which is housed in the school building with what actually is finding expression and a chance to grow within those walls, a visit to even a better-than-average school is a most depressing experience.' Instead of growth in personality, in too many cases we see amputations of personality. (Sladen, F.J. *Psychiatry and the War,* Thomas, Springfield, Ill., 1943)

personality, anal See *character, anal.*

personality, antisocial See *personality, psychopathic.*

personality, 'as if' A pre-psychotic condition indicative of loss of object cathexis in which the individual's whole relation to life has something about it that is lacking in genuineness. The phenomenon is closely related to depersonalization, but, unlike the latter, the 'as if' personality is not perceived as a disturbance by the patient himself. The expressions of emotion in such patients are formal, and interpersonal relationships are devoid of any traces of warmth. The individual gives the impression of a good adjustment to reality, but this is based on mimicry and identification with the environment and leads to a completely passive attitude toward the environment and a readiness to adopt whatever attitudes or reactions seem to be expected. Thus there is no single, integrated personality; instead, the individual seems to shift with the tide of his surroundings. Deutsch believes that the schizophrenic goes through an 'as if' stage before there is any delusional formation. ('Some Forms of Emotional Disturbance and Their Relationship to Schizophrenia,' *Psychiatric Quarterly 11*, 301, 1942) She believes that the 'as if' personality represents a deep disturbance of the process of sublimation which re-sults in a failure to synthesize various infantile identifications into an integrated personality; this leads to an imperfect, one-sided, and purely intellectual sublimation of the instinctual strivings.

personality, compulsive See *personality trait disturbance; defense, character.*

personality, crowbar An example of post-traumatic mental deterioration that occured in a patient who had a segment of a crowbar imbedded in his left forebrain as a result of a premature dynamite explosion. Before the accident he had been a stable individual of good character and exemplary conduct. After his head injury, he became a vulgar, short-tempered, irritable, disagreeable person who drank to excess, abused his wife and children, and finally abandoned them.

personality, cyclothymic (sī-klō-thī′mik) See *personality pattern disturbance.*

personality disorder Behavioral reaction; according to the 1952 revision of psychiatric nomenclature, this term refers to those cases in which the personality, in in its struggle for adjustment to internal and external stresses, utilizes primarily a pattern of action or behavior rather than symptoms in the mental, somatic, or emotional spheres. There is minimal subjective anxiety and little or no sense of distress. As thus defined, there are three main groups of personality disorder: personality pattern disturbance (including inadequate personality, schizoid personality, cyclothymic personality, and paranoid personality), personality trait disturbance (including emotionally unstable personality, passive-aggressive personality, and compulsive personality), and sociopathic personality disturbance (including antisocial reaction, dyssocial reaction, sexual deviation, and addiction).

personality disorder, post-traumatic The changes occurring in the disposition or personality of an individual, as a result of head- or brain-injury due to force directly or indirectly applied to the head. The manifest symptoms may include headache, explosive emotional reactions, low resistance to alcohol, fatigability, vasomotor instability, and occasionally convulsive seizures.

personality, emotionally unstable See *personality trait disturbance.*

personality, epileptic It is not clear

whether what is called epileptic personality is a true epileptic character or merely a reaction to the chronic invalidism of epilepsy. As usually described, in any event, it probably does not occur in more than 20 per cent of known epileptics. The characteristics of this personality type include: rigidity, egocentricity, selfishness, seclusiveness, explosive outbursts of emotion, and extreme rage reactions when frustrated (children especially become frenzied when refused their wishes). Enuresis is also said to be common. Probably the most frequently observed abnormality is a tendency to a certain morose egotism; and only one psychodynamic feature occurs in epilepsy which would in any way support the belief in a specific epileptic psychic constitution—phantasies of death and rebirth, which are more common here than in any other illness.

personality, ideal See *ego* (Jung's definition of).

personality, inadequate See *personality pattern disturbance.*

personality, intraconscious (in-trà-kon′-shus) A co-conscious personality that knows another personality's thoughts. In one type of multiple personality, one personality functions subconsciously, and when it is aware not only of the outer world but of the thoughts of the conscious personality in the same individual, it is termed intraconscious personality.

personality, multiple The presence of two or more relatively distinct and separate sub-personalities in a single individual, as in Dr. Jekyl and Mr. Hyde, or in Morton Prince's case of Miss Beauchamp, or in Cleckley and Thigpen's case of Eve. Multiple personality is popularly known as split personality, and this has led to the logical but incorrect inference that schizophrenia ('split personality') is identical with multiple personality. The latter is actually a dissociative reaction, and thus a form of hysteria. Splitting is seen in both hysteria and schizophrenia, but the splitting is quite different in each. In hysteria, the splitting is massive or molecular and consists of division into complicated and relatively complete sub-personalities. In the schizophrenias, on the other hand, individual psychic functions are split off from the personality as a whole and attain an autonomy of their own which is unrelated to and often contradictory to the major personality trends; thus the splitting in schizophrenia is often termed discrete, nuclear, or atomic.

In multiple personality, the original personality is termed the primary personality, and the dissociated or split-off personality is termed the secondary (and tertiary, etc.) personality.

personality, multiplication of Schizophrenic patients in particular often express the delusion that they are many other people, that others actually reside in them, often displacing the patient entirely. One patient changed her identity many times within a short period. 'Most remarkable, however, is the division and multiplication of the personality unit into various separate persons which appear to her as strange, though, as she also distinctly feels, they represent her own thought complexes and aspirations.' (Storch, A. *The Primitive Archaic Forms in Schizophrenia,* tr. by Willard C., Nervous and Mental Disease Publishing Company, New York and Washington, 1924)

personality, panels of See *panels, personality.*

personality, paranoid (par′à-noid) See *personality pattern disturbance.*

personality pattern disturbance In the 1952 revision of psychiatric nomenclature, this term is used to refer to personality types or character structures which are more or less fixed and only minimally liable to any basic alteration. 'The depth of the psychopathology here allows these individuals little room to maneuver under conditions of stress, except into actual psychosis.' (*Diagnostic and Statistical Manual of Mental Disorders,* American Psychiatric Association of Mental Hospital Service, Washington, D.C., 1952). Included in this group are:

(1) Inadequate Personality—inadaptability, ineptness, poor judgment, lack of physical and emotional stamina, social incompatibility, etc.

(2) Schizoid Personality—avoidance of close interpersonal relationships, inability to express hostility, autistic thinking, etc.

(3) Cyclothymic Personality—extraverted type of relationships with reality, competitive, frequently alternating moods, etc.

(4) Paranoid Personality—hypersensitivity in interpersonal relationships, sus-

piciousness, envy, jealousy, stubbornness, and similar projection mechanisms.

personality, prepsychotic (prē-sī-kot′ik) The patient's personality make-up or the character structure considered usual for him before the development of a psychotic disorder.

personality, pretraumatic (prē-traw-mat′ik) In the case of a person who has developed an emotional or mental illness in consequence of an injury, this psychiatric term denotes the personality as it was before the injury and illness. Knowledge of the details of the patient's pretraumatic personality is essential for proper therapeutic understanding and management in any of the traumatic neuroses and psychoses, i.e. psychiatric disorders attributable to injury.

'The traumatic neurosis is the record of the lasting consequences of an abrupt change in the external environment to which the resources of the individual are unequal. This situation we designated as a trauma. The neurosis is, therefore, the record of the disturbance created by the trauma on the previously established adaptations [i.e. pretraumatic personality].'

It is necessary to understand 'the relation of the traumatic neurosis to the personality as a whole, and the relation of the trauma to the pretraumatic personality, or the predisposition to the neurosis.' (Kardiner, A. *War Stress and Neurotic Illness,* Hoeber, New York and London, 1947)

personality, primary See *personality, multiple.*

personality, psychopathic See *psychopathic personality.*

personality, schizoid (skiz′oid) See *personality pattern disturbance.*

personality, secondary 'In the unconscious may be conserved a vast number of life's experiences ranging in time almost from the cradle to the grave. The hopes, the wishes, the anxieties of childhood may still be there, lying fallow, but capable of injecting themselves under favoring conditions into our personalities. Properly speaking, from this point of view, aside from certain artificial and pathological conditions, there is, *normally,* no distinct "subconscious *self,*" or "subliminal *self,*" or "secondary *self,*" or "hidden *self.*" In artificial and pathological conditions there may be, as has been fre-

quently shown, a splitting of consciousness and the aggregation into a secondary co-conscious system of large systems of ideas which have all the characteristics of personality. This secondary personality (of which the primary personality is not aware) may have its own memories, feelings, perceptions, and thoughts. . . . Such a co-conscious system may properly be spoken of as a subconscious *self.*' (Prince, M. *The Unconscious,* Macmillan, New York, 1916) See *personality, multiple.*

personality, split This general expression describes the individual personality that shows a separation or splitting of certain components of the personality. After the splitting has taken place, the part split off functions as an entity, without any correlation with the remaining parts of the personality.

The phenomenon is observed in many psychiatric states, notably hysteria and schizophrenia. A hysterical patient may at one time function as one individual, while at another time, he may behave as a person entirely different from the first (double or multiple personality).

'Where the hysterical dissociation becomes so extreme as to eventuate in amnesia in one state for another the different systems of complexes are easily recognized as so many phases of *multiple personality.*' (Prince, M. *The Unconscious,* Macmillan, New York, 1916)

In schizophrenia or dementia praecox, splitting of another type may be encountered. The ideational components may be separated from the emotional ones; or, the elements of the unconscious may be more or less completely split from those of consciousness. See *personality, multiple.*

personality, stormy Arieti's term for a personality type, found often in preschizophrenic patients, consisting of repeated changes in the individual's attitude to life which may be slow or abrupt and commonly are sudden, violent, and drastic. Such individuals have no stable sense of self-identity and are forever searching for their role in life, without success. Life often seems to be little more than a series of crises in these patients.

personality, subconscious 'A subconscious personality is a condition where complexes of subconscious processes have been constellated into a personal system, manifesting a secondary system of self-consciousness endowed with volition, intelligence, etc. Such a subconscious personality is capable of communicating with the experimenter and describing its own mental processes. It can, after repression of the primary personality, become the sole personality for the time being, and then remember its previous subconscious life, as we all remember our past conscious life, and can give full and explicit information regarding the nature of the subconscious process.' (Prince, M. *The Unconscious,* Macmillan, New York, 1916)

personality trait disturbance In the 1952 revision of psychiatric nomenclature, this term is used to refer to '. . . individuals who are unable to maintain their emotional equilibrium and independence under minor or major stress because of disturbances in emotional development. Some individuals fall into this group because their personality pattern disturbance is related to fixation and exaggeration of certain character and behavior patterns; others, because their behavior is a regressive reaction due to environmental or endopsychic stress.' (*Diagnostic and Statistical Manual of Mental Disorders,* American Psychiatric Association of Mental Hospital Service, Washington, D.C., 1952) Included in this group are:

(1) Emotionally unstable personality—excitability, ineffectiveness and poor judgment when under even minor stress; poorly controlled hostility, guilt, and anxiety; formerly called 'psychopathic personality with emotional instability.'

(2) Passive-aggressive personality — passive-dependent type, passive-aggressive type, and aggressive type.

(3) Compulsive personality—overinhibited, overconscientious, rigid adherence to standards of conscience or conformity. See *defense, character.*

personality types Psychiatrists speak of types of personality, referring by that term to what might be called personality syndromes. For a psychoanalytic description of personality types, see *defense, character.* Jung recognizes two 'general attitude' types, described from the standpoint of the direction of the flow of libido. When the general direction of the flow of libido is away from the individual, the expression *extraversion* is used and the individual is called an *extravert.* When the libido is mainly turned inwardly upon the individual himself, the condition is

known as *introversion* and the individual as an *introvert.* These two are known as *temperamental* types.

Jung describes four basic *functional* types known as thinking, feeling, sensation, and intuition. Any one of these four functions may be(come) preponderant over the other three and, in that case, it is called the *superior function.* On the other hand, an *inferior function* is one less powerful than the other three. The remaining two functions are then said to occupy an intermediate position.

Kretschmer speaks of two general biotypes, the *schizothymic* and the *cyclothymic,* each of which is subdivided into several other types, such as 'gushing jolly people,' 'quiet humorists,' etc. (Kretschmer, E. *Physique and Character,* tr. by Sprott, W.J.H., Kegan Paul, Trench, Trubner, London, 1925)

personality, unity of A psychiatric term indicating that the patient's personality is emotionally well balanced and that there is a normal unity in its functioning. In a normal individual, as also in a neurotic individual, unity of personality is maintained. This unity, however, is affected in persons suffering from a psychosis, especially schizophrenia. Janet maintained that in a schizophrenic patient, the connection between the ego and certain complexes is more or less completely lost. This split is not relative but, rather, absolute. Jung expressed himself in a similar way: 'The dissociation is no longer liquid and changeable as it is in a neurosis, but is more like a mirror broken up into splinters.' In schizophrenia the unity of personality is broken into fragments. (Baynes, H.G. *Mythology of the Soul,* Williams and Wilkins, Baltimore, 1940)

persona, organic Burrow's term for the constellation of reactions embodied in the organism's total principle of motivation. The subjective correlate of the organism's primarily integrated or total behavior-pattern. Contrasted with 'I'-persona, symbolic persona. Synonym: organic identity. (Burrow, T. *The Biology of Human Conflict,* Macmillan, New York, 1937, pp. 387–8)

person, composite A figure in a dream who is not an actual person at all but a composition or 'composite' of two or more actual persons. The dreamer is not able to identify the composite person as any person known to him but, upon psychoanalytic interpretation of his dream, he is able to see that two or more persons who *are* known to him have been fused into one.

The composite person is produced by the mechanism of *condensation* in dream-making. 'The condensation is effected in several ways. A figure in a dream may be constituted by the fusion of traits belonging to more than one actual person, with some belonging to another, or by making prominent the traits common to the two and neglecting those not common to them. . . . The same process frequently occurs with names. . . . The neologism thus produced closely resembles those met with in the psychoses. . . .' (Jones, E.J. *Papers on Psycho-Analysis,* Williams and Wilkins, Baltimore, 1949)

person, disturbances in the One of the fundamental symptoms of the schizophrenias, according to Bleuler. Such disturbances arise by reason of the tendency to splitting of the psyche and domination of the personality by one or another of the patient's complexes. The ego is never fully intact, and there results a lack of homogeneity and wholeness and stability of the personality organization.

personification (pĕr-son-i-fi-kā'shun) A psychiatric term denoting the habit or process of endowing another individual with pleasant or unpleasant attributes as a result of frustration of one's desires or wishes. For example, one schizophrenic patient whose letter was not answered accused his doctor of intercepting the mail. Personification is a form of projection wherein the desirable or undesirable properties of reality are attributed to some person, even though the latter is unrelated to the happening itself. Thus schizophrenic persecutory delusions develop only after an obstacle to gratification is felt by the patient; a persecutor is chosen to take on the qualities necessary to explain the frustration. Delusions of persecution convert obstacles into machinations of certain people, the persecutors.

personology (pĕr-son-ol'ō-jē) The science or study of the personality as a whole, of man's functioning in society, his perceptions, his actions, and especially his thoughts and feelings and their reasons for being. The scope of personology includes the totality of mental life, the dynamics and economics of the entire personality; and its task is to trace the laws and phases of personality development in the individual life. In contrast, metapsychology is the pure-science aspect of the study of personality and yields information regarding the general laws of mental life. Personology supplies the understanding of how to use this knowledge in relation to the specific individual. Personology regards the individual as an organic-psychic whole whose every action can be understood only in terms of the whole. See *holism.*

persuasion While almost universal in application, *persuasion* has not gained distinction as a clear-cut form of psychotherapy. It is perhaps a part of all types of psychotherapy, achieving merit as an adjunct. Dubois was particularly instrumental in fostering persuasion, yet it never became known as a method, in the sense that the psychoanalysis of Freud, or the analytical psychology of Jung, are methods. 'In this method, the physician tries to clarify the development of the symptoms, their relation to situational and personality difficulties; and he explains to the patient the interrelations of these factors and how the difficulties and symptoms can be overcome.' (Diethelm, O. *Treatment in Psychiatry,* Macmillan, New York, 1936)

Persuasion is a method of carrying conviction that aims to prompt the acceptance of a point of view.

perverse, polymorphous (po-li-mor'fus) Pertaining to an individual who possesses the potentialities for many forms of sexual perversion. Though it often appears during mental disorders, polymorphous perversion is said to be normal in early childhood, embracing as it does the multiple forms of sexual activities observed in the period of infancy and also in adulthood in the form of perversions. As Freud says, 'sexual excitation of the child flows from diverse sources.' There are the excitations associated with the erotogenic zones; furthermore, there is 'gratification which is experienced with other organic processes: excitation of erotogenic zones by peripheral stimulation; sexual excitation through looking, showing, cruelty, etc.; excitation through rhythmic activities, such as swinging, dancing, rocking, etc.; sexually exciting influence of some painful affects, such as fear, shuddering, and horror, is felt by a great many people. . . .'; and 'mental application or the concentration of attention on an intellectual accomplishment will result, especially often in youthful persons, but in older persons as well, in a simultaneous sexual excitement.' (Freud, S. *Three Contributions to the Theory of Sex,* 4th ed., tr. by Brill, A.A., Nervous and Mental Disease Publishing Company, New York and Washington, 1930)

Abraham says that 'we learn from his [Freud's] investigations that the first traces of sexual activity appear very early and that for some time they are of an auto-erotic character. A stage follows in which the child turns to "object-love"; but its sexual object need not be of the opposite sex. In addition to heterosexual and homosexual impulses certain other impulses, that of a sadistic and masochistic character, find expression. Hence Freud speaks of a polymorphous-perverse stage.' (Abraham, K. *Selected Papers,* tr. by Bryan, D. and Strachey, A., Leonard and Virginia Woolf and The Institute of Psychoanalysis, London, 1927)

perversion Homogenitality, pederasty, fellatio, and cunnilinction are but a few of the many perversions.

In psychiatry this term almost invariably refers to sexual practices looked upon as deviations from the normal or average. As knowledge of sexual matters increases, there is less tendency among psychiatrists to stress the question of perversion. For instance, masturbation, as an act performed by and for oneself, alone, is now considered 'a physiological by-product of sex development in youth and serves as a compensation of repressed desires in the adult.' (Tenenbaum, J. *Encyclopaedia Sexualis,* ed. by Robinson, V., Dingwall-Rock, New York, 1936) But mutual masturbation among adults, as also masturbation in an exhibitionistic setting, is believed to be a perversion.

Psychoanalysts assert that 'everyday experience has shown that most of these transgressions, at least the milder ones, are seldom wanting as components in the sexual life of normals who look upon them as upon other intimacies. Wherever the conditions are favorable such a perversion may for a long time be substituted by a normal person for the normal sexual aim or it may be placed near it. In no normal person does the normal sexual aim lack some designable perverse element. . . .' (Freud, S. *Three Contributions to the*

Theory of Sex, 4th ed., tr. by Brill, A.A., Nervous and Mental Disease Publishing Company, New York and Washington, 1930) In the foregoing quotation the words 'these transgressions' do not refer to the perversions mentioned in the second paragraph. They refer principally to the sexual acts called *fore-pleasures* (q.v.).

perversion, affective 'False affective accentuations in the sense of perversions, in which the instinctive side stands in the foreground (sex impulse, hunger impulse). . . .' (Bleuler, E. *Textbook of Psychiatry,* tr. by Brill, A.A., Macmillan, New York, 1930)

perversion, negative of the The neuroses are the 'negative' of the perversions, 'because in the neuroses the perverse tendencies come to expression from the unconscious part of the mind, after the repression, and because they contain the same tendencies in a state of repression that manifest perverts exhibit.' (Freud, S. *Collected Papers,* vol. 2, tr. by Riviere, J., Leonard and Virginia Woolf and The Institute of Psychoanalysis, London, 1924–25)

pervert (pĕr′vĕrt) One who practices perversions or forms of genital activity not in accordance with the general culture or mores of his community or state.

pervigilium (pĕr-vi-jil′i-um) (L. 'an all-night watching') Coma vigil.

petit mal (p'tē′ mȧl′) (F. 'little disease') See *epilepsy.*

petrification (pet-ri-fi-kā′shun) Punishment by being turned to stone. The sensations associated with looking are a source of erotic pleasure. This pleasure may become the object of specific repressions. As a result inhibitions of looking arise. The inhibitions are a defense against either temptations for the scopophilia or a feared punishment associated with it.

There are several factors involved in the inhibition of scopophilic impulses. First, through episodes in his life, the child may have learned to fear voyeuristic impulses. For example, he may have been threatened with severe punishment (which the child might interpret as castration) because of efforts to observe his parents in the 'primal scene.' Secondly, pleasurable looking has in the infant the archaic quality of incorporation through the eyes and frequently destruction of the perceived object. Thus, with the erotic pleasure of looking will be associated the animistic dread of retaliation from the environment. Coming as it does from the 'evil eye,' this retaliation turns the person into stone and destroys him.

The punishment appears to be specific for scopophilic interests. It can be found in myths, fairy tales, and dreams. Petrification signifies a paralyzing fright associated with castration or death. (Fenichel, O. *The Psychoanalytic Theory of Neurosis,* Norton, New York, 1945)

pettifog (pet′i-fog) A popular term denoting mental confusion.

peyotism (pā-yot′iz′m) Intoxication with peyote, the dried blossoms of the mescal cactus. Peyote was used by the Southwest American Indians to produce ectasies as part of a religious ritual. Results included beautiful visual and sometimes auditory hallucinations, a sense of timelessness, and a complete withdrawal from reality. Mescaline, the active principle of the cactus, has been used more recently in experimental psychiatry to produce a model psychosis. See *mescaline.*

PGR Psychogalvanic reflex. See *reflex, psychogalvanic.*

phaged(a)ena (faj-ē-dē′nà) Bulimia.

-phagia, -phagy (-fā′ji-à, -fa-jē) Combining form meaning eating, food, from Gr. *phagein,* to have eaten, devoured.

phagomania (fag-ō-mā′ni-à) Uncontrollable or insatiable desire to eat.

phagophobia Fear of eating.

phallic (fal′ik) In psychoanalysis the term relates to the penis during the phase of infantile sexuality.

phallicism (fal′i-siz′m) Phallic worship.

phallic love See *love, phallic.*

phallism Phallic worship.

phallus (fal′us) In psychoanalysis the term refers to the penis during the period of infantile sexuality when it is intensely charged or cathected with narcissistic love. When the narcissistic qualities, associated with one's own genital organ, are directed outwardly upon a love-object, it is said that the stage of *genital love* has been reached. Thus, genital love in the male may be called penile love, in contrast to phallic love.

phallus girl See *girl, phallus.*

phaneromania (fan-ēr-ō-mā′ni-à) An ir-resistible impulse to touch some part of one's own body especially an exterior growth on it. It is a form of repetition-compulsion, related to tic-like movements. A patient had the compulsion to rub his nose; to him the nose, a centrally placed, unpaired organ, was equated with the penis. A homosexual woman, infuriated by all manifestations of effeminacy, constantly stroked her breasts, as if trying to rub something off them.

phantasia Phantasy, a figment of the imagination, a mental picture, a day-dream.

phantasm (fan′taz′m) From the psychiatric point of view a phantasm is a sense perception, appearing in the form of either an illusion or a hallucination.

'The most important psychopathic manifestations in the centripetal fields are the sensory deceptions (Phantasms).' (Bleuler, E. *Textbook of Psychiatry,* tr. by Brill, A.A., Macmillan, New York, 1930)

Phantasms are classed as pseudo-hallucinations in that they are usually recognized as being illusory or imaginary; often the illusion is of an absent person seen in the form of a spirit or ghost.

phantasmagoria (fan-taz-mà-gō′ri-à) The raising or recalling of spirits of the dead.

phantasmatomoria (-ma-tō-mo′ri-à) Dementia with delusions.

phantasmophrenosis (-mō-fren-ō′sis) Day-dreaming (coined by Schultz).

phantasmoscopia (-mo-skō′pi-à) Hallucinations involving spectres, ghosts, or spirits.

phantastica (fan-tas′tē-kà) See *psychotomimetic.*

phantasy, fantasy From the psychiatric point of view this is the equivalent of *day-dream,* and in psychoanalysis, at times, also the equivalent of *night-dream.* 'Thus, for example, I remember a dream which on waking seemed so particularly well-constructed, flawless and clear that I made up my mind, while I was still in a somnolent state, to admit a new category of dreams—those which had not been subject to the mechanism of condensation and distortion, and which might thus be described as "phantasies during sleep." ' (Freud, S. *The Interpretation of Dreams,* 3rd ed., tr. by Brill, A.A., Macmillan, New York, 1933)

'The material you have to work with in the analysis of the unconscious does not consist of dreams only. There are products of the unconscious which one calls phantasies. Those phantasies which are forms of imaginative activity, are either products of day-dreaming or reverie or else they are perceived by intuition as a sort of vision or inspiration.' (Jung, C.G. *Contributions to Analytical Psychology,* tr. by Baynes, H.G. and C.F., Kegan Paul, Trench, Trubner, London, 1928)

phantasy, anal rape Among the multitude of phantasies, certain ones seem to be met with frequently enough to merit individual mention. The phantasy of being raped per anum is not uncommon. It is believed by psychoanalysts that mouth, anus, and vagina form an equivalent series for the female organ. Fixation of libido in the anal zone may lead to the phantasy.

phantasy-cathexis See *cathexis.*

phantasy, conscious Phantasies may be formed in the realm of consciousness or in that of unconsciousness. For a description of the former see *phantasy-life.*

phantasy, creative Creative phantasy is the equivalent of symbol-forming activity. 'Besides the will . . . we have also creative phantasy, an irrational, instinctive function, which alone has the power of yielding the will a content of such a character as can unite the opposites. It is this function which Schiller intuitively apprehended as the source of symbols.' (Jung, C.G. *Psychological Types,* tr. by Baynes, H.G., Harcourt, Brace, New York and London, 1923)

phantasy, death Death phantasies are common in psychiatric conditions, but they are also common among mentally healthy individuals. They may appear in the conscious or unconscious field. 'Perhaps it is not too much to say that the response to every insoluble psychic conflict is a taking flight in what appears to be a death phantasy—i.e., a return to the place whence one came, a creeping back into the mother.' (Jones, E. *Papers on Psycho-Analysis,* 4th ed., Wood, Baltimore, 1938) Death phantasies have innumerable ways of expressing themselves; in fact, they may employ any one of the many dynamisms—transference, symbolizations, introjection, dream-work, etc.

phantasy, forced The term, introduced by Ferenczi, is based upon the finding that there is a type of person 'who both in analysis and life is particularly poor in

phantasies, if not actually without them, on whom the most impressive experiences leave no apparent trace.' These people may reproduce experiences, but the latter are devoid of adequate or significant affects, that is, the individual does not develop any reaction to the memories. Ferenczi tries to force affect into the memories. He may ask the individual to fabricate or to guess about the memories, hoping that in this way he may be able to produce phantasies. He may at other times tell the patient what he should have felt and phantasied.

Ferenczi asserts that phantasies may be forced only at the end of a psychoanalysis. Moreover, he believes that there are mainly three topics that lend themselves to forced phantasies. They are (1) positive and negative phantasies of the transference, (2) phantasies relating to infancy, and (3) onanistic phantasies. (Ferenczi, S. *Further Contributions to the Theory and Technique of Psycho-Analysis,* tr. by Suttie, J.I., Leonard and Virginia Woolf and The Institute of Psychoanalysis, London, 1926)

phantasy-formation See *phantasy-life.*

phantasy, hetaeral (hē-tē'ral) Phantasy formed in women of being, and in men of possessing, a courtesan or female paramour.

phantasy, king-slave 'Another extraordinary type of phantasy which has received as yet too little attention at the hands of psychoanalysts is the king-slave phantasy, in which the individual phantasies himself perhaps as now king, now slave, bound to service even by invisible golden chains.' (Healy, W., Bronner, A.F., and Bowers, A.M. *The Structure and Meaning of Psychoanalysis,* Knopf, New York, 1930)

phantasy-life Day-dreaming in contradistinction to thinking that is logical and realistic. Varendonck says that phantasy-life 'gives the illusion that wishes and aspirations have been fulfilled; it thinks obstacles away; it transforms impossibilities into possibilities and realities.' He adds that it is 'a search for pleasurable representations and an avoidance of everything likely to cause pain.' (Varendonck, J. *The Psychology of Day Dreams,* Macmillan, New York, 1921)

Freud holds that there are two principal groups of phantasies, egoistic and erotic. Varendonck likens phantasy to a safety valve for the abreaction of strong affects.

Often the real meaning of a phantasy is not clear. In this condition it is called screen-phantasy (see *phantasy, screen*), for it is believed to cover up a deeply lying urge.

Phantasies may be conscious or unconscious. Unconscious phantasies are said to express the impulses of the infantile period of life. See *day-dream; phantasy, unconscious*.

phantasy, magic The phantasy based upon the idea of limitless power and authority attributed to the analyst by the patient, who, consequently, expects the impossible from the analyst. In his phantasies, under hypnosis, the patient may seek a complete fulfillment of all his wishes and expect a kind of miraculous abatement of all his symptoms. (Wolberg, L.R. *Hypnoanalysis,* Grune and Stratton, New York, 1945)

phantasy, masturbation A psychiatric term which denotes any of the sexual, erotic phantasies accompanying the act of masturbation. 'There seems to be a difference between the way the child masturbates during the oral and early anal-sadistic periods and the way he masturbates later. Perhaps during these first periods the child does not have sufficient concepts or is too unaware of his concepts either to have or be aware of phantasies. He is only aware of the pleasure in the sensory experience. On the other hand, the content of the masturbation phantasies during the later part of the anal-sadistic, phallic, and latency periods and adolescence is either erotic or aggressive, although both elements may be combined at the same time. The erotic phantasies are sensual in nature, and the love object is the parent of the opposite sex, if the phantasy is heterosexual, and the parent of the same sex, if homosexual. Since aggression is combined with the erotic sensual drives, the phantasies will also have a sadistic or masochistic and an active or passive coloring. The aggressive phantasies are hostile and destructive in nature and have as the object one or the other parent.' (Pearson, G.H.J. *Emotional Disorders of Children,* Norton, New York, 1949)

phantasy, night In distinguishing night-phantasies from dreams, in the psycho-analytic sense, Freud holds that night-phantasies occur during the sleeping state,

but unlike dreams, do not undergo additions or alterations of any kind and in all other ways are similar to day-dreams.

phantasy of being eaten See *eaten, phantasy of being.*

phantasy, Pompadour (Jeanne Antoinette Poisson le Normant d'Étioles, Marquise de Pompadour [1721–64], mistress of Louis XV [1710–74], King of France [1715–74]) 'One could give this name to that type of hetaeral phantasy in which even the most chaste women indulge—in day-dreams. The exaltation of the partner to kingly rank makes thoughts and wishes possible which would otherwise be rejected as immoral.' (Ferenczi, S. *Further Contributions to the Theory and Technique of Psycho-Analysis,* tr. by Suttie, J.I., Leonard and Virginia Woolf and The Institute of Psychoanalysis, London, 1926)

phantasy, primal See *phantasy, unconscious.*

phantasy, screen A sublimated expression that serves to conceal the deeper significance of mental impulses. In *Character and Anal Erotism* Freud relates money (a screen-phantasy) to feces. 'In reality, wherever archaic modes of thought predominate or have persisted—in ancient civilizations, in myth, fairy-tale and superstition, in unconscious thoughts and dreams, and in the neurosis—money comes into closest relation with excrement. We know how the money which the devil gives his paramours turns to excrement after his departure. . . .' (Freud, S. *Collected Papers,* vol. 2, tr. by Riviere, J., Leonard and Virginia Woolf and The Institute of Psychoanalysis, London, 1924–25)

It seems that a phantasy that stands for another phantasy is a screen-phantasy. See *memory, screen; phantasy-life.*

phantasy, secondary See *phantasy, unconscious.*

phantasy-thinking Autism.

phantasy, unconscious Unconscious phantasies 'have either always been unconscious and formed in the unconscious, or more often, they were once conscious phantasies, day-dreaming' which were repressed into the unconscious. (Freud, S. *Collected Papers,* vol. 2, tr. by Riviere, J., Leonard and Virginia Woolf and The Institute of Psychoanalysis, London, 1924–25)

Such phantasies are revealed through mental analyses of adults and children, and dream-analyses. The unconscious phantasies of young children, the 'primal phantasies' of Freud, are derived from several sources, such as the Oedipus situation, ideas of procreation, the phenomena of birth, the castration complex, etc.

Secondary unconscious phantasies are as a rule some modification of the foregoing primal phantasies. For instance, the revival of the Oedipus complex at puberty gives rise to a new set of phantasies with certain adult sexual issues added.

The so-called 'wish for illness,' that is, the unconscious phantasy to be ill, is widespread among psychiatric patients. It may be derived from one of the several sources of unconscious conflict. There may be other reasons for wishing for illness: it may serve as a so-termed attention-getting device or it may be economically determined as a means for gaining financial compensation. As a rule, however, both of the latter sources are believed to be secondary representations of some unconscious complex.

In *Psychoanalyse der Weiblichen Sexualfunktionen,* Helene Deutsch describes three unconscious phantasies in adolescent girls: (1) the parthenogenetic phantasy or that of having a child by herself (virginal birth); (2) the phantasy of being a prostitute; (3) the rape phantasy.

Other phantasies of the unconscious are those based upon projection, identification, and introjection. Indeed, according to many investigators, it is possible to include all repressed tendencies as phantasies; dreams then would be regarded as such.

phantasy, womb Of the vast number of phantasies, this is one of the commonest in psychiatric patients. It is as a rule a phantasy of the unconscious and is almost always symbolically expressed. When it appears in consciousness it is highly disguised. It is commonly depicted as living alone on an island void of all things or as living in a cave of mother-earth, or as being alone in a room or church. The possible representations are legion.

Freud draws a distinction between womb-phantasy and rebirth. For instance, while speaking of the homosexual fixation of a boy for his father, Freud says: 'This instance, I think, throws light upon the meaning and origin of the womb-phantasy

as well as that of re-birth. The former, the womb-phantasy, is frequently derived (as it was in the present case) from an attachment to the father. There is a wish to be inside the mother's womb in order to replace her during coitus—in order to take her place in regard to the father. The phantasy of re-birth, on the other hand, is in all probability regularly a softened substitute (a euphemism, one might say) for the phantasy of incestuous intercourse with the mother.' (Freud, S. *Collected Papers,* vol. 3, tr. by Strachey, A. and J., Leonard and Virginia Woolf, Hogarth Press, London, 1925)

phantom From the psychoanalytic point of view a phantom is an unconscious representation of another individual. 'Psychoanalysis is very familiar with the conceptions of identification and projection. It is less outspoken about the obvious difference between the mechanism of identification, and its effect: a figure, a phantom existing in one as a result of identification.' (Wittels, F. *Psychoanalytic Quarterly 8,* 1939)

phantomatize, phantomize To create a phantom.

phantom-limb See *limb, phantom.*

pharmacomania (fär-må-kō-mā′ni-á) Morbid impulse to take medicines. It is particularly common among hypochondriacal patients, to whom drugs achieve magical significance. To possess such magic the medicines must be prescribed by a physician to whom the patient is emotionally bound and assumes the role of a child toward a parent. Some patients are uninfluenced by solid medicines (pills, powders) and are gratified only when they take medicine in liquid form.

pharmacophobia Fear of medicines.

pharmaco-psychoanalysis (fär-må-kō-sī-kō-á-nal′i-sis) 'We mean the principle that psychic influences may be supported by medical devices, and that, *vice versa,* medicinal and physical influences may be brought to their full effectiveness by psychic means.' (Schilder, P. and Kauders, O. *Hypnosis,* tr. by Rothenberg, S., Nervous and Mental Disease Publishing Company, Washington, D.C., 1927)

pharmacopsychosis (-sī-kō′sis) A term suggested by Southard for psychoses associated with alcohol, drugs, and other similar poisons.

pharmacothymia (-thim′i-à, -thī′mi-à) A neurotic or temperamental avidity for drugs.

phase, anal A psychoanalytical term designating (chronologically) the second libidinal or psychosexual development, immediately following the primary or oral stage. The anal phase (or stage) is subdivided into the early or *first anal phase,* commonly occurring in the third and fourth year of life, and the late or *second anal phase,* occurring between the ages of four and six.

(1) The first anal phase is characterized by pleasure in the passage of the fecal mass (or 'fecal stick') over the anal mucous membrane at the sensitive mucocutaneous junction area. At this period children will hold back their stools for the purpose of increasing the sensory stimulus through increased size of the mass with secondary increased expulsive pressure. In addition to direct anal sensory pleasure, there may occur 'hostility intent' pleasure, as the expelled stool mass may represent to the child an object which is destroyed in the expulsion.

(2) The second anal phase occurs usually in the period between four and six years of age, in the libidinal (emotional) development of a child. It is marked by a predominant interest and pleasure in the *retention,* or holding back, of stool. This is in direct contrast to the first anal phase, which is characterized by *expulsive* excretory *anal pleasure.* In this second anal phase, stool is treated as a possession with an inordinately high value.

Many adult traits of stinginess, hoarding, and interest in hobby collections find here their original prototype. All folklore is replete with observations equating the identity of excrement with money and gold. As examples of this unconscious identity, we have such phrases as 'filthy rich,' 'filthy with money,' 'money stinks' (Latin—*pecunia olet*), 'he likes to be around the smell of money,' etc.

Often a mother's or nurse's oversolicitude toward the child's stool 'regularity' serves to intensify this tendency to overvalue the stool; thus, when withheld, it becomes a powerful tool for getting inordinate attention and solicitude focused upon the child. When the stool is finally 'passed,' it is bestowed as a gift, reward, or largess on the anxious mother or nurse. (Sterba, R. *Introduction to the Psycho-analytic Theory of the Libido,* Nervous and Mental Disease Monographs No. 68, New York, 1942)

phase, magic A phase in the evolution of thinking in which the mere imagining of an object seems to the individual the equivalent of his having created it. In other words, this is the magic-phase stage of thinking in which the world is seemingly created by the thinker. Freud referred to it as 'omnipotence of thought.' The various phases in the evolution of thinking can be studied in the development of thought in primitive man, in the child, in the schizophrenic, and in the normal adult. Thinking receives its direction toward reality, its respect for facts, only in the last phases of its evolution. Before this maturity takes place, there is the magic-phase stage in which the individual operates directly (without any intervening medium) in his thoughts in such a way that every effect will seem to him to be the result of his wish, or, in other words, that there can be action by wish only. (Schilder, P. *Mind, Perception and Thought,* Columbia University Press, New York, 1942)

phase, oral incorporative From the psychoanalytic point of view the period (in early infantile development) marked by the appearance of possessiveness and its derivatives: voracity, greed, and envy, in association with 'cannibalistic' urges toward incorporation of bodily parts, such as mother's nipple, breast, finger, etc. In this way the danger of loss or separation from the 'loved' or 'security' object is obviated. Oral incorporation thus represents the ultimate of closeness.

When thwarted, the urge to possess becomes the drive for aggression, i.e. taking by force that which has been withheld. Later, these possessive, aggressive drives become the source of primary guilt-feelings, or early conscience.

(Alexander, F. *Psychosomatic Medicine,* Norton, New York, 1950)

phase, preambivalent (prē-am-biv′à-lent) In the development of object-love this psychiatric term denotes the earlier phase of the oral stage, when no conception of objects as yet exists. As infantile sexuality develops, it passes through several stages associated with the various erogenous zones. The libido is organized successively around these various erogenous zones. The earliest stage in infantile sexuality is the oral stage, in which the libido is organized around the mouth, for the earliest tensions and satisfactions which the infant experiences are those of hunger and the satiation of the hunger.

The development of object-love is interwoven with the development of sexuality. As infantile sexuality develops, the type of relationship to objects changes, for associated with each stage and related to the particular erogenous zone around which the libido is being organized is a different type of relationship to objects. The stages of object-love before real love is reached are denoted as ambivalent: in these stages, the process of achieving satisfaction destroys the object. This is based chiefly on the physiological nature of oral and anal erogeneities which are the usual models for these object relationships. For example, in the oral stage, the libidinous aim is to incorporate the object, that is, to put it into the mouth. 'However, incorporation destroys the object objectively.'

Oral incorporation is the first object relationship, for the first awareness of an object was the longing for something already familiar to the infant which could gratify his needs but which was not present at the moment. And the gratification of hunger was the earliest need.

Before this concept of object arose, the infant was not yet aware of the outside world: he was aware only of his own tension and relaxation. Thus, since in the earlier phase of the oral stage oral eroticism had no object, there could not be an ambivalent attitude toward the object. As a result this early objectless period of the oral stage in the development of infantile sexuality is known as the preambivalent phase. It has been noted that in the preambivalent phase oral erotic pleasure is gained not only from the gratification of hunger but also from stimulation of the erogenous oral mucous membrane. This is easily seen in thumb-sucking. Accordingly, this preambivalent phase is also characterized as the 'early oral sucking stage of libidinal organization' or as the 'autoerotic stage' in the development of object-love. (Fenichel, O. *The Psychoanalytic Theory of Neurosis*, Norton, New York, 1945)

phase, pre-superego This term denotes the early years of an individual's life before the superego has been formed. It is generally believed that the superego comes into being when it replaces the Oedipus complex. The pre-superego stage lasts until the child is five or six years of age, and includes the oral, anal, and phallic phases, as well as the development of the Oedipus complex in the phallic stage. A clear distinction is made between the pre-superego stage and the superego stage because of the different type of anxiety that is typical of each. In the pre-superego stage, anxiety is objective and more closely related to reality situations than in the adult superego stage: here anxiety is typically determined by the precepts of the fully developed superego, of whose role the individual is not consciously aware.

-phasia (-fā′zhi-à) Combining form meaning faculty or power of speech, from Gr. *phásis,* saying, word, from *phánai,* to speak.

phasmophobia (faz-mō-fō′bi-à) Fear of ghosts.

phengophobia (feng-gō-fō′bi-à) Fear of daylight (comfort being felt only at night).

phenocopy (fē′no-ko-pē) Imitation of the phenotype of a well-known mutant by a nonhereditary, externally produced variation which is virtually indistinguishable from an inherited variation.

phenomena, release Hughlings Jackson (1834–1911) conceived the term and mechanism of what he called the 'release phenomena.' By this he meant the unhampered activity of a lower center when a higher inhibiting center acting as a control is removed or destroyed, so that the 'released' structure can spontaneously discharge motor impulses.

phenomenon, Aschner ocular (Bernhardt Aschner, Austrian gynecologist, 1883–   ) Pressure exerted over eyeball produces a slowing of the pulse; also known as the oculocardiac reflex.

phenotype (fē′nō-tīp) The changeable picture of an organism's appearance as produced and modified by its external life situation. In contrast to the *genotypical* structure, the *phenotype* of an organism is the sum of all its manifested attributes.

phenylketonuria (fē-nil-kē-tō-nūr′i-à) A hereditary disorder of phenylalanine metabolism, inherited as a Mendelian recessive, which appears in infancy and whose most striking manifestation is severe mental deficiency (most patients are idiots, with intelligence quotients below 20). Normally, phenylalanine is almost completely converted into tyrosine; in phenylketonuria, this metabolic pathway is blocked and phenylalanine is instead converted into phenylpyruvic acid (which is excreted as phenylketones in the urine). The associated mental defect is believed to be due to intoxication by the accumulated phenylalanine and/or its breakdown products in the brain.

phenylpyruvic oligophrenia (fē-nil-pī-roo'vik ol-i-gō-frē'ni-à) See *phenylketonuria.*

philo-, phil- (fil'ō-, fil-) Combining form meaning loving, from Gr. *phílos,* loving, friend(ly).

philoenia (fi-lē'ni-à) *Obs.* Love of wine.

philogenitive (fil-ō-jen'i-tiv) *Rare.* Erotic.

philomimesia (-mi-mē'si-à) Morbid impulse to imitate or mimic.

philoneism (fi-lon'ē-iz'm) Intense passion for novelty (Lombroso).

philopatridomania (fil-ō-pà-tri-dō-mā'-ni-à) Nostalgia.

philoprogeneity (-prō-jē-nē'i-tē) *Rare.* Love of offspring.

philoprogenitive (-prō-jen'i-tiv) Erotic; manifesting abnormal love for children.

phlebotomomania (flē-bot-ō-mō-mā'ni-à) *Obs.* A mania for bloodletting as a curative measure.

phlegmatic (fleg-ma'tik) See *type, phlegmatic.*

phobanthropy (fō-ban'thrō-pē) Fear of people; anthropophobia.

phobia (fō'bi-à) A phobia is a morbid fear associated with morbid anxiety. After excluding *traumatic* obsessions and phobias, because they are 'nothing but memories, unaltered images of important experiences,' Freud says: 'We must distinguish: (a) obsessions proper; (b) phobias. The essential difference between them is the following:

'Two components are found in every obsession: (1) an idea that forces itself upon the patient; (2) an associated emotional state. Now in the group of phobias this emotional state is always one of "morbid anxiety," while in true obsessions other emotional states, such as doubt, remorse, anger, may occur in the same capacity as fear does in the phobias.' (Freud, S. *Collected Papers,* vol. 1, tr. by Riviere, J., Leonard and Virginia Woolf and The Institute of Psychoanalysis, London, 1924–25)

According to Freud phobias may be divided into two groups, 'according to the nature of the object feared: (1) common phobias, an exaggerated fear of all those things that everyone detests or fears to some extent; such as night, solitude, death, illness, dangers in general, snakes, etc.; (2) specific phobias, the fear of special circumstances that inspire no fear in the normal man; for example, agoraphobia and the other phobias of locomotion.' (Freud, S. ibid) See *anxiety-hysteria.*

phobia, bathroom A fear of the toilet or bathroom, seen often in children and obsessive-compulsive neurotics. The phobia is frequently expressed as a fear of falling into the toilet, of being attacked by some monster coming from it, or as a fear of being infected. As a rule, such phobias represent a condensation of ideas of dirt (representing anal-erotic temptations) with ideas of castration.

phobia, bug Fear of small animals such as insects, spiders, flies, etc. Although animal phobias are usually distorted representations of the passionate, sexual, aggressive, 'animal-like' father, fears of small animals may be a direct projection of one's own drives. Creatures of this sort commonly represent genitals, feces, or little children (brothers and sisters).

phobia, cancer A fear of being eaten away or eaten up by neoplastic cells. The fear of being eaten up, whatever rationalized form it takes, is common in neurotics and is based upon fears of retaliation for having sadistically introjected an object. The dangerous introject may have different meanings on different psychic levels; thus it may represent a child, a penis, the breast, milk, etc. In like manner, the fear may be expressed in various ways—as a phantasy of impregnation, as a delusion or fear of being poisoned, as a fear of infection, as a fear of cancer, etc.

phobia, death A morbid fear of dying, most commonly an outgrowth of the idea of death as a punishment for death wishes against other persons, or of the idea of death as the ultimate in relaxation consequent upon orgastic relief of one's own excitement, or of the idea of death as a reunion with a dead person.

phobia, doorknob This is a phobia in which the situation to be avoided (because it produces anxiety) is the touching of a doorknob. On first examination it would appear that this anxiety is related to touching an object which is believed to be dirty, as a doorknob must be. Thus the patient is protected against 'anal-erotic wishes to be dirty or to soil,' for in magical thinking the characteristics of an object are communicated by touching it. As Fenichel points out, however, occasionally what appears to be only a protection against anal-erotic wishes may in reality be a protection against other impulses altered by regression, so that they seem to be anal-erotic impulses. He explains that the goal of all impulses involves touching an object, whether it be another person or one's own body. In this way, for example, the patient can achieve security against a wish to masturbate. 'Not infrequently a wish to masturbate that has been warded off has been altered by regression, so that the phobia appears to be a protection against anal-erotic wishes to be dirty or to soil.' (Fenichel, O. *The Psychoanalytic Theory of Neurosis,* Norton, New York, 1945)

phobia, hypochondriacal (hī-pō-kon-drī'-à-kal) Morbid fear of organic disease in the absence of known pathology. 'At the very beginning she had suffered from the fear of becoming insane, a hypochondriacal phobia common enough among women who are not satisfied by their husbands, as she was not.' (Freud, S. *Collected Papers,* vol. 1, tr. by Riviere, J., Leonard and Virginia Woolf and The Institute of Psychoanalysis, London, 1924–25)

phobia, hysterical Morbid fear in a hysterical person. 'It is scarcely possible to exaggerate the pathogenic significance of the comprehensive tie uniting the sexual and the excremental, a tie which is at the basis of a very large number of hysterical phobias.' (Freud, S. *Collected Papers,* vol. 3, tr. by Strachey, A. and J., Leonard and Virginia Woolf, Hogarth Press, London, 1925)

phobia, impregnation See *phobia, cancer.*

phobia, infection See *phobia, cancer.*

phobia, insect See *phobia, bug.*

phobia, landscape Morbid fear which arises when the patient finds himself in some particular locale: e.g. mountains, plains, the sea, gently rolling woodlands, etc. This fear may reach the intensity of a landscape phobia, that is, morbid avoidance of the particular type of landscape causing the fear. Animism is at work in such a phobia. The individual has projected certain of his painful emotions or feelings onto a particular type of landscape. Whenever he finds himself in such an environment, these painful feelings are aroused in him by a sort of introjection. Probably there are certain landscapes which can more readily than others communicate a particular type of feeling, even to different sorts of people—that is, they can more easily give rise to certain emotions. Thus, endless prairies bring on melancholy, mountains engender activity and energy, etc.

Fenichel states that the painful emotions aroused by particular landscapes are associated with unmastered infantile excitation. Finding himself in the particular landscape toward which he is phobic, the patient feels threatened with a loss of the forces protecting him against dangerous infantile excitement. (Fenichel, O. *The Psychoanalytic Theory of Neurosis,* Norton, New York, 1945)

phobia, light-and-shadow A phobia or a morbid fear concerning light-and-shadow effects which works in a way similar to the mechanisms described in the *landscape phobia.* With respect to this particular type of phobia, Fenichel states specifically that 'probably many phobias of darkness or twilight contain memories of primal scenes.' The influences exerted by light-and-shadow effects can be very noticeable in certain cases. A patient with a diagnosis of pseudoneurotic schizophrenia was particularly affected by bright, clear days. His overt schizophrenic symptomatology was restricted to attacks of feelings of unreality. These feelings would be well marked on particularly sunny days and diminished to the point of absence on dark, overcast days. As a result, he had a strong preference for gray, rainy weather and a fear of bright, clear days which in its severity bordered on a phobia. (Fenichel, O. *The Psychoanalytic Theory of Neurosis,* Norton, New York, 1945)

phobia, live burial A fear of being buried

alive is a special 'mother's womb' type of claustrophobia which represents the mother's womb, one's own body sensations, and/or the interior of one's own body. The patient attempts to rid himself of his aggressive or sexual sensations by projection and, as with other claustrophobias, the need for sudden escape is a need for escape from one's own feared excitement as soon as it has reached a certain intensity.

phobia, poisoning See *phobia, cancer.*

phobia, street A common, morbid fear of being in a street; agoraphobia.

'Hans's anxiety, which thus corresponded to a repressed erotic longing, was, like every infantile anxiety, without an object to begin with: it was still anxiety and not yet fear. The child cannot tell what it is afraid of; and when Hans, on the first walk with the nursemaid, would not say what he was afraid of, it was simply that he himself did not yet know. He said all that he knew, which was that in the street he missed his mother, whom he could coax with, and that he did not want to be away from her. In saying this he quite straightforwardly confessed the primary meaning of his dislike of streets.' (Freud, S. *Collected Papers,* vol. 3, tr. by Strachey, A. and J., Leonard and Virginia Woolf, Hogarth Press, London, 1925)

As with all phobias, the feared street may represent a temptation (especially a situation which would ordinarily call forth an aggressive or a sexual response), or it may represent punishment for the forbidden impulse directly or indirectly through symbolism, or it may be a fear that the anxiety will return because the initial anxiety attack occurred in the street. Any phobia may represent castration and punishment directly, or it may represent a loss of love.

phobia, toilet See *phobia, bathroom.*

phobia, traumatic (traw-mat'ik) See *obsession, traumatic.*

phobia, vehicle A fear of trains, boats, airplanes, automobiles, and/or other forms of transportation. Often these represent a struggle against sexual excitation as perceived in the pleasurable sensations of equilibrium, or a fear that one will be unable to escape from a confined area, this latter representing a need for escape from one's feared excitement as soon as it has reached a certain intensity.

phobic reaction *Anxiety-hysteria* (q.v.).

phobo-, phob- (fō'bō-, fōb-) Combining form meaning fearing, from Gr. *phóbos,* flight, (panic) fear.

phobodipsia, phobodipson (fō-bō-dip'si-à, -dip'sun) *Obs.* Hydrophobia.

phobophobia Fear of fearing.

phoneme (fō'nēm) In linguistics, a speech-sound that serves to distinguish words of different meanings; a word- (or meaning-) distinguishing sound: the vowels in: tan, ten, tin, ton, tun; the consonants in pan, ban, ten, den, seal, zeal, sink, zinc. There is a rigid sequence in the process of acquisition of new phonemes by a child learning to speak, and, accordingly, this process is reversed in various species of aphasia speech disorders: the patient loses those phonemes first which he has acquired most recently. In other words, the successive stages of speech disintegration are exactly contrary to the chronological process of their having been learned or acquired.

phonism (fō'niz'm) See *sensation, secondary.*

phonomania (fō-nō-mā'ni-à) Homicidal mania.

phonophobia (fō-nō-fō'bi-à) Fear of sounds; fear of one's own voice.

photic driving (fō'tik) See *electroencephalogram.*

photism See *sensation, secondary.*

photomania (fō-tō-mā'ni-à) Morbid craving for light.

photophobia Literally, fear of light, but rarely used to indicate a phobic avoidance reaction. More commonly the term is used to refer to an organically determined hypersensitivity to light (as in many acute infectious diseases with conjunctivitis) which results in severe pain and marked tearing when the patient is exposed to light.

-phrasia (-frā'zhi-à) Combining form meaning phrase, phraseology, from Gr. *phrásis,* speech, way of speaking, phraseology.

phren (fren) The mind.

phrenalgia (fre-nal'ji-à) Guislain classified mental disorders as follows: phrenalgia or melancholy; phrenoplexia or ecstasy; hyperphrenia or mania; paraphrenia or folly; ideophrenia or delirium; aphrenia or dementia.

phrenasthenia (fren-as-the′ni-à) Bianchi says that 'under the name *phrenasthenia* are comprised all the forms of defective evolution of the mind.' He referred to feeblemindedness. (Bianchi, L. *A Text-Book of Psychiatry*, tr. by MacDonald, J.H., Baillière, Tindall & Cox, London, 1906)

phrenatrophia (fre-nà-tro′fi-à) *Obs.* Atrophy of the brain.

phrenesia (fre-ne′zhi-à) *Obs.* Encephalitis.

phrenesis (fre-ne′sis) *Obs.* Phrenitis.

phrenetiasis (-net-i-a′sis) *Obs.* Phrenitis.

phrenetic (fre-net′ik) Relating to or affected by phrenesis, phrenitis.

phrenhypnotic (fren-hip-not′ik) *Obs.* Pertaining to phrenology and hypnosis.

-phrenia (-fre′ni-à) Combining form meaning mind, mentality, from Gr. *phren*, mind.

phreniatry (fre-ni′à-tre) *Obs.* Cure of mental disorders.

phrenic (fren′ik) Pertaining to the mind or the diaphragm.

phrenicula (fre-nik′u-là) *Obs.* Brain fever.

phrenismus (fre-niz′mus) *Obs.* Encephalitis.

phrenitic (fre-nit′ik) Phrenic.

phrenitis (fre-ni′tis) This term was used by Hippocrates (Aphorisms, 1248 ff.) for inflammation of the brain.

Celsus distinguished three forms: mental disorders accompanied by fever; a second form, characterized by melancholy and caused by black bile, was without fever; and a third class, with two subdivisions, 'for some err in having false images, and not in their whole mind, as Ajax and Orestes are represented in poetic fables; in others, the whole mind or judgment is affected.'

phrenitis aphrodisiaca (fre-ne′tes à-frò-de-ze′à-kà) (Mod.L. 'sexual phrenitis') *Obs.* Erotomania.

phrenitis apyreta (a-pe-ra′tà) *Obs.* Mania.

phrenitis potatorum (pô-tä-to′room) *Obs.* Delirium tremens. See *delirium potatorum.*

phreno- (fren′o-) Combining form meaning brain, mind; diaphragm, from Gr. *phren, phrenós,* mind, brain.

phrenoblabia (fren-o-blä′bi-à) *Obs.* Dementia.

phrenocardia (-kär′di-à) Herz uses this term for a special form of cardiac neurosis, called by him 'sexual psychogenic cardiac neurosis—phrenocardia.' The basis of the neurosis relates to the absence of sexual gratification. Herz's phrenocardia is the equivalent of Freud's anxiety neurosis with reference to the heart.

phrenolepsia (-lep′si-à) *Obs.* Insanity.

phrenology (fre-nol′o-je) 'The doctrine that the different mental faculties have their seats respectively in particular tracts of brain-surface, and that the relative predominance of the faculties can be diagnosticated from the conformation of the parts of the skull overlying those traits.' (Foster, F.P. *Medical Dictionary,* Appleton, New York, 1892–94)

phrenomania (fren-o-mä′ni-à) Collapse delirium; delirious mania; Bell's mania; typhomania. See *mania.*

phrenomesmerism (-mez′mer-iz′m) Theory of animal magnetism.

phrenonarcosis (-när-ko′sis) Stupefaction; dulling of mental faculties.

phrenoparalysis (-pà-ral′i-sis) *Rare.* Psychogenic paralysis.

phrenopath (fren′o-path) *Obs.* An alienist.

phrenopathia, phrenopathy (-path′i-à, fre-nop′à-the) *Obs.* Disorder or disease of the mind.

phrenophagia (-fä′ji-à) A term suggested by Radzinski to refer to the suppression and/or liquidation of individuals whose personalities and convictions are incompatible with or non-conforming to existing authoritarian standards, such as is practiced by the Communist party in Russia today.

phrenoplegia, phrenoplegy (-ple′ji-à, fren′o-ple-je) A sudden attack of mental derangement.

phrenoplexia (-plek′si-à) Guislain's term for the clinical syndrome then (early part of 19th century) known as *ecstasy* (q.v.).

phrenopraxic (-prak′sik) One of the many terms used to describe the drugs which have an action on the mind or psyche;

viz. the tranquillizers, ataractics, psychotropics, etc.

phrenorthosis (frēn-or-thō'sis) *Obs.* Sound-mindedness.

phrenotherapy (fren-ō-ther'à-pē) *Obs.* Psychiatry.

phrenotropic (-trō'pik) Having an action on the mind. The term is usually used to describe certain pharmacologic agents, such as psychotomimetics, tranquillizers, and energizers, which have an effect on mental processes.

phrenzy (fren'zē) *Obs.* Phrenitis.

phricasmus (fri-kaz'mus) *Obs.* Shivering of psychic origin.

phrictopathia (frik-tō-path'i-à) Sensation of touch, as unpleasantly tingling.

phronemophobia (fro-nē-mō-fō'bi-à) Fear of thinking.

phthinoid ([f]tin'oid) In Kretschmer's system of constitutional types this term refers to the variety of the *asthenic* type which is so underdeveloped as to represent a morbid condition in itself. This category of the asthenic type is contrasted with the *oligosthenic* and *eusthenic* varieties of moderately or considerably greater vigor, respectively.

In a more general sense, the term refers particularly to the flat, narrow chest characteristic of the tuberculous individual. Sometimes it applies to any characteristic of the asthenic physique.

phthisical insanity ([f]tiz'i-kal) *Obs.* A psychotic state associated with pulmonary tuberculosis.

phthisiophobia ([f]tiz'i-ō-fō'bi-à) Fear of tuberculosis.

phylo- (fī'lō-) Combining form meaning tribe, race, from Gr. *phylon,* race, tribe, clan, people, nation.

phyloanalysis (fī-lō-à-nal'i-sis) A method developed by Burrow which induces in an individual an awareness of his partitive or dissipative behavior, personally and socially, by contrasting the internal tensions concomitant to this type of behavior-reaction with an internal pattern of reaction that is concomitant to the organism's total motivation individually and as a phylum. Phyloanalysis regards the symptoms of the individual and of society as but outer aspects of impaired tensional processes which affect the balance of the organism's internal reaction as a whole,

(Burrow, T. *The Biology of Human Conflict,* Macmillan, New York, 1937)

phylobiology (-bī-ol'ō-jē) A term introduced by Burrow to denote the science of behavior that studies the organism's reactions in their phyletic motivation as these reactions mediate man's basic rapport with the external environment. Phylobiology posits a biological unity as a central governing principle motivating the behavior of the organism as an individual and as a species. (Burrow, T. *The Biology of Human Conflict,* Macmillan, New York, 1937)

phylogenesis, phylogeny (fī-lō-jen'ē-sis, fī-loj'ē-nē) Originally a biological term denoting the genealogical history and evolutionary development of a species or group as distinguished from the *ontogenetic* development of the individual. According to Haeckel's 'biogenetic law,' phylogeny is always recapitulated by *ontogeny* (q.v.).

The biological concept of phylogenesis has been used in different ways for analytical analogies in the psychological sphere, in order to emphasize the role of racial elements in the manifestations of the psyche. In accordance with the theory of analytical psychology that the mind or psyche, as an organ of the individual, has archaic history, it is believed that patterns of the psyche are derived from racial activities.

As Dewey expressed it: 'We need to know about the social conditions which have educated original activities into definite and significant dispositions before we can discuss the psychological element in society. . . . Native human nature supplies the raw materials, but custom furnishes the machinery and the designs.' (Dewey, J. *Democracy and Education,* Macmillan, New York, 1916)

Jung speaks of psychic elements called *archetypes,* which he considers to be 'the fundamental elements of the unconscious mind, hidden in the depths of the psyche, or to use another comparison, they are the roots of the mind, sunk not only in the earth in the narrower sense, but in the world in general. Archetypes are symptoms of preparedness that are at the same time images and emotions. They are inherited with the structure of the brain of which they represent the psychic aspect.' (Jung, C.G. *Contributions to Analytical Psychology,* tr. by Baynes, H.G. and C.F.,

Kegan Paul, Trench, Trubner, London, 1928)

If applied in such a special metaphorical sense, the term phylogeny becomes synonymous with *archaic inheritance*, thus losing all connection with its original biological meaning. It is obvious that the psychoanalytical interpretation of the continuation of social and cultural conditions through 'inheritance' has been derived without reference to the biological conception of inheritance as expressed in the laws of human genetics.

Nietzsche said that 'the dream carries us back to a condition of human culture far removed from the present and furnishes us with the means of a better understanding of that former condition.'

'The extension of the field of individual psychology into that of racial psychology, the psychological analysis of the myths, fairy tales, and magic practices of primitive peoples and early societies, opened up to the clinician a surprising perspective and gave rise to a multitude of new and stimulating problems.' (Storch, A. *The Primitive Archaic Forms in Schizophrenia*, tr. by Willard, C., Nervous and Mental Disease Publishing Company, New York and Washington, 1924)

'Primitive man is known to us by the stages of development through which he has passed: that is, through the inanimate monuments and implements which he has left behind for us, through our knowledge of his art, his religion and his attitude towards life, which we have received either directly or through the medium of legends, myths and fairy tales; and through the remnants of his ways of thinking that survive in our own manners and customs.' (Freud, S. *Totem and Taboo*, tr. by Brill, A.A., New Republic, New York, 1931)

phylogenetic symptoms See *schizophrenia, hebephrenic.*

phyloörganism (fī-lō-or′gan-iz′m) Burrow's term to denote the species man regarded as an organismic whole in which the element or individual is a phylically integrated unit.

phylopathology (-pà-thol′ō-jē) The scientific investigation of the underlying causal factors in behavior-disorders as envisaged from the background of phylobiology. In its scope it includes disturbances of behavior not only in neurotic but also in so-called normal individuals. Phylopathology has developed principles which are applicable to these behavioral disturbances on a broad, organismic basis. (Burrow, T. *The Biology of Human Conflict*, Macmillan, New York, 1937)

physiatrist (fiz′i-a-trist) See *physical medicine.*

physical Pertaining to the *physique*, or body build, of an individual.

physical medicine The diagnosis and treatment of disease by physical means, which are a form of applied medical biophysics. The term includes physical therapy and rehabilitation. In 1947, a specialty board was established for this branch of medicine in the United States; a physician certified by this board is known as a physiatrist.

physical therapy See *therapy, physical.*

physiogenesis (fiz-i-ō-jen′e-sis) Origin in the functioning of an organ of the body. Thus, intellectual deficiencies due to impairment of organic (cerebral) functioning are described as physiogenic manifestations.

physiognomy (fiz-i-og′nō-mē) The physical appearance of the face; also, judging personality from facial appearance.

physioneurosis (fiz-i-ō-nū-rō′sis) From the psychoanalytic point of view the term *physioneurosis* is synonymous with *actual neurosis*. Two physioneuroses are described, namely, neurasthenia and anxiety-neurosis.

physiopathology (-pà-thol′ō-jē) The study of disturbances of physiology, whether functional or organic in nature. The capacity for growth and adjustment inheres in physical structure and function. 'The general psychological factors of an individual's personality are inherent in, and depend upon: (1) the nature of his physical state, (2) the degree of its effect upon his personal goals, (3) the cumulative effect of a physical deficiency affected by any other dysgenic element in the personality, (4) the local effect of the physical condition, but more especially in terms of the total personality, (5) the secondary effects of the physical condition in the light of social response to it as it conditions his education, occupation, recreation, social responsiveness and adaptability.' (Wile, I.S. 'Physiopathology in Child Guidance' in *Handbook of Child Guidance*, ed. by Harms, E., Child Care Publications, New York, 1947)

physioplastic See *stage, physioplastic.*

physiotherapy See *therapy, physical.*

physique (fĭ-zēk′) The *physical* structure of a human organism, the general build of the body as it is to be classified according to the various systems of *constitutional types* (q.v.).

pia mater (pē′à mä′ter) (L. 'tender mother') A delicate fibrous membrane closely enveloping the brain and spinal cord.

pica (pī′kà) *Rare.* In psychiatry, a craving. 'Besides these, nervous patients evince peculiar cravings (*picae*). . . .' (Bleuler, E. *Textbook of Psychiatry,* tr. by Brill, A.A., Macmillan, New York, 1930)

The young infant brings to his mouth everything his hand or mouth can reach. Gradually in the course of development, as well as a result of training, the child learns to discriminate between articles fit for oral consumption and those that are not. Pica is the recurrence of this early developmental characteristic at a later age and is found in children suffering from neurosis, or as a psychotic manifestation. It is also found in some children without any of these characteristics. 'Some children will constantly pluck out hairs and eat them, or will devour particles of fluff from the blankets. Others will seize every opportunity to eat unpleasant things, such as earth, sand, mud, or dirt of any sort.' (Cameron, H.C. *The Nervous Child,* Oxford University Press, Oxford, 1929)

picatio (pē-kà′tē-ō) *Obs.* Pica.

Pick's disease (Arnold Pick, Prague psychiatrist, 1851–1924) Specific form of progressive dementia occurring in the presenile age, although somewhat later than Alzheimer's disease; it is characterized pathologically by circumscribed atrophy of the cerebral cortex. There is a gradual disintegration of the higher faculties and a progressive development of aphasia. Dulling of the emotions, stereotypy of action and speech, and loss of moral judgment and memory impairment gradually develop.

The pathological picture shows focal atrophy of cortical cells, mainly of the three upper layers, in the temporal and frontal regions. There are also glial changes and swelling of nerve cells.

The diagnosis is difficult to make clinically. The disease may last up to ten years or even more.

picture, concrete Storch writes: 'Perhaps the most prominent feature of primitive thinking is the tendency to employ "full concrete pictures," instead of abstract ideas. The thought of primitive man works with total percepts of phenomena without analytic discrimination of their essential constituent parts; he thinks in full concrete pictures just as they are encountered in real experience. . . . In this connection it should be remembered that our own ideas of number have grown out of concrete sensory perceptions. The word *five* is derived from the Sanskrit *pancha,* meaning hand; the Roman number V represents the hand.' (Storch, A. *The Primitive Archaic Forms in Schizophrenia,* tr. by Willard, C., Nervous and Mental Disease Publishing Company, New York and Washington, 1924) This concept gains significance in that many psychiatric patients, particularly those with schizophrenia, abandon the use of abstract ideas, concrete ideas taking their place.

picture, inward An internally apprehended image or picture, as commonly presented in dreams, phantasies, and visions: the pictorialized expression of material from the deeper levels of the unconscious part of the psyche. It is an 'inward picture' not only because it *occurs* 'inwardly' but also because (according to Jung, whose expression it is) it is a picture of our most 'inward,' innermost self—the *true* SELF.

Jacobi says: 'In Jungian dream-analysis . . . the psychic images [i.e. inward pictures] in the dream as in all their other manifestations are at once reflection and essence of the dynamics of the psyche. They are at once reflection and essence of the dynamics of the mind, just as in the case of a waterfall the waterfall is at once reflection and essence of force itself. For without force, i.e. physical energy (which in itself is only a working hypothesis), there could be no waterfall, whose essence it therefore is; but simultaneously it reflects too in its form of being this energy, which without the waterfall, in which it becomes visible as it were, would be wholly inaccessible to observation and verification. They are the real energy-transformers in psychic events. They have at the same time expressive and impressive character, expressing on the one hand internal psychic happenings pictorially, and on the other hand influencing—after having been transformed into images—through their meaningful content these same happenings, thus furthering the flow of the psychological processes. For example, the symbol of the withered Tree of Life, which was meant to convey the idea of an overintellectualized existence that had lost its natural instinctive basis, would on the one hand express this meaning pictorially before the very eyes of the dreamer, and on the other hand, by thus presenting itself to him, would impress him and thereby influence his psychic dynamism in a certain direction. One can continually observe in the course of an analysis how the various pictorial motives determine and lead into one another. In the beginning they still appear in the guise of personal experiences; they bear the characteristics of childhood or other remembrances. As the analysis penetrates to deeper levels, however, they exhibit the outlines of the archetypes ever more clearly, the field becomes dominated ever more definitely by the symbol alone.' (Jacobi, J. *The Psychology of C.G. Jung,* Kegan Paul, Trench, Trubner, London, 1942)

pigmentary retinal lipoid neuronal heredo-degeneration (pig′men-tēr-ē ret′in-al lip′-oid nū′ron-al he-red-ō-dē-gen-er-ā′shun) Spielmeyer-Vogt's disease, a type of *amaurotic family idiocy* (q.v.).

Pilcz, Alexander (1871–   ) (pēlts) Austrian psychiatrist.

Pinel's system Named after Philippe Pinel, a Parisian psychiatrist, 1745–1826, through whose efforts forcible restraint in the management of the mentally ill was abolished.

pink disease *Acrodynia* (q.v.).

pithiatism (pith′i-à-tiz′m) A forced suggestion; a method of removing hysterical symptoms by way of persuasion. The word was coined by Babinski, who held that everything that is hysterical may be caused by suggestion.

'In no case, however, can I accept Babinski's "explanation," according to which stigmata (like hysterical symptoms in general) are only pithiatisms suggested by the doctor.' (Ferenczi, S. *Further Contributions to the Theory and Technique of Psycho-Analysis,* tr. by Suttie, J.I., Leon-

ard and Virginia Woolf and The Institute of Psychoanalysis, London, 1926)

pithiatric (pith-i-at′rik) Curable by persuasion or suggestion, referring to the class of hysterical symptoms which can be made to disappear or be reproduced by means of suggestion.

pituitarism (pi-tū′i-tēr-iz′m) Overactivity of the pituitary gland.

pituitary cachexia See *cachexia, hypophysial.*

placebo (plà-sē′bō, plà-kā′bō) (L. 'I am to placate') Any medication used to relieve symptoms, not by reason of specific pharmacologic action but solely by reinforcing the patient's favorable expectancies from treatment. Although a placebo may be an inert substance, as used in present-day research placebos more commonly contain active substances that at least in part mimic the side-effects of the specific therapeutic agent with which the placebo is being compared. Placebo effects include all those psychologic and psychophysiologic benefits and undesirable reactions which reflect the patient's expectations; they depend upon the diminution or augmentation of apprehension produced by the symbolism of medication or by the symbolic implications of the physician's behavior and attitudes.

plane, subjective Jung uses this expression in relation to dream interpretation. 'By interpretation upon the subjective plane, I understand that conception of a dream or phantasy in which the persons or conditions appearing therein are related to subjective factors entirely belonging to the subject's own psyche. It is common knowledge that the image of an object existing in our psyche is never exactly like the object, but at most only similar.'

'In the analytical treatment of unconscious products, therefore, it is essential that the image shall not immediately be assumed to be identical with the object; it is wiser to regard it as an image of the subjective relation to the object. That is what is meant by the consideration of a product upon the subjective plane.' (Jung, C.G. *Psychological Types,* tr. by Baynes, H.G., Harcourt, Brace, New York and London, 1923)

plan, life With this term Adler indicates the entire system of behavior by means of which the individual prevents his 'superiority' from being subjected to the test of reality.

planomania (plan-ō-mā'ni-à) Morbid impulse 'to wander from home and throw off the restraints of society.' Clouston, from whom the quotation is taken, said elsewhere: 'I think it is the instinct of mental self-preservation that makes young men sometimes fly from the influences of civilization and to take to the backwoods, the "planomania" of some authors.' (Clouston, T.S. *Clinical Lectures on Mental Diseases,* 6th ed., Churchill, London, 1904)

planophrasia (plan-ō-frā'zhi-à) Wandering speech; usually used to refer to flight of ideas in manic syndromes.

plasm, germ The theory developed by Weismann conceives the *germ plasm* (the reproductive tissue which produces the germ cells) as separate and distinct from the other body tissues representing the *somatoplasm.* It is the basis of the important genetic concept that attributes acquired by the organism during the lifetime of its phenotype are never inheritable.

According to this concept (true only in higher animals and therefore of limited value) the germ plasm is the sole seat of hereditary characters and thus represents the potentially immortal part of an organism, through the continuing succession of its reproductive cells. The environment may cause many variations in the somatoplasm, but it has been shown by Weismann and other geneticists that these changes are not transferred to the germ plasm and, therefore, cannot be hereditarily transmitted to the offspring.

plasmon (plaz'mon) This biological term was introduced by von Wettstein to characterize the independent gene-like elements in the cytoplasm, in contradistinction to the nuclear system of Mendelian gene-units, for which he proposed the term *genome.*

plate, neural (nū'ral) See *cephalogenesis.*

platonic nymphomania See *nymphomania, platonic.*

platonization (From *platonize,* to make platonic in character, idealize, as in platonic love, which in Plato's view passed from physical passion on to higher contemplation of the ideal, i.e. to love free from sexual desire.) A mental mechanism

consisting of considering the desired act without actually performing it. Platonization is thus a mechanism of defense against impulses and would be considered by some as evidence of prelogical, primitive thinking wherein thought has become an equivalent of action by reason of infantile belief in the magical omnipotence of thought. Platonization is typical of paranoia, where thought rather than action reigns supreme. But, like any other mechanism of defense, such as repression, sublimation, or projection, platonization need not imply gross psychiatric abnormality in the individual who uses the mechanism.

platybasia (pla-ti-bā'zhia) Basilar impression; an abnormality of the base of the skull, often congenital, in which the angle between the basisphenoid and the basilar portion of the occipital bone is widened. The neck is abnormally short and the head is sometimes mushroom-shaped.

platycephaly (pla-ti-sef'à-lē) Flattening of the crown of the head.

play See *activity, ludic.*

pleasure-ego See *ego, pleasure.*

pleasure, function Enjoyment of functioning or doing or exercising one's own capacities. Function pleasure is obtained when an act can be accomplished without anxiety; such pleasure is the basis for subsequent repetitions of situations which originally induced excitation and anxiety, as is seen frequently in children who enjoy endless repetitions of the same game or of the same story, which has to be retold in exactly the same words.

pleasure, muscle Pleasure connected with body movements.

pleasure-pain-principle See *principle, pleasure.*

pleasure-principle See *principle, pleasure.*

pleasure-sucking See *sucking, pleasure.*

-plegia, -plegy (-plē'ji-à, -plē'jē) Combining form meaning (paralytic) stroke, attack, from Gr. *plēge,* blow, stroke.

pleniloquence (plē-nil'ō-kwens) Excessive talking.

pleocytosis (plē-ō-sī-tō'sis) Excess of cells; pleocytosis of the cerebrospinal fluid indicates meningeal irritation.

pleonexia (plē-ō-nek'si-à) Excessive greediness; a psychosis characterized by an uncontrollable desire for acquisition or gain.

pleurothotonos, pleurotetanus (ploo-rō-thot'ō-nos, -tet'à-nus) Lateral bending or arching of the body; sometimes observed in hysteria.

plot, melody See *speech, plateau.*

pluralism In psychiatry pluralism refers to the concept that behavior is causally determined by a multiplicity of complexly interrelated factors. 'Freud and Meyer were among the first to appreciate the importance of the setting, the *theme,* the emergence of a behavior item or action tendency from a complexly-integrated set of experiences and their meaning to the experiencing individual. Freud could show how the early "family drama" was a theme which had a profound significance throughout a person's life, influencing his ambitions, identifications, choice of a mate, and even the contents of his dreams. Meyer's pluralistic orientation could not be satisfied with the study of behavior as a self-contained phenomenon: he was too much aware of the multiplicity of factors at play in any situation. His relativistic mode of thinking caused him to look for the cohesion and interdependence of these factors. . . .

'Behavior, thus considered, is an integral function which derives its existence, its form and its meaning from the totality of its setting. Hence it can be understood only in terms of its setting. The setting is the resultant of relationships and experiences which have begun to exert themselves from the beginning of life and toward which a person has formed his own accepting or rejecting, defensive, aggressive or submissive reaction tendencies. Behavior of the moment thus appears as the temporarily last scene of an uninterrupted plot or theme, during which a person has developed a certain readiness to perform in the particular manner in which he does perform.' (Kanner, L. *Child Psychiatry,* Thomas, Springfield, Ill., 1948)

plutomania (plōō-tō-mā'ni-à) Wealth-greediness.

pneuma (nū'mà) The principle of life, according to Hippocrates.

pneumatopathy (nū-mà-top'à-thē) *Obs.* Healing by psychic cure; mind cure.

pneumoencephalogram (nū-mō-en-sef'a-lō-gram) An X-ray of the skull following replacement of measured quantities of cerebrospinal fluid with air or some other gas by means of lumbar or cisternal puncture.

pnigerophobia (nī-jē-rō-fō'bi-à) Fear of smothering.

pnigophobia (nig-ō-fō'bi-à) Fear of choking.

Po Rorschach scoring symbol for a position response, i.e. a response determined or suggested by the location of the particular stimulus area on the card.

poena talionis (poi'nà tà-lē-ō'nēs) (L. 'punishment by retaliation') This refers to a law of ancient Rome according to which the culprit was subjected to the identical injury or material loss as he had caused to the plaintiff.

poikilothymia (poi-ki-lō-thī'mi-à, -thim'-i-à) By this term E. Kahn designates a mental constitution closely akin to cyclothymia, differing from the latter in that in poikilothymia the mood variations are more intense.

poinephobia (poi-nē-fō'bi-à) Fear of punishment.

point, critical Described by S.R. Slavson as the event, occurrence, or situation in which the patient's problem comes to a head and he mobilizes his resources for dealing with the problem. Slavson, who suggested the term, believes that in nearly all therapy an ultimum point is reached in the specific intrapsychic or environmental situation which is the culminating point of therapy. See *problem, nuclear.*

point, flicker-fusion Same as critical flicker frequency. See *flicker.*

pointing A test for vestibular rather than pure cerebellar function; patient is requested to extend his arm and perform the movements at the shoulder; examiner stands in front of him, and patient touches with his extended index finger the examiner's two index fingers which are held together in a fixed position; with eyes open, there is no deviation normally; on closing the eyes, and knowing the position of the examiner's fingers, the patient should be able to touch the same spot every time; if he deviates to the left or right there is said to be past-pointing.

poisoning, deadly nightshade Strychnomania. Deadly nightshade is a plant of the genus Solanum. Poisoning may follow ingestion of the black berries of the plant. The mouth and tongue become dry and vision is impaired; any or all of the following symptoms may then appear: visual hallucinations, mutism, restlessness, unresponsiveness, widely dilated pupils, disorientation and confusion, with increasing agitation. The patient then falls into a deep sleep and awakes asymptomatic but with amnesia for the agitated period. During the disturbed period, a misdiagnosis of acute schizophrenic reaction is commonly made.

polar body See *body, polar.*

polarity (pō-lar′i-tē) Possession of opposite properties, as if opposite pole.

From the psychoanalytic point of view, 'mental life as a whole is governed by *three polarities,* namely, the following antitheses:
Subject (ego)—Object (external world),
Pleasure-Pain,
Active-Passive.'
The foregoing arrangement is taken from Freud, S. *Collected Papers,* vol. 4, tr. by Riviere, J., Leonard and Virginia Woolf and The Institute of Psychoanalysis, London, 1924–25.

policy, open-door See *open-door policy; community, therapeutic.*

polio-encephalitis hemorrhagica superior (pō-li-ō-en-sef-à-lī′tis hem-or-à′ji-ka sooper′i-or) See *Wernicke's encephalopathy.*

poliomyelitis (pō-li-o-mī-e-lī′tis) Infantile paralysis; Heine-Medin's disease. An acute infectious disease due to a virus which attacks the anterior horn cells of the spinal cord and brain-stem. The usual route of infection is the alimentary tract via personal contact with healthy carriers and abortive cases, and via the fecal contamination of food. It has been suggested that the virus travels from the alimentary tract to the central nervous system by way of the autonomic nerves. The peak incidence is in the late summer and early fall; the young are most susceptible, and the disease is rare after the age of 25, although in both the United States and Great Britain the age incidence has been rising. Reports to date indicate that 'Salk vaccine' affords highly efficacious prophylaxis at least against the paralytic symptoms.

Symptoms may appear in several ways: there may be development of immunity without any symptoms of illness; the symptoms may never be more than those of a mild general infection; symptoms of general illness may be combined with pleocytosis of the cerebrospinal fluid, without further progression (this is the most usual form during epidemics); and in a minority, the infection runs its full course and causes paralysis.

Symptoms are divided into two stages, the pre-paralytic and the paralytic. In the pre-paralytic stage, there is an early phase with symptoms of general infection and a late phase with more severe headache, pain in the back and limbs, and hyperesthesia of both superficial and deep tissues. Symptoms of the paralytic stage depend upon the area of central nervous system attacked, i.e. spinal or brain-stem symptoms. Paralysis may be widespread or localized, and usually maximal damage is done within the first 24 hours. Thus only a portion of the muscles initially affected will remain permanently paralyzed. In the brain-stem form, there is danger of involvement of the cardiac and respiratory centers.

poliomyelitis, chronic See *sclerosis, amyotrophic lateral.*

politico-social See *constant, extrinsic.*

pollakiuria (pol-à-ki-ū′ri-à) Abnormally frequent urination.

pollution The discharge of semen and seminal fluid in the absence of sexual intercourse; the term is often used synonymously with *nocturnal emission.*

poltergeist (pōl′tĕr-gīst) The word or concept finds little usage in psychiatry. Nandor Fodor borrowed it from the field of occultism in his effort to explain allegedly mysterious head noises telepathically induced. (*Psychiatric Quarterly 22,* 195, 1948)

polyandry (pol′i-an-drē) Having more than one husband.

polychromate, abnormal (pol-i-krō′māt) One who distinguishes most colors, but fails to perceive one or two, or confuses two colors.

polyclonia epileptoides continua (pô-lē-klō′nē-à e-pē-lãp-tô-ē′dās kôn-tē′noo-à) See *epilepsy, continuous.*

polycratism (pō-lik′rà-tiz'm) (From Polycrates, tyrant of Samos [535–512 B.C.] who wished to allay the envy of the gods, because all his enterprises were invariably highly successful. In a galley fitted out with regal splendor Polycrates sailed out on a pleasure trip. As if inadvertently his favorite signet-ring fell overboard and with ostentatious grief Polycrates returned home, inwardly happy that he had appeased the gods. Two or three days later a fisherman brought to the palace a huge fish he thought fit only for the ruler's table. When Polycrates carved the fish at the repast, he found his ring, which the fish had swallowed. The gods were not to be appeased—Polycrates met death by crucifixion.) 'By analogy with Schiller's poem "The Ring of Polycrates" one could give this name to the superstition that dreads lest things should "go too well" with one, because then a proportionately heavier punishment is to be expected from God. In an analysis it could be traced to a bad conscience due to personal phantasies that were reprehensible.' (Ferenczi, S. *Further Contributions to the Theory and Technique of Psycho-Analysis*, tr. by Suttie, J.I., Leonard and Virginia Woolf and The Institute of Psychoanalysis, London, 1926)

polydipsia (pol-i-dip'si-à) Excessive thirst.

polydipsia ebriosa (pô-lē-dēp'sē-à ā-brē-ō'zà) A craving for intoxicants.

polygamy (po-lig'à-mē) Having more than one mate. This term is thus more general than *polyandry* and *polygyny* (qq.v.), both of which it includes.

polyglot (pol'i-glot) See *reaction, polyglot*.

polyglot neophasia See *neophasia, polyglot*.

polygraph, Keeler Lie detector.

polygyny (pol'ig-i-nē) Having more than one wife.

polyhybrid (pol-i-hī'brid) In genetics this characterizes *hybrids* which differ in more than three hereditary characters. See *hybrid*.

polylogia (-lō'ji-à) See *tachylogia*.

polymorph, polymorphous perverse See *perverse, polymorphous*.

polyneuritis (-nū-rī'tis) A disease in which there usually is simultaneous inflammation of a large number of peripheral nerves. The signs and symptoms are usually bilateral and frequently symmetrical, although not all the nerves are affected with equal severity. The condition is due either to an infectious agent or an endogenous or exogenous poison, probably operating through the circulatory system. Prominent symptoms include severe pain, wasting of the muscles and paralysis. Clinical examples are alcoholic polyneuritis, arsenic polyneuritis, diabetic polyneuritis, polyneuritis of pregnancy, etc.

polyneuritis, acute infective *Guillain-Barré's syndrome* (q.v.).

polyneuritis, acute toxic *Guillain-Barré's syndrome* (q.v.).

polyneuritis, erythroedema (e-rith-rō-ē-dē'mà) *Acrodynia* (q.v.).

polyneuritis, rheumatic (rū-ma'tik) *Guillain-Barré's syndrome* (q.v.).

polyopsia, hysterical (pol-i-op'si-à) A condition in which the visual apperception of one object appears to the individual as two or more objects. Such a phenomenon may be observed in hysteria. It is synonymous with polyopsia. According to Schilder, this hysterical optic multiplication may be produced by alterations of the innervations of the ocular muscles. The condition can be binocular (diplopia) or monophthalmic—in the latter case an object viewed with one eye appears double to the individual. In the opinion of some authors, this condition constitutes a symptom of conversion phenomenon similar to so-called hysterical blindness. Such optic multiplication can have other etiological sources, not only in the field of psychiatry but in purely ophthalmological diseases. (Schilder, P. *Mind, Perception and Thought*, Columbia University Press, New York, 1942)

polyparesis (-par'ē-sis) General paralysis of the insane.

polyphagia (-fā'ji-à) Excessive eating; gluttony.

polyphallic (-fal'ik) Individuals may dream of, or patients may overtly or symbolically give expression to, multiple phalli. The manifestation is usually rooted in a very strong castration complex. Fluegel maintains that polyphallic representations are, among other things, evidence of an overcompensating wish-fulfillment.

polyphobia (-fō'bi-à) Fear of many things.

polypnoea (pol-ip'nē-à) Deep, labored, and rapid respiration. It may be physically or psychically determined. Among psychiatric patients, particularly those exhibiting a compulsive-obsessive syndrome, disorders of breathing are not uncommon. The condition has been observed in the psychoneurotic patient who has a vivid fear of impending death or in the hysterical patient with globus hystericus. Polypnoea may be one of the symptoms of schizophrenia, when the patient believes that by deep and rapid breathing he is able to ward off the evil and demoniacal forces of the environment.

When polypnoea is but one of a great number of symptoms associated with a psychogenic syndrome and it has no relationship with organic disorder, its causes are considered to lie in the psyche.

polyposia (pol-i-pō'si-à) Craving for intoxicating drinks.

polypsychism (-sī'kiz'm) The concept (often found in psychotic patients) that each person possesses several souls.

polyradiculoneuritis (-ra-dik-ū-lō-nū-rī'-tis) *Guillain-Barré's syndrome* (q.v.).

polyuria (-ū'ri-à) Excessive excretion of urine; profuse micturition.

Pompadour phantasy See *phantasy, Pompadour*.

ponopathy (pō-nop'à-thē) Synonymous with *nervous exhaustion*. See *neurasthenia*.

ponophobia (pon-ō-fō'bi-à) Fear of overwork.

pons That portion of the metencephalon which forms the floor of the fourth ventricle; the pons is continuous with the midbrain anteriorly, and with the medulla oblongata posteriorly. The pons contains the pontine nuclei which connect the cerebellum with the cerebrum, and the nuclei of cranial nerves 4, 5 (in part), 6, and 7. Transverse fibers of the pons form the brachium pontis, or middle cerebellar peduncle; the longitudinal fibers of the pons contain the pyramidal tracts and the corticopontile fibers.

pontocerebellar angle tumor (pon-tō-ser-e-bel'ĕr) See *syndrome, pontocerebellar angle*.

popular In Rorschach scoring, this refers to a response which occurs commonly or frequently.

porencephaly (pō-ren-sef'à-lē) A developmental anomaly in which there occur small or large unilateral or bilateral cavities in the brain substance.

poriomania (pō-ri-ō-mā'ni-à) An irresistible impulse to journey. The latter may be carried out with the full and complete knowledge of the individual or there may be complete amnesia for all of the individual's activities associated with the trip. Brill describes a patient with such an impulse, who was entirely amnesic for his acts; he was a patient with psychic epilepsy. 'He had what we called a "fugue" or "poriomania." ' (Brill, A.A. *Fundamental Conceptions of Psychoanalysis*, Allen & Unwin, London, 1921, p. 54) States of poriomania may or may not be associated with criminal acts. Some individuals, while amnesic, commit crimes; others, while also amnesic, conduct themselves exemplarily. Thus a patient with epilepsy left his family, went to a distant city, and worked honestly and industriously for two years, without any memory of his family.

poriomaniac One affected by poriomania. 'There are people who, under the influence of a strong inner affect, feel themselves compelled to run around for hours; they seek, so-to-say, the land of their longing, of their desire.' They are, as Stekel says, in a twilight state. 'Those gruesome sexual crimes reported again and again by newspapers are usually committed in similar twilight states by pathological poriomaniacs.' (Stekel, W. *Encyclopaedia Sexualis*, edited by Robinson, V., Dingwall-Rock, New York, 1936)

pornerastic (por-nĕr-as'tik) Fond of prostitutes.

pornographomania (por-nō-graf-ō-mā'ni-à) Morbid impulse to write obscene letters.

pornography (por-nog'rà-fē) Expression of lewdness, lasciviousness, or obscenity by word or image.

pornolagnia (por-nō-lag'ni-à) A perverted lustful attraction for prostitutes.

porphyria, acute intermittent (por-fē'-ri-à) A familial metabolic disorder of the pyrroles, resulting in the production of abnormal types of porphyrins, which appear in the urine; first described by Gunther and Waldenstrom. Females are four times as frequently affected as males, usually between the ages of 20 and 35. The first symptom is usually abdominal pain, often with nausea, vomiting, low-grade fever, leukocytosis, and tachycardia. These symptoms continue and to them are added psychic changes (irritability, tension, and often progression to a schizophreniform psychosis) and, later, neurologic symptoms (muscular weakness and other signs of peripheral neuritis). There is no known treatment. The disease is fatal in about half of the cases; mortality is higher (60–90%) in those with cranial nerve involvement.

porphyrinuria (por-fē-ri-nur′i-à) See *porphyria, acute intermittent.*

porropsia (po-rop′si-à) Inability to gauge the real distance of objects, which appear more distant than they really are, without any alteration in their size.

posiomania (pō-si-ō-mā′ni-à) Dipsomania.

possessed An old concept, that persons were entered and dominated by the devil. 'The heathen philosophers believed that the devil took up his abode in the soul, and that an insane person became thus possessed. They believed that he forced an entrance into the soul from without the body.' (Mann, E.C. *A Manual of Psychological Medicine and Allied Nervous Diseases,* Blakiston, Philadelphia, 1883, p. 37)

possession, demoniacal (dē-mō-nī′à-kal) See *demon.*

postambivalence See *stage, postambivalent.*

postcentral gyrus (gī′rus) See *lobe, parietal.*

post coitum triste (pôst′ kô′ē-toom tris′-te) (L. 'gloom after sexual intercourse') See *impotence, psychic.*

postconcussion neurosis See *neurosis, postconcussion.*

post-encephalitic syndromes See *post-traumatic and post-encephalitic syndromes, classification of.*

posterolateral sclerosis See *sclerosis, posterolateral.*

post-traumatic and post-encephalitic syndromes, classification of (post-traw-ma′-tik, post-en-sef-à-li′tik) Blau (*Research Publications, Association for Nervous and Mental Diseases 34:* 404–423, 1954) has suggested the following classification:

I. Etiologic Classification
   A. Cerebral birth injury
      1. Direct injury—prolonged molding, disturbed labor, breech ex-

traction, instrumental delivery, etc.
      2. Anoxemia — prolonged labor, abnormalities of pregnancy, placenta previa, strangulated cord, etc.
   B. Cerebral trauma—accidental head injury with or without skull fracture, concussion, contusion, subdural hematoma, etc.
   C. Cerebral inflammatory and degenerative diseases
      1. Encephalitis—epidemic, variola, vaccinia, rubella, measles, mumps, meningitis, etc.
      2. Encephalopathy—pertussis, burns, lead, epilepsy, etc.
II. Psychiatric Classification
   A. Intellectual defect conditions
      1. Focal defects—memory disturbances, paraphasias, attention defects, concentration, etc.
      2. Generalized intellectual defect —general mental retardation, secondary dementia, learning difficulties, etc.
   B. Personality disorders—conduct and behavior disorders, delinquency, psychoneurosis, psychosis, character disorders, etc.

potamophobia (pot-à-mō-fō′bi-à) Fear of rivers.

potence, potency This term is most commonly used in psychiatry to designate the ability (of the male) to consummate the act of sexual intercourse.

potestas coeundi (pô-tes′tàs kô-e-oon′dē) (L. 'ability to copulate') Sexual potency.

potomania (pō-tō-mā′ni-à) Morbid impulse for intoxicating drinks; *dipsomania; delirium tremens* (qq.v.).

pototromania (pō-tot-rō-mā′ni-à) *Obs.* Delirium tremens.

pototromoparanoia (pō-tō-trom-ō-par-à-noi′à) *Obs.* Delirium tremens.

Pötzl, Otto (1877–   ) (pēts′l) Austrian psychiatrist and neurologist.

POW See *syndrome, prisoner of war.*

power, traumatic (traw-ma′tik) A term used by Freud in connection with the etiology of hysteria. He states 'that tracing an hysterical symptom back to a traumatic scene assists our understanding only if the scene in question fulfils two conditions—if it possesses the required *determining quality* and if we can credit it with the necessary *traumatic power.*' (Freud, S. *Collected Papers,* vol. 1, tr. by Riviere, J., Leonard and Virginia Woolf and The Institute of Psychoanalysis, London, 1924–25)

By this he means that a traumatic scene must be sufficient alone, or by another association, to explain the hysterical symptom. For example, a hysterical symptom of vomiting was attributed to eating a fruit which had a rotten spot in it. This derivation of the symptom lacks *traumatic power,* although it may be said to possess determining quality, i.e. vomiting determined by disgust. However, on further analysis, the rotting apple roused the memory of a former experience of picking up fallen apples in a garden when the patient happened to come on the loathsome carcass of an animal. This experience now fulfills both requirements of determining quality and traumatic power, i.e. an event capable of producing psychic injury.

praecox, heboid (prē'koks, hē'boid) F.M. Barnes, Jr. says: 'Not infrequently the principal changes [in dementia praecox] are shown in an emotional dulling, indifference and stupidity without the occurrence of hallucinations or developed delusions. These cases in which the dementia seems to be the principal symptom, and in which the accessory symptoms play a small part, have also been spoken of as simple or heboid precox.' (Barnes, F.M. *An Introduction to the Study of Mental Disorders,* 2nd ed., Mosby, St. Louis, 1923)

praecox, predementia (prē-dē-men'shi-à prē'koks) This expression refers to the personality constitution of the schizophrenic individual prior to the appearance of the symptoms of the disorder.

'Dementia praecox is thus the culmination of a long-continued series of faulty mental habits. The predementia praecox character is one in which the individual habitually ceases to apply himself vigorously to the real facts of life. His thoughts are devoted to day-dreams and fantasies, and by constantly seeking refuge in evasions he loses the capacity for grappling with difficulties. Thus, in the presence of some added stress, which the ordinary individual would be prepared to meet, "the sensitive and weakened individual will react with manifestations constituting the deterioration process" of dementia prae-

cox.' (Kraepelin, E. *Lectures on Clinical Psychiatry,* 3rd ed., revised and edited by Johnstone, T.H., Baillière, Tindall & Cox, London, 1913) Kraepelin credits Adolf Meyer with having first delineated the character syndrome observed in predementia praecox.

-praxia (-prak'si-à) Combining form meaning acting, doing, act(-ion), from Gr. *prāxis,* a doing, acting, action, from *prássein,* to achieve, accomplish, practice, do.

praxiology (prak-si-ol'ō-jē) Dunlap's term for the science of behavior which excludes the study of consciousness and similar non-objective, metaphysical concepts.

praxi-therapeutics (-ther-à-pū'tiks) An old term for occupational treatment; ergotherapy.

pre- (prē-) Prefix meaning earlier, before, ahead, from L. *prae-,* before.

preadaptive attitude See *attitude, preadaptive.*

preambivalence See *phase, preambivalent.*

precaution In occupational therapy this term means certain restrictions placed upon patients who are dangerous to themselves or others. Patients 'on precautions' are denied the use of tools or are limited to harmless tools, because they need special observation by those in charge.

precentral area, convolution, gyrus See *lobe, frontal; motor cortex.*

precocity (prē-kos'i-tē) In a child, the premature or exceptionally early development of certain mental or physical capacities and endowments normally and characteristically exhibited only by children of a more advanced age group.

precognition Prescience; knowledge of future events, presumably by means of extra-sensory perception.

preconscious Foreconscious; in psychoanalysis, one of the three topographical divisions of the psyche, and often abbreviated Pcs. The preconscious division includes those thoughts, memories, and similar mental elements which, although not conscious at the moment, can readily be brought into consciousness (Cs.) by an effort of attention. This is in contrast to the unconscious (Ucs.) division, whose elements are barred from access to consciousness by some intrapsychic force such as repression.

preconscious Burrow uses this term to denote the primary phase or mode of consciousness described by him; it represents the infant's original identification with the mother organism. This mode relates to a non-libidinal, pre-objective phase in the organism's development. It finds symbolic expression in poetry and in literature, in dreams, in the phantasies both of the psychoneurotic and of the normal individual. Not to be confused with the psychoanalytic term 'preconscious' or 'foreconscious.' Synonyms: primary identification, the nest instinct. (Burrow, T. 'The Origin of the Incest-Awe,' *The Psychoanalytic Review* 5, 245, 1918; also Burrow, T. *The Biology of Human Conflict*, Chapter IV, Macmillan, New York, 1937). See *co-conscious*.

predementia praecox See *praecox, predementia*.

predisposition The inherited ability of an organism to develop a certain attribute or morbid trait when the necessary peristatic conditions for the given character are present. According to the genetic principles, there is no inheritance of fully developed hereditary characters, but only a transmission of *predisposing* genetic factors depending for their phenotypical manifestation on various constitutional and dispositional influences. See *heredity*.

pregenital In psychiatry as used by psychoanalysts, the term means antedating the phase of genital primacy. See *organization, pregenital*.

pregenital organization See *organization, pregenital*.

prehension (prē-hen′shun) Sullivan uses this word to mean 'an intelligible alteration of the personality by an impinging event.' (Sullivan, H.S. in *Psychiatry,* vol. 1, p. 124, 1938)

pre-industrial Pre-vocational.

prejudice, race See *race-prejudice*.

pre-logical The mode of thinking may regress, as it often does in schizophrenic subjects, from the logical to the pre-logical. It has frequently been pointed out that thought and language in their development change from *feeling, concreteness* and *perception* in the direction of *reasoning, differentiation and abstraction*.

premaniacal (prē-mȧ-nī′ȧ-kal) Preceding a maniacal outbreak.

premium, incitement *Fore-pleasure* (q.v.).

premotor area See *lobe, frontal*.

prenatal Relating to the phase of development before birth.

prenubile Referring to the period of life from birth to puberty.

preoccipital area (prē-ok-sip′i-tal) See *lobe, occipital*.

preoccupation See *stupor*.

pre-oedipal (prē-ed′i-pal) Relating to the stages of infantile development antedating the Oedipus complex (psychoanalysis).
   'The pre-oedipal phase . . . is for both sexes that earliest period of attachment to the first love object, the mother, before the advent of the father as a rival. It is the period during which an exclusive relation exists between mother and child.' (Brunswick, R.M., 'The Pre-oedipal Phase of the Libido Development,' *The Psychoanalytic Quarterly IX*, 295, 1940)

prephallic (-fal′ik) Referring to the period of psychosexual development preceding the phallic phase; i.e. the oral and anal phases or stages. While the term pregenital is often used interchangeably with the term prephallic, this is not technically correct since the phallic and genital phases are quite distinct and separate.

prepotent Ascendant; dominant. In neurophysiology, that reflex is prepotent which, when two stimuli that would evoke dissimilar reflexes are applied simultaneously, displaces the second reflex. 'The outcome of the rivalry depends upon a number of circumstances: (i) the nature of the reflexes, (ii) the intensity of the several stimuli and (iii) the duration of action of the reflex.' (Fulton, J.F. *Physiology of the Nervous System,* 3rd ed., Oxford University Press, New York, 1949) In general, nociceptive reflexes, such as the flexion reflex, are prepotent to all other types of reflex competing for the final common pathway; other things being equal, the more intense stimulus results in prepotency of its reflex; and the longer a reflex has been in operation, the easier will its prepotency be lost.

pre-psychic form See *form, pre-psychic*.

prepsychotic (-sī-kot′ik) Relating to the period of life prior to the appearance of a psychosis.

prepubertal (-pū'bĕr-tal) Relating to the phase of life antedating puberty.

presbyophrenia (pres-bi-ō-frē'ni-ȧ) Clinically the term means early senile dementia, that is, dementia that has its onset at a much earlier age than is characteristic of an average comparable group. It is closely related to Alzheimer's and to Pick's diseases.
'Presbyophrenics comprehend occurrences in the environment, but seem to be unable to grasp their own relationship to these occurrences, and have no insight for their own condition.' (Henderson, D.K. and Gillespie, R.D. *A Text-Book of Psychiatry*, 4th ed., Oxford University Press, London, 1936) Retention defects and confabulation are common in this condition.

presence, psychic (sī'kik) This term, introduced by Edoardo Weiss, refers to images 'with almost hallucinatory vividness' . . . 'which pursue the guilty person.' Weiss cites the case of a young man who 'thought that he would be able to commit the crime [stealing] without a sense of guilt. . . . While he was arranging the details of the theft, the reproachful image of his father appeared in his mind with almost hallucinatory vividness.' (*Bulletin of the Menninger Clinic, 3,* 179, 1939)

presenile (prē-sē'nīl) Relating to the period of life antedating senility or old age.

presentation Freud uses this term to mean the mode by which an instinct expresses itself. He says that it is not possible to identify an instinct existing as an entity by itself; it is recognizable only when it is conveyed or presented by some vehicle of expression. For example, a patient had a dread of sharp instruments; the instruments comprised the *presentation* by which the dread was expressed.
'It follows that the fate of the charge of affect belonging to the presentation is far more important than that of the ideational content of it. . . .' (Freud, S. *Collected Papers,* vol. 4, tr. by Riviere, J., Leonard and Virginia Woolf and The Institute of Psychoanalysis, London, 1924–25)
This is a term used in a special sense by Jung (analytical psychology). 'To my mind, a simple stringing together of representations, such as is described by cer-

tain psychologists as *associative thinking* is not thinking at all, but mere *presentation.* The term "thinking" should, in my view, be confined to the linking up of representations by means of a concept, where, in other words, an act of judgment prevails, whether such act be the product of one's intention or not.' (Jung, C.G. *Psychological Types,* tr. by Baynes, H.G., Harcourt, Brace, New York and London, 1923)

presentation, metapsychological (met-à-sī-kō-loj'i-kal) Freud suggests that 'when we succeed in describing a mental process in all its aspects, dynamic, topographic and economic, we shall call this a *metapsychological* presentation.' (Freud, S. *Collected Papers,* vol. 4, tr. by Riviere, J., Leonard and Virginia Woolf and The Institute of Psychoanalysis, London, 1924–25)

pressure of ideas See *thought pressure.*

pressures, social 'Socially created sanctions which emanate from less sanctioned or less responsible sources [than the] direct authoritarian controls, effected through officials or other accredited social agents and expressive of established codes.' (McIver, R.M., 'Pressures, Social'; *Encyclopaedia of the Social Sciences,* vol. 11, Macmillan, New York, 1933, p. 344)
'A distinction may be drawn here between mass social pressures directed against minorities which do not conform to the demands of a dominating and emotionally charged popular movement and group social pressures emanating from particularistic groups which seek to advance their interests through activities intended to restrain or direct the behavior of resistant elements.' (ibid., p. 345)

prestige-suggestion See *suggestion; suggestion, prestige.*

prevalence (pre'va-lens) In epidemiology, prevalence is the number of cases presently existing and active in a given population at any particular time. See *rate; incidence.*

pre-vocation In occupational therapy this denotes the occupation prescribed primarily for the disability of the patient, but with a possible future vocation taken into consideration; 'prescribed occupations are employed for the studied purpose of leading up to definite education and training for some industry, trade or profession.' (Slagle, E.C. and Roberson,

H.H. *Syllabus for Training of Nurses in Occupational Therapy*, State Hospitals Press, Utica, N.Y., 1933)

priapism (prī'ap-iz'm) A term used by many in its psychiatric meaning as the equivalent of satyriasis. It is also used to denote persistent erection of the penis, particularly when the erection is due to organic disease and not to sexual desire.

Priapus (prī-ā'pus) (Priapus, the son of Venus and Mercury (or Bacchus) is the god of procreation and hence of gardens and vineyards, as the embodiment of the generative force in nature. The Priapic cult was associated with the worship of the membrum virile, and Priapus became equivalent with a satyr and the phallus, and *priapism* became a synonym of lewdness.) Priapus has become a common noun and means the penis, though rarely so in psychiatry.

pride, penis A term employed to designate the feeling of superiority and power attendant to the possession of the male genital organ. The concept has been emphasized by Melanie Klein in her analysis of the child's instinctual life. 'In describing the development of the boy, I have drawn attention to certain factors which tend, as I think, to increase yet more the central importance which the penis possesses for him. They may be summed up as follows: (1) The anxiety arising from his earliest danger situations, his fears of being attacked in all parts of his body and inside it, which include all his fears belonging to the feminine position, are displaced onto the penis or an external organ, where they can be more successfully mastered. The increased pride the boy takes in his penis and all that this involves may also be said to be a method of mastering those fears and disappointments which his feminine position lays him open to more particularly. (2) The fact that the penis is a vehicle first of the boy's destructive and then of his creative omnipotence, enhances its importance as a means of mastering anxiety. In this ministering to his sense of omnipotence, assisting him in the task of testing by reality and promoting his object—relationships . . . in fact, in subserving the all-important function of mastering anxiety—the penis is brought into specially close relation with the ego and is made into a representative of the ego and the conscious; while the interior of the body,

the imagos and the faeces—what is invisible and unknown, that is—are compared to the unconscious.' (Klein, M. *The Psycho-Analysis of Children*, tr. by Strachey, A., Norton, New York, 1932)

primacy, complete genital From the psychoanalytic point of view, genitality is divided into two principal sub-stages. The first is the phallic phase. The second is reached only at puberty; it is the stage of late genital, or complete genital primacy.

primacy, early genital See *primacy, phallic.*

primacy, oral This term refers to the infant's contracting and first comprehending the world primarily in terms of the mouth. According to Freud, this is determined by the erotic satisfaction derived from mouth contact. Other analysts believe that Freud overemphasized the erotization of a situation that may be purely developmental, and that the infant first contacts the world by mouth because it is his most efficient and adequate organ. Thus oral primacy is a generally recognized organic fact, but to many psychoanalysts the important aspect of the oral phase is not so much the biological background as the differences in experience which occur during this biologically determined period. 'Moreover, the kind of world contacted through the mouth is not universally the same, and the differences in experience make a more significant impression on personality development than does the organic fact of a period of oral primacy.' (Thompson, C. *Psychoanalysis, Evolution and Development*, Hermitage House, New York, 1950)

primacy, phallic (fal'ik) A psychoanalytic concept. During the pregenital stage of infantile sexuality, libido spreads over various parts of the body, with greatest concentration at two principal erogenous zones, the oral and the anal. The third erogenous zone of special significance is the genital, which at this early stage is called phallic. As Freud says, 'from all one hears in analyses one could not guess that the male genitals consist of anything more than the penis.' When libido becomes preponderantly associated with the penis, during the stage of infantile sexuality, the expression *phallic primacy* is used to designate such concentration.

According to Freud the phallic phase is as much a part of the girl's growth as it is the boy's. 'Third comes the *phallic* phase, in which for both sexes the penis (and what corresponds to it in the girl) achieves an importance which can no longer be overlooked.' (Freud, S. *New Introductory Lectures on Psychoanalysis,* tr. by Sprott, W.J.H., Norton, New York, 1933)

'In the phallic stage the genitals become an erotogenic zone with pleasure possibilities comparable to those of the oral and anal zones. The penis (and clitoris) absorbs to a large extent the erotogenicity of the other zones and Freud speaks of "phallic primacy." ' (Healy, W., Bronner, A.F., and Bowers, A.M. *The Structure and Meaning of Psychoanalysis,* Knopf, New York, 1930)

primal scene See *scene, primal.*

primary behavior disorders See *behavior disorders.*

primary ictal automatism (ik'tal aw-tō'-ma-tiz'm) A type of psychomotor epilepsy. See *epilepsy.*

primary psychic process See *process, primary psychic.*

primary thought-disorder See *thought-disorder, primary.*

primitivation (prim-i-ti-vā'shun) A name given by Fenichel to the regression of the ego to the early primitive stage in its development. Apparently this term is used only in reference to those states of regression which involve the loss of all the higher ego functions. Thus objective thinking will have been replaced by magical thinking or wish-fulfilling hallucinations; object relationships and love will be of the helpless, passive dependent type, or there may even be a lack of objects; sexuality will be colored with oral eroticism; all perceptions, even those associated with incorporation, may be completely blocked; unco-ordinated discharge movements will replace purposeful actions. According to Fenichel, this primitivation state of marked regression occurs in both the traumatic neuroses and schizophrenia. In the former, the patients often exhibit an attitude of utter helplessness and passive dependence in which the behavior is that of an infant. But in traumatic neuroses the regression of the ego comes out most dramatically when perceptions and actions are tempor-arily blocked. The patient may show constant weakness and fatigue, be unable to undertake any active tasks, encounter difficulty in concentration and memory, show various levels of disturbance of consciousness. Of course, fainting is the most primitive response to a trauma. Fenichel explains that this primitivation appears in the traumatic neuroses as an emergency phenomenon. All mental energies are required to master the intruding overwhelming excitation. Thus the ego functions are blocked and have to relinquish their energies in favor of the emergency task. Moreover, in this way further excitations are excluded.

In schizophrenia, too, many of the symptoms are 'direct expressions of a regressive breakdown of the ego and an undoing of differentiations acquired through mental development.' There is a 'return to the time when the ego was not yet established or had just begun to be established.' For example, world-destruction phantasies are caused by the inner perception of the loss of object relationships; feelings of grandeur express the increase in narcissism that occurs as the psychic energy withdrawn from objects is invested in the ego; schizophrenic thinking is the archaic magical thinking that precedes the development of reality-testing in the small child; hebephrenia is a vegetative existence expressing the old passive receptive or even intra-uterine adaptations. (Fenichel, O. *The Psychoanalytic Theory of Neurosis,* Norton, New York, 1945)

primitivization *Primitivation* (q.v.).

Prince, Morton (1854–1929) American psychiatrist and neurologist.

principle, echo This psychiatric term denotes in children the echo-like repetition or imitation whereby they pattern themselves after their parents and exhibit certain behavior or behaviorisms similar to those seen in their parents but not necessarily indicative of inheritance. For example, a child learns to speak English or French, says Allport, 'not because of specific genetic predisposition, but because English or French is spoken in his home.' (Allport, G.W. *Personality: A Psychological Interpretation,* Holt, New York, 1937) Allport suggested the term echo-principle to designate imitative patterning of this kind. Characteristic parental gestures and postures are similarly 'echoed.'

principle, homeopathic (hō-mē-ō-path′ik)
See *principle, isopathic.*

principle, isopathic (ī-sō-path′ik) An expression coined by Jones, which he had
earlier called the *homeopathic principle,*
'according to which the cause cures the
effect.' (Jones, E. *Papers on Psycho-
Analysis,* 4th ed., Wood, Baltimore, 1938)
'It is curious, and seemingly a paradox,
that guilt can be relieved by an exhibition
of the very thing—namely, hate—which
was the generating occasion of the guilt
itself. We are familiar with the talion
principle in psychology and with the
exactness with which the punishment is
made to fit the crime. We have here an
example of a very similar principle, which
might be termed the *isopathic principle,*
according to which the cause cures the effect.' (ibid.)

principle of anticipatory maturation See
maturation, anticipatory, principle of.

principle of inertia (in-ēr′shi-à) The *principle of inertia,* a term introduced in
psychoanalysis by Alexander, is the same
as the principle of *repetition-compulsion*
(q.v.). Alexander lays stress upon the
consideration that the tendency to automatic action is greater than that involving
constantly changing and active mental
efforts.

principle, pleasure A regulatory mechanism of mental life whose function is to
reduce psychic tension that has arisen as
a result of drives pressing for discharge.
The pleasure-pain principle tries to undo
the effects of disturbing stimuli (pain) in
a way that will most easily provide satisfaction (pleasure). It comes into operation later than the repetition-compulsion
principle and is concerned mainly with
the stimuli afforded by the action of the
drives or instincts, while the earlier principle is concerned with damping external
stimuli and merely tries to restore the
organism to as near its original state as
possible. (Jones, E. *Papers on Psycho-
Analysis,* 5th ed., Ballière, Tindall and
Cox, London, 1948) The pleasure-pain
principle operates earlier than the reality
principle. See *repetition-compulsion.*
'The *Nirvana*-principle expresses the
tendency of the death instincts, the
pleasure-principle represents the claims of
the libido and that modification of it, the
reality-principle, the influence of the outer
world.' (Freud, S. *Collected Papers,* vol.

2, tr. by Riviere, J., Leonard and Virginia
Woolf and The Institute of Psychoanalysis, London, 1924–25, p. 257)

principle, reality In normal growth the
individual adapts himself to what Freud
calls the pleasure-principle. This means
that mental life and personality development are shaped to meet the requirements
of internal needs. Subsequently, in healthy
mental progress, the demands of reality
compel an inclusion of these needs within
the personality of the individual. The
reality-principle, while entering into the
service of the pleasure-principle, causes
the latter to be appreciably modified. As
Freud maintains, 'the *Nirvana*-principle
expresses the tendency of the death-in-
stincts, the *pleasure*-principle represents
the claims of the libido and that modification of it, the *reality*-principle, the influence of the outer world.' (Freud, S.
Collected Papers, vol. 2, tr. by Riviere, J.,
Leonard and Virginia Woolf and The
Institute of Psychoanalysis, London, 1924–
25)

principle, treble safeguard The variable
regulation of all growth functions by
means of integration of endocrine and
individual organ activities with the molecular dynamics of the nervous system.

prison psychosis See *psychosis, prison.*

privacy 'Withdrawal from the group with,
at the same time, ready access to it.'
(Park, R.E. and Burgess, E.W. *Introduction to the Science of Sociology,* University of Chicago Press, Chicago, 1921)

privation, sexual Sexual privation is a
common concept in psychoanalysis.
'In the conditions of life in modern
society there is certainly no lack of sexual
privation.' (Freud, S. *Collected Papers,*
vol. 1, tr. by Riviere, J., Leonard and
Virginia Woolf and The Institute of
Psychoanalysis, London, 1924–25)
'It follows, and my analytical experience fully confirms the conclusion, that
sheer privation comes of course in both
sexes, to have just the same meaning as
deliberate deprivation on the part of the
human environment. We thus reach the
formula: *Privation is equivalent to frustration.*' (Jones, E. *Papers on Psycho-
Analysis,* 4th ed., Wood, Baltimore, 1938)

privilege See *communication, privileged.*

proband (prō′band) In genetic studies of
tainted families this term designates the

original cases constituting the starting point of a family study. These cases are called *probands,* or *probati,* because they must be proved representative of the type of trait-carrier whose blood-relations are to be investigated as to the recurrence of the trait under observation. Although the probands are not the main object of such a family study, their examination comes first and is of pre-eminent importance, since it must determine the hereditary trait so positively that a group of their blood-relations must have likewise inherited that trait.

The practicable statistical method of probands in the study of selective population groups was devised by Weinberg and is called the *proband method.*

probatus (prô-bä′toos) See *proband.*

problem As used by psychiatric social workers this term 'denotes not the major general problem of the case, but the component problem situations as they arise for treatment by interview or modification of the material situation.' (*Proceedings* of the American Association of Hospital Social Workers, 1926)

problem, behavior See *behavior disorders.*

problem child See *child, problem.*

problem drinker See *alcoholism, chronic.*

problem, family behavior This expression is used in social work to denote 'anti-social conduct of someone within the patient group. Behavior which has the status of offenses or delinquency is here included; as *Assault, Stealing,* etc.' (Hamilton, G. *A Medical Social Terminology,* Presbyterian Hospital, New York, 1930)

problem, feeding See *feeding-problem.*

problem, nuclear The patient's central conflict on which therapy should be focused. It is believed that the manifestations of a number of maladjustments and defenses in a patient usually emanate from one central conflict. Examples of these are inadequate resolution of the oedipal conflict, feelings of inadequacy, unwholesome sexual identifications, sibling rivalry, and so forth. The critical event has a dynamic relation to the nuclear problem. (Slavson, S.R. *An Introduction to Group Therapy,* The Commonwealth Fund, Oxford University Press, New York, 1943, p. 124) See *conflict, actual; conflict, root.*

process, cultural The process by which the folkways, mores, and social values are transmitted from generation to generation and are modified in adjustment to social change.

'It is the function of the cultural process to shape and define the social forms and the social patterns which each generation imposes upon its successors.' (Park, R.E. and Burgess, E.W. *Introduction to the Science of Sociology,* University of Chicago Press, Chicago, 1921)

process, elementary D. Nachmansohn's theory of neural excitation and transmission: excitation of the neural membrane results in a dissociation of bound acetylcholine into an active form (the ester); free acetylcholine acts on a protein receptor and thereby increases the permeability of nerve membrane to ions. Thus the bioelectric potential is generated and acts as a stimulus to adjoining nerve segments or to the synapse, resulting in propagation and transmission of the impulse. Meanwhile, the free ester of acetylcholine undergoes hydrolysis by the enzyme cholinesterase, and the protein receptor returns to its resting condition. The barrier to ionic movement is thus re-established.

processes, unconscious The processes going on in the unconscious part of the psyche. In Freud's conception of the total personality the psyche is divided into: (1) the conscious, or consciousness, which exists within the level of awareness; (2) the preconscious, which exists outside awareness, but can be readily called into awareness when needed; and (3) the unconscious, which exists outside the level of awareness and is not subject to recall into consciousness under ordinary circumstances. Freud also divided the psyche into ego, id, and superego, and these three areas are not to be confused with the three described above, for they are not synonymous. 'Freud saw the newborn infant as chiefly Id, that is, masses of impulse without an organizing or directing consciousness. Contact with the world gradually modifies a portion of this Id, and the Ego, a small area of consciousness, slowly emerges from it. It is developed out of the necessity for reality testing. However, the Ego is not synonymous with consciousness. Only a small part even of the Ego is conscious at any one time. A great part of the Ego as now defined exists outside of awareness, but can readily be recalled when needed. This part was called the preconscious. Still another part of the Ego is unconscious and cannot readily be made conscious. This consists of the experiences and feelings which have been repressed. By the repression these experiences are somehow brought into more intimate contact with the forces of the Id.

'The Id is a mass of seething excitement which cannot become conscious directly. Many of its forces never reach awareness, but from time to time portions of its energy can find some expression in the Ego by becoming connected with the memory-traces of repressed experience and thus participating in the formation of symptoms; becoming distorted as in dream symbols; or by undergoing modification chiefly as a result of the influence of the Super-ego as in sublimation. The Id Freud conceived of as of tremendous size in comparison with the Ego. He thought of it as the generator of energy, the dynamo of the personality. It is somehow closely associated with the organic processes of the body.

'In the course of time, the Ego takes over certain standards from the culture, chiefly through the training by parents in early childhood. These standards become incorporated as parent images within the Ego as a part of itself and this part is called the Super-ego. It exercises a criticizing and censoring power. The functions of dream censor and resistance described in Freud's earlier writings are now seen as part of the Super-ego. The Super-ego, in brief, represents the incorporated standards of society. It includes the parental attitudes, especially as these attitudes were understood and interpreted by the child in his early years. It includes also the person's own ideals for himself, and Freud even indicates that certain phylogenetic experiences such as those described by Jung under the concept of the collective unconscious may also be part of the Super-ego. Much of the Super-ego is unconscious, because it was incorporated by the child very early and without his awareness. This means that like all unconscious material this portion is not available for reality testing.' (Thompson, C. *Psychoanalysis, Evolution and Development,* Hermitage House, New York, 1950)

Unconscious processes, then, refer to

methods of handling the environment and the instinctual needs on a level outside that of conscious awareness. These include repression, regression, reaction-formation, isolation, undoing, introjection, turning against the self, reversal, sublimation, and the development of character structure. These terms are defined elsewhere individually.

process, interpersonal In psychoanalysis, this term refers to the fact that in the therapeutic situation the analyst is more than a mirror reflecting the patient's problems. Just as there is transference on the patient's part, so is there counter-transference on the analyst's part. Still, not every attitude toward the analyst is a transference attitude. The patient can like or dislike the analyst for what he really is, and the analyst cannot completely conceal what kind of person he is. The analyst sometimes transfers elements from his past or present problems to the analytic situation.

'I think it is clear that Freud's conception of countertransference is to be distinguished from the present-day conception of analysis as an interpersonal process. In the interpersonal situation, the analyst is seen as relating to his patient not only with his distorted affects but with his healthy personality also. That is, the analytic situation is essentially a human relationship in which, while one person is more immediately detached than the other and has less at stake, he is nevertheless an active participant.' (Thompson, C. *Psychoanalysis, Evolution and Development,* Hermitage House, New York, 1950)

processomania (pros-es-ō-mā′ni-à) Bianchi's term for mania for litigation.

process, primary (psychic) A name given by Freud to the laws that govern unconscious processes. The intense forces operating in the unconscious or in the id are the organic instincts, which are continually striving for discharge, for satisfaction. This striving goes on according to what is known as the primary process, according to certain laws utterly different from those that have become familiar in conscious thought. An understanding of the primary process has been gained through the study of dreams, for in the formation of dreams instinctual impulses play the major role; they have forced themselves upon the ego and into consciousness. At the same time the unconscious material retains its own ways of working. The primary process can be observed at work in dreams.

The term primary process is used to refer to a type of thinking, characteristic of childhood, and/or to the way in which libidinal or aggressive energy is mobilized and discharged. The basic characteristics of the primary process are a tendency to immediate discharge of drive energy (i.e. immediate gratification) and an extreme mobility of cathexis so that substitute methods of discharge can be achieved with relative ease. Primary process thinking is characterized by the absence of any negatives, conditionals, or other qualifying conjunctions; by the lack of any sense of time; and by the use of allusion, analogy, displacement, condensation, and symbolic representation. Drive energy characteristically remains unneutralized during the period of operation of the primary process.

In essence, the primary process is identical with Freud's formulation of the pleasure-principle. The difference between them is that while the pleasure principle is described in subjective terms, the primary process is described in objective terms.

process psychosis See *psychosis, process.*

process, secondary (psychic) A name given by Freud to the laws 'which regulate events in the preconscious or ego.' The ego is that part of the individual's mental apparatus which regulates the discharge of excitations arising either from external stimuli or from internal stimuli (instinctual demands). In executing this function, the ego is concerned with self-preservation, i.e. avoiding danger. In the case of external stimuli, the ego determines when they should be avoided, when it should adapt itself, and when the external world can be modified. In the case of internal stimuli (those arising from instinctual demands) the ego decides when the demands can be satisfied, when the satisfaction should be postponed, and when the demands or excitations should be completely suppressed. (The dangers of instinctual demands are, first, that their satisfaction might involve dangers in the external world, and, second, that an excessive strength of instinct can damage the organization of the ego.)

Thus the most important part of the ego is its intellectual process.

This intellectual activity, 'after considering the present state of things and weighing up earlier experiences, endeavors by means of experimental actions to calculate the consequences of the proposed line of conduct.' Thus by means of its faculties of judgment and intelligence, by the application of logic and reality-testing, the ego blocks the tendency of the instincts toward immediate discharge. Instead, the ego decides under what conditions it would be safe to satisfy the instincts, if at all. The process by which the ego regulates the discharge of instinctual demands, that is, through the above-mentioned logical thinking, is the mode of operation of the conscious and preconscious mind and is called the secondary process. (Freud, S. *An Outline of Psychoanalysis,* Norton, New York, 1949)

process, social A process means 'continuous change taking place in a definite manner through the operation of forces present from the first within the situation.' (McIver, R.M. *Society, A Textbook of Sociology,* Farrar & Rinehart, New York, 1937)

The idea of social process 'must be seen as the center of a whole configuration of concepts ranged around it which are both historically related to it and logically implicit in it. These are: first, the concept of process itself; second, the concept of social interaction, or of society as a flow of relations between individuals; third, the concept of historical and social continuity; fourth, the concept of the organic connection between the individual and society; fifth, the concept of the social heritage; sixth, the concept of society as an organic unity; seventh, the concept of multiple factors.' (Lerner, M. 'Social Process'; *Encyclopaedia of the Social Sciences,* vol. 14, Macmillan, New York, 1934, p. 149)

The four chief social processes are: competition, conflict (social), accommodation, and *assimilation* (social) (q.v.).

process, subconscious 'A subconscious process may be provisionally defined as one of which the personality is unaware, which, therefore, is outside of the personal consciousness, and which is a factor in the determination of conscious and bodily phenomena, or produces effects analogous to those which might be directly or indirectly induced by consciousness.' (Prince, M. *The Unconscious,* Macmillan, New York, 1916)

proctophage (prok'tō-fāj) This term, derived from Greek nomenclature, was resorted to in official reports during World War II in order to translate 'apt but scarcely printable G.I. slang' characterizing driving, ruthless officers: 'he is an ass-eater' (not very common) and 'he'll eat; work; beat your ass off' (not infrequent). (Rosen, H., and Kiene, H.E. 'The Paranoic Officer and the Officer Paranee,' *American Journal of Psychiatry 103,* 620, 1946–47)

prodigy See *child, bright.*

prodigy, idiotic Idiot-savant.

prodromata (prō-drom'ä-tà) The aggregate of prodromes.

prodrome (prō'drōm) Precursor. An early or premonitory symptom of a disease or disorder. From the psychiatric point of view, withdrawal from reality, oversensitiveness as regards the remarks of others, and ideas of reference are frequently prodromata of schizophrenia.

progeria (prō-jē'ri-à) Gilford introduced this term for a special form of dwarfism characterized by a combination of infantilistic traits and premature senility. The dwarfs of this type show infantile proportions of the skeleton, complete absence of hair, a senile face with a long, aquiline nose, deficient secondary sexual characteristics in spite of a fairly normal development of the sex organs, thickened ends of the long bones, average intelligence, and a tendency to vascular sclerosis; they are practically identical with the sub-group of drawfism called *senile nanism* by Variot and Pironneau.

prognosis (prog-nō'sis) Forecast or estimation of the course, outcome, and duration of an illness—the opinion being formed during the course of the illness.

prognosis, direction This is a term used by Bleuler to designate the type of reaction that a disorder may be expected to develop. Thus, 'within the realm of schizophrenia there are again different directions such as the paranoid, catatonic dementia, etc., that have to be considered in the prognosis.' (Bleuler, E. *Textbook of Psychiatry,* tr. by Brill, A.A., Macmillan, New York, 1930)

Direction prognosis is distinguished

from *extent prognosis,* which has to do with the prediction relating to the progress of the disorder in a given period of time.

prognosis, extent See *prognosis, direction.*

progredient See *neurosis, progredient.*

progressive degenerative subcortical encephalopathy (de-jen'er-à-tiv sub-kor'tikal en-sef-al-op'à-thē) See *sclerosis, diffuse.*

project In occupational therapy this term usually means the occupation or activity which has been planned to fulfill the requirements noted on the patient's prescription card. See *projection.*

projection As used by psychiatrists, this means the process of throwing out upon another the ideas or impulses that belong to oneself. It is the act of giving objective or seeming reality to what is subjective. The expression implies that what is cast upon another is considered undesirable to the one who projects. The person who blames another for his own mistakes is using the projection mechanism.

Freud explains that the individual orients himself by means of both inner and outer perceptions. The latter can be managed by motor activity, which is another way of saying that if reality is uncomfortable the individual may alter or avoid it. Inner perceptions, such as the instincts and their representations, cannot be handled with the same facility; one cannot flee from one's 'merciless claims of his instincts.' Therefore, the individual, who has an inner problem that is painful to him, may project the problem upon another person or upon some part of reality. When the conflicting issue has been externalized, he may engage it as if it were originally an external situation. For example, the paranoid schizophrenic individual, beset with unconscious homosexual urges, projects the urges upon some man or men in the environment and then struggles against the urges as they seem to arise from outside sources.

In its morbid manifestations, the projection mechanism is clearly an unconscious process, at least, in the sense that the conscious ego is not at all aware of the process.

According to Ferenczi, projection is one of the first defensive or protective measures employed by the child in defense of its narcissism. When the child realizes that he is not omnipotent, he begins to ascribe omnipotence to those about him and comes to realize that others control him. He does not, however, abandon the feeling of his own importance and of his magical powers.

Alexander says that the projection mechanism serves to create harmony between reality (which the child reshapes) and the id. See *reference, ideas of.*

projection, impersonal Projection alone means attributing one's own ideas or impulses to another. By implication, this is done because one finds his own ideas or impulses objectionable. Impersonal projection refers to the same mechanism applied not to objectionable material but to impersonal or neutral material. One example of impersonal projection is found in the echo of reading aloud, when the subject feels that someone else is saying the words which he himself is reading. Approximately 47 per cent of patients who admit to auditory hallucinations also hear the echo of reading. These patients do not feel that the echo occurs more with one type of reading material than with another, and it is therefore difficult to think of apparently innocuous reading material selected at random as having assumed some objectionable significance to such a large percentage of patients. Marjorie C. Meehan feels that impersonal projection may indicate the extreme feeling of passivity and domination by an external agent so characteristic of certain schizophrenics; the symptom may also suggest that there is some mechanism, possibly physiological, which transforms internal speech so that it seems to the patient to be heard from without. (*Psychiatric Quarterly 16*, 156, 1942)

projective test See *test, projective.*

prolonged sleep therapy See *treatment, continuous sleep.*

promiscuity (prō-mis-kū′i-tē) 'Intimate behavior upon the basis of casual association.' (Burgess, E.W. in 'Introduction' to Cressy, P.G., *The Taxi-Dance Hall,* University of Chicago Press, Chicago, 1932)

Examples of promiscuity are to be found in behavior in the taxi-dance hall, the public dance, and prostitution.

proneness, accident A relationship exists between personality organization and the occurrence of accidents. Insurance companies have compiled statistics which

show that only 20 per cent of all accidents can be ascribed to mechanical causes and that 80 per cent are due to personality factors. For some years it has been known that a high percentage of accidents were limited to a comparatively small number of individuals. In L.D. Bristol's study, 10 per cent of a group were responsible for 75 per cent of the accidents, and P.G. Moorad estimated that 12 to 15 per cent were responsible for 100 per cent of accidents. In the army similar observations were made. Many soldiers were wounded because of their emotional state. Under stress of battle many individuals used poorer judgment because of their tenseness and fear. In some individuals accident proneness is due to an emotional state present prior to the injury. In others, deep-seated personality traits (such as unconscious wishes to be punished) lead to repeated accidents. (Menninger, W.C. *Psychiatry in a Troubled World,* Macmillan, New York, 1948)

propaganda (prop-à-gan′dà) 'A deliberately worked and guided campaign to induce people to accept a given view, sentiment, or value.' (Blumer, H.E., in Park, R.E., *Principles of Sociology,* Barnes & Noble, New York, 1939)

'The technique of influencing human action by the manipulation of representations.' (Lasswell, H.D., 'Propaganda'; *Encyclopaedia of the Social Sciences,* vol. 11, Macmillan, New York, 1933, p. 521)

propfschizophrenia (propf-skiz-ō-frē′ni-à) A schizophrenic syndrome superimposed, engrafted, so to speak, upon an intellectual deficiency (oligophrenia). However, schizophrenia may be engrafted upon any organic disease. It is generally considered that the disease facilitates the development of the schizophrenic syndrome in a predisposed individual.

prophase (prō′fāz) The initial stage of a cell division by mitosis. See *division, cell.*

prophylaxis (prof-i-lak′sis) The branch of medical science which has to do with protection against the onset of a disease or disorder. For example, the treatment of an individual showing marked schizoidism in an effort to prevent the development of schizophrenia is termed prophylaxis.

propinquity (prō-pin′kwi-tē) Proximity; in genetics, nearness of blood relationship.

proprioception (prō-pri-ō-sep′shun) The

ability to appreciate sensations of muscle, joint, tendon, and vibration.

proprio-social See *constant, central.*

propulsion Rapid, forward running with short steps, in paralysis agitans.

prosencephalon (pros-en-sef′à-lon) *Fore-brain* (q.v.).

prosopagnosia (prō-so-pag-nō′si-à) Inability to recognize faces. This may be congenital or acquired, but it rarely occurs as an isolated defect.

prosopalgia (prō-sō-pal′ji-à) See *tic douloureux.*

prosoplegia (prō-sō-plē′ji-à) Bell's palsy. See *nerve, facial.*

prosopoplegia (prō-sō-pō-plē′ji-à) Peripheral facial paralysis or Bell's palsy.

protanopia (prō-tan-op′i-à) A form of color-blindness, usually referred to as red-blindness, in which red and blue-green are confused.

protest, body A term coined by Esther L. Richards to indicate that physical dysfunctions may serve as outlets for worries, disappointments, frustrations, etc.

protest, masculine This is a technical term applied by Adler both to male and female individuals, to describe a desire to escape from the feminine role. This concept he regards as the main motive force in neurotic disease. It represents the distorted apprehension of sex-differences caused by the striving for superiority. If it takes an active form in women, they attempt from an early age to usurp the male position. They become aggressive in manner, adopt definitely masculine habits or 'tricks' of behavior, and endeavor to domineer everyone about them.

The masculine protest in a male individual indicates that he has never fully recovered from an infantile doubt as to whether he really is male. He strives for an ideal masculinity invariably conceived as the possession by himself of freedom, love, and power, 'which in this egoistic conception amounts simply to irresponsibility, the *conquest* of women or friends, and the surpassing or overthrowing of others.' (Mairet, P. *ABC of Adler's Psychology,* Kegan Paul, Trench, Trubner, London, 1928)

prothymia (prō-thī′mi-à, -thim′i-à) Mental alertness.

proto- (prō′tō-) Combining form meaning first, original, primitive, from Gr. *prōtos,* first, foremost.

protocol The individual case record; the 'raw material' of a study or experiment before it has been included into the conclusions or overall results of the study. In clinical psychiatry, the protocol commonly refers to the complete case history and workup, in contrast to the case summary or final conclusions about the individual case.

protomasochism (prō-tō-maz′ok-iz'm) The primary, ancestral tendency of the death instinct to lead all human beings into annihilation; a drive into nothingness. Reik uses the term to describe 'a pleasure of destruction directed against the ego, a kind of sadism which has chosen the ego for its victim.' In Freud's opinion, the death-instinct that is not neutralized by the erotic urges or channeled into the outer world remains effective within the organism, directing its forces against the ego proper, as it did in primitive man. (Reik, T. *Masochism in Modern Man,* Farrar and Rinehart, New York, 1941)

protopathic (-path′ik) Of primary sensitiveness, i.e. pertaining to sensory nerves in the skin with a primary, grosser, or more limited sensibility to stimuli. Opposed to *epicritic.*

The ability to appreciate deep pain sensation and marked variations in temperature such as hot and cold; distinguished from epicritic sensibility.

proto-phallic (-fal′ik) Jones says that there are two stages to what Freud calls the phallic phase: 'The first of the two— let us call it the *proto-phallic* phase— would be marked by innocence or ignorance—at least in consciousness—where there is no conflict over the matter in question, it being confidently assumed by the child that the rest of the world is built like itself and has a satisfactory male organ—penis or clitoris, as the case may be. In the second, or *deutero-phallic* phase, there is a dawning suspicion that the world is divided into two classes; not male and female in the proper sense, but penis-possessing and castrated (though actually the two classifications overlap pretty closely).' (Jones, E. *Papers on Psycho-Analysis,* 4th ed., Wood, Baltimore, 1938)

protoplasm (prō′tō-plaz'm) In biology, the cellular substance with which the life of living beings is associated. All vital activities of an organism, such as growth, repair, and reproduction, are ultimately referred to the properties of this transparent and jelly-like cell material which usually shows a fibrillar structure with a honeycombed reticulum and consists of a mixture of proteins, carbohydrates, fats, lipoids, salts, and water.

The protoplasmic matter of each cell is endowed with the structural and functional peculiarities characteristic of the species of animals or plants to which the cell belongs. It is subject to the complex biochemical processes which are the fundamental basis of all cell functions.

Of particular importance in the biological mechanism of inheritance are the proteins, which are built up of one or more of the amino acids. They are very specific in their chemical relations and do certain things with such great precision that the enormous number of different kinds of organisms can be maintained with a high degree of persistence.

protopsyche (-sī'kē) In discussing *The Phenomena of Hysterical Materialization,* Ferenczi says: 'If, therefore, the reflex process is considered not only as a prototype but as a preliminary stage of the psychic process, a stage to which indeed the highest psychic elaboration always remains inclined to regress, then the puzzling leap from mental to bodily in the conversion symptom and the reflex wish-fulfilling phenomenon of materialization become less amazing. It is simply regression to the "protopsyche."' (Ferenczi, S. *Further Contributions to the Theory and Technique of Psycho-Analysis,* tr. by Suttie, J.I., Leonard and Virginia Woolf and The Institute of Psychoanalysis, London, 1926)

proviso, parapathic (pro-vī'zō, par-à-path'ik) Stekel's term for a compromise or bargain which the neurotic makes with his illness—e.g. the patient who thinks that as long as he remains ill, his father will not die: it is a 'clause,' or stipulation with the neurosis in order to justify its existence. In other words, 'if the patient accepts his neurosis, some disaster which he dreads will not happen.' Adler referred to this mental mechanism as *junctim;* another name for it is *neurotic proviso.* (Stekel, W. *The Interpretation of Dreams,* Liveright, New York, 1943)

prudery Exaggerated concern about minor points of the moral or ethical code. This is almost always a reaction-formation, the prude decrying in others the very impulses and behavior he must deny in himself.

pruritus, psychogenic (proō-rī'tus, sī-kō-jen'ik) An itching dermatitis of a functional nature. The diagnosis of psychogenic pruritus is made only after organic factors have been ruled out by complete allergy studies, search for foci of infection, physical examination, blood count, serology, chest X-ray, etc. Psychogenic pruritus is produced or aggravated by environmental stress, and for this reason it has been felt that men with a predisposition to the disease should be excluded from the armed forces. Patients with functional pruritus are usually of the obsessive-compulsive character type, are rigid, defensive, and not readily susceptible to suggestion or reassurance. The disease is difficult to cure.

Sullivan and Bereston distinguish four psychosomatic dermatological syndromes: psychogenic pruritus, neurodermatitis, psychogenic urticaria, and hyperhidrosis. (Sullivan, D.J., and Bereston, E.S. 'Psychosomatic Dermatological Syndromes in Military Service,' *American Journal of Psychiatry 103,* 42, 1946)

psammoma-body (sam-ō'mà-) A collection of fibroglia, collagen fibers, and small calcified concretions seen often in meningiomas.

psellism ([p]sel'iz'm) Stammering; indistinct or faulty pronunciation.

psellismus haesitans (sel-ēs-moos hes'i-tans) *Obs.* Stammering; ischnophonia.

pseudacusis (sū-dà-kū'sis) *Obs.* Auditory hallucinations and illusions.

pseudamnesia (sū-dam-nē'zhi-à) *Obs.* A transitory amnesia, usually associated with an organic brain disease.

pseudesthesia (sū-des-thē'si-à) Sensation or perception without a corresponding stimulus. An imaginary or illusory sensation, such as phantom limb.

pseudo- (sū'dō-) Combining form meaning false, spurious, from Gr. *pseŭdos,* falsehood, lie, *pseudēs,* lying, false.

pseudoaggression A false aggressiveness developed in neurotics as a result of denial of their basic psychic masochism. In other words, the basic desire is to be mistreated. This desire gains only reproach from the superego, and a defense of pseudoaggression is constructed. 'No, I do not want to be mistreated by this person. The situation is just the opposite —I want to kill this person or mistreat him.' This pseudoaggression also receives reproach from the superego and is itself denied, but the neurotic is more willing to accept the guilt for his pseudoaggression than that for his underlying masochism. Bergler believes that neurotics have no true ego aggression, for almost all of their aggression is in the superego. He explains stage fright in actors in this way. Superficially, the symptom refers to a fear of one's aggressive exhibitionism. In reality, however, this aggressiveness is a false front with which the patient deludes himself and others to deny the basic fear, that his masochism will be uncovered. Under successful psychoanalytic treatment, a more equitable distribution of aggression between superego and ego can be achieved and the patient can become truly aggressive as the need for aggression arises in reality situations. (E. Bergler, *Psychoanalytic Quarterly Supplement 23,* 317, 1949)

pseudo-angina (sū-dō-an-jī′nà) It is believed by many psychiatrists that anxiety is one of the many conditions that may give rise to anginoid attacks.

'Turning to the physical symptoms of anxiety we note the same admixture of over-excitation and inhibition phenomena as that referred to in connection with the mental symptoms. . . . Pseudo-angina is merely a symptom of precordial anxiety. . . .' (Jones, E. *Papers on Psycho-Analysis,* 4th ed., Wood, Baltimore, 1938)

pseudoasthma A functional disorder of respiration characterized by breathing difficulties very similar to those observed in true asthma, but differing from those present in the latter disease by reason of emotional origin. Instances of pseudoasthma are often traceable to a severe anxiety arising out of some conflict going on in the unconscious. The following case, excerpted and condensed from Kanner (*Child Psychiatry,* 2nd ed., Thomas, Springfield, Ill., 1948) is illustrative. George H., age nine and a half, was the son of parents who were oversolicitous and overprotective to a damaging degree. At the age of one year, George had an upper respiratory infection which lasted one month. A physician diagnosed the condition as asthma. He warned the parents that the asthma might return in the future and advised that the child be watched closely and brought back whenever the slightest sign of breathing disorder was noticed. But George had no trouble with breathing until he was nine years old. In the interim, however, his parents had kept waiting for the anticipated return of asthma and had frequently reminded George of such a contingency. They had him sleep in their bedroom so that nocturnal panting would not escape their attention, and suggested that he open the window and loosen his belt as soon as he had trouble breathing. Thus, poor George had been conditioned to expect asthma. Through the years he learned that the slightest hint of this condition instantly brought him the loving solicitude and care of his parents. A major environmental change made by the family resulted in a change of schools for George, then nine years old. The boy was very reluctant, extremely fearful, and filled with anxiety about this change. On his very first day at the new school, George at lunch time hurried home, rushed into the house struggling for breath, opened the window, and loosened his belt. The doctor's prediction, made eight years before, seemed to have come true. George had 'asthma.' Of course, he could not continue at school. This time, the condition was properly diagnosed as pseudoasthma. Over a period of time it gradually yielded to diligent psychiatric treatment of the underlying anxiety situation from which it had developed.

pseudo-athetosis (sū-dō-ath-ē-tō′sis) Athetoid movement which is not spontaneous, but elicited when the patient closes his eyes and extends his hands; it occurs in those whose sense of position is impaired such as in tabes or combined sclerosis.

pseudoblepsis (-blep′sis) *Obs.* Visual hallucinations or illusions.

pseudocatatonia, traumatic (-kat-à-tō′ni-à, traw-ma′tik) A catatonic-like state following an injury.

pseudocommunity Norman Cameron's term for the progressive desocialization seen in the schizophrenias in which social language habits are replaced with personal, highly individual habits. The pseudocommunity is a behavioral organization which the patient constructs from his distorted observations, inferences, and phantasies; most commonly, the patient sees himself as the victim of some concerted action.

pseudoconvulsion An attack which simulates a convulsion, with falling and muscular contractions, but with no loss of consciousness, no pupillary changes, amnesia, or postconvulsive confusion. Such an attack usually occurs in hysteria. It may be consciously or unconsciously exaggerated for the sake of gaining sympathy or attention.

pseudocyesis (sū-dō-sī-ē′sis) Spurious pregnancy.

pseudodebility (-de-bil′i-tē) *Pseudoimbecility* (q.v.).

pseudodementia (-dē-men′shi-à) A condition of exaggerated indifference to one's surroundings without actual mental impairment.

pseudodementia, hysterical Wernicke thus denotes a syndrome of hysteria in which the patient appears unable to answer the simplest questions, or to give any information about himself. The patient gives the appearance of being feebleminded.

As a rule the patient, exhibiting this syndrome, regresses to the behavior of early childhood, showing the condition known as *hysterical puerilism.* See *feeblemindedness, affective.*

pseudo-feeblemindedness Feeblemindedness sometimes indicated by a low I.Q. but actually non-existent. Untoward psychological and emotional factors operative at the time of testing can result in a low score misrepresenting the actual mental endowment: this blunder is especially likely to come about when children are tested. The label feeblemindedness resulting from a score of this nature is a misnomer, and the proper term is pseudofeeblemindedness.

pseudo-flexibilitas (psew-dō-flek-sē-bē′-lē-tàs) When an individual, whose movements are more or less normal, maintains for a relatively long period a posture imposed upon him, the condition is known as *pseudo-flexibilitas.*

pseudogeusia (sū-dō-gū′si-à) False perception of taste.

pseudo-giftedness Apparent unusual talents in a child, resulting not from specific or permanent trends but rather from the ability of the bright child to imitate, adopt, and assimilate the behavior patterns of others. Pseudo-giftedness is usually inspired by momentary influence from without rather than by any inborn ability or urge from within. 'The current educational fad for child art has, at the moment, America's parents gasping for breath. As simple art technics are very easy to adopt, and as children in the preintellectual period have a natural urge for self-expression of a formalistic type, art is a natural and vital sort of juvenile language just as it has always been to primitive man.' (Harms, E., ed. *The Guidance of the Superior Child and the Prodigy* in *Handbook of Child Guidance,* Child Care Publications, New York, 1947) Such juvenile abilities commonly disappear after adolescence, with the advance of intellectual and scientific forms of expression.

pseudographia (sū-dō-graf′i-à) 'Katatoniacs perform all sorts of tricks with their writing, just as they do in other departments of voluntary action. Their style is apt to be stilted and circumlocutory. They form their letters with unnecessary care or perhaps have some fantastic alphabet of their own (*pseudographia*).' (Stoddart, W.H.B. *Mind and Its Disorders,* 5th ed., Lewis, London, 1926)

pseudo-hallucination A hallucination, which the patient knows to be such. It is not uncommon for schizophrenic individuals to realize in the early phases of the development of hallucinations that the morbid sensory impressions are the result of abnormal activity of the psyche.

'Hallucinations, the morbidness of which is recognized in spite of the vividness of the deceptive perception (pseudo-hallucinations), occur most readily in the visual sense.' (Bleuler, E. *Textbook of Psychiatry,* tr. by Brill, A.A., Macmillan, New York, 1930)

'In pseudo-hallucinations the patient has the vivid sensory experience, but realizes that it has no external foundations.' (Henderson, D.K. and Gillespie, R.D. *A Text-Book of Psychiatry,* 4th ed., Oxford University Press, London, 1936)

pseudo-hydrophobia (-hī-drō-fō′bi-à) Cynophobia.

pseudohypersexuality (-hī-pĕr-sek-shoo-al′i-tē) A term used by Fenichel interchangeably with the term *hypersexuality.* (Fenichel, O. *The Psychoanalytic Theory of Neurosis,* Norton, New York, 1945)

pseudo-hypnosis (-hip-nō′sis) See *captivation*.

pseudo-identification A method of dealing with people in the environment by apparently identifying oneself with, or assimilating oneself to, the person with whom one chances to be in contact at any given moment. Pseudo-identification is illustrated by the case of the man who asserted that he had found the ideal way of adapting himself to reality: he assimilated himself to the person with whom he chanced to be talking and so had no external conflicts. But in reality, such a method of adaptation led to many conflicts; the man found that he had assimilated himself to A at one time, to B at another, and that A and B were in disagreement. Since pseudo-identification is not insincerity, but rather the conviction that the individual has in fact become one with the other person, such conflicting identifications lead to many reality problems. Pseudo-identification appears somewhat akin to paranoid projection in that the patient's ideas are prevented from entering consciousness and are ascribed to the object, with whom the patient then identifies himself. Unlike the ideas of paranoia, however, those of pseudo-identification are apparently innocent. The dynamics of the process are still poorly understood.

pseudo-imbecility A psychiatric term for the imbecility consisting in the pathological limitation and restriction of intellectual functions of the ego. This intellectual restriction or inhibition may mean (1) that intellectual functions have been erotized and so are given up to escape-conflicts; (2) that the restriction disguises aggression in order to escape retaliation; (3) that it is a display of castration to escape the fear of literal castration and the loss of a love-object; or (4) that it represents an attempt to restore or maintain a secret libidinous rapport within the family. A mask of stupidity enables the child or infantile adult to participate in the sexual life of the parents and other adults to an amazingly unlimited extent which, if overtly expressed, would be strictly and definitely forbidden. Such utilization of stupidity is widespread, because it affords an opportunity for the mutual sexual desires of parent and child to be gratified on a preverbal affective level without becoming conscious through word pictures. Thus, repression or other defense measures are unnecessary, and the child and his parents can maintain a distorted but gratifying affective communion that would otherwise be limited to mother and infant.

The analysis of an 18-year-old pseudo-imbecile, who had manifested his pathological behavior since early childhood, revealed that in the phallic stage of psychic development he had had to give up competition with his aggressive twin brother. He was unable to pass the phallic stage successfully and so regressed to the immediately preceding anal stage. Acting as a counterpart to anal exhibitionism was an intense sexual curiosity against which he had to maintain strong defenses, because of the threats of his father. With pseudo-imbecility, however, he was able unconsciously to satisfy his curiosity, for his parents and siblings permitted his presence even during intercourse. He was regarded as a pet animal that does no harm by its presence and neither understands nor participates in what it sees.

pseudo-insanity *Obs.* Simulation.

pseudo-intoxication *Obs.* A trance-like state in which there is a tendency to staggering and stammering with excitement and irritability.

pseudolalia (sū-dō-lā′li-à) This uncommon term was suggested by Stoddart to denote 'meaningless sounds' produced by patients.

'Patients presenting this symptom apparently pretend to speak; but in reality they utter a series of meaningless sounds, such as "camalaba, dink-a-di-dink-goosey-goosey-wadlum." The reduplicative tendency of this mode of speech suggests that it is of instinctive origin.' (Stoddart, W.H.B. *Mind and Its Disorders,* 5th ed., Lewis, London, 1926)

pseudologia fantastica (psew-dō-lō′ji-à fan-tas′ti-kà) A clinical syndrome characterized by phantasy construction, usually extensive, consisting of a superstructure of some actualities erected upon a foundation of phantasy. Pseudologia fantastica is seen mainly in the so-called psychopathic group and in other acting-out types of disturbance, and appears often to arise in an attempt to produce an ego lift; the phantasy is believed only momentarily and is quickly dropped when the patient is confronted with contradictory evidence. Pseudologia fantastica is to be differentiated from *confabulation* (q.v.).

pseudologue (sū′dō-log) Pathological liar. Kraepelin used the term as a subgroup of 'psychopathic personality.' His distinction between the criminal liar and the pseudologue was not very clear.

pseudomania A symptom in which the patient accuses himself of having committed crimes of which he is really innocent; shame psychosis.

pseudo-melancholia (-mel-an-kō′li-à) *Obs.* Juliusburger's term for the clinical syndrome characterized by subjective inhibition and depersonalization.

pseudomnesia (sū-dom-nē′zhi-à) *Obs.* The patient's belief in having a clear recollection of events that had never taken place or things that had never existed.

pseudomotivations Bleuler uses this term to refer to those after-the-fact justifications of behavior which are common in schizophrenia. One hebephrenic patient stated that he got into debt only to show that he could obtain money without his wife's assistance. Another patient flew into a rage and stated that he did so because his doctor was wearing a gray suit. 'According to my experience the patient really becomes furious for quite different reasons which have some relationship to his complexes. He then, purely at random, mentions the grey suit as the reason for his fury.' (Bleuler, E. *Dementia Praecox or the Group of Schizophrenias,* International Universities Press, New York, 1950) Although the patient himself believes in his ex post facto pseudo-motivations, he may subsequently become aware that he has made up the motivations. Ordinarily, however, the patient is unaware of, and indifferent to, even the grossest contradictions.

pseudonarcotism (sū-dō-när′kō-tiz′m) Stupor of hysterical nature, not induced by drugs.

pseudoneurasthenia (-nū-ras-thē′ni-à) Bleuler believes that most cases called neurasthenia are not to be regarded properly as such, but rather as pseudoneurasthenia. See *neurasthenia.*

pseudoneurotic (-nū-rot′ik) See *psychoneuroid; schizophrenia, pseudoneurotic.*

pseudonomania (-nō-mā′ni-à) Morbid impulse to falsify, to lie.

pseudoparanoia (-par-à-noi′à) An uncommon term for unsystematized paranoid trends that are not strictly associated with schizophrenia. For example, paranoid delusions may occasionally be observed in deaf people, sometimes in feebleminded individuals; the delusions are generally scattered and transitory or at least they do not constitute the preponderant part of the disorder.

pseudo-paresis, alcoholic (-par′ē-sis) When a clinical syndrome resembling general paresis appeared as a result of alcoholic encephalopathy it was customary to speak of alcoholic pseudo-paresis, or, as Kraepelin called it, alcoholic paresis. Usually the diagnosis was suggested because of the Argyll Robertson pupils and the slurring speech. With recent advances in diagnostic technique the inclination to make such a diagnosis has been diminishing.

'*Alcoholic paresis* is a mental deterioration with ideas of grandeur, emotional dulness, hallucinations, delusions of jealousy, sometimes pupils stiff to light, speech defect, tremors and polyneuritis. Epileptiform attacks are frequent.' (Strecker, E.A. and Ebaugh, F.G. *Practical Clinical Psychiatry,* 4th ed., Blakiston, Philadelphia, 1935)

pseudopersonality The term for a constellation of habits and reaction patterns consciously recognized as false by the individual. The development of a pseudo-personality is characteristic of many prostitutes, who strive to maintain an incognito quality in their sexual contacts and fortify this with fictitious tales about themselves and their families. Their pseudopersonality usually includes a false toughness, meanness, and indifference. It is obvious that, with time, the recognition of the falseness of the pseudopersonality may gradually dwindle so that it finally becomes a true *character defense,* and in therapy must be handled as such. See *defense, character.* (Agoston, T. *International Journal of Psychoanalysis 26,* 321, 1945)

pseudopsia (sū-dop′si-à) *Obs.* Visual hallucination or illusion.

pseudopsychopathic schizophrenia (sū-dō-sī-kō-path′ik skiz-ō-frē′ni-à) See *schizophrenia.*

pseudo-querulant 'The *pseudo-querulants* are usually described as a separate type. . . . They are very irritable. Hence they readily come into collision with other people, and regard trifling differences as grave injustices. They are also arrogant, and this combination of irritability and arrogance leads them not only into quarrels, but into actual lawsuits.' They are to be distinguished from the litigous paranoid type 'by the fact that in the pseudo-querulants the tendency exists from youth up.' (Henderson, D.K. and Gillespie, R.D. *A Text-Book of Psychiatry*, 4th ed., Oxford University Press, London, 1936)

pseudo-reminiscence Pseudologia fantastica.

pseudoschizophrenia (-skiz-ō-frē′ni-à) See *psychosis, process.*

pseudosclerosis of Westphal-Strümpell (-skle-rō′sis) (Adolf von Strümpell, German physician, 1853–1925; Alexander Karl Otto Westphal, German neurologist, 1863–1941) See *degeneration, hepatolenticular.*

pseudo-sexuality See *masturbation, compulsive.*

pseudosmia (sū-doz′mi-à) False sense of smell.

pseudosphresia (sū-dos-frē′z[h]i-à) Pseudosmia.

pseudotumor cerebri (psew-dō-tōō′môr kā′rà-brē) A condition of uncertain etiology consisting of increased pressure of cerebrospinal fluid and formation of small cysts in the arachnoid. Symptoms include headaches, vomiting, diplopia, papilledema, somnolence, and few if any focal signs. Also known as serous meningitis; arachnoiditis; toxic hydrocephalus.

psi (sī) In parapsychology, this term refers to whatever it is that enables an individual to perceive extra-sensorially. See *perception, extra-sensory.*

psi- (or ψ) **system** See *system.*

psopholalia (sō-fō-lā′li-à) Lallation; babbling, infantile, slovenly, incomprehensible speech.

psychagogy (sī′kà-gō-jē) In the field of psychiatry A. Kronfeld has extensively developed the concept *psychagogy.* It involves educational and re-educational psychotherapeutic procedures, with special emphasis upon the relationship of the individual to his environment. The general principles behind psychagogy are essentially in agreement with those be-

hind objective psychobiology; both stress the socialization of the individual.

psychal (sī′kal) *Rare.* Psychical.

psychalgalia (sī-kal-gā′li-à) See *psychalgia.*

psychalgia (sī-kal′ji-à) Certain patients speak of pain in the mind, psychalgia, when they wish to distinguish the 'pain' from that which they consider to be organic. The symptom is vividly expressed by certain hypochondriacal patients as a pain due to the pressure of intolerable anxiety. Depressed patients also complain of peculiar head pains due to their horrible ideas. The schizophrenic patient complains, often with laughter, of the unbearable pains in his 'head,' induced by electric currents that come from a distant machine operated by a persecutor.

Patients with psychalgia almost invariably say they would far prefer organic pain (somatalgia).

psychalia (sī-kā′li-à) *Rare.* A mental syndrome characterized by auditory and visual hallucinations.

psychanopsia (sī-kan-op′si-à) Psychic blindness.

psychasthenia (sī-kas-thē′ni-à) This term is steadily losing in favor. Formerly it denoted the nosologic syndrome characterized by fears or phobias. Strecker and Ebaugh say that 'in the anxiety states belongs much of the material that was formerly described as psychasthenia, with a prominent display of the so-called phobias or fears.' (Strecker, E.A. and Ebaugh, F.G. *Practical Clinical Psychiatry*, 4th ed., Blakiston, Philadelphia, 1935)

Pierre Janet recognizes two subgroups of psychoneuroses, namely, hysteria and psychasthenia. In general he includes under psychasthenia all psychoneurotic syndromes which are not classified under hysteria.

'Psychasthenia resembles hysteria in that both of these psychoneurotic disorders may be traced to a conflict over a forbidden pleasure. The essential difference lies in the fact that the conscience of the hysterical person is intolerant of even the thought of such pleasure while the psychasthenic has an ambivalent attitude.' (Henry, G.W. *Essentials of Psychiatry*, 3rd ed., Williams and Wilkins, Baltimore, 1938)

psychataxia (sī-kà-tak′si-à) Mental confusion, inability to fix the attention or to make any continued mental effort.

psychauditory (sī-kaw'di-tō-rē) Relating to the mental perception and interpretation of sounds.

psyche (sī'kē) The psyche is the mind. In modern psychiatry the psyche is regarded in its own way as an 'organ' of the individual. The human organism is made up of a large number of organs or organic systems, such as the cardiovascular, neuromuscular, hepatic, nephritic, cerebral, endocrinal, etc. There is the 'organ' called the psyche which, like other organs, possesses its own form and function, its embryology, gross and microscopic anatomy, physiology, and pathology.

The most comprehensive schematization of the psyche is that drawn by Freud, consisting in general of the conscious and unconscious divisions, each of which is made up of a great number of components. The mind, like all other organs of the body has its own local functions and those functions that are intimately associated with adjacent and distant organs. It is like the cardiovascular system in that it reaches all parts of the body; it also serves to adjust the total organism to the needs or demands of the environment.

psycheclampsia (sī-kek-lamp'si-à) *Obs.* T.S. Clouston's synonym for *mania*.

psyche, contrasexual component of Jacobi's term for the 'repressed side' in Jung's theory of analytical psychology. Jung maintains that there is a male and a female side to everyone, the side which is not dominant being repressed; i.e. in the male the female side is repressed and vice versa. 'The second stage of the individuation process (self-realization through Jungian analysis) is characterized by the meeting with the figure of the "soul-image," named by Jung the ANIMA in the man, the ANIMUS in the woman. The archetypal figure of the soul-image stands for the respective contrasexual portion of the psyche, showing partly how our personal relation thereto is constituted, partly the precipitate of all human experience pertaining to the opposite sex. In other words, it is the image of the other sex that we carry in us, both as individuals and as representatives of a species. "Jeder Mann trägt seine Eva in sich" (Every man carries his Eve in him-self) affirms a popular saying. According to psychic law . . . everything latent, unexperienced, undifferentiated in the psyche, everything that lies in the unconscious and therefore the man's "Eve" and the woman's "Adam" as well, is always projected. In consequence one experiences the elements of the opposite sex that are present in one's psyche no otherwise than, for example, one experiences his shadow—in the other person. One chooses another, one binds one's self to another, who represents the qualities of one's own soul.

'The soul-image is a "more or less firmly constituted functional complex, and the inability to distinguish one's self from it leads to such phenomena as those of the moody man, dominated by feminine drives, ruled by his emotions, or of the rationalizing, animus-obsessed woman who always knows better and reacts in a masculine way, not instinctively.' (Wolff, T. *Einfuhrung in die Grundlagen der Komplexen Psychologie,* p. 112) 'One has then the impression that another, a strange person, has "taken possession" of the individual, "a different spirit has got into him," etc., as proverbial speech so profoundly expresses it. Or we see the man who blindly falls victim to a certain type of woman—how often one sees precisely highly cultivated intellectuals abandon themselves helplessly to hussies because their feminine, emotional side is wholly undifferentiated—or the woman who, apparently incomprehensibly, falls for an adventurer or swindler and cannot get loose from him. The character of our soul-image, the anima or animus of our dreams, is the natural measure of our internal psychological situation. It deserves very special consideration in the way of self-knowledge.' (Jacobi, J. *The Psychology of C.G. Jung,* Kegan Paul, Trench, Trubner, London, 1942)

psychedelic (sī-ke-del'ik) Mind-manifesting; sometimes used to describe certain pharmacologic agents which have an effect on mental processes.

psychehormic (sī-ke-hor'mik) Mind-rousing; sometimes used to describe certain pharmacologic agents which have an effect on mental processes.

psycheism Mesmerism; animal magnetism.

psychelytic (sī-ke-li-tik) Mind-releasing; sometimes used to describe certain pharmacologic agents which have an effect on mental processes.

psychentonia (sī-ken-tō'ni-à) Mental (usually high) tension.

psychephoric (sī-ke-for'ik) Mind-moving; sometimes used to describe certain pharmacologic agents which have an effect on mental processes.

psycheplastic (sī-ke-plas'tik) Mind-molding; sometimes used to describe certain pharmacologic agents which have an effect on mental processes.

psycherhexic (sī-ker-ek'sik) Mind-bursting forth; sometimes used to describe certain pharmacologic agents which have an effect on mental processes.

psychezymic (sī-ke-zī'mik) Mind-fermenting; sometimes used to describe certain pharmacologic agents which have an effect on mental processes.

psychiasis (sī-kī'à-sis) Spiritual healing.

psychiater (sī-kī'à-tĕr) Psychiatrist.

psychiatria (sī-ki-at'ri-à) Psychiatry.

psychiatric disorders, classification of See *nomenclature, 1952 revision.*

psychiatrics The theory or practice of psychiatry.

psychiatric social work See *social work, psychiatric.*

psychiatrism (sī-kī'à-triz'm) The injudicious and fallacious application of psychiatric principles in an unwarrantedly mechanistic way, without careful investigation of the dynamics of the individual case to which the principle is applied. Psychiatrism is perhaps best illustrated by the novice student of psychology who reads Freud's work on dream-interpretation and begins blandly to interpret all his friends' dreams on the basis of the symbols mentioned by Freud. Thus psychiatrism tends to standardize and oversimplify complex problems of relationship and causality, and ignores the enormous importance of individual variation. It is based on the fallacy of hypothetical concepts of unconscious personality forces being accepted in an unscientific, matter-of-fact fashion.

psychiatrist One versed in that branch of medicine which deals with the prevention, diagnosis, and treatment of mental and emotional disorders. A psychiatrist is a physician who has had advanced training in the diagnosis and treatment of mental disorders. This advanced training ordinarily includes the study of *psychotherapy* (q.v.), and since the methods of psychotherapy are often based on a particular theory or system of psychology, the individual psychiatrist will often characterize his orientation as 'psychoanalytic,' 'Freudian,' 'Jungian,' 'Adlerian,' etc. Such appellations are to be considered as indicative of the philosophy or psychological system to which the psychiatrist adheres; they are, as it were, subgroupings within the more general field of psychiatry. A certain amount of confusion has arisen in regard to differentiation between the terms psychiatrist and psychoanalyst. In the United States, the term psychoanalyst generally refers to a physician who has had advanced training in the specialty of psychiatry and whose theoretical background is psychoanalytic. There are, however, certain individuals (particularly in Europe) who are psychoanalysts but not psychiatrists; these 'lay analysts' are individuals who are not physicians but who have had intensive training in the psychoanalytic method of psychotherapy and whose theoretical orientation is psychoanalytic. Certain such individuals in the United States have been trained in academic psychology and may thus be termed clinical psychologists.

psychiatrize (sī-kī'à-trīz) To exert psychiatric influence.

psychiatry (sī-kī'à-trē) The science of curing or healing disorders of the psyche.

psychiatry, asylum A term used by Ernest Jones to describe the field of psychiatry which deals with major mental disorders under treatment in institutions.

psychiatry, child The science of healing or curing disorders of the psyche in children.

psychiatry, experimental As used today, this term generally refers to the use of chemical agents in the development of a science of human behavior, and particularly to research on the properties and pathways of action of the *psychotomimetics* (q.v.). In experimental psychiatry, drugs which alter behavior are used as devices for the detection and manipulation of significant variables in naturally occurring mental disorders.

psychiatry, forensic (fō-ren'sik) This term refers to psychiatry in its legal aspects, including criminology, penology, commitment of the mentally ill, the psychiatric role in compensation cases, the problems of releasing information to the court, of expert testimony, etc.

psychiatry, pastoral The branch of psychiatry that is related to religion, and particularly to the integration of psychiatry and religion for the purpose of alleviating emotional ailments—the psychotherapeutic role which the clergyman must often play in his relationship to his parishioners. The term includes such things as vocational and marriage counseling.

Organized religion as a whole represents centuries of interpersonal experiences which have given pragmatic validation to certain tenets and doctrines. Therefore, when based on these doctrines, advice and other therapeutic measures are often psychologically valid, even though the dynamics as such may not be recognized or understood. And, at least with certain types of patients, the results may be excellent. The many 'cures' at the shrine of Lourdes, France, afford an example of this.

Pastoral psychiatry at the present time is confined largely to reassurance and relief of guilt-feelings, affording opportunity for catharsis, and alleviation of anxiety in general by directive and noninterpretive methods. In addition religion offers the possibility of identification with the omnipotent Father, and engenders reaction formations and sublimation. In certain aspects, organized religion may be likened to group psychotherapy of an educative type. Unlike the latter, however, religion is generally devoid of an understanding of the psychodynamics involved.

psychiatry, political The application of psychiatric knowledge to politics is called political psychiatry.

psychiatry, psychoanalytic (sī-kō-an-à-lit′-ik) See *psychoanalysis.*

psychiatry, social In psychiatry, the stress laid on the environmental influences and the impact of the social group on the individual. This emphasis is made not only with regard to etiology, but also for purposes of treatment and, more important, in preventive work.

psychic (sī′kik) Relating to or affected in the mind or psyche.

psychical (sī′ki-kal) Psychic.

psychical reality See *reality, psychical.*

psychic equivalent Psychomotor epilepsy. See *epilepsy.*

psychicism (sī′ki-siz'm) Psychical research.

psychics (sī′kiks) Psychology.

psychic suicide See *suicide, psychic.*

psychinosis (sī-ki-nō′sis) *Rare.* Psychosis.

psychlampsia (sī-klamp′si-à) *Obs.* Mania.

psychnosia (sik-nō′si-à) A term used by Moshcowitz to cover syndromes of physical symptoms on the basis of emotional conflicts (e.g. essential hypertension, Grave's syndrome, cardiospasm, irritable colon, mucous colitis). (Moshcowitz, E. 'The Psychogenic Origin of Organic Disease,' *New England Journal of Medicine 212,* 603–11, 1935)

psychnosis (sī-knō′sis) *Rare.* Synonym of psychopathy.

psychoanaleptica (sī-kō-an-a-lep′ti-kà) See *psycholeptica.*

psychoanalysis (-an-al′i-sis) The separation or resolution of the psyche into its constituent elements. The term has three separate meanings: (1) a procedure, devised by Sigmund Freud, for investigating mental processes by means of free-association, dream-interpretation, and interpretation of resistance and transference manifestations; (2) a theory of psychology developed by Freud out of his clinical experience with hysterical patients; and (3) a form of psychiatric treatment developed by Freud which utilizes the psychoanalytic procedure (definition 1 above) and which is based on psychoanalytic psychology (definition 2 above). Freud considered the cornerstones of psychoanalytic theory to be: the assumption of unconscious mental processes, recognition of resistance and repression, appreciation of the importance of sexuality (and aggressivity), and the Oedipus complex. Ernest Jones has delineated seven major principles of Freud's psychology: (1) determinism—psychical processes are not a chance occurrence; (2) affective processes have a certain autonomy and can be detached and displaced; (3) mental processes are dynamic and tend constantly to discharge the energy associated with them; (4) repression; (5) intrapsychic conflict; (6) infantile mental processes—the wishes of later life are important only as they ally themselves with those of childhood; (7) psychosexual trends are present in childhood. For a short summary of Freud's instinct theories, see *neurosis*.

Other schools of thought within psychology and psychiatry are sometimes referred to (loosely, and not wholly correctly) as 'psychoanalytic.' Chief among these are:

(A) Jung's 'analytical psychology,' which emphasizes the collective unconscious, a concept bearing on ethnological psychology. Jung considers that libido arises not from the sexual instinct but from a universal force or life urge; mind is not only a Has Been but also a Becoming, that is, it has aims and strives to realize certain goals within itself. Reminiscences of experience are relegated to the personal unconscious and then link up with and are used to express fundamental ideas and trends, the 'archetypes,' which represent not only the past stages but also the future potentials of race development.

(B) Adler's 'individual psychology,' which is based on the egoistic side of man's nature, on the striving for power as a compensation for inferiority (psychic and organic). Neurosis is an attempt to free oneself from the feeling of inferiority.

(C) Meyer's *psychobiology* (q.v.).

psychoanalyst One who adheres to the doctrine and/or uses the methods of psychoanalysis. See *psychoanalysis; psychiatrist*.

psychoanalysis, wild A term used to describe psychotherapeutic techniques which use a limited amount of interpretation or which attack the patient directly with deep interpretations.

psychoataxia (sī-kō-à-tak′si-à) *Rare.* Synonym of intrapsychic ataxia. See *ataxia*.

psychobacillosis (-bas-i-lō′sis) Treatment of schizophrenia by bacterial preparations.

psychobioanalysis See *bioanalysis*.

psychobiogram (-bī′ō-gram) E. Kretschmer devised the psychobiogram for purposes of practical investigation of the personality. It is made up of several parts. The first two parts consist of the data concerning the patient's heredity and past history. The other parts consist of a detailed description of the person's temperament, his sociological attitude, intelligence, physical findings, etc., and the classification from the point of view of the somatotype. (*Textbook of Medical Psychology,* tr. by Strauss, E.B., Oxford Medical Publications, London, 1934)

psychobiology The study of the biology of the psyche. It includes such subdivisions as the organization ('anatomy'), physiology, and pathology of the mind.

Janet credits Bernheim with having written as follows in 1886: 'The mind is not a negligible quantity. There is such a thing as psychobiology. There is also such a thing as psychotherapy. This is a powerful lever, and one which the human intelligence and medical therapeutists must turn to full account.' (Janet, P. *Psychological Healing,* vols. 1–2, tr. by Paul, E. and C., Macmillan, New York, 1925)

The term was used with a variety of meanings in the early part of the 20th century. Thus, in 1900, Small wrote an article in which he referred to the 'psychobiological character' of the rat. In 1909 Charles Henry published a book on *Psychobiologie et Energétique.* In 1912 Oskar Kohnstamm wrote on 'Willensfreiheit and Zeilstrebigkeit (Psychobiologische Abhandlungen I).' Adolf Meyer first used the term in 1915, and in the United States, it is generally associated with his name. Meyer generally calls his point of view *objective psychobiology,* with particular stress upon the relationship of the individual to his environment.

The term is also known as *biopsychology*.

Meyer's school of objective psychobiology concerns itself with the overt and implicit behavior of the individual, which is a function of the total organism. The mind is the integration of the whole-functions of the total personality. Ideal mental health is the maximal ability of, plus the best opportunity for, getting along with people, without the interference of inner conflicts or external frictions, in a manner that would make for full mutual satisfaction on a constant give-and-take basis. Psychobiology is a genetic-dynamic science which studies personality development in the light of environmental setting and longitudinal growth. Meyer's central theme is 'the mind in action' and he stresses the relationship between the conscious drives and the environment. The aim of objective psychobiology as it is applied to patients (distributive analysis and synthesis) is to adapt the patient to his surroundings, both directly by working with him and indirectly via environmental manipulation and work with other social agencies. The therapist attempts to correct the patient's faulty mental habits. Psychobiology is particularly useful in the psychoses, where the conflict to a large extent is between the ego and the environment; but in the neuroses, the conflict is between the ego and the id.

psychobiology, objective See *psychobiology.*

psychocatharsis (sī-kō-ka-thär′sis)   L. Frank uses this term as equivalent with the psychic process of catharsis. He recommends that psychocatharsis be carried out through light hypnosis.

'The goal of catharsis is the full emotional re-experience of markedly affective experiences which have not settled, the discharge of pent up emotions and the elimination of neurotic emotional tension.' (Diethelm, O. *Treatment in Psychiatry*, Macmillan, New York, 1936)

psychochemist A term used by Freeman for a chemist 'grounded in biochemistry as well as in psychiatry' and equipped to 'investigate the problems of normal and abnormal behavior from the standpoint of altered chemical reactions in . . . the central nervous system.' (Freeman, W. *Journal of the American Medical Association 97*, 293, 1931)

psychochemistry Freeman's term for biochemistry as applied to psychiatric problems.

psychocinesia (sī-kō-si-nē′z[h]i-a) See *psychokinesia.*

psychocoma (-kō′ma) *Obs.* T.S. Clouston's term for *stupor.*

psychocortical (-kor′ti-kal) Relating to the cortex of the brain as the seat of the mind.

psychodiagnostics (dī-ag-nos′tiks) A term used by German writers to designate the Rorschach test.

psychodietetics (-dī-e-tet′iks) A psychiatric term coined by Martin F. Fritz to denote 'the science of the feeding of an individual in sickness and in health with particular reference to the mental aspect. . . . This definition clearly designates the field which concerns the relationship between diet and mental life. Broadly speaking, the term psychodietet-

ics may be used to cover not only those cases where diet is a factor in the direct causation of mental phenomena but also where behavior has a dietary expression as, for example, in the case of food fads due to peculiar notion on the part of the individual.' (Fritz, M.F. 'The Field of Psychodietetics,' *The Psychological Clinic XXII, 3*, 181–6, Sept.–Nov. 1933.) See also *dietary fads.*

psychodometer (-dom′ē-tēr) An instrument for measuring the rapidity of psychic processes.

psychodometry The measurement of psychic processes.

psychodrama 'The psychodrama deals with the private personality of the patient and his catharsis, with the persons within his milieu and with the roles in which he and they have interacted in the past, in the present, and in which they may interact in the future. Techniques have been devised to bring the underlying spontaneous processes to expression. Psychodramatic work is usually best organized in a therapeutic theatre, but it may be carried out wherever the patient lives, if his problem requires it.

'One of the techniques is that of self-presentation. The psychiatrist asks the patient to live through and portray or duplicate situations which are a part of his daily life, especially crucial conflicts in which he is involved. He must also enact and represent as concretely and as thoroughly as possible every person near to his problem. This may be done in collaboration with a partner or partners, either real or a person or persons functioning as substitutes—auxiliary egos.

'Another technique of the psychodrama is that of soliloquy. Here a deeper level of the inter-personal world is brought to expression. It is used by the patient to duplicate hidden feelings and thoughts which he actually has or had in a situation with a partner in real life, but which he did not or does not express. Expression of these hidden feelings, in the psychodrama, has a cathartic value for the patient.

'In the technique of spontaneous improvisation the patient acts in fictitious or symbolic roles which are carefully selected by the psychiatrist on the basis of the patient's problem. During the acts the patient reveals many elements of his private personality which offer an open target for analysis without the patient's awareness.

'In the psychodrama on a non-semantic level, feeling complexes—the pantomime, the dance, music, and the (apparently) nonsensical—are trained with therapeutic effect. An example is the technique of nonsensical expression where the patient is told to resist the emergence of verbal utterance and to produce sounds and words at random. The vowels and consonants are to be brought together into any possible combinations as they come to him spontaneously. This exercise has been useful in the training of patients with vocal defects.

'In the case of patients with whom any sort of communication is reduced to a minimum, the psychodrama attempts to create an auxiliary world, or a world within which the patient functions. This may require the use of a staff of auxiliary egos who are to embody the psychotic world of the patient. In this manner, the psychiatrist (through the auxiliary egos making up the auxiliary world) is able to "act with" the patient on the patient's spontaneous level.

'*Psychodramatic catharsis* is a process which takes place between the actual partners in a problem or mental disturbance. Analysis before or after psychodramatic action may prepare a cathartic development, but the genuine phase of catharsis takes place in the course of the psychodrama itself.' (Moreno, J.L. *Das Stegreif Theater*, Potsdam, Germany)

psychodrama, forms of
(1) *Psychodrama.* Focuses on the individual, being a synthesis of psychological analysis with drama (action). Psychodrama aims at the *active* building up of private worlds and individual ideologies.
(2) *Sociodrama.* Focuses on the group, being a synthesis of the *socius* with psychodrama. It aims at the active structuring of *social* worlds and collective ideologies.
(3) *Physiodrama.* Focuses on the soma, being a synthesis of physical culture (sports) and psychodrama. The physical condition of the individuals before, during, and after the production is *measured*. It gives diagnostic (possibly also prognostic) clues for training requirements, provides the set-up for retraining.
(4) *Axiodrama* (Gr. *áxios,* worth, wor-

thy of value, goodly.) Focuses on ethics and general values, and aims to dramatize eternal verities (truth, justice, beauty, grace, piety, eternity, peace, etc.).
(5) *Hypnodrama.* The synthesis of *hypnosis* (q.v.) and (psycho)drama.
(6) *Psychomusic.* A synthesis of *spontaneous* music with (psycho)drama.
(7) *Psychodance.* A synthesis of *spontaneous* dancing with (psycho)drama. 'The synthesis of all other forms of art as: sculpture, painting, creative writing etc. with psychodrama opens the way for action—as well as group methods.'
(8) *Therapeutic motion picture.* A synthesis of motion picture with psychodrama. (Moreno, J.L. 'Forms of Psychodrama; Terms and Definitions,' *Sociatry 1,* 4, 447–8, and bibliography, 1947)

psychodynamic (-dī-nam'ik) The term *psychodynamic* relates to the forces of the mind. Ideas and impulses are charged with emotions, to which the general expression *psychic energy* is given. For example, delusions of persecution or obsessions or compulsions are described as psychodynamic phenomena, in that they are said to represent the results of activity of psychic forces.

psychodynamic cerebral system See *psychodynamics, adaptational.*

psychodynamics The science of mental forces in action.

psychodynamics, adaptational Rado's system of psychoanalytic psychiatry. 'This science is based on the psychoanalytic method of investigation. As we have just seen, it studies the part played by motivation and control in the organism's interaction with its cultural environment. It deals with pleasure and pain, emotion and thought, desire and executive action, interpreting them in terms of organismic utility, that is, in an adaptational framework. In the theory of evolution, the pivotal concept is adaptation; since the organism's life cycle is but a phase of evolution, it is consistent to make the same concept basic to the study of behavior.

'We define ontogenetic adaptations as improvements in the organism's pattern of interaction with its environment that increase its chances for survival, cultural self-realization, and perpetuation of its type. Autoplastic adaptations result from changes undergone by the organism itself; alloplastic adaptations from changes wrought by the organism on its environment. In ontogenetic adaptations, the master mechanisms are learning, creative imagination, and goal-directed activity.' (Rado, S. *Psychoanalysis of Behavior,* Grune & Stratton, New York, 1956)

'The organism's systemic requirements are known as its needs. Like its other traits, they are an outcome of the interaction between inherited predisposition (genotype) and environment. We speak of aboriginal needs that show predominantly the forming influence of the culture in which the organism lives.' (ibid.)

In Rado's terminology, the psychodynamic central system refers to mind and unconscious mind and includes (1) that range of the brain's neurophysiologic activity which comes to the awareness of the organism, the self-reporting range, and (2) that range of non-reporting activity which is accessible to extrapolative investigation by psychodynamic methods and/or to investigation by physiologic methods. The aim of adaptational psychodynamics is to discover the mechanisms by which the psychodynamic cerebral system accomplishes its integrative task. The integrative apparatus of the system is composed of four units, which are hierarchically ordered levels reflecting the course of evolutionary history—hedonic, brute emotions, emotional thought, and unemotional thought. At the hedonic level, the organism moves toward pleasure and away from pain. In the next two levels, the emotions are the controlling means of integration (divided into the emotions based on present pain or the expectation of pain, such as fear, rage, retroflexed rage, guilty fear, and guilty rage; and the welfare emotions based on present pleasure or the expectation of pleasure, such as pleasurable desire, affection, love, joy, self-respect and pride). At the level of unemotional thought, reason, common sense and science prepare the ground for intelligent action and self-restraint.

Behavior disorders are disturbances of psychodynamic integration which interfere with the organism's adaptive life performance, its attainment of utility and pleasure. The simplest forms of behavior disorder occur when the organism responds to danger with an overproduction of the emergency emotions; such emergency dyscontrol is in itself a threat to the organism from within and leads to processes of miscarried prevention and miscarried repair.

More complex behavior disorders arise when emergency dyscontrol acts in combination with additional pathogenic agents. With emergency dyscontrol as a point of departure, Rado classifies behavior disorders according to the increasing complexity of their patterns and mechanisms as follows:

'Class I. Overreactive Disorders.

'(1) Emergency Dyscontrol: The emotional outflow, the riddance through dreams, the phobic, the inhibitory, the repressive, and the hypochondriac patterns; the gainful exploitation of illness. (2) Descending Dyscontrol. (3) Sexual Disorders: The impairments and failures of standard performance. Dependence on reparative patterns: Organ replacement and organ avoidance; the criminal, dramatic and hidden forms of sexual pain-dependence; the formation of homogeneous pairs. Firesetting and shoplifting as sexual equivalents. (4) Social Overdependence: The continuous search for an ersatzparent; the mechanisms of forced competition, avoidance of competition, and of self-harming defiance. (5) Common Maladaptation: A combination of sexual disorder with social overdependence. (6) The Expressive Pattern (expressive elaboration of common maladaptation): Ostentatious self-presentation; dreamlike interludes; rudimentary pantomimes; disease-copies and the expressive complication of incidental disease. (7) The Obsessive Pattern (obsessive elaboration of common maladaptations): Broodings, rituals, and overt temptations. Tic and stammering as obsessive equivalents; bed wetting, nailbiting, grinding of teeth in sleep, as precursors of the obsessive pattern. (8) The Paranoid Pattern (nondisintegrative elaboration of common maladaptation): The hypochondriac, self-referential, persecutory and grandiose stages of the Magnan sequence.

'Class II. Moodcyclic Disorders.

'Cycles of depression; cycles of reparative elation; the pattern of alternate cycles; cycles of minor elation; cycles of depression marked by elation; cycles of preventive elation.

'Class III. Schizotypal Disorders.

'(1) Compensated schizo-adaptation. (2) Decompensated schizo-adaptation.

(3) Schizotypal disintegration marked by adaptive incompetence.

'Class IV. Extractive Disorders.

'The ingratiating ("smile and suck") and extortive ("hit and grab") patterns of transgressive conduct.

'Class V. Lesional Disorders.

'Class VI. Narcotic Disorders.

'Class VII. Disorders of War Adaptation.' (Rado, S. ibid.)

Rado divides the methods of psychotherapy into two classes—reconstructive (adaptational technique of psychoanalytic therapy) and reparative (less ambitious treatment methods with limited goals but in general also of shorter duration).

psychodynamy (-dī'nam-ē) Animal magnetism.

psychodysleptica (-dis-lep'ti-kà) See *psycholeptica.*

psychoepilepsy (-ep'i-lep-sē) By some, this term is used synonymously with idiopathic or genuine epilepsy; an unfortunate term in that it implies a psychogenic basis for epilepsy, evidence for which is minimal. See *epilepsy.*

psychoexploration A generic term used to refer to the various procedures known as abreaction, psychocatharsis, narcoanalysis, narcosynthesis, etc.

psychogenesis (-jen'ē-sis) Origination within the mind or psyche. The psyche is now regarded by many as one of the organs of the body or individual, in its own way analogous to any other organ of the body. The liver, for example, is an organ with its own *anlage,* embryology, gross and microscopic anatomy, physiology, and pathology. The same may be said about the psyche. But, the liver is not strictly an entity; on the contrary, it is an intimate part of several other divisions of the body; it is, for instance, a part of the blood system, of the system of sugar metabolism, water metabolism, etc. The same may be said about the psyche.

The 'bile pigment is secreted by the liver cells into the bile capillaries, but whether or not the pigment is actually produced by these cells is a subject that has given rise to much discussion.' (Howell, W.H. *Text-book of Physiology,* 12th ed., Saunders, Philadelphia and London, 1933) The instincts and their various manifestations are 'secreted' by the psyche; it is likely, however, that they are produced through the agency of the soma.

The term *psychogenesis* means, insofar as present knowledge extends, that certain activities of the individual, called psychic activities, may be traced back at least to the psyche.

psychogenia (-jē'ni-à) *Rare.* Mental disorder due to impaired mentality.

psychogenic, psychogenetic (-jen'ik, -jē-net'ik) Relating to or characterized by psychogenesis.

psychogeny (sī-koj'ē-nē) Psychogenesis.

psychogeusic (sī-kō-gū'sik) Pertaining to taste perception.

psychognosis (sī-kog'nō-sis) *Rare.* Diagnosis of psychic disorders or psychiatric states.

psychogonical (sī-kō-gon'i-kal) Psychogenic.

psychogony (sī'-kog'ō-nē) The doctrine of the development of the mind.

psychogram (sī'kō-gram) A chart depicting personality traits. The term is often synonymous with psychograph.

psychograph More frequently used in psychology than in psychiatry. It has two special meanings. It refers to a chart depicting personality traits or it may relate to the history of an individual from the point of view of personality.

psychography (sī-kog'rà-fē) In psychiatry, the natural history of the mind. It includes description of the phenomena of the mind. The psychoanalysis of Freud, analytical psychology of Jung, the individual psychology of Adler and the psychobiology of Meyer represent divisions of psychography.

psycho-hygiene (sī-kō-hī'jēn, -hī'ji-ēn) *Obs.* Mental hygiene.

psycho-infantilism (-in-fan'ti-liz'm) The term for a condition often encountered in psychiatric practice which 'is a persistence, in the adult, of mental qualities characteristic of the child. Psycho-infantile behavior is referable to the hopelessness, uncertainty and desire for guidance and authority distinctive of childhood. It is manifested in tractability and dependence, which often takes the form of a strong emotional fixation frequently to the mother or the father, but sometimes to other persons, even chance acquaintances. The psycho-infantile person gives the normal adult the same feeling of detachment and the same urge to protect as the child. It is the latter attribute which lies back of the terms "naive," "childish" and "artless" so often used to describe his personality.' (Lindberg, B.J. *Psycho-Infantilism,* Ejnar Munksgaard, Copenhagen, 1950)

'*Psycho-infantilism* is not a disease, nor is it the common denominator for psychoneurotic or psychosomatic disorders. It is a form of mental weakness, inasmuch as the psycho-infantile person is particularly vulnerable to mental insufficiency when confronted with decisive events in his life. He is specially apt to break down when he himself has to make an important decision, the more so if circumstances have deprived him of the person he has been used to leaning upon.

'A psycho-infantile attitude is often met with outside the hospital walls and may be adopted by almost anyone in the face of crisis. Although psycho-infantilism as defined here is easy to recognize and to define as an independent syndrome, it is not a sufficient diagnosis in itself for a psychiatric case. The word "psycho-infantilism" must always be complemented with information regarding the other personality traits and naturally regarding the mental insufficiency in question.' (ibid.)

psychokinesia, psychokinesis (-kī-nē′-z[h]i-à, -nē′sis) T.S. Clouston's term for defective inhibition; formerly it also referred to the clinical syndrome known as *impulse insanity.*

psychokym(e) (-kīm′) 'Psychic processes conceived physiologically, namely, that which is conceived analogous to a form of energy, that something which flows through the central nervous system and which is at the basis of psychic processes. "Neurokym" is used to designate the nervous processes in general.' (Bleuler, E. *Textbook of Psychiatry,* tr. by Brill, A.A., Macmillan, New York, 1930)

psycholagny (sī′-kō-lag-nē) Sexual excitation that begins, continues, and ends with mental imagery. So-called mental masturbation, that is, the occurrence of masturbatory phenomena stimulated by mental forces alone, is an example of psycholagny.

psycholepsy, psycholepsis (sī′ko-lep-sē, -lep′sis) Sudden, intense lowering of psychic tension, associated with morbid ideas and actions.

'Individuals in whom psychological tension is unstable, suffer from sudden relaxations of this tension, succumb to psycholeptic crises which have been brought on by their relationships with certain persons in their immediate circle.' (Janet, P. *Psychological Healing,* vols. 1–2, tr. by Paul, E. and C., Macmillan, New York, 1925) When so-termed psychic tension mounts to great heights, 'in which feelings of ecstacy and indescribable happiness' appear, there may be a sudden fall in tension 'culminating in a psycholeptic crisis and even in an epileptic fit.' (ibid) Some individuals who have triumphed in a given work may terminate the triumph with a morbid clinical syndrome.

psycholeptica (-lep′ti-kà) Delay's term for phrenotropic drugs, whose principal effect is on the psyche, in contrast to neuroleptica, whose principal effect is on psychomotor activity. The psycholeptica include: (1) the 'minor' tranquillizers or ataractics, i.e. diphenylmethane derivatives and substituted propanediols (see *tranquillizers*); (2) psychoanaleptica (psychic 'tonics,' euphoriants, and antidepressives); and (3) psychodysleptica, which produce disintegration of psychic functions (lysergic acid, mescaline, etc.).

psychological Relating to psychology.

psychologist One versed in psychology.

psychologist, clinical One versed in psychology who deals with clinical cases and who uses his training in the theory and techniques of psychology to aid in the diagnosis and (under medical supervision) in the treatment of mental and emotional disorders. See *psychiatrist.*

psychology The science which deals with the mind and mental processes—consciousness, sensation, ideation, memory, etc.

psychology, atomistic Any psychology based on the doctrine that perceptions, thoughts, and all mental processes are built up through the combination of simple elements or atoms. According to the doctrine of atomism, the physical universe (or, as is sometimes taught, the whole universe both physical and mental) is composed of simple, indivisible, and minute particles or atoms. Many thinkers have endeavored to interpret atomism from a psychical point of view, treating the atoms either as mind stuff or as composed of sense elements. Mind stuff, a term first used by W.K. Clifford, is 'the elemental material, internally of the nature of mind, externally, or as it appears to us, in the form of matter, which is assumed to be the ground of reality.' (*Webster's New International Dictionary*, 2nd ed., Merriam, Springfield, Mass., 1948) 'The distinguishing feature of Freud's instinct theory is that it is based on a conative-appetitive-striving, rather than a structural principle like sensation or reflex. But, as with the classical psychologies and behaviorism, psychoanalysis is an *atomistic psychology* which attempts to derive complex entities from the action of a synthetic principle (association, conditioning, integration) on or about a basic unit. A conative principle is used as an atomic unit to reconstruct the molecules of experience.' (Kardiner, A., and Spiegel, H. *War Stress and Neurotic Illness,* Hoeber, New York, 1947)

psychology, 'blame' In persons with serious inhibitions in social competitive relationships, this psychiatric term denotes their tendency to find expression for these inhibitions in hatred and persecution of some blameless scapegoat. 'This blame psychology also permits the individual to harbor a secret grandiose conception of himself.' (Kardiner, A., *et al. The Psychological Frontiers of Society,* Columbia University Press, New York, 1945)

psychology, Gestalt (ge-stalt') A school of psychology which is concerned primarily with perceptual processes. Its development is associated particularly with the names of Max Wertheimer, Wolfgang Koehler, and Kurt Koffka, and represents an outgrowth of opposition to the traditional association psychology.

'Gestalt psychology holds that the whole or total quality of the image is perceived. This is in contrast to association psychology, which states that stimuli are perceived as parts and built into images. According to gestalt psychology, the organization of the stimuli into the image is based upon laws of perception which include proximity, similarity, direction, and inclusiveness of parts of the stimuli. The perceptual experience is a gestalt or configuration or pattern in which the whole is more than the sum of its parts. Organized units or structuralized configurations are the primary form of biological reactions. In the sensory field,

these gestalten correspond to the configuration of the stimulating world. 'The organism has a "gestalt function" which is defined as that function of the integrative organism whereby it responds to a given constellation of stimuli as a whole, the response being a constellation or pattern or gestalt which differs from the original stimulus pattern by the process of the integrative mechanism of the individual who experiences the perception. The whole setting of the stimulus and the whole integrative state of the organism determine the pattern or response.

'There is a tendency not only to perceive gestalten but to complete gestalten and to reorganize them according to principles biologically determined by the sensory motor pattern of action which may be expected to vary in different maturation or growth levels and in pathological states organically or functionally determined.' (Bender, L. *Child Psychiatric Techniques,* Thomas, Springfield, Ill., 1952)

psychology, individual This term denotes Adlerian psychology, a discipline elaborated by the Viennese psychiatrist Alfred Adler. The complete name of his system is 'comparative individual-psychology.' He describes it as follows: 'By starting with the assumption of the *unity of the individual,* an attempt is made to obtain a picture of this unified personality regarded as a variant of individual life-manifestations and forms of expression. The individual traits are then compared with one another, brought into a common plane, and finally fused together to form a composite portrait that is, in turn, individualized.' (Adler, A. *The Practice and Theory of Individual Psychology,* tr. by Radin, P., Kegan Paul, Trench, Trubner, London, 1924)

Mairet states: 'Individual psychology is not psycho-analysis. It is a method initiated by Dr. Adler of Vienna, of gaining knowledge of individuals, including knowledge of their inner life, but it is a method founded upon a view of the individual as whole in himself, an indivisible unit of human society. It relates everything that the individual does in such a way as to obtain a picture of a single, coherent and intelligible tendency, expressed in most various ways, direct and indirect. Thus it is a method of unifying the psyche much more than of dissecting it.' (Mairet, P. *ABC of Adler's Psychology,* Kegan Paul, Trench, Trubner, London, 1928)

psychology, mob The psychology of mob behavior is considered by Fenichel to have much in common with a certain type of character defense against guilt-feelings. In this type of defense, the guilt-laden character feels admiration and relief when someone else does something which he has been striving to do, but has been inhibited from doing through guilt-feelings. The meaning of the admiration and relief is 'Since others do it, it cannot be so bad, after all.'

The attainment of relief from guilt-feelings in this way is a powerful force for group formation. Others have dared to do what the individual has felt guilt about doing. And 'If my whole group acts this way, I may, too.' In this way, the relief from guilt-feelings is described as 'one of the cornerstones of "mob psychology."' Indeed Fenichel points out that 'individuals acting as a group are capable of instinctual outbreaks that would be entirely impossible for them as individuals.' (Fenichel, O. *The Psychoanalytic Theory of Neurosis,* Norton, New York, 1945)

psychology, rational Any system of psychology in which *a priori* assumptions (usually of a philosophical or theological nature) form the background into which any observed facts must be fit.

psychology, topographical See *topography, mental.*

psychology, uprooted This psychiatric term denotes the changed mentality exhibited by an individual who has been uprooted by force of circumstance, i.e. has had to leave his native place with its physical, social, and cultural background that had surrounded him all his life.

When removed from their customary environment and dislocated from their protective moral background, uprooted individuals deviate markedly from their inculcated reverence for original values and show symptoms parallel to those found in migrating hordes: recklessness, unregulated and indiscriminate sexuality, a marked lowered responsibility toward human life and property. (Baynes, H.G. *Mythology of the Soul,* Williams and Wilkins, Baltimore, 1940)

psychomathematics The use of certain formulas in working out variations of human character and capabilities.

psychometrics Mental testing. See *examinations, psychometric.*

psychometry (sī-kom'ē-trē) Measurement of the duration and force of mental processes.

psychomotility (sī-kō-mō-til'i-tē) The term for any motor action, attitude, or habit pattern which is influenced by mental processes and thus reflects the individual's personality make-up. Certain psychomotor phenomena such as tics, stereotypies, catatonia, dysarthria, stammering, and tremor have long been used in diagnosis as signs of psychomotor disturbance. Recently, postural attitudes and gait have been under investigation by clinicians as objective signs of psychomotor disturbance. Handwriting, also, has long been known as a valuable aid in investigating psychomotility, for it gives some indication of the individual's motivation. Certain features of handwriting have been regarded as suggestive of certain personality traits. Preliminary investigations of a nature more scientific than mere palmistry indicate that correlations do exist between handwritings of different types and symptoms, syndromes, and character traits noted in the patients' records.

psychomotor The term *psychomotor* relates to the mental origin of muscular movement. From the standpoint of psychiatry it denotes movement that is psychically determined in contradistinction to that which is definitely recognized as extra-psychic or organic in cause. A patient felt compelled to repeat all actions three times, lest something dreadful happen to his wife. The impulse came from the psyche. Another patient had to perform a rotatory movement about the abdomen with his hand 'in order to hasten vegetation.'

psychoneuroid (sī-kō-nū'roid) A psychiatric term intended to convey the idea of 'resembling or like psychoneurosis or psychoneurotic.' When a patient is falling sick with a psychiatric disorder, the nature of his symptoms will depend on his previous personality make-up. For instance, a patient who had a cycloid personality may develop a manic-depressive psychosis, a schizoid patient may show a schizophrenic psychosis, a psychoneuroid individual may develop one of the different kinds of psychoneurosis.

The term psychoneuroid is also used in a different sense. If, for instance, a patient's neurotic symptoms are based on an organic disease such as general paresis or arteriosclerosis, they are called psychoneuroid or pseudoneurotic symptoms. The same term is applied if neurotic manifestations occur in a schizophrenic psychosis. In these patients the neurotic manifestations, fears, obsessions, etc. are not due to a neurosis, even though they appear to be similar in their clinical manifestations. (Hinsie, L.E. *Understandable Psychiatry*, Macmillan, New York, 1948)

psychoneurosis (-nū-rō′sis) Modern conceptions of the large group of clinical disorders classified under the heading *psychoneurosis* center around the hypothesis that a psychoneurosis is a disorder of the psyche. From the theoretical as well as the practical point of view the causes of the disorders have been traced as far back, so to speak, as the psyche, particularly to that division of the mind called the unconscious. The psyche has its own physiology and pathophysiology (psychopathology). A psychoneurosis is best known today as a psychopathological syndrome, characterized in the main by special combinations of anxiety, phobias, compulsions, obsessions, and conversion phenomena. These are but a few of the possible symptoms. Ordinarily a psychoneurotic individual possesses insight, that is, he is aware that his symptoms are manifestations of morbidity.

Generally a psychoneurosis results only in partial disorganization of the psyche, in contradistinction to a psychosis that usually disrupts all the functions of the psyche. See *neurosis*.

psychoneurosis, battle War neurosis. See *neurosis, traumatic*.

psychoneurosis, cardiac See *neurosis, cardiac*.

psychoneurosis, defense Freud's term for hysteria and various neuroses and psychoses caused by some idea or sensation, so painful that the sufferer endeavors to dismiss it from the mind; at times, instead of being absolutely forgotten, the thought sinks down into the unconscious and acts as the hidden cause of the psychoneurotic disturbances.

psychoneurosis maïdica (mȧ-id′i-kȧ) Pellagra.

psychoneurosis, psychoneurotic reaction (sī-kō-nū-rot′ik) The 1952 revision of psychiatric nomenclature defines this as a reaction in which anxiety, generated by the conflict between the organism and internal or external stresses, is typically defended against by such mechanisms as depression, conversion dissociation, displacement, phobic avoidance, and/or repetitive thoughts and acts. The following subgroups are included: anxiety reaction, dissociative reaction, conversion reaction, phobic reaction, obsessive compulsive reaction, and psychoneurotic depressive reaction.

psychonoetism (-nō′e-tiz′m) A term introduced by L.E. Hinsie to designate the transference of personal conflicts to the intellect. Often patients are seen 'who shift their doubts, fears, obsessions and delusions from their original source in the unconscious to the sphere of the intellect. Thus a patient who was a great objector and had to contradict everything and everyone was really denying a strong Oedipus complex and unconscious instinctual demands directed toward his mother. However, he had transferred his denial of his unconscious instincts to the intellectual sphere, where it became an obsessive doubting of all ideas and statements. This is the process termed psychonoetism.' (Hinsie, L.E. *Understandable Psychiatry*, Macmillan, New York, 1948)

psychonomics (-nom′iks) The science of the laws of mind: psychology.

psychonomy (sī-kon′ōmē) The branch of psychology treating of the laws of mental action.

psychonosema (sī-kō-nō-sē′mȧ) *,Obs.* Mental disease.

psychonosology (-nō-sol′ō-jē) The classification of mental disorders.

psychoparesis (-par′ē-sis) *Rare.* Mental enfeeblement.

psychopathia (-path′i-ȧ) Psychopathy.

psychopathia martialis (psē-kô-pá′thē-ȧ mȧr-tē-ȧ′lēs) Shell-shock.

psychopathia sexualis (sek-soo-ä′lēs) The expression, referring to sexual perversions, was introduced by the German sexologist Richard von Krafft-Ebing (1840–1903), whose classical book on sexology bears that title.

psychopathic personality Although the 1952 revision of psychiatric nomenclature does not recognize psychopathic personality as a discrete entity, the attempts to define more clearly the nature of the various behavior patterns which make up this poorly understood group have not been wholly successful, and the term continues to appear in the psychiatric literature.

It was J.C. Prichard who first offered a systematic description of the so-called 'moral disorders'; in 1835 he described a series of cases (which he termed 'moral insanity' and 'moral imbecility') which were the prototypes of the psychopathic state as it is generally understood today. In 1888 Koch introduced the term 'psychopathic inferiority,' and Kraepelin later included in this group a variety of syndromes described in terms of the most obvious presenting symptom, e.g. excitability, impulsivity, lying, criminality. The term 'constitutional psychopathic inferior' was used by Adolf Meyer in 1905; it should be noted, however, that Meyer did not use the term constitutional in the sense of congenital, but rather to indicate that the traits in question were acquired early and were thoroughly ingrained in the personality.

Cleckley (1941), who considers psychopathic personality a psychosis because of the lack of integration of the affective components into the personality, lists the following characteristics: '(1) Superficial charm and good "intelligence." (2) Absence of delusions and other signs of irrational "thinking." (3) Absence of "nervousness" or psychoneurotic manifestations. (4) Unreliability. (5) Untruthfulness and insincerity. (6) Lack of remorse or shame. (7) Inadequately motivated antisocial behavior. (8) Poor judgment and failure to learn by experience. (9) Pathologic egocentricity and incapacity for love. (10) General poverty in major affective reactions. (11) Specific loss of insight. (12) Unresponsiveness in general interpersonal relations. (13) Fantastic and uninviting behavior with drink and sometimes without. (14) Suicide rarely carried out. (15) Sex life impersonal, trivial and poorly integrated. (16) Failure to follow any life plan.' (Cleckley, H. *The Mask of Sanity*, Mosby, St. Louis,

1941) The maladjustment is a chronic one, and the psychopath tends to project the blame for his actions onto others. He tends to act out his conflicts so that the environment suffers, rather than the patient. He is a rebellious individualist and a non-conformist.

The etiology is unknown; some claim an exclusively organic etiology, others maintain that it is due to psychogenic factors. Many writers have emphasized difficulties in identification leading to a formless or confused ego-ideal. An unstable, inconsistent maternal figure or rejection and emotional deprivation early in life are believed to produce such difficulties in identification. According to M.S. Guttmacher (in Hoch, P. and Zubin, J. *Current Problems in Psychiatric Diagnosis,* Grune and Stratton, N.Y., 1953), psychopathic behavior is '. . . generally the result of affect starvation during the first years of life. The most malignant anti-social psychopaths are probably the products of affect starvation plus sadistic treatment in early childhood.'

Karpman suggests that those cases of psychogenic etiology be termed secondary or symptomatic psychopathy; the others he calls primary psychopathy or *anethopathy* (q.v.). See also *psychopathy, passive parasitic.*

Various workers have noted a high incidence of cerebral dysrhythmia in patients diagnosed psychopathic personality; a high alpha index and theta activity are among the most commonly observed abnormalities.

psychopathist (sī-kop′à-thist) *Obs.* Psychiatrist; alienist.

psychopathologist (sī-kō-pà-thol′ō-jist) A person who specializes in psychopathology.

psychopathology The branch of science which deals with morbidity or pathology of the psyche or mind.

psychopathosis (sī-kō-pa-thō′sis) Southard's term for what is more commonly termed *psychopathic personality* (q.v.).

psychopath, sexual See *psychopathia sexualis.*

psychopathy (sī-kop′à-thē) General term for mental disease or disorder.

psychopathy, passive parasitic (par-à-sit′ik) A term which defines a clinical subdivision of anethopathy (psychopathic personality). Karpman suggests the term *anethopathy* (q.v.) to replace idiopathic, constitutional, or primary psychopathy. Anethopathy is subdivided into two distinct clinical types: the aggressive predatory type and the passive parasitic type. In regard to the latter, Karpman says: 'Instead of being actively aggressive, this type of an individual has much less of energy output and feeds himself by "sponging" on his environment for all his needs in a passive and entirely parasitic way. Its victims are willing, yet unwilling hosts. Such aggression as there may be, is very minimal and no more than is absolutely necessary to satisfy immediate needs.' ('Passive Parasitic Psychopathy,' *Psychoanalytic Review 34*, 102, 1947) Typical of such patients is the lack of any positive or generous human emotions, of sympathetic or tender affect, of gratitude or appreciation. These patients show no guilt, remorse, or regret. Their total picture is one of self-gratification. There are almost no unconscious mechanisms, because there is no repression of instinctual demands and no deferment of pleasure. Further, the patients are completely lacking in insight into the nature of their disturbances.

psychopedagogy (-ped′à-gō-jē) A combination of conventional pedagogy and Adlerian psychology which aims to stimulate, cultivate, and amplify the natural qualities of the child and do away with unnecessary authority.

psychopetal (sī-kop′ē-tal) The term *psychopetal* literally refers to objects that seek the psyche. Ordinarily, however, psychiatrists prefer the term *centripetal*. Bleuler says: 'I do not speak of "psychopetal" functions, because although there is a given "direction" yet both incoming and outgoing functions, as far as psychology is concerned, take place within the psyche.' (Bleuler, E. *Textbook of Psychiatry*, tr. by Brill, A.A., Macmillan, New York, 1930)

psychophobia (sī-kō-fō′bi-à) Fear of psyche or mind.
'In philosophy ultra-idealistic solipsism means a relapse into egocentric infantilism; the purely materialistic psychophobic standpoint signifies a regression to the exaggerations of the projection-phase. . . .' (Ferenczi, S. *Further Contributions to the Theory and Technique of Psycho-Analysis*, tr. by Suttie, J.I., Leonard and Vir-

ginia Woolf and The Institute of Psychoanalysis, London, 1926)

psychophore (-fōr) See *archaism*.

psychophysical (-fiz′i-kal) Psychosomatic.

psychophysics (-fiz′iks) The science of the relation between mental action and physical phenomena.

psychophysiologic autonomic and visceral disorders (sī-kō-fiz-i-ō-loj′ik aw-tō-nom′ik, vis′er-al) This is the diagnostic term preferred in the 1952 revision of psychiatric nomenclature to the older categories 'psychosomatic disorders,' 'somatization reactions,' 'organ neuroses,' etc. These disorders are disturbances of visceral function secondary to chronic attitudes or long-continued insufficiency of affective discharge and may present themselves as dysfunction involving any of the organ systems: skin, musculoskeletal, respiratory, cardiovascular, hemic and lymphatic, gastro-intestinal, genito-urinary, endocrine, nervous system or organs of special sense. In this system of classification, ulcerative colitis, for example, would be labeled 'psychophysiologic gastro-intestinal reaction.'

psychophysiology (-fiz-i-ol′ō-jē) Physiology in relation to the mind and its processes.

psychoplegia (-plē′ji-à) *Rare*. A rapidly developing form of dementia.

psychopneumatology (-nū-mà-tol′ō-jē) Study of the interactions of mind and body; psychosomatology.

psycho-reaction Much and Holzmann used this expression for psychophysical interrelationship. They asserted that when they injected cobra poison into patients with schizophrenia, they observed lysis of the red blood corpuscles in a way that was characteristic of schizophrenia. Their claims were short-lived.

psychorhythm (-riTH′m) T.S. Clouston's term, synonymous with *alternating insanity*.

psychorhythmia (-riTH′mi-à) Involuntary repetition, by the mind, of its formerly volitional action.

psychorrhagia, psychorraghy (sī-kō-rā′-ji-à, sī-ĸor′à-jē) The death-struggle.

psychorrhea (-rē′à) A mental syndrome characterized by vague and often bizarre theories of philosophy; usually the stream of thought is incoherent. The condition is not uncommon in schizophrenia.

psychorrhexis (-rek′sis) A malignant type of anxiety reaction seen in 2 to 3 per cent of war neuroses, according to Emilio Mira. Anguish and perplexity, rather than fear or excitement, are the cardinal features. Pulse remains above 120, respiration above 40. Temperature rises rapidly after seven days, the tongue becomes ulcerated, and jaundice and tympanitic abdomen may appear. Patients become restless, develop automatic movements and facial spasms. In fatal cases, death ensues after three or four days. Psychorrhexis occurs in patients with pre-existing lability of the sympathetic system, with sudden severe mental trauma in conditions of physical exhaustion, and when there is long delay before sedative treatment is instituted.

psychoscopy (sī-kos′kō-pē) The term psychoscopy is used by L.E. Hinsie to characterize Freud's contribution to psychiatry in which the function of the human mind was dissected in microscopic detail. (Hinsie, L.E. *Understandable Psychiatry,* Macmillan, New York, 1948)

psychosensory (sī-kō-sen′sō-rē) Pertaining to: 1. The mental perception and interpretation of sensory stimuli, or

2. A hallucination which, by an effort, the mind is able to distinguish from an actuality.

psychoses, alcoholic (sī-kō′sēs) See *alcoholism.*

psychoses, combined When psychiatrists use the expression *combined psychoses* they do not mean that a single individual has more than one psychotic diagnosis, but that almost every psychosis contains, in addition to the basic elements characterizing the disorder, a number of phenomena that may be common to other psychiatric states. Compulsive-obsessive symptoms are usual in states of manic-depressive psychosis; conversion symptoms occur with much regularity among schizophrenic patients. The term *combined psychoses* is rarely used, to avoid the chance of misinterpretation.

psychosexual Relating to sexuality as it manifests itself in the mind, in contradistinction to its physical or somatic manifestations.

psychosexuality Psychosexual condition

or state. *Psychosexuality* is distinguished from sexuality expressed somatically (somatosexual). For example, ideas of a sexual character are manifestations of psychosexuality.

psychosis (sī-kō′sis) In current psychiatry, mental disorder of a more or less special kind, which may or may not be associated with an organic disease. It is not considered in keeping with the available facts to refer to a psychosis as a disease, since the term *disease* is traditionally identified with pathology of tissues. For want of a better term psychiatrists speak of mental *disorder* when they refer to pathology of the psyche.

A psychosis is usually a severer type of mental disorder in the sense that all the forms of adaptation (e.g. social, intellectual, professional, religious, etc.) are disrupted. In other words, the disorganization of the personality is extensive. The principal psychotic syndromes are schizophrenia and manic-depressive psychosis. When the psychic disorder is associated with an organic disease, such as general paresis, brain tumor, etc., the term *organic psychosis* is used for the sake of convenience.

From the psychoanalytic point of view 'unconscious wish-impulses evidently strive to assert themselves even during the day, and the fact of transference, as well as the psychoses, tells us that they endeavor to force their way through the preconscious system to consciousness and the command of motility.' Normally the wish-impulses are checked by the critical censorship, located between the unconscious and preconscious. When the censorship is enfeebled or when unconscious excitations are pathologically reinforced, the wish-impulses gain domination over the preconscious realm, 'thus directing an apparatus not designed for them by virtue of the attraction exerted by perceptions on the distribution of our psychic energy. We call this condition psychosis.' (Freud, S. *The Interpretation of Dreams,* 3rd ed., tr. by Brill, A.A., Macmillan, New York, 1933)

psychosis, accidental This expression is not in common usage. 'Upon the basis of these observations it may be concluded that individuals who suffer from psychoses may be considered to form two great classes: 1. Those who develop psychoses irrespective of environment; for example, paranoia and manic-depressive psychoses. 2. Those who develop psychoses, provided there exist the proper environment and exciting causes; for example, puerperal and other toxic psychoses, general paralysis and organic dementias. These in this sense may be termed *accidental* psychoses.' (Buckley, A.C. *The Basis of Psychiatry,* Lippincott, Philadelphia and London, 1920)

psychosis, acute shock An acute psychiatric disturbance occurring during war. Its most prominent symptoms are a completely unconscious state (with flaccid limbs and closed eyes), lasting from minutes to hours; insensitivity to pain with no reaction to external stimuli; the eyelids flutter, the eyeballs are mobile and are rolled outward and upward. The condition occurs most commonly during active warfare, especially on forced marches and in active campaigns.

psychosis, affective A general term used to refer to any of those psychoses whose prominent feature is a disturbance in mood or emotion, viz. manic-depressive psychosis and involutional melancholia.

psychosis, akinetic (ak-i-net'ik) Wernicke used the term akinetic motor psychosis to refer to that extreme of catatonia which is marked by stupor, 'attonita,' and cerea flexibilitas. Flexor action of the musculature predominates, and movement may be reduced almost to zero. At the other extreme of catatonia is the hyperkinetic motor psychosis, which corresponds to what in present-day use is termed catatonic excitement.

psychosis, alcoholic Psychosis brought on by drinking alcohol. See *alcoholism.*

psychosis, alcoholic Korsakoff When associated with alcoholism, the *Korsakoff psychosis* is also known as *chronic alcoholic delirium.* Some authors also refer to it as *chronic delirium tremens,* because the syndrome frequently follows (acute) delirium tremens. Bleuler says that 'the Korsakoff psychosis in the majority of cases begins with a delirium tremens that recedes somewhat slowly and leaves behind the organic syndrome.' The basic symptomatology comprises memory defects, confabulations, impairment of apperception and attention, disorientation, ideational and affective disorders, in addition to such physical symptoms as are associated with general neuritis (pains,

paralyses, atrophies, etc.). (Bleuler, E. *Textbook of Psychiatry,* tr. by Brill, A.A., Macmillan, New York, 1930)

psychosis, alternating The so-called circular form of manic-depressive psychosis in which manic episodes alternate with depressive episodes in the same patient. This form was originally described by Falret, Jr. as 'folie circulaire.' It is not as common as either the recurrent depressive or the recurrent manic types of manic-depressive psychosis.

psychosis, anxiety This is a term used by Bleuler for a psychosis characterized by anxiety. As a rule, however, anxiety does not play an important part in a psychosis, save, perhaps, in states of agitated depression.

psychosis, arteriosclerotic (ar-tēr-ī-ō-skle-rot'ik) Chronic brain syndrome associated with cerebral arteriosclerosis. The term cerebral arteriosclerosis refers to degenerative changes in the arteries of the brain, the most important causes of which are: (1) primary degeneration of the intima; (2) degeneration secondary to high blood pressure; (3) endarteritis (usually syphilis); (4) thromboangiitis obliterans; (5) polyarteritis nodosa or periarteritis nodosa; and (6) temporal arteritis. The effect of progressive occlusion of the cerebral blood vessels is an impairment of circulation in the regions they supply. As a result of this, impairment of cerebral function occurs before any vessel is completely blocked.

Pathologically, the primary and most important changes are in the elastic tissues, especially in the internal elastic membrane of the cerebral arterioles. Two main types of elastic alterations are seen, hyperplastic and hypoplastic degeneration. Focal parenchymatous changes in the brain tend to be associated with hyperplastic degeneration, while gross hemorrhagic softenings are more prevalent in the hypoplastic type. The hyperplastic type tends to be associated with focal neurologic symptoms; the hypoplastic type shows predominantly mental symptoms.

The onset of the disease is often insidious, and its course is slowly progressive. Mental symptoms consist of a general reduction in intellectual capacity with memory impairment and emotional instability. The patient becomes self-centered and hostile to change in all forms.

In more severe cases, loosely constructed delusions occur, often with a paranoid coloring. Depression is not uncommon and there may be attacks of confusion. Still greater deterioration leads to a profound dementia.

Neurologic symptoms include epileptiform attacks, various forms of aphasia, agnosia, and apraxia, signs of pyramidal tract lesions, senile tremor, athetosis, Parkinsonism, and often some degree of visual impairment.

psychosis, association In discussing unconscious complexes Prince refers to the relationship of obsessions and fears. 'Although biologically fear is useful as a defense for the preservation of the individual, when perverted by useless associations it becomes harmful, in that it is not only painful, but prevents the adjustment of the individual to his environment and thereby takes on a pathological taint. Complexes with other emotions are less likely to be harmful and therefore less frequently apply for relief. Yet imperative ideas with jealousy, anger, hatred, love, disgust, etc., centered about an object are exceedingly common, though their possessors less often resort to a physician.' (Prince, M. *The Unconscious,* Macmillan, New York, 1916)

'From another point of view abnormal complexes, represented by these examples, may be regarded as "association psychoses." Sometimes the physiological bodily accompaniments form the greater part of the complex which is for the most part made up of physiological disturbances (vasomotor, cardiac, gastric, respiratory, secretory, muscular, etc.); almost pure association *neuroses* they then become.' (ibid)

psychosis, autistic (aw-tis′tik) See *psychosis, symbiotic infantile.*

psychosis, barbed wire A psychosis developing in prisoners or war, characterized by irritability and loss of memory for prewar occurrences.

psychosis, biogenic (bī-ō-jen′ik) Craig and Beaton write that 'the group of disorders called the biogenic psychoses are abnormal reactions to experience which should normally build up the personality; they have no other cause than the patient's failure to master life. The conception originated with Kraepelin, who differentiated by the term dementia prae-

cox a class of reactions which he supposed to run a dementing course.' The psychoses known as biogenic are dementia praecox (schizophrenia), dementia paranoides, paraphrenia, paranoia, manic-depressive psychosis, and the involutional states, according to Craig and Beaton.

psychosis, buffoonery A form of hyperkinetic catatonia (catatonic excitement) in which the patient constantly makes disconnected caricatured grimaces and gestures. This psychosis probably represents a flight into disease as an escape from reality. 'One has the impression that these patients want to play the buffoon, though they do this in a most awkward and inept fashion. They contrive any number of stupidities and sillinesses, such as beating their own knees, interchanging pillows for blankets when they go to bed, pouring water out on the floor instead of into a cup, lifting doors off their hinges. The patients will do all this while they are seemingly well oriented. As a rule they speak very little or not at all and what they have to say is, in the main, completely illogical cursing or other nonsense. Undoubtedly the "faxen-psychosis" has an origin similar to that of the Ganserian twilight state. It usually involves individuals who for some unconscious reason pretend to be mentally deranged.' (Bleuler, E. *Dementia Praecox or the Group of Schizophrenias,* International Universities Press, New York, 1950) Also called *faxen-psychosis.*

psychosis, cardiac Confused mental state associated with heart failure.

psychosis, Cheyne-Stokes (John Cheyne, Scottish physician, 1777–1836, and William Stokes, Irish physician, 1804–1878) An abnormal mental state, characterized by anxiety and restlessness, associated with Cheyne-Stokes breathing.

psychosis, circular See *mania.*

psychosis, circulatory Confused mental state associated with cardiovascular failure.

psychosis, climacteric (klī-mak-ter′ik) Any psychotic reaction associated with the climacterium or 'change of life.' See *psychosis, involutional.*

psychosis, collective The term for psychic defense mechanisms that are utilized by an entire group in adapting to other cultures and societies. Freud's instinctual theories recognized two basic drives, sex and aggression. Freud felt that the aggressive trends of man lead him and his culture to fatal conflicts. Man's aggressiveness within a culture is diverted to people outside his own 'psychic mass.' This diversion of hostile trends implies a process of projection of the superego's aggressive component, so that the individual's hostility can be ascribed to other groups. Flescher thinks that this paranoid projection is inherent in the formation of the mass and constitutes the collective psychosis. Present-day Russia affords an example of collective psychosis, with the Russians accusing the United States, for one, of capitalistic war-mongering and aggression. According to the theory above, these accusations represent a projection of the Russians' own aggression, which cannot be openly expressed against their government.

psychosis, compound *Obs.* A mixture of different psychoses. The term was used by Wernicke, whose system of classification of mental diseases was such that almost every patient would have to be considered as suffering from many of the most diverse mental diseases. Wernicke, therefore, hypothesized that more than one psychosis could be present in the same individual. As a rule, modern-day psychiatric thought rejects such a concept.

psychosis, defect *Obs.* Feeblemindedness. 'The first group of disorders which will be discussed are those classed as the defect psychoses—idiocy, imbecility, and other degrees of mental debility.' (Paton, S. *Psychiatry,* Lippincott, Philadelphia and London, 1905)

psychosis, defense Now obsolete, this was a general term used by Freud to express the concept of the defensive value of a psychosis. He then employed the phrase *defense-neurosis* to express a similar concept in the neuroses.

psychosis, degenerative (dē-jen'ĕr-à-tiv) A general term for regression or falling back upon a form of mental adjustment characteristic of some earlier type of adaptation. For example, the schizophrenic patient may abandon adaptation to reality and then recede or regress through adolescence, puberty, late childhood, early childhood, and infancy. In this sense the term *degenerative* has no anti-social or immoral import. Likewise,

when patients with hysteria adapt themselves to puerilism, they are said to show a degenerative disorder, *degenerative hysteria.*

'One should avoid working with such an ambiguous conception as degeneration and its designation.' (Bleuler, E. *Textbook of Psychiatry,* tr. by Brill, A.A., Macmillan, New York, 1930)

psychosis, epochal (ep'ok-al) White says: 'In the past it has been the custom to describe certain other psychoses occurring at physiological epochs and to give them the name of the epoch during which they occurred. Thus we find the group of *puerperal psychoses,* especially *puerperal mania,* and the *lactational psychoses.*' White adds: 'There is no such thing, for example, as a puerperal psychosis, strictly speaking. Mental disorder frequently occurs during the puerperium but must be classified in accordance with the symptoms it presents rather than the time at which it occurs.' (White, W.A. *Outlines of Psychiatry,* 12th ed., Nervous & Mental Disease Publishing Company, Washington, D.C., 1929)

psychosis, exhaustive The symptomatology of *exhaustive psychosis* is essentially that of *collapse delirium.* Binswanger subdivides exhaustive psychosis as follows: *exhaustion stupor; exhaustive amentia; delirium acutum exhaustivum.*

psychosis, febrile (fē'bril, feb'ril) *Obs.* Infective-exhaustive psychosis.

psychosis, functional See *functional.*

psychosis, 'furlough' The term for an episode of the acute schizophrenic type secondary to the sudden emotional readjustments required by a military furlough or leave. Dynamically, the outbreak of the psychotic behavior seems to be related to the sudden release of the individual from military authority, on which he has become dependent. Symptoms appear suddenly a few days after the apparently well-adjusted person has returned home. Affect becomes inappropriate, delusional trends and ideas of reference are prominent, and suicidal tendencies are frequent. In the ensuing week or two, severe confusion with blocking of thought processes becomes marked. Gradual improvement occurs within two months, irrespective of any particular form of therapy. The patient cannot return to duty, because flattening of affect and unpredictable behavior usually remain. (*American Journal of Psychiatry 102,* 670, 1945–46)

psychosis, gestational (jes-tā'shun-al) *Obs.* Psychosis developing during pregnancy. Synonymous with *gestational insanity.*

psychosis, governess 'For decades, the idea has been preserved that governesses were especially prone to develop schizophrenia. Some authors even spoke of a "governess-psychosis"; and it has even been maintained that governesses suffer a particularly severe (and unpleasant) form of the disease. There may be something in this, inasmuch as young women become governesses who have ambitions of raising their social standing beyond their capacities and among whom there must be many with schizophrenic predisposition.' (Bleuler, E. *Dementia Praecox or the Group of Schizophrenias,* International Universities Press, New York, 1950) Statistics do not, in fact, indicate that the incidence of schizophrenia is higher in governesses than in other vocations.

psychosis, hallucinatory wish (ha-lū'sinà-to-rē) 'The formation of the wish-phantasy and its regression to hallucination are the most essential parts of the dream-work, but they do not belong exclusively to dreams. On the contrary, they are found similarly in two morbid states: in acute hallucinatory confusion (Meynert's "amentia"), and in the hallucinatory phase of schizophrenia. The hallucinatory delirium of amentia is a clearly recognizable wish-phantasy, often perfectly framed like a beautiful day-dream. One might speak in quite general terms of an *hallucinatory wish-psychosis,* ascribing it equally to dreams and to amentia.' (Freud, S. *Collected Papers,* vol. 4, tr. by Riviere, J., Leonard and Virginia Woolf and The Institute of Psychoanalysis, London, 1924–25)

psychosis, housewife's 'From the accounts given me by the girl and her father I was led to imagine her as an uncultivated woman and above all as a foolish one, who had concentrated all her interests upon domestic affairs, especially since her husband's illness and the estrangement to which it led. She presented the picture, in fact, of what might be called the "housewife's psychosis."' (Freud, S. *Collected Papers,* vol. 3, tr. by Strachey, A

and J., Leonard and Virginia Woolf, Hogarth Press, London, 1925)

psychosis, hysterical At present this term is synonymous with hysteria, which is more commonly looked upon as a psychoneurosis rather than a psychosis. However, at times a hysteroid condition seems closely allied to a psychosis (e.g. certain stuporous and hallucinatory states) and then it is called a hysterical psychosis or a hysteriform condition.

psychosis, iatrogenic (ī-at-rō-jen'ik) See *iatrogeny.*

psychosis, idiophrenic (id-i-ō-fren'ik) *Obs.* Organic psychosis.

psychosis, infective-exhaustive An older term for acute brain syndrome associated with systemic infection; also known as acute toxic encephalopathy, acute toxic encephalitis, or acute serous encephalitis.

psychosis, influenced Gordon's term for psychosis of association. See *association, psychosis of.*

psychosis, involutional ('pertaining to the period of involution or regression, as opposed to evolution or development') As a rule any psychiatric disorder, arising for the first time in the involutional period and presumably associated etiologically with it, is called an involutional psychosis. There are many forms of psychiatric states occurring during this period of life, two of which are outstanding. The foremost is called *involutional melancholia* and is characterized by intense agitation and depression. A second form, usually also depressive, contains components that have close kinship with schizophrenia.

psychosis, juvenile A psychosis occurring between the ages of 15 and 25, approximately. This term is sometimes used, incorrectly, as synonymous with schizophrenia. All psychoses occur in this age group, and, because schizophrenia is the most common of the psychoses, it is also the most common in this age group. But there is no characteristic juvenile psychosis or psychosis typical for the age of puberty.

psychosis, Korsakoff (Syergey Syergeyvich Korsakoff, Russian neurologist, 1854–1900) This is characterized by mental and physical disorders. The outstanding physical symptom is polyneuritis. The organic mental syndrome is 'the result of a combination of attention and memory disorders. The memory disorder is of the nature of a lack of impressibility. The result of this combination is a special type of amnesia. There is defect in the recording of current events. The patient is usually disoriented, to some extent at least, and the things that have recently happened cannot be recalled.' (Jelliffe, S.E. and White, W.A. *Diseases of the Nervous System,* 6th ed., Lea & Febiger, Philadelphia, 1935) The amnesic periods are generally filled in by confabulations.

The Korsakoff psychosis may be caused by a variety of agents—alcohol, metallic poisons, infections, or any of the encephalopathies. See *psychosis, alcoholic Korsakoff.*

psychosis, lactation *Rare.* This expression refers to any type of psychiatric condition that occurs during the period of lactation.

psychosis, malignant By this term Fenichel designates that type of schizophrenia which is progressive (slowly or rapidly) and terminates in permanent dementia. He contrasts these malignant psychoses with schizophrenic episodes which are temporary attacks in persons who are apparently well both before and after their psychotic episode.

The question arises whether these two general types of schizophrenia can have anything in common. Fenichel believes that both the malignant 'schizophrenic process' and the shorter-termed 'schizophrenic episode' have certain common features. These are 'the bizarrity of the symptoms, the absurdity and unpredictability of the affects and intellectual ideas and the obviously inadequate connection between these two.' Moreover, the symptomatology in both types can be explained by the concept of regression of the ego to a much deeper level than in the neurosis, i.e. to the time of 'primary narcissism' when 'the ego was not yet established or had just begun to be established.' Apparently no factors, of either an organic or a psychogenic nature, have yet been discerned which might explain the different courses taken by these different types of schizophrenic illness. (Fenichel, O. *The Psychoanalytic Theory of Neurosis,* Norton, New York, 1945)

The term malignant psychosis is approximately equivalent to the terms process psychosis and nuclear schizophrenia, and to 'dementia praecox' as used by contemporary European psychiatrists.

psychosis, manic-depressive A term introduced by Kraepelin in 1896 to differentiate between those psychoses which typically progress to profound dementia (dementia praecox, or the group of schizophrenias) and those which do not lead to a true deterioration (manic-depressive psychosis). The term thus came to include periodic and circular insanity, simple mania, melancholia, and many types of confusion or delirium. Although involutional melancholia was later included in the manic-depressive group, the tendency in both the United States and Great Britain has been to keep the involutional group separate; and in many classificatory schemes, involutional melancholia and manic-depressive psychosis are considered the two major subdivisions of the broader category, affective psychoses.

Manic-depressive psychosis accounts for 15 per cent of the total first admissions to mental hospitals in the United States; it occurs more frequently in women, who account for approximately 70 per cent of cases, and is more common among Jews than is any other mental illness. Kallmann estimates that the general average frequency of manic-depressive psychosis does not exceed 0.4 per cent; but the expectancy in half-siblings is approximately 17 per cent, in siblings and in parents approximately 23 per cent, in di-zygotic co-twins approximately 26 per cent, and in one-egg twin partners approximately 100 per cent. These numbers are based upon fairly strict diagnostic criteria; Kallmann uses as manic-depressive subjects only those whose illness is cyclic, with periodicity of acute, self-limited mood swings before the fifth decade and with no progressive or residual personality disintegration before or after psychotic episodes of elation or depression. Reactive and situational depressions, hallucinatory episodes, and agitated anxiety states associated with hypertension are excluded. Primary menopausal and presenile depressions, and other non-periodic forms of depressive behavior in the involutional period are placed in the category of involutional psychosis. Kallmann concludes: 'The recurring ability to exceed the normal range of emotional responses with extreme but self-limited mood alterations seems to be associated with a specific neurohormonal disturbance, which depends on the mutative effect of a single dominant gene with incomplete penetrance. The dynamics identified with this specific ability cannot be considered to be part of a person's normal biological equipment nor are they out of line with current concepts of psychodynamic phenomena as observed in potentially vulnerable persons.' (Kallmann, Franz J. *Genetic Principles in Manic-Depressive Psychosis*, in Hoch, P.H., and Zubin, J. *Depression*, Grune & Stratton, New York, 1954)

Clinically, manic-depressive psychosis may appear in any of several forms: as a depressive episode in varying degrees of severity (simple depression or simple retardation, acute depression and, according to some, depressive stupor, although many feel that this latter form is always a manifestation of catatonic schizophrenia); or as an elated or manic episode in varying degrees of severity (simple mania or hypomania, acute mania, and delirious mania, the latter being also known as Bell's mania, typhomania, delirium grave, and collapse delirium). A fourth type of mania, chronic mania, has also been described; the symptoms here are of the same degree as acute mania, but they continue uninterruptedly for an indefinite number of years.

Some manic-depressive patients have only manic attacks throughout their lives (recurrent mania); others have only depressive episodes (recurrent depressions), and in a few the circular or alternating form is seen: a continuous alternation for years between states of depression and states of elation. In addition to these types, Kraepelin described a number of mixed states (e.g. maniacal stupor, unproductive mania), but closer scrutiny usually reveals these to be types of schizophrenic episodes.

In the 1952 revision of psychiatric nomenclature, three types of manic-depressive psychosis are included among the 'affective reactions'—manic-depressive reaction, manic type; manic-depressive reaction, depressed type; and manic-depressive reaction, other.

See *melancholia*.

psychosis, masturbatic This is an older diagnostic term, formulated when masturbation was viewed as a causative agent in the production of a psychosis. Modern authorities consider the concept erroneous.

psychosis, menstrual Psychiatric state associated with the menses. Bleuler says that 'menstrual moodiness which is not uncommon in "normal women" might be heightened to a degree that may be designated as melancholic depression; at all events suicides among women occur noticeably often at this time.' He adds that a 'menstrual insanity' 'in any definite sense has not been demonstrated in spite of different attempts.' (Bleuler, E. *Textbook of Psychiatry*, tr. by Brill, A.A., Macmillan, New York, 1930)

psychosis, model Experimental psychosis and, particularly, such as is produced by mescaline or lysergic acid or similar psychotomimetic drugs.

psychosis, motility A type of manic-depressive psychosis described by Ewald; symptoms are mainly hyperkinetic in character, and the episode often occurs only once in a lifetime, with complete remission.

psychosis, motor See *psychosis, sensory*.

psychosis, night Intense anxiety about night or darkness, particularly an aversion to darkness.

'Some rebel at this period [i.e. 'the dawn of sexual life'] against the necessity of losing so much time from the life of active consciousness, dread night, and rejoice every morning on waking up that they have a long day before sleep is again imperative.' (Hall, G.S. *Adolescence*, vol. 1, Appleton, New York, 1908, p. 264)

psychosis of association See *association, psychosis of*.

psychosis of degeneracy An obsolescent expression, used by Siefert to denote that class of psychoses intimately associated with the environment, in contradistinction to the so-called real psychoses in which the environment plays no essential role.

psychosis, organic Psychosis associated with a recognizable organic pathological condition, such as general paresis, brain tumor, traumatic encephalopathy, alcoholism, pellagra, etc. The type of psychosis may vary considerably, though the organic pathology may be more or less constant. Thus, in general paresis, the mental clinical syndrome may be essentially that of manic-depressive disorder, schizophrenia, psychopathic personality, or any one of the psychoneuroses. It is believed that the psychiatric state is a reflection of the organization of the psyche as it was represented prior to the onset of the organic pathology. For example, when an organic brain disease afflicts an individual who is substantially schizoid, the psychiatric syndrome will be of a schizophrenic character. In the 1952 revision of psychiatric nomenclature, the organic psychoses are termed acute and chronic brain syndromes.

The organic syndrome produces its own special symptomatology. This means that in any so-called organic psychosis there are two principal syndromes, an organic and a psychic, one of which may be dominant or both may be of approximately the same force.

The organic reaction-type of psychiatric disorder is a mental disease which may occur in either an acute or chronic form. Pathologically the difference is observed in the fact that the acute organic reaction usually follows a temporary toxic process affecting the brain substance. Clinical examples of the acute type of organic reaction are the delirium of acute fevers, and acute alcoholism. The chronic organic reaction is produced by a more severe tissue change, usually a progressive degeneration. Clinical examples are general paresis and the senile psychoses.

The organic reaction-type in general manifests the following signs:

'1) In the intellectual sphere there is impairment of comprehension, interference with elaboration of impressions, defects in orientation and retention, difficulty in activation of memories and marked fluctuation of the level of attention.

'2) Affective disorder in the form of emotional instability, the patient laughing or weeping without sufficient cause, and often in an explosive way.

'3) Character-change in the form of conduct foreign to the patient's natural disposition, e.g., indecent behavior in a hitherto self-respecting individual.' (Henderson, D.K. and Gillespie, R.D. *A Text-Book of Psychiatry,* 4th ed., Oxford University Press, London, 1936)

psychosis, overwhelming According to Freud, a 'psychosis through simple intensification—overwhelming-psychosis.' He cites the case of a young girl who, out of a sense of guilt, developed obsessive reproaches. When, for instance, 'she read in the papers about counterfeiting coinage the thought occurred to her that she also had forged coins; if an unknown criminal had committed a murder, she asked herself anxiously, whether she had not done

the deed.' (Freud, S. *Collected Papers,* vol. 1, tr. by Riviere, J., Leonard and Virginia Woolf and The Institute of Psychoanalysis, London, 1924–25)

psychosis, perplexity This is a subdivision of manic-depressive psychosis, characterized by 'peculiar distress that goes with subjective perplexity.' Hoch and Kirby first described this type in 1919, in a communication entitled 'A Clinical Study of Psychoses Characterized by Distressed Perplexity.' (*Archives of Neurology and Psychiatry 1,* 415–58, 1919)

psychosis, polyneuritic Korsakoff's psychosis.

psychosis, post-infectious Mental disturbances may follow such acute diseases as influenza, pneumonia, typhoid fever, acute rheumatic fever, etc. in their postfebrile period or may occur during the period of convalescence. These mental disturbances may be observed as mild forms of confusion, or suspicious, irritable, depressive reactions. Occasionally states of mental enfeeblement occur following such acute infectious diseases.

psychosis, prison A mental disorder precipitated by anticipated or actual incarceration; the form of psychiatric syndrome depends upon the type of individual; thus, a prison psychosis may resemble or be a schizophrenic, manic-depressive, or psychoneurotic disorder.

'There is no doubt in my mind but that we have here a beginning psychosis and that in all probability, if the sentence of hanging were sustained, the mental symptoms would become progressively aggravated as time went on. It is quite certain, also, that if this patient were relieved from the stress under which she is suffering, if, for example, she were pardoned and set free, that the mental symptoms would melt away almost immediately.' (White, W.A. *Insanity and the Criminal Law,* Macmillan, New York, 1923)

'Another group of psychopaths who are prone to develop prison psychoses are those primitive, superficially endowed individuals with a high degree of autosuggestibility, a marked tendency to phantastic lying and instability of mood, individuals who have always led a sort of humdrum existence without aim or goal of any kind in view.' (Glueck, B. *Studies in Forensic Psychiatry,* Little, Brown, Boston, 1916)

psychosis, private The expression *private psychosis* is used by Ferenczi as a synonym of *neurotic character,* because, as he says, it is tolerated by the ego.

psychosis, process A term applied to the malignant type of schizophrenic psychosis which terminates in permanent dementia. It has always been recognized that schizophenic phenomena have many diverse manifestations: there are the passing schizophrenic episodes in persons who apparently are well both before and after these periods; then, there are the severe psychoses which sooner or later end in permanent dementia. All the schizophrenic manifestations, however, have the common features of queer and bizarre symptoms, absurd and unpredictable affects and intellectual ideas, and the obviously inadequate connection between these two.

The question arises whether there is any etiological basis for differentiating schizophrenic episodes and schizophrenic processes. Some authors have felt that schizophrenic episodes result from traumata and impediments in early infantile life, whereas the process psychosis is due to unknown organic factors. Fenichel feels, however, that there is no basis for such a differentiation and that both psychogenic influences and organic disposition are contributory causes in the majority of cases. Certainly the prognosis in the 'process' type of cases (in which there has been slow chronic development of the disease) is very poor. The prognosis is better in the acute cases, because some of them recover quickly and entirely. This is especially true of the cases in which the episode is the retroaction to an acute and severe frustration or narcissistic hurt. (Fenichel, O. *The Psychoanalytic Theory of Neurosis,* Norton, New York, 1945) See *psychosis, malignant.*

'The European tendency is to use the term nuclear or process schizophrenia, or dementia praecox, to refer to unquestionable cases with a high tendency to deterioration and little tendency to remission or recovery. The others are called by Ruemke the pseudoschizophrenias, by Lunn (Denmark) the schizophreniform psychoses. The nuclear types may or may not show the accessory symptoms of Bleuler (delusions, hallucinations, etc.), but the fundamental symptoms are prominent. In the other types, the accessory symptoms are in the foreground and the fundamental symptoms may not be readily apparent. As Bleuler pointed out, the accessory symptoms are not diagnostic of schizophrenia for they occur also in many other disorders, especially in the organic group.' (Campbell, R.J. *Psychiatric Quarterly 32,* 318–34, 1958)

psychosis, progressive Same as *psychosis, process.*

psychosis, puberty As Bleuler says, 'A "puberty psychosis" peculiar to the period of development is not yet known.' Many psychiatric conditions may appear at the period of puberty, such as schizophrenia, hysteria, etc. (Bleuler, E. *Textbook of Psychiatry,* tr. by Brill, A.A., Macmillan, New York, 1930)

psychosis, puerperal When a psychiatric syndrome is associated with the puerperium (the period from the termination of labor to the complete involution of the uterus), it is generally designated as a puerperal psychosis. Strictly speaking, there is no single psychiatric condition that occurs during this period, and except for those states that are definitely connected with organic disorders, there is nothing in the puerperium as such, save psychic factors, which gives rise to a psychosis. The expression puerperal psychosis has about the same weight as that given to *pregnancy psychosis, lactation psychosis,* etc.

'But there are no special psychoses either in the wider or narrower sense of the term.' (Bleuler, E. *Textbook of Psychiatry,* tr. by Brill, A.A., Macmillan, New York, 1930)

psychosis, purpose While it is generally acknowledged by psychiatrists that all psychiatric states serve a purpose, usually an unconscious one, there are some whose motives are quite clear-cut. 'The wish to be insane and to appear irresponsible is fulfilled through the Ganser state which is a mental disease, or the wish to be innocent and pardoned is realized in the prison delirium which deludes the patients with the fact that they are innocent or forgiven. The maximum of wish fulfillment is achieved by the ecstasies. These syndromes are also called *purpose psychoses.*' (Bleuler, E. *Textbook of Psychiatry,* tr. by Brill, A.A., Macmillan, New York, 1930)

psychosis, reactive When a psychosis is

believed to be instigated principally by an environmental condition, it is designated as a *reactive* or *situational* psychosis. For example, the prisoner who develops the Ganser syndrome is said to have in mind the avoidance of paying the penalty for the crime.

'One class of the psychoses shows itself as a morbid reaction to an affect experience, as a prison psychosis to a confinement, and an hysterical twilight state to a jilting on the part of the beloved (*reactive psychoses, situation psychoses*).' (Bleuler, E. *Textbook of Psychiatry*, tr. by Brill, A.A., Macmillan, New York, 1930)

psychosis, schizoaffective (skiz-ō-a-fec'tiv) A subtype of schizophrenia in which manic or melancholic symptoms are prominent. The affective symptoms are often so pronounced in the early stages as to mask the underlying schizophrenic process, and such cases account for the majority of diagnoses of manic-depressive psychosis in children and adolescents. Later in the course of the disease, however, the affective symptoms tend to abate as the schizophrenic elements become more obvious. Such cases usually end in hebephrenic or simple deterioration. (Campbell, R.J. *Psychiatric Quarterly* 32, 318–34, 1958)

psychosis, schizophreniform (skiz-ō-fren'i-form) See *psychosis, process.*

psychosis, senile A mental disorder occurring in and peculiar to old age. It is characterized by a progressive intellectual enfeeblement, with loss of memory for recent events, and an alteration in the personality with irritability, lack of consideration for others, grouchiness, indifference, and apathy. There is a marked tendency to reminisce, and the patient may hoard things. Paranoid delusions, ideas of infidelity, and hypochondriacal complaints may appear. Unmotivated crying and laughing are fairly common. Moral delinquency with complete failure of judgment may occur. As the deterioration progresses, the memory defect becomes more marked and there is loss of comprehension of the environment with complete disorientation, the patient wetting and soiling himself.

Physical signs of the dotage are present.

The pathological picture of the senile brain shows numerous foci of generalized atrophy, necrosis and fatty infiltration, degeneration of nerve cells and neuroglia, and the presence of senile plaques in the cerebral cortex. These plaques consist of dense neurofibrils, which are thought to represent aggregations of microglia.

Senile psychosis differs from psychosis with cerebral arteriosclerosis in that it occurs considerably later in life, presents a greater disintegration of the personality, and shows less insight, and focal signs are much less frequent than in the cerebral arteriosclerosis.

In certain cases of senile psychosis the outstanding picture may be one of deep confusion; of a delirious condition; of pronounced depression and persistent agitation; of well-marked paranoid delusional trends or delusions of an expansive nature.

In the 1952 revision of psychiatric nomenclature, senile psychosis is termed 'chronic brain syndrome associated with senile brain disease.'

psychosis, sensory Bucknill and Tuke suggested that mental disorders be divided into two large classes, called sensory psychoses and motor psychoses. The former were to include all forms of psychiatric syndromes in which feeling, emotion, sensory perception, and ideation predominated. The latter would comprise those reactions characterized by disorders in the intellectual and motor spheres. The classification (suggested in the latter half of the 19th century) was not adopted.

psychosis, septicemia (sep-ti-sē'mi-å) An acute organic psychosis due to a severe infection of the blood and characterized mainly by a delirium. Nosologically, this condition belongs to the toxic psychoses (deliria) associated with toxic-infectious diseases, and would today be classified as acute brain syndrome associated with systemic infection, with psychotic reaction.

psychosis, shock By the term shock psychosis Kardiner describes the particular type of mental reaction observed in soldiers overcome by shock or fright in combat. He writes: 'Many of the acute reactions to shock terminated in what may be called *"shock psychosis."* Many of the soldiers who were picked up immediately after the shock and sent to a hospital had initial anxious deliriums, during which they regarded everything in the environment as hostile, and anybody who approached them excited violent fear reactions. Wild motor activity with mutism, depression, and disturbances of sleep sometimes followed.

'The most common form of this psychosis was perhaps the acute, passive, negativistic stupor, with mutism, complete immobility, total anesthesia, inability to take food, incontinence, total unconsciousness at first and cloudy states later, and inability to stand or walk. These patients had gradually to relearn sphincter control and the enunciation of words; at first they said only "yes" and "no" and then answered to their names. Very gradually they were taught how to grasp objects and how to feed themselves. Familiarity with the environment was also regained slowly; some time elapsed before these patients began to take an interest in their destiny. Of interest is the fact that most of them were able to recall the traumatic event; they remembered some details of their behavior such as making certain efforts to save themselves just before they lost consciousness. Gaupp reported a patient with no recollection of the accompaniments of the exploding shell which caused him to lose consciousness. This observation is important, because the psychic experience—the feelings and ideas excited by the explosion—called forth the powerful action of the entire organism, that is, unconsciousness and other symptoms of fright, as a defense against it. Gaupp believes that, between the moment of the explosion and the following psychic disturbance, an interval exists during which the perception of the effects of the explosion, the sight of mutilated comrades, and the excitation of fright aggravate the reaction to the trauma.

'Patients in fright stupor were not always passive and without feeling. Very frequently they shouted in their stupor: "The enemy is coming!" "They are coming!" "Get em!" "Fight em!" ' (Kardiner, A., and Spiegel, H. *War Stress and Neurotic Illness,* Hoeber, New York, 1947)

psychosis, situational See *psychosis, reactive.*

psychosis, somatic (sō-mat′ik) In discussing diabetes from the standpoint of psychosomatic diagnosis, Dr. Dunbar uses this term for the somatic expression of tension, aggression, and resentment in diabetic patients. 'Much of the aggression and resentment in these patients seems to have been driven inward in a manner which suggests patients with rheumatic heart disease, but they have not given in so much to the passive masochistic role.

In addition to being expressed in tension of striated and smooth musculature, it gnaws at their vitals, and, probably because of their infantile regression and extreme ambivalence, brings about what might be called a *somatic psychosis.*' (Dunbar, F. *Psychosomatic Diagnosis,* Hoeber, New York, 1943)

psychosis, symbiotic infantile (sim-bi-ot′-ik) Mahler's term for a disturbance seen in certain children at the time when separation from the mother would ordinarily be effected. Under the threat of separation, the symbiotic child's rage and panic are projected onto the world, which is perceived as hostile and destructive. The child defends himself by maintaining or restoring the infantile delusion of omnipotence and oneness with the mother, by means of omnipotence phantasies, introjection, projection, delusions, and hallucinations.

Mahler differentiates between the symbiotic psychosis and the autistic psychosis. The latter arises in a child with a constitutionally defective ego anlage and thus the symbiotic mother-infant relationship is interfered with from the beginning. Autism is used as a major defense against external stimuli and inner excitations. See *depression, anaclitic; anxiety, separation.*

psychosis, symptomatic (sim-tō-ma′tik) Whenever the brain function is affected as a result of some general physical disease, the mental condition is known as a symptomatic psychosis, the most common feature of which is a delirious state. This may occur in the course of an acute infectious disease such as penumonia, influenza, typhoid fever, meningitis, etc., or in the course of acute chorea, pellagra, or pelvic infections following childbirth.

These disorders would today be classified as acute or chronic brain syndromes with psychotic reaction.

psychosis, toxic Psychic disorders caused by the great variety of agents called toxins are known as toxic psychoses. The symptomatology varies considerably, depending upon the nature of the toxin, its virulence, the response of the host, etc. In the 1952 revision of psychiatric nomenclature, these psychoses are termed acute and chronic brain syndromes due to intoxication.

psychosis, toxic-infectious This term indicates a mental condition accompanying or following an infective illness or poisoning by some exogenous toxin. The symptoms include delirium, dazed and stuporous conditions, epileptiform attacks, hallucinoses, incoherence, and confusion. Examples of diseases which may produce this reaction-type include influenza, malaria, acute rheumatic fever, pneumonia, typhoid and typhus fever, smallpox, and scarlet fever. In the 1952 revision of psychiatric nomenclature, the toxic-infectious psychoses are classified as acute and chronic brain syndromes associated with systemic infection, and acute and chronic brain syndromes due to drug or poison intoxication.

psychosis, transitory According to Kasanin, a transitory psychosis is 'characterized by emotional turmoil, various kinetic phenomena, and dissociation with confusion and hallucinations, followed by complete recovery and amnesia' for the episode. (Kasanin, J. 'The Syndrome of Episodic Confusions,' *American Journal of Psychiatry 93,* 637, 1936–37)

psychosis, traumatic (traw-ma'tik) When an injury is linked with a psychosis etiologically, that is, as a competent producing cause, the clinical syndrome is called a traumatic psychosis. Fenton found traumatic psychoses in 28 of 830 patients, who had earlier in their illness been diagnosed as traumatic neuroses.

In 1904 Adolf Meyer classified the traumatic psychoses as follows:

1. Direct post-traumatic deliria.
2. Post-traumatic constitution.
3. Traumatic defect states.
4. Post-traumatic psychoses.
5. Post-traumatic psychoses not directly involving the head.

In the 1952 revision of psychiatric nomenclature, traumatic psychoses are classified as brain syndromes (acute or chronic) associated with brain trauma.

psychosis with cardio-renal disease See *cardio-renal disease, psychosis with.*

psychosis with mental deficiency See *deficiency, mental, psychosis with.*

psychosis, zoöphil (zō'ō-fil) *Obs.* A psychosis marked by morbid affection for or interest in animals.

psychosoma (sī-kō-so'mà) The union of physical and psychical components is often designated by the term *psychosoma.* For example, conversion hysteria comprises psychosomatic phenomena, in that a mental conflict gains outlet through somatic agencies.

Infrequently the term *psychosoma* is condensed into *psysoma* (Draper, G.).

psychosomatiatria (-sō-mat-ī-at'ri-à) *Obs.* Medical treatment of mind and body.

psychosomatic (-sō-ma'tik) This term may be used in a methodological sense only, to refer to a type of approach in the study and treatment of certain disturbances of body function. More commonly, however, the term is used in a nosological or classificatory sense to refer to a group of disorders whose etiology at least in part is believed to be related to emotional factors; in the 1952 revision of psychiatric nomenclature such 'psychosomatic disorders' are called 'psychophysiologic autonomic and visceral disorders.'

As used in the second sense, the term psychosomatic is unfortunate, for it implies a dualism which does not exist. No somatic disease is entirely free from psychic influence, just as even in the purest psychic disturbances there are organic-constitutional factors, somatic compliance, etc. While it is generally recognized that many symptoms and diseases occur in the setting of difficult life situations, there is no accepted answer as to why some people get one disease, some get another. Various hypotheses have been put forward: some have tried to show that there is a personality pattern common to all patients with the same disease; others have tried to demonstrate a single personality trait associated with a particular disease; others have maintained that a specific nuclear conflict or dynamic configuration is unique to a particular disease; others have emphasized what has happened to the patient previously, especially in childhood, as in a search for toilet-training problems in patients with intestinal disorders; and, finally, some have tried to correlate the occurrence of particular symptoms with particular life situations. None of these attempts has been wholly satisfactory. Not all patients fit into the pattern they should; many patients show more than one of the illnesses in question, and this is difficult to reconcile with the idea of fixed personality patterns; many patients show the specific dynamic configuration without developing the expected disease; and often there is little similarity between the various situations which provoke recurrences in the same patient.

Many psychoanalysts (e.g. O. Fenichel, *The Psychoanalytic Theory of Neurosis,* Norton, New York, 1945) prefer the term 'organ neurosis' to 'psychosomatic disorder.' An organ neurosis is defined as a type of functional disorder which is physical in nature and which consists of physiologic changes caused by the inappropriate use of the function in question. Thus organ neuroses and conversion neuroses are quite different—in conversion neuroses, the symptom has a specific unconscious meaning and is an expression of a phantasy in 'body language'; in organ neuroses, the change in function *per se* has no unconscious meaning, but instead the chronic, unconscious attitudes of the patient have secondarily produced a change in function. In other words, in the organ neuroses a persistent emotional disturbance has secondarily altered the physiology of an organ system; but in the conversion neuroses, a persistent emotional disturbance is directly symbolized by a disturbance in bodily function, and the physiology of the organ system in question need not be altered.

F. Alexander (*Psychosomatic Medicine, Its Principles and Applications,* Norton, New York, 1950) maintains the theory of specificity in organ neuroses: physiological responses to emotional stimuli, both normal and morbid, vary according to the nature of the precipitating emotional states. He differentiates two types of organ neuroses, the sympathetic and the parasympathetic. 'Whenever the expression of competitive, aggressive, and hostile attitudes is inhibited in voluntary behavior, the sympathetic adrenal system is in sustained excitation. The vegetative symptoms result from the sustained sympathetic excitation, which persists because no consummation of the fight or flight reaction takes place in the field of coordinated voluntary behavior, as exemplified by the patient suffering from essential hypertension who in his overt behavior appears inhibited and under excessive control.' Besides essential hypertension, the sympathetic group includes migraine and hyperthyroidism. 'In those cases in which the gratification of help-seeking, regressive tendencies is absent from overt behavior either because of internal denial of these tendencies or because of external circumstances, the vegetative responses are apt to manifest themselves in dysfunctions which are the results of an increased parasympathetic activity. Examples are the overtly hyperactive, energetic peptic ulcer patient who does not allow gratification of his dependent needs, and the patient who develops chronic incapacitating fatigue whenever he tries to engage in some activity requiring concentrated effort.' Bronchial asthma and ulcerative colitis are also in this parasympathetic group.

psychosomatic disorders See *psychophysiologic autonomic and visceral disorders.*

psychosomatism (-sō'mà-tiz'm) Used by L.E. Hinsie as a synonym for the term body-mindedness. In the development of the infant's mind, his mental energy first becomes attached to the various internal and external organs of the body: indeed, the first imprints on the infant's mind come from these organs. Also the various organs of the child's body such as mouth, gastro-intestinal tract, etc. are trained by the mother to appropriate responses. Thus 'The prime layer of the mind is made up of images of one's body . . . and . . . the child's first emotions are heavily invested in its body-minded mind.' Moreover, that layer of the mind the mental energy of which is invested in the body and its organs is the layer of body-mindedness.

Although body-mindedness naturally exists throughout life, its dominance should gradually diminish and even disappear as the child grows. Sometimes, however, body-mindedness or psychosomatism continues dominant into adulthood. This type of individual develops preoccupations with his bodily organs and their functions or he may feel extreme fatigue and weakness. In the first case he is known as a hypochondriac, in the second, as a neurasthenic. (Hinsie, L.E. *Understandable Psychiatry,* Macmillan, New York, 1948)

psychosomimetic (-sō-mi-met'ik) *Psychotomimetic* (q.v.).

psychosurgery 'Psychosurgery is a general term now used to describe any form of brain operation done to relieve mental illness or intractable pain. The usual operation in psychosurgery has been lateral transcranial lobotomy. In addition to this transorbital lobotomy, topectomy, gyrectomy, thalamotomy, and so on, have been performed. Such operations have been found to lead to an amelioration of mental illness in a fair proportion of cases.' (Landes, C. and Erlick, D. 'An Analysis of the Porteus Maze Test as Affected by Psychosurgery,' *American Journal of Psychology LXIII,* No. 4, 557, Oct. 1950)

psychosynthesis (-sin'thē-sis) Often in psychiatry the term *psychosynthesis* is generally referred to merely as *synthesis,* the text providing the idea that the synthesis has to do with psychic components. The act of combining individual components of the mind into a whole; it is the opposite of *psychoanalysis.*

'I employ "constructive" and "synthetic," in describing a method that is opposed to the reductive. The constructive method is concerned with the elaboration of unconscious products (dreams, phantasies, etc.). It takes the unconscious product as a basis or starting point, as a *symbolical* expression, which, stretching on ahead as it were, represents a coming phase of psychological development.' (Jung, C.G. *Psychological Types,* tr. by Baynes, H.G., Harcourt, Brace, New York and London, 1923)

'They [Freudians] state that the Jungian transference and the active role played in the attempts at psychosynthesis create a permanent state of dependence upon the analyst.' (Henry, G.W. *Essentials of Psychiatry,* 3rd ed., Williams and Wilkins, Baltimore, 1938)

'In the final synthesis one must try to harmonize the various strivings and tendencies and consider whether they may co-exist in a personality or whether they disturb or exclude each other, and with what result.' (Diethelm, O. *Treatment in Psychiatry,* Macmillan, New York, 1936)

'I cannot imagine, however, that any new task for us is to be found in this psycho-synthesis. If I were to permit myself to be honest and uncivil I should say it was nothing but a meaningless phrase.' (Freud, S. *Collected Papers,* vol. 2, tr. by Riviere, J., Leonard and Virginia Woolf and The Institute of Psychoanalysis, London, 1924–25)

psychotaxis (-tak'sis) A psychiatric term suggested by T.V. Moore 'to signify the mental adjustments of individuals to pleasant and unpleasant situations. . . . We wish a root to designate the tendency of the mind to adjust itself to pleasant

and unpleasant situations. Though taxis suggests a passive arrangement rather than an active adjustment, those of us who have become familiar with its use to designate the movements of the protozoa will feel that no great violence is done if it is used to signify the mental adjustments of individuals to pleasant and unpleasant situations, especially since such reactions often consist in a rearrangement of one's ideas in which some drop below consciousness and others appear on the surface. . . . The tendency to enjoy pleasant states of mind or to make use of pleasant emotions and feelings . . . by analogy with the tropism or taxis could be termed a positive psychotaxis. The opposite tendency to avoid unpleasant situations is a negative psychotaxis.' (Moore, T.V. 'The Parataxes,' *Psychoanalytic Review 8,* 258, 1921)

psychotechnics (-tek'niks) The practical application of psychological methods in the study of economics, sociology, and other problems.

psychotherapeusis (-ther-à-pū'sis) Same as *psychotherapy* (q.v.).

psychotherapeutics Psychotherapy.

psychotherapy (-ther'a-pē) The art of treating mental diseases or disorders. 'Psychotherapy is a form of treatment for problems of an emotional nature in which a trained person deliberately establishes a professional relationship with a patient with the object of removing, modifying or retarding existing symptoms, of mediating disturbed patterns of behavior, and of promoting positive personality growth and development.' (Wolberg, L.R. *The Technique of Psychotherapy,* Grune & Stratton, New York, 1954) The same author distinguishes three types of psychotherapy:

(1) *Supportive therapy,* whose objectives are to strengthen existing defenses, elaborate better mechanisms to maintain control, and restore to an adaptive equilibrium. Included in supportive therapy are guidance, environmental manipulation, externalization of interests, reassurance, pressure and coercion, persuasion, catharsis, desensitization, and inspirational group therapy.

(2) *Re-educative therapy,* which aims at giving the patient insight into the more conscious conflicts, with deliberate efforts at goal modification and maximal utilization of existing potentialities. Included

in re-educative therapy are relationship therapy, attitude therapy, psychobiology, counseling, reconditioning, and re-educative group therapy.

(3) *Reconstructive therapy*, which aims at giving the patient insight into his unconscious conflicts and extensive alteration of his character structure. Included in reconstructive therapy are psychoanalysis (Freudian), Adlerian and Jungian therapy, the treatment techniques of the 'cultural-interpersonal' school (Sullivan, Horney), and psychoanalytically oriented psychotherapy.

psychotherapy, active analytical See *analysis, active.*

psychotherapy, analytic group See *psychotherapy, group.*

psychotherapy, co-operative See *psychotherapy, multiple.*

psychotherapy, didactic group A strictly tutorial practice in which definite outlines, texts, and visual aids are used for teaching patients in special subjects.

psychotherapy, group A method of treating emotional disturbances, social maladjustments, and psychotic states in which two or more patients participate simultaneously in the presence of one psychotherapist or more.

The techniques in group psychotherapy vary to a great extent in accordance with the different schools of psychiatric thought and the preferences of individual psychiatrists and other psychotherapists. S.R. Slavson separates group psychotherapy under three major categories: I. activity; II. analytic; III. directive.

I. *Activity group therapy*, which he originated, is suitable for children in latency. Children selected by criteria which he had described are given the opportunity to act out their aggressions or withdrawal in the presence of a neutral, permissive, and understanding adult. The patients draw upon one another for support. The accessibility of the patients to each other and to the environment, and their interaction, generate certain inhibitive controls which improve the superego formation and strengthen the ego of each participant. Slavson believes that this type of therapy is predominantly ego therapy and is an experience in which character changes occur. He, therefore, commends selecting patients on the basis of these two factors. No interpretation is given to

the children and a minimal restraint of their behavior is exercised by the therapist and, at that, only when the group cannot bring itself under control.

II. *Analytic group psychotherapy* is a technique in which interpretation is given to the patients, activity and verbalization are encouraged and interpreted, and insight is evoked. In this technique the therapist is more active than he is in activity group psychotherapy, where he is predominantly a passive agent. Slavson divides analytic group psychotherapy into three subdivisions: (1) play group psychotherapy; (2) activity-interview group psychotherapy; (3) interview psychotherapy. (1) *Play group psychotherapy* is suitable for young children in the prelatency period, where the catharsis occurs through play with specially selected materials through which the children in the group can act out their preoccupations, phantasies, and anxieties. (2) *Activity-interview group psychotherapy* has been designed by him for children in latency who suffer from severe psychoneuroses, who are given the opportunity to act out against each other and against their environment as in activity group psychotherapy, but interpretation of the latent meaning of the behavior is given by the children to each other and by the therapist. Spontaneous and planned discussions are held with individual children or with a number of the children in the group or the group as a whole. These are intended to stimulate understanding by the children of the meaning of their behavior and to evoke insight into their unconscious motivations and phantasies. (3) *Interview group psychotherapy* is intended for adolescents and adults who are selected by definite criteria and are grouped together so that the patients would have a therapeutic effect upon one another. The basic criterion suggested by Slavson is syndrome (not symptom or diagnosis) homogeneity. Other group psychotherapists do not use this criterion but group the patients without any special considerations, provided the patients can accept and gain from a group experience. In analytic group psychotherapy the procedure is the same as in individual psychotherapy. Since the patients are adolescents and adults, the catharsis occurs through verbalization and free association. The psychotherapist here, as in individual treatment, interprets, explores, and helps patients to un-cover their repressed, guilt-producing, and anxiety-evoking feelings, attitudes, values, and behavior.

III. Under *directive group treatment* Slavson includes such activities as didactic or therapeutically educational group work, particularly with psychotics, group guid-ance, group counseling, therapeutic recreation, and many other group efforts to help patients, particularly psychotic patients, adjust to their environment.

Group psychotherapy is also referred to as *group therapy.* The two terms are synonymous. (Slavson, S.R. *An Introduc-tion to Group Therapy,* The Common-wealth Fund, Oxford University Press, New York, 1943; *Analytic Group Psy-chotherapy,* Columbia University Press, New York, 1950)

psychotherapy, multiple Role-divided, three-cornered therapy; co-therapy; co-operative psychotherapy; dual leadership —all refer to the use of more than one therapist at one time in individual or group psychotherapy.

psychotherapy, reconstructive See *psycho-dynamics, adaptational; psychotherapy.*

psychotherapy, short-contact Treatment of mental disorders, similar to brief psy-chotherapy, but used in child-guidance clinics when the therapy is of short dura-tion.

psychotic (sī-kot′ik) Pertaining to or af-fected by psychosis.

psychotica (sī-kot′i-kà) See *psychotomi-metic.*

psychotic disorder The 1952 revision of psychiatric nomenclature defines a psy-chotic disorder or psychotic reaction as one in which the personality, in its struggle for adjustment to internal and external stresses, utilizes severe affective disturb-ance, profound autism and withdrawal from reality, and/or formation of delu-sions or hallucinations. As thus defined, the following are included in the group *psychotic disorders:* involutional psychotic reaction, affective reactions (including the various forms of manic-depressive reac-tion and psychotic depressive reaction), schizophrenic reactions, and paranoid re-actions. Cases formerly classified as or-ganic psychoses are now included in the categories, acute and chronic brain dis-orders.

psychotogen (sī-kot′ō-gen) See *psychoto-mimetic.*

psychotogenic *Psychotomimetic* (q.v.).

psychotoid (sī-kot′oid) According to Selling, psychotoid personalities are 'in-dividuals who might be classed as very mild cases of some psychosis, by virtue of their symptoms. However, they are not psychotic persons and their symptoms are of long standing without change and do not respond to the same treatment as the true psychoses which have similar but more exaggerated symptoms. They have more insight than psychotics.' (Sell-ing, L.S. *Synopsis of Neuropsychiatry,* Mosby, St. Louis, 1947)

psychotomimetic (sī-kot-ō-mi-met′ik) Re-sembling or mimicking naturally occur-ring psychosis, especially schizophrenia; also known as psychosomimetic, schizo-mimetic. While any number of drugs can produce a psychosis, the term psychoto-mimetic agent is confined to those sub-stances which produce psychological changes in a high proportion of subjects exposed to the drug without producing the gross impairment of memory and ori-entation characteristic of the organic re-action type. Among the known psychoto-mimetics are lysergic acid diethylamide (LSD), mescaline, adrenochrome, har-mine, tetrahydrocannabinol, diisopropyl flourophosphates (DFP), tetraethylpyro-phosphate (TEPP), N-allylnormorphine and bufotenin.

psycho-toxicomania (sī-kō-tok-si-kō-mā′-ni-à) Toxicomania.

psychralgie (psē-kràl′zhē) 'A morbid state characterized by painful subjective sensa-tions of cold.' (Foster, F.P. *Medical Dic-tionary,* Appleton, New York, 1892–94)

psychrophobia (sī-krō-fō′bi-à) Fear of cold.

psychrotherapy (-ther′à-pē) Treatment by the application of cold in any form. It was at one time extensively employed in the form of hydrotherapy as a stimu-lating agent for inactive or retarded pa-tients, e.g. those with the depressive type of manic-depressive psychosis.

psysoma (sī-sō′mà) *Rare.* Contracted form of *psychosoma.*

P-system See *system.*

pteronophobia ([p]ter-ō-nō-fō′bi-à) Fear of feathers.

ptosis (tō'sis) Lid-drop. See *nerve, oculomotor.*

ptosis, waking A functional paralysis of the upper eyelid, occurring temporarily in the anemic or neurotic individual on awaking.

puberal, pubertal (pū'bĕr-al, -tal) Relating to the age of puberty, extending from the termination of the period of puerilism to the beginning of the adolescent period.

puberism, persistent Condition characterized by hypogenesis and prolongation, or even lifelong persistence, of puberal characteristics. The individual seems an eternal adolescent with incompletely developed secondary sexual characteristics in contrast with the types distinguished by *infantilism* or *juvenilism.*

pubertas praecox (pōō-ber'tàs prī'kôks) (L. 'premature puberty') Premature puberty. See *macrogenitosomia.*

puberty, puberism (pū'bĕr-tē, -iz'm) The stage of growth extending from the termination of the puerile to the beginning of the adolescent period. It begins with the acquisition of secondary sexual characteristics and continues for approximately two or three years thereafter.

puberty, precocious Macrogenitosomia.

pubescence, pubescency (pū-bes'ens, pū-bes'en-sē) Puberty.

pubescent (pū-bes'ent) Pubertal.

public 'A group of people (a) who are confronted by an issue, (b) who are divided in their ideas as to how to meet the issue, and (c) who engage in discussion over the issue.' (Blumer, H.E., in Park, R.E. *Principles of Sociology,* Barnes & Noble, New York, 1939)

The public, according to Tarde, is a product of the printing press. (Tarde, G. *L'Opinion et la foule,* Paris, 1901)

While the members of the crowd are in face-to-face communication, interaction in the public occurs without presence, and 'contagion without contact' takes place.

pudendal (pū'den'dal) Pertaining to or subserving the genitals.

pudendum, pl. **pudenda** (pū-den'dum, pū-den'da) Genitals; the private parts.

pudibilia (pū-di-bil'i-à) Pudenda, the private parts.

pudibund (pū'di-bund) *Obs.* Bashful.

pudic (pū'dik), rarely **pudical** (pū'dikal) *Obs.* Modest; *Anat.* pudendal.

pudicity (pū-dis'i-tē) Modesty, chastity.

puella publica (poo-el'là pōō'blē-kà) (L. 'public girl') Hirschfeld's term for a prostitute.

puer aeternus (poo'er ī-ter'noos) (L. 'eternal lad, youth') A term denoting a specific archetype of Jung, viz. the eternal youth, *puer aeternus.* See *archetype (in Jung's psychology); archetype, mother.*

puerilism (pū'ĕr-il-iz'm) From the standpoint of psychiatry *puerilism* is childishness; it is the stage following infantilism or infantility and is followed by the stage of puberism or puberty.

puerilism, hysterical See *pseudo-dementia, hysterical.*

puerperium (poo-ĕr-per'i-um) The period of time and/or the state of the mother following childbirth. See *psychosis, puerperal.*

pulling, ear Pulling of the ears is believed by Kanner to be a substitute for thumbsucking; in psychoanalysis it is believed to be a masturbatory equivalent.

pulvinar (pul'vi-nàr) See *thalamus.*

punch-drunk Martland uses this term to denote a concussion syndrome observed among pugilists; the symptoms are a reflection of an encephalopathy following repeated concussions.

'The early symptoms of punch-drunk usually appear in the extremities. There may be only an occasional and very slight flopping of one foot or leg in walking, noticeable only at intervals; or a slight unsteadiness in gait or uncertainty in equilibrium. . . . In some cases periods of slight mental confusion may occur as well as distinct slowing of muscular action. . . . Many cases remain mild. . . . In others a very distinct dragging of the leg may develop and with this there is a general slowing down in muscular movements, a peculiar mental attitude characterized by hesitancy in speech, tremors of the hand and nodding movements of the head.' (*Journal of the American Medical Association 91,* 1103, 1928)

punch-drunkenness A chronic traumatic encephalopathy, occurring frequently in boxers, characterized by deterioration of the personality, impairment of memory, dysarthria, tremor, and ataxia.

puncture, cistern (sis'tẽrn) A technique for gaining access to the subarachnoid space by means of introduction of a needle into the cisterna magna. Cistern puncture is performed when lumbar puncture is for some reason impossible; it is also used for the injection of air or opaque media for diagnostic purposes and for the introduction of therapeutic substances. It is contraindicated in cases of tumor or abscess in the posterior fossa, in cases of increased intracranial pressure, and when the cisterna magna is likely to be obliterated by inflammatory adhesions. See *puncture, suboccipital.*

puncture, lumbar (lum'bẽr) A technique for gaining access to the subarachnoid space by means of introduction of a needle into the lumbar cul-de-sac of the subarachnoid space below the termination of the spinal cord at the first lumbar vertebra. Lumbar puncture (L.P.) is used to obtain cerebrospinal fluid for diagnostic purposes, to relieve increased intracranial pressure, to introduce therapeutic substances or local anesthetics, to introduce air preparatory to encephalography and myelography, and to introduce opaque media for radiography.

puncture, suboccipital (sub-ok-sip'i-tal) Suboccipital or *cisternal puncture* is a procedure, introduced by Ayer and his coworkers, for determining spinal subarachnoid block and for therapeutic purposes. 'The method consists in withdrawing fluid from the cisterna magna at the base of the brain behind the medulla. With the patient on the side, the head bent forward, the needle is introduced in the midline at a point midway between the external occipital protuberance and the spine of the axis or second cervical vertebra. The needle is directed forward and upward in the direction of the eyes or glabella. One should never penetrate to a depth beyond 4½ to 5 cm., generally 3½ to 4 are sufficient. . . The same click is felt when the dura is pierced as in spinal puncture.' (Wechsler, I.S. *Textbook of Clinical Neurology,* 4th ed., Saunders, Philadelphia, 1939) See *puncture, cistern.*

puncture, ventricle (ven'tri-k'l) A surgical technique for gaining access to the intraventricular space of the lateral ventricles. The principal indications for ventricle puncture are: (1) to relieve increased intracranial pressure before operation for intracranial tumor; (2) to inject air for ventriculography; (3) to inject therapeutic substances such as penicillin or streptomycin; (4) to obtain cerebrospinal fluid for diagnostic examination when lumbar or cisternal puncture cannot be performed.

punishment, Midas See *masturbation, compulsive.*

punishment, unconscious need for See *criminal from sense of guilt.*

pupil, Adie's See *pupil, tonic.*

pupil, Argyll Robertson (Argyll Robertson, Scottish physician, 1837–1909) 'A usually but not invariably myotic pupil with sound vision that does not respond to light, even in a darkroom, but does to accommodation, and reacts slowly to mydriatics is known as an Argyll Robertson pupil.' (Jelliffe, S.E. and White, W.A. *Diseases of the Nervous System,* 6th ed., Lea & Febiger, Philadelphia, 1935)

It is usually found in patients with neurosyphilis, although it may appear in other conditions (traumatic brain injury, brain tumor, infectious disorders of the brain, multiple sclerosis, etc.).

pupil, fixed A pupil which does not react to light, to accommodation, or to convergence.

pupillary reflex The alterations in size of the pupil in response to light, convergence, and accommodation. Certain abnormalities of reaction are associated with lesions affecting portions of the pupil reflex arc.

pupil, tonic (of Adie) (William John Adie, British neurologist, 1886–1935) A unilateral condition in which the pupil responds poorly to light and very slowly to convergence.

puppy-love A state of love in the late adolescent or young adult period, highly romantic in nature, with little stability in the relationship formed, so that the courtship swiftly disintegrates. This is in the nature of a developmental activity, occurring in the course of emotional maturation; another designation for this emotional phenomenon is *calf-love.*

pure line See *line, pure.*

Purkinje cell See *cell, Purkinje; cerebellum.*

purpose From the psychoanalytic point of view this is defined as follows: 'We do not merely accept as basal concepts certain conventions which we apply to the material we have acquired empirically, but we also make use of various complicated postulates to guide us in dealing with psychological phenomena. We have already cited the most important of these postulates; it remains for us expressly to lay stress upon it. It is of a biological nature, and makes use of the concept of "purpose" (one might say, of adaptation of the means to the end). . . .' (Freud, S. *Collected Papers,* vol. 4, tr. by Riviere, J., Leonard and Virginia Woolf and The Institute of Psychoanalysis, London, 1924–25)

'Now purpose implies mind or mental activity. To speak of purpose without implying mind is meaningless. Commonly, when we speak of purpose, we have in view our most clearly defined and self-conscious purposes. But we must recognize that mental purposive operations go on on very different planes of consciousness; that, besides our most fully conscious purposes, our organs express and are controlled by purposes of which we may be only very obscurely aware, and also by purposes which operate wholly on the subconscious plane.' (McDougall, W. *Outline of Abnormal Psychology,* Scribner, New York, 1926)

purposeful In occupational therapy this common term indicates that an activity has been planned with a definite result or effect in view. It may apply to the practical use of a project.

purposive Characterized by or serving a purpose.

putamen (poo-tà'men) See *basal ganglia.*

Putnam, James Jackson (1846–1918). American psychiatrist.

pycnic (pik'nik) See *type, pyknic.*

pycnoepilepsy (pik-nō-ep'i-lep-sē) Repeated slight epileptic seizures.

pycnolepsy (pik'nō-lep-sē) Same as *pyknolepsy.*

pygmalionism (pig-mā'li-on-iz'm) The condition of falling in love with a creation of one's own is not uncommon in psychiatric patients. The patient feels toward the object as one might naturally be expected to feel toward a living subject. A patient with paranoia, strongly homosexual, devised what he called a 'perpetual-motion' machine, to which he ascribed all masculine attributes; the ma-

chine was given a masculine name. The patient avowed his 'unqualified love for Albert' and acted toward Albert as if Albert were a living human being. Another patient, also paranoid, made a model of himself; the model always 'slept' in the same bed with the patient and to the disgust of the patient 'had sexual intercourse with me every night.'

pygmeism (pig'mē-iz'm) The constitutional anomaly characterized by a *dwarfed,* but well-proportioned stature as compared with the average type of the given racial group. It corresponds to the other special forms of *microsomia,* called *nanosomia primordialis* by Hansemann and *heredo-familial essential microsomia* by E. Levi and occurs in certain peoples as a more or less physiological condition (African Negrillos and Negritos, Bushmen, etc.). Nevertheless, as has been stressed by Pende, 'this extreme variant must not be regarded as without detriment to health, but must rather be looked upon as a constitutional inferiority.' (Pende, N. *Constitutional Inadequacies,* tr. by Naccarati, S., Lea & Febiger, Philadelphia, 1928)

pyknic (pik'nik) Compact, thick-set, round-bodied. See *type, pyknic.*

pyknoepilepsy (pik-nō-ep'i-lep-sē) See *pyknolepsy.*

pyknolepsy, pycnolepsy (pik'nō-lep-sē) A disorder characterized by frequent, brief interruptions in consciousness, and usually discussed in conjunction with epilepsy, although Fürstner, Heilbronner, and others have classified it as a hysterical disorder. In children who are otherwise healthy, it occurs, as a rule before the age of seven, as frequent, short, and incomplete cloudings of consciousness. The onset is usually abrupt, the disease runs a monotonous course without intellectual deterioration and shows little response to therapy, but the prognosis is generally favorable. During attacks, which may be as frequent as 150 times a day, the eyes turn upward, arms and trunk become somewhat tonic; but pulse and respiration are unaffected, there are no convulsive movements, and spontaneous recovery is common. Owen and Berlinrood ('Clinical Electroencephalographic Studies in Pyknolepsy,' *American Journal of Psychiatry 98,* 757–66, 1941–42) believe that '. . . pyknolepsy is a form of petit mal epilepsy because of:

1. the similarity in the clinical picture; 2. the electroencephalographic pattern in the active phase showing a wave and spike formation found in petit mal epilepsy; 3. the lack of evidence of definite psychogenic factors; 4. the high incidence of epilepsy in families of patients with pyknolepsy as revealed by a study of the literature.' Lennox used *pyknoepilepsy* (which is by many considered synonymous with pyknolepsy, or dart and dome dysrhythmia) for the ordinary *petit mal* form of epilepsy (q.v.).

pyknophrasia (pik-nō-frā′zhi-à) Thickness of utterance.

pyramid The prominence on the anterior surface of the medulla oblongata where the pyramidal tract decussates. See *tract, pyramidal.*

pyramis See *cerebellum.*

pyrexiophobia (pī-rek-si-ō-fō′bi-à) Fear of fever.

pyrolagnia (pī-rō-lag′ni-à) Sexual excitement aroused by the sight of conflagrations; erotic pyromania.

pyromania Morbid impulse to set fire to things; the term, however, generally means the actual setting on fire.

'The analysis of many neurotics and the observation of the doings of children show us that "setting on fire," the delight in conflagrations, indeed, too, the tendency to incendiarism, is an urethra-erotic character trait. Many incendiarists were excessive bed-wetters. . . . In a collection of criminal cases of incendiarism there were quite a number in which incendiaries set fire to their *beds,* as though to indicate the still active enuristic primitive source of their pyromanic character trait.' (Ferenczi, S. *Further Contributions to the Theory and Technique of Psycho-Analysis,* tr. by Suttie, J.I., Leonard and Virginia Woolf and The Institute of Psychoanalysis, London, 1926)

pyromania, erotic *Pyrolagnia* (q.v.).

pyrophobia Fear of fire. See *pyromania.*

pyrosis (pī-rō′sis) Heartburn.

Q

quadrantanopia, quadrantanopsia (kwad-ran-tan-ō'pi-à, -op'si-à) See *field defect*.

quadrantic hemianopia (kwad-ran'tik hē-mi-an-op'i-à) See *field defect*.

quadriplegia (kwad-ri-plē'ji-à) Tetraplegia; paralysis affecting the four extremities.

quadruplet In human genetics the plural signifies four children born at the same birth (see *birth, multiple*).

quality, determining A term used by Freud in connection with the etiology of hysteria. He states, 'That tracing an hysterical symptom back to a traumatic scene assists our understanding only if the scene in question fulfills two conditions—if it possesses the required *determining quality* and if we can credit it with the necessary *traumatic power*.' (Freud, S. *Collected Papers*, vol. 1, tr. by Riviere, J., Leonard and Virginia Woolf and The Institute of Psychoanalysis, London, 1924–25)

By this he means that a traumatic scene must be sufficient, alone, or more usually through another association, to explain the hysterical symptom. For example, a hysterical symptom of vomiting was attributed to the shock of a railway accident. This derivation of the symptom lacks *determining quality*, although it may be said to possess traumatic power. However, on further analysis this accident woke the memory of another event which had happened previously, during which the patient saw a decomposing corpse, a sight which aroused in her horror and disgust. This connection now supplies the *determining quality* for the hysterical symptom of vomiting. The antecedent experience justifiably gave rise to a high degree of disgust.

quasi-action See *activity, ludic*.

quaternity (kwà-tēr'ni-tē) Any unit composed by the union of four factors; a group of four. In psychiatry, the term quaternity refers to the fact that Jung's system of psychology 'is based on an archetype that finds its special expression as "tetrasomy," four-foldness—cf. the theory of the four functions, the pictorial arrangement of the four, the orientation according to the four points of the compass, etc. The number four can often be

observed in the arrangement of dream contents as well. Probably the universal distribution and magical significance of the cross or the circle divided into four can be explained through the archetypal quality of the quaternity.' (Jung, C.G. *The Integration of the Personality*, Farrar and Rinehart, New York, 1939, p. 154) Jung says: 'It is a peculiar *lusus naturae* [play of nature] that the principal chemical constituent of the bodily organism is carbon, characterized by four valences; the "diamond" too is, as is well known, a carbon crystal. Carbon is black; the diamond is "brightest water." . . . Such an analogy would be a regrettable lack of intellectual taste if the phenomenon of the four were a mere creation of consciousness and not a spontaneous product of the objective-psychic, of the unconscious.' (ibid., p. 198) 'It might even be considered more than a mere coincidence that in an epoch which, particularly in consequence of revolutionary discoveries in the domain of the exact natural sciences, stands on the verge of transition from "three-dimensional" to "four-dimensional" thinking, the most modern system of depth psychology, the complex-psychology of Jung, taking its start from an altogether different point, has elevated the archetype of the four to the central structural concept of its doctrine.' (Jacobi, J. *The Psychology of C.G. Jung*, Kegan Paul, Trench, Trubner, London, 1942)

querulent Ever suspicious, always opposing any suggestion, complaining of ill-treatment and of being slighted or misunderstood, easily enraged, and dissatisfied with conditions as they exist.

question, Pigem's A projective question asked of the patient such as, 'What three things would you like most to change (or to do, or to be) in your life?' or, 'If you could be changed into something else by a fairy, what would it be?'

Quételet-Gauss, binomial law of The study of human constitution is facilitated by the use of a method introduced by A. Quételet and perfected by Karl Pearson. Quételet was the first to show that the distribution of human characters, such as height, may be adequately described by the normal curve. This law was first described in mathematical language by A. De Moivre, a French Huguenot who lived in exile in London, and was later rediscovered independently by Laplace and Gauss. According to this law, frequencies which may be adequately described by it are distributed symmetrically about a mean value, which is also the maximum or mode. The frequencies decrease regularly on either side of the mean. For any deviation above the mean there will be a frequency equal to that between the mean and a corresponding deviation below the mean. Frequencies taper off very rapidly from the mean to the end of the curve in either direction, approaching the base line as an asymptote.

Quincke disease (Heinrich Irenaeus Quincke, physician in Kiel, 1842–1922) See *edema, angioneurotic.*

quintuplet In human genetics the plural signifies five children born at the same birth (see *birth, multiple*).

quotient, intelligence The ratio of an individual's intelligence (determined by mental measures) to so-called average or normal intelligence for his age. The most common method for determining the intelligence quotient is to divide the assigned mental age by the chronological age.

R

R In Rorschach test scoring, the total number of responses to the cards.

race 'Applied to human beings, the term race implies a blood related group with characteristic and common hereditary traits. . . . Primary races or sub-species—the Caucasian, the Mongoloid, and the Negroid—are generalized racial types, hypothetical stocks, rather than living races. . . . Aside from all questions of a biological nature, it [race] is made the symbol of cultural status and thus serves to justify the exploitation of the weaker group with the inevitable political and cultural consequences.' (Reuter, E.B. *The American Race Problem*, Crowell, New York, 1938)

race, disease Group of individuals susceptible to the same disease. Draper uses the term *race* in a special way. In his efforts to establish correlations between constitutional characteristics of an individual and disease entities, he uses such expressions as gastric ulcer race, gall-bladder race, etc. Thus, he says, 'by the same token, any other series of constant similarities, whether physiologic, psychologic or immunologic, might as justifiably be used as proper criteria of racial entity. One might conceive, therefore, as well of a gastric ulcer race, a manic-depressive race, a meningococcus susceptible race, or gall-bladder race, as of the present customarily accepted black, yellow, or white divisions of mankind.' (Draper, G. *Disease and the Man*, Macmillan, New York, 1930)

race prejudice 'A function of conflict (arising) in those situations and areas where one group feels its security or existence menaced by the presence or behavior of another.' (Reuter, E.B. *The American Race Problem*, Crowell, New York, 1938)

In race prejudice 'color, or any other racial mark that emphasizes physical differences, becomes the symbol of moral divergences which perhaps do not exist.' (Park, R.E. and Burgess, E.W. *Introduction to the Science of Sociology*, University of Chicago Press, Chicago, 1921)

'Race prejudice may be regarded as a spontaneous, more or less instinctive defense-reaction, the practical effect of which is to restrict free competition between races.' (Park, R.E., in 'Introduction' to J.F. Steiner, *The Japanese Invasion*, McClurg, Chicago, 1917)

Race prejudice arises from 'an aversion to strange appearances and ways of life which are often held to be proof of inferior standards; such attitudes are strengthened by the desire of the dominating group to maintain its solidarity. Intermarriage and social intercourse are legally or tacitly prohibited, and the superior race generally asserts its superiority by reserving all economic advantages to its members.' (Kohn, H. *Encyclopaedia of the Social Sciences*, vol. 13, Macmillan, New York, 1934, p. 39)

rachischisis (rā-kis'ki-sis) See *spina bifida*.

racial saturation point See *saturation point, racial*.

radiation In neurophysiology, the spreading of excitation to adjacent neurons.

radiculitis (rȧ-dik-ū-lī'tis) Inflammation of the intradural portion of a spinal nerve root prior to its entrance into the intervertebral foramen or of the portion between that foramen and the nerve plexus.

radix (ra'diks) Nerve root.

rage Fury; violent, intense anger; often used in psychoanalytic writings to emphasize the overpowering and unbridled aspect of infantile anger.

rage, retroflexed See *psychodynamics, adaptational*.

rage, sham The term first used to denote the spontaneous outbursts of motor activity resembling fear and rage which occur in decorticate or diencephalic animals. (Cannon, W.B. and Britton, S.W. 'Studies on the Conditions of Activity in Endocrine Glands,' *American Journal of Physiology 72*, 283, April 1925) Such outbursts are accompanied by changes in the internal organs and in the composition of the blood which are similar to those characteristic of human emotional behavior. It has been shown that sham rage depends on the functional integrity of the caudal hypothalamus. The question naturally is: 'How real or sham is such behavior? Does uninhibited action of the hypothalamus give rise to the experience of fear and rage, or does it affect merely the sympathetic and motor concomitants of the emotions?' Sham rage differs from normal rage in animals as follows: (1) the animal rarely attempts to avoid the stimulus that called forth the reaction; and (2) the response of sham rage rarely outlasts the duration of the stimulus, i.e. after-discharge is minimal. These differences are also seen in cases of sham rage in humans, which is never purposeful. In humans sham rage has been observed as a result of extensive cortical damage secondary to prolonged hypoglycemia and carbon monoxide poisoning: the response pattern was uniform to all strong stimuli, it lasted from 30 seconds to one minute, and the strength of stimulus had no apparent effect on the duration of the sham rage. In these cases, loud noises and painful stimuli produce dilation of the pupil, widening of the palpebral fissures, exophthalmos, and marked increase in pulse rate and systolic pressure. A patient with carbon monoxide poisoning clenched and ground her teeth and emitted hissing sounds.

All in all, both animal and human data would seem to imply that the hypothalamus is not the emotional center. 'It would, therefore, seem that while subcortical centers (the hypothalamus) may integrate and possibly reinforce the effector neural responses controlling some of the sympathetic and motor manifestations of fear and rage, there is little or no basis for the thesis that the hypothalamus governs or even mediates the emotional experiences themselves.' (Wortis, H. and Maurer, W.S. 'Sham Rage in Man,' *American Journal of Psychiatry 98*, 637–44, 1941–42)

rami communicantes (rà-mē kō-moo-nē-kan'tēs) Branches of the spinal nerves which pass to the sympathetic trunk. The white ramus is present only in thoracic and upper lumbar nerves; the gray ramus is present in all spinal nerves.

random Uncontrolled, spontaneous, unplanned, occurring by chance. The term is used most commonly in statistics to refer to the choosing of experimental subjects on the basis of chance rather than on the basis of particular selective factors.

rank Position in a series when the components of the series are arranged in order of magnitude; thus a rank of 20 indicates that the component-part is 20th from the top (or bottom) when all components have been arranged in order of size. Be-

cause the meaningfulness of any given rank will depend upon the number of component-parts in the series, rank is more meaningful if expressed in relative terms as a percentile rank. See *rank, percentile.*

Rank, Otto (1884–1939) Viennese psychoanalyst; birth trauma, will therapy.

rank, percentile Position in a series expressed as a number which represents the per cent of cases in the total group lying below the given score value. Example: if an individual makes a score of 82 in an examination, and it is found that this score is higher than that made by 93 per cent of the total number of individuals taking that examination, we would say that the individual is at the 93rd percentile on this particular examination. Percentile ranks are used to facilitate the interpretation of a single measure in a distribution of such measures, as a means of describing the variability and form of a frequency distribution, and as a means of comparing measures which were originally expressed in different units. Thus an individual may make a score of 82 on one test and a score of 127 on a second; as raw scores these would be relatively meaningless, but when it is known that the score of 82 represents the 93rd percentile on the first test, and that the score of 127 represents the 92nd percentile on the second, the subject's performance on the two tests is seen in more meaningful perspective.

rape-phantasy, anal See *phantasy, anal rape.*

rapport (rà-pawr') (F. 'relation, ratio, proportion') Harmonious relation, accord. In the group: 'the existence of a mutual responsiveness such that every member reacts immediately, spontaneously, and sympathetically to the sentiments and attitudes of every other member.' (Park, R.E. and Burgess, E.W. *Introduction to the Science of Sociology,* University of Chicago Press, Chicago, 1921)

'In his treatment of her case, Breuer could make use of a very intense suggestible *rapport* on the part of the patient, which may serve us as a prototype of what we call "transference" today.' (Freud, S. *Collected Papers,* vol. 1, tr. by Riviere, J., Leonard and Virginia Woolf and The Institute of Psychoanalysis, London, 1924–25)

raptus (rap'tus) A type of action seen in some catatonic schizophrenics consisting of unco-ordinated discharge movements which tend to relieve extreme tension. Cataleptic general muscular rigidity is a common form of raptus action.

raptus impulsive A rarely used expression, meaning a sudden, unprovoked attack of extreme agitation. It appears in one of its most vivid forms in the catatonic state of schizophrenia.

raptus melancholicus (ràp'toos me-làng-kô'lē-koos) (L. 'melancholic seizure') An attack of extreme agitation or frenzy occurring in the course of melancholia.

R.A.S. Reticular activating system. See *formation, reticular.*

rate In epidemiology, the rate is the level of occurrence of a disease or reaction in relation to a given population, such as 10 cases per 1,000 population, or per 10,000, or per 100,000. See *incidence; prevalence.*

rate, death The ratio of the number of persons dying within a specified period, usually a year, to the number who were in the original group. In institutional statistics the true death rate is usually approximated by finding the ratio of deaths to the average number under treatment during the period. The number of admissions and the total number under care have been used incorrectly as the base for the death rate.

Example: There were 5,758 deaths among patients in the New York civil State hospitals during the fiscal year ended June 30, 1939, representing a rate of 76.9 per 1,000 of their average daily population.

However, some patients are present at the beginning of the year, and may be discharged before the close of the year. Others are admitted during the year and hence are present for only varying portions of the year. As death rates are based upon the assumption that a population is observed for a complete year, it is necessary to convert shorter periods of residence into an equivalent number of years, called annual exposures.

rate, discharge The ratio of the number discharged within a given period (usually a year) to the total number in the original group. In institutional statistics this rate is usually approximated by relating the number discharged in a given period to the number who were admitted during the same period.

Example: If there are 620 admissions to a mental hospital during the calendar year, and if there are 527 discharges from that hospital during the same period, the discharge rate is $\frac{527}{620} = 85$ per cent.

rate, improvement The improvement rate is the ratio of the number discharged as improved within a given period (usually a year) to the total number in the original group. In institutional statistics this rate is usually approximated by relating the number discharged as improved in a given period to the number who were admitted during the same period.

Example: In one psychiatric hospital in New York City, 616 patients were admitted during the calendar year 1958. During the same period, 542 patients were discharged as improved. The improvement rate is $\frac{542}{616} = 88$ per cent. See *rate, discharge.*

rate, of first admissions The rate of first admissions (i.e. to hospitals for mental disease) is the ratio of all first admissions within a year to the average general population during that year.

Example: There were 12,635 first admissions to the New York civil State hospitals during the year ending June 30, 1938, giving a rate of 84.9 per 100,000 estimated population. Rates of first admission for the more important groups of mental disorders were as follows: senile psychoses, 8.3; psychoses with cerebral arteriosclerosis, 16.2; general paresis, 6.1; alcoholic psychoses, 5.6; manic-depressive psychoses, 6.2; dementia praecox (schizophrenia), 21.2.

The rate of first admissions is higher among males than females; it is higher for urban than for rural populations; it is higher among the unmarried than among the married; it is higher among the illiterate than among the literate; it is higher among Negroes than whites; it is higher among the older than among the younger population.

rate, recovery The ratio of the number discharged as recovered within a given period (usually a year) to the total number in the original group. In institutional statistics this rate is usually approximated by relating the number discharged as recovered in a given period to the number who were admitted during the same period.

Example: There were 3,236 patients discharged as recovered from the New York civil State hospitals during the year ending June 30, 1939, representing 19.4 per cent of the admissions during the same year.

rate, residence In institutional statistics, the residence rate is based upon the population actually in institutions of a given type on any specified date. For example, it is the ratio of the resident population to the total population of the State.

Example: On June 30, 1938 there were 66,572 patients in the New York civil State hospitals, a rate of 432.8 per 100,000 general population. Corresponding rates for the more important groups of mental disorders were as follows: general paresis, 23.2; alcoholic psychoses, 13.7; psychoses with cerebral arteriosclerosis, 29.4; senile psychoses, 14.6; manic-depressive psychoses, 33.3; dementia praecox (schizophrenia), 254.3.

rate, specific A rate is specific when it is based upon a population and a class of that population both of which are homogeneous, or nearly so, with respect to a specific character: e.g. the number of male patients dying at ages 20–24 per 1,000 male patients aged 20–24.

Example: The average annual death rate from 1929 to 1931 among patients in the New York civil State hospitals was 86.8 per 1,000 exposures. The specific rate for males aged 20–24 was 45.7 per 1,000 corresponding exposures.

rate, standardized A hypothetical rate which would prevail if a given population had the same relative distribution (i.e. with respect to age) as another population called the standard.

Example: Patients with mental disease under treatment in the New York civil State hospitals from 1929 to 1931, inclusive, had an average annual death rate of 86.8 per 1,000 exposures. Based upon the age and sex distributions of the general population of New York State in 1930, the patients had a standardized rate of 64.9, which may be compared with a rate of 13.5 for the general population.

ratio, affective The ratio of the total number of responses to the colored Rorschach cards (cards VIII, IX, and X) to the total number of responses to the achromatic cards (I through VII). This ratio is an expression of the degree to which color increases responsiveness and is interpreted as an index of affectivity.

rational Reasoning, sensible. From the standpoint of Jung 'the rational is the reasonable, that which accords with reason. I conceive reason as an attitude whose principle is to shape thought, feeling, and action in accordance with objective values.' (Jung, C.G. *Psychological Types,* tr. by Baynes, H.G., Harcourt, Brace, New York and London, 1923)

'Thinking and feeling are rational functions in so far as they are decisively influenced by the motive of reflection. They attain their fullest significance when in fullest possible accord with the laws of reason. The irrational functions, on the contrary, are such as aim at pure perception, e.g., intuition and sensation; because, as far as possible, they are forced to dispense with the rational (which presupposes the exclusion of everything that is outside reason) in order to be able to reach the most complete perception of the whole course of events.' (ibid.)

rationalization This term was introduced into psychoanalysis by Ernest Jones. It means in psychiatry practically the same as in other fields: making a thing appear reasonable, when otherwise its irrationality would be evident. It is, perhaps, synonymous with *justification.* It is said that an individual 'covers up,' justifies, rationalizes an act or an idea that is unreasonable and illogical. For example, when a dehypnotized individual obeys a command received while under hypnosis and of which he is not consciously aware, and then proceeds to give a specious explanation for his act, he resorts to rationalization. Let us assume that he had been commanded to remove his shoes, when there was no reason for the removal. When the hypnotic stage is ended and he begins to take off his shoes, he explains that the shoes are too tight, or there are pebbles in them, or he gives some explanation that has the appearance of rationality.

Psychoanalysts hold that 'rationalization is the work of the unconscious Ego by which it evades the recognition of irrational and inconsistent behavior which really arises on the basis of unconscious urges. It can be seen that the Ego's narcism is always largely involved in the process of rationalization.' (Healy, W., Bronner, A.F., and Bowers, A.M. *The Structure and Meaning of Psychoanalysis,* Knopf, New York, 1930)

rationalize To invent a reason 'for an attitude or action, the motive of which is not recognized.' (Jones, E. *Papers on Psycho-Analysis,* 4th ed., Wood, Baltimore, 1938)

rational type See *type, rational.*

ratio, sex This statistical term relates to the proportional distribution of males and females at birth with the slight but constant excess of male births. The usual sex ratio 106:100 has always been cited as evidence that boys are stronger and better able to survive the ordeal of being born.

Recent genetic studies have shown, however, that more boys are born, because more boys are *conceived,* and that the excess of males over females conceived is still greater than the ratio at birth. Investigation of embryos aborted when about three months old has shown that males outnumber females almost four to one. It must be assumed, therefore, that male embryos are not stronger, but just on the contrary, *weaker* than female ones, and therefore more likely to perish under adverse intrauterine conditions.

ratio, type token An index of the balance between repetition and variety of words, used as a quantitative measurement of certain aspects of verbal communication during psychiatric sessions. Repetition gives a low index, variety of words gives a high index.

Rat-Man This refers to the patient reported on by Freud in his 1909 paper, 'Notes upon a Case of Obsessional Neurosis.' The patient is so called because of the experience which was the direct occasion of his consulting a psychiatrist: on military maneuvers he had heard a story of a type of punishment used in the Far East, the punishment consisting of overturning a pot of rats onto the buttocks of the prisoner so that the rats would bore their way into his anus.

Ray, Isaac (1807–81) American psychiatrist; mental hygiene.

reaction Counter-action; response to a stimulus.

reaction, adjustment See *maladjustment.*

reaction, alarm The first stage of the general adaptation syndrome. The alarm reaction is a response to stress and as observed in experimental animals consists of: adrenocortical enlargement with histologic signs of hyperactivity, thymicolymphatic involution, gastrointestinal ulcers, and often other manifestations of damage or shock. See *syndrome, general adaptation.*

reaction, alcohol-Antabuse See *Antabuse.*

reaction, all-or-none In psychiatry this expression means that instinctive processes, when stimulated, respond with full force or not at all.

Jung distinguishes pathological psychic symptoms, such as phobias and obsessions, from instincts, but says that 'they share the character of the "all-or-none" reaction.' (Jung, C.G. *Contributions to Analytical Psychology,* tr. by Baynes, H.G. and C.F., Kegan Paul, Trench, Trubner, London, 1928)

In neurophysiology, the all-or-none (or all-or-nothing) principle refers to the fact that individual neurons either transmit their messages maximally or not at all. Differences in intensity are conveyed by means of spatial and temporal summation of impulses.

reaction, antisocial See *antisocial reaction.*

reaction, anxiety According to the 1952 revision of psychiatric nomenclature, this is the acceptable term for conditions formerly diagnosed anxiety state, or anxiety-neurosis. See *anxiety-neurosis.*

reaction, aversion A response of avoidance or turning away from disturbing or frightening stimuli.

reaction, behavioral See *personality disorder.*

reaction, defensive The expression refers to the response (e.g. fear, compulsion, hallucination, delusion, etc.) occasioned by the conflicting interaction of two or more psychic structures. Each psychic unit has its own special structure and functions; the results of its activities are called mechanisms or dynamisms; when the latter operate defensively the result is called a defensive reaction. A phobia is a form of defensive reaction against an undesirable impulse.

reaction, delirious See *syndrome, organic.*

reaction, dissociate-dysmnesic substitution By this expression Adolf Meyer designates 'the main dynamic principle' in hysterical reactions. Diethelm says: 'An analysis of symptoms in the older sense, i.e., an analysis in order to find the meaning of the symptoms, is not desirable.' He adds: 'An understanding of the personality setting is desirable before one decides on a definite therapeutic plan.' In other words, 'the main dynamic principle' in hysteria is to be found, according to Meyer, in some form of memory dissociation. (Diethelm, O. *Treatment in Psychiatry,* Macmillan, New York. 1936)

reaction-formation Reaction-formation (or reversal-formation) is a psychoanalytic term, meaning 'the development in the ego of conscious, socialized attitudes and interests which are the antithesis of certain infantile unsocialized trends which continue to persist in the unconscious.' (Healy, W., Bronner, A.F., and Bowers, A.M. *The Structure and Meaning of Psychoanalysis,* Knopf, New York, 1930) When, for instance, oversolicitude is the conscious response to unconscious hate, the condition (oversolicitude) is known as a reaction-formation.

Reaction-formation is a form of defense against urges which are unacceptable to the ego. It is one of the earliest of the defense-mechanisms and one of the most fragile. As Freud says it is 'insecure and constantly threatened by the impulse which lurks in the unconscious.' There is always the danger in reaction-formation of a return of the repressed impulse to consciousness.

'Repression, as it invariably does, has brought about a withdrawal of libido, but for this purpose it has made use of a *reaction-formation,* by intensifying an antithesis. So here the substitute-formation has the same mechanism as the repression and at bottom coincides with it, while yet chronologically, as well as in its content, it is distinct from symptom-formation.' (Freud, S. *Collected Papers,* vol. 4, tr. by Riviere, J., Leonard and Virginia Woolf and The Institute of Psychoanalysis, London, 1924–25)

Reaction-formation, then, is a type of repression, but it is distinguished from the latter by two features: (1) in reaction-formation, the counter-cathexis is manifest in the form of the denying attitude, and thus the necessity for often repeated secondary repressions is avoided; and (2) the counter-cathexis is constantly manifested as a definitive change of per-

sonality rather than a momentary arousal of defensive maneuvers in response to an immediate danger.

'In a sense the superego can be considered a reaction formation of the ego, a complicated reaction to the oedipus complex. The fully developed superego in turn stimulates the ego to further reaction formations. The ego has to change its structure according to internal and external needs. It has the difficult task of maintaining itself in the face of three kinds of influences—the superego, the external world, and the id. Although its core is stable, the structure of the ego as a whole changes according to the influences to which it is subjected. Instead of reacting to these influences, that is, perceiving and discharging or abreacting them, the ego assimilates them and creates something new.' (Nunberg, H. *Principles of Psychoanalysis,* International Universities Press, New York, 1955) Such reaction-formations contribute extensively to the final structure of the character. Two commonly observed reaction-formations are disgust (a reaction-formation of the ego to an oral sexual impulse) and shame (a reaction-formation to exhibitionistic impulses).

It is to be emphasized that reaction-formation is an unconscious defense mechanism of the ego; conscious dissimulation or hypocrisy is not reaction-formation. Further, reaction-formation is not to be confused with sublimation; in the former, the unconscious impulse is repressed, and the constant counter-cathexis required to maintain such constant repression drains off energy which would otherwise be available to the ego. In the case of sublimation, on the other hand, the original impulse is superseded and its energy remains available to the ego for the fulfillment of its various tasks.

'To clarify the relation between reaction formation and sublimation let us compare (a) a child who learns to write well and enjoys it very much, (b) a child who has an inhibition for writing, (c) a child who writes very constrainedly and meticulously, and (d) a child who smears. All of them have displaced anal-erotic instinctual quantities to the function of writing. In the first child a sublimation has taken place; he no longer wishes to smear but to write. The other children have not succeeded in channelizing this impulse. They are forced to inhibit it through a countercathexis, or to "robot" through reaction formations, or even to retain the original impulse in an unchanged way.' (Fenichel, O. *The Psychoanalytic Theory of Neurosis,* Norton, New York, 1945)

While reaction-formation can be seen as an element of any neurosis or psychosis, it is a typical mechanism of the obsessive-compulsive psychoneurosis.

reaction, hand-to-mouth Observed in young infants, bringing to the mouth, for the purpose of sucking, all objects within reach of the infant's hand. These may be parts of the infant's body (hand, foot) or any outside object. According to Gesell, this reaction disappears at about twelve months of age.

reaction, manic-depressive See *psychosis, manic-depressive.*

reaction, Much-Holzmann (Hans Much, W. Holzmann, German physicians.) The alleged property of the serum from a person affected with schizophrenia or manic-depressive psychosis, to inhibit hemolysis by cobra venom.

reaction, polyglot In aphasia, any exception to the general rule that in individuals who are multilingual, the mother tongue is the first to return.

reaction, psychotic See *psychosis; psychotic disorder.*

reaction, spoiled child Behavior reaction of children due to parental oversolicitude, overindulgence, and overprotection. Such children do not learn the value or even the meaning of regularity, self-care, responsibility, or independence.

reaction, thymonoic (thĭ-mō-nō'ik) 'Thymonoic reactions are closely related to catathymic reactions. They are distinguished by the presence of strong affective factors and equally strong tendency to systematization of thought (in the direction of depressive delusion), each factor springing from the same experiential and personality sources, and each feeding on and becoming more strongly fixed because of the other. These are the strongly "intellectualized" and "rationalized" depressions, with marked systematized content, at times entirely autopsychic, but also at times with allopsychic manifestations.' (Muncie, W. *Psychobiology and Psychiatry,* Mosby, St. Louis, 1939)

reaction-time 'The lapse of time between the stimulus word and the reply.' (Jung, C.G. *Contributions to Analytical Psychology,* tr. by Baynes, H.G. and C.F., Kegan Paul, Trench, Trubner, London, 1928.) From the psychiatric point of view a long reaction-time signalizes a so-termed complex and is believed to be due to emotions. When the stimulus word 'lake' promptly gives rise to a reply, it is not likely that a complex has been touched; when the subject hesitates long and perhaps feels uncomfortable, it is said that a complex has been traced.

reaction-type In the field of objective psychobiology, this general expression designates psychiatric syndromes from the point of view of the preponderating or essential symptomatology. For example, Adolf Meyer describes six reaction-types: organic, delirious, affective, paranoic, substitutive, and deteriorated.

reaction-type, affective When the principal response in a psychiatric syndrome is of an affective or emotional nature, the expression *affective* reaction-type is used. Manic-depressive psychosis is an example of this type of reaction.

reaction-type, delirious Adolf Meyer's expression for a type of psychiatric response due to toxic, infective, or exhaustive influences. The syndrome is characterized by dream-like imaginations, hallucinations, and impairment of the sensorium.

reaction-type, deterioration When regression, accompanied as a rule by delusional and hallucinatory phenomena, is a principal characteristic of a psychiatric syndrome, as it is in schizophrenia, Adolf Meyer classifies the syndrome as a deterioration reaction-type.

reaction-type, organic See *syndrome, organic.*

reaction-type, paranoic This term, common in objective psychobiology, denotes a psychiatric syndrome the essential nature of which is a paranoid, delusional formation. The paranoid form of schizophrenia comes under this classification.

reaction-type, substitutive When mental conflicts are repressed into the unconscious and appear in the field of consciousness in disguised or substituted form, Adolf Meyer classifies the syndrome as *substitutive.* The psychoneuroses in general are substitutive reaction-types.

reactive depression See *depression.*

reactive mania See *mania, reactive.*

readiness, complex The tendency of unconscious feelings or impulses to find substitute expression in the behavior or routine of everyday life. We have frequent lapses in speaking, reading, and writing. These mistakes are unconsciously motivated. Brill gives among others the following example: he was once speaking to a French patient, who had the annoying habit of wandering from the subject, meandering, and wasting a considerable amount of time. On one occasion he wanted to tell her to go on (en avant), but instead of this he said good-by (au revoir). Another time he wrote to a doctor about a Mr. K.: 'I am very glad to do so, as Mr. K. has considerable experience inn this matter.' The doctor returned the letter to the writer asking him to explain why he had in with two n's instead of one. Mr. K. was addicted to alcohol and was always to be found in a certain inn which Brill knew very well and he associated this in his mind with a particular experience that occurred there in connection with Mr. K. These slips or errors occur because the mind is in a state of complex readiness. The real state of mind on certain matters is betrayed owing to the unconscious feelings behind it. (Brill, A.A. *Basic Principles of Psychoanalysis,* Doubleday, New York, 1949)

readiness, explosion Readiness to explode, or burst forth violently.

An individual, having experienced a painful reaction, may repress the experience and its affects. 'Every new similar experience increases the tension; thus there is on the one hand an *explosion-readiness* to certain experiences, and on the other hand, an unconscious affective search for such processes.' (Bleuler, E. *Textbook of Psychiatry,* tr. by Brill, A.A., Macmillan, New York, 1930) See also *diathesis, explosive.*

reading, disabilities of The term 'reading disability' includes a variety of clinical entities of apparently different etiology and treatment need.

'In our total caseload, which now numbers some 250 children and adolescents, we have been impressed with the emergence of three major groups:

'1. Those in whom the reading retardation is due to frank brain damage manifested by gross neurologic deficits. In these cases there are clearly demonstrable major aphasic difficulties, and they are similar to adult dyslexic syndromes. An example is that of a 9-year-old boy who sustained a severe head injury with prolonged coma, followed by a right hemiparesis and expressive aphasia.

'2. Those with no history or gross clinical findings to suggest neurologic disease but in whom the reading retardation is viewed as primary. The defect appears to be in basic capacity to integrate written material and to associate concepts with symbols. On the basis of findings to be presented later in this paper a neurologic deficit is suspected and, because the defect is basic or biologic in its origin, we have called these cases *primary reading retardation.*

'3. Those cases demonstrating reading retardation on standard tests but in whom there appears to be no defect in basic reading learning capacity. These children have a normal potential for learning to read but this has not been utilized because of *exogenous* factors, common among which are anxiety, negativism, emotional blocking and limited schooling opportunities. We diagnose these cases as *secondary reading retardation.*' (Rabinovitch, R.D., Drew, A.L., De Jong, R.N., Ingram, W., and Withey, L. 'A Research Approach to Reading Retardation,' *Research Publications, Association for Nervous and Mental Diseases 34:* 363–96, 1954, p. 366)

Failure to distinguish between these major types of reading disability has led to confusion among workers in the field, and innumerable terms have been coined to describe various types of reading defects, many terms frequently referring to the same concept. Among such terms currently in use are: word-blindness, congenital symbolamblyopia, congenital typholexia, congenital alexia, amnesia visualis verbalis, congenital dyslexia, developmental alexia, analfabetia partialis, bradylexia, strephosymbolia, constitutional dyslexia, specific dyslexia.

In the primary group described above, '. . . the defect appears to be part of a larger disturbance in integration. Our findings suggest that we are dealing with a developmental discrepancy rather than an acquired brain injury. The specific areas of difficulty manifested in the clinical examinations are those commonly associated with parietal and parietal-occipital dysfunction.' (ibid, p. 387)

readmission An individual admitted more than once to any institution of a given class (i.e. hospitals for mental disease).

Example: The following table shows the number of readmissions to the New York civil State hospitals during the year ended June 30, 1938, classified according to sex and type of mental disorder.

Mental Disorders	Number		
	Males	Females	Total
General paresis	82	37	119
With other syphilis of central nervous system	12	5	17
With epidemic encephalitis..	20	8	28
With other infectious diseases	6	3	9
Alcoholic	203	35	238
Due to drugs or other exogenous poisons	6	6	12
Traumatic	29	...	29
With cerebral arteriosclerosis	117	120	237
With other disturbances of circulation	4	2	6
With convulsive disorders...	27	26	53
Senile	22	44	66
Involutional	30	125	155
Due to other metabolic, etc., diseases	2	10	12
Due to new growth........	...	1	1
With organic changes of nervous system	6	8	14
Psychoneuroses	57	53	110
Manic-depressive	268	516	784
Dementia-praecox	626	603	1229
Paranoia and paranoid conditions	10	22	32
With psychopathic personality	73	46	119
With mental deficiency.....	42	50	92
Undiagnosed	2	2	4
Without psychosis	47	14	61
Primary behavior disorders..	6	2	8
Total	1697	1738	3435

reality In psychiatry the term means the whole of the objective world, embracing all that may be perceived by the five senses.

reality, coefficient of This term applies to the very limited range or extent of the knowledge that the individual has of his own day-dreaming. In the opinion of Stekel, 'complete knowledge of a day-dream will completely destroy it,' and, furthermore, this knowledge 'must be an affective process, not a purely logical or intellectual one which remains in the upper levels of consciousness without exerting a fermentative influence in the depths.' (Stekel, W. *The Interpretation of Dreams*, Liveright, New York, 1943)

reality-ego See *ego, reality.*

reality-principle See *principle, reality.*

reality, psychical A term indicating that in his phantasy a neurotic creates scenes to which he reacts, as if they were real events. This term is the antithesis of *actual reality.* 'If hysterics trace back their symptoms to fictitious traumas, this new fact signifies that they create such scenes in phantasy, and *psychical reality* requires to be taken into account alongside actual reality.' (Freud, S. *Collected Papers,* vol. 1, tr. by Riviere, J., Leonard and Virginia Woolf and The Institute of Psychoanalysis, London, 1924–25)

reality, requisition of See *pathogenesis.*

reality-system See *ego, stability of.*

reality-testing A fundamental ego function which consists of the objective evaluation and judgment of the world outside the ego or self. Reality-testing depends upon the simpler ego-functions of perception and memory and upon differentiation between ego and non-ego. Reality-testing provides the ego with a mechanism for handling both the external world and its own excitation, for it makes it possible for the ego to anticipate the future in the imagination. External objects represent a threat to the ego and/or potential gratification, and the ego can best protect itself against threats and can secure maximal gratification by using reality-testing to judge reality objectively and direct its actions accordingly.

A stage of primary hallucinatory wish-fulfillment precedes the development of reality-testing, and a counterpart of the former is the ability to deny unpleasant parts of reality. As reality-testing develops along with the acquisition of speech and thinking proper, such wholesale falsification of reality becomes impossible. Serious and important denials, then, are seen only in very early childhood and in pathological conditions such as psychosis, where the ego has been weakened by narcissistic regression. Projection, too, can be used extensively only when reality-testing is seriously impaired, as in psychosis, or when adequate demarcation between ego and non-ego has not yet been achieved, as in childhood. Only when the boundaries between ego and non-ego are blurred can the ego ward off the unpleasant by 'spitting it out' and feeling it as being outside the ego.

Neurotics do, however, show some impairment of reality-testing at least to the extent that warded-off impulses and their derivatives interfere with differentiated thinking and block the ego's capacity to organize its experiences, and insofar as present-day objects become mere 'transference' representations of past objects and are reacted to with inappropriate and anachronistic feelings.

reassociation A process of renewed or refreshed association occurring in hypnoanalysis of the war neurosis, during which the patient relives the traumatic event with emotional vividness. Such forgotten experiences will then become a part of his normal personality and consciousness.

reassurance A type of supportive psychotherapy. See *assurance*.

rebirth The concept of rebirth possesses considerable importance in psychiatry. It is almost a universal inclination among human beings, normal and abnormal, to think of rebirth. It is encountered in its most literal forms of expression in patients with schizophrenia, who openly believe that they have gone through the phase of living again in the mother's womb. They add that they are being reborn, this time in the form of God.

The similarity between the concepts of patients with schizophrenia, and of primitives has been repeatedly emphasized by psychiatrists.

'In schizophrenics the ascent to cosmic union, with the all, with deity, often takes the form of an archaic experience of rebirth.' (Storch, A. *The Primitive Archaic Forms in Schizophrenia,* tr. by Willard, C., Nervous and Mental Disease Publishing Company, New York and Washington, 1924)

Storch cites an initiation ceremony, held in ancient India, and called *Upanayana*. 'The teacher, who leads the disciple in, makes him an embryo and he is carried three days in the womb of the teacher. Then the one is born whom the gods come to see.' The quotation, appearing in Storch's monograph, is taken from Brahmacharin song (Atharvaveda, XI, 5).

rebound phenomenon of Gordon Holmes (British physician, 1876–   ) A test for ataxia, specifically illustrating the loss of cerebellar 'check' on co-ordinated movement; if an attempt is made to extend the flexed forearm against resistance and suddenly let go, the hand or fist flies unchecked against the mouth or shoulder.

recapitulation, pubertal sexual The concept that the successive stages in the development of adult sexuality recapitulate those of infantile sexuality. The development of adult sexuality begins with puberty and is normally completed somewhere between the ages of sixteen and twenty-one. The developmental stages of adult sexuality 'repeat' those of infantile sexuality and rarely are conflicts found which have not had their forerunners in the earlier development. 'At puberty a regression takes place in the direction of infancy, of the first period of all, and the person lives over again, though on another plain, the development he passed through in the first five years of life. This correlation between adolescence and infancy is of considerable importance as affording the key to many of the problems of adolescence.' (Jones, E.J. *Papers on Psycho-Analysis,* Williams and Wilkins, Baltimore, 1949)

While it is true that conflicts in adolescent sexual development which have not had their forerunners in infantile sexual development are rarely encountered, nevertheless 'experiences in puberty may solve conflicts or shift conflicts into a final direction; moreover, they may give older and oscillating constellations a final and definitive form. Many neurotics give an impression of adolescence. They have not succeeded in getting on good terms with their sexuality. Therefore, they continue the behavior patterns of adolescent children, that is, of an age at which it is usually considered normal not to have achieved these good terms and to feel life as a provisional state, with "full reality" still waiting in an indefinite future.' (Fenichel, O. *The Psychoanalytic Theory of Neurosis,* Norton, New York, 1945)

receptive Passive, accepting, dependent. See *character, receptive.*

recessiveness The meaning of this genetic term is best understood as the mirror image of *dominance,* since the behavior of a recessive factor in Mendelian inheritance is characterized by the principle that it remains *hidden* as an independent genetic entity, as long, and as far, as it is covered by the dominant member of a given allelic pair of hereditary factors. See *dominance.*

According to modern genetic theories, a recessive character does not really 'disappear' as was suggested by the old presence-absence theory of Bateson, but it can be phenotypically manifested only in a *homozygous* condition when it is inherited by a hybrid from both parents. In the case of a single-recessive cross, this is true in 25 per cent of the entire hybrid generation.

In the recessive or *indirect* mode of inheritance we observe as a rule that the heterozygotes are germinally affected, but phenotypically healthy. Since a recessive trait can appear only in the phenotype of a homozygote, all trait-carriers must be homozygous. The occurrence of such a trait among the offspring is not possible, unless both parents are, at least, heterozygotes.

The probability of a union between two recessive taint-carriers (heterozygotes) is clearly the greater the more frequent this recessive trait is in the general population. The probability is the greatest in the cases of *intermarriage* between blood-relations, unless the trait in question is very common in the normal average population. Apart from this particular instance of *cousin marriages,* the direct transmission of a recessive trait is the exception and the indirect inheritance through the collateral lines is the rule.

recidivism (rē-sid'i-viz'm) The term refers to the repetition of delinquent or criminal acts by the same offender who is called, accordingly, a recidivist. (Healy, W. *The Individual Delinquent,* Little, Brown, Boston, 1915)

'A large proportion of the inmates of penal institutions in most countries are "repeaters"; persons who have been committed to a penal institution after having served one or more terms.' (Cantor, N. *Encyclopaedia of the Social Sciences,* vol. 13, Macmillan, New York, 1934, p. 157)

Less commonly, recidivism is used to refer to relapse or recurrence of a psychiatric disorder. See *schizophrenia, recidives in.*

recombination The genetic process by which linked factors break up their original combinations, so that originally separate genes become united in one gamete, or originally united genes become separated. These recombining phenomena are also known as *crossovers.*

'Under independent assortment the parental combinations and the recombinations are approximately equal in number. Under linkage the parental combinations are always more numerous than the recombinations. Linkage may vary greatly with different genes, producing all the way from very few to nearly 50 per cent of recombinations.' (Sinnott, E.W. and

Dunn, L.C. *Principles of Genetics,* 3rd ed., McGraw-Hill, New York and London, 1939)

When crossovers occur and lead to a separation of linked genes, the genes which have crossed over are bound to enter different gametes and to appear in different individuals among the progeny. See *linkage.*

recommencement, mania of Janet's term for the behavior of some obsessive-compulsive patients who must do things many times before they can feel some assurance that they have been done correctly—opening and shutting doors, locking and unlocking doors, dressing and undressing, constant repetition of prayers and penances, etc.

reconditioning A type of psychotherapy based on the belief that neurosis is a result of faulty conditioning. In Salter's method, the patient is authoritatively directed to abandon destructive patterns of behavior and to practice new habits which will be of value to him. The patient is considered to be in a state of pathologic inhibition which is itself a conditioned response that blocks free emotional expression ('excitation'). Treatment is directed to unlearning conditioned inhibitory reflexes and replacing them with conditioned excitatory reflexes by means of deliberate practicing of excitatory emotional reactions until they are established as conditioned reflexes.

reconstruction See *psychotherapy.*

recreation In social work 'recreation is leisure activity engaged in for its own sake.' (Worman, E.C. *Social Work Year Book,* edited by Kurtz, R.H., Russell Sage Foundation, New York, 1939)

The term is also used to refer to a type of ancillary treatment and is then called recreation(al) therapy or R.T. John E. Davis (*Clinical Applications of Recreational Therapy,* Thomas, Springfield, Ill., 1952) defines recreation therapy as '. . . any free, voluntary and expressive activity; motor, sensory or mental, vitalized by the expansive play spirit, sustained by deep-rooted pleasurable attitudes and evoked by wholesome emotional release; prescribed by medical authority as an adjuvant in treatment.' Recreation therapy includes such activities as dressmaking, drama, puppetry, lectures, films, music appreciation, dancing, discussion groups, clubs, painting, singing, excursions, bowling, and athletic games of all sorts.

recreation, active In occupational therapy this term denotes any form of diversional endeavor or pastime in which the patient actually engages and in the participation of which it is necessary for him to make some physical exertion. For example, dancing is a form of active recreation.

recreation, passive In occupational therapy this term denotes a form of entertainment or amusement which is planned and presented by others for the patient and in which he does not participate, but plays the passive part of onlooker. For example, moving pictures or a concert are forms of passive recreation.

recruiting system See *system, intralaminar.*

redintegration (red-in-tē-gra'shun) Hollingworth's term for the process in which part of a complex antecedent provokes the complete consequent that was previously made to the antecedent as a whole. The conditioned response is an example of redintegration. Redintegration is the basis of the value of souvenirs and keepsakes, which tend to arouse the same attitudes as were originally connected with the experiences to which they pertain.

Redintegration is also sometimes used synonymously with reintegration. See *integration.*

red nucleus See *midbrain.*

reductive 'I employ this expression to denote that method of psychological interpretation which regards the unconscious product not from the symbolic point of view, but merely as a *semiotic* expression, a sort of sign or symptom of an underlying process. Accordingly the reductive method treats the unconscious product in the sense of a leading-back to the elements and basic processes, irrespective of whether such products are reminiscences of actual events, or whether they arise from elementary processes affecting the psyche. Hence, the reductive method is orientated backwards (in contrast to the constructive method), whether in the historical sense or in the merely figurative sense of a tracing back of complex and differentiated factors to the general and elementary.' (Jung, C.G. *Psychological Types,* tr. by Baynes, H.G.,

Harcourt, Brace, New York and London, 1923)

re-education See *psychotherapy.*

reefers Slang expression for marihuana cigarettes. Possibly the weed was first brought by sailors (?) from the 'reefs' of Mariguana Island in the Bahamas.

re-enactment, emotional See *abreaction.*

reference, delusion of See *reference, ideas of.*

reference, ideas of When an individual projects his own, usually unconscious, ideas upon another or other persons and then proceeds to act toward those ideas as if they originated from an outside source, he is said to show *ideas of reference.* For instance, a patient with an unconscious impulse to steal, was preoccupied with the idea, delusional, that others asserted he intended to steal. The psychic process involves criticism of the projected urges, so that the patient may not know that he is really criticizing some undesirable impulse within himself.

The paranoid patient almost always exhibits ideas of reference. He misinterprets the activities of others, believing that they have personal reference of a derogatory character to him. See *projection.*

referred pain See *pain, referred.*

reflection In psychiatry and psychology, this may refer (1) to a type of thinking characterized by introspection, deliberation, or contemplation, or (2) to a psychotherapeutic technique in which a patient's statements are restated or rephrased to the patient so as to emphasize their emotional significance.

reflex A sensorimotor reaction, the simplest form of involuntary response to a stimulus. Stimulation of the receptor organ or cell excites the afferent neuron, from which the impulse travels to one or more intercalated neurons in the central nervous system and thence, via the efferent neuron, to the effector organ or cell.

reflex, abdominal The upper (or epigastric) and lower abdominal reflexes are superficial skin reflexes tested by stroking the skin of the abdomen. This results in contraction of the abdominal muscles beneath the skin area stroked and usually also movement of the umbilicus in the direction of the area stroked. The upper abdominals depend on thoracic nerves 7 to 10; the lower abdominals depend on thoracic nerves 10 to 12.

reflex, accommodation See *accommodation*.

reflex, acute affective Kretschmer's term for the earliest indications of emotional discharge (usually, tremors) in response to great stress.

reflex, biceps A deep reflex; patient's forearm is placed half-way between flexion and extension and slightly pronated; examiner's finger is on the tendon, and a blow on this digit results in flexion of the forearm. This reflex depends upon the musculocutaneous nerve for its afferents and efferents; its center is C_{5-6}.

reflex, Chaddock (Charles Gilbert Chaddock, American neurologist) Dorsal extension of the great toe, induced by stroking the skin over the external malleolus. This is one of several pathologic reflexes which may be seen when the lower motor neuron is released from the normal suppressor effect of higher centers, as in pyramidal tract lesions.

reflex, consensual When light enters the pupil of one eye only, the iris of the other eye contracts; the phenomenon is known as the consensual light reflex.

reflex, corneal Bilateral blinking induced by touching the cornea with a wisp of cotton. The afferent nerve of the corneal reflex is the 5th cranial nerve; its efferent is the 7th cranial nerve, and its center is in the pons.

reflex, cremasteric (krē-mas-ter'ik) A superficial reflex; stroking the inner and upper side of the thigh causes contraction of the cremaster and elevation of the testicle on the same side. The afferents of this reflex depend upon the femoral nerve, the efferents on the genitofemoral nerve; the center is L_1.

reflex, cuboidodigital (kū-boi-dō-dij'i-tal) See *Bechtereff-Mendel reflex*.

reflex, deep Any one of the tendon and periosteal reflexes, which include the jaw-jerk, pectoral, triceps, biceps, radial, ulnar, knee-jerk, suprapatellar, tibio-adductor, flexion of the leg, ankle-jerk, and Bechtereff-Mendel reflexes.

reflex, dorsocuboidal (dor-sō-kū-boid'al) See *Bechtereff-Mendel reflex*.

reflex, emptying See *reflex, gastrocolic*.

reflex, epigastric See *reflex, abdominal*.

reflexes, grasping and groping These reflexes are elicited when the palms and the fingers are stroked, causing a closure of the hand on the stimulating object. Normally this occurs in infants below one year of age. Otherwise it is indicative of frontal lobe lesions.

reflex, flexion, of the leg A deep reflex; patient's leg is semiflexed at the knee; the examiner's finger grasps the tendons of the semimembranosus and semitendinosus muscles; this finger is tapped, and that results in contraction of these muscles and flexion of the leg.

reflex, gastrocolic (gas-trō-kol'ik) Contraction of the colon following stretching of the muscle wall of the stomach (as by filling of the stomach); also known as emptying reflex.

reflex, gluteal (glōō'tē-al) A superficial reflex; stroking the buttocks causes contraction of the glutei.

reflex, Gordon (Alfred Gordon, American neurologist, 1869–   ) Dorsal extension of the great toe, induced by compression of the calf muscle.

reflex, grasp Same as forced grasping, forced groping, or instinctive grasp reaction. See *lobe, frontal*.

reflex, mass In very severe injury to or complete interruption of the spinal cord, stimulation below the level of the lesion produces the following reflexes: (1) flexion reflex, (2) contraction of the abdominal wall, (3) automatic evacuation of the bladder, (4) sweating of the skin below the level of the lesion. This *mass-reflex* was described by Riddoch.

reflex, oculocardiac (ok-ū-lō-kar'di-ak) Slowing of the pulse in response to pressure exerted on the eyeball; also known as the Aschner ocular phenomenon.

reflex, Oppenheim (H. Oppenheim, 1858–1919, German neurologist) The dorsal extension of the great toe, induced by stroking distally along the median side of the tibia. This is one of several pathologic reflexes which may be seen when the lower motor neuron is released from the normal suppressor effect of higher centers, as in pyramidal tract lesions.

reflex, palmar A superficial reflex; scratching or irritation of the palm results in flexion of the fingers.

reflex, palmomental (pal-mō-men'tal) A

pathologic reflex observed in pyramidal tract disease. It is elicited by tapping the thenar eminence, whereupon a contraction of the ipsilateral muscles of the lower jaw below the angle of the mouth occurs.

reflex, patellar (pa-tel'ẽr) See *reflex, suprapatellar.*

reflex, periosteal (per-i-os'tē-al) The reflex; patient's arm is placed half-way between adduction and abduction; the examiner's finger is on the muscle tendon near the humerus; a sharp blow on this finger produces adduction and slight internal rotation of patient's arm.

reflex, periosteal (per-i-os'tē-al) The response to tapping certain bones which lie just beneath the skin; for example, the radial and ulnar periosteal, and the tibial adductor reflexes.

reflex, plantar A superficial reflex; stroking the sole of the foot causes flexion of the toes. This reflex depends upon the tibial nerve for its afferents and efferents; its center is at S_{1-2}.

reflex, psychogalvanic (sī-kō-gal-van'ik) Changes in skin resistance to the passage of a weak electric current which occur as part of the physicochemical response to emotional stimuli. Also known as PGR, galvanic skin response (GSR), electrodermal response (EDR), Féré phenomenon.

reflex, quadrupedal extensor (kwad-roo-pē'dal ek-sten'sor) Russel Brain described this reflex in organic hemiplegia. It consists in the extension of the hemiplegic flexed arm on the assumption of the quadrupedal position. An additional feature may be the further flexion of the arm if the head is bent forward and extension of the arm if the head is bent back.

reflex, radial A deep reflex; also known as the extension reflex of the wrist. When the styloid process of the radius is tapped, the wrist extends. This reflex depends upon the radial nerve for its afferents and efferents; its center is C_{7-8}.

reflex, Ros(s)olimo's (Grigoriy Ivanovich Rosolimo, Russian neurologist, born in Odessa in 1860 of Greek parents) Plantar flexion of the toes, induced by tapping the balls of the toes. This is one of several pathologic reflexes which may be seen when the lower motor neuron is released from the normal suppressor effect of

higher centers, as in pyramidal tract lesions.

reflex, Schaeffer (Max Schaeffer, German neurologist, 1852–1923) Dorsal reflexion of the great toe, induced by pinching the tendo Achillis. This is one of several pathologic reflexes which may be seen when the lower motor neuron is released from the normal suppressor effect of higher centers, as in pyramidal tract lesions.

reflex, scrotal (skrō'tal) By stroking the perineum or applying a cold object to it, a slow, vermicular contraction of the dartos muscle occurs. This is a purely automatic reflex with the cremasteric reflex.

reflex, superficial The response to stroking or pressing upon certain portions of the skin; for example, the plantar, cremasteric, and abdominal reflexes.

reflex, suprapatellar (sū-pra-pa-tel'ẽr) A deep reflex; patient's leg is extended with patella movable; examiner places index finger above patella, pushing down slightly, then striking this finger; the result is a kick-back of the patella.

This reflex is also known as the patellar reflex. It depends upon the femoral nerve for its afferents and efferents; its center is L_{2-3-4}.

reflex, tendon The contraction of a muscle in response to tapping its tendon; for example the triceps, quadriceps femoris (patellar), and gastrocnemius (Achilles or ankle) reflexes.

reflex, triceps (trī'seps) A deep reflex; the patient's forearm, partly flexed at the elbow, is held by the examiner; the striking of the tendon just above the olecranon process results in extension of the forearm. This reflex depends upon the radial nerve for its afferents and efferents; its center is C_{6-7}.

reflex, ulnar (ul'nẽr) A deep reflex; also known as the flexion reflex of the wrist; when the styloid process of the ulna is tapped, the wrist flexes (pronation and adduction of the hand). This reflex depends on the median nerve for its afferents and efferents; its center is C_{6-7-8}.

reflex, visceral (vis'ẽr-al) In physiology, the term is restricted to the response of a viscus or organ innervated by the sympathetic or vegetative nervous system. In clinical neuropsychiatry, the term has a broader application and refers to the response not only of a single viscus but of these organs as a group to a stress which alters body function as a whole. As an example there is the dysfunction of the alimentary tract in certain psychoneurotic patients with anxiety-states.

reflex, wrist See *reflex, radial; reflex, ulnar.*

reform Reform 'does not seek to change the mores but rather to change conditions in conformity with the mores.' (Park, R.E. and Burgess, E.W. *Introduction to the Science of Sociology,* University of Chicago Press, Chicago, 1921)

refractory Resistant, unresponsive, unmanageable, obstinate, stubborn. In neurophysiology, the refractory period is the time following stimulation during which a nerve or muscle remains unresponsive to a second stimulus. The absolute refractory period is that during which there is no response to any stimulus; the relative refractory period is that during which response can be elicited only if the stimulus is very strong.

regimen The specific details of a treatment plan, including the scheduling and regulation of diet, medication, and other therapeutic measures designed to operate over a period of time. The term regime is often used incorrectly in this sense.

registration In learning psychology, registration refers to impressibility or notation ability and implies either the ability to notice, or the ability to make a record, or both. Impaired registration of recent impressions is the most striking symptom of Korsakoff's psychosis.

regression From the psychiatric point of view *regression* refers to the act of returning to some earlier level of adaptation. The mentally healthy individual progresses through many so-called levels. Following the designations of Freud, they are (1) intrauterine; (2) infancy (early and late; extending from birth to approximately the fifth year; this period includes, among other things, the phases of oral, anal, and genital organization); (3) latency (extending from about the age of five to puberty; one of its chief characteristics is sublimation); (4) puberty (beginning at the onset of manhood and womanhood and continuing for two or three years; one of its main attributes is adult sexuality); (5) adolescence (begin-

ning at the termination of puberty and ending in the early or middle twenties; its principal characteristics revolve around the reality-principle, heterosexuality, and sublimated interest); (6) adulthood (extending from the termination of the adolescent period to senescence; the characteristics of adolescence are amplified during this stage); (7) senescence (the phase of decadence).

When an individual, say, at the age of forty, begins to show symptoms of schizophrenia and subsequently undergoes deep regression, he sometimes passes through the various levels of adaptation formerly lived through by him. Thus, with the abandonment of the qualities of adulthood, he regressively becomes, so to speak, adolescent, pubertal, puerile, and finally infantile; he may also regress to a stage resembling that of the intrauterine period of existence. As a rule, regression in schizophrenia or in any of the psychogenic psychiatric disorders is accomplished by means of symbolic manifestations.

From the psychoanalytic standpoint, regression and *fixation* (q.v.) are commonly associated with each other. When fixation is intense, frustrations on the part of reality may easily lead to regression. But, internal frustrations are even more important, according to Freud.

'According to the concept of finality, causes are understood as means to an end. A simple example is the process of regression. Regarded causally, regression is determined, for example, by "mother fixation." But from the final standpoint, the libido returns to the mother-imago in order to find there the memory associations by means of which further development can take place, as, for instance, from an emotional system into an intellectual system.' (Jung, C.G. *Contributions to Analytical Psychology,* tr. by Baynes, H.G. and C.F., Kegan Paul, Trench, Trubner, London, 1928)

regression, temporal 'When we investigate psychoneurotic conditions, we find in each of them occasion to comment upon a so-called *temporal regression,* i.e., the particular extent * to which each of them retraces the stages of its evolution. We distinguish two such regressions—one in the development of the ego and the other in that of the libido.' (Freud, S. *Collected Papers,* vol. 4, tr. by Riviere, J., Leonard

* *i.e. extent in time.*

and Virginia Woolf and The Institute of Psychoanalysis, London, 1924–25)

regression, topographical According to Freud, topographical regression or regression in space is well exemplified in dreams. He speaks of day-residues, namely, events of the waking state, that occupy the realm of the pre-conscious. 'The process begun in the Pcs [preconscious] and reinforced by the Ucs [unconscious] pursues a retrogressive course, through the Ucs, to perception, which forces itself upon consciousness. . . . We call this kind of regression a *topographical* one to distinguish it from the previously mentioned temporal or developmental regression.' (Freud, S. *Collected Papers*, vol. 4, tr. by Riviere, J., Leonard and Virginia Woolf and The Institute of Psychoanalysis, London, 1924–25)

regressive EST See *therapy, regressive electro-shock.*

rehabilitation The use of all forms of physical medicine in conjunction with psychosocial adjustment and vocational retraining in an attempt to achieve maximal function and adjustment, and to prepare the patient physically, mentally, socially, and vocationally for the fullest possible life compatible with his abilities and disabilities. Rehabilitation is a dynamic, purposeful program in which, ideally, activities are scheduled for each patient for the entire day; such schedules are built around activities prescribed by the physician, with guidance, psychological services, adult education, prevocational shop training, and directed socialization supplementing the prescribed therapy and retraining. The chief areas to which rehabilitative efforts are directed are: (1) the highest degree of physical improvement; (2) vocational placement that enables the patient to work at maximal capacity; and (3) satisfactory adjustment in personal and social relationships so the patient can again function as a useful member of society.

Rehabilitation is sometimes called the fourth leg of medical practice, the others being prevention, diagnosis, and treatment.

rehearsal, obsessional The term for a preliminary 'try-out' often used by obsessional patients, who must carry out their compulsions but at the same time try to make their behavior conform to the requirements of the social milieu. In the obsessional rehearsal the patient performs his compulsion, but surveys the scene to determine how he can best work his compulsive activity into the pattern of behavior expected of him at some later date. Reik cites the case of the man whose compulsion was a stamping of the foot to ward off danger as he crossed the border of a country. The patient had arranged to go driving with a woman friend, and their tour was to include crossing a border. On the day before their meeting, the patient drove out to the border and surveyed the scene. On the following day, when he was in his car with the woman friend, he was able to introduce a discussion of waltz music at just the right moment, so that when the car did cross the border he could beat time with his foot. In this way his compulsion could be performed without alerting anyone to its pathological features. The obsessional rehearsal was necessary so that the patient would know when he was approaching the border, and so know when to introduce his discussion of waltz music. (Reik, T. 'Neurotic Camouflage and Thought-Rehearsal,' *American Imago 2,* 86, 1941)

The obsessional neurotic also often shows peculiar deliberations and anticipations in thought. These are test phantasies, which Reik calls thought-rehearsals.

reification (rē-if-i-kā'shun) Treating the abstract as though it were concrete; a type of thinking seen often in schizophrenia but observable also in essentially normal subjects.

reinforcement In neurophysiology, facilitation; i.e. the enhancement of response to a stimulus by simultaneous excitation of response(s) in other neural circuits, as when the knee-jerk is facilitated by having the subject clasp his hands tightly at the same time that his patellar tendon is tapped. In conditioning theory, reinforcement refers to re-introduction of the original, unconditioned stimulus along with the conditioned stimulus, thus strengthening the conditioned response; reinforcement in this sense is sometimes loosely referred to as reward.

reinforcement, Jendrassik (Ernst Jendrassik, Slovakian physician, 1858–1922) A weak response of the knee-jerk may often be reinforced, that is, strengthened, by having the patient grasp his own hands and pull vigorously on them.

reinforcement (of affect) According to Freud, two of the psychic 'institutions,' namely, the suppressed and the suppressing, often engage in the act of mutual inhibition, but they may also combine their forces, thus producing mutual co-operation. The latter process is called *reinforcement of affect.*

'The cases in which the two institutions bring about a pathological result by co-operation and mutual reinforcement deserve just as much attention.' (Freud, S. *The Interpretation of Dreams,* 3rd ed., tr. by Brill, A.A., Macmillan, New York, 1933)

reinforcement, reactive This term is used by Freud to indicate that opposite thoughts are always closely connected with each other and are frequently paired off in such a way that one thought is plainly in the conscious while its counterpart is repressed in the unconscious.

'This relation between the two thoughts is an effect of the process of repression. For repression is often achieved by means of an excessive reinforcement of the thought contrary to the one which is to be repressed. This process I call *reactive reinforcement,* and the thought which asserts itself exaggeratedly in consciousness and (in the same as a prejudice) cannot be removed I call a *reactive thought.*' (Freud, S. *Collected Papers,* vol. 3, tr. by Strachey, A. and J., Leonard and Virginia Woolf, Hogarth Press, London, 1925)

reinstinctualization (rē-in-stinkt-choo-al-ĭ-zā′shun) Deneutralization of drive energy which would normally be available to the ego for the execution of its various functions. As a result, the functions may be affected adversely by the wishes or conflicts arising from the drives. Reinstinctualization is one aspect of the phenomenon of regression.

In hysterical blindness, for example, the neutralized drive energy which made seeing possible regardless of inner conflict has been lost to the ego; the energy is deneutralized or reinstinctualized so that the function of seeing must be suspended just as the drive itself (aggression or sexuality) must be denied.

reintegration See *integration.*

reintegration, affective See *integration.*

rejuvenation (rē-jōō-vē-nā′shun) A special *vasectomy* operation introduced by Steinach to mitigate in men certain pathological symptoms of old age, sexual impotence, hypertrophy of the prostate, or eunuchoidism.

While the ordinary vasectomy technique resulting in sterilization is bilateral and leaves the proximal end of the seminal ducts open, the 'rejuvenating' operation is performed unilaterally and provides for ligatures at both ends of the given vas deferens. The effect of rejuvenation is said to be achieved by a renewed activity of the proliferating and regenerating interstitial secretory tissue of the testicles, which is considered to be the hormone-bearing apparatus mainly responsible in men for sexual libido and potency, as well as by an equally favorable response of the other endocrine glands.

No similar surgical technique has as yet been developed for the rejuvenation of women.

relapse A patient who has recovered or improved and who subsequently suffers a recurrence of the symptoms is said to have experienced a relapse.

relatedness, functional The arrangement of objects that are organically and dynamically related to each other: for example, placing woodworking tools near the woodworking bench and nails and other objects involved in woodworking near by; placing drawing paper near crayons and paints in the proximity of an easel.

relationship, inversion of From the social worker's point of view: 'A transposition of natural roles, as a young girl taking the mother's responsibilities or place in the home, or an adult playing the child's role in the family group.' (Hamilton, G. *A Medical Social Terminology,* Presbyterian Hospital, New York, 1930)

release In neurology, the removal of the inhibitory effect of higher centers on the activity of lower nervous centers. In psychiatry, a form of psychotherapy in which the patient is allowed to express wishes, thoughts, and impulses which he is unable to discharge adequately under usual environmental conditions; in this sense, release is approximately equivalent to catharsis. In child psychiatry, release therapy refers to the use of play methods as an avenue for the expression of the child's anxieties.

release phenomena See *phenomena, release.*

reliability The degree to which a test measures consistently; the dependability of a measure; the standard deviation is used as a measure of variability and when so used is known as the standard error. See *deviation, mean.* Reliability is inversely proportional to the standard error.

religion 'Since religion is largely a spontaneous product, it may be regarded as a kind of *lingua franca* of human nature, so that man's conflicts and their resolution (when resolution is possible) can be stated and dealt with in its terms.' (Casey, R.P. 'The Psychoanalytic Study of Religion,' *Journal of Abnormal and Social Psychology,* October 1938, p. 439)

Fromm regards religious thought as an interaction between social forces and the deeper unconscious responses in the individual.

reminiscence Recalling or recollection of past experiences, particularly when the recall has a 'now you see it, now you don't' quality. In contrast to memory, reminiscence consists of a peculiarly irregular alternation between remembering and forgetting so that a memory apparently lost suddenly appears, while one that was just there disappears.

remission The term *remission* means the abatement of the symptoms and signs of a disorder or disease. The abatement may be partial or complete. Physicians use the expression *remission* to denote amelioration, which even if complete for the time being, does not necessarily imply permanent cure; in fact, the term carries the idea that the amelioration of the symptoms is temporary.

renifleur (rē-nē-flēr′) See *osphresiolagniac.*

renunciation, instinctual The phrase used by Freud to denote the situations in which the ego foregoes the satisfaction of an instinctual demand of the id.

Instinctual demands of an erotic or aggressive nature keep rising continually in the human being. Through its control of thinking and motility, the ego usually satisfies these demands by some action. This satisfaction is felt as pleasure. There are, however, circumstances under which the ego refrains from satisfying the instincts. In the first place, instinctual renunciation takes place in obedience to the reality-principle when the satisfying action would bring serious danger to the ego from the outside world. In this case, the unsatisfied instincts would engender a lasting painful tension unless the strength of the instinctual urge were diminished through a displacement of its energies. Second, instinctual renunciation takes place in obedience to the demands of the superego. That is, the ego will not satisfy the instincts if such a satisfying would run counter to the individual's conscience, the prohibitions of his superego. In this case, too, painful tension will spring from the unsatisfied instinct. When, however, the instinctual renunciation takes place because of the superego's objections, it brings about, besides the pain, 'a gain in pleasure to the ego—as it were, or substituted satisfaction.' This gain in pleasure through obedience to the superego is a direct outgrowth of the child's relationship to its parents. In early childhood, the individual was concerned with retaining his parents' love. He achieved this by renouncing his instincts and, instead, obeying his parents' precepts and thus avoiding a threatened loss of love. This gave the individual security and satisfaction. In later life, 'the super-ego is the successor and representative of the parents (and educators)' and 'perpetuates their functions almost without a change.' Thus the ego is concerned with retaining the love and appreciation of the superego, which it feels as relief and satisfaction, a pleasurable feeling. This will occur when an instinctual renunciation, a sacrifice to the superego, has taken place. (Freud, S. *Moses and Monotheism,* Hogarth Press, London, 1939)

repersonalization (rē-pēr-sun-al-i-zā′-shun) Morton Prince suggested this term in place of *hypnotism.* ('Society Transactions,' *Archives of Neurology and Psychiatry 15:* 800–802, 1926)

repetition-compulsion 'The blind impulse to repeat earlier experiences and situations quite irrespective of any advantage that doing so might bring from a pleasure-pain point of view.' (Jones, E. *Papers on Psycho-Analysis,* 4th ed., Wood, Baltimore, 1938)

The impulse to redramatize or to reenact some earlier emotional experience. The principle is more fundamental, according to Freud, than the pleasure-principle and generally differs widely from it, in that the experience repeated is usually a painful one, that contains 'no potentiality of pleasure and which could at no time have been' satisfactory.

'It must be explained that we are able to postulate the principle of a *repetition-compulsion* in the unconscious mind, based upon instinctual activity and probably inherent in the very nature of the instincts—a principle powerful enough to overrule the pleasure-principle, lending to certain aspects of the mind their daemonic character, and still very clearly expressed in the tendencies of small children.' (Freud, S. *Collected Papers*, vol. 4, tr. by Riviere, J., Leonard and Virginia Woolf and The Institute of Psychoanalysis, London, 1924–25)

'It is also possible that certain early infantile unconscious pathogenic psychic contents, which never were conscious (or preconscious) but which date from the period of "uncoördinated gestures or magical behavior," cannot be simply remembered at all, but can only be reproduced by a re-living in the sense of Freud's repetition.' (Ferenczi, S. *Further Contributions to the Theory and Technique of Psycho-Analysis,* tr. by Suttie, J.I., Leonard and Virginia Woolf and The Institute of Psychoanalysis, London, 1926)

repetition-reaction See *repetition-compulsion.*

replacement In psychiatric occupational therapy this term denotes the substitution of normal and healthy thoughts and actions for unhealthy, abnormal ones. The means used to achieve this result include the employment of various activities such as the handicrafts, recreation, and other interests of a constructive nature.

replacement-formation See *formation, replacement.*

replacement-memory See *memory, replacement.*

representability, regard for This is a phrase used by Freud to refer to such psychic processes as condensation, displacement, exchange of the verbal expression, etc., the purpose of which is to meet the requirement of the censorship for representation of the unconscious impulses in consciousness.

representation, coitus (kō′i-tus) The representation of sexual intercourse in terms of symptom formations or by other symbolizations during the course of a psychoanalysis. 'In this analysis the girl's stammering proved to be determined by the libidinal cathexis of speaking as well as of singing. The rise and fall of the voice and the movements of the tongue represented coitus.' (Klein, M. *Contributions to Psycho-analysis 1921–1945,* Hogarth Press, London, 1948)

representation, indirect This term, when used by Freud, indicates that a patient when talking in the course of free association may make no direct reference to his unconscious conflict, but may indirectly give some hint of it by remote or veiled allusions.

representation, key Paul Schilder writes: 'A suggestion and a mental process become efficient only by way of specific representations which are in connection with the situation. I have called these representations "key representations," and in order to influence a specific organ one has to find the key representation which fits this specific organ. This is merely an expression of the general principle that we live in specific situations.' (Schilder, P. *Psychotherapy,* Norton, New York, 1938)

representation, object A psychoanalytic term denoting the intrapsychic unity of ideas and memories, pertaining to perceptions that were experienced in relation to a specific individual object in the external world. To the individual the idea and memory unit of an external object (i.e. its internal object representation) are often of greater psychic importance than the reality object, whence it stems. Hence the psychiatric truism that, in patients, psychological reality often transcends in importance the objective reality of the external world.

R. Sterba (*Introduction to the Psychoanalytic Theory of the Libido,* Nervous and Mental Disease Monographs No. 68, New York, 1942) states: 'The concept of object representation will help us to understand the psychic devouring of an object either at the cannibalistic level, or in a regression to this phase, and how, at the first level of the anal phase [of infantile development] an object can be expelled psychically as excrement.'

representations, collective Collective representations are 'the concepts which embody the objectives of group activity.'

(Park, R.E. and Burgess, E.W. *Introduction to the Science of Sociology*, University of Chicago Press, Chicago, 1921)

representatives, instinct The psychic manifestations, such as strivings and emotions which ally themselves with ideas and give rise to wishes, of an instinct or drive. The instincts are not observable directly but are expressed by means of such representatives.

repress From a psychiatric point of view, to *repress* is to force material from the realm of consciousness into the unconscious; it implies also that force is continuously exerted to keep the material in the unconscious. A second function of repression is to prevent material which was never conscious from gaining the level of consciousness.

repressed, return of the This phrase, very common in psychoanalysis, means the return to consciousness of an idea or set of ideas that had been repressed into the sphere of the unconscious.

'So far as we know at present, it seems probable that the two [i.e. substitute-formation and symptom-formation] are widely divergent, that it is not the repression itself which produces substitute-formations and symptoms but that these latter constitute indications of a *return of the repressed* and owe their existence to quite other processes.' (Freud, S. *Collected Papers*, vol. 4, tr. by Riviere, J., Leonard and Virginia Woolf and The Institute of Psychoanalysis, London, 1924–25)

repression The concept is used extensively in psychiatry. The most exhaustive description of it was made by Freud. It may be briefly defined as the active process of keeping out and ejecting, banishing from consciousness, the ideas or impulses that are unacceptable to it.

When an instinct-presentation (i.e. an idea or group of ideas charged with affect) is painful to the contents of consciousness, an effort is made to thrust it into the sphere of the unconscious. It is possible to reduce to a minimum the influence of such an instinct-presentation by first breaking it up into its two basic components: the idea and the affective charge. This means that there are three things that are subject to repression: (1) the instinct-presentation; (2) the idea; (3) the affect. In many instances, when

the entire instinct cannot be successfully repressed, either the ideational or the affective part may be. If the idea is repressed, the affect with which it was associated may be transferred to another idea (in consciousness) that has no apparent connection with the original idea. Or, if the affect is repressed, the idea, remaining, so to speak, alone in consciousness may be linked with a pleasant affect. Finally, if the whole instinct-presentation is repressed, it may at some later time return to consciousness in the form of a symbol.

For example, a son may consciously hate his father. The idea and the affect are repellent to him. He may repress both, but if the idea is strongly charged with affect, it strives to re-enter consciousness. It may return to consciousness in disguised form, for example, as hatred for some superior, unconnected with the father. If the idea alone of the father is repressed, the hate may be transferred to someone else, who is not recognized by the individual as standing for the father. If the hate alone is repressed, the idea (father) may be cathected with love; in this last instance the hate may return to consciousness to be connected with someone not known to be a father-substitute.

All the foregoing observations refer to *repression proper*, which Freud at times calls *after-expulsion*, because the material repressed is that which was once in the conscious realm.

There is another subdivision called *primal repression*. The ego has also the task of keeping repressed in the unconscious the material that has never been in consciousness. 'Now we have reason for assuming *a primal repression*, a first phase of repression, which consists in a denial of entry into consciousness to the mental (ideational) presentation of the instinct. This is accompanied by a *fixation*; the ideational presentation in question persists unaltered from then onwards and the instinct remains attached to it.' (Freud, S. *Collected Papers*, vol. 4, tr. by Riviere, J., Leonard and Virginia Woolf and The Institute of Psychoanalysis, London, 1924–25)

Primal repression is maintained by means of anti-cathexis, which Freud says 'is the sole mechanism of primal repression.'

According to Jung, repression plays an important role. For example, when the *superior function* is *thinking* (e.g. the extraverted thinking type), the *feeling function* is subordinated. When the individual tries to meet all the requirements of living by the *thinking function,* 'sooner or later—in accordance with outer circumstances and inner gifts—the forms of life repressed [i.e. feeling, intuition and sensation] by the intellectual attitude become indirectly perceptible, through a gradual disturbance of the conscious conduct of life. Whenever disturbances of this kind reach a definite intensity, one speaks of a neurosis.' (Jung, C.G. *Psychological Types,* tr. by Baynes, H.G., Harcourt, Brace, New York and London, 1923)

repression, organic The term for a special type of amnesia which occurs in cases of head injuries independently of any personal problems that the individual wishes to forget. It is a retroactive amnesia: as in (the so-called) psychogenic amnesia, the individual turns away from a part of his experiences. In this organic repression, however, no specific personal motives are discernible. The individual forgets, more or less extensively, the events of his life prior to the accident, as if he were trying to get rid of knowledge of his experiences, although such a desire is not present even in the subconscious. We find no personal problems responsible for this attitude. Heinz Hartmann and Schilder have described this phenomenon in the Freudian term of 'organic repression.' In Schilder's opinion, we deal with an organic condition the nature of which is unknown, and at the present time the psychological description of the event is more to the point than are physiological theories. (Schilder, P. *Mind, Perception and Thought,* Columbia University Press, New York, 1942)

repression, primal See *repression.*

repression, proper See *repression.*

repression-resistance One of the resistances encountered in the patient under psychoanalysis. The neurotic patient is protecting himself against the perception of inner impulses which are dangerous to him. He expends much energy in various defenses, the purpose of which is to repress these instinctual impulses, to keep them in the unconscious. As the analysis proceeds, and these threatening ideas and impulses begin to be made conscious, the ego fights even harder to maintain its

defenses, in order to prevent the further appearance of threatening instinctual impulses. The patient's ego 'shrinks from undertakings that seem dangerous and threaten unpleasure; it must be constantly spurred on and soothed down if it is not to fail us. This resistance, which persists through the whole treatment and is renewed with every fresh piece of work, has been named, though not quite correctly, repression-resistance.' Thus, repression-resistance is the unpleasure felt by the ego 'at undertaking the severe work imposed upon it' by the analysis.

Once the resistance has been overcome under the direction and with the assistance of the analyst, the ego may either accept or reject again—but this time finally—the repressed instinctual demand. 'In either case a permanent danger has been disposed of, the compass of the ego has been extended and a wasteful expenditure of energy . . . [for defense] . . . has been made unnecessary.' (Freud, S. *An Outline of Psychoanalysis,* Norton, New York, 1949)

repression, secondary Synonymous with *repression;* the word 'secondary' is seldom used.

repression, subsequential See *repression.*

repression, topography of A psychoanalytic concept. 'So far we have gathered from our discussion that repression is essentially a process affecting ideas, on the border between the systems Ucs and Pcs (Cs). . . .' (Freud, S. *Collected Papers,* vol. 4, tr. by Riviere, J., Leonard and Virginia Woolf and The Institute of Psychoanalysis, London, 1924–25) Freud calls this the topographical hypothesis of repression, in contradistinction to the functional hypothesis.

reproduction The creative process by which organic life is transmitted from one individual to a succession of new ones. Although the origin of new organisms takes place in very different ways, the ultimate aim and sense of the reproductive process is always to maintain the preservation of a species and to guarantee the continuity between successive generations.

Plants and the simplest types of animals originate by *asexual* or *vegetative* reproduction, which simply divides the parental body into two or more parts, each of which grows into a new individual. The division into two *equal* new cells usually occurs in unicellular organisms like amoebae and is called *fission*. However, even in the case of an *unequal* division, or *budding*, it holds true that the offspring can be expected to be practically identical with the parent. If differences between offspring and parents arise in asexual reproduction, they may primarily be attributed to *mutations* which do not depend on the type of reproduction and constitute the basis of most evolutionary developments. See *mutation*.

The typical form of *sexual* reproduction is biparental and presupposes the differentiation of a species into two sexes capable of producing individual germ cells. Among higher animals, the two types of specialized *sexual cells* or *gametes* are known as *spermatozoa* and *ova,* according to whether they are produced in the testis of a male or in the ovary of a female. At fertilization a male and a female gamete unite, the nucleus of one fusing completely with that of the other, and they form one *single* cell, the fertilized ovum or *zygote,* from which a new individual develops by cell division.

Wherever sexual reproduction occurs, it is bound to lead to variations among the offspring as well as to differences between offspring and parents. Mature germ cells have only half of the chromosomes of the individual producing the germ cells, and homologous chromosomes are similar, but not usually identical. The nature of a germ cell depends on which of the two chromosomes it has received from each pair. See *meiosis*.

In certain groups of animals, for instance in the honey-bee, an ovum may develop into a new individual without having been fertilized by a spermatozoön. Such uniparental mode of reproduction is called *parthenogenesis* and is regarded as sexual, although offspring produced parthenogenetically have only one parent.

repulsion A modifying process in the recombination of genetic factors, which was discovered by Bateson and Punnett both as an exception to the Mendelian principle of independent assortment and as the antithesis of the phenomenon of *coupling* (q.v.). Its mechanism consists of an 'aversion' of the genes introduced by different parents to entering the same gametes, and its effect is similar to that of coupling, leading to the formation of an excess of the parental combinations of

genes and a deficiency of the new type of combinations.

According to Morgan's chromosome theory repulsion and coupling are manifestations of a single important phenomenon now usually called *linkage*.

requisition (of reality) See *pathogenesis*.

research, action A field of social psychology, associated especially with the name of Kurt Lewin, which is concerned with discovering the causes of real social problems, finding the means for dealing with them, and applying these means as the most effective methods of bringing about change. Various methods are used to determine the role of personality in such problems as group tension, morale, conflict, and prejudice.

reserve, schizophrenic Reserve is very common in schizophrenic patients. Being insecure in themselves, they cannot easily establish emotional relationships with other individuals and are afraid to deliver themselves emotionally into the hands of different personalities, no matter how much they may be inclined to trust them.

residua, brain (re-zid′ū-á) See *neurogram*.

residual schizophrenia See *schizophrenia*.

residue, archaic Remnants of primitive mentality; see *function-engram*.

resistance From the psychoanalytic point of view resistance is 'the instinctive opposition displayed towards any attempt to lay bare the unconscious; a manifestation of the repressing forces.' (Jones, E. *Papers on Psycho-Analysis,* 4th ed., Wood, Baltimore, 1938)

'As you are aware, the whole of psychoanalytic theory is in fact built up on the perception of the resistance exerted by the patient when we try to make him conscious of his unconscious.' (Freud, S. *New Introductory Lectures on Psycho-Analysis,* tr. by Sprott, W.J.H., Norton, New York, 1933) Much of this resistance stems from the ego and hence is called ego resistance. See *resistance, ego*.

resistance, character See *defense, character*.

resistance, conscious Freud's term for the intentional withholding of information by the patient because of distrust of the analyst, shame, fear of rejection, or the like. In his early work, Freud discovered that patients cannot maintain free association uninterruptedly, and sooner or later fail to mention something that occurs to them. They show other signs of difficulty with the treatment process—tardiness or failure to keep appointments, loss of interest in their own problems, and turning all their attention to trying to win the analyst's love or to engaging in a battle of wits with him, etc. Exhortation can usually induce the patient to overcome these conscious difficulties.

Unconscious resistance, on the other hand, is more significant and more difficult to overcome, arising as it does from the ego as a defense against uncovering the repressed material, which the ego constantly strives to avoid, since it produces anxiety. Unconscious resistance is more than a phenomenon appearing early in treatment and later overcome once and for all: it is a conservative force seeking to maintain the *status quo* and appearing throughout the analysis whenever significant data are under discussion. See *silence, selective; resistance, ego.*

resistance, ego This psychiatric term denotes the type of resistance encountered in psychoanalysis which is produced by the ego. Much of the resistance to be overcome in analysis is produced by the ego, 'which clings tenaciously to its anti-cathexes.' In other words, the ego 'finds it difficult to turn its attention to perceptions and ideas the avoidance of which it had until then made a rule, or to acknowledge as belonging to it impulses which constitute the most complete antithesis to those familiar to it as its own.' This resistance of the ego is known more specifically as repression-resistance. It is often unconscious. When the resistance has been made conscious, logical arguments are used to induce the ego to give it up, and the gains that will result therefrom are pointed out.

Freud describes two more categories of ego-resistance. One, which is of the same character as repression-resistance but exists specifically with reference to the analytical situation, is the transference-resistance: the repression constantly exerted by the ego is in this case related specifically to the person of the analyst and thus appears in the analysis in different and more definite ways than simple repression-resistance. The other (third) category of ego-resistance is related to the gain of the illness. Symptoms in warding

off dangerous instinctual impulses both relieve anxiety and serve as a means of gratifying these instinctual impulses. The ego opposes the renunciation of both the gratification and relief which are 'based upon the inclusion of the symptom in the ego.'

It should be added that in analysis there are also resistances which derive from sources other than the ego. These are (1) the 'resistance of the unconscious' or of the id, which derives from the 'repetition-compulsion,' and (2) the 'resistance of the super-ego,' which derives from 'the sense of guilt or need of punishment.' (Freud, S. *The Problem of Anxiety,* Norton, New York, 1936)

resistance, stage of See *syndrome, general adaptation.*

resistance, transference See *transference-resistance.*

resistivity (rē-zis-tiv'i-tē) Applied to materials in arts and crafts employed in education and therapy, especially activity group psychotherapy, this term indicates the amount of physical effort required to produce results with these materials. 'Water is the least resisting material, then come paint, clay, wire, wood, metal and so on. A frightened, sensitive child will naturally turn to materials which can be used directly and are easily manipulated without the use of tools, such as clay and water colors. More aggressive children prefer more resisting materials, such as wood and metals.' (Slavson, S.R. *An Introduction to Group Therapy,* The Commonwealth Fund, Oxford University Press, New York, 1943, p. 36)

resocialization (rē-sō-shal-i-zā'shun) In occupational therapy this term usually denotes the replacement of tendencies in an individual by habits which will aid in adjustment to the group and community and to the accepted social standards.

response, galvanic skin See *reflex, psychogalvanic.*

response (in marriage) Understanding, co-operative, sympathetic, or affectionate interreaction between two persons married to each other. 'The human being appears to have a basic need to live with some one of the other sex to the fullest possible meaning of the words "live with." This need has been termed the need for "response." Mowrer says: "The desire for response is universal among human beings. In the marriage relation it involves the demonstration of affection, the sharing of interests, aspirations, and ideals by husband and wife." ' (Lemkau, P.V. *Mental Hygiene in Public Health,* McGraw-Hill, New York, 1949)

response, negativistic (neg-à-tiv-is'tik) A tendency to do the exact opposite of what is requested or ordered. When asked to open his eyes, the patient shuts them tightly; when asked to come forward, he backs away. This condition is most common in the catatonic type of schizophrenia.

responsibility, limited See *insanity, partial.*

responsibility, test of See *rule, M'Naghten.*

R.E.S.T. Regressive electric shock therapy. See *therapy, regressive electroshock.*

rest-cure The term is usually associated with the psychiatrist Silas Weir Mitchell (1829–1914), who stressed the value of rest, environmental change, fattening diet, massage, and mild exercise. It has not achieved much distinction as an isolated method of treatment, though the individual procedures (rest, environmental change, etc.) are known to be highly valuable.

restitution See *schizophrenia, restitutional symptoms.*

restraint In the treatment of the violently psychotic patient, a measure whereby he is prevented (by the camisole or restraint-sheet) from doing injury to himself or others.

restraint, situational Employed especially in activity group psychotherapy, this type of restraint is differentiated from direct or authoritative restraint in that it is practiced by creating a situation which by its very nature will prevent the individual from committing dangerous or destructive acts. In activity group psychotherapy, windows are screened so that they will not be broken and furniture is placed in such a way that the children will not need to or cannot move it about. Placing materials in a relation to *functional relatedness* is also a form of situational restraint.

resymbolization A new symbolization adopted in the life of a patient on regaining a healthy mentality. 'A recovered patient, as he makes a new adaptation to life, must redefine all his conceptions, particularly those related to his own conflict. This is essentially a resymbolization of his life concepts and in itself denotes a healthy attitude and a good prognosis. . . . Resymbolization is a universal phenomenon in our daily life and of which the resymbolization as used by psychotics is only one of the pathological forms.' (Karpman, B. *Psychoanalytic Review 9,* 348, 1922)

retardation Slowness or backwardness of intellectual development; when used in this sense, mental retardation is the usual phrase. Slowness of response, a slowing down of thinking and/or a decrease in psychomotor activity; in this latter sense, the term psychomotor retardation is the appropriate phrase. Psychomotor retardation is characteristic of clinical depressions.

retardation, mental From the standpoint of mental deficiency, this term means dullness, backwardness.

retardation, reading A term suggested by Rabinovitch *et al.* (1954) to describe all subjects in whom the level of reading achievement is two years or more below the mental age obtained in performance tests. See *reading, disabilities of.*

retardation, simple See *melancholia; psychosis, manic-depressive.*

retention Non-evacuation of the bladder or bowels. In psychological testing, retention refers to the ability to learn, remember, or recall. In psychoanalytic psychology, retention refers to any number of traits or symptoms believed to develop on the basis of the need or desire to withhold the feces during the anal stage of development; collecting mania, stubbornness, secretiveness, niggardliness, etc. are generally considered to be instances of anal retention or retentiveness.

retention, anal In psychoanalysis, the term retention refers to the holding back of the fecal mass as part of toilet training and to the characterologic or symptomatic carry-overs of this in later life. Frugality, for example, is considered to be a continuation of the anal habit of retention; stubbornness and obstinacy are more complicated developments of this same habit which are related to the child's ability to spite parental efforts by tightening his sphincters. Psychodynamically, anal retention is seen to contain two components, fear of loss of body contents or of control over instinctual impulses, and enjoyment of erogenous pleasure; and later anal character traits represent an outgrowth of one or the other or both of these components. See *anal-erotism; character, anal.*

reticular activating system See *formation, reticular.*

reticular formation See *formation, reticular.*

reticulum (re-tik'ū-lum) (L. 'a little net') *Biol.* A finely meshed network in a cell or in some delicate tissue system.

rétifism (rā'ti-fiz'm) (Rétif de la Bretonne (1734–1806), a famous French educator, known for this sexual perversion.) Ivan Bloch coined this term for fetishism of the foot and shoe; in this form of sexual perversion the foot or shoe or both possess the value of the genital organs for the rétifist. A patient 'loved,' as he put it, the female shoe to the same degree that 'others are attracted to the female genitals.' He looked upon the shoe as if it were a real person—gaining full and complete sexual satisfaction, including 'intercourse,' with the object; he used it as an agency of masturbation.

retreat, vegetative The tendency of certain neurotic persons to meet an inimical or dangerous reality situation not by appropriate self-assertive behavior and actions, but by recourse to infantile or childish function of the visceral apparatus, which, to them, anachronistically stands for praise or succor from strong or omnipotent parents. It thus represents a return to the pseudo-power of the 'helpless' and dependent child and warrants the descriptive term 'regressive,' because it is a resort to the old infantile ways of handling frustration and stress. See also *hypoglycemia.*

A common example of this phenomenon is the man who develops diarrhea when in danger, instead of carrying out an appropriate action directed against the dangerous enemy or situation. As a harbinger of protection and approval, this vegetative reaction, or achievement, is inappropriate for adult life, but logical for infancy, where it brought mother's care. There is on record the case of a married woman who found herself sucking her thumbs whenever thwarted or rejected by her husband. (Alexander, F.

Psychosomatic Medicine, Norton, New York, 1950)

retrogenesis (ret-rō-jen'e-sis) 'It is remarkable to know in the matter of conscience the universal rule once more applies: that that which is newly formed does not develop from the highest (in the sense of the most recent) existing formation but out of a lower part which has remained hitherto undeveloped. Every line of development is a blind-alley: the new sprouts from a bud which is further, sometimes much further, down. The path of development is not that of *evolution* but of *revolution.* Only out of temporary chaos does renewal proceed. Before development can take place, there must be regression. We will give this rule a name and call it the *law of retrogenesis.*' (A. Staercke, *International Journal of Psychoanalysis X,* 186, 1929)

retrogression A return to earlier behavior or techniques when more recently developed techniques prove unsatisfactory. The term is synonymous with regression but avoids the psychoanalytic connotations of the latter.

retropulsion Rapid running backward with short steps, in paralysis agitans; as if drawn by an uncontrollable force.

return of the repressed See *repressed, return of the.*

reverie, revery A type of phantasy in which the subject is lost in thought or abstract musing which is not purposively directed.

reverie, hypnagogic (hip-nȧ-goj'ik) The phantasies occurring when the individual is in a state intermediary between sleep and waking. Kubie has shown that the institution of a state of hypnagogic reverie can bring about easier access to unconscious material. When employing hypnosis, the analyst can take advantage of it by 'permitting his patients to associate freely in the waking state, until a resistance is manifested. Hypnosis is then induced and the last few statements uttered by the patient before the onset of resistance are repeated to him. Usually free association will continue during hypnosis from this point on.' (Wolberg, L.R. *Hypnoanalysis,* Grune and Stratton, New York, 1945)

reversal In psychoanalysis the *reversal* of an instinct into its opposite means a change of it from an active to a passive instinct or vice versa. The *aim* of the instinct does not change; its object does. For example, the destructive instinct may be directed outwardly, as sadism, or it may operate upon oneself, as masochism. 'The reversal here concerns only the aims of the instincts. The passive aim (to be tortured . . .) has been substituted for the active aim (to torture . . .).' (Freud, S. *Collected Papers,* vol. 4, tr. by Riviere, J., Leonard and Virginia Woolf and The Institute of Psychoanalysis, London, 1924–25)

Freud says also that there may be *reversal* of content. 'Reversal of content is found in the single instance of the change of love into hate.' (ibid) See *opposite, reversal into the.*

reversal-formation See *reaction-formation.*

reversal of affect See *affect, inversion of.*

reversal, sex An individual's turning by external influences to the opposite sex both as to gonads and ducts and as to secondary characters. It has been produced in many animals 'to the extent of changing the histological character of the gonads and to some extent the ducts, but the change has seldom gone far enough in an adult animal, to permit the individual to function as of the new sex.' (Shull, A.F. *Heredity,* 3rd ed., McGraw-Hill, New York and London, 1938)

The most remarkable instance of complete sex reversal was observed by Crew, in an adult hen that had laid normal eggs producing normal chicks, before she changed into a cock that became the father of two normal chicks. An autopsy showed that the original ovary had been destroyed by a tumor, and a testis had been produced in its place by regeneration.

reversion A genetic phenomenon which occurs in crosses between true-breeding varieties and produces offspring resembling a remote ancestor more than either parent. These 'throwbacks' had been observed for many years by plant and animal breeders, but for lack of satisfactory explanation had been regarded as due to some mysterious force which caused the retention and subsequent reappearance of a remote ancestral trait.

According to E.W. Sinnott and L.C. Dunn (*Principles of Genetics,* 3rd ed.,

McGraw-Hill, New York and London, 1939) every kind of reversion is now readily explained in terms of ordinary Mendelian inheritance. 'The reappearance of an old trait is usually due to the reunion of the two or more factors, necessary for its production, which had become separated in the history of the plant or animal.'

Reversion is also used synonymously with regression or retrogression; less commonly, it is used synonymously with reversal-formation or reaction-formation.

revindication, delirium of, insanity of (rē-vin-di-kā'shun, dē-lir'i-um) See *interpretation, delirium of.*

revolution The term revolution connotes 'a sudden and far reaching change, a major break in the continuity of development.' (Mensel, A. *Revolution and Counter-Revolution; Encyclopaedia of the Social Sciences,* vol. 13, Macmillan, New York, 1934, p. 367)

A revolution is 'a mass movement which seeks to change the mores by destroying the existing social order.' (Park, R.E. and Burgess, E.W. *Introduction to the Science of Sociology,* University of Chicago Press, Chicago, 1921)

Three major types of revolution are: *cultural,* where profound changes take place in the mores; *industrial,* where sudden changes result from technological discoveries and inventions; and *political,* where violent change takes place in the political order.

rhabdophobia (rab-dō-fō'bi-à) Fear of the rod, instrument of punishment.

rhathymia (ra-thī'mi-à) Outgoing, carefree, happy-go-lucky behavior such as is seen in so-called oral optimists.

rhembasmus (rem-baz'mus) Indecision, mental uncertainty.

rheumatism, psychogenic (rōō'mà-tiz'm, sī-kō-jen'ik) This psychiatric term denotes rheumatism that is of psychic (emotional) origin. Rheumatic symptoms based on emotional conflicts were seen frequently in the army during World War II, the soldiers complaining about low back pain, muscle pain, and joint pain. (Menninger, W.C. *Psychiatry in a Troubled World,* Macmillan, New York, 1948)

rhinencephalon (rīn-en-sef'a-lon) A phylogenetically old portion of the cerebral hemispheres which includes: olfactory bulb and tract, anterior perforated substance, subcallosal gyrus, hippocampus, uncus, amygdala, fornix, and anterior commissure. Rhinencephalon is sometimes used synonymously with olfactory brain. In man, the olfactory brain is overshadowed by the neocortex (isocortex), but olfaction appears to be important in the psychic apparatus of the human. The physiology of the rhinencephalon is poorly understood and is largely based on inferences drawn from its anatomical relations. Animal experiments indicate that the olfactory tract terminates in the prepyriform area, the amygdala, the periamygdaloid cortex, and the opposite olfactory bulb. Although the hippocampus is generally regarded as part of the olfactory system, it is to be noted that no anatomical connections of the hippocampus with the olfactory tract have been demonstrated. Instead, the hippocampus appears to be primarily an efferent system projecting to the medial and lateral mammillary nuclei of the hypothalamus, and as such it is probably concerned with control of autonomic functions. Rhinencephalic structures may exert an inhibitory effect on brain-stem mechanisms concerned with emotional expression. Lesions of these structures result in restlessness and hyperactivity. The limbic system is sometimes referred to as the 'visceral brain'; it includes the limbic lobe (Brodmann's area 24) and infolded hippocampus, and also certain subcortical structures: amygdala, septal nuclei, hypothalamus, anterior thalamic nuclei, parts of the basal ganglia, and the epithalamus.

rhinolalia (rīn-ō-lā′li-à) Nasality of speech. Rhinolalia is of two types: rhinolalia aperta, in which the passages at the back of the nose and mouth fail to close during speech; and rhinolalia clausa, in which obstructions in the nasopharynx interfere with nasal resonance.

rhombencephalon (rom-ben-sef′à-lon) *Hindbrain* (q.v.).

rhypophagy (rī-pof′à-jē) The eating of filth; scatophagy.

rhypophobia (rī-pō-fō′bi-à) Fear of dirt or filth.

riddance This term, coined by S. Rado, refers to 'many reflexes designed to eliminate pain-causing agents from the surface or inside of the body. The scratch reflex, the shedding of tears, sneezing, coughing,

spitting, vomiting, colic bowel movement are but a few well-known instances of this principle of pain control in our bodily organization. This principle I have called the *riddance principle*, and its physiological embodiments the *riddance reflexes*.' ('Developments in the Psychoanalytic Conception and Treatment of the Neuroses,' *The Psychoanalytic Quarterly, VIII*, 434–35, 1939)

right and left When the concepts *right* and *left* appear in dreams they are understood in an ethical sense. 'The right-hand path always signifies the way to righteousness, the left-hand path the path to crime. Thus the left may signify homosexuality, incest, and perversion, while the right signifies marriage, relations with a prostitute, etc. The meaning is always determined by the individual moral standpoint of the dreamer.' (Stekel, W. *Bi-Sexual Love,* tr. by van Teslaar, J.S., Badger, Boston, 1922)

right-handedness See *dextrality-sinistrality*.

rigidity, affective When the emotions or affects remain constant in the face of topics that normally call for changes in affect, the condition is known as affective rigidity. It is encountered in purest form in patients with schizophrenia, who show no mood changes in spite of discussions covering a wide variety of experiences.

Rigidity of the affect, or affect-block, is common also in obsessive-compulsive neurosis.

rigidity, decerebrate (dē-ser′e-brāt) A syndrome of exaggerated posture in continuous spasm of muscles produced by transection of the brain at a pre-pontine level. The extensor muscles are particularly affected and exhibit lengthening and shortening (clasp-knife) reactions.

rigidity, lead pipe *Rare* (humorously, as lead possesses practically no rigidity) Waxy flexibility.

ring, Kayser-Fleischer (Bernhard Kayser, German ophthalmologist, 1869–   , and Richard Fleischer, German physician, 1848–1909) See *degeneration, hepatolenticular*.

risk level *Confidence level* (q.v.).

rites, puberty In many primitive cultures it is customary for boys at puberty to undergo certain initiatory rites as a part of the religious pattern of that culture.

Ritual [651] Rooming-in

One of the commonest rituals is a pretense of killing the boy and bringing him to life again. In another primitive group, part of the proceedings consists of knocking out a tooth and giving a new name to the boy being initiated, indicating thereby the change from youth to manhood. In still another tribe, the puberty rites comprise the operations of circumcision and subincision. All of these ceremonies are conducted in absolute secrecy and only those already initiated may attend them. No female is ever permitted to witness these events.

ritual 'Formal behavior for occasions not given over to technological routine [which occur] both as the spontaneous invention of the individual, especially of the compulsion neurotic, and as a cultural trait.' (Benedict, R. *Ritual; Encyclopaedia of the Social Sciences*, vol. 13, Macmillan, New York, 1934, p. 397)

rivalry 'A sublimated form of conflict where the struggle of individuals is subordinated to the welfare of the group.' (Park, R.E. and Burgess, E.W. *Introduction to the Science of Sociology*, University of Chicago Press, Chicago, 1921)

rivalry, sibling A term much used in child psychiatry and in the study of childhood experiences and personality development in general. It refers specifically to the usual family situation wherein brothers and sisters engage in an intense and highly emotional competition, one against the other, for the love, attention, affection, and approval of one or the other or both of the parents. This intense competition between rival sibs (brothers or sisters) can be an important determinant of later specific character or personality traits.

Sibling rivalry, however, is usually evaluated in relation to other important universal and unique experiences in the child's early life, such as the oedipal relationship to the parents; the discovery of and reaction to sexual differences; that specific reaction which is called 'the castration complex'; self-comforting trends, such as thumb-sucking and masturbation, and conflicts concerning their prohibition and gratification.

Important though it may be in certain specific family constellations, sibling rivalry cannot be isolated from the total familial, developmental situation of the individual child. Lois Barclay Murphy (*Personality and the Behavior Disorders*,

ed. by J.McV. Hunt, vol. 2, Ronald Press, New York, 1944) states: 'The Oedipus complex is primarily a way of describing one aspect of the child's relation with its parents; and there are many other aspects. The relation between sibling rivalry (D. Levy, 1936 B) and the Oedipus picture is now seen to be quite as important as the relationship with parents.'

RLS person A person who finds difficulty in pronouncing the sounds of *r, l, s;* by hardly justified extension—a *stammerer* (q.v.).

role The role of a person is 'the pattern or type of behavior which the child—and the adult—builds up in terms of what others expect or demand of him.' (Young, K. *An Introductory Sociology*, American Book, New York, 1934)

romance, family The expression *family romance* is often used synonymously with *Oedipus complex* or *parental complex*.

romance, memory In psychoanalysis, the phantasy standing between infantile impressions and later symptoms. Thus, in speaking of hysteria Freud says that the symptoms 'now no longer appeared as direct derivations of repressed memories of sexual experiences in childhood; but, on the contrary, it appeared that between the symptoms and the infantile impressions were interpolated the patient's phantasies (memory-romances), created mostly during the years of adolescence and relating on the one side to the infantile memories on which they were founded, and on the other side to the symptoms into which they were directly transformed.' (Freud, S. *Collected Papers*, vol. 2, tr. by Riviere, J., Leonard and Virginia Woolf and The Institute of Psychoanalysis, London, 1924–25)

Romberg sign See *sign, Romberg*.

rooming-in The modern concept in pediatrics which recognizes the essential unity of mother and child after the birth of the child in a hospital. The mother and child are housed in the same room, the infant's crib standing alongside or near the mother's bed. It is essentially a rooming-in of the baby with the mother. The usual hospital nursery plays no role in this practice. The rooming-in process permits the mother to touch, fondle, and caress her child, to feed it when it is hungry, and to diaper it when it soils. This is said to make her immediately familiar with her baby and to allay considerable anxiety in the mother as well as in the child.

root-pain Pain in the segmental area innervated by the affected nerve root, usually excited or intensified by coughing, sneezing, or changes of posture.

Rorschach test See *test, Rorschach.*

Rosenbach's sign See *sign, Rosenbach.*

Rosolimo's reflex See *reflex, Rosolimo.*

rotation See *system, rotation.*

R.T. Reaction time; also, recreation(al) therapy. See *recreation.*

Rüdin, Ernst (1874–   ) (rü'din) German psychiatrist and geneticist.

rule, M'Naghten (or McNaughton) In 1843 Daniel M'Naghten shot and killed Drummond, private secretary to Sir Robert Peel. He mistook Drummond for the latter. The killing was the outcome of delusions of persecution and gave rise to judicial opinions that in principle have guided jurists in similar cases.

In the Penal Law of New York State (section 1120) it is stated that 'an act done by a person who is an idiot, imbecile, lunatic or insane is not a crime. A person cannot be tried, sentenced to any punishment or punished for a crime while he is in a state of idiocy, imbeciiity, lunacy, or insanity so as to be incapable of understanding the proceeding or making his defense. A person is not excused from criminal liability as an idiot, imbecile, lunatic, or insane person, except upon proof that, at the time of committing the

alleged criminal act, he was laboring under such defect of reason as:

1. Not to know the nature and quality of the act he was doing; or

2. Not to know that the act was wrong.'

'The knowledge test [M'Naghten test] laid down by the judges of England after M'Naghten's Case is still our most important criterion of criminal responsibility. In twenty-nine American states it is the only test, and in the others it is still the main test supplemented only by the irresistible impulse test.' (Weihofen, H. *Insanity as a Defense in Criminal Law,* Commonwealth Fund, New York, 1933)

ruler, negative, of the soul See *ego, negation of.*

ruminate To regurgitate, remasticate, and reswallow; to ponder; to meditate.

rumination From the psychiatric point of view, rumination or merycism is the act of voluntary regurgitation, remastication, and swallowing again. The practice is sometimes observed in psychiatric patients. It also means meditation.

ruminative tension state *Obsessive ruminative tension state* (q.v.).

Rumpf's sign See *sign, Rumpf's.*

rupophobia (rōō-pō-fō'bi-à) Same as *rhypophobia.*

Rush, Benjamin (1745–1813) Father of American psychiatry.

rypophobia (rī-pō-fō'bi-à) Same as *rhypophobia.*

S

S An abbreviation for experimental subject or for stimulus; also used as a Rorschach scoring symbol to indicate a response to the white space on the card.

sabotage, masochistic (maz-ok-is'tik) Reik uses this expression to describe the irritating attitude shown by certain individuals in order to achieve masochistic satisfaction. The individual does or says things that will bring humiliation or debasement upon himself. Sometimes these masochistic subjects appear sadistic, but only in order to obtain their unconsciously desired punishment. During the analytical treatment, this attitude is revealed in many forms, varying from obstinate silence to insolent remarks and behavior. The patient who comes into the analytical room and spends the entire hour of treatment in obstinate silence, or one who from the moment of entering the room finds fault with everything from the psychiatrist's remarks to the furnishings, shows masochistic sabotage. 'The unconscious aim in these cases is: to be insulted or scolded.' (Reik, T. *Masochism in Modern Man,* Farrar and Rinehart, New York, 1941)

sadism (sad'iz'm; often, although incorrectly, sād'iz'm) (After Donatien Alphonse François Sade, usually called Marquis de Sade (1740–1814), a French writer who described individuals whose sexual pleasure depended upon inflicting cruelty upon others) A sexual perversion in which orgasm is dependent upon torturing others or inflicting pain, ill-treatment and humiliation on others. Krafft-Ebing defined sadism as sexual emotion associated with the wish to inflict pain and use violence. Moll defined it as a state in which the sexual impulse is manifested as a tendency to strike, misuse, or humiliate the love-object.

Viewed as a perversion, sadism is a defense against castration fears and fears of one's own sexual excitement. What might happen to the subject passively is done actively to others—'identification with the aggressor.' Further, the castration performed in the sadistic act is a symbolic one, not a real one, and such pseudo-castration assures the sadist that his fears are ungrounded. The sadist tries to force his victim to love him; this love is conceived of as a forgiveness, which removes the guilt feelings that interfere with sexual satisfaction.

While sadism is sometimes considered to be a deflection outside the self of the destructive or death-instinct, it will be seen that the perversion of sadism depends upon fusion of destructive energy with libidinal energy. The discharge of aggression in itself may be pleasurable, but sadism further implies pleasure in the destruction of others. But at the same time, the manifestations of the aggressive drive progress through the same developmental stages as the sexual (oral, anal, phallic), and in this context such manifestations are generally called sadistic— thus, oral-sadistic, anal-sadistic, and phallic-sadistic.

sadism, anal The expression anal-sadism, derived from the school of psychoanalysis, refers to the aggressive instinctual quality associated with the anal region. It is said that the anal zone occupies a position of great importance in the very early life of the child, antedating the genital phase. Hence, anal-sadism is regarded as pregenital. The infant is interested not only in the act of defecation, but also in the product of the act. The earliest interests, thoroughly ingrained in the mind of the child, are never abandoned, although they take on a different type of expression as the child grows up. For example, the resentment expressed by the infant at having to give up something (e.g. feces) very important to him, later takes the form of resentment against the relinquishment of any object valuable to him (e.g. money, securities, etc.). In other words, the earliest organic habits are to a large extent carried on into later life in sublimated form, that is, in the guise of character traits.

'Many infants feel it as an injustice that what they have so interestedly produced should at once be taken away from them, and this goes to strengthen the resentment against the general interference on the subject, resulting in an intense feeling against any form of injustice.' (Jones, E. *Papers on Psycho-Analysis,* 4th ed., Wood. Baltimore, 1938)

'The anal stage is always characterized by sadistic or cruelty impulses, but just what the connection is between anal erotism and sadism does not yet seem to be clear to psychoanalysts.' (Healy, W., Bronner, A.F., and Bowers, A.M. *The Structure and Meaning of Psychoanalysis,* Knopf, New York, 1930)

sadism, complicated When the patient experiences not only pleasure but also horror, disgust, and pain in performing a sadistic act, the term 'complicated sadism' is used in psychiatry to describe his particular ailment, which involves several varieties of emotions. (Stekel, W. *Compulsion and Doubt,* Liveright, New York, 1949)

sadism, id A psychoanalytic term referring to the primary primitive instinctual destructive urges, which are seen in their unmodified form in the early years of infancy. They are closely tied up with drives toward omnipotent gratification and security, and seem to be brought out by frustration in early infancy. Much of this primary sadism suffers repression under the aegis of the striving for goodness and approval, and the fear of the reality consequences to the individual of external retaliation and its internal equivalent, conscience pangs.

E.F. Sharpe (*Collected Papers on Psycho-analysis,* Hogarth Press and The Institute of Psychoanalysis, London, 1950) states: ' . . . in the different neuroses . . . the ego's severest task is in connection with the sadism of the id and the superego. The two severities are complementary.'

sadism, infantile See *sadism, id.*

sadism, larval (lär'val) (L. *larva,* 'ghost, specter, mask') Hirschfeld uses the term larva in one of its original meanings, a mask; hence, larval sadism is masked or concealed sadism.

sadism, manual A type of sadism in which the torture of the object is achieved through muscular eroticism, the use of the hand(s), in the sadistic act. Any sadistic activity in which the sexual pleasure achieved by the sadist is intimately associated with the use of his musculature (as, for example, in beating or kicking his partner) would be classified as manual sadism. The term manual has been chosen probably because in this type of sadism muscular activity and eroticism are so frequently expressed through the use of the hands and arms.

Different types of sadism correspond to the different erogenous zones, and the particular erogenous zone employed by the sadist to achieve his sexual pleasure depends on the particular fixations his ego has undergone. However, 'sadistic impulses are . . . not limited to strivings from one specific erogenous zone.' For example, 'in the perversion of sadism . . . the sexual aims may be the destructive tendencies of the oral period.' Thus the aim of muscular eroticism is not the only aim that is being pursued in manual sadism. (Fenichel, O. *The Psychoanalytic Theory of Neurosis,* Norton, New York, 1945)

sadism, omnipotent infantile See *sadism, id.*

sadism, oral A psychoanalytic term referring specifically to the expression of infantile, primordial, aggressive, instinctive urges toward omnipotent mastery, through phantasy function of the mouth, lips, and teeth. These phantasy functions represent distortions of the reality functions of the mouth, lips, teeth, tongue, cheeks, and pharynx.

Oral sadistic wishes, strivings, and phantasies appear normally in the earliest stages of infantile development, immediately after birth. As the child matures and develops, these wishes and strivings undergo various vicissitudes, to appear and persist later in adult life in modified and disguised form as components of neurotic symptoms; as perversions and foreplay desires and gratifications; as character traits; and as socially approvable and desirable sublimation activities.

In the acting-out symptomatology of the psychotic and criminally insane, we see many examples of this primordial and infantile violent, oral sadistic 'stuff' persisting, in an unregenerate and unmodified fashion, directly into adult life. (Sharpe, E.F. *Collected Papers on Psycho-analysis,* Hogarth Press and The Institute of Psychoanalysis, London, 1950) See *sadism, unconscious; phase, oral incorporative.*

sadism, phallic (fal'ik) In psychoanalysis, this term refers to sadism and aggression associated with the phallic stage of development. The child ordinarily comprehends sexual intercourse as an aggressive and sadistic act on the part of the male, and specifically on the part of the penis. Evidence that the penis is phantasied as a weapon of violence and destruction comes from unconscious productions of normal adults. Limericks, for instance, often refer to the penis as square, or too large, etc., so that intercourse is dangerous and painful for the partner. This may well be a projection of the male's own fear of coitus.

Scop(t)ophilia may result at the phallic stage, secondary to such sadism. The looking gives reassurance that the sadistically perceived object is not yet dead.

sadism, primal A certain portion of the death-instinct always remains within the individual; it is called *primal sadism* and according to Freud is identical with masochism. 'After the chief part of it [i.e. the death-instinct] has been directed outwards towards objects, there remains as a residuum within the organism the true erotogenic masochism, which on the one hand becomes a component of the libido and on the other still has the subject itself for an object.' (Freud, S. *Collected Papers*, vol. 2, tr. by Riviere, J., Leonard and Virginia Woolf and The Institute of Psychoanalysis, London, 1924–25)

sadism, superego A psychoanalytic term referring specifically to the intense cruelty, rigidity, and pain-giving punitive aspects of conscience (superego). In the developing child, the infantile sadism (primordial aggressivity) is eventually mastered by the erection and development within the child of equally powerful controlling and countervailing forces. These forces of character, warning the child of the reality consequences of its unbridled aggressive trends, become organized into what is called *the conscience,* 'that still small voice' that silently warns us when we are about to succumb to our urges and do something wrong. The warnings emanate from the internalized (introjected) pictures or images that the child has, not necessarily of his real parents, but rather of what he conceives the parents would be if they discovered the attempt to carry out his own violently aggressive wishes against them.

The internal image of the violently angry, discovering parent is formed in the old talionic formula of an 'eye for an eye.' The child feels that the discovering parent must become the punishing parent, seeking vengeance in proportion to the strength and enormity of the child's own

phantasies and aggressive wishes. Thus, in the last analysis, the intensity of the sadism of the superego, or conscience, stems from the enormity and violence of the child's own infantile, primordial, sadistic phantasies and strivings, which have succumbed to the control of an equal and opposite repressive power. (Sharpe, E.F. *Collected Papers on Psycho-analysis,* Hogarth Press and The Institute of Psychoanalysis, London, 1950)

sadism, unconscious A psychoanalytic term referring to the primordial aggressive and destructive instinctive wishes and trends with which all infants and children have to deal as part of their constitutional and biological inheritance and endowment. An infant's aggressivity trends are in the direction of magical omnipotence and control, through phantasies of the power to destroy. The ability to destroy by magical means is entertained in the unconscious phantasies of power-hungry adults seeking omnipotence and security. Persistence of such infantile aggressive strivings in the repressed and unconscious areas of adults makes for symptomatic (neurotic) difficulties in later life.

E.F. Sharpe (*Collected Papers on Psycho-analysis,* Hogarth Press and The Institute of Psychoanalysis, London, 1950) states: 'He [i.e. the neurotic] fears his own dreaded power. The ego is in a constant state of anxiety because of the unconscious sadism.'

sadomasochism (sad′ō-maz′ok-iz′m) A condition of combined sadism and masochism: the simultaneous existence, in an individual, of submissive and aggressive attitudes in his social and sexual relations to other persons, with a considerable degree of destructiveness present; a condition assumed to be charged with a libidinous energy. The individual is affected by an interplay between the two instinctual components of love and hate, in which the destructive impulses momentarily have the upper hand. In a general way, in human relations the individual may have three different kinds of attitude toward other persons: first, the individual is interested in having the other exist as his equal; second, the individual considers himself either superior or inferior to the other person, though still remaining interested in the other person's existence; and third, the individual is swayed by aggression and submission simultaneously in such a way that he wishes the other person's destruction and preservation at the same time. In normal social relations the existence of the other person not only is necessary but fulfills the inner psychic demands, although a certain amount of destructive impulse is always present. Only when a high degree of destructiveness is present in the relationship between two persons may one speak of sadomasochism.

safeguard, treble See *principle, treble safeguard.*

Saint Dymphna's disease See *disease, Saint Dymphna's.*

Saint John's evil Epilepsy.

Saint Martin's evil Dipsomania.

Saint Vitus' dance (St. Vitus, a Christian child [martyred under Diocletian, 245–313 A.D.] whose chapels, especially the one at Ulm, were filled with sufferers from epilepsy, invoking the saint for cure.) Chorea; Sydenham's chorea.

Sakel, Manfred (1900–1957) Polish psychiatrist, trained in Vienna; in 1933 reported his discovery of the hypoglycemic insulin treatment of schizophrenia and soon after came to the U.S.A., where he remained until his death.

salaam spasm See *spasm, salaam.*

salad, word See *word-salad.*

Salk vaccine See *poliomyelitis.*

salpingectomy (sal-pin-jek'tō-mē) This is a general medical term for the operation which aims at, or results in, the *sterilization* of the woman. It is performed, for surgical or eugenic reasons, by cutting and tying off the Fallopian tubes. *Tubectomy* or *fallectomy* are other expressions for this sterilizing operation on the female, while *vasectomy* is the corresponding operation on the male. The operation removing the ovaries and resulting in the *castration* of the woman is usually called *ovariotomy* or *oöphorectomy.* See *sterilization; castration.*

sanable (san'ȧb'l) Curable.

sanatorium An institution for the treatment of chronic diseases, such as tuberculosis, nervous and mental disorders, chronic rheumatism, etc., and as a place for recuperation under medical supervision; often improperly called sanitarium.

sanction By this term Freud denotes the

defensive measure which the obsessional neurotic is obliged to adopt in order to prevent a phantasy from being fulfilled. This may take the form of a formula, as in the case of the rat man, in which he employed the following formula: 'but,' accompanied by a gesture of repudiation, and the phrase 'whatever are you thinking of?' (Freud, S. *Collected Papers,* vol. 3, tr. by Strachey, A. and J., Leonard and Virginia Woolf, Hogarth Press, London, 1925)

sane Sound of mind.

sanguine See *type, sanguine.*

sanguinem menstruationis amicae lambit et devorat The phrase denotes a form of sexual perversion, namely, to drink and swallow menstrual blood. Quoted from Stekel.

sanity Soundness of mind. See *rule, M'Naghten.*

sanity, legal See *rule, M'Naghten.*

sa(p)phism (saf'iz'm) (Greek poetess *Sapphô,* or in her native Aeolian dialect *Psapphô,* a Lesbian by birth (born 600 B.C. in the island Lesbos), who was a female homosexual) The sensual and sexual desire of woman for members of her own sex; known also as Lesbianism. Neither of these terms is in common usage: female homosexuality is the usual term.

Satanism (sā'tan-iz'm) Satanism is pictured in the Middle Ages in the framework of a Black Mass. Satan (who in the guise of Mephistopheles introduces himself to Goethe's Faust with the words: 'I am the spirit that denieth') represents a spirit of negativism that wants to deny the meaning of love and reality of God. Satanism expresses a blasphemous attitude toward the church. (Baynes, H.G. *Mythology of the Soul,* Williams and Wilkins, Baltimore, 1940)

satanophobia (sā-tan-ō-fō'bi-ȧ) Fear of the devil.

satisfaction Psychoanalysts give a special meaning to *satisfaction.* 'A better term for a stimulus of instinctual origin is a "need"; that which does away with this need is "satisfaction." This can be attained only by a suitable (adequate) alteration of the inner sources of stimulations.' (Freud, S. *Collected Papers,* vol. 4, tr. by Riviere, J., Leonard and Virginia

Woolf and The Institute of Psychoanalysis, London, 1924–25)

In occupational therapy this term means a feeling of gratification, of accomplishment; often used in relation to the progress of an activity or interest.

saturation point, racial 'A given population may be saturated with a certain minority group at a given time. If an excess of members of the minority group move into the community from the outside in numbers exceeding this point— the racial saturation point—frictions and various disturbances break out.' (Moreno, J.L. *Who Shall Survive?* Nervous & Mental Disease Publishing Company, Washington, D.C., 1934)

satyriasis (sat-i-rī′à-sis) Pathological, excessive heterosexuality in man.

'It is a violent desire of venery, even so that reason is deprived by it.' (Motherby, G. *A New Medical Dictionary,* 5th ed., for J. Johnson, St. Paul's Church-Yard, etc., London, 1801)

Obs. Formerly, *leprosy.*

satyrismus (-riz′mus) *Obs.* Satyriasis.

satyromania (-rō-mā′ni-à) *Rare.* Synonym of *satyriasis.*

savants, idiots (så-vänz′, id′i-uts) Tredgold states that 'amentia is often characterized by an irregular as well as a defective mental development, and in a small number of patients this is so marked as to result in special aptitudes which are quite phenomenal, not merely in comparison with aments, but often with the acquirements of ordinary persons. These persons are conveniently described as "idiots savants." ' Usually such 'idiots' are not of the lowest grade of mental deficiency. (Tredgold, A.F. *A Text-Book of Mental Deficiency,* 6th ed., Wood, Baltimore, 1937)

scabiophobia (skå-bi-ō-fō′bi-à) Fear of scabies.

Scarpa's ganglion (Antonio Scarpa, Italian anatomist and surgeon, 1748–1832) See *nerve, acoustic.*

scar, psychic (sī′kik) Bleuler states that '*cure with a defect* is also spoken of by formulating the conception, suitable only to few cases, that the acute disease has left a defect just as a healed wound leaves a scar. A "psychic scar" may be formed by definite "residual symptoms," as in the case of a delusion which in spite of re-

turned clearness following a delirium is no longer corrected.' (Bleuler, E. *Textbook of Psychiatry,* tr. by Brill, A.A., Macmillan, New York, 1930)

scatology Study relating to excrement. It acquires significance in psychiatry, because of the many normal and abnormal manifestations connected with excrement.

See the several words beginning with *copro-.*

'The whole significance of the anal zone is mirrored in the fact that there are but few neurotics who have not had their special scatologic customs, ceremonies, etc., which they retain with cautious secrecy.' (Freud, S. *The Basic Writings of Sigmund Freud,* tr. by Brill, A.A., Random House, New York, 1938)

scatophagy (skà-tof′à-jē) Eating of excrement; see *rhypophagy.*

scatophobia (skat-ō-fō′bi-à) A morbid dread of contamination by excrement.

scattering In clinical psychiatry, this term generally refers to one of the schizophrenic thinking disorders in which associations are sometimes irrelevant or tangential, with the result that speech productions are occasionally incomprehensible. The term is also used in clinical psychology to refer to widely divergent test scores, as when a schizophrenic patient passes all the year X items in an intelligence test but shows many failures at the year VI level, or as when there is marked inconsistency on subtest scores.

scene, primal Primal scene is a psychoanayltic expression, referring to a child's first observation of sexual intercourse between the parents. In his description of the 'wolf-man' case, Freud claims that the primal scene was influential in determining later morbid personality reactions.

scene, traumatic (traw-mat′ik) This term describes any psychic experience which the individual wishes to forget or repress as disagreeable, painful, or unbearable. Freud speaks of traumatic situations and emphasizes that neurotic symptoms are 'complete reproductions of such situations.' It is as if the patient cannot get rid of the original painful experience and remains attached to it, an attachment which Freud called 'fixation to traumas.' Such is the case of the girl who had developed an abnormal erotic attachment to her father (traumatic situation, or scene) and was constantly ill after his death, so that she would be in no condition to marry and could thus remain with her father, her original love-object.

In the opinion of Breuer and Freud, the psychic energies that cannot be lived out in the normal way, when the patient tries to forget or repress the traumatic scene, are diverted into other pathways and there provoke symptoms in the somatic sphere. Later, Freud referred to it as a 'psychosexual trauma,' the term used especially by Schilder. (Schilder, P. *Psychotherapy*, Norton, New York, 1938) See *trauma*.

Schaeffer reflex See *reflex, Schaeffer*.

schedule A form on which may be given many summarized items of information concerning an individual; it is arranged so that each item may be easily abstracted and made available for tabulation.

schedule, self-demand See *feeding, demand*.

Scheid, cyanotic syndrome of Scheid attempted to explain sudden death in excited manic patients and in catatonic states as a somatic condition somehow related to a somatic febrile or toxic etiology of the psychosis itself. This view is not widely held at the present time, it being more generally believed that such deaths are due to physiologic exhaustion secondary to pathologic overactivity; but some authors continue to speak of a catatonic cerebral paralysis as a primary somatic change which explains the occasional (probably not more than 1 per cent) occurrence of unexpected death in this group.

Schicksal analysis See *analysis, Schicksal*.

Schilder's disease (Paul Ferdinand Schilder, Vienna and New York neurologist, 1886–1940) Encephalitis periaxialis diffusa. See *sclerosis, diffuse*.

schizo- (skiz′ō-) Combining form meaning split(ting), cleavage, rift, division, from Gr. *schizein*, to split, cleave, rive.

schizo-affective schizophrenia See *schizophrenia*.

schizocaria (skiz-ō-kā′ri-à) An acute and highly malignant form of schizophrenia which leads to rapid deterioration of the personality. Mauz uses the term 'catastrophic schizophrenia' synonymously with schizocaria.

schizogen (skiz′ō-gen) See *psychotomimetic*.

schizoid (skiz′oid) Resembling the division, separation or split of the personality that is characteristic of schizophrenia.

schizoidia (skiz-oi′di-à) Schizoidism.

schizoidism (skiz′oid-iz′m) In psychiatry this term means the splitting or schism of the psyche which is a characteristic feature of schizophrenia. Schizoidism is not, however, in itself a morbid feature. It is an expression used to denote the aggregate of personality traits known as introversion, namely, quietness, seclusiveness, 'shut-in-ness.' The schizoid individual splits or separates from his surroundings to a greater or lesser degree, confining his psychic interests more or less to himself.

The intensely schizoid individual may become schizophrenic; it is estimated that not less than 60 per cent of schizophrenic patients show exaggerated schizoid tendencies prior to the development of schizophrenia.

Many contemporary European writers use the term schizoidism to refer to the hereditary or 'nuclear' factor in schizophrenia. These same authors tend to use the term 'dementia praecox' to refer to a type of schizophrenia showing a high tendency to deterioration and little tendency to remission or recovery. (Campbell, R.J. *Psychiatric Quarterly 32*, 318–34, 1958)

schizoid personality See *personality pattern disturbance*.

schizomania (skiz-ō-mā′ni-à) A psychotic state presenting a mixture of schizophrenic and manic symptoms.

schizomimetic (-mi-me′tik) *Psychotomimetic* (q.v.).

schizophasia (-fā′zhi-à) Word-salad.

schizophrene (skiz′ō-frēn) One affected by schizophrenia.

schizophrenia (skiz-ō-frē′ni-à) A term which Bleuler suggested as a replacement for the now generally obsolete term *dementia praecox* (q.v.). By the term, Bleuler meant to designate what he considered to be one of the fundamental characteristics of patients so diagnosed, namely, the splitting off of portions of the psyche, which portions may then dominate the psychic life of the individual for a time and lead an independent existence even though these may be contrary and contradictory to the personality as a whole. Bleuler rejected the term dementia praecox because in his experience profound deterioration (dementia) was not the inevitable end-result of the disease process, and because it did not always appear by the time of adolescence.

'In 1911, Eugen Bleuler described the schizophrenias as a slowly progressive deterioration of the entire personality, which involves mainly the affective life, and expresses itself in disorders of feeling, thought and conduct, and a tendency to withdraw from reality. Bleuler noted that the schizophrenias were at times progressive, at times intermittent, and could stop or retrogress at any stage; but that they showed a tendency toward deterioration and, having once appeared, did not permit of a full *restitutio ad integrum*. Bleuler established the multidimensional nature of the schizophrenias and believed them to be organic; but at the same time, he stressed the interaction of psychogenic and physiogenic features in their psychopathology and development.' (Campbell, R.J. *Psychiatric Quarterly 32*, 318–34, 1958)

Bleuler subdivided the symptoms of the schizophrenias into two groups: (1) the fundamental, primary, or basic symptoms, which are characteristic and pathognomonic of the disease process; and (2) the accessory or secondary symptoms, which are often seen in the schizophrenias and which may even occupy the forefront of the symptom-picture, but which are seen in other nosologic groups as well and particularly in the organic reaction types (acute and chronic brain syndromes). In this second group are included such symptoms as hallucinations, delusions, ideas of reference, memory disturbances (e.g. déjà fait, déjà vu), etc. The fundamental symptoms of the schizophrenias include: (1) disturbances in associations, (2) disturbances of affect, (3) ambivalence of the affect, intellect, and/or will, (4) autism, (5) attention defects, (6) disturbances of the will, (7) changes in 'the person,' (8) schizophrenic dementia, and (9) disturbances of activity and behavior.

While the specific etiology remains unknown, mounting evidence favors the conception of the schizophrenias as a heredogenetic disease involving particularly certain enzyme systems of the body. The average expectancy of schizophrenia in the general population probably does not exceed 1 per cent; it is not, therefore, a universal potentiality and not everyone could become a schizophrenic under certain conditions. It occurs in every segment of the population, without regard for race, culture, or social class. It occurs, too, in all the forms generally recognized, although the content of the symptoms appears to be determined in large part by the culture. To state this in a different way: the fundamental symptoms are the same, no matter where schizophrenia appears. 'Kallmann reports the following findings: (a) the majority of schizophrenic hospital patients (90 per cent) come from non-schizophrenic parents; (b) one schizophrenic parent is not enough to produce the disease in his offspring, although one schizophrenic parent will raise the expectancy of schizophrenia in his off-spring to 16 per cent; (c) at the same time, a non-schizophrenic, adequate home is not able to prevent the development of schizophrenia in vulnerable offspring; (d) both one-egg twins are six times more likely to develop schizophrenia than both two-egg twins, regardless of whether they are reared alone or apart.' (ibid.) Kallmann feels that schizophrenia is a gene-specific, metabolic deficiency transmitted as a receptive unit-factor and manifested as a lack of ability to respond to certain environmental stimuli. The basic integrative deficiency is not yet identified; it may be an overproduction or underproduction of central synaptic neurohumors such as norepinephrine or serotonin; it may be a production of abnormal metabolites such as adrenochrome or adrenolutin; it may be production of abnormal forms of copper-containing enzymes, such as Heath's 'taraxein'; it may be inadequate production of enzymes normally responsible for the breakdown of various potentially toxic amines.

Forms of the disease. Bleuler subdivided the schizophrenias into acute and chronic forms, depending upon the predominant symptoms of any particular episode. As already indicated, the predominant symptoms are often the accessory symptoms, and before subtyping of an episode is made the diagnosis of schizophrenia is first established by reason of the presence of the fundamental symptoms.

The acute syndromes are:

(1) melancholia—in contrast to non-schizophrenic depressions, the affect here tends to be superficial, inappropriate,

and/or unconvincing, and hypochondriacal delusions are frequent.

(2) mania—the prevailing mood is capriciousness rather than euphoria or triumph, and withdrawal can usually be seen.

(3) catatonia—stupor, cerea flexibilitas, *faxenpsychosis* (q.v.) or other hyperkinetic syndromes.

(4) delusional states with hallucinations, which are often visual and less stereotyped than the hallucinations seen in the chronic syndromes.

(5) twilight states—including religious ecstasies and other dream-like conditions in which desires, impulses, or fears are represented in a direct or symbolic way as being already fulfilled.

(6) Benommenheit (psychic 'benumbing')—in which there is a slowing up of all psychic processes, usually in conjunction with an incapacity for dealing with any relatively complicated or unusual situation.

(7) confusion, incoherence—as a result of fragmentation of associations, speech is disconnected, sentences are half broken, and activity is excessive, purposeless, and random.

(8) anger states—with cursing, vilification, uncontrolled rage outbursts, often in relation to seemingly insignificant external events.

(9) anniversary excitements—episodes of agitation appearing only on definite calendar days, usually related to a specific event in the patient's past.

(10) stupor.

(11) deliria—acute hallucinatory episodes often resembling the fever deliria. These states are sometimes termed oneirophrenia and include those patients who become dazed and bewildered with narrowing of consciousness, often following specific traumata such as childbirth, postoperative exhaustion, and battlefield experiences. While such cases are often said to be benign, there is a percentage of cases that recur with decreasing recovery after each episode.

(12) fugue states—running away in intercurrent episodes of agitation and excitement, sometimes in response to a hallucinatory command.

(13) dipsomania — tense, anxious moods drive some patients to drink heavily until they become exhausted.

The chronic forms are:

(1) paranoid—see *schizophrenia, paranoid.*

(2) catatonic—see *schizophrenia, catatonic.*

(3) hebephrenic—see *schizophrenia, hebephrenic.*

(4) simple—see *schizophrenia, simple.*

Various other forms have been described since Bleuler's subdivision, among which are:

(1) *schizophrenia, childhood* (q.v.).

(2) *schizophrenia, pseudoneurotic* (q.v.).

(3) *schizophrenia, ambulatory* (q.v.).

(4) schizophrenia, acute undifferentiated—those acute forms in which clear-cut crystallization into one of the generally recognized chronic forms has not yet occurred.

(5) schizophrenia, chronic undifferentiated—mixed forms and also those termed 'latent,' 'incipient,' 'borderline,' 'prepsychotic,' etc.

(6) schizophrenia, schizo-affective—including the acute melancholic and manic forms of Bleuler; this type often has its onset during adolescence and with recurrences the affective picture tends to abate and to be replaced by hebephrenic or simple or paranoid symptoms.

(7) schizophrenia, pseudopsychopathic —with predominant asocial, dyssocial, or antisocial trends.

(8) schizophrenia, residual—cases in a state of relative remission or improvement between acute psychotic episodes.

schizophrenia, ambulatory The term ambulatory schizophrenia (non-hospitalized) has been applied to the disease of the group of schizophrenics who, on the surface, appear normal, but can suddenly commit acts which reveal their abnormality. (Zilboorg, G. 'Ambulatory Schizophrenics,' *Psychiatry, Journal of the Biology and Pathology of Interpersonal Relations 4,* No. 2, p. 154, May 1941) The puzzling aggressive, asocial acts committed by apparently sane persons have very often turned out to be acts of ambulatory schizophrenics. (Abrahamsen, D. *Crime and the Human Mind,* Columbia University Press, New York, 1944)

schizophrenia, arrest of The subsidence of acute schizophrenic symptoms. This may occur at any time in the process of the disease, and if the disease itself is not too far advanced, there may be little of a pathological nature to appear. In other words, schizophrenia does not necessarily imply positive deterioration.

schizophrenia, catastrophic See *schizo-caria*.

schizophrenia, catatonic (ka-ta-ton'ik) One of the subgroups of schizophrenia (in the older literature, dementia praecox) which may appear as a chronic form or as an acute episode in the course of a schizophrenic pattern. As with any type of schizophrenia, the fundamental symptoms afford the basis for the diagnosis, although the subgrouping into the catatonic type is largely dependent upon certain secondary or accessory symptoms—catalepsy, stupor, hyperkinesiae, stereotypies, mannerisms, negativism, automatisms, and impulsivity.

Onset is acute in 41 per cent of cases; in 31 per cent of cases chronic paranoid symptoms precede the development of catatonic symptoms, and in the remaining cases the onset is subacute. In general, symptoms may be seen to fall into one of two categories: (1) catatonic stupor, including catalepsy, stupor, and negativism; and (2) catatonic excitement, including hyperkinesiae, stereotypies, mannerisms, automatisms, and impulsivity.

Catalepsy may appear as immobile or mask-like facies, as posturing, resistance to movement, decreased spontaneity in movement, or, less commonly, as cerea flexibilitas (waxy flexibility). The hyperkinesiae include arbitrary, automatic, pseudospontaneous movements while the stereotypies include movements, actions, posturings, speech, writings, or drawings which are monotonously repetitive and which bear little obvious relationship to external reality. *Schnauzkrampf* (q.v.) is a particular type of stereotypy. Mannerisms are not necessarily stereotyped but they are nonetheless inappropriate, inadequately modifiable, and caricature-like. Negativism may appear in several forms: (a) external negativism, or negation of commands; (b) inner negativism, or oppositional thoughts (actually a type of intellectual ambivalence, but often misinterpreted as 'obsessive thinking'); (c) active negativism, the active opposition of commands; (d) passive negativism, which often appears as stubbornness or unco-operativeness; (e) command-negativism, or doing exactly the opposite of what is ordered. Automatisms may also be expressed in various ways, such as echopraxia or echolalia (forms of command-automatism), or as fugues, self-injuries, or coprolalia. Impulsivity is commonly seen in catatonic schizophrenia and on occasion can lead to suicidal attempts or homicidal outbursts.

schizophrenia, childhood A clinical entity occurring in childhood, usually after the age of one and before the age of 11, characterized chiefly by disturbance in the ability to make affective contact with the environment and by autistic thinking. It has long been believed by many clinicians that such pictures represented early-appearing schizophrenia rather than any different or unique syndrome, and Kallmann's genetic studies support this view. The criteria for establishing such a diagnosis, however, are not as well defined as in adult schizophrenia, so that various definitions of the disorder (or group of disorders) are given by various authors. Thus Bender says: 'We now define childhood schizophrenia as a maturational lag at the embryonic level in all the areas which integrate biological and psychological behavior; an embryonic primitivity or plasticity characterizes the pattern of the behavior disturbance in all areas of personality functioning. It is determined before birth and hereditary factors appear to be important. It may be precipitated by a physiological crisis, which may be birth itself, especially a traumatic birth.' (In Caplan, G. *Emotional Problems of Early Childhood*, Basic Books, New York, 1955) Mahler distinguishes between symbiotic infantile psychosis, which she described in 1952, and early infantile autism (Kanner's term), and considers both of them types of childhood schizophrenia. Others would limit the term childhood schizophrenia more narrowly and consider it as a separate entity from early infantile autism and from psychoses associated with mental deficiency. See *psychosis, symbiotic infantile*.

schizophrenia, compensation Term coined by N.D.C. Lewis for the type of schizophrenia characterized by overcompensation for the feelings of inferiority. Delusions of grandeur form the core of this psychosis.

schizophrenia deliriosa (skē-zô-fre'nē-à dā-lē-rē-ô'zà) Menninger's term for a form of schizophrenia which starts as a delirium and is frequently associated with or directly follows a physical illness such as influenza. (*American Journal of Psychiatry 1*, 573–88, 1921–22)

schizophrenia, engrafted See *Propfschizophrenia.*

schizophrenia, hebephrenic (hē-be-fre′nik) A chronic form of schizophrenia characterized by marked disorders in thinking, incoherence, severe emotional disturbance, wild excitement alternating with tearfulness and depression, vivid hallucinations, and absurd, bizarre delusions which are prolific, fleeting, and frequently concerned with ideas of omnipotence, sex change, cosmic identity, and rebirth (the so-called phylogenetic symptoms). The hebephrenic forms tend to have an early onset, usually before the age of 20. Bleuler classified as hebephrenic all those schizophrenias with an acute onset that were not characterized by catatonic symptoms (e.g. the manic, melancholic, amented, and twilight states) and also all those chronic forms where the accessory symptoms are not dominant. Others have depended upon the presence of the silly, inappropriate 'teenager' symptoms to establish the diagnosis.

Hebephrenic schizophrenia in almost all reported series has been associated with a poor prognosis; i.e. with a relatively rapid deterioration and schizophrenic dementia. It is this form which contributes most heavily to the group termed nuclear or process schizophrenia by other workers.

schizophrenia, induced This psychiatric term denotes delusions or other schizophrenic symptoms imposed by one member of the family on other members. In one such case, a schizophrenic mother transmitted her ideas of grandeur to her two daughters, one of whom was clearly schizophrenic, while the other could be convinced of the falsity of her beliefs and then showed no further evidence of the disease. This case, incidentally, is an example of *folie à trois.* 'Therefore, we must assume that an energetic patient can suggest his delusions to other members of the family if and when they articulate with the complexes (wishes and desires) of these same members. However, schizophrenia will only develop if the disease is already latent in those individuals. In induced insanity, not the disease as such is determined by induction but only its delusional content, and perhaps also the manifest outbreak.' (Bleuler, E. *Dementia Praecox or the Group of*

Schizophrenias, International Universities Press, New York, 1950) See *folie à deux.*

schizophrenia, latent Bleuler often uses this expression for personality states which he believes to be schizophrenia, though others call them schizoidism.

'*Latent schizophrenias* are very common under all conditions, so that the "disease" schizophrenia has to be a much more extensive term than the pronounced psychosis of the same name. . . . At what stage of the anomaly anyone should be designated as a "schizoid" psychopath, or as a schizophrenic mentally diseased, cannot at all be decided as yet.' (Bleuler, E. *Textbook of Psychiatry,* tr. by Brill, A.A., Macmillan, New York, 1930)

schizophrenia, mixed An instance of schizophrenia that cannot be classified under any one of the disease's four generally accepted and clearly distinguished categories: simple, paranoid, catatonic, hebephrenic. The patient is said to suffer from mixed schizophrenia when he shows symptoms of two or more of the above-named categories. In the 1952 revision of psychiatric nomenclature, such cases are often called chronic undifferentiated schizophrenia.

schizophrenia, paranoid (par′à-noid) One of the chronic forms of schizophrenia. In addition to the fundamental schizophrenic symptoms, the paranoid type shows the following features: a feeling that external reality has changed and somehow become different; suspiciousness and ideas of dedication; ideas of reference; hallucinations, especially of body sensations; delusions of persecution or of grandiosity. Some paranoid schizophrenics may act in accord with their delusions and turn on their tormentors, while others may become suicidal in an attempt to escape their persecutors.

Several types of paranoid schizophrenia are recognized: litigious, depressed, persecutory, grandiose, erotomaniacal, etc. In general, paranoid forms of schizophrenia develop later than do the other forms, the highest incidence being between the ages of 30 and 35. In contrast to paranoia, in paranoid schizophrenia the delusions are multiple, less highly systematized, changeable, illogical, and bizarre.

schizophrenia, postemotive (pōst-ē-mō′tiv) This term indicates that in a constitutionally predisposed individual, schizophrenia may be precipitated by an emotional trauma, particularly when the situation is actually or threateningly inimical to the bodily self. Such emotional stress is met with varying degrees of adequacy by different individuals. Postemotive psychotic reactions are more usual in the manic-depressive predisposed individual, but schizophrenia may also follow such insupportable trauma, especially in the face of situations which threaten self-preservation, the social self, or the sexual life.

A 21-year-old schizoid man, who had made a happy work adjustment for the preceding six years in a candy factory, developed postemotive schizophrenia. His right arm was caught in a machine pulley belt and he suffered severe muscular contusions. He was hospitalized for two weeks, but was unable to return to work after discharge from the hospital, because of his 'nervous state caused by the accident.' After two months, he finally went back to work, but did poorly and seemed terrified by machine work. He worked for several days but had to leave his job, because he began to tremble all over, could not sleep, developed numerous hypochondriacal complaints and crying spells, became generally apprehensive, with acute fear reactions. Shortly thereafter he began to neglect his personal appearance, and a widespread retraction of interest was noted. He became absorbed in himself, talked and laughed senselessly in a childish voice, and at times demonstrated verbigeration. He was institutionalized, and a diagnosis of schizophrenia, hebephrenic type, was made. After seven years, there was no improvement in his condition.

Most postemotive reactions eventually and spontaneously disappear and are self-limited syndromes. But when emotional stress precipitates a psychosis in a predisposed individual, prognosis is made on the basis of the psychosis itself rather than on the nature of the precipitating factor. Many authorities feel that schizophrenia is nearly always postemotive, that detailed anamnestic investigation would reveal specific emotional traumata as precipitating factors in the majority of cases. (*Psychiatric Quarterly 13,* 278, 1939)

schizophrenia, pseudoneurotic (sū-dō-nū-rot′ik) Hoch and Polatin ('Pseudo-neurotic Forms of Schizophrenia,' *Psychiatric Quarterly 23,* 248, 1949) apply this term to those patients whose defense mechanisms are, at least superficially, neurotic in type, but who, on close investigation, show the basic schizophrenic mechanisms. The most important diagnostic feature is pan-anxiety and pan-neurosis. The all-pervading anxiety structure leaves no life-approach of the person free from tension. Usually not only one or two different neurotic mechanisms are seen, but all symptoms known in neurotic illness tend to be present at the same time—anxiety, conversion symptoms, gross hysterical or vegetative manifestations, phobias, and obsessive-compulsive mechanisms. These neurotic mechanisms dominate the patient; they constantly shift but are never completely absent.

The life-approach of these patients is always autistic and dereistic, although this may be very subtly expressed. Withdrawal from reality is more general than is the case even in the neurotic with schizoid features. Some inappropriate emotional connections are usually manifest, and there is a lack of modulation and flexibility in emotional display. Often, these patients appear cold and controlled in responding to major frustrations, but over-react to trivial ones. Hate reactions, particularly toward the family, are more open and less discriminating than in the neurotic. Commonly there is depression or an anhedonic state wherein the patient derives pleasure from nothing. Thinking disorders may also be too subtle to be on the surface: condensations and concept displacements, catathymic thinking, expression of omnipotence emanating from the patient, or the feeling of an omnipotential attitude of the environment toward the patient. Unlike neurotics, such patients do not try to rationalize their symptoms in a logical and coherent fashion. Instead, the component elements of their story always remain vaguely conflicting; they are unable to give details of the development of the symptoms, and repeat and reiterate their complaints in a stereotyped and sterile way. There is usually an inability to associate freely in spite of their ordinarily good intelligence and signal ability to verbalize. Psychosexually, such patients show a chaotic organization and a mixture of all levels of libidinal development. Marked sadistic or sadomasochistic behavior is often linked with this sexual material. The Rorschach test in such patients often shows thinking disorders such as concrete thinking, an unpredictable attitude toward various situations, lack of constructive planfulness, passive opportunism, and marked anxiety. In the Rorschach results there is often noticed that marked variability of performance which is so characteristic of schizophrenia. Amytal interviews frequently release some of the more overtly psychotic material.

Many of these patients develop psychotic episodes which are often of short duration with complete reintegration. These short-lived attacks are called 'micropsychoses' and are characterized by the simultaneous development of three very significant features: hypochondriacal ideas, ideas of reference, and feelings of depersonalization. These patients zig-zag, repeatedly trespassing beyond the reality line.

The following case illustrates pseudoneurotic schizophrenia. The patient was a single white female, 38 years old. Though an unwanted child, she had a normal early development, was very affectionate and obedient, and mixed well with her contemporaries. With advancing age the patient appeared to grow progressively more schizoid in personality, but never enough to interfere with her functioning. After completing high school, she obtained a position with a dentist, and several years later was discharged, because her employer felt that she had lost interest in her work, had become listless. Her arms hung down at her sides and she slouched along as she walked. After that, the patient found employment in a hospital and began to complain of abdominal pain. Appendectomy was performed, but her complaints continued, including new ones about marked weakness and lack of strength, but there was no real depression. Later, constipation and a 'foggy feeling' began to trouble her. She was much irritated by her mother and sister, because they did not understand her and regarded her complaints as caused by laziness. She also complained that her heart hurt her. On admission to the hospital, the patient appeared cooperative but somewhat self-absorbed. Whenever she had to talk with people in the course of social contacts, she showed fear and shame, and marked feelings of inferiority. Later the patient complained that her subconscious mind played tricks

on her, that she had a feeling as if a voice were telling her to go to sleep. Finally, this last complaint crystallized into frank ideas of reference and persecution and auditory hallucinations.

schizophrenia, recidives in (res′i-divz) Recurring, intermittent, acute episodes of schizophrenia, or other evidences of deterioration which begin after prolonged remission. The recurring attacks often duplicate the previous ones, but new features may appear. There is no definite correlation between initial disease symptoms and recidives.

schizophrenia, regressive symptoms Those schizophrenic symptoms which represent an undoing or primitivization of differentiations acquired through mental development; included here are such symptoms as phantasies of world destruction, physical sensations and delusions, depersonalization, delusions of grandeur, archaic speech and thought, most hebephrenic symptoms, and certain catatonic symptoms (negativism, echolalia, echopraxia, automatic obedience, posturing, stereotypy). See *schizophrenia, restitutional symptoms.*

schizophrenia, restitutional symptoms Those schizophrenic symptoms which represent an attempt at regaining reality, which has been lost by regression; included are such symptoms as hallucinations, delusions, most of the social and speech peculiarities of schizophrenia, and certain catatonic symptoms (stereotypy, mannerisms, automatic obedience, rigidity).

schizophrenia, reversible Menninger's term for a schizophrenic state with a potentiality for recovery. Its significance is prognostic rather than nosological. (*American Journal of Psychiatry 1*, 573–88, 1921–22)

schizophrenia, simple One of the chronic forms of schizophrenia; also called dementia praecox, simple type; dementia simplex; schizophrenia simplex; primary dementia.

In the simple form of schizophrenia, there is an insidious psychic impoverishment which affects the emotions, the intellect, and the will. Chronic dissatisfaction or complete indifference to reality are characteristic, and the simple schizophrenic is isolated, estranged, and asocial. Affect is markedly blunted and dulled, there is little phantasy life, and there may be few or no accessory symptoms. Dementia, in Bleuler's sense, is marked—patients make many foolish mistakes, are highly suggestible and gullible, and speech is filled with senseless generalizations. Thought is vacuous and banal, ideas are insipid and unintegrated. Such patients tend to sink to low and relatively simple social levels that make little or no demands on them and may come to lead almost a vegetative existence. They often become day laborers, peddlers, or vagabonds, and they contribute heavily to the group of eccentric recluses.

schizophrenia, toxic Toxiphrenia.

schizophreniform (skiz-o-fren′i-form) Resembling schizophrenia. See *psychosis, process.*

schizophrenosis (-frē-nō′sis) Southard's term for schizophrenic reactions in general.

schizothyme (skiz′ō-thīm) One who has a schizothymic personality.

schizothymia (-thī′mi-à, -thim′i-à) Introversion; schizoidism.

schizotypal disorders (skiz′ō-tī-pal) See *psychodynamics, adaptational.*

Schmidt's syndrome (Johann Friedrich Moritz Schmidt, German laryngologist, 1838–1907) A bulbar syndrome due to involvement of the vagus and spinal accessory nerves. Symptoms are: homolateral paralysis of the soft palate, pharynx, and larynx, and homolateral sternocleidomastoid paralysis.

Schnauzkrampf (shnouts′krämpf) This term, coined by Karl Ludwig Kahlbaum (1828–99), has almost been 'naturalized.' It means protrusion of the lips so that they resemble a snout. The condition is found almost exclusively in the catatonic form of schizophrenia.

Scholz's disease (Willibald Scholz, German neurologist, 1889–　) See *sclerosis, diffuse.*

school-marmitis Patry's term designating a particular type of personality difficulty which had been brought to his attention as one of many types occurring in an average professional group of women. Placed next to last in a list of some sixteen different types of these personality difficulties, *school-marmitis* is thus described: 'magnified self-awareness of herself in the role of dispenser of knowledge

and wisdom to children and, on occasion, to their parents; a tendency to "lord it over" and a patronizing attitude toward others.' (Kanner, L. *Child Psychiatry,* Thomas, Springfield, Ill., 1948) For psychiatry the importance of the term school-marmitis lies in the fact that the emotional attitudes of a schoolteacher can be powerful determinants of the child's own attitude, for good or ill, as the case may be. This is especially true if the child is already emotionally insecure in his home life. Happily, there also exist teacher-attitudes that reflect a healthy degree of emotional integration at a high level of personal maturity. If at present the greater number of children come out of their school years without serious emotional damage, it is in part due to the salutary influence of such teachers; otherwise it is unlikely that many children would leave school without emotional injury.

schoolsickness J.V. Treynor classifies schoolsickness as an occupational neurosis. It is said to appear in children maladjusted to their school situation and is characterized by anxiety, restlessness, and irritability. (*Iowa State Medical Society Journal 19,* 451, 1929)

Schreber, Schreber-case In 1911, Freud published *Psycho-Analytic Notes Upon an Autobiographical Account of a Case of Paranoia (Dementia Paranoides).* This consisted of an analysis of *Memoirs of a Neurotic,* a previously published (1903) autobiographical account by Dr. jur. Daniel Paul Schreber. Freud's analysis of these memoirs formed the basis for the psychoanalytic view of paranoid delusions which, at least in the male, are interpreted as attempts to contradict the underlying homosexual wish-phantasy of loving a man.

Schrenck-Notzing, Albert (1862–1929) German psychiatrist.

Schuele's sign See *sign, Schuele.*

Schüller-Christian-Hand's syndrome *Xanthomatosis* (q.v.).

sciatica (sī-a′ti-ka) See *disk, herniated lumbar intervertebral.*

sclerosis, amyotrophic lateral (skle-rō′sis, am-i-ō-trō′fik) Progressive muscular atrophy; progressive bulbar palsy; chronic poliomyelitis. Some authorities believe that amyotrophic lateral sclerosis is a hereditary disorder; but most feel that it is due to a toxin with a predilection for the anterior horn cells. It begins between the ages of 50 and 70, is twice as frequent in males as in females, and usually has an insidious onset. Pathological changes include progressive degeneration of the anterior horn cells of the spinal cord, the medullary motor nuclei, and the pyramidal tracts. Wasting begins in the upper limbs, first in the hands and later in the forearm and shoulder. Then it spreads to the tongue, palate, larynx, and pharynx, resulting in slurred speech. Degeneration of both pyramidal tracts above the medulla produces pseudobulbar palsy: dysarthria, dysphagia, and spasticity of the muscles; when severe, pseudobulbar palsy results in impaired voluntary control over emotional reactions which may be exaggerated, explosive, and quite inappropriate. The disease is fatal within 3 to 10 years.

sclerosis, atrophic lobar (a-trō′fik lō′bĕr) *Little's disease* (q.v.).

sclerosis, diffuse 'A group of progressive diseases usually occurring early in life and characterized pathologically by widespread demyelination of the white matter of the cerebral hemispheres, and clinically in typical cases by visual failure, mental deterioration, and spastic paralysis. Both sporadic and familial cases are encountered. The aetiology of these disorders is unknown and there is no general agreement as to their classification. At present their resemblances to one another appear to outweigh their differences and they are therefore included under a common title.' (Brain, W.R. *Diseases of the Nervous System,* 4th ed., Oxford University Press, London, 1951) The various entities which Brain includes are: encephalitis periaxialis diffusa (Schilder's disease), centrolobar sclerosis, encephaloleukopathia scleroticans, progressive degenerative subcortical encephalopathy, leukodystrophy, leuko-encephalopathia myeloclastica primitiva, encephalomyelomalacia chronica diffusa, concentric demyelination (Baló's disease), Krabbe's disease, Scholz's disease, and Pelizaeus-Merzbacher's disease.

The demyelination typically begins symmetrically in both occipital lobes and spreads forward. Onset is usually before the age of 14; males are more frequently affected than females. Symptoms may be-

gin acutely or insidiously and include: headache, giddiness, visual impairment progressing to blindness; diplopia, nystagmus; spastic diplegia, aphasia and/or spastic dysarthria, epileptiform attacks, and progressive dementia. Survival period is rarely longer than three years after the onset of symptoms. There is no known treatment.

sclerosis, disseminated Multiple sclerosis.

sclerosis en plaque (sklē-rō′sis äN plàk′) (F. 'in patches') Multiple sclerosis.

sclerosis, multiple Insular sclerosis; disseminated sclerosis. One of the demyelinating diseases of the nervous system and, at least in temperate zones, one of the most common neurological disorders. It is characterized pathologically by swelling and then demyelination of the medullary sheath, which is followed by glial proliferation. The result is an irregular scattering of well-demarcated sclerotic plaques throughout the white and gray matter of the brain and spinal cord. The lesions show a predilection for the pyramidal tracts and posterior columns of the spinal cord, the posterior longitudinal bundle and cerebellar connections of the brain-stem, the white matter of the frontal lobes, and the optic tracts. The disease was first described by Cruveilhier in 1835 and Carswell in 1838. Charcot described a triad of symptoms—nystagmus, intention tremor, and scanning speech—but this is found only in about 10 per cent of cases and even then usually only when lesions are far advanced.

The etiology of multiple sclerosis is unknown; some would implicate a spirochetal or viral agent, but the modern tendency is to stress constitutional factors. The highest incidence of the disorder is in Northern Europe and Switzerland; the incidence in Great Britain is about half that in Switzerland, and the incidence in the United States is about one-quarter that in Great Britain. In the United States, incidence is considerably greater in the North than in the South. While heredity may be a contributing factor in the genesis of the disorder, evidence does not substantiate its designation as a major factor.

The disease usually begins between the ages of 20 and 40; the average age at onset is 30 years for females and 34 years for males. The age at onset tends to be lowest in those areas with the highest incidence. In 50 per cent of cases, the initial symptom is weakness or loss of control over one or more limbs; in 29 per cent the initial symptom involves the visual apparatus (blindness, dimness of vision, double vision, field defects, etc.); in 11 per cent the initial symptom is numbness or similar painless paresthesia. The earliest symptoms tend to be fleeting and fluctuating, so that a misdiagnosis of hysteria is often made. The disappearance or alleviation of symptoms may last for months or years until the patient suffers another exacerbation. In general, three main types can be distinguished: an acute form, with a survival period of one to two years; a chronic, progressive form with a slowly downhill course that may last for 20 or 30 years; and a remittent form in which there is almost complete relief from symptoms during the period between acute exacerbations. The average life expectancy after the onset of the illness has been estimated to be 20 to 25 years.

'The end is distressing. An account of it is given by a sufferer who was also a graphic writer, W.N.P. Barbellion, in *The Diary of a Disappointed Man* and *Enjoying Life*. Ataxia, weakness, and spasticity confine the patient to bed and prevent him from carrying out the simplest actions for himself. Swallowing becomes difficult and speech almost unintelligible. Urinary or cutaneous infection or pneumonia finally releases the sufferer. In rare cases the last event is an acute exacerbation of the disease itself, taking the form of an acute myelitis or encephalomyelitis.' (Brain, W.R. *Diseases of the Nervous System,* 4th ed., Oxford University Press, London, 1951)

In the mental sphere, euphoria with a sense of mental and physical well-being despite obvious handicaps is characteristic, although dejection, irritability, and emotional lability are seen in some patients. Usually there is some reduction in intellectual capacity, and a few patients develop a delusional state or a terminal dementia.

There is no known treatment for the disorder.

sclerosis, posterolateral (post-ĕr-o-lat'ĕr-al) Subacute combined degeneration of the spinal cord; a deficiency disease due to lack of intrinsic factor (which combines with extrinsic factor to form the cobalt-containing complex, or vitamin B_{12}), seen in pernicious anemia, sprue, cachexia, and post-gastrectomy cases. Pathological changes include irregular demyelination of the posterolateral columns and peripheral nerves. Symptoms are: paresthesiae; early loss of position and vibratory sensation; later loss of touch and pain sensation, often with a glove and stocking type of anesthesia; sphincter disturbances; moderate muscular wasting; and ataxia. Symptoms usually begin in the lower limbs. Various mental changes may be seen: mild dementia, confusional psychosis, Korsakoff psychosis, or affective reactions. Associated with the neuropsychiatric changes are gastric achlorhydria, glossitis, and anemia. Duration of life in untreated cases is approximately two years. Present-day treatment with vitamin B_{12} can restore the patient to good health indefinitely.

sclerosis, tuberous (tū'bĕr-us) A chronic disease from unknown cause, beginning in early childhood. It is characterized by mental deterioration often resulting in idiocy, epileptic convulsions, and special tumors (adenoma sebaceum) of the skin and viscera. Pathologically, there are various malformations and numerous glial tumors within the brain. The disease was originally described by Bourneville.

-scopia, -scopo, -scopy (-skō'pi-a, -skō'pō, -skō'pē) Combining form meaning looking at, examination, scrutiny, from Gr. *skopein,* to look at, examine, inquire.

scopolagnia (skō-pō-lag'ni-à) Voyeurism; scop(t)ophilia.

scopophilia Sexual pleasure derived from contemplation or looking. It is a component-instinct and stands in the same relation to exhibitionism as sadism does to masochism. Freud calls them paired instincts.

Autoscopophilia refers to the pleasure of looking at one's own body. Active scopophilia is the pleasure derived from looking at the sexual organs of another. Passive scopophilia is the desire to be looked at by others and is thus seen to be equivalent to active exhibitionism.

'The pleasure which a person takes in his own sexual organ may become associated with scoptophilia (or sexual pleasure in looking) in its active and passive forms. . . .' (Freud, S. *Collected Papers,* vol. 3, tr. by Strachey, A. and J., Leonard and Virginia Woolf, Hogarth Press, London, 1925)

In Freudian literature the German *Schaulust* has been translated as scoptophilia, but scopophilia is the more correct form.

scopophobia Fear of being looked at.

scoptophilia See *scopophilia*.

scotoma (skō-tō′ma) An abnormal blind spot in the visual field.

scotoma, mental This phrase is used somewhat synonymously with *lack of insight*.

The patient 'has a "blind spot" for the problem before his eyes (a mental "scotoma"), and it is absolutely futile to expect the analyst to secure insight into the patient's conflicting situation by relying solely upon the patient's free associations.' (Gutheil, E.A. *The Language of the Dream,* Macmillan, New York, 1939)

scotomization (skot-ō-mi-zā′shun) In psychiatry this term means formation of mental blind spots.

'In an earlier work I have defined scotomization (or the forming of mental "blind spots") as a process of psychic depreciation, by means of which the individual attempts to deny everything which conflicts with his ego.' (R. Laforgue. *International Journal of Psychoanalysis VIII,* 473, 1927)

scotophobia (skō-tō-fō′bi-à) Fear of darkness.

screen In psychoanalysis this means a form of concealment. When, for instance, in a dream one person stands for another or others, in virtue of some common feature, the person so standing is called a screen.

'Identification consists in giving representation in the dream-content to only one of two or more persons who are related by some common feature, while the second person or other persons appear to be suppressed as far as the dream is concerned. In the dream this one "screening" person enters into all the relations and situations which derive from the persons whom he screens.' (Freud, S. *The Interpretation of Dreams,* 3rd ed., tr. by Brill, A.A., Macmillan, New York, 1933)

screen-memory See *memory, screen.*

screen-phantasy See *phantasy, screen.*

scruple, defloration Hirschfeld's term for a compulsion neurosis in young men about to marry; it implies a dread of being the first one to 'injure' a woman and carries with it also the fear of castration on the part of the male. From the standpoint of both sexes, it appears that castration is the basic theme.

scruple, virginity Hirschfeld uses this expression for a compulsive syndrome—doubt on the part of the man regarding his wife's virginity. The symptom is not uncommon as an early manifestation of the paranoid form of schizophrenia.

sebastomania (sē-bas-tō-mā′ni-à) *Obs.* Religious psychosis.

secondary defense symptom See *symptom, secondary defense.*

sedation threshold See *threshold, sedation.*

Séglas type See *type, Séglas.*

segmentation Synonymous with *cleavage.*

segregation Segregation is a 'form of isolation in which social distance is based upon physical separation.' (Wirth, L. *Segregation; Encyclopaedia of the Social Sciences,* vol. 13, Macmillan, New York, 1934, p. 643)

'Segregation is the sifting of like social and population types, as well as industrial and commercial facilities, into specific districts where each unit tends to have the same economic function and competitive strength.' (Hollingshead, A.B., in Park, R.E. *Principles of Sociology,* Barnes & Noble, New York, 1939)

In genetics this term relates to that most essential principle in the Mendelian mechanism of inheritance, which implies that the gene units derived from the two parents segregate out in the hybrid, as if independent of each other. This phenomenon allows the gene units to enter into new combinations, especially in those involving more than one pair (see *Mendelism*).

As a eugenic term, segregation means placing in mental hospitals or special institutions (colonies) the insane, mentally defective or criminal individuals until the end of their capacity for reproduction, in order to prevent their having offspring.

Séguin, O. Edouard (1812–1880) (sē-gwin′, sā-gâN′) French-American psychiatrist.

seizure An attack, or sudden onset of a

disease or of certain symptoms, such as convulsions.

seizure, audiogenic (aw-di-ō-gen′ik) Convulsion or fit induced by prolonged exposure to intense sounds of high frequency.

seizure, erotic See *epilepsy, erotic.*

seizure, gustatory Epileptics often have seizures which involve the motor apparatus or certain sense organs or both. In connection with these attacks some of these patients experience a peculiar taste known as a gustatory seizure. The seizures are often also associated with experiencing peculiar odors. (Hinsie, L.E. *Understandable Psychiatry,* Macmillan, New York, 1948)

seizure, psychic (sī′kik) A type of psychomotor epilepsy. See *epilepsy; psycholepsis.*

seizures, automatic A type of psychomotor epilepsy. See *epilepsy.*

seizure, subjective A type of psychomotor epilepsy. See *epilepsy.*

seizure, temporal lobe Psychomotor epilepsy. See *epilepsy.*

sejunction (sē-jungk′shun) Wernicke's term for blocking and other forms of dissociation. The concept is seldom used today, because it includes forms of dissociation which are widely removed both psychologically and nosographically.

selaphobia (sē-là-fō′bi-à) Fear of a flash.

selection In a specific biological sense, this term applies in a mixed population to the intentional or unintentional choice of those individuals who possess a particular genetic character or a certain combination of characters. This choice may be exercised by the failure to reproduce or by the lack of an adequate partner for marriage, if preference is given to other types or the given type is biologically incapable of reproduction.

According to the doctrine of survival of the fittest, *natural selection* takes place in evolution through a variety of processes which enable types (adapted to their environment) to reproduce their kind in marked degree, so that an improvement is gradually carried on from one stage of development to the other.

In human genetics, one usually distinquishes between *positive* and *negative* factors of selection, according to (1) whether a given factor is favorable to the reproduction of healthy or tainted family stocks, or (2) whether the general life conditions of a poulation facilitate or hinder the reproduction of the average type.

seleniasmus (sē-lē-ni-az′mus) *Obs.* Lunacy.

selenogamia (-nō-gam′i-à) ('state of being wedded to the moon') *Obs.* Somnambulism.

self See Jung's definition of *ego.*

self-abuse The expression *self-abuse,* as a synonym for masturbation, is steadily becoming obsolete, for the act is no longer regarded by authorities as normally abusive in effect. See *masturbation.*

self-accusation A common psychiatric symptom, encountered in its most intense form in the depressive phase of manic-depressive psychosis. The patient condemns himself to misery, often because of some trivial error.

self-analysis The analysis of oneself, that is, of one's psychic components. According to the most acceptable doctrines today, self-analysis cannot be expected to be successful save in the understanding of the most superficial aspects of oneself. It has psychotherapeutic value only in this meagre way and is regarded by psychiatrists as merely an adjunctive procedure.

self, bad A psychoanalytic concept referring to the tendency on the part of both analyst and patient to project on each other their guilty images of their instinct-ridden selves. Behind the shield of unconscious counter-transference, an analyst may make the patient a whipping boy for his own unconscious image of his infantile instinctual self. Conversely, the analyst must frequently tolerate (and analyze) the patient's tendency to project his own instinctual urges onto the analyst and to castigate him (the analyst) for them.

Much 'holier than thou' missionary zeal in the psychopathology of everyday life finds its source in this process of projection of the 'bad self' upon others. E.F. Sharpe (*Collected Papers on Psychoanalysis,* Hogarth Press, and The Institute of Psychoanalysis, London, 1950) says: 'The analyst must be sufficiently analysed to enable him to detect, and so consciously control, any tendency to regard the patient as the "Bad Self" who needs reforming.'

self-dynamism The fabric of the motivational forces and processes which lead to the development of the *self-system,* in Sullivan's theory of interpersonal relations. The human personality is founded on a biological substrate and is the product of the interpersonal and social forces acting on the individual from the time of birth. The human being is concerned with two goals: (1) the pursuit of satisfaction, which deals chiefly with biological needs; and (2) the pursuit of security, which deals primarily with cultural pressures. To maintain security and avoid anxiety, the child develops and strengthens those sides of his nature which are pleasing or acceptable to the significant adults. The resulting configuration of traits is the *self-system.*

self-esteem Psychodynamically, self-esteem refers to a state in which narcissistic supplies emanating from the superego are maintained so that the individual does not fear punishment or abandonment by the superego. In other words, self-esteem is a state of being on good terms with one's superego. Pathologic loss of self-esteem is characteristic of clinical depression.

self, ethical See *superego.*

self-extension In social work, the 'effort to assert one's ego generally as a compensation for inferiorities and inadequacies; drive for ascendency; showing off; aggressiveness.' (Hamilton, G. *A Medical Social Terminology,* Presbyterian Hospital, New York, 1930)

self-fellator See *auto-fellatio.*

self, hidden See *personality, secondary.*

selfhood G.W. Jacoby in *Suggestion and Psychotherapy* uses this term to mean what he called 'I-ness,' the individual personality.

self-hypnosis (-hip-nō'sis) See *auto-hypnosis.*

self-identification When an individual loves someone else, who is like himself, the state is known as self-identification. The individual projects his own personality upon another and then proceeds to admire himself as he appears in the other person. While this is the usual process of self-identification, it is possible to include under the term the process of projecting one's undesirable traits upon another and

then hating his own traits, as if they belonged to another. The latter happens in paranoid states.

Self-identification is based upon narcissism and homosexuality.

self-irrumation (-ir-ōō-mā'shun) Auto-fellatio.

self-maximation The drive (involving a part of the ego) associated with the numerous competitive situations the individual encounters in the course of living, such as competitions for affection, attention, and status, at home, at school, in groups of peers, and elsewhere. There are competitions in the vocational, intellectual, and social fields, as well as for love-objects. This drive is to maintain feelings of personal adequacy.

self-peeping, narcissistic (när-si-sis'tik) This term denotes self-voyeurism on the basis of primary *narcissism* (q.v.). It is generally believed by psychoanalysts that voyeurism is at first narcissistic self-voyeurism. But reality demands that objects be included in the child's scheme of things, and the original self-voyeurism is transformed into voyeurism directed against the parents. Bergler considers this voyeurism to be the true basis for choosing acting as a profession. In the beginning, the child says: 'I want to be a voyeur of mother and father, later of intimacies between them.' But the superego reproaches the child for this wish, and the child denies having this wish by asserting the opposite: 'No, I am not a voyeur, I am just the opposite—an exhibitionist.' This, too, receives reproaches from the superego, and the desire is sublimated: 'I am neither a voyeur nor an exhibitionist; I merely want to give other people pleasure, so I am an actor.' (Bergler, E. 'On Acting and Stage Fright,' *Psychoanalytic Quarterly Supplement 23,* 313, 1949)

self-punishment See *ego-suffering; illness as self-punishment; masochism.*

self-reporting See *psychodynamics, adaptational.*

self, secondary See *personality, secondary.*

self, subconscious See *personality, secondary.*

self, subliminal (sub-lim'i-nal) See *personality, secondary.*

self-system A term used by Sullivan, in his theory of personality development, to denote final formation of self from a limited number sifted out of a greater number of potentialities, through parental influence on the developing personality of the child. Security rests on the feeling of belonging and being accepted. The child's actions or attributes that meet with disapproval tend to be blocked out of awareness and dissociated. As the child realizes that certain earlier devices for obtaining satisfaction, such as crying when hungry, bring on disapproval in the environment, the earlier pattern of behavior is inhibited: the child tends to develop and emphasize those aspects of his nature which are pleasing or acceptable to the significant adults, and the configuration of the traits which have met with approval constitutes the self-system.

After the self-system has been established, secondary anxiety appears whenever there is a possibility that the dissociated thoughts or feelings will become conscious: the dissociated impulses are not necessarily destructive, but because there is an emotional stake in maintaining the self-system, anything threatening it will nonetheless produce anxiety. It is obvious that the self-system tends to lead to a rigidity in personality and that even many positive potentialities of the person may never be realized or put into operation.

'The self-system of Sullivan has this in common with Freud's concept of character: it is formed as a result of the influence of the parents on the developing personality of the child. Freud presents this idea more mechanistically when he says character is the result of the sublimation of instincts under the influence of the Superego, the Superego being mainly the incorporated attitude of the parents and society. The self-system is different from the concept of character in that it includes more than sublimation, whereas Freud seems to conceive of character as nothing but sublimation. No true comparison of the two can be made, because the frames of reference are entirely different. Freud's system emphasizes what happens to instincts. Sullivan's system stresses what goes on between people. For Sullivan personality does not develop mechanically. Always the emphasis is on a dynamic interaction between people. Freud's orientation is mechanistic-biological; Sullivan's dynamic-cultural (interpersonal).' (Thompson, C. *Psychoanaly-*

sis, Evolution and Development, Hermitage House, New York, 1950)

self, true The sum total of an individual's potentialities which might be developed under the most favorable social and cultural conditions. Fromm considers neurosis in terms of cultural pressures (which often thwart potentialities) and the interaction of people. Since some of the patient's best potentialities are repressed, therapy aims at helping the patient to become himself and discover his 'true self.' Neurosis stems from the new needs a person's culture creates in him and, as a secondary concomitant to cultural pressures, from the person's deprivations and the frustrations of his potentialities.

'Fromm points out that in the course of therapy one often needs to stress the essential healthiness of some of the patient's tendencies which had met with the disapproval of his environment. The goal of therapy is not primarily to make the person adjusted to his culture but to develop a sense of integrity and a respect for his true self. All adjustments to the culture which violate a person's integrity produce the feeling of guilt and shame and a loss of self-esteem. Fromm sees a real respect for oneself as essential to genuine love and respect for others.' (Thompson, C. *Psychoanalysis, Evolution and Development,* Hermitage House, New York, 1950)

semiconscious Imperfectly conscious.

semi-obsession à deux (à -dē′) 'The name "semi-obsession *à deux*" follows the expression *folie à deux,* by which is understood an identical and simultaneous psychosis in two members of a family group. However, while in *folie à deux* the psychosis in one individual is induced and/or influenced by the partner, we wish to call a symptom a phenomenon *à deux* when it occurs in two members of a group independently from each other.' (Wilder, J. 'A Semi-Obsession A Deux,' *American Journal of Psychotherapy 1,* 193, 1947)

semiopathic (sē-mi-ō-path′ik) Term applied by Burrow to the organism's affective or emotionally distorted use of the symbol. The result of the impingement of the symbolic or semiotic (partitive) reaction-pattern upon the organism's total pattern of behavior and the concomitant substitution of projected affects for intrinsic feeling. (Burrow, T. *The Biology* *of Human Conflict,* Macmillan, New York, 1937)

semiotic (sē-mi-ot'ik) Relating to symptoms. 'Every view which interprets the symbolic expression as an analogous or abbreviated expression of a known thing is *semiotic.* A conception which interprets the symbolic expression as the best possible formulation of a relatively unknown thing which cannot conceivably, therefore, be more clearly or characteristically represented is symbolic.' . . . 'the explanation of the Cross as a symbol of Divine Love is *semiotic,* since Divine Love describes the fact to be expressed better and more aptly than a cross, which can have many other meanings.' (Jung, C.G. *Psychological Types,* tr. by Baynes, H.G., Harcourt, Brace, New York and London, 1923)

senile (sē'nīl) Relating to, characterized by, or manifesting old age.

senility (sē-nil'i-tē) Old age, but almost invariably it is intended to convey the idea that the individual or some part of him has undergone involution or degeneration attendant upon advanced age. The onset of senility varies considerably from one individual to another, though in general it begins clinically at about the age of seventy.

senium (sē-ni-um) Feebleness of old age; also, the period of old age. In general, psychoses, psychoneuroses, or behavioral reactions appearing in old age are not considered due to senility and senile brain deterioration unless the patient is seventy years or older.

senium praecox (prē'koks) (L. 'premature old age') Premature senility. As average senility begins, at least clinically, at about the age of 70, senile manifestations in individuals under the age of fifty-five may be regarded as definitely premature. In psychiatry senium praecox is associated, for example, with Pick's disease or Alzheimer's disease; presbyophrenia is also looked upon by some as a form of premature senile deterioration.

sensation, feeling See *feeling-sensation.*

sensation, kinesthetic (kin-es-thet'ik) ('pertaining to the perception of muscular movement') The sensation derived from muscles, joints, and inner ear, giving the individual the perception of body weight, position, location, and movement. If an individual raises an arm with his eyes closed, he senses the position of his arm in space; he feels the limb as heavy or light, and realizes clearly the different stages of the movement of the arm. This is done mainly through kinesthetic sensation. Schilder points out that primitive perception shows in motion in the majority of the senses, and emphasizes his belief that this inner motion is an important factor for the recognition and understanding of the space in which the body moves. Kinesthetic sensation is an important element 'for the final evaluation of space in our minds.' Without such a knowledge, achieved through kinesthetic sensation, the individual would not have a complete perception of his own body, nor would he be able to evaluate his relationship to all other objects. (Schilder, P. *Mind, Perception and Thought,* Columbia University Press, New York, 1942)

sensation, proprioceptive (prō-pri-ō-sep'tiv) See *proprioception.*

sensation, secondary Stoddart uses this expression as synonymous with the *synesthesias.* They are those sensations 'which accompany sensations of another modality; for example, some people experience with every auditory sensation an accompanying visual sensation: the tone G is perhaps associated with the colour red or the tone D with blue. Similar sensations of color may accompany perceptions of taste, touch, pain, heat or cold: they are called "photisms." With some people certain words are accompanied by a sense of color, varying with different words (verbochromia). Again, there are secondary auditory sensations called "phonisms," secondary taste sensations called "gustatisms," secondary smell sensations called "olfactisms," and so on.' (Stoddart, W.H.B. *Mind and Its Disorders,* 5th ed., Lewis, London, 1926)

sensorium (sen-sō'ri-um) (L. 'the seat of organ of sensation') The hypothetical 'seat of sensation' or 'sense center,' located in the brain, is usually contrasted with the *motorium,* the two constituting the so-called 'animal organ-system,' while the *nutritive* and *reproductive* apparatus make up the 'vegetative organ-system.' Occasionally this term is applied to the entire sensory apparatus of the body.

With our present knowledge it does not seem possible to give a clear description of the sensorium. When psychiatrists use the term, however, they commonly have in mind the state of 'mental' clarity or unclarity the individual possesses at a given time. It seems that the condition of the sensorium is a reflection of an organic, rather than a psychic state, although it is not possible to be certain of such a concept.

When an individual is clearly aware of the nature of his surroundings, his sensorium is said to be 'clear' or 'intact.' For example, correct orientation is a manifestation of a clear sensorium. When an individual is unclear, from a sensory (not a delusional) standpoint, his sensorium is described as impaired or 'cloudy.'

Psychiatrists interchange the term *sensorium* with (organic) *consciousness*.

The sensorium may appear to be disordered, when the psyche is intensely active, as it is in severe manic states, or when the patient is completely out of the environment, as he may be while in a phase of depressive stupor.

sensory deprivation See *deprivation, sensory*.

sentiment 'Inasmuch as a sentiment . . . involves an affective element, it is obvious that *a sentiment is an idea of an object with which one or more emotions are organized*.' (Prince, M. *The Unconscious*, Macmillan, New York, 1916) The italicized words constitute the definition given by Shand.

According to McDougall, a sentiment is an organized system of emotional tendencies concerning an object or a class of objects. It is a learned form of behavior, built upon the experiences of the individual, and acting in the form of emotional tension. Sentiments are not pure emotions or motives because they cannot exist apart from a relationship to some person or object. The object may call forth different emotional behavior at different times, but this behavior is still consistent with the sentiment.

sentinel-activity *Vigilance* (q.v.).

separation See *depression, anaclitic; anxiety, separation*.

seriatim functions See *functions, seriatim*.

serotonin (ser-ō-tō'nin) A potent cerebral synaptic inhibitor, also known as 5-hydroxytryptamine, and identical with enteramine (which is found in the enterochromaffin system of the mammalian gastro-intestinal tract). Various functions have been attributed to serotonin, but its chief interest in psychiatry lies in the evidence that serotonin is normally involved as a synaptic agent in the regulation of centers in the brain concerned with wakefulness, temperature regulation, blood-pressure regulation, and various other autonomic functions. The nature of the effects produced makes it likely that serotonin, rather than acetylcholine, is the synaptic transmitter in the central parasympathetic system (the 'trophotropic' system, in Hess' terminology); and nor-epinephrine might well be the chemical transmitter in the central sympathetic ('ergotropic') nervous system. *Monoamine oxidase* (q.v.) is believed to be one of the most important agents in the metabolic breakdown of serotonin.

setting, social Milieu.

sex The fundamental biological mechanism which differentiates higher animals as males, females, or intermediate sex forms.

As *maleness* is the state associated with the production of spermatozoa, a male is an individual that is efficiently equipped for the elaboration of functional sperms and for the conveyance of these to the site of fertilization. *Femaleness* is always associated with the elaboration of ova and in mammals, in addition to possessing the property of producing eggs, the female has an equipment for the prenatal care of the embryo and foetus and for the nurture of the offspring. If both maleness and femaleness are exhibited in one and the same individual he is called a *hermaphrodite*.

Where the sexes are distinct, male is to be distinguished from female by differences in (1) the form and structure of the gonads or reproductive organs, the male's being testes, the female's, ovaries; (2) the accessory sexual apparatus of ducts and associated glands concerned with the transit of the products of the gonads; (3) the external organs of reproduction; and (4) certain skeletal, cutaneous, and other less definite physiological, biochemical, and psychological characters.

The organs that carry on the reproductive functions are known as *primary* sex organs. Those that distinguish the sexes from each other but play no direct part in reproduction are called *secondary* sexual characters.

sex-chromosome (-'krō'mō-sōm) The term

sex-chromosome denotes the pair of heterosomal chromosomes which differ in the male and female members of a species, in contrast to the other pairs of autosomal chromosomes which are alike in both sexes. See *heterosome*.

In human beings the female has the like pair of chromosomes designated as the X chromosomes. The male has only one X chromosome plus an odd chromosome. This antagonistic chromosome, empty as far as genes are concerned, is the Y chromosome. Thus the male being XY has 47 ordinary chromosomes, while the female is XX and has 48 chromosomes altogether.

The mechanism of sex-determination rests upon the genetic phenomenon that at the time of the ripening period of the eggs of the female there is a reduction of the number of the chromosomes by one half. Therefore, the ripe egg of the female has one X. Since there are two kinds of sperms—one with an X, the other with a Y—any egg fertilized by an X sperm produces an XX female, and any egg fertilized by a Y sperm produces an XY male.

In the converse condition of sex-determination found chiefly in birds and moths it is the female that is 'heterogametic,' being characterized by a pair of unlike sex-chromosomes, while the male is determined by the homologous chromosomes. In this case it is customary to describe the two sexes of animals as ZW and ZZ, respectively.

sex-determination In biology the term *sex-determination* relates to the genetic mechanism, by which in bisexual organisms the primary difference between the sexes originates in accordance with the laws of heredity. It is a difference in the heterosomal chromosome constitution between male and female individuals which explains the generally sharp segregation of the two sexes. See *sex-chromosome*.

In the female homogametic animals sex is determined by whether an X-bearing or Y-bearing sperm fertilizes the ovum, resulting in a female and a male offspring respectively. In male homogametic animals sex depends on whether a sperm fertilizes an X-bearing or Y-bearing egg, resulting in male and female offspring respectively.

Before the era of physiological genetics it was dogmatically held that the fully developed sex characters in the phenotype are dependent on this simple mechanism of sex-determination. Since Goldschmidt's studies of sex-differentiation it has been realized, however, that it is only the *predisposition* to sex that is transmitted by heredity, and that the expression in the phenotype is furthered or inhibited by physiological and environmental conditions as well as by age factors. See *sex-differentiation*.

sex-differentiation Although this term sometimes embraces both sex-determination and also sex-differentiation, it actually relates only to the developmental processes operating in the manifestation of sex differences in higher animals as expressed by Goldschmidt's 'balance theory.' The term thus indicates what happens during development after two sexually different types of zygotes have been formed by the chromosomal mechanism of *sex-determination* (q.v.).

The conception of sex-differentiation in terms of a ratio between male-determining and female-determining elements is based upon the observation that in a number of species of animals there have appeared, in addition to normal males and females, peculiar individuals which are neither typical males nor typical females. These *intersexes* (q.v.) have some male and some female characters which 'may be so intimately mixed as to give their possessors the appearance of being true intermediates between maleness and femaleness.' (Sinnott, E.W. and Dunn, L.C. *Principles of Genetics,* 3rd ed., McGraw-Hill, New York and London, 1939) They suggest that sex-differentiation is 'a competition between opposed tendencies in which the race is eventually won by that type of process (either male or female) which proceeds most rapidly at the critical period of determination.'

sex-limitation The principle of a trait occurring in one sex only, namely, one characterized by the phenotypical development of those physiological sex characters that are the necessary anatomical basis of the trait in question.

In contrast to *sex-linked* characters produced by genes which are bound to the X or Y chromosomes, the phenomenon of *sex-limitation* is *not* due directly to differences in the manifestation of the effects of genes located in one sex-chromosome. See *sex-linkage*.

sex-linkage The genetic phenomenon of

the coupling of a hereditary factor with an individual's sex-chromosome structure responsible for the development of the respective sex. It rests upon the fact that in bisexual organisms the sex distinction is transmitted by heredity in accordance with the Mendelian law of segregation, and is not to be confused with the more common mechanism of *sex-limitation*. If one of the sex-chromosomes carries a gene for a certain character, the transmission of the character and the distribution of the sexes must run together. See *sex-determination*.

The particular distribution of the sex-chromosomes in man, having heterogametic XY males, explains why sex-linkage gives different sex proportions of linked characters with respect to dominance or recessiveness. *Dominant* sex-linked characters are able to appear when only one predisposition is present. Their manifestation is therefore twice as frequent in females as in males, since the number of X chromosomes is double in females.

Recessive sex-linked anomalies can be manifested by a female only when she is a homozygote for the factor in question. As the female has two X chromosomes, one from each parent, the heterozygotic manifestation of a recessive trait, transmitted on a mother's X chromosome to her daughter, is antagonized by the effect of the X chromosome which she has from her father. In males, however, the anomaly is manifested in the heterozygotic condition, since in the case of a son who receives his single X chromosome from his mother, there is no paternal X chromosome with a dominant gene to overcome the recessive gene on the X chromosome of the mother.

Consequently, these recessive traits, of which hemophilia and color blindness are the classic examples, are usually transmitted by the female and suffered for by the male. They do not appear in both father and son unless the mother also possesses the gene. It is the rule that, through their daughters, who do not exhibit it, men transmit the trait to half of the daughters' sons.

sexology (seks-ol'ō-jē) The science of the sexes and their interrelationship.

sexopathy (seks-op'à-thē) Sexual abnormality; sexual perversion. Roland Dalbiez uses this term in preference to perversion, because of the undesirable moralistic con-

notation of the latter. Sexopathy includes both anomalies of sexual aim and anomalies of sexual object, no matter what their etiology. 'Like Havelock Ellis he [Dalbiez] is disinclined to preserve the word perversion in sexology, being of the opinion that it carries with it the moralist's veto; he suggests the word sexopathy instead.' (O'Connor, W.A. *Psychiatry, A Short Treatise,* Williams and Wilkins, Baltimore, 1948)

sex, third Freud speaks of three series of sexual characteristics; (1) 'physical sexual characteristics (physical hermaphroditism); (2) mental sexual characteristics (masculine, or feminine attitude); (3) and kind of object-choice.'

'Moreover, the tendencious publications block the way leading to a deeper insight into all that is uniformly designated homosexuality by rejecting two fundamental facts which have been revealed by psychoanalytic investigation. The first of these is that homosexual men have experienced a specially strong fixation in regard to the mother; the second, that, in addition to their manifest heterosexuality, a very considerable measure of latent or unconscious homosexuality can be detected in all normal people. If these findings are taken into account, then, to be sure, the supposition that nature in a freakish mood created a "third sex" falls to the ground.' (Freud, S. *Collected Papers,* vol. 2, tr. by Riviere, J., Leonard and Virginia Woolf and The Institute of Psychoanalysis, London, 1924–25)

sexual (sek'shoo-al) Pertaining to, characterized by, springing from or endowed with sex. In biology the term *sexual,* pertaining to the property of being male or female, is used not only to characterize what is peculiar to sex or the sexes, but also to denote the method of reproduction by sexes, as distinguished from *asexual* reproduction.

sexual, contrary Synonymous with *homosexual* and (*sexual*) *invert*.

sexualism Sexuality (q.v.); rarely used in psychiatry.

sexualitas senilis (sek-soo-ä'lē-tàs se-nē'-lēs) (Mod.L. 'senile sexuality') Krafft-Ebing's expression for sexual potency exhibited in the senile period of life.

sexuality (sek'shoo-al'i-tē) The meaning of *sexuality* to Freud apparently is twofold; rather, one should say that the sexual instincts serve two major functions—those associated with self-preservation and those with race-preservation.

The race-preservative component is really not put into actual service of reproduction until some time after puberty. There seems to be no objection, indeed, there is universal agreement, to referring to the instincts, devoted to the reproductive act, as sexual.

It has been difficult, however, to accept the idea that the sexual instincts are present and operative during the so-called latency period (from the age of five to puberty). It is not reasonable to believe that, without any conditioning whatever, the sexual instinct is dormant somewhere for 12 or 14 years, only to put in a sudden appearance at puberty in an individual wholly unprepared for adult sexuality. Freud holds that the preparations for adult sexuality are intensive and cover a long period. The sexual instincts, so universally acknowledged after puberty, are given definite assignments already during the latency period, for purposes of preparing the individual for the severest test of all, the harmonious union of the sexes, culminating in reproduction. During the latency period, however, the sexual energies do not possess specific sexual coloring; they are sublimated or hidden under the cloak of non-reproductive forms of activities. But, their purpose is race-preservation. It might have been more expedient to have given the sexual instincts of the latency period other names, which should more aptly describe the immediate nature of their service. Wheat is not bread until it has passed through many processes. It will eventually be a part of bread. The sexual instincts of the latency period are the 'wheat' of adult sexuality. See *altrigenderism; suigenderism.*

Freud uses the term *sexual* to refer to many activities of the infantile period (extending from birth until approximately the fifth year). There is sexuality, for instance, associated with infantile oral, anal, and genital organization. It seems true that part of the energies of the erogenous zones is destined for final adult sexual participation; moreover, that the zones themselves, particularly the oral and genital, are prepared from early life for the participation.

Freud's concept of sexuality is to be understood in a broad sense. Psychic energy connected with sensual and somatic satisfactions is said to be sexual energy; the latter is expressed also in the multiple forms of sublimation. 'We suppose that there are two fundamentally different kinds of instincts, the sexual instincts in the widest sense of the word (*Eros*, if you prefer that name) and the aggressive instincts, whose aim is destruction.' (Freud, S. *New Introductory Lectures on Psychoanalysis,* tr. by Sprott, W.J.H., Norton, New York, 1933)

'An attempt to formulate the general characteristics of the sexual instincts would run as follows: they are numerous, emanate from manifold organic sources, act in the first instance independently of one another and only at a later stage achieve a more or less complete synthesis. The aim which each strives to attain is "organ-pleasure"; only when the synthesis is complete do they enter the service of the function of reproduction, becoming thereby generally recognizable as sexual instincts.' (Freud, S. *Collected Papers,* vol. 4, tr. by Riviere, J., Leonard and Virginia Woolf and The Institute of Psychoanalysis, London, 1924–25)

Jung is not as comprehensive as Freud in the meaning of sexuality. What he includes under the term more closely approximates the general opinion of scientists. 'We ought to be able to recognize and to admit that much in the psyche really depends on sex, at times even everything, but that at other times little depends on sex, and nearly everything comes under the factor of self-preservation, or the power-instinct, as Adler calls it. . . . At times sex is dominant, at other times self-assertion or some other instinct. . . . When sex prevails, everything becomes sexualized, as everything then either expresses or serves the sexual purpose.' (Jung, C.G. *Contributions to Analytical Psychology,* tr. by Baynes, H.G. and C.F., Kegan Paul, Trench, Trubner, London, 1928)

Adler's general concept of sex is not greatly unlike Jung's. 'The desire for knowledge of sex differences, the uncertainty concerning his own sexual role, may be looked upon as causes of the arousing of the feeling of inferiority. Likewise the realization and grouping of traits believed to be feminine, the vacillating, doubting, hermaphroditic apperception and hermaphroditic predisposition. Predisposition to and psychic gestures of the feminine role always entail greater passivity, anxious anticipation, etc., but call forth the masculine protest, stronger emotivity.' (Adler, A. *The Neurotic Constitution,* tr. by Glueck, B. and Lind, J.E., Moffat, Yard, New York, 1917) The foregoing is said by Adler to be a 'typical cause of the onset of a neurosis.' Other typical causes, described by him, are: onset of menstruation, epoch of menstrual activity, epoch of sexual activity, the stage of fitness for marriage, pregnancy, puerperium, climacteric, reduction of potency, etc.

In biology the term *sexuality* relates to the state of being distinguished by sex. See *sex-determination.*

sexuality-index See *index of sexuality.*

sexuality, infantile The expression *infantile sexuality* is common in psychoanalysis. It is maintained by psychoanalysts that 'this period of life, during which a certain degree of directly sexual pleasure is produced by the stimulation of various cutaneous areas (erotogenic zones), by the activity of certain biological impulses and as an accompanying excitation during many affective states, is designated by an expression introduced by Havelock Ellis as the period of auto-erotism.' (Freud, S. *Collected Papers,* vol. 2, tr. by Riviere, J., Leonard and Virginia Woolf and The Institute of Psychoanalysis, London, 1924–25)

This stimulation of the oral and anal zones, as well as of the genital, is connected with infantile sexuality.

'Freud and his co-workers have produced abundant evidence to show that this instinct [i.e. sexual] is actively operative long before this time [i.e. puberty], and probably from early childhood, though what is called infantile sexuality widely differs from the adult form, being, like other childhood manifestations, much more diffuse, tentative, and preliminary in nature. Amongst other striking differences, two special ones may be briefly mentioned here: the close association between infantile sexuality and excretory functions, and the sexual coloring in the child's relation to its near relatives (the so-called "incest-complex").' (Jones, E. *Papers on Psycho-Analysis,* 4th ed., Wood, Baltimore, 1938)

sexualization (sek-shoo-al-i-zā'shun) The act of sexualizing. See *sexuality.*

sexualize (sek'shoo-al-īz) To endow with sexual energy or instinct. The genitals become sexualized at an early age. Other parts of the body (breasts, oral region, hands, etc.) may possess sexual qualities. Thoughts may be sexualized, as for example, when they appear in the form of sexual jokes.

shadow In Jung's analytical psychology this term means the unconscious.

'For the sake of understanding, it is, I think, a good thing to detach the man from his shadow, the unconscious. . . . One sees much in another man which does not belong to his conscious psychology, but which gleams out from his unconscious, and one is rather tempted to regard the observed quality as belonging to the conscious ego.' (Jung, C.G. *Psychological Types,* tr. by Baynes, H.G., Harcourt, Brace, New York and London, 1923)

shame Psychodynamically, shame is considered to be the specific force directed against urethral-eroticism, just as the fear of being eaten is the specific oral fear, and the fear of being robbed of body contents is the specific anal fear. Ambition is the fight against this shame.

Shame is also used as a defense against exhibitionism and voyeurism; 'I feel ashamed' means 'I do not want to be seen.'

shell-shock A general term, particularly wide in its application to psychic disorders occurring during active warfare. Many of the illnesses called shell-shock are encountered in civil life and are then usually regarded as traumatic neuroses.

'The purposive aspect of hysterical dissociations is of unusually direct importance in the "traumatic neuroses." This was very evident in the War hysterias, the hysterical disability making further service in the danger zone impossible. . . . Ross has pointed out that it was often easy enough to remove a hysterical paralysis from "shell-shock" by suggestion, and that the patient appeared pleased and grateful for perhaps two days afterwards. Then, however, he began to have signs of considerable mental unrest—because he now realized that there was nothing between him and a return to active service.' (Henderson, D.K. and Gillespie, R.D. *A Text-Book of Psychiatry,* 4th ed., Oxford University Press, London, 1936)

shock 1. A sudden physical or mental disturbance.

2. A state of profound mental and physical depression consequent upon severe physical injury or an emotional disturbance.

shock, color A term used in Rorschach scoring for a response to the introduction of color into the series of cards which indicates disturbance. The most frequent expression of color shock is an increase in reaction time to the colored cards.

shock, psychodramatic In psychodramatics 'a procedure which throws a patient, barely escaped from a psychosis, back into a re-experience of the psychotic attack is a psychodramatic shock treatment. The patient is asked to throw himself back into the hallucinatory experience when it is still most vivid in his mind. He is not asked to describe it; he must act. He puts his body into the position as it was then and acts as he acted then. He may select any members of the staff to recreate the hallucinatory situations. This makes the procedure a "psychodrama." The patient usually shows a violent resistance against being thrown back into the painful experience from which he has just escaped. Doing this, despite a violent fear, produces a "shock."

'Acting upon a psychotic level at a time when he is extremely sensitive to the vanished mental syndrome, the patient learns to check himself. It is a training in mastering of psychotic invasions, not through analysis but through a reconstruction of the psychotic experiences from act to act, from role to role, and from delusion to delusion, until the whole sphere of the psychosis is projected upon the therapeutic stage. It is a preventative therapy. The patient is trained to develop spontaneous controls with which to ward off the sudden onset of a psychotic invasion. The procedure produces a cathartic effect. Psychodramatic procedure, as differentiated from other shock procedures which leave a patient helpless and inarticulate, insists that the patient reproduce with his own body that fantastic world in which he has been lost.' (Moreno, J.L. *Sociometry 2, 6, 1939*)

shock-therapy See *therapy, shock; treatment, shock.*

shock-treatment See *treatment, shock.*

shortening reaction See *rigidity, decerebrate.*

short stare epilepsy A type of petit mal epilepsy. See *epilepsy.*

shower, cold Sands writes: '*Cold showers* are usually given to those who are physically able to stand them. These showers are valuable as stimulants to the nervous system, as well as general cleansing agents. Cold baths, though once popular, are now rarely employed. The cold plunge, so popular several years ago, has been judiciously replaced by the cold shower.' (Sands, I.J. *Nervous and Mental Diseases for Nurses,* 3rd ed., Saunders, Philadelphia and London, 1937)

show, half See *half-show.*

shut-in August Hoch's term for the premorbid personality which is seen in approximately 60 per cent of schizophrenics: quiet, reserved, asocial, withdrawn, seclusive, 'lone-wolf' types, those who live among but not with, etc. Bleuler's term, schizoid, is approximately equivalent to 'shut-in.'

sialorrh(o)ea (sī-à-lo-rē′à) Excessive salivation.

sibling (sib′ling) In human genetics, one of two or more children not simultaneously born of the same two parents. It thus excludes twins or other multiples as well as half-brothers and half-sisters, and step-brothers and step-sisters. However, the definition in all leading dictionaries makes it a far less restricted term.

sibship A genetic term pertaining to one series of siblings, that is, to all the biological children of a union of two parents, excluding multiples. See *birth, multiple.*

sibship method See *method, sibship.*

sicchasia (si-kā′z[h]i-à) Disgust for food.

side-impulse See *impulse, side.*

siderodromophobia (sid-ĕr-ō-drom-ō-fō′-bi-à, -drō-mō-fō′bi-à) Fear of railroads or trains.

siderophobia (sid-ĕr-ō-fō′bi-à) Fear of the heavens and what comes from them— the elements, etc. Bianchi writes that 'the subject turns pale, suffers from tremors, dryness of the mouth, visceral movements, diarrhoeic discharges, sometimes nausea, palpitation, oppression, or even a fit of real anguish (*siderophobia*).' (Bianchi, L. *A Text-Book of Psychiatry,* tr. by MacDonald, J.H., Baillière, Tindall & Cox, London, 1906)

Sidis, Boris (1876–1923) American psychiatrist.

Siemerling, Ernst (1857–1931) (zē'mĕr-ling) German psychiatrist and neurologist.

sigmatism (sig'mà-tiz'm) Difficulty in pronouncing of the S (and Z) sound.

signal, anxiety A psychoanalytic term designating the concept, based upon clinical observations, that the emergence of previously repressed and suppressed instinctual trends from the unconscious, or id, into the conscious (mind), or ego, is heralded in consciousness by a warning signal—anxiety. This warning signal is of a painful nature, usually so painful that, as a result, immediate defensive suppression of the dangerous emergent instinct takes place, with the result that the ego is relieved of this pain.

R. Sterba (*Introduction to the Psychoanalytic Theory of the Libido,* Nervous and Mental Disease Monographs No. 68, New York, 1942) states: 'One has to assume that in these cases [anxiety hysteria] anxiety is not caused by libido but is the result of libido, that the Ego fears the dangerous libidinal tendency and that the anxiety, owing to the intense sensation of pain which it creates, is usually able to block libido processes.'

sign, Brudzinski (broo-jĕñ'ski) (J. Brudzinski, Polish physician, 1874–1917) The Brudzinski sign is essentially indicative of meningitis. By passively flexing the head on the chest, a flexion of the lower limbs is produced.

sign, echo *Rare.* The term refers to a speech-disorder observed in epileptic patients and is characterized by the repetition of a word in some part of a sentence.

sign, eyelash In a case of unconsciousness due to functional disease, such as epilepsy or hysteria, stroking the eyelashes will make the lids move, but no such reflex will occur in case of organic brain lesion such as apoplexy, fracture of the skull, or other severe traumatism.

sign, Hoffmann (Johann Hoffmann, German neurologist, 1857–1919) In hemiplegia due to organic brain disease, snapping of the index or ring finger produces flexion of the thumb.

sign, Kernig's (Waldemar Kernig, Russian physician, 1840–1917) The Kernig sign is observed in meningitis. Flexing the

thigh at the hip, and extending the leg at the knee, produces pain and resistance.

sign, Litten's (Moritz Litten, German physician, 1845–1907) In paralysis of the diaphragm, non-projection of shadow by the diaphragm x-rayed during respiration.

sign, Marcus Gunn (Marcus Gunn, contemporary British surgeon) The raising of a ptosed lid on opening the mouth and moving the jaw to the opposite side.

sign, mirror A symptom seen frequently in schizophrenic patients, who tend to stand in front of a mirror or other shining surface for an unduly long time. The mirror sign is generally regarded as an expression of the patient's autistic withdrawal.

sign, Romberg (Moritz Heinrich Romberg, German physician, 1795–1873) Swaying of the body when the patient stands with the feet together and the eyes closed, indicating a condition of ataxia.

sign, Rosenbach's (Ottomar Rosenbach, German physician, 1851–1907) Inability of neurasthenics to close the eyes immediately and completely on command.

sign, Rumpf (Theodor Rumpf, German physician, 1862–1923) In cases of neurasthenia pressure over a painful point will accelerate the pulse from ten to twenty beats per minute.

sign, Schuele's (Heinrich Schuele, German psychiatrist, 1839–1916) See *omega melancholicum.*

sign, Stiller's (Berthold Stiller, Budapest physician, 1837–1922) The presence of a floating tenth rib as indicative of a neurasthenic tendency; called also costal stigma.

sign, Strümpell (Adolf von Strümpell, German neurologist, 1853–1925) In organic hemiplegia, dorsiflexion of the hand occurs on making a fist.

sign, tibialis In organic hemiplegia, dorsal flexion of the foot occurs on flexion at the knee and hip.

sign, Westphal's (vest'fàlz) (Carl Friedrich Otto Westphal, German neurologist, 1833–1890) Loss of the knee jerk.

silence, insane An older expression used by T.S. Clouston to denote insanity with mutism.

silence, selective This psychiatric term denotes the deliberate silence and the withholding of response, information, or free-association which a patient resorts to at a point of anxiety or negative transference toward the therapist or the group in order to resist the therapeutic situation.

Simmonds' disease (Morris Simmonds, German physician, 1855–1925) See *cachexia, hypophysial.*

Simon-Binet tests See *tests, Binet-Simon.*

simple schizophrenia See *schizophrenia, simple.*

simulant Simulator.

simulate Malinger, deceive.

singultus (sing-gul'tus, L. sēng-gool'toos) Hiccough.

sinistrality See *dextrality-sinistrality.*

sinistrosis (sin-is-trō'sis) Shell-shock.

sitiophobia (sit-i-ō-fō'bi-à) Sitophobia.

sitomania (sī-tō-mā'ni-à) Boulimia; a morbid, voracious appetite.

sitophobia Fear of (eating) food.

situational reaction See *transient situational personality disorders.*

situation, danger See *anxiety.*

situation, either-or The term for a situation of doubt and vacillation in which the neurotic places himself, especially in dreams. In such situations the patient desires two different things at the same time and does not know which to choose. An example of this is the neurotic patient with a strong mother attachment who is also deeply in love with his fiancée: in his dreams he symbolizes either his mother or his fiancée, but always with a profound doubt about which of them he should love more. The patient vacillates between two principles and this vacillation may refer to persons, objects, or ideas.

sixty-nine A slang expression referring to fellatio and/or cunnilinction practiced simultaneously by two persons, the head of each being near the feet of the other.

sketch, biographic This expression is often used in the field of objective psychobiology (Adolf Meyer) to refer to the life history of the patient as the latter records it. To facilitate the recording Meyer devised what he calls *The Life Chart,* consisting of topical guides for the individual who is writing his biographic sketch.

skew-deviation See *deviation, skew.*

skoptsy (skop-tsē') A Russian religious sect (a subdivision of the *raskol'niki,* the schismatics or dissenters) whose adherents practice castration, in conformity with the passage: 'And there be eunuchs, which have made themselves eunuchs for the kingdom of heaven's sake. He that is able to receive it, let him receive it.' (St. Math. XIX, 12; cf. also V, 29–30; XVIII, 8–9; St. Mark IX, 43–7; Rom. VIII, 13; Col. III, 5)

Castration among the skoptsy is of two degrees: (1) *the small seal (first purity; mounting a piebald horse),* involving removal of scrotum only, with the testicles. (2) *the grand seal (second purity; mounting a white horse),* total castration, with the excision of both the scrotum and the reproductive organ. Women, too, undergo castration and even remove their breasts.

The skoptsy seek salvation through mortifying the flesh by castration. They await the Second Advent when the Savior will 'roll in on a fiery chariot, will ring the bell of St. John's Church in Moscow and assemble for his Kingdom his faithful little children.'

The sect of skoptsy is an outgrowth of the *Kristovshchina* (Christist faith), who elect a Christ, Theotokos (Mother of God, Virgin Mary), the Apostles, and an Old Maid from among their numbers.

In economic life, the skoptsy have plied the trade of money-changers almost exclusively and 'all their passions have turned into profit and acquisitiveness.' In appearance they usually look bloated, with a flabby, livid skin, light-colored sparse hair (none on the upper lip or chin), piping effeminate voice, and phlegmatic movements.

slavering *Obs.* Drooling.

sleep, continuous See *treatment, continuous sleep.*

sleep-drunkenness Somnolentia; a half-waking condition in which the faculty of orientation is in abeyance, and, under the influence of nightmare-like ideas, the person becomes actively excited and violent, sometimes to the extent of inflicting injury upon others.

sleep, paroxysmal Sleep epilepsy, narcolepsy; a sudden uncontrollable disposition to sleep occurring at irregular intervals, with or without obvious predisposing or exciting cause.

sleep-walking See *somnambulism.*

sleep, yen (Chinese *yen,* smoke, opium) A slang expression used by morphine or heroin addicts for the somnolence that affects them when the drug is withdrawn.

slip of tongue See *lapsus linguae.*

slum A slum is an urban area characterized by physical deterioration and social disorganization so marked as to result in the personal disorganization of its residents in the form of juvenile delinquency, adult crime, vice, alcoholism, gambling, mental disorders, etc.

The term slum connotes 'the worst structural and sanitary conditions and the most degraded occupancy, usually on the lowest income groups, of any period.' (Newman, B.J. *Slums; Encyclopaedia of the Social Sciences,* vol. 14, Macmillan, New York, 1934, p. 93)

smother-love See *love, smother.*

snake, symbol of Symbols of snakes are based on symbolization of the male genital. Before he knew the principles of biology, primitive man could think of only one thing: that because the genitals produce life they were, therefore, the symbols of life; hence snakes or symbols of them were carried in processions and worshipped. Though there is no obvious resemblance between the snake and the male genital, to the conscious eye there is nevertheless suggested a hidden similarity for the unconscious to draw the analogy. The story of Adam and Eve has a truly allegorical significance. Adam and Eve represent humanity in its infancy, when it was untroubled, naked, and free, when life was a paradise. But then comes the snake, the symbol of sex, and the situation takes on an altogether different aspect. Dreams about snakes are very common, but we must guard against the conclusion that the snake always signifies the male genital. (Brill, A.A. *Basic Principles of Psychoanalysis,* Doubleday, New York, 1949)

snow (From the cocaine powder's resemblance to snow both in whiteness and powder consistence) Slang expression for cocaine.

snow-bird Slang expression for a cocaine addict.

social impulse, fundamental See *impulse, fundamental social.*

socialization In sociology, socialization is 'the development of a social nature or character—a social state of mind—in the individuals who associate.' (Giddings,

F.H. *Theory of Socialization,* Macmillan, New York, 1897)

'The interactional process by which the individual is taught his place in the social order.' (Young, K. *An Introductory Sociology,* American Book, New York, 1934)

The form 'in which individuals on the basis of interests grow together into a unity and within which these interests come to realization.' (Simmel, G. *American Journal of Sociology XV,* 297, 1909)

'From the standpoint of the group, [socialization] is the psychic articulation of the individual into the collective activities. From the standpoint of the person, socialization is the participation of the individual in the spirit and purpose, knowledge and methods, decision and action of the group.' (Burgess, E.W. *The Function of Socialization in Social Evolution,* University of Chicago Press, Chicago, 1910)

In occupational therapy this term is applied to the development (in a patient) of those tendencies which induce him to be companionable and inclined to seek and mingle easily with a group.

In psychiatry the term means the condition in which inner impulses (i.e. instincts and their derivatives) are expressed or lived out in conformity with the cultural demands of the environment.

It is synonymous with *sublimation* (q.v.).

socialize 1. Synonymous with *sublimate* (q.v.) 2. To mix in a group.

social type See *type, social.*

social work, family 'Family social work is a field of organized practice having to do with human relationships. Its main purpose is to help individuals deal effectively with difficulties experienced in relating themselves to others in their families and in their communities. This practice is based on a growing body of knowledge about human beings as functioning members of society and it employs the technique and art termed social case work.' (Lund, H.H. *Social Work Year Book 1939,* ed. by Kurtz, R.H., Russell Sage Foundation, New York)

social work, psychiatric The adaptation and application of social psychiatry and mental hygiene to case-work practice. 'Psychiatric social workers are usually concerned with the social case study and treatment of children or adults whose personal and social maladjustments are primarily due to mental health problems, including nervous and mental diseases and defects, and emotional behavior, and habit disorders.' (C. Bassett. *Social Work Year Book 1939*, ed. by R.H. Kurtz. Russell Sage Foundation, New York)

The term has also been defined as 'the branch of social case work that deals with cases of social maladjustment in which a mental factor or a behavior problem is of primary importance.' ('Vocational Aspects of Psychiatric Social Work,' *Mental Hygiene*, 1925)

society Society may be regarded 'as the most general term referring to the whole complex of the relations of man to his fellows.' (Parsons, T. *Society: Encyclopaedia of the Social Sciences*, vol. 14, Macmillan, New York, 1934, p. 225)

It is 'the system of social relationships in and through which we live' (MacIver, R.M. *Society, A Textbook of Sociology*, Farrar & Rinehart, New York, 1937), and 'the sum total of social institutions.' (Park, R.E. and Burgess, E.W. *Introduction to the Science of Sociology*, University of Chicago Press, Chicago, 1921)

Society is 'a highly intricate network of partial or complete understandings between the members of organizational units of every degree of size and complexity, ranging from a pair of lovers or a family to a league of nations.' (Sapir, E. *Communication; Encyclopaedia of the Social Sciences*, vol. 4, Macmillan, New York, 1931, p. 78)

sociogram (sō'shi-ō-gram) 'The sociogram projects the results of sociometric, spontaneity and population tests into a pattern and makes visible the relationship of every individual to every other individual of the group tested. Thus, the position of every individual is defined as well as the configuration of the total structure.

'The sociogram is primarily a method for exploring the invisible structure of society. As a guide it has led to discoveries of social structures which could not have been revealed through other means. It showed, for example, the positions of emotional isolates in a group, of pair attractions and pair rejections, of triangles, of chains of interpersonal relations, the positions of leader structures and the cliques of individuals who are separated from the group as a whole.' (Moreno, J.L. *Sociometry 1*, 212, 1937)

sociometry (sō-shi-om'i-trē) 'Sociometry is the study of the actual psychological structure of human society. This structure, rarely visible on the surface of social processes, consists of complex interpersonal patterns which are studied by quantitative and qualitative procedures.

'Sociometry proceeds upon the premise that there is some sort of order in the phenomena with which it deals. The psychological situation of a community viewed as a whole has a discernible ordered pattern. It presents itself in laws and tendencies which are discoverable by means of experiment and analysis.

'From the point of view of a "medical" sociology, it is essential to know the actual structure of human society at a given moment. The sociometric procedure obtains this knowledge by considering every individual in his concreteness and not as a symbol. Every relationship an individual may have with another person or persons is also considered in its concreteness. The actual structure is best obtained when the individuals are placed in a situation where they spontaneously uncover their relationships. A fundamental part of the sociometric procedure is to apply to a community an actual social situation which is confronting its people at the moment. The social situation applied is of such a nature as to make repetition possible at any time in the future without loss of spontaneous participation. In this manner, the procedure reveals the organization and evolution of groups and the position of individuals within them.' (Moreno, J.L. 'Inter-Personal Therapy,' *Sociometry 1*, 19, 1937)

sociopath (sō'shi-ō-path) A term that was proposed to designate the psychopathic personality, since the symptoms of psychopathy are manifested in the field of social behavior. The term has not achieved any considerable degree of acceptance.

sociopathic personality disturbance In the 1952 revision of psychiatric nomenclature, this term is used to refer to individuals who are ill primarily in terms of society and of conformity with social, cultural, and ethical demands. This group does *not* include those whose conduct and behavior is symptomatic of more primary personality disturbance. Included in this group are:

(1) *Antisocial reaction* (q.v.)—approximately equivalent to the older terms

'constitutional psychopathy' and 'psychopathic personality.'

(2) Dyssocial reaction—disregard for and conflict with the social code as the result of having lived their lives in an abnormal moral environment.

(3) Sexual deviation—such as homosexuality, transvestism, pedophilia, fetishism, sexual sadism.

(4) *Addiction* (q.v.).
   (a) *Alcoholism* (q.v.).
   (b) Drug Addiction.

sociopathology (sō-shi-ō-pà-thol'ō-jē) The pathology of society. Society at large, or any segment of society, is composed of or comprises an aggregate of individuals, and the psychopathology of the patient as an individual or of a few or many of the group is quantitatively and qualitatively reflected ultimately as the psychopathology of the society that contains the individuals. Individual psychopathology is thus closely intermeshed with communal sociopathology. And the reciprocal importance of this fact should find the agencies of preventive mental hygiene teamed with those of public health in a common purpose.

sociopathy (sō-shi-op'à-thē) 1. This term has generally been used to designate an abnormal or pathological mental attitude toward the environment. Thus criminality and vagabondage are regarded by some authorities as manifestations of sociopathy. In this sense the term refers to mental states that are commonly subsumed under psychopathy.

2. Abnormality or pathology of society or social units.

sodomist (sod'um-ist) One who practices sodomy; a sodomite.

sodomite One who practices sodomy; a sodomist.

sodomy (sod'um-ē) 'Sodomy, in the widest use, is carnal copulation by human beings with each other against nature or with a beast. In the narrower sense, "sodomy is carnal copulation between two human beings per anum, or by a human being in any manner with a beast." Present sodomy laws may cover homosexual acts, certain acts between heterosexual partners, acts with animals, fowls, or corpses, and, in one or two states, mutual masturbation or incitement to masturbation. In the act per anum, the term mankind includes females.' (Bowman, K.M.,

and Enger, B. *American Journal of Psychiatry 112:* 577–83, 1956)

soiling See *encopresis.*

soliloquy, sexual Hirschfeld says that many sexually timid individuals, who find difficulty in suppressing or repressing their sexual impulses, engage in long soliloquies as a means of relieving their sexual tensions.

solipsism (sol'ip-siz'm) The doctrine that *my self, alone,* is the essence of existence and that nothing counts except my ego, in which all else is reflected.

soma (sō'mà) The organic tissues of the body. Thus, the brain, heart, musculature, bone, constitute parts of the soma. Whether entirely correctly or not, the terms *soma* and *psyche* are often employed as if they were opposites. The psyche, however, is currently considered as an organ of the total individual; it is not looked upon as an antithesis of the soma, but rather as a harmonious constituent of the entire organism. See *psyche.*

somatalgia (sō-mà-tal'ji-à) Pain due to organic causes, is to be distinguished from psychalgia or pain due to psychical causes.

To a patient, pain may have all the appearances of being organically determined, yet the organ from which the pain seems to come may serve merely as the vehicle for expressing psychical pain. This is a common phenomenon in conversion hysteria, in which condition complaints of a severe character about an organ have no connection with known organic anatomy, physiology, or pathology, but are identified closely with matters in the psyche. See *hypochondriasis; psychalgia.*

somatic (sō-mat'ik) Relating to or involving the soma.

somatist (sō'mà-tist) Psychiatrist or scientist who regards any particular neurosis or psychosis as of organic or physical origin.

somatization (sō-mà-ti-zā'shun) Stekel's term for a type of bodily disorder arising from a deep-seated neurotic cause. It is as if the organs of the body were translating into a physiopathological language the mental troubles of the individual. The term somatization is identical with the phenomena Freud calls 'conversion.' Stekel refers to it also in terms of 'organ-speech of the mind,' meaning the organic expression of mental processes. Such physical expressions are also encountered in dreams, and when they occur, the oneiric phenomena or process is known as 'functional dream.' See *dream, functional.*

It seems that in somatization there are 'certain areas of predilection' for the organic expression of the psychic conflicts. (Stekel, W. *The Interpretation of Dreams,* Liveright, New York, 1943)

somato- (sō'mȧ-tō-) Combining form meaning body, from Gr. *sōma, -atos,* body.

somatobiology The study of the biology of the body, as contrasted with psychobiology, which is the study of the biology of the mind. (Hinsie, L.E. *Understandable Psychiatry,* Macmillan, New York, 1948)

somatogenesis (so-mȧ-tō-jen'e-sis) Origination in organic tissue (the soma). For example, paralysis of an extremity, associated with arteriosclerosis, is said to be somatogenic.

somatoplasm (sō'mȧ-tō-plaz'm) In biology, the somatic tissues of an animal body, to distinguish them, according to the *germ plasm* theory, from the reproductive tissue which produces the germ cells.

Hence, from the genetic standpoint, the somatoplasm represents the temporary, perishable envelope of an organism, the body, which the *gametes* can produce anew in each generation. While the germ plasm gives rise to both new germ cells and body cells, the soma never gives rise to germ plasm.

However, since the distinction between germ plasm and somatoplasm does not seem to exist in plants and lower animals, 'it cannot be considered as of fundamental or universal importance.' (Sinnott, E.W. and Dunn, L.C. *Principles of Genetics,* 3rd ed., McGraw-Hill, New York and London, 1939)

somatopsychic (sō-mȧ-tō-sī'kik) Relating to or originating in both body and mind.

somatopsychonoologia (-sī-kō-nō-ō-loj'-i-ȧ) *Obs.* Psychosomatism. The term was introduced in 1823 by Thomas Forster.

somatopsychosis (-sī-kō'sis) Southard's term for a psychosis associated with visceral disease.

somatosexual (-sek'shoo-al) Pertaining to or characterized by organic manifestations of sexuality.

somatosexuality (-sek-shoo-al'i-tē) Somatosexual condition or state, or sexuality

as it exists in the tissues or soma or organs. For example, sexuality, expressing itself through the genitals, is a form of somatosexuality.

somatotonia -(tō'ni-ȧ) A personality type described by Sheldon which is correlated with the mesomorph body type and which shows a predominance of vigorous assertiveness and muscular activity.

somatotopagnosia (top-ag-nō'zhi-ȧ) *Autotopagnosia* (q.v.).

somatotype (sō-ma'tō-tīp) In some systems of constitutional medicine, this means the physical structure and build of a person as assessed by particular photographic techniques of *anthropometry.* Its scientific meaning thus applies only to one aspect of an *anthrotype* which has physiological, immunological, and psychological aspects as well. See *anthrotype.*

-some (-sōm) Combining form meaning body, from Gr. *sōma,* body.

somesthetic area (som-es-thet'ik) See *lobe, parietal.*

somite (sō'mit) In the development of an embryo, a mesodermic segment formed by the medial portions of the third germ layer or *mesoderm.*

Sommer, Robert (1864–1937) (zôm'mēr) German psychiatrist.

somnambulism Sleep-walking. 'Somnambulisms are dissociated states identical with the above [i.e. fugue] except that they begin during sleep. They are common in childhood, when their motivation often appears on the surface. For example, a patient who in late life developed a depressive illness had been in his childhood much attached to his mother, and antagonistic to his father, who treated him badly. In his somnambulism he would make for his parents' bedroom and endeavor to get in at the side of the bed on which his mother slept.' (Henderson, D.K. and Gillespie, R.D. *A Text-Book of Psychiatry,* 4th ed., Oxford University Press, London, 1936)

The individuals are not always asleep in the usual sense of the word. 'Incidentally, however, the nature of these states [i.e. hypnoidal] and the degree of their inaccessibility to the rest of conscious processes would very probably vary in a fashion similar to that of hypnosis, which ranges from light sleepiness to somnambulism, from complete recollection to absolute amnesia.' (Freud, S. *Collected Papers*, vol. 1, tr. by Riviere, J., Leonard and Virginia Woolf and The Institute of Psychoanalysis, London, 1924–25)

somnambulism, cataleptic (kat-à-lep'tik) A cataleptic state occurring during somnambulism.

somnambulism, complete Janet speaks of restoring patients to a state of 'artificially induced health' through hypnosis. But sometime after the hypnosis is over the former symptoms return and the patient forgets the period of artificially induced health. 'In a word, the forgetfulness supervening upon the relapse, gave the aspect of somnambulism to the period of quasi-normal health. That is why, in order to denote the periods of temporary restoration, I use the term "complete somnambulism," which had already been employed by Azam to denote kindred phenomena.' (Janet, P. *Psychological Healing*, vols. 1–2, tr. by Paul, E. and C., Macmillan, New York, 1925)

somnambulism, ecstatic When, during the somnambulistic state 'the expression is fervid and suggests abstract contemplation while unconscious of surrounding objects, the case is labelled ecstasy.' (Tuke, D.H. *A Dictionary of Psychological Medicine*, vols. 1–2, Blakiston, 1892)

somnambulisme pathologique (sôm-näN-bü-lism' pà-tô-lô-zhēk') (F. 'pathological sleepwalking') Janet says that emotion 'is in reality nothing more than a kind of fatigue.' During hypnosis 'attention is speedily fatigued,' and consciousness is narrowed to the ideas suggested by the hypnotist. 'At the moment of suggestion there occurs a shock, there is felt an emotion which destroys the subject's enfeebled personal synthesis, so that the suggested idea remains isolated.' The condition just described is known as *somnambulisme pathologique*. (Janet, P. *Psychological Healing*, vols. 1–2, tr. by Paul, E. and C., Macmillan, New York, 1925)

somnambulisme provoqué (prô-vô-kà') (F. 'induced or hypnotic sleep') 'When a subject is in a natural somnambulist crisis, or has a fit of hysterics accompanied by delirium and babbling which resembles somnambulism, his condition may be easily transformed, and he may be made to pass into the hypnotic state.' (Janet, P. *Psychological Healing*, vols.

1–2, tr. by Paul, E. and C., Macmillan, New York, 1925)

somnambulism, monoideic (mon-ō-ī-dē'-ik) When the ideational content associated with the state of somnambulism revolves about a single idea, Janet speaks of monoideic somnambulism. When the content contains many ideas he calls it polyideic somnambulism.

somnambulism, polyideic (pol-i-ī-dē'ik) See *somnambulism, monoideic*.

somnial (som'ni-al) *Rare*. Pertaining to dreams.

somnifacient (som-ni-fā'shent) Hypnotic; sleep-inducing.

somniferous (som-nif'ēr-us) Hypnotic; somnific.

somnific Somniferous; hypnotic.

somnifugous (som-nif'ū-gus) Driving sleep away; agrypnotic.

somniloquism (som-nil'ō-kwiz'm) Talking in sleep.

somniloquy Talking in sleep.

somnipathist (som-nip'à-thist) One affected by or under the influence of somnipathy.

somnipathy 1. Any sleep disorder; 2. hypnotism.

somnocyclism (som-nō-sīk'liz'm) *Obs*. Bicycle-riding in a state of somnambulism.

somnolence (som'nō-lens) Unnatural sleepiness, drowsiness.

somnolentia (sôm-nō-len'tē-à) 1. Sleep-drunkenness. 2. Somnolence.

somnolism (som'nō-liz'm) Hypnotism.

somnovigil (som-no-vij'il) *Obs*. Somnambulism.

sophomania (sof-ō-mā'ni-à) A form of megalomania in which the patient stresses the excellence of his wisdom.

sopient (sō'pi-ent) Soporific.

sopite (sō-pīt') *Rare*. Drowsy.

sopor (sō'por) (L. 'deep sleep') Torpor.

soporiferous (sō-pō-rif'ēr-us) Soporific, making drowsy.

soporific, soporifical Any sleep-inducing agent.

soporose (sop'ō-rōs) Characterized or affected by morbid sleepiness.

soul See *anima*.

soul, folk A kind of mystical group-mind, the presence of which is deduced from the way each individual displays properties and modes of reaction not present when he remains outside the group. The folk soul is considered a sort of supermind which is transcendental and possesses more good than the individual minds that contribute to it. The following terms are nearly synonymous with folk soul: group-mind (McDougall); general will (Rousseau); collective consciousness (Renan); social consciousness (Espinas, Durkheim, Wundt); group consciousness (Heard). Many do not accept the presence of a folk soul or group-mind and, instead, would explain collective reactions like communism and anarchism as racial neurosis (see *psychosis, collective*). Freud explains group psychology on the basis of individual identification with one another, secondary to the sharing of a common emotional situation.

source In psychoanalysis the term *source* (of an instinct) refers to 'that somatic process in an organ or part of the body from which there results a stimulus represented in mental life by an instinct.' (Freud, S. *Collected Papers*, vol. 4, tr. by Riviere, J., Leonard and Virginia Woolf and The Institute of Psychoanalysis, London, 1924–25) Freud claims that 'the study of the sources of instincts is outside the scope of psychology,' because it probably involves physiochemical processes. He then adds that 'although its source in the body is what gives the instinct its distinct and essential character, yet in mental life we know it merely by its aims.' (ibid.)

Southard, Elmer Ernest (1876–1920) American psychiatrist.

space, subarachnoid (sub-ar-ak'noid) See *meninges*.

spasm A slow, at times prolonged, pattern movement of a muscle or groups of muscles occurring anywhere in the body.

spasm, masticatory Tonic closure of the jaw; it may be part of a syndrome of hysteria, meningitis, tetanus, epilepsy; it occasionally occurs in tumors or other diseases of the pons.

spasm, nodding This term designates a disorder that occurs in infants and is characterized by head-shaking and nystagmus. Kanner describes the spasm as 'continuous or intermittent, mostly arrhythmic, involuntary, horizontal, vertical or rotary movements of the head.' The head-shaking is usually accompanied by unilateral or bilateral nystagmus and by vertical, horizontal, or rotary eye movements. 'The condition is confined to the first two or three years of life. It is an involuntary reaction and does not seem to be (specifically) associated with emotional disturbances.' (Kanner, L. *Child Psychiatry*, Thomas, Springfield, Ill., 1948)

spasmophemia (spaz-mō-fē'mi-à) *Obs.* Speaking in spasms; stammering or stuttering.

spasmophilia (spaz-mō-fil'i-à) In general and constitutional medicine this term means a syndrome characterized by undersecretion of the parathyroids and frequently associated with a generalized hypoparathyroid constitution. See *constitution, hypoparathyroid*.

spasm, salaam (or **salutation**) A variety of spasm seen in young children. Salaam spasms are described by Kanner as consisting of 'periodic and rhythmic movements of the head and upper part of the body of about two seconds duration with intervals of approximately ten seconds. They resemble the oriental form of greeting. The condition is mostly associated with neuro-pathologic findings.' (Kanner, L. *Child Psychiatry*, Thomas, Springfield, Ill., 1948)

spasm, saltatory (sal'tà-tō-rē) Spasm of the muscles of the lower extremities producing jumping or skipping movements, occurring in hysteria.

spasmus nutans (spàz'moos nōō'tàns) (L. 'nutant, nodding spasm') A rhythmic nodding or rotatory tremor of the head occurring in infants between the ages of six and twelve months; frequently accompanied by nystagmus.

spatial summation See *summation*.

species In natural science, a group of animals or plants which rank below the genus and divisible into varieties or *subspecies*. The individuals forming a species are assumed to resemble one another in the essential features of their organization and to produce fertile offspring that vary from the general type of the group to a limited extent only.

The criterion of *specific status* of Darwin's *Origin of Species* has frequently been regarded as an arbitrary matter having a purely systemic value, because Darwin suggested that species cannot be regularly discriminated from other categories as a distinct and standardized evolutionary grade. However, as knowledge advanced with modern genetics, there came considerable tendency to rehabilitate the special status of a species—as having some objective genetic basis—as well as the doctrine rejected by Darwin that the criterion of a species is 'successful breeding inter se.'

The origin of species was still unexplained owing to the scant data on genetics in general and mutations in particular at that time. Natural selection, which Darwin held to be a gradual creative process bringing new types into existence, is considered in modern genetics a discontinuous process with considerable gaps due to mutations, which create new types whose numbers tend to increase or to dwindle on the principle of survival of the fittest.

specific *Biol.* Pertaining to a *species.*

specific dynamic pattern Franz Alexander's term for the specific nuclear conflict or dynamic configuration which is unique to a particular psychosomatic disorder or organ-neurosis. See *psychosomatic.*

spectrophobia (spek-trō-fō′bi-à) 'The hysterical phobia for mirrors and the dread of catching sight of one's own face in a mirror had in one case a "functional" and a "material" origin. The functional one was dread of *self-knowledge;* the material, the flight from the *pleasure of looking and exhibitionism.* In the unconscious phantasies the parts of the face represented, as in so many instances, parts of the genitals.' (Ferenczi, S. *Further Contributions to the Theory and Technique of Psycho-Analysis,* tr. by Suttie, J.I., Leonard and Virginia Woolf and The Institute of Psychoanalysis, London, 1926)

spectrum, psychotherapeutic (sī-kō-ther-à-pū′tik) A psychiatric term based on the concept (in optics) of the nature of the light spectrum as containing the entire range of colors from red to violet. Similarly, the term psychotherapeutic spectrum embraces all the branches and varieties of psychotherapeutics or psychotherapy.

'Group psychotherapy . . . is an area which has not been fully explored. It is capable of a wide range of modifications and is still in a fluid state. The various modifications thus far evolved are instruments which act on particular elements of the psychotherapeutic spectrum more or less predominantly.' (Klapman, J.W. *Group Psychotherapy,* Grune and Stratton, New York, 1946)

speech, cerebellar (ser-e-bel′ĕr) In diseases of the cerebellum, the speech may be jerky, explosive, irregular, and scanning. This condition is also called *asynergic* or *ataxic speech.*

speech disorders Disorganization of speech. The term is here synonymous with *language. Language* may be expressed as gesture, voice, and picture. Accordingly speech disorders fall into three groups:

1. *Amimia* (absence of or disordered gestures).

2. *Aphonia* (absence of or disordered sound or voice).

3. *Agraphia* (absence of or distorted pictorial symbols).

Since all communication involves at least two persons—the communicator and the communiquee—speech disorder may be found at either end of the line of communication.

These two aspects of speech (motor and sensory) really move the source a step further back; inability to produce speech goes back to *apraxia,* 'the loss of previously acquired skilled acts (without paralysis), or failure to develop normal skills'; and the inability to grasp speech goes back to *agnosia,* the inability to recognize the import of sensations.

In this way *motor* disabilities in the three groups of communication are of like nature when compared one with the other, namely:

1. Inability to utter (speak) a sound, syllable, word, or phrase—*aphasia.*

2. Inability to write a certain letter, syllable, word, or phrase—*agraphia.*

3. Inability to gesticulate—*amimia.*

The foregoing are paralleled by *sensory* or *perceptive* disabilities in the same three groups:

1. Inability to perceive or understand certain sounds, syllables, words, or phrases —*sensory aphasia.*

2. Inability to read certain letters, syllables, words, or phrases—*alexia.*

3. Inability to understand gestures— *sensory amimia.*

Disorders of speaking in the strict sense

of the word are denoted by the same term on both the *-praxia* side and the *-gnosia* side.

Certain sounds are habitually mispronounced. For example:

r's may become burrs or guttural grunts or *w*'s or *l*'s (*rhotacism*);

l's may become *w*'s or *oo*'s or *y*'s (*lambdacism*);

s's may become *sh*'s or *h*'s, *th*'s, *f*'s (*sigmatism*);

g's and *k*'s become *d*'s and *t*'s (*gammacism*).

An individual may form letters satisfactorily or range or align them badly, or interchange them within the words or reverse them 'mirror-fashion' (*strephosymbolia*) or he may substitute other letters, syllables, or words for the appropriate ones, or write meaningless combinations.

Some individuals retain their ability to read or write and yet be afflicted with the specific disorder *asymbolia* (*asemia, asemasia*)—the inability to grasp or write various signs and symbols, such as are used in mathematics or chemistry; a switchman or a trainman may lose all understanding or ability to distinguish the railroad signals; or a musician past middle age may suddenly find himself staring blankly at a sheet of music that no longer conveys any meaning to him. Naturally in all these cases of aphasia, alexia, and agraphia, the symptoms may be milder and fall under the categories denoted by the prefixes *brady-, dys-, mogi-, moli-,* and *para-,* instead of the total *a-*.

Similarly the disorder may occur in the field of gestures or mimicry, with analogous results, which would be fatal to an actor, or to a pantomimist.

Although various authorities have introduced their own terms, there are certain combining forms which have gained universal acceptance. Almost without exception these terms have been treated under respective title-entries.

1. *a-* or *an-* means absence of a faculty or (total) loss of one acquired: *aphasia, aphemia, alalia, aphonia, alexia, agraphia, agnosia, apraxia, asemasia, asemia, asymbolia, amusia, anarthria, aphthongia, asyllabia, aphrasia, agrammatism, akataphasia, acatamathesia*. A modifying word or phrase may narrow the scope of the disorder and make it more specific: *sensory aphasia, functional aphasia, syntactic aphasia*.

2. *dys-* denotes a partial disorder or a specific disability; inability to produce certain elements; faulty or distorted performance or function: *dysarthria, dyslexia, dysmimia, dyslalia, dyslogia,* all imply that only particular sounds, letters, words, or gestures are outside one's powers or are produced or perceived faultily or imperfectly.

3. *mogi-, moli-* refer to the difficulty in or a labored, effortful functioning: *mogilalia, mogimimia, mogiphrasia,* etc.

4. Excess or insufficiency of functioning, though the mechanics of speech are otherwise unimpaired:

(a) *swift* or above normal is denoted by *tachy-: tachy*lalia, *tachy*glossia.

(b) *slow* or subnormal is denoted by *brady-: brady*lalia, *brady*arthria, *brady*glossia, *brady*lexia, *brady*logia, *brady*phasia, *brady*phrasia.

(c) *above normal: hyper*logia; *hyper*mimia; *macro*mimia.

(d) *subnormal: hypo-*.

5. *para-* means qualitative perversion of the faculty, the substitution of a wrong element (something inappropriate) for the correct or proper one: *para*lalia, or the habitual production of wrong sounds, substitution of one sound for another (proper) one; *para*phasia (or less commonly and properly, *para*phemia) is the improper use of a word; *para*phrasia is the use of a wrong phrase in the sentence; *para*grammatism is the employment of a wrong grammatical construction; *thematic paraphrasia* (wandering, incoherent speech) denotes a still larger unit in the scale of speech-elements—the theme or subject of a speech.

*Para*graphia is the transposition of letters or words, or the use of wrong ones in writing; *para*lexia is misreading, substitution of wrong letters or meaningless words; *para*mimia is inappropriate gesture or facial expression; *para*praxia is symptomatic misaction like a slip of the tongue.

As for the means to denote more specific aspects of speech disorders (that is, smaller or larger *elements* of speech), the terms range through:

Alalia—inability to produce sounds.

Anarthria—inability to produce articulate speech.

Asyllabia—inability to form syllables from individual sounds.

Aphrasia—inability to mold separate words into phrases.

Agrammatism—inability to subject separate words to the rules of grammar.

Asyntacticism or *syntactic aphasia*—inability to arrange words into sentences.

Other sundry prefixes denoting various specific aspects of speech disorders are:

agito-, to denote a state of agitation, e.g. *agito*lalia.

embolo-, interlarding of speech, writing, or gestures at intervals with meaningless words, phrases, or mimicry.

echo-, repetition of words or gestures coming from others: *echo*lalia, *echo*phrasia, *echo*mimia, *echo*pathy, *echo*praxia.

Instead of the more generally accepted prefix *para-* for 'perversion' in the sense of *substitution* of another or inappropriate element, some authorities use *hetero-;* for example, *hetero*phasia, *hetero*lalia, *hetero*phonia, *hetero*phemy.

Likewise excess or insufficiency or lack of speech are denoted by such terms as: *pheniloquence, hyperlogia, logodiarrhea, logorrhea, logomania, logomonomania*—each of these denoting excessive talking; *tachylogia, tachyphemia, tachyphrasia, tachyglossia, lerema, leresis, leschenoma*—all meaning rapid speech.

speech, labyrinthine See *labyrinthine.*

speech, organ Communication or self-expression by means of an organ or organs of the body. 'Schizophrenic speech displays a hypochondriac trait: it has become "organ-speech." ' (Freud, S.) He quotes from Tausk, whose patient said that her eyes were not right, they were twisted. This type of 'speech' is very common in schizophrenia. Freud 'would call attention to the manner in which the whole train of thought is dominated by that element which has for its content a bodily innervation (or, rather, the sensation of it). An hysteric would . . . have convulsively rolled her eyes,' without knowing why she did so; but, schizophrenic patients draw a direct connection between the organ-speech and the alleged cause for it.' (Freud, S. *Collected Papers,* vol. 4, tr. by Riviere, J., Leonard and Virginia Woolf and The Institute of Psychoanalysis, London, 1924–25)

speech, plateau Each vowel has its (average) specific pitch, which, in pronunciation, constantly rises and then steadily falls to the end, thus forming (if graphically represented) a bulging curve, termed its 'melody plot' by Drs. L. Pierce Clark and E.W. Scripture. It is the result of plotting and joining on graph paper the points representing the consecutive pitches in the vowel. These are obtained by measuring the successive waves registered on a smoked drum of the kymograph, or wave-register, by the inscribing point set in vibration by 'air puffs' from the lungs of the patient speaking into the 'tambour' or mouthpiece covered with thin rubber material. The typical epileptic voice has been proven 'monotonous' (i.e. the individual pitches of the various vowels are reduced to an average pitch or 'tone' in contrast to a normal person's speech) and, accordingly, it keeps to a certain more or less uniform level or 'plateau,' i.e. the epileptic's 'melody proceeds by even steps.'

speech, scattered A psychiatric term used to designate a type of speech commonly found in hebephrenic schizophrenia and marked especially by the lack of relevancy and coherence. This lack is due primarily to the patient's tendencies to condensation and the formation of neologisms. The patient condenses 'a whole series of allied events into a single word or phrase.' Thus many ideas are expressed in one or two words. He will also string together several words, 'one each from separate series of events,' the result sounding 'like a hodge-podge to which the technical term neologism is given.' (Hinsie, L.E. *Understandable Psychiatry,* Macmillan, New York, 1948) See *scattering.*

spell, vacant Absence.

sperm, spermatozoön (spĕrm, spĕr-mȧ-tō-zō′on) In contradistinction to the large and passive reproductive cells in the female, which are called *eggs* (or ova), the *spermàtozoa* (or sperms) are the very small male germ cells. They are of peculiar form, unlike any other kind of cell, and like the eggs, are subject to *meiosis* (q.v.). When mature they have only half the number of chromosomes characteristic of the individual that produces the germ cells.

Before undergoing meiosis, the spermatozoa multiply by repeated cell divisions of the ordinary duplicating type and are called *spermatogonia.* When these cells cease to divide by ordinary division, they become *primary spermatocytes,* but grow considerably less than the oöcytes. See *egg.*

The first meiotic division produces in the male two *equal* cells, both functional, which are known as *secondary spermatocytes.* Each cell produced by this first *maturation division* immediately proceeds to divide again (*equation division*). The two identical new cells are called *spermatids* and, by changing shape, produce the *mature spermatozoa.*

In the process of fertilization, a spermatozoön enters an egg either after the maturation is completed or at some earlier time during the maturation process. When an egg is fertilized, a new individual is started.

spermatid (spẽr'mȧ-tid) In genetics a certain stage in the development of a mature *spermatozoön* (q.v.).

spermatocyte (spẽr-ma'tō-sīt) In sexual reproduction, the *spermatogonium* divides into *primary* and *secondary spermatocytes*, before maturing into a *spermatozoön* (q.v.).

spermatogonium (spẽr-ma-tō-gō'ni-um) In sexual reproduction, the *spermatogonium* represents the first stage in the development of a male's mature reproductive cell. See *spermatozoön*.

spermatophobia Fear of semen.

spes phthisica (spās' ftē'zē-kȧ) (Neo L. 'tubercular hopefulness') The feeling of hopefulness and confidence of recovery experienced by many sufferers from tuberculosis even in the later stages of the disease.

sphacelismus (sfas-ē-liz'mus) *Obs.* Phrenitis.

spheresthesia (sfer-es-thē'zhi-à) Globus hystericus.

sphincter morality See *morality, sphincter.*

Spielmeyer-Vogt's disease (Walter Spielmeyer, German neurologist, 1879–1935, and Oskar Vogt, contemporary German neurologist) A type of *amaurotic family idiocy* (q.v.); pigmentary retinal lipoid neuronal heredodegeneration.

spike-and-wave The dart-and-dome type of electroencephalographic tracing seen in petit mal epilepsy. See *epilepsy.*

spina bifida (spē'nȧ bē'fē-dȧ) (L. 'cleft spine') Rachischisis; a developmental defect in the spinal column due to failure of fusion of the dorsal walls of the primitive ectodermal neural canal. Although this defect may exist anywhere along the spine, it is usually situated posteriorly in the median line in the lumbar region.

spina bifida occulta (ôk-kool'tȧ) (L. 'hidden cleft spine') A condition of spina bifida in which the bony defect is covered by skin.

spine, railway A general term for injuries, real or feigned, to the back or spine, sustained during a railway accident.

'Some railway spines must be cases of pure malingering, but exaggeration added to traumatic neurosis will account for the majority of them.' (Huddleson, J.H. *Accidents, Neuroses and Compensation,* Williams and Wilkins, Baltimore, 1932)

Spitzka, Edward Charles (1852–1914) American neurologist and psychiatrist.

splanchnic (splangk'nik) Referring to the viscera. In psychiatry, the term ordinarily has reference to Viola's system of typology. See *type, normosplanchnic; type, megalosplanchnic; type, microsplanchnic.*

splitting See *personality, multiple.*

splurge, stealing A form of behavior disorder in children: the child strives to attain status in the group either by proving itself daring and competent in acts of stealing or by using the articles or money stolen as gifts to purchase the favor of the other members of the group.

spoiled-child reaction See *reaction, spoiled-child.*

spondylitis (spon-di-lī'tis) Inflammation of one or more of the vertebrae.

spontaneity See *state, spontaneity.*

spontaneous imagery See *imagery, spontaneous.*

spoonerism See *cluttering.*

spoon feeding Certain patients may refuse to eat spontaneously, but they may eat when spoon-fed, so to speak. Although technically this means the feeding of another person (e.g. an infant) by putting a spoon filled with food to his lips, the expression has come to refer to any manifestation of oversolicitude that prevents or obstructs the development of independence on the part of the one being 'fed.' Psychiatric residents, for example, who receive so much individual case supervision that they are never in the position of handling a patient completely by themselves are spoken of as being spoon-fed.

spot, hypnogenic (hip-nō-jen'ik) In susceptible patients the body sometimes presents a spot or point, pressure upon which will throw the person into a hypnotic state.

spot, hysterogenic (his-tĕr-ō-jen'ik) In a susceptible subject, the body sometimes presents a spot, pressure upon which will induce a paroxysm of hystero-epilepsy.

spray, needle A form of hydrotherapy, 'the application of water to the body through horizontal jets the size of a needle.' (Steele, K.M. *Psychiatric Nursing,* Davis, Philadelphia, 1937)

stage, biting A subdivision of the oral phase of libido development. Abraham divided this phase into two parts. One is the sucking stage and the other, in consequence of the appearance of teeth, is the biting stage. Based on the nature of the fixation at the oral stage the distinguishing marks of the oral character will be: (1) submissive, if the fixation takes place in the sucking stage, or (2) aggressive, if in the biting stage. Thus, psychoanalysts speak of oral receptive and oral aggressive characters.

stage-fright A type of anxiety hysteria in which the patient, an actor, fears to go onto the stage, or if he goes on, forgets his lines and/or begins to stutter. Stage-fright is often based upon a need to ward off heightened exhibitionism and scopophilia, which if indulged in might provoke castration, and at the same time to gain reassurance from the audience that the dreaded castration has not occurred.

stage, ideoplastic (id-ē-ō-plas'tik) Verworn's term, which refers to the fact that the young child draws what he knows rather than what he sees. In the ideoplastic stage the child tends to exaggerate items which seem important or interesting and to minimize or omit the other parts.

stage, physioplastic (fiz-ē-ō-plas'tik) Verworn's term which refers to the ability to draw what is seen, in contrast to the ideoplastic stage, in which the child draws what he knows. See *stage, idoplastic.*

stage, postambivalent The final stage in the development of object-love in which real love for an object is possible. As infantile sexuality develops, it passes through several stages associated with the various erogenous zones. The libido is organized successively around these various erogenous zones. The final stage in the development of sexuality is the genital stage and it occurs when all sexual excitations can be discharged through the use of the genital apparatus.

Development of object-love is interwoven with the development of sexuality. As infantile sexuality develops, the type of relationship to objects changes, for associated with each stage and related to the particular erogenous zone around which the libido is being organized is a different type of relationship to objects. In general, the development proceeds from an objectless state associated with the early oral (sucking) stage to the final stage of real love.

The stages of object-love before real love is reached are ambivalent: in these stages, the process of achieving satisfaction destroys the object. This is based chiefly on the physiological nature of oral and anal erogeneities—that is, biting, swallowing, defecating, etc.—which are the usual models for these object-relationships. The personality of the object itself does not matter, as the object is important only insofar as it can give satisfaction to the individual. When satisfaction has been achieved, the object itself may disappear—as far as the infant is concerned.

The final stage of object-relationship, real love, is termed the postambivalent stage. No traces of hateful or destructive feelings toward the object remain. Instead, 'consideration of the object goes so far that one's own satisfaction is impossible without satisfying the object, too.' The prerequisite for real love is genital primacy, the ability to attain full satisfaction through genital orgasm. This emerges only in the final genital stage of libidinal organization. (Fenichel, O. *The Psychoanalytic Theory of Neurosis,* Norton, New York, 1945)

staleness See *neurasthenia, aviator's.*

stammering A speech disorder characterized by spasmodic, halting, or hesitating utterance. The term is used by many authorities interchangeably with *stuttering* (q.v.), apparently a more violent form of stammering.

stammer, mental A patient drew a picture of several heads joined to each other by wavy lines. He interpreted this as a picture of a mental stammer, to indicate the stammerer's helplessness on having started the crucial syllable. The stutterer may go on indefinitely until something happens to break the spasm. (Baynes, H.G. *Mythology of the Soul,* Williams and Wilkins, Baltimore, 1949) See *stammering.*

standard deviation See *deviation, standard.*

'standing mute' A defendant, who refuses to plead or say anything when arraigned, is said to be *standing mute.*

'Today, almost without exception, it is provided by statute in the American states that if a defendant refuses to plead, the court may order a plea of not guilty entered for him, and the mere fact that a defendant refuses to plead does not of itself require the question of his physical or mental capacity to be submitted to a jury.' (Weihofen, H. *Insanity as a Defense in Criminal Law,* Commonwealth Fund, Oxford University Press, New York, 1933)

Starr, Moses Allen (1854–1932) American neurologist.

stasibasiphobia (stas-i-bā-si-fō′bi-à) Déjérine and Gauckler define this as 'a phobic phenomenon. Sometimes the patients are so convinced of their helplessness that they do not even make enough effort to enable them to stand up on their feet or to take a single step. They just let themselves go, and sink down helpless.' (Déjérine, J. and Gauckler, E. *The Psychoneuroses and their Treatment by Psychotherapy,* 2nd ed., tr. by Jelliffe, S.E., Lippincott, Philadelphia and London, 1915) See *astasia; abasia.*

stasiphobia (stas-i-fō′bi-à) Fear of standing (up), due to a delusion of inability to stand. See *astasia.*

stasis, libido (stā′sis, stas′is, li-bēd′ō) The term used by Freud to denote an accumulation of libidinous excitations or tensions consequent upon blockage of their motor discharge. When the free flow of libido has been thus dammed, a stasis (libido stasis) results, giving rise to the feeling of anxiety.

According to Kardiner, 'Freud made an early attempt to describe the *Aktualneurosen,* and in this category were anxiety neurosis and neurasthenia. In connection with these neuroses Freud noted irritability, a diminished ability to tolerate accumulations of excitation, auditory hyperesthesia, anxious expectation, hypochondria, paresthesias, vasomotor disturbances, and so on. The essential pathology Freud considered an "accumulation of tensions which were prevented from motor discharge." '

The physiological accompaniments of anxiety are mediated by way of the autonomic nervous system. Kardiner points out that stasis phenomena resulting from overactivity of this system do not necessarily produce anxiety. He writes: 'The autonomic phenomena need to be explained as regards their role in the failure reaction which is traumatic neurosis. . . These phenomena may be considered "discharge" manifestations. One may say that [the inhibitions of a traumatic neurosis] . . . produce stasis phenomena, on the principle that since the demands of the external world continue to be the same as those before the neurosis was established, and the executive apparatus cannot carry out the necessary adaptive manipulations, stasis of some kind will accumulate. In other words it is as if the internal environment were geared for action, and the executive apparatus not. Hence autonomic activity that is shunted from its proper function continues unaccompanied by the activity of which it was originally an integral part.

'In the traumatic neurosis the place of the autonomic system in the action system is quite clear. It stands in direct relation to activity that is inhibited and in this neurosis is a part of the disorganization phenomena. The relations of autonomic disturbances in other neuroses are more difficult to disentangle. . . .

'The disorders of this autonomic system can be classified roughly by their correspondence to the normal physiologic accompaniments of anxiety. Such a picture is found in the usual autonomic imbalance of what is called by Lewis "the soldier's heart" or "effort-syndrome." This autonomic picture may or may not be accompanied by the affect of anxiety or terror in the chronic forms of the disturbance. The affect of anxiety may completely disappear and in proportion as it disappears the more obtrusive these autonomic disturbances may become. In place of the anxiety or terror there remains a residual irritability. In the chronic cases the affect is generally not present nor are there any displacement phobias. But there is one constant in the traumatic neurosis, the fact that the motility is blocked or guarded while the need tensions which can only be released by activity continue unabated. Hence one can regard these autonomic phenomena as evidence of stasis, since the autonomic system is not susceptible to inhibition—

at least not by the same quantities of stimuli that are effective in inhibiting the skeletal system.' (Kardiner, A., and Spiegel, H. *War Stress and Neurotic Illness*, Hoeber, New York, 1947)

stasobasophobia (stas-ō-bā-sō-fō′bi-à) Stasibasiphobia.

stasophobia (stas-ō-fō′bi-à) Stasiphobia.

state, anxiety A diagnostic expression, used by Henderson and Gillespie synonymously with anxiety reaction. See *reaction, anxiety*.

state, central excitatory See *summation*.

state, clouded See *sensorium*.

state, dreamy A state of arrested consciousness, akin to epileptiform seizures, but unaccompanied by convulsions. The patient suddenly passes off into a dream world, often with olfactory, auditory and/or visual hallucinations, and usually recovers within a few minutes. Such states are most commonly associated with temporal lobe lesions.

state, fatigue See *hypoglycemia*.

state, paraphonic (pà-rà-fon′ik) See *action, automatic*.

state, spontaneity 'Spontaneity state is the condition which a subject has to attain in order to produce an emotion or role at will. The state is usually felt by the subject as a novel experience and frequently without a concrete precedent in his life history. Ordinarily, emotions like anger and jealousy are determined by the influence of common tensions and stresses. The emotions produced during the spontaneity state are voluntary. The subject must make an effort to reach the state or to warm up to it. Getting angry or jealous may be enforced upon the subject in life situations by determinants he cannot control, but getting angry or jealous in a spontaneity state is exactly the opposite. The subject voluntarily realizes a state which he usually experiences as something coming up against his will. In the spontaneity state he develops a relative distance from the states or roles which he ordinarily embodies. Spontaneity and spontaneity state are operational terms and cannot be fully understood by intellectual definition.' (Moreno, J.L. *Das Stegreif Theater*, Potsdam, Germany)

state, twilight In Bleuler's classification, one of the acute syndromes in *schizo-*

phrenia (q.v.). The twilight-states appear as waking dreams which portray desires, wishes, or fears in a direct or symbolic way as being already fulfilled. They often persist for long periods; duration for six months is not uncommon.

statistical trend See *trend, statistical*.

statistics The branch of mathematics which deals with data that vary relatively as a result of the interaction of many causes. A body of data, numerical facts, or enumerations which must be analyzed in accordance with the statistical method.

status (stā′tus) (L. 'mannner of standing, position in society, condition, state, rank') Status is the 'relative position, rank, or standing of a person in a group, or of a group in reference to some larger grouping.' (Young, K. *An Introductory Sociology*, American Book, New York, 1934) 'The status of any individual means the sum total of all the statuses he occupies. It represents his position with relation to the total society. (It) derives from a combination of all the statuses which he holds.' (Linton, R. *The Study of Man*, Appleton-Century, New York, 1936)

In medicine this term implies the presence of some abnormal state or pathological condition in an individual and requires further qualification by an adjective for the particular type of condition.

status degenerativus (stà′toos dā-ge-ne-rā-tē′voos) (Mod.L. 'degenerative condition') Bauer describes this as an accumulation, in a given person, of extreme variants of certain constitutional characteristics which, taken alone, may have little, if any, pathological significance, such as a scaphoid shoulder-blade, a supernumerary breast, a deformed ear lobe or an anomalous distribution of hair. However, any combination of these anomalies in the same individual may be taken to indicate a type of general constitution which deviates too much from the average type and, therefore, is to be regarded as 'biologically inferior.'

This definition shows that from the constitutional standpoint *degeneration* simply implies a marked deviation from the type of a species, without regard to the clinical value of the deviation itself. It is equally clear that the actual *status degenerativus* 'includes not only those variants that are extreme in deficit, but also those extreme in excess.' (Pende, N. *Constitution Inade-*

quacies, tr. by Naccarati, S., Lea & Febiger, Philadelphia, 1928)

status dysraphicus (dēs-rà′fē-koos) (Mod. L. 'dysraphic condition') A variety of developmental anomalies resulting from a particular disturbance in the closure of the neural groove at an early embryological stage. It seems to be hereditary and is believed to be the basis of such neurological diseases as hereditary ataxia and spinal gliosis (syringomyelia).

status epilepticus (e-pē-lep′tē-koos) (L. 'epileptic state') The recurrence without interruption of grand mal seizures in an epileptic.

status hypnoticus (hēp-nō′tē-koos) (Mod. L. 'hypnotic state') The hypnotic state.

status hypoplasticus (hē-pô-plàs′tē-koos) (Mod.L. 'hypoplastic condition') Bartel and Wiesel use this term for a constitutional type characterized by generalized hypoevolutism, fibrous diathesis, hyperplasia of the lymphatic tissue, and the ready aging of the differentiated elements. This general hypoplastic condition is bound to lead to a poor functional capacity of the natural defense mechanisms and to a tendency on the part of the connective tissue to replace the elements constituting the parenchyma, which easily undergoes atrophy.

According to Bartel and Wiesel, the *status thymico-lymphaticus* is one of the most important manifestations of a hypoplastic constitution. Pende asserts, however, that this condition, embracing both the fibroplastic diathesis and lymphatism, is most characteristic of the *megalosplanchnic* constitutions, which have been shown especially by Viola to be morphologically hypoevolute. (Pende, N. *Constitutional Inadequacies,* tr. by Naccarati, S., Lea & Febiger, Philadelphia, 1928)

status hystericus (his-te′rē-koos) (L. 'hysterical state') 'In some instances one attack [of grand hysteria] follows another without appreciable interval, or some feature of the attack, as the stupor of the first period or the delirium of the fourth, may be prolonged for hours and days, constituting a *status hystericus.*' (Church, A. and Peterson, F. *Nervous and Mental Diseases,* 8th ed., Saunders, Philadelphia and London, 1916)

status lymphaticus (lēm-fä′tē-koos) (Mod. L. 'lymphatic condition') A constitutional condition of the body characterized by hyperplasia of the lymphatic tissue system and by commonly poor development of the blood vessels. Slight injuries to a person in this state may prove fatal.

status marmoratus (màr-mō-rà′toos) See *dystonia, torsion.*

status, mental See *mental status.*

status nervosus (ner-vō′zoos) (L. 'nervous condition') *Obs.* Neurasthenia.

status psychicus (psē′kē-koos) (L. 'psychic state') Mental state.

status raptus (ràp′toos) (L. 'ecstatic state') Ecstasy.

status thymico-lymphaticus (thē′mē-kō-lim-fä′tē-koos) (Mod.L. 'thymicolymphatic condition') This term refers to those cases of status lymphaticus in which an enlargement of the thymus is conspicuous. The condition may be *primary* and congenital or acquired *secondarily* in extra-uterine life, especially through changes in other endocrine glands, occurring before the period of physiological involution of the thymus.

The symptomatology of both forms chiefly consists of enlarged thymus, gener hyperplasia of the glands, dissemination of hyperplastic lymphatic tissue throughout the body, hyperthyroidism, sclerosis of ovaries and testes, and hypoplasia of the circulatory system. This condition attains its significance for constitutional medicine from the fact that the persons affected by it are under constant threat of infection and even of sudden death from minor psychical or physical traumata.

status thymicus (thē′mē-koos) (Mod.L. 'thymic condition') The meaning of this term in constitutional medicine is practically identical with that of *status thymico-lymphaticus* (q.v.), as it refers to those cases of status lymphaticus in which an enlargement of the thymus is conspicuous.

statuvolence (stach-ū-vō′lens) Statuvolent state; self-induced hypnotism.

steatopygia, steatopygy (stē-à-tō-pī′ji-à, stē-à-top′i-jē) Excessive fatness of the buttocks, a biological peculiarity observed among Hottentot and Bushman women.

'Whether or not this is due to a special gene confined to these peoples, or due to the overactivity of a gene also found among White females (who might, therefore, have relative degrees of *steatopygia*) is not known.' (Scheinfeld, A. *You and Heredity*, Book-of-the-Month Club, New York, 1939)

Stekel, Wilhelm (1868–1940) German sexologist and psychoanalyst; advocated activity as a means to shorten the duration of treatment. Through sympathy and imaginative or intuitive insight the therapist alerts himself to the patient's repressed complexes and then is expected to intervene actively to make the patient aware of them.

stema (stē'mà) *Obs.* Penis.

stem, brain This refers to the *pons* (q.v.) and *medulla oblongata* (q.v.).

stereognosis (stē-rē-og-nō'sis) The ability to judge the shape and form of an object by means of touch.

stereopsyche (stē-rē-ō-sī'kē) The primitive part of the mind which has to do with primitive types of motility. Storch applied this term to certain motor manifestations seen in schizophrenia: the catatonic postures and movements which seem to be isolated from the personality and to have a meaning independent of the rest of the psychic structure. These archaic types of motility arise from the deeper layers of the motor apparatus after the ego has disintegrated. They indicate an indistinct apperception of objects, indistinct ego boundaries, and a deep ambivalence toward reality objects in general. An example is the fetal position often assumed by catatonics: this position suggests that at least certain motor manifestations in the catatonic are carry-overs from the intra-uterine period of existence.

stereotypy (stē-rē-ot'i-pē) The constant repetition of any action. It is observed in its most florid form in the patient with the catatonic form of schizophrenia in the so-called phase of excitement. The patient may and often does engage in repetitious acts, such as incessantly rubbing some part of the body; or he may continuously reiterate some phrase (verbigeration); or he may write the same word over and over again.

The foregoing is often called stereotypy of motion. There is also stereotypy of posture, the patients maintaining a given posture for inordinately long periods. And there is sterotypy of place; catatonic patients may occupy an identical place month in, month out, year in, year out.

sterile Incapable of producing offspring.

sterility Sterility is the state or quality of being unfertile or barren. This condition may be produced either by primary genetic disturbances in the sex chromosome constitution of an individual, or by secondary effects on the phenotype both of internal pathological processes and of surgical interference for medical or eugenic purposes. See *sterilization*.

The pathological processes disturbing the physiology of normal reproduction may affect (1) the sexual center in the hypothalamus, (2) the anterior pituitary gland with the follicle-stimulating and the luteinizing hormones, (3) the ovaries with the follicle and the corpus luteum hormones and (4) the uterus. About 50 per cent of sterile women are reported by Wiesbader to show evidence of endocrine disturbance, a form of sterility which is usually subdivided into the pituitary, ovarian, and hyperthyroid types. The Froehlich syndrome and Cushing's pituitary basophilism are the best-known instances of the pituitary type of sterility.

sterilization The process (brought about spontaneously or by deliberate action) which causes a person to become sterile.

When performed for *eugenic* reasons, it aims at rendering conception impossible, without affecting the ovaries or testes, respectively. Accordingly it is not an 'unsexing' operation, and neither inhibits sex desires nor interferes with normal sex-functioning. In men it is the simple process of cutting and tying the vas deferens, while in women it requires an abdominal incision to tie the fallopian tubes. See *eugenics*.

Stewart-Morel syndrome See *syndrome, Stewart-Morel*.

STH Somatotrophic or growth hormone; one of the anterior pituitary hormones. See *syndrome, general adaptation*.

sthenia (sthē'-ni-à) In a general medical sense, this term designates strength and vigor.

sthenic (sthen'ik) In general medicine, strong and active. It is applied especially to morbid states with excessive action of the vital processes, as for instance, in sthenic fever or sthenic mental (delusional) reaction.

In constitutional medicine, the term is applicable in a general way to all types which correspond to Kretschmer's *athletic type* or its equivalents in other systems. It is even used by Mills for one of his three types. See *type, athletic.*

In general psychology, the term indicates strength and vigor in different fields of emotional reactivity and adaptability. In accordance with this concept, the psychopathological behavior of a sthenic type has been described by Kretschmer as inclined to delusional reactions of a predominantly aggressive nature (paranoia, querulous ideas of reference), in contrast to the introspective tendency of paranoid or hypochondriac reactions in sensitive types.

sthenoplastic (sthen-ō-plas'tik) In constitutional medicine, this term denotes a type contrasted by Bounack with the *euryplastic,* and corresponding to the *asthenic* in Kretschmer's system, the *microplanchnic hypovegetative* constitution of Pende.

stick, fecal Fecal mass. See *phase, anal.*

stigmata (stig-mà'tà) Marks resembling the wounds on the crucified body of Christ. Most psychoanalytic writers would consider these monosymptomatic conversions, the afflicted areas unconsciously symbolizing the genitals, the hyperemia and swelling representing erection, and abnormal sensations imitating genital sensations. The first person known to have experienced stigmata was St. Francis of Assisi; since that time, more than 300 cases have been reported, most of them in women.

Stiller's sign See *sign, Stiller.*

stimuli, accidental Among the four general types of dream-stimuli, which are (1) external sensory; (2) internal sensory (subjective); (3) internal physical (organic); (4) psychic, the group of accidental stimuli belongs to the first type—external sensory. Accidental stimuli denote those chance happenings which take place in the environment of the sleeper and seemingly precipitate dreams or become part of them. For example, the backfire of an automobile passing in the street may emerge in the dream as the firing of a gun or as the 'pop' of a champagne cork. The pain of muscles cramped by an awkward position during sleep may start a dream of being hurt in that area of the body. An alarm clock ringing may be heard by the sleeper simultaneously dreaming of that very thing.

stimulus, dream See *dream-stimulus.*

stimulus-tension The tension produced by a stimulus. 'But we have unquestioningly identified the pleasure-pain-principle with this Nirvana-principle. From this it would follow that every "pain" coincides with a heightening, every pleasure with a lowering, of the stimulus-tension existing in the mind.' (Freud, S. *Collected Papers,* vol. 2, tr. by Riviere, J., Leonard and Virginia Woolf and The Institute of Psychoanalysis, London, 1924–25)

stimulus-word The word used in association tests to provoke a response is called a stimulus-word. 'Its [association method] principle is the finding out of the main complexes through irregularities in responding to selected stimulus-words.' (Jung, C.G. *Contributions to Analytical Psychology,* tr. by Baynes, H.G. and C.F., Kegan Paul, Trench, Trubner, London, 1928)

stir-fever See *psychosis, prison.*

strabismus (stra-biz'mus) Squint; deviation of one or both eyes from the normal axis. See *nerve, oculomotor.*

strait-jacket See *camisole.*

strait-jacket, chemical An uncommonly used term to denote the arresting of psychomotor overactivity by chemical means, specifically by the hypodermic injection of morphin sulphate, $\frac{1}{4}$ grain and hyoscine hydrobromide, $\frac{1}{50}$ grain.

Stransky, Erwin (1877–) Viennese neuropsychiatrist, pupil of Wagner von Jauregg; first to publish textbook on mental health in Germany; concept of intrapsychic ataxia, the dissociation of the thymopsyche from the noöpsyche, as the essential characteristic of schizophrenia.

strength, ego See *ego-strength.*

strephosymbolia (stref-ō-sim-bō'li-à) The perception of objects or graphic symbols reversed as if in a mirror. A term coined by Orton for the specific reading disability due, he believes, to poorly established hemisphere dominance, so that visual impressions, coming to both hemispheres are not clearly differentiated, and symmetrical engrams oriented in opposite directions are confused, as *b* and *d, p* and *q.* 'At the outset it is characterized by confusion between similarly formed, but oppositely oriented letters and a tendency to a changing order of direction in reading.' (Orton, S.T. *Reading, Writing and*

Speech Problems in Children, Norton, New York, 1937)

Strephosymbolia is frequently encountered in left-handed children converted to right-handedness.

stridor dentium (strē'dôr den'tē-oom) (L. 'grating of teeth') Grinding of teeth; see also *bruxism, bruxomania.*

striving, appetitive Striving in one particular direction, toward the particular goal appropriate for the gratification of the appetite involved. 'The distinguishing feature of Freud's instinct theory is that it is based on a conative-appetitive-striving, rather than on a structural principle like sensation or reflex. But, as with the classical psychologies and behaviorism, psychoanalysis is an atomistic psychology which attempts to derive complex entities from the action of a synthetic principle (association, conditioning, integration) on or about a basic unit.' (Kardiner, A., and Spiegel, H. *War Stress and Neurotic Illness,* Hoeber, New York, 1947)

striving, compensatory Kempf says that 'the herd, beginning with the parental influence in the home, trains the infant to contribute to the general progress of the herd's development. The infant's segmental cravings (as nursing and defecation) are early counterbalanced by developing wishes to control them in order to please the mother and win her favors. These wishes are jeopardized by heedless self-indulgence and the *fear* of losing favor and esteem initiates more vigorous *compensatory* striving to prevent a recurrence of submitting to the segmental indulgence.' (Kempf, E.J. *Psychopathology,* Mosby, St. Louis, 1921)

stroke, emotional A term used by L.E. Hinsie to designate hysterical paralysis. (Hinsie, L.E. *Understandable Psychiatry,* Macmillan, New York, 1948)

structure, character The term for a relatively permanent constellation of habitual ways of reacting to the world, connoting only habitual attitudes developed as reactions to life-situations. This is not to be confused with *temperament.*

'Character structure, as Freud saw it, is the result of sublimation or reaction formation. That is, it is formed unconsciously through the efforts of the Superego to bind the forces of the Id in such a way that the Ego accepts them, and its relation to the outside world is not jeopardized. It is, in effect, a defensive mechanism. Although the result, sublimation, seems to be a positive attitude of the Ego, it is formed primarily as a defense against instincts. Freud's philosophy of character makes it the result of the transformation of instinctual drives.' (Thompson, C. *Psychoanalysis, Evolution and Development,* Hermitage House, New York, 1950) See *defense, character.*

structure, mental The organization of the *psyche* (q.v.).

strychnomania (strik-nō-mā'ni-à) An obsolescent term for deadly nightshade poisoning. See *poisoning, deadly nightshade.*

stupemania (stū-pē-mā'ni-à) Manic stupor. See *mania.*

stupor (stū'pēr) A state in which the sensibilities are deadened or dazed and the individual has little or no appreciation of the nature of his surroundings. The term is commonly synonymous with *unconsciousness,* in an organic, not in a psychic sense.

Further, in a second meaning that has no relationship with the condition of the sensorium, stupor is synonymous with *mutism.* For example, a patient may possess all the characteristics of the manic or depressed phase of manic-depressive psychosis, save that of talking; he is said to exhibit a manic or a depressive stupor; there need not be any essential disorder in intellectual or sensorial clarity. In the condition known as catatonic stupor the patient is ordinarily well aware of the nature of his surroundings.

stupor, affective See *stupor, emotional.*

stupor, akinetic (a-ki-net'ik) *Cairns' stupor* (q.v.).

stupor, anergic (an-er'jik) Stupor with immobility. As a rule patients showing the psychogenic stuporous reaction are inactive, immobile, anergic.

According to older concepts *anergic stupor* was synonymous with *primary dementia* and *stuporous insanity.*

stupor, benign *Benign stupor* denotes a stuporous syndrome from which recovery is the rule. The term *benign* refers to the nature of the symptoms rather than to the duration or course of the disorder. When the symptoms are those commonly associated with a recoverable psychiatric state, the syndrome is called benign. Thus, when a patient in a stupor of psychogenic character exhibits the basic symptomatology of the manic-depressive psychosis, he is said to have a benign stupor. When a patient in a stupor possesses the symptomatology of schizophrenia, he is said to be in a phase of *malignant stupor.*

stupor, Cairns' See *Cairns' stupor.*

stupor, catatonic See *schizophrenia, catatonic.*

stupor, depressive See *stupor, benign.*

stupor, diencephalic (dī-en-se-fal′ik) *Cairns' stupor* (q.v.).

stupor, emotional Emotional stupor (or affective stupor) commonly designates the psychiatric state characterized by mutism and intense anxiety or depression. The syndrome is not uncommon in states of depression associated with manic-depressive psychosis or with hysteria.

'*Emotional stupor* is a syndrome seen in different conditions, especially in the different kinds of "nervosities," in the widest sense, and in the oligophrenias.' (Bleuler, E. *Textbook of Psychiatry,* tr. by Brill, A.A., Macmillan, New York, 1930)

stupor, examination When the affects are so strong as to 'bring to a standstill thoughts and actions,' Bleuler speaks of *examination* or *emotional stupor.*

stupor, exhaustive When, as a consequence of severe response to toxic influences, the patient collapses and becomes stuporous, the condition is known as exhaustive stupor.

stupor, malignant See *stupor, benign.*

stupor, manic See *mania.*

stuporous Relating to or under the influence of stupor.

stupor, partial 'We consequently regard stupor and partial stupor as different degrees of the same psychotic process, which we term the stupor reaction.' (MacCurdy, J.T. *The Psychology of Emotion,* Harcourt, Brace, New York, 1925)

stupor vigilans (stoo′pôr vē′gē-làns) (L. 'vigilant, wakeful stupor') An old term for catalepsy.

Sturge-Weber's disease Intracranial hemangioma.

stuttering A spasmodic utterance with involuntary halts, breaks, and repetitions, usually characterized (in severer cases)

externally by sputtering due to violent expulsion of breath following a halt or stop. For the sake of convenience, stuttering will be assumed a visually more violent or explosive form of stammering without intention to settle the prevailing disagreement as to whether *stutter* or *stammer* is the more appropriate term and whether they denote two different disorders or not.

The long-standing controversy in medical literature as to whether the halts and reiterations involved only consonants, vowels, or parts of words, and likewise initially or medially, was an academic discussion with useless waste of energy, practically without foundation, as has been proven by closer studies and experimental phonetics, particularly by Dr. E.W. Scripture and Dr. S.T. Orton. Any sound, in any position, any part of a word and any word may be the obstacle in stuttering, varying with the individual stutterer or the severity of the symptom.

Some authorities hold that stuttering is the result of an organic brain disease or physiological defect, but that is still a moot question. The first hesitations and halts in a child's speech are as normal as the missteps, stumbles, and falls in the child's earliest attempts in walking, due to lack of co-ordination and control of the walking-mechanism, which in comparison with the speech-mechanism is as simple as that of a wheelbarrow by the side of a delicate watch-movement. The staggering burden on the child's powers to reproduce the movements of speech organs (many of them concealed from his view within the other people's mouths) can be surmised from the exertions adults have to make in learning the sounds of a new language even from a teacher with the aid of diagrams, illustrations, and mirrors.

Whether originating in a physiological disorder or not, in its subsequent stages, the symptom is evidently a psychic condition—shrinking from speaking through fear of not succeeding, and the remedy of *relaxation* (to reduce or entirely do away with the nervous and muscular tension) has worked nearly always in the various institutions for stutter-curing.

'Of the initial stage of speech development, the mental process is in advance of the powers of muscular control, and the resulting lack of muscular co-ordination often produces a *temporary stammer* [read *stutter*]. If the child is worried and nervous during this period of adjustment, he will become conscious of his speech and of the difficulties surrounding its acquisition, and at once the second stage is reached—that of fear or dread of speech —unconscious probably, but none the less potent.' (Boome, E.J., Baines, H.M.S., and Harries, D.G. *Abnormal Speech,* Sherwood Press, Cleveland, 1939)

Stuttering is seen in about 1 per cent of the population and usually appears between the ages of two and six years. It occurs more frequently in males, in individuals who are twins, and in those who are left-handed. It is rarely seen among diabetics and it is most uncommon among primitive peoples.

From the psychoanalytic point of view, stuttering is regarded as due in most instances to displacement of anal libido onto the throat and mouth and onto the act of word-forming. The anal-sadistic stutterer equates words with feces, and the expulsion or retention of words mean the expulsion or retention of feces. Further, words acquire the same omnipotence they had in the infantile stage; 'words can kill' and the stutterer is constantly anxious about using so dangerous a weapon. While anal sadism forms the core of the problem, other component instincts typically contribute to the symptom. Phallic impulses, for example, often lead to an equation of speaking ability with potency and of disability with castration.

stygiophobia (sti-ji-ō-fō′bi-à) Fear of hell; hadephobia.

subacute combined degeneration of the spinal cord See *sclerosis, posterolateral.*

subconscious The term subconscious is often considered synonymous with *co-conscious* (q.v.).

'Unfortunately, however, the term [unconscious] has been also employed to characterize another distinct class of facts, namely, *Co-* [*or Sub-*] *conscious Ideas.*' (Prince, M. *The Unconscious,* Macmillan, New York, 1916)

But, other authors use it as MacCurdy does, namely, as a term essentially 'synonymous with "unconscious," as I use that term.' (MacCurdy, J.T. *The Psychology of Emotion,* Harcourt, Brace, New York, 1925)

subconsciousness 1. Partial unconsciousness.

2. The state in which mental processes

take place without conscious perception on the individual's part.

subcortical encephalopathy (sub-kor′ti-kal en-sef-a-lop′à-thē) See *sclerosis, diffuse.*

subject homoerotic (hō-mō-e-rot′ik) See *homosexuality, male.*

subject-ill A term used by Stekel to describe the patient suffering from phobias who expresses his emotional conflicts through his own organs. The subject-ill patient uses his own body to symbolize his emotions. This is achieved through somatization, which constitutes an organic language of the mind. See *somatization.*

In opposition to this type, Stekel calls object-ill the patient who is the victim of compulsions and expresses his emotions through symbolization of objects outside his body—usually a close member of the family.

'The "subject-ill" makes efforts to extravert himself in order to adjust himself to the world; the "object-ill," however, is introverted and makes no attempts at extraversion.' (Stekel, W. *Compulsion and Doubt,* Liveright, New York, 1949)

subjective mentation Autism.

subject-system See *complex, subject.*

sublimate (sub′li-māt) To externalize or objectivate instinctual impulses in ways that meet the situation. To sublimate is to refine, to purify instinctual manifestations. The instincts are not changed; their mode of expression is altered.

sublimation (sub-li-mā′shun) In psychoanalytic psychology, the process of modifying an instinctual impulse in such a way as to conform to the demands of society. Sublimation is a substitute activity which gives some measure of gratification to the infantile impulse which has been repudiated in its original form. Sublimation is an unconscious process and is a function of the normal ego. It is not technically a defense mechanism, for unlike the latter it does not lead to any restriction or inhibition of ego-functioning by requiring a constant counter-cathexis; rather, the impulse or wish is modified in such a way that gratification can be achieved without disapprobation or disapproval. Unlike the usual defenses, in sublimation the ego is not acting in opposition to the id; on the contrary, it is helping the id to gain external expression. Sublimation, in other words, does not involve repression. It is to be noted that the original impulse is never conscious in sublimation.

E. Bergler (*Psychiatric Quarterly Supplement 23*, 313, 1949) considers acting a sublimation and he notes that, contrary to popular opinion, it is not exhibitionism which is the original id wish, for were this the case the original impulse would be conscious. Instead, according to him, it is voyeurism which is being sublimated. The id wish is: 'I want to look at mother (the breast) or father (the penis) or both (intercourse)'; but the superego vetoes this wish, and the ego defends itself against the reproach: 'I am not really interested in peeping; indeed, I do the opposite, I want to show off my own body.' But the exhibitionism is also forbidden, and the ego evades this second superego reproach by finding a socially approved and accepted outlet: 'I am neither aggressive in exhibitionism nor am I a voyeur. I am only socially minded and want to give pleasure to others.'

Interesting as this formulation is, it implies that reversal into the opposite or reaction-formation is necessary before sublimation can occur, a viewpoint to which not all would subscribe. See *reaction-formation.*

subliminal fringe (sub-lim'in-al) See *summation.*

submania Hypomania.

sub-psyche (sub'-sī'kē) A term introduced by Bumke as synonymous with unconscious life. Bumke refused to accept the unconscious and preferred to speak in terms of 'a consciousness of which one does not know anything.' Freud pointed out very pertinently, however, that 'a consciousness about which one does not *want* to know anything' seems more appropriate. This psychic material, unknown to the consciousness, constitutes the unconscious life of the individual. (Stekel, W. *Compulsion and Doubt,* Liveright, New York, 1949)

sub-shock See *treatment, ambulatory insulin.*

substantia nigra (sub-stan'tē-à nē'grà) See *midbrain.*

substitute See *surrogate.*

substitute, displacement An idea and its affect may be repressed into the sphere of the unconscious. At some later time the repressing influences may fail to keep the complex therein; the latter breaks through, re-enters consciousness. 'The vanished affect is transformed, without any diminution, into dread of the community, pangs of conscience, or self-reproaches; the rejected idea is replaced by a *displacement-substitute,* often by displacement on to something utterly trivial or indifferent.' (Freud, S. *Collected Papers,* vol. 4, tr. by Riviere, J., Leonard and Virginia Woolf and The Institute of Psychoanalysis, London, 1924–25)

substitute-formation Symptom-formation; the tendency of repressed impulses to use any opportunity for indirect discharge. The energy of the warded-off instinct is displaced to any other impulse that is associatively connected with the repressed one, and the intensity of this substitute impulse is increased and often, in addition, the affect connected with it is changed in quality. Such substitute impulses are known as derivatives; most neurotic symptoms are derivatives.

substitute-manifestation In Freud's use this term means a symptom observed in a psychoneurosis, in consequence of a repression of a perverse sexual impulse.

These 'inhibited sexual impulses are not expressed as such—and to that extent the inhibition is successful—but they are expressed in other ways [substitute-manifestations] which are quite as injurious to the person concerned, and make him quite as useless to society as satisfaction of these suppressed impulses in their original form would have done.' (Freud, S. *Collected Papers,* vol. 2, tr. by Riviere, J., Leonard and Virginia Woolf and The Institute of Psychoanalysis, London, 1924–25)

substitute, regressive Freud applies this term to the phenomenon of displacing the unconscious sexual aim or object in the course of psychosexual development to a chronologically earlier one from which pleasure was derived.

In describing a patient with a phantasy of being beaten by the father, Freud states that 'it is not only the punishment for the forbidden genital relation [*incest*], but also the *regressive substitute* for it.' (Freud, S. *Collected Papers,* vol. 2, tr. by Riviere, J., Leonard and Virginia Woolf and The Institute of Psychoanalysis, London, 1924–25)

substitution neurosis See *neurosis, substitution.*

subthalamus (sub-thal′a-mus) That portion of the brain which is bounded by the dorsal thalamus anteriorly, the tegmentum of the midbrain posteriorly, the hypothalamus medially, and the internal capsule laterally. The subthalamus contains the rostral extensions of the red nucleus and substantia nigra from the midbrain, the fields of Forel (which are probably a rostral extension of reticular nuclei), and the subthalamic nucleus (body of Luys). The last is functionally connected with the globus pallidus.

subwaking Being or held in a state intermediate between sleeping and waking; hypnoidal.

success, failure through A term used by Freud to describe the self-injuring conduct of those individuals who, on the verge of achieving a long-desired aim, renounce it, obtaining gratification through its renunciation. We have, for instance, 'the clinical assistant who for so long desired to become professor and renounced the position on his predecessor's sudden death,' or 'the girl who withdrew from the beloved man at the sudden death of his wife, her rival.' It is a moral veto. The fact is that at such a moment the force of conscience prevents the enjoyment, and even the acceptance, of success. The moral veto can enforce itself in different ways. 'A young man who has been dependent on an uncommonly thrifty, rich father, is suddenly notified that his father had died from apoplexy. He is the only heir. A few hours later he is so clumsy when driving his car that he perishes in an accident.' In a less spectacular reaction, this young man could have wasted his heritage, or he could have acquired a severe neurosis. It seems that this moral veto, with its reaction of renunciation, occurs only when it is preceded by a period of phantasy which anticipates the misfortune or the death of the rival. (Reik, T. *Masochism in Modern Man,* Farrar and Rinehart, New York, 1941)

succubus (suk′ū-bus) A demon said to have sexual intercourse with human beings in their sleep. The concept is not uncommon among psychotic patients. See *incubus.*

sucking, pleasure The sucking of objects, such as the thumb or finger, is called pleasure-sucking by psychoanalysts. It is looked upon by Freud as a form of sexual activity which 'became separated from the nourishment activity and the strange object was given up in favor of one from his own body.' (Freud, S. *Three Contributions to the Theory of Sex,* 4th ed., tr. by Brill, A.A., Nervous and Mental Disease Publishing Company, New York and Washington, 1930)

sucking, thumb The earliest and one of the most common manipulations of the body found in young children. In some children, it is observed at birth, to continue on through infancy and early childhood, when it becomes an undesirable habit and is classified as a neurotic trait. During the first months of life, thumb-sucking is a physiological and common, but not universal, characteristic of the infant. With the waning of the hand-to-mouth reaction phase, which takes place at about twelve months of age, according to Gesell, the habit ceases. Even past the age of twelve months and on through three and four years (two years according to Kanner) it is considered normal when recurring before nap, sleep, or at times of fatigue or emotional stress. Thumb-sucking is accompanied by movements and positions of the free hand, as well as the remaining fingers of the sucked thumb hand, which are characteristic of and constant for the individual child, the so-called accessory movements. (Levy, D.M. 'Finger Sucking and Accessory Movements in Early Infancy: An Etiologic Study,' *American Journal of Psychiatry* 7, 881–918, 1928) According to Levy, who has made an anamnestic and an experimental study of the subject, thumb-sucking occurs in children with insufficient lip movements or incompleteness of the sucking phase of earlier feeding, breast or other type.

The psychoanalytic school considers thumb-sucking an auto-erotic gratification, as an expression of infantile sexual cravings, the oral erogenic zone being in this case the level of stimulation and gratification.

suckling, eternal 'Perhaps Christoph Haitzmann was only a poor devil, one of those who never had any luck; perhaps he was too poorly gifted, too ineffective to make a living, and belonged to that well-known type, the "eternal suckling"—to those who are unable to tear themselves away from the joyous haven at the mother's breast, who hold fast all through their lives to their claim to be nourished by someone else.' (Freud, S. *Collected Papers*, vol. 4, tr. by Riviere, J., Leonard and Virginia Woolf and The Institute of Psychoanalysis, London, 1924–25)

suffocatio hysterica (soof-fô-kä'tē-ō hē-ste'rē-kà) Hysterical suffocation; hysterical spasm of the muscles of the throat; often seen as part of the symptom picture in globus hystericus. Like the latter, suffocatio hysterica is often based on the unconscious rejection of incorporation phantasies of a sexual and/or aggressive nature.

suggestibility The capability of becoming suggested appears in different forms and different degrees in individuals. '*Suggestibility* becomes abnormal when the patient habitually conforms with unusual readiness to suggestions made to him. It is common in psychoneurotics, and Babinski has attempted to make suggestibility the fundamental factor in hysteria, on which all the wide variety of symptoms depend.' (Henderson, D.K. and Gillespie, R.D. *A Text-Book of Psychiatry*, 4th ed., Oxford University Press, London, 1936)

Suggestibility may be positive or negative. 'The *exaggerations* of suggestibility are more important. We can produce it experimentally in a state of hypnosis.' (Bleuler, E. *Textbook of Psychiatry*, tr. by Brill, A.A., Macmillan, New York, 1930) This is the positive form.

Negative suggestibility is doing the opposite of what is suggested to the patient. See *schizophrenia, catatonic.*

suggestibility, negative Bleuler says that 'to a certain degree "negative suggestibility" is a normal characteristic, which is often disagreeably conspicuous especially in little children, in that they reject all sorts of things.' Negative suggestibility denotes the refusal to conform to suggestions. It appears to be synonymous with *active negativism.*

suggestion The process of influencing an individual so that he shows uncritical acceptance of an idea, belief, or other cognitive process. This acceptance is typically expressed as an attitude of belief and/or some action preparatory to carrying out the idea. Some would differentiate between heterosuggestion (when the source of the idea is someone outside the individual) and autosuggestion (when the source of the idea is the individual himself, as when an individual keeps saying to himself that he is getting better and better every day, perhaps in hopes that he will one day come to believe his own statement).

While suggestion does not afford a complete explanation of hypnosis, it is obvious that it plays a large part in it, in that the subject comes to accept the hypnotist's repeated suggestions that he is becoming drowsy and soon finds that this is so. This is even more clear with post-hypnotic suggestion, when an individual after coming out of the hypnotic trance will carry out some action which has been proposed to him during the trance-state.

The psychoanalytic method is a modification of hypnosis and, like the latter, depends upon suggestion. '. . . we readily admit that the results of psycho-analysis rest upon a basis of suggestion; only by suggestion we must be understood to mean that which we, with Ferenczi, find that it consists of—influence on a person through and by means of the transference-manifestations of which he is capable.' (Freud, S. *Collected Papers*, vol. 2, tr. by Riviere, J., Leonard and Virginia Woolf and The Institute of Psychoanalysis, London, 1924–25)

Prestige-suggestion is another form of psychotherapy; unlike psychoanalysis, however, it does not attempt to uncover or deal with the unconscious determinants of behavior. Its efficacy is chiefly dependent upon gratification of the patient's security needs; the patient submits to and identifies with the omnipotent authority (the therapist) and gives up his symptoms as part of his obedience to the therapist.

suggestion, affective See *hypotaxia.*

suggestionist One who employs suggestion in the treatment of disease.

suggestion, post-hypnotic Suggestion given during the hypnotic stage to be acted upon after the hypnotic phase has passed.

suggestion, prestige A form of supportive psychotherapy in which the therapist, because he occupies a position of omnipotence in the eyes of the patient, is able to dictate the disappearance of symptoms. 'The motivation to comply is usually conditioned by a wish to gratify important security needs through archaic mechanisms of submission to and identification with an omnipotent authority.' (Wolberg, L.R. *The Technique of Psychotherapy,* Grune & Stratton, New York, 1954) Prestige-suggestion is probably the least successful of all treatment methods.

suggestion, verbal See *ideoplasty.*

suggestive In psychiatry this usually relates to hypnotic suggestion; thus, one speaks of hypnotic or suggestive therapeutics.

suicide The act of killing oneself. While it is believed by some that all suicides are psychotic, the more widely accepted view is that suicide can occur in any psychiatric disorder although the psychoses (depressions, including involutional psychoses, and the schizophrenias) account for the majority of cases. Men outnumber women by three or four times when 'successful' suicides are considered; if attempted suicides are considered, however, the ratio is reversed. Suicide increases with increasing age, although particularly in females there is a large rise in incidence in the third decade and in both sexes there is another rise in the involutional period (40–55 years for females; 50–65 years for males). In the United States, suicide occurs less frequently in the Negro than in any other race. The larger the family, the smaller the risk of suicide; when classified by marital status and family constellation, suicides are seen to be most frequent among those who are divorced. While some series indicate that almost all suicides have had a relative or mate who committed suicide or otherwise met a violent, tragic, or dramatic death (the so-called 'death trend'), not all writers agree on the prognostic significance of the presence or absence of such loss of a loved one. Most suicides occur in the early morning hours (the time at which clinically depressed patients typically awake from their fitful, unrefreshing sleep), and more occur on Monday and Tuesday than on any other day of the week. The spring is the season with highest incidence of suicide. It is a common misconception that the patient who threatens suicide is not likely to commit suicide. The reverse is probably closer to the truth, for about 75 per cent of successful suicides had previously threatened or attempted it. Typically, the genuinely suicidal patient departs with a surge of

hatred for the world and pejorative accusations of the self, leaving definite instructions and restrictions for those he has purposely deserted. Among the clinical depressions, those with prominent anxiety features, a feeling of losing ground, and/or a marked hypochondriacal trend are the most likely to make a suicide attempt. Ill-health is a prominent motive for suicide in both sexes, accounting for 40 per cent of the males and 20 per cent of the females, and such motives are likely to be associated with a high degree of success (50 per cent of the males and 25 per cent of the females). Other common motives include domestic difficulties, which account for 50 per cent of suicide attempts by women and 30 per cent of attempts by men; and unhappy love affairs (10 per cent of the women, 4 per cent of the men). Suicide often occurs when the patient seems to be recovering from an emotional crisis; approximately half occur within 90 days of such crisis.

The following table of suicide rates (per 100,000 adults) is adapted from the 1956 report of the World Health Organization:

	Total	Male	Female
U.S.A.	10.1	16.1	4.3
U.S.A.—whites	10.8	17.2	4.6
U.S.A.—non-whites	3.8	6.4	1.3
Scotland	5.9	8.3	3.7
Spain	5.9	9.1	2.9
Switzerland	22.6	33.9	12.0
Denmark	23.3	31.4	15.4
Japan	23.4	29.2	17.8

Psychodynamically, suicide or a suicide attempt is seen most frequently to be an aggressive attack directed against a loved one or against society in general; in others, it may be a misguided bid for attention or it may be conceived of as a means of effecting reunion with the ideal love-object or mother. That suicide is in one sense a means of release for aggressive impulses is supported by the change of wartime suicide rates. In World War II, for example, rates among the participating nations fell, sometimes by as much as 30 per cent; but in neutral countries, the rates remained the same.

In involutional depressions and in the depressed type of manic-depressive psychosis, the following dynamic elements are often clearly operative: the depressed patient loses the object which he depends upon for narcissistic supplies; in an attempt to force the object's return, he regresses to the oral stage and incorporates (swallows up) the object, thus regressively identifying with the object; the sadism which was originally directed against the deserting object is taken up by the patient's superego and is directed against the incorporated object, which now lodges within the ego; suicide occurs, not so much as an attempt on the ego's part to escape the inexorable demands of the superego, but rather as an enraged attack on the incorporated object in retaliation for its having deserted the patient in the first place.

suicide, psychic A psychiatric term denoting the killing of one's self without resorting to any physical agency; used in reference to those individuals who make up their minds to die and actually do so. It is presumed that the same forces which lead a person to commit physical suicide are active in psychic suicide cases, but that, instead of operating overtly, these forces work endopsychically.

suicidogenic (sū-i-si-dō-jen′ik) Pertaining to suicidogenesis; causing suicide.

'Manic-depressive psychosis, this material tends to show, is "suicidogenic" in Western society, but "non-suicidogenic" in the non-westernized portions of Mohammedan society.' (Alpert, H. *Emile Durkheim and His Sociology,* Columbia University Press, New York, 1939)

suigenderism (sū-i-jen′dĕr-iz′m) The natural drift on a child's part to associate or group with others of one's own *gender.* During the latency period of human growth the activities of boys are largely confined to boys, while those of girls are mainly limited to girls. For the manifestation of these natural, wholesome, unerotic relationships between members of one's own gender, the term *suigenderism* is recommended. When sex-feelings begin to crop up in suigenderism, it may become *homoerotism, homosexuality,* or *homogenitality,* as the case may be.

Sullivan, Harry Stack (1892–1949) The chief proponent of the so-called dynamic-cultural school of psychoanalysis, which emphasizes sociologic rather than biologic events, present-day contacts with people rather than past experiences, current interpersonal relationships rather than infantile sexuality. Orthodox Freudians consider this a superficial approach that limits itself to a single facet of experience, the cultural.

summation Kempf explains that to his way of thinking the term *summation* means the following: 'the tendency to suppress our affections may accumulate; that is, a *summation* of the *repressing* or *suppressing* egoistic wishes may occur, usually through the influence of puritanical associates. Also, a summation of the *repressed* and *suppressed* autonomic tensions may occur and they cannot be prevented from showing their influence on the postural tensions of the striped muscle apparatus, as in the summation of fear through a series of dangerous experiences.' (Kempf, E.J. *Psychopathology,* Mosby, St. Louis, 1921)

Freud uses the term *summation* in regard to the etiology of anxiety-neurosis. He feels that the specific sexual noxia contained in coitus interruptus increases quantitatively with each new indulgence in this act until the anxiety neurosis develops.

'According to the disposition of the person concerned and the other burdens on his nervous system, a longer or shorter time will be required before the effect of this *summation* becomes evident. Those persons who tolerate coitus interruptus apparently without harmful results are in reality becoming thereby disposed to the disorder of anxiety neurosis, which may break out either at any time spontaneously or after an ordinary and otherwise insufficient trauma; just as the chronic alcoholic will in the end develop a cirrhosis or other illness as an effect of *summation,* or under the influence of a fever will go down with a delirium.' (Freud, S. *Collected Papers,* vol. 1, tr. by Riviere, J., Leonard and Virginia Woolf and The Institute of Psychoanalysis, London, 1924–25)

In neurophysiology, summation refers to a response obtained when two stimuli are applied, neither of which by itself is of sufficient intensity to elicit a response. In this sense, there are two types of summation, temporal and spatial. Temporal summation is seen when two successive stimuli, each of them too weak to elicit a response, are applied to the same nerve trunk within 0.1 to 0.5 millisecond of each other, in which case a response will be evoked because of the enduring character of the local excitatory process. Spatial summation is seen when two different afferent nerves, which play upon the same reflex center, are stimulated either simultaneously or within a short interval (not more than 15 milliseconds); a response is evolved even though neither stimulus alone will elicit a response. Spatial summation is believed to be a result of additive excitatory alterations in the neurons involved. Sherrington and his associates refer to this excitatory alteration as the 'central excitatory state,' which is often abbreviated as c.e.s. The nerves affected are said to be in the 'subliminal fringe of excitation.'

summation, spatial See *summation.*

summation, temporal See *summation.*

superconscious This term is seldom used in current psychiatric literature. What it is supposed to designate is unclear. It has been considered by some as synonymous with *unconscious.* The prefix *super-* means 'above' in a functional, not a structural sense. Hence, anything that controls consciousness is superconscious.

'We must also steer clear of the distinction between the *super-conscious* and the *subconscious,* which has found such favour in the more recent literature on the psychoneuroses, for just such a distinction seems to emphasize the equivalence of what is psychic and what is conscious.' (Freud, S. *The Interpretation of Dreams,* 3rd ed., tr. by Brill, A.A., Macmillan, New York, 1933)

superego In psychoanalytic psychology, there are three functional divisions of the psyche: the id, the ego, and the superego. The superego is the last of these to be differentiated. It is the representative of society within the psyche (i.e. conscience or morality) and also includes the ideal aspirations (ego-ideal). The superego is mainly unconscious; its functions include: (1) approval or disapproval of the ego's actions, i.e. judgment that an act is 'right' or 'wrong'; (2) critical self-observation; (3) self-punishment; (4) demands that the ego repent or make reparation for wrongdoing; (5) self-love or self-esteem as the ego reward for having done right. (Brenner, C. *An Elementary Textbook of Psychoanalysis,* International Universities Press, New York, 1955)

In general, the superego may be re-

garded as a split-off portion of the ego which arises on the basis of identification with certain aspects of the introjected parents. Since introjection and identification are among the earliest defense mechanisms to appear, it is obvious that the precursors of the superego are in evidence early in life, in the prephallic or preoedipal phase. Such precursors consist mainly of the various effects which the demands and prohibitions of the parents (and their surrogates) have on the child, and these are particularly evident in regard to bowel training (and thus Ferenczi's term, 'sphincter morality'). Yet until the oedipal phase, the superego does not make itself felt as a disturbance of the harmonious accord between the strivings of the ego and the strivings of the id. Morality in the young child, such as it is, is more a response to immediate external demands of the environment than obedience to an inner authority. It is only with the oedipal phase that the superego begins to take its final form as an internal authority which stands between ego and id, compelling the individual on his own to renounce certain pleasures, and imposing punishment (loss of self-esteem, guilt-feelings, etc.) for violations of its orders. The superego develops as a reaction to the Oedipus complex; as is often said, it is the heir of the Oedipus complex. It is a solution to the impulses of this period which have no prospect of succeeding in reality and which, if allowed to continue unchanged, would have been dangerous. These impulses, deriving from the id, are allowed access to the ego; the forbidden impulses (love for the mother, hatred of the father) are withdrawn from their objects and deposited in the ego, which thus becomes changed. The changed portion of the ego is the superego, and it contains the sadism which was originally directed against the father; so also does it contain the love originally felt for the mother, but the very process of introjecting the mother and changing the libido attached to the maternal object into ego libido has resulted in desexualization. Thus the love portion of the superego (the ego-ideal) is a non-sensual love.

What has happened, in short, is that the frustrations of the Oedipus complex have caused the ego to resort to primitive methods of defense; viz. introjection and identification. As a result, the oedipal objects are regressively replaced by identifications, and sexual longing for the maternal object has been replaced by an asexual alteration within the organization of the ego. These newly introjected objects, which replace the sexual and hostile impulses toward the parents, combine with the parental introjects from the prephallic period (internalized parental prohibitions), and the superego is formed.

In practice it is difficult to differentiate sharply between the superego, which is an image of the hated and feared objects, and the ego-ideal, which is an image of the loved objects in the libido. 'The ego ideal seems to contain more maternal libido, the superego, more of the paternal; in reality both are fused. Furthermore, just as there are some destructive elements to be found within the ego ideal because the libido is desexualized, there are also libidinal forces at work in the formation of the superego, since it develops through identification with the ambivalently loved father. The predominantly maternal ego ideal starts to develop as early as the pregenital stages, but the predominantly paternal superego is observed first in the genital stage. The impetus for the formation of the superego is the danger of castration, a danger which threatens the entire ego in consequence of its identification with the genitals. By taking the father into his ego, the boy not only escapes the danger of castration but also gains a protector in the image of the father absorbed by the ego.' (Nunberg, H. *Principles of Psychoanalysis,* International Universities Press, New York, 1955)

Melanie Klein and her followers believe that the superego begins to function much earlier than Freud (and most psychoanalysts since him) believed. 'Where I differ is in placing at birth the processes of introjection which are the basis of the superego. The superego precedes by some months the beginning of the Oedipus complex, a beginning which I date, together with that of the depressive position, in the second quarter of the first year. Thus the early introjection of the good and bad breast is the foundation of the superego and influences the development of the Oedipus complex. This conception of superego formation is in contrast to Freud's explicit statements that the identifications with the parents are the heir of the Oedipus complex and only succeed if the Oedipus complex is successfully overcome.' ('On the Development of Mental Functioning,' *International Journal of Psychoanalysis 39,* 84–90, 1958)

superego, autonomous The normal superego, which demands that the ego behave in a 'good' way, in contrast to a heteronomous superego, which demands that the ego behave in accordance with what is expected. The heteronomous superego is a possible outcome of inconsistent handling of a child by his parents. The inconsistency makes it impossible for him to foresee what particular conduct might ensure continued affection from the parents; the child consequently renounces attempts to differentiate between good and bad, and instead responds only to the demand of the moment.

superego, double This term refers to the double conscience sometimes seen in *psychic dualism.* The two consciences, or superegos, are usually antagonistic and regard each other vigilantly and belligerently. One conscience is usually considered masculine, the other feminine. Oberndorf cites the case of a male physician as an illustration of double superego. The patient's courtesy, conscientiousness, and consideration for others was often exaggerated to the point of masochistic subservience. The patient complained of depression secondary to the constant criticism which he underwent at the hands of his second superego. This second conscience, which never agreed with his masculine conscience, was traced to the story of the Dybbuk he had heard from his mother. In the story, the Dybbuk is the disembodied spirit of a wicked person which can reach heaven only after purification by entering the body of a young, virtuous girl. Thus the second conscience, which required almost absolute goodness, was viewed as feminine, and the patient's goodness became almost synonymous with femininity.

superego, group S.R. Slavson differentiates between the group superego and the infantile superego (*An Introduction to Group Therapy,* The Commonwealth Fund, Oxford University Press, New York, 1943, p. 232). He considers that this superego is an outcome of the adaptations to and experiences with various groups of individuals beyond the relationship with parents. For children, these group experiences are particularly important, according to Slavson, because of the emergence of a group superego.

superego, heteronomous (het'ĕr-on'ō-mus) See *autonomy-heteronomy*. A special type of superego which demands of the ego that it behave according to what is expected at the moment. As a result, the individual with this kind of superego is irresolute and weak, for his behavior at any given moment is controlled by the desire to secure the approval of those about him; and he is likewise in constant fear of being criticized or punished—i.e. he has 'social anxiety.' This is in contrast to the normal type of superego, which demands only that the ego behave in a 'good' way, according to a certain set of standards or ideals. Here the individual goes by the rule of thumb and is thus free of constant fear of criticism; he can come to decisions and carry out behavior independently of the approval or disapproval at the moment.

The heteronomous superego arose, for example, 'when the parents had shown so inconsistent a behavior that it became impossible for the child to foresee what conduct on his part would be most likely to ensure the continuance of their affection; whereupon, renouncing all attempts to distinguish between good and bad, he would take his bearings according to the demand of the moment.' (Fenichel, O. *The Psychoanalytic Theory of Neurosis,* Norton, New York, 1945)

superego, parasites of the Ideals and values absorbed by the individual 'which usurp the functions of the super-ego.' After one has entered the latency period, ideals usually continue to undergo modification. As the emotional ties to the family begin to loosen, becoming less intense, the individual's ideals and standards become more independent of the infantile models based upon the parents. Other persons or ideas begin to serve as models. These become part of the original superego which was formed at an earlier age from the parents' attitudes and activities. In this way the content of the superego is modified as the individual matures. When the new ideals are only 'a slight modification of old ideals, the situation is not difficult. . . Sometimes, however, internal or external situations may create parasites of the super-ego which usurp the functions of the super-ego for a varying length of time.' Even though the later

identifications with authorities other than the parents are usually superficial, they may be very influential. An example of a parasitic superego may develop through the influence of mass suggestion. An individual in whom a normal superego has been established may, under mass suggestion, yield to impulses which would normally be suppressed and yet show no guilt-feelings: '. . . individuals acting as a group . . . (or mob) . . . are capable of instinctual outbreaks that would be entirely impossible for them as individuals.'

Another example of a parasitic superego occurs under hypnosis, when the hypnotist takes over the functions of the patient's superego. In the patient's psyche the hypnotist acts as a parasitic superego. 'As such he tries to undo the previous work of the super-ego that gave rise to the defensive struggle.' (Fenichel, O. *The Psychoanalytic Theory of Neurosis,* Norton, New York, 1945)

superego, primitive This psychiatric term refers to a superego that exists apart from the parental superego and is older in origin than the force established by parents and teachers. The primitive superego would be hereditary and susceptible to the influence of hereditary factors in contrast to the parental superego which reflects tradition.

'For my part, I believe we must envisage, at least in theory, the existence of some sort of primitive super-ego having the function, according to us, as "organizer" of differentiating cells of the fetal organism, of assigning to them their places and functions in the physical framework, and of eliminating or destroying their tendencies to fulfill other functions. This organizer differentiates the activities of cells according to principles peculiar to each species.' (Laforgue, R. *The Relativity of Reality,* Nervous and Mental Disease Monographs No. 66, 1940, New York)

supergene (sū'pĕr-gēn) A type of variation of hereditary traits caused by chromosomal rearrangement; such a mutation affects an entire section of a chromosome but simulates the single factor type of inheritance (which is produced by one major mutant gene).

superior paraplegia See *paraplegia*.

supermoron (sū-pĕr-mō'ron) A person

slightly subnormal mentally, but in a grade above that of a moron.

super-ordinated See *ego* (Jung's definition of).

supersex (sū'pēr-seks) A sexually abnormal type of sterile organisms, first observed by Bridges, which show intersexual features owing to the disturbed ratio of autosomes to heterosomes.

Supersexual individuals are either *'superfemales'* characterized by three X chromosomes and two sets of autosomes, or *'supermales'* with one X chromosome and three sets of autosomes. The female characters of a superfemale are modified, because 'the preponderance of female genes in the three X chromosomes over the male genes in the autosomes is more marked than in the normal female with two X's.' (Sinnott, E.W. and Dunn, L.C. *Principles of Genetics,* 3rd ed., McGraw-Hill, New York and London, 1939) Conversely, in a supermale the male characters are exaggerated. See *intersexuality*.

support See *psychotherapy*.

suppression The act of consciously inhibiting an impulse, affect, or idea, as in the deliberate attempt to forget something and think no more about it. Suppression is thus to be differentiated from *repression* (q.v.), which is an unconscious process. It is probable that there is no sharp line of demarcation between suppression and repression, and it seems also likely that on occasion the unconscious defense of repression may be directed against material which the individual consciously suppresses. Nonetheless, it seems advisable in most instances to regard suppression and repression as distinctly different mechanisms.

suppression of affect In discussing affects in dreams, Freud says: 'In general, a dream is less rich in affects than the psychic material from which it is elaborated.' He adds that dreams are often 'colourless and devoid of any very intensive affective tone.' Freud explains such a condition as being due to a *suppression of the affects*. (Freud, S. *The Interpretation of Dreams,* 3rd ed., tr. by Brill, A.A., Macmillan, New York, 1933)

suppression-neurosis See *neurosis, suppression*.

supra-individual See *collective*.

suprarenalism (su-pra-rēn'al-iz'm) Overactivity of the suprarenal glands.

surface-ego H. Sachs maintains that 'Freud conceives the ego as essentially a "surface-ego," that is to say, one which in its principal function is directed toward the outside world, whose stimuli it receives or wards off. It is therefore more readily able to assimilate a piece of knowledge presented to it from without than one which proceeds from within the psychic apparatus.' (*International Journal of Psychoanalysis VI,* 7, 19, 1925)

surrender, schizophrenic (skiz-ō-fren'ik) A term used by C.MacFie Campbell to characterize the type of schizophrenia in which the mechanism is one of passive repression without initial anxiety or any conspicuous restitutional attempts.

The symptoms of schizophrenia can be divided into two major groups: (1) the regressive symptoms and (2) the restitutional symptoms. The first category comprises those symptoms that are a direct expression of the regressive breakdown of the ego and an undoing of differentiations acquired through mental development. Some examples are phantasies of world destruction, feelings of depersonalization, delusions of grandeur, and physical sensations. In the second category are those symptoms that express the schizophrenic's attempt to regain the lost objective world; hallucinations, delusions of persecution, and some catatonic symptoms are in this category.

Hebephrenia is the purely regressive type of schizophrenia in which there are no restitutional or defensive attempts. The ego takes refuge in successively older and older types of adaptation, finally arriving at a vegetative existence and perhaps even intra-uterine attitudes. The loss of the objective world and of any interest in it has become complete. The patient has undergone a 'schizophrenic surrender.' (Fenichel, O. *The Psychoanalytic Theory of Neurosis,* Norton, New York, 1945)

surrender, will to This psychiatric term denotes the psychic process through which the neurotic patient comes to the point of giving up his neurosis: it is a renunciating mental attitude through which the patient expresses his desire to submit to the analyst's aim of curing the illness. At the beginning of his psychotherapy, the patient's only aim seems to be a 'desire to protect and cherish his illness in defiance of the doctor's therapeutical endeavor.' It is only through the development of the will to surrender that the patient is ready to renounce his neurosis.

According to Stekel, a positive transference during analysis is a manifestation of this will to surrender. This desire is the opposite of the patient's 'will to power,' which is the expression of the patient's wish to master the analyst by love and attention, and defend his neurosis by so doing. (Stekel, W. *The Interpretation of Dreams,* Liveright, New York, 1943)

surrogate (sĕr'ŏ-gāt) One who takes the place of another is a surrogate or substitute. From the standpoint of instinctual psychology, during the growth of the individual, affective states originally expressed upon the parents are normally transferred from them to others who stand for them. Thus, a sister may be the first mother-surrogate, later a teacher, still later the mother of a friend, and finally a lover. With each new surrogate there is normally less and less resemblance to the original (mother). See *surrogate, mother.*

surrogate, father See *surrogate, mother.*

surrogate, mother One who takes the place of the mother. In psychiatry this is one of the nuclear themes. In normal growth youthful attachments to the mother should gradually be directed upon other women. The female schoolteacher, for instance, takes over part of the care of the child; she becomes a mother-surrogate; later, with the development of heterosexual interests, the individual, in the adolescent stage, substitutes other women for his mother. However, if strongly fixated upon the mother, the child may be unable to affect any substantial shift to another woman. It may select its later love-objects more or less genuinely on a basis of the earlier fixations. From the standpoint of the (now grown-up) child, the qualities of the mother-surrogate may be essentially those of the mother.

The expression *mother-substitute* is synonymous with *mother-surrogate.*

The same concepts hold true with regard to the father; hence, the expressions *father-surrogate* and *father-substitute.*

suspenopsia (sus-pen-op'si-à) Literally, 'suspension of sight.' 'A tendency for the image arising in either eye to be entirely disregarded for a short period of time

so that the individual is using one eye only for the time being.' (Orton, S.T. *Reading, Writing and Speech Problems in Children,* Norton, New York, 1937)

Sweetser, William (1797–1875) American psychiatrist who wrote the first American treatise on mental hygiene (1843).

swindler, epileptic See *epilepsy, affective.*

swindler, pathological (path-ŏ-log'i-kal) See *liar, pathological; impostor.*

syllable-stumbling A form of stuttering or stammering: the patient halts on syllables which he finds it difficult to enunciate.

symbiotic infantile psychosis See *psychosis, symbiotic infantile.*

symbol An object that stands for or represents something else. E. Jones ('The Theory of Symbolism,' *Papers on Psychoanalysis,* Baillière, Tindall & Cox, London, 1948) has pointed out that a symbol (1) is a representative or substitute of some other idea; (2) represents the primary element through having something in common with it; (3) is typically sensorial and concrete, whereas the idea represented may be relatively abstract and complex; (4) utilizes modes of thought which are more primitive, both ontogenetically and phylogenetically; (5) is a manifest expression of an idea that is more or less hidden, secret, or kept in reserve; and (6) is made spontaneously, automatically, and, in the broad sense of the word, unconsciously.

Further, Jones has this to say in regard to the extraordinary predominance of sexual symbols: 'A Swedish philologist, Sperber, has in a remarkable essay elaborated the theory, which has been several times suggested on other grounds by biologists, that sexual impulses have played the most important part in both the origin and later development of speech. According to this theory, which is supported by very weighty considerations, the earliest speech sounds were those that served the purpose of calling the mate (hence the sexual importance of the voice to this day), while the further development of speech roots accompanied the performance of work. . . . Words used during these common tasks thus had two meanings, denoting the sexual act and the equivalent work done respectively. In time the former meaning became detached and the word, now applying only to the work, thus "desexualized." . . . The symbolic association is the relic of the old verbal identity; things that once had the same name as a genital organ can now appear in dreams, etc., as a symbol for it. Freud aptly likens symbolism to an ancient speech that has almost vanished, but of which relics still remain here and there.' (ibid.)

As psychiatric symptoms, symbols may be expressed in any one or all of these general categories: (1) affects alone; thus, in anxiety-hysteria the symbol is intense anxiety without any relevant ideas; other symptoms (rapid pulse and breathing, feelings of impending collapse, etc.) are generally secondary symptoms; (2) affects with ideas, the latter being looked upon as thoroughly foreign and painful to the conscious ego. For example, a patient was 'tormented to death with the idea that I am slowly but certainly killing my children; that thought is furthest removed from my mind. I love them too dearly,' or (3) organic symptoms: the patients whose mental symptoms take an organic route of expression usually complain of a disease and not of symptoms; a woman, 35 years old, inordinately attached to her mother since early childhood, developed a deep sense of guilt when she left her invalid mother, who had a hemiplegia at the time. She repressed the guilt, replacing it with good intellectual reasoning, that is, with rationalization. The daughter later developed symptoms identical with those of her mother, and although these were not organically determined, the repressed guilt and its associated impulses returned to consciousness in the guise of a physical ailment.

Symbols may appear as delusions, hallucinations, morbid affects, compulsions, obsessions, conversions (i.e. hysterical), hypochondriasis, personalization of organs or organic systems, etc. Dreams form a special class of symbols.

While the term *symbolism* is in general synonymous with *symptomatology,* according to psychiatric usage, it is sometimes used in a more limited sense to refer to material objects. Thus a wand may be a phallic symbol; the earth may stand for femininity. See *symptom.*

symbolamblyopia, congenital (sim-bol-am-blī-ō'pi-à) Claiborne's term (1906) for a type of reading disability. See *reading, disabilities of.*

symbolism The act or process of representing an object or idea by a substitute object, sign, or signal. In psychiatry, symbolism is of particular importance since it can serve as a defense mechanism of the ego, as where unconscious (and forbidden) aggressive or sexual impulses come to expression through symbolic representation and thus are able to avoid censorship. The symbolic expression of the unconscious impulse may then appear as the patient's symptom. In one of Freud's cases, for example, Dora's cough was a hysterical symptom which symbolized her unconscious phantasy of oral intercourse between her father and another woman, and this phantasy in turn covered her own erotic feelings for this other woman's husband. See *symbol.*

symbolism, abstract Abstract symbolism—for instance, the cross, the crescent, the swastika—played a great role in religious mythology. For the most part, the origin of the symbols has been forgotten. Nevertheless, the timely ideas which were behind them have remained. They are called archaic expressions of the *collective unconscious* (see *collective*). (Baynes, H.G. *Mythology of the Soul,* Williams and Wilkins, Baltimore, 1940)

symbolism, anagogic (an-à-goj'ik) In modern dictionaries of the English language the word anagogic is accorded a specific definition when used in psychoanalytical connotation. Thus, Webster defines anagogic as: 'Pertaining to or arising from the striving of the inner psychic forms toward progressive ideals; pertaining to the interpretation and psychotherapy of dreams, symptoms, etc., with emphasis on such striving: as, *anagogic methods.*' (*Webster's New International Dictionary,* 2nd ed., Merriam, Springfield, Mass., 1948)

In psychoanalysis symbolism refers to the indirect representation of objects or ideas by means of symbols. The term anagogic symbolism originated with Silberer. He ascribes an anagogic significance to symbolism when the symbols are presumed to contain mystical, spiritual, magical, or religious doctrine. In such instances (as explained by Jones) Silberer takes the symbol 'to be the expression of a striving for a high ethical ideal, one which fails to reach this ideal and halts at the symbol instead; the ultimate ideal, however, is supposed to be implicit in the symbol and to be symbolized by it.' (Jones, E.J. *Papers on Psycho-Analysis,* Williams and Wilkins, Baltimore, 1949)

Therapists who embrace this concept of anagogic symbolism regularly make use of it in their treatment of patients. Recognition and understanding of anagogic symbols is stressed and the striving for the achievement of the ideals expressed therein is encouraged.

symbolism, cryptogenic (krip-tō-jen'ik) Silberer uses the term *cryptogenic symbolism* for any form of pictorial representation or image formed in mental functioning. In other words, all functions of the mind, save the ideational, are represented by cryptogenic symbolism.

symbolism, cryptophoric (krip-tō-for'ik) See *symbolism, metaphoric.*

symbolism, dream See *dream-symbolism.*

symbolism, functional Silberer subdivides symbolism into the first and second types; his first is called by Jones the 'material' type; his second, the 'functional' type. 'The first type is that which arises on the basis of an apperceptive insufficiency of purely intellectual origin, where the symbolized idea is not hindered by the influence of any affective complex; the second type arises, on the other hand, on the basis of an apperceptive insufficiency of affective origin.' (Jones, E. *Papers on Psycho-Analysis,* 4th ed., Wood, Baltimore, 1938)

Formerly Silberer used the expression *functional symbolism* with reference to the speed with which the mind was working, whether it was fast, slow, etc.

symbolism, material See *symbolism, functional.*

symbolism, metaphoric Jones emphasizes that *'the thesis will here be maintained that true symbolism, in the strict sense, is to be distinguished from other forms of indirect representation. . . .'*

Metaphoric symbolism, according to Jones, is a form of indirect representation. It seems that he prefers the expression *indirect pictorial representation* to *symbolism,* or *metaphoric symbolism.* The latter may be defined, then, as a pictorial representation based on a metaphor.

Jones says that J.C. Flügel 'suggested to me that, as an alternative to my proposal, the term "cryptophor" be used as a counterpart of "metaphor" so that one might speak of cryptophoric as contrasted with

metaphoric symbolism, instead of, as I propose, speaking of symbolism as contrasted with metaphoric representation.' (Jones, E. *Papers on Psycho-Analysis,* 4th ed., Wood, Baltimore, 1938)

symbolism, polyphallic (pol-i-fal'ik) In many clinical syndromes, also in dreams, it is not uncommon, particularly among women, to meet with the affirmation of possessing many penises. Flügel believes that such polyphallic symbolism (the patient represents the penis-wish symbolically) is developed to avoid rejection by the ego and the superego and the motive is furnished by overcompensatory wish-fulfillment. The impulse to have many male organs stems from the castration complex, courses through the oedipal situation and may finally be achieved in one of several ways. It may appear in the form of mental symptoms, expressed, for example, as a fear rather than a wish; the fear of sharp things is a case in point. It may appear as a polygamous tendency. It may be manifested in actual prostitution.

symbolism, threshold Silberer's term for symbolism occurring during the transition from one state of consciousness to, i.e. on the threshold of, another, for example, from sleep to wakefulness or *vice versa.* The term seems to be the equivalent of *hypnagogic hallucination.* It is a subdivision of what Silberer calls *functional symbolism.*

symbolism, true 'The typical attributes of *true symbolism,* as modified from the description given by Rank and Sachs, are: (1) representation of unconscious material; (2) constant meaning, or very limited scope for variation in meaning; (3) non-dependence on individual factors only; (4) evolutionary basis, as regards both the individual and the race; (5) linguistic connections between the symbol and the idea symbolized; (6) phylogenetic parallels with the symbolism as found in the individual existing in myths, cults, religions, etc.' (Jones, E. *Papers on Psycho-Analysis,* 4th ed., Wood, Baltimore, 1938)

symbolization In psychiatry, the process of expressing psychic disorder in terms (viz. affective, ideational, organic) dissimilar from, but standing for, the underlying disorder itself.

'Symbolization according to psychoanalytic usage is an unconscious process built up on association and similarity whereby one object comes to represent or stand for (symbolize) another object, through some part, quality, or aspect which the two have in common. The resemblance is generally so slight or superficial that the conscious mind would overlook it.' (Healy, W., Bronner, A.F., and Bowers, A.M. *The Structure and Meaning of Psychoanalysis,* Knopf, New York, 1930) Other schools of psychiatric thought define symbolization in a similar way, though they may ascribe different reasons for the formation of symbols.

symbol, memory A memory-symbol is a memory or idea that stands for, i.e. is substituted for, some other idea.

symbolophobia Fear of symbolism, i.e. of having a symbolical meaning attached to one's acts or words.

symbol, phallic (fal'ik) Anything which represents the penis. Many phallic symbols have been described: knife, spear, gun, and other similar weapons; tree, column, pillar, skyscraper, automobile, airplane, bird, snake, wild animals, cigar, cigarette, pen, pencil, key, screw, hammer, etc.

sympathetic nervous system See *autonomic nervous system.*

sympathicotonia (sim-path-i-kō-tō'ni-á) Eppinger and Hess described a clinical syndrome in which there is increased tonus of the sympathetic nervous system with a marked tendency to vascular spasm and high blood pressure. This they named *sympathicotonia.* Here there is excessive functioning of the adrenals and a hypersensitivity to adrenalin.

sympathin (sim'pa-thin) See *epinephrine.*

sympathism Suggestibility.

sympathize To experience. Experience a feeling similar to that possessed by another. Usually reciprocal motivation is implied.

sympathy In general, the existence of feeling identical with or resembling that which another experiences. According to Freud, identification may arise when there is no emotional attachment with the person imitated: for example, an individual may copy the feelings and actions of another, because the imitator has an unconscious impulse set free upon hearing about or looking at the one copied. In *sympathy* the feelings of the imitator remain essentially within him. When one or both share similar feelings, based upon some common unconscious quality, the term *identification* is used. See *empathize.*

symptom A symptom is any sign, physical or mental, that stands for something else. In a medical sense the term *symptom* generally implies pathology, although in its broader meaning a symptom may reflect physiological action (as in hunger).

Before the advent of modern psychiatric knowledge, when almost all psychic manifestations were traced directly to cells of the body, the term *symptom* denoted a sign relating to mental and physical phenomena, that is to say, by tradition it carried with it thoughts of the soma or tissues. With the expansion of psychiatric understanding, the expression *symbol* has become identified with the realm of the psyche, i.e. a symptom of the psyche is a symbol. However, in this transitional period, many psychiatrists prefer symptom to symbol, particularly when there is any doubt concerning the origin of the symptom. But there is general agreement when a signal from the psyche is called a symbol. See *symbolism.*

symptom, accessory Bleuler differentiates between fundamental symptoms and accessory symptoms of the schizophrenias. The accessory, secondary symptoms include hallucinations, illusions, delusions, certain memory disturbances (e.g. déjà vu, déjà fait), some of the disturbances of the person (e.g. speaking of one's self in the second or third person and other pronominal reversals), speech and writing disturbances (e.g. coprolalia, verbigeration, neologisms, metonymy, asyndesis, interpenetration), and physical symptoms such as headache, paresthesiae, 'will-of-the-wisp' gait, weight loss, and general signs of metabolic asthenia. See *symptom, fundamental.*

symptomatize In psychiatric usage, equivalent to *symbolize* (q.v.).

symptom, biphasic (bī-fāz'ik) A compulsive symptom or action that has two component parts, the second of which is the direct reverse of the first: e.g. the patient has the compulsion first to open the water tap and then to close it again. Obsessive thoughts or impulses may likewise have two parts, the second directly contradicting the first.

The first phase of the symptom represents an instinctual demand, whereas the second phase represents the *anti-instinctual force* (q.v.), or threat of the superego. 'The patient behaves alternately, as though he were a naughty child and a strict punitive disciplinarian.' (Fenichel, O. *The Psychoanalytic Theory of Neurosis,* Norton, New York, 1945)

symptom, defense Any symptom of psychical disorder was thus called by Freud in his earliest writings. The term is becoming obsolete.

'Now self-reproach becomes connected with the memories of those pleasurable activities, and the relation with the initial passive experience makes it possible to repress them and substitute for them a *primary defense-symptom*—often only after conscious and remembered efforts.' (Freud, S. *Collected Papers,* vol. 1, tr. by Riviere, J., Leonard and Virginia Woolf and The Institute of Psychoanalysis, London, 1924–25)

symptom, fundamental Bleuler differentiates between fundamental symptoms and accessory symptoms of the schizophrenias. The fundamental, primary, or principal symptoms are those that are characteristic of and pathognomonic of schizophrenia. The accessory symptoms, on the other hand, while they may overshadow the fundamental symptoms in their intensity, are not the essential or basic elements of the schizophrenias since they are seen also in other diseases, and particularly in the organic brain syndromes. The fundamental symptoms include disturbances in the associations, in the affect, in the person, in the will, in attention, in activity and behavior, and also ambivalence (of affect, intellect and/or will), autism, and schizophrenic dementia.

symptom, primary See *symptom, fundamental.*

symptom, primary defense A term used by Freud in describing the early development of obsessional neurosis. At the onset of sexual 'maturity,' self-reproach for the memories of pleasurable sexual activities in childhood is avoided by primary defense-symptoms, such as conscientiousness, shame, and self-distrust. These introduce the period of 'apparent health or, better—that of successful defense.' (Freud, S. *Collected Papers,* vol. 1, tr. by Riviere, J., Leonard and Virginia

Woolf and The Institute of Psychoanalysis, London, 1924–25)

symptom, principal See *symptom, fundamental.*

symptoms, compulsive This psychiatric term designates the orderly and systematic behavior exhibited by the compulsion-neurotic in order to protect himself against dangerous anal-erotic instinctual demands. The compulsion-neurotic feels threatened by unconscious anal-sadistic drives. He is protecting himself against a rebellion of sensual and hostile demands (such as murder and incest) which through regression have become anal-erotic in nature. He accomplishes this by doing things in a compulsive systematic way, according to a prearranged plan, a routine. This protects him against the danger associated with spontaneity. He can be sure he is not committing a sin of which he is both unconscious and afraid. He knows beforehand what he will do and how he will do it and thus he overcomes his fear that his own excitement may induce him to do things he is afraid of. The systemization is especially noticeable with respect to money and time. 'Many compulsion neurotics have an exaggerated interest in all kinds of timetables.'

The unconscious anal-sadistic drives, however, 'usually sabotage orderliness and clinging to a "system." They may reappear in the form of disorder or events that disturb the system. . .' Furthermore, the compulsion-neurotic never can feel that he has provided enough rules to govern all possibilities, that he knows all the rules sufficiently well, or that he is actually following out the rules. This is because the unconscious drives have actually permeated the systems themselves.

Frequently, people around the compulsion-neurotic are bidden to follow his systems in an effort to ensure their validity. The others' refusal to submit increases the patient's hostility as well as his attempts to compel those around him to conform, with the end result that the fear engendered by this show of hostility increases the patient's systematizing needs.

The systematization of the compulsion-neurotic often leads him to make false generalizations. All ideas are classified into certain mutually exclusive categories. Thus the likelihood of an unforeseen new event is excluded. The attitude is that the phenomenon or idea is already known—

that is, has been classified—for unforeseen events are dangerous and are interpreted as temptations. (Fenichel, O. *The Psychoanalytic Theory of Neurosis,* Norton, New York, 1945)

symptom, secondary See *symptom, accessory.*

symptom, secondary defense The expression applied by Freud to the protective measures to which the ego resorts in obsessional neurosis, when the primary defense (against repressed memories and self-reproach) has failed. These secondary defense-symptoms include obsessive actions, obsessive speculating, obsessive thinking, the compulsion to test everything, *folie du doute;* Freud continues their elaboration by stating that 'secondary defense against the obsessional affects calls into being a still wider series of protective measures, which may be transformed into obsessive acts. These may be grouped according to their tendencies: *penitential* measures (burdensome ceremonials, the observation of numbers), *precautionary* measures (all kinds of phobias, superstitions, pedantry, exaggeration of the primary symptom of conscientiousness), *dread of betrayal* (collecting paper, misanthropia), *hebetude* (dipsomania).' (Freud, S. *Collected Papers,* vol. 1, tr. by Riviere, J., Leonard and Virginia Woolf and The Institute of Psychoanalysis, London, 1924–25)

symptoms, phylogenetic (fī-lō-ge-net'ik) See *schizophrenia, hebephrenic.*

symptoms, withdrawal A term for the symptoms (restlessness, yawning, chills, characteristic pilomotor activity, excessive nasal secretion, lacrimation, sneezing, cramps in abdomen and lower extremities, vomiting and diarrhea, excessive perspiration, muscular twitching) experienced by addicts to morphine and heroin when the drug is suddenly withdrawn, that is, no longer taken.

synchiria (sin-kī'ri-a) Perception of a stimulus to one side of the body as having been applied to both sides of the body.

synchronism The simultaneous occurrence of several developmental faults. In mongolism, for example, all organ systems of ectodermal, mesodermal, and entodermal origin which undergo specific development during the neofetal period are impaired; the particular synchronism of mongoloid symptoms points to the period

between the sixth and twelfth weeks of fetal life as the time when the etiologic factors exert their greatest effect.

syncope (sing'kō-pē) Fainting; a swoon.

syncretism (sin'kre-tiz'm) See *thinking, physiognomonic.*

syndrome (sin'drōm; more rarely sin'drō-mē) Group or set of concurrent symptoms which together are indicative of a disease.

syndrome, akinetic-abulic (à-kin-et'ik-à-bū'lik) A group of symptoms which frequently appear in the course of treatment with 'tranquilizers' or 'ataractics': pseudoparkinsonism (tremor), bradykinesia, hypertonia, decreased mental drive, and lack of interest.

syndrome, Brown-Sequard (Charles Edouard Brown-Sequard, French physiologist, 1818–1894) This syndrome, which follows hemisection of the spinal cord, consists of lower motor neuron type paralysis and loss of touch sensation at the level of the lesion; ipsilateral upper motor neuron type paralysis and loss of proprioception and vibratory sense below the level of the lesion; and contralateral loss of pain and temperature sense below the level of the lesion.

syndrome, buffoonery 'The *buffoonery syndrome* is not always easily separated from catatonic states. In this syndrome the entire picture is taken up with playing demonstrative striking tricks, and with giving wrong answers; like the Ganser twilight state it probably only occurs as a reaction to a situation from which unconsciously one wants to escape through insanity.' (Bleuler, E. *Textbook of Psychiatry,* tr. by Brill, A.A., Macmillan, New York, 1930)

syndrome, Capgras' (kà-gràz') A psychotic state in which the individual is unable to identify the person confronting him even though recognizing his appearance and behavior. He feels he is confronted by a 'double.' This condition is usually associated with suspicion and distrust. Another term for this syndrome is 'illusion of negative doubles'; the misidentification results from a perception of nonexistent differences between the person confronted and his double. When imaginary resemblances are recognized, the term 'illusion of positive doubles' is used. (Coleman, S.M. 'Misidentification and Non-Recognition,' *Journal of Mental Science 79,* 42–51, 1933)

syndrome, effort Neurocirculatory asthenia.

syndrome, Foster Kennedy (Foster Kennedy, American neurologist, 1884–1955) See *nerve, olfactory.*

syndrome, Freud's P. Janet coined this expression: 'The mania for repression . . . is still an interesting symptom; and it explains certain remarkable phenomena, such as monstrous and sacrilegious longings. It will continue to form a part of mental pathology under the name of "Freud's syndrome." ' (Janet, P. *Psychological Healing,* vols. 1–2, tr. by Paul, E. and C., Macmillan, New York, 1925)

syndrome, general adaptation The various changes in the body in response to and/or as defense against stress. Selye distinguishes three stages in this syndrome: the alarm reaction, in which adaptation is not yet acquired; the stage of resistance, in which adaptation is optimal; and the stage of exhaustion, in which the acquired adaptation is lost again. The hypophysis-adrenal interrelationships, which largely determine the various elements of the syndrome, are as follows: the stress agent, or stressor, acts not only upon the cells of the target organ but also acts (humoral or neural route?) upon the anterior pituitary and stimulates the latter to produce ACTH; in certain circumstances it may also induce a release of somatotrophic hormone (STH). ACTH, in turn, induces the adrenal cortex to produce glucocorticoids (such as cortisone). The latter exert primarily an inhibitory effect upon the various target organs—catabolism, diminution of granuloma formation and of allergic responses, etc. STH, on the other hand, by stimulating connective tissue, enhances defensive reactions in the target organs—anabolism, augmentation of granuloma formation and of allergic responses, etc. This action occurs by means of direct sensitization of the connective tissue elements to mineralo-corticoids (such as desoxycorticosterone) and also by stimulating the adrenal cortex to produce mineralo-corticoids. This latter corticotrophic effect, however, depends upon the simultaneous availability of ACTH. Thus the target organ response to stressors depends largely upon the balance between STH and the mineralo-corticoids on one hand, and ACTH and gluco-corticoids on the other.

syndrome, Horner's (Johann Friedrich Horner, Swiss ophthalmologist, 1831–86) Caused by paralysis of the cervical sympathetic, this condition has the following signs and symptoms: (1) miosis, (2) enophthalmos, (3) pseudoptosis, (4) occasionally ipsilateral vasodilatation and anhidrosis on the side of the face and neck.

syndrome, Horton's (Bayard T. Horton, contemporary American physician) See *histamine.*

syndrome, hyperventilation Subjective symptoms (especially breathlessness, palpitation, dizziness or faintness, paresthesiae and excessive sweating) due to the progressive hypocapina produced by overbreathing. The overbreathing is itself a form of reaction to anxiety or fear, but the importance of recognizing the syndrome lies in the fact that the subjective symptoms secondarily produced are of physiologic origin rather than specific symbolic representatives of the underlying neurotic conflict.

syndrome, Kleine-Levin A syndrome consisting of episodes of hypersomnia, bulimia, and abnormal mental states such as clouded sensorium, partial or total amnesia for certain periods of the attack, and psychomotor retardation. The syndrome is distinct from narcolepsy, although it may be related to the latter. The Kleine-Levin syndrome appears to be a result of disturbance of function of the frontal lobe and/or the hypothalamus. Amphetamine drugs are often useful in treatment of the disorder.

syndrome, Klippel-Feil (klē-pel' fāl') (Maurice Klippel, 1858–1942, French neurologist; André Feil, contemporary French physician) A congenital anomaly characterized by absence and fusion of portions of the cervical spine, producing a shortness and stiffness of the neck. Compression of the cord may occur with motor and sensory changes. Mirror writing may occur in association with the syndrome.

syndrome, Klumpke-Déjérine (Mme. Auguste Klumpke-Déjérine, French neurologist, 1859–1927) A combination of paralysis of the cervical sympathetic with paralysis and atrophy of the small muscles of the hand.

syndrome, Klüver-Bucy A syndrome, described originally by Klüver and Bucy in monkeys who had been subjected to bilateral removal of the temporal lobes. In the human, symptoms include: (1) loss of recognition of people; (2) loss of fear and rage reactions; (3) increased sexual activity (especially masturbation and homosexuality); (4) bulimia; (5) hypermetamorphosis, and (6) memory defects. (Terzian, H., and Ore, G. *Neurology 5:* 373–80, 1955)

syndrome, Laurence-Moon-Biedl (J.Z. Laurence, British ophthalmologist, 1830–74; Moon; A. Biedl, German physician, 1869–1933) A syndrome consisting of six cardinal signs in the following order of frequency: obesity, retinitis pigmentosa, mental deficiency, genital dystrophy, familial occurrence, polydactyly.

syndrome, Marin Amat A syndrome described in 1918 consisting of closing of the eyelid on chewing or opening the mouth. Paralysis or spasm of the ipsilateral facial nerve usually precedes the appearance of the syndrome, which is probably due to a disturbance of intrinsic nuclear functions.

syndrome, Melkersson-Rosenthal Recurrent, gradual, persistent swelling of the lips and facial paresis; the syndrome occurs in individuals with an unstable vegetative nervous system and is usually precipitated by stress or other psychic factors.

syndrome, night-eating A syndrome seen in some obese patients consisting of nocturnal hyperphagia, insomnia, and morning anorexia. The syndrome tends to appear episodically, and during such periods weight control is especially difficult or even impossible for the patient.

syndrome, nonsense Popular synonym for Ganser syndrome.

syndrome of approximate answers See *answers, syndrome of approximate.*

syndrome, organic The group of symptoms characteristic of the acute and chronic brain disorders. In any specific case, one or more of the characteristic symptoms may predominate. The basic syndrome consists of: (1) disturbances in orientation; (2) impairment of memory; (3) impairment in the maintenance of the level of attention; (4) impairment of all intellectual functions (comprehension, calculation, knowledge, learning, etc.);

(5) defective judgment; (6) lability, shallowness, and similar instabilities of the affect; and (7) overall changes in the personality, with the appearance of conduct which is foreign to the patient's natural or usual behavior. In the acute brain disorders, alteration in consciousness (with preoccupation, stupor, or coma) and defects in orientation and memory tend to predominate; the acute organic syndrome is sometimes called the delirious reaction. In the chronic brain disorders (e.g. the Korsakoff psychosis), intellectual defects are prominent (loss of general efficiency, inability to plan, judgment defects, disturbances in orientation and memory, confabulation), and disturbed affect and personality changes are also frequent.

syndrome, pedunculopontile (ped-ung-kŭ-lō-pon′tĭl) Weber's syndrome; see *hemiplegia alternans.*

syndrome, pontocerebellar angle (pon-tō-ser-e-bel′ĕr) A group of symptoms caused by acoustic neuromas. Involvement of the acoustic nerve produces persistent tinnitus, progressive deafness, and vertigo. Involvement of the facial nerve produces homolateral facial anesthesia with loss of corneal and sneeze reflexes. Cerebellar involvement produces homolateral ataxia with staggering, and pontine involvement results in contralateral hemiplegia and slight hemianesthesia. In addition, there are general symptoms of brain tumor and increased intracranial pressure.

syndrome, prisoner of war (POW) Psychopathologic manifestations occurring in prisoners of war, presumably a reaction to capture and imprisonment. Various types of reaction have been described, among them a syndrome of withdrawal, apathy, and sometimes death which has been likened to the anaclitic depression reported by Spitz in hospitalized or otherwise deprived children.

syndromes, acute Bleuler differentiated between the acute and chronic forms of schizophrenia. The acute syndromes are transitory states of various kinds that may occur as simple exacerbations of the chronic state or as reactive episodes, in response to emotionally charged experiences. The acute syndromes occur more frequently in the early years of the disease process; they may last for hours only, or they may persist for years. Subsequent memory for these episodes varies, but complete amnesia for them is unusual. Bleuler listed the following acute syndromes: melancholic conditions, manic conditions, catatonic states, delusions ('amentia' in the terms of the Viennese school), twilight-states, Benommenheit, confusional states, fits of anger, anniversary excitements, stupor, deliria, fuguestates, and dipsomania. See *schizophrenia.*

syndrome, Stewart-Morel Internal frontal hyperostosis with adiposity and mental disturbances.

syndrome, stiff-man A poorly understood syndrome, related to abnormal phosphorus metabolism, consisting of painful, iron-like spasms of muscle groups in various parts of the body. The spasms can be so severe as to cause fractures of the long bones, and most patients show secondary hypertrophy of affected muscles as well as varus deformity of the feet. Course is prolonged, and death may occur after a number of years during or shortly after a severe spasm.

syndrome, striatal (stri-ā'tal) Disease of the striatum or strio-pallidal system, characterized, in general, by the following: (1) rigidity (a general increase of muscle tonus); (2) tremor (abnormal involuntary movements); (3) hypokinesia (poverty of voluntary, especially spontaneous movements); (4) impairment of associated movements; (5) absence of sensory disturbances; (6) absence of 'true' paralysis, that is, absence of signs of involvement of pyramidal tracts.

syndrome, Tapia's See *Tapia's syndrome.*

syndrome, thalamic (thal-a'mik) See *thalamus.*

syneidesis (sīn-ī-dē'sis) This Greek word was proposed by Monakow to replace our English *conscience,* from Latin conscientia, which, in itself, was literally and morphologically nothing but the classical Roman writers' slavish replica and equivalent of the proposed syneidesis. Monakow suggests that conscience is not a specifically human phenomenon and does not belong to the sphere of consciousness, but is a characteristic of all living beings in any stage of development. This concept is at variance with prevailing psychiatric opinion, which believes that conscience is a product of the interaction of the child with frustration-producing elements in the child's environment. See *conscience.*

synergia (sin-ĕr'ji-à) See *synergy.*

synergism, sexual (sin'ĕr-jiz'm) A sexual excitation that arises from a combination of various stimuli acting simultaneously. The manifold aspects of this combination range from pleasurable stimulation of the surface of the body to unpleasant, or even painful, processes within the organism. Freud considered that perhaps every important physical process contributes to the genesis of sexual excitement. Even the combination of the two opposed instinctual tendencies—love and hate—may arouse sexual excitement: sexual synergism can be aroused provided the intensity of discomfort and pain does not pass a certain limit. According to the individual sexual constitution, this synergism manifests itself in different ways. Reik asserts that sexual synergism 'constitutes the physiological basis for the psychic superstructure of masochism.' This peculiar sexual excitement is independent of the attitude of the subject toward the object: in many children mechanical concussions may produce this kind of sexual excitement, and, similarly, certain affective processes such as fright or horror may act as sexual stimuli, even in adults. In this respect one may cite the patients who distinguish between 'disagreeable' and 'interesting' pain. (Reik, T. *Masochism in Modern Man,* Farrar and Rinehart, New York, 1941)

synergy Co-ordination of muscular movements; co-operation in action, primarily a function of the cerebellum.

synesthesia (sin-es-thē'z[h]i-à) See *sensation, secondary.*

syngamy (sing'gà-mē) This term is synonymous with *fertilization,* the biological phenomenon which brings about the intermingling of paternal and maternal hereditary material.

'It is accomplished by a great variety of means in animals and plants. In the lowest groups the gametes may be equal in size and similar in structure (an *isogamous* condition), but in the great majority of all animals and plants they are unequal (*heterogamous*), the male gamete being relatively small and consisting of little but a nucleus, and the female gamete (egg) being very much larger and possessing a considerable amount of cytoplasm in addition to its nucleus.' (Sinnott, E.W. and Dunn, L.C. *Principles of Genetics,* 3rd ed., McGraw-Hill, New York and London, 1939)

syngignoscism (sin-jig′nos-iz′m) Hypnotism; suggestion.

synkinesis (sin-ki-nē′sis) An involuntary movement accompanying a voluntary one; such as the movement (occurring in a paralyzed muscle) accompanying motion in another part.

synthesis The combination or grouping of parts or elements so as to form an integrated whole; the integration of the various factors making up the personality and, thus, the opposite of analysis. This term has been used with various shades of meaning by different writers. Morton Prince used it to refer to the ability to keep the component parts of the psyche together in close association; any weakening of synthesis tends to produce dissociation and, hence, neurosis. Synthesis has also been used to refer to maintenance of intactness of personality; in this sense, synthesis is the opposite of 'splitting' in Bleuler's sense. Gestalt psychologists use the term synthesis to refer to the tendency to perceive and appreciate situations as a whole. In psychoanalytic psychology, synthesis is considered to be a complex ego-function, probably a derivative of libido, which impels the individual to harmonious unification and creativity in the broadest sense of the term. Synthesis includes a tendency to simplify, to generalize, and ultimately to understand—by assimilating external and internal elements, by reconciling conflicting ideas, by uniting contrasts, and by seeking for causality.

synthesis, distributive In objective psychobiology this denotes the 'synthesis of the various factors and strivings which will offer the patient security. . . . The material for such a synthesis is obtained by analysis of all the factors and situations which are of importance in the study of the human personality and more specifically in the pathologic reactions which bring a patient to the physician. . . . Every analysis should lead to synthesis, and after each consultation physician and patient should be able to formulate what has been obtained from the analysis and how it can be used constructively.' (Diethelm, O. *Treatment in Psychiatry,* Macmillan, New York, 1936)

synthesis, syllabic (si-lab′ik) The combination of syllables of several words to form a new word or neologism. The process is common in the productions of schizophrenic patients and in dreams.

'The condensation-work of dreams becomes most palpable when it takes words and names as its objects. Generally speaking, words are often treated in dreams as things, and therefore undergo the same combinations as the ideas of things. The results of such dreams are comical and bizarre word-formations.' (Freud, S. *The Interpretation of Dreams,* 3rd ed., tr. by Brill, A.A., Macmillan, New York, 1933) See *neologism; condensation.*

synthesize See *psychosynthesize.*

syntone (sin′tōn) In psychiatry, one whose personality is in harmony with the environment. The term implies emotional rapport, in particular. Bleuler at times uses the expression interchangeably with *cyclothyme.*

'According to a more recent theory of these two groups of psychoses one observes *even in normal people* a syntonic ("cyclothymic") reaction type, in which the whole personality uniformly participates in a definite and relatively vivid affect, suitable for the situation of the moment, and the train of ideas follows substantially quite logical laws. . . .' (Bleuler, E. *Textbook of Psychiatry,* tr. by Brill, A.A., Macmillan, New York, 1930)

The term *syntone* implies normality, while usually *cyclothyme* describes a personality that is an exaggeration of the syntonic but is less intense than that observed in the manic-depressive reaction.

syntropy (sin′trō-pē) The state of wholesome association with others (Adolf Meyer).

syphilis (sif′i-lis) An infectious venereal disease caused by Treponema pallidum; lues.

syphilis, cerebral (ser′e-bral) Meningovascular syphilis; interstitial syphilis. The term includes syphilitic leptomeningitis, vascular neurosyphilis, or luetic endarteritis and the gummatous subtype. The essential lesion in cerebral syphilis is vascular and perivascular inflammation of varying degrees. Symptoms, which typically appear about three years after the primary infection, depend upon the site and extent of involvement. Thus there may be primarily a picture of acute or chronic leptomeningitis with signs of increased intracranial pressure and involvement of the cranial nerves (especially III, VI, and VII); or luetic endarteritis may lead to occlusion and thus to hemiplegia or convulsions; or development of a gumma may simulate the appearance of intracranial neoplasm. Superimposed on these neurological signs are mental symptoms such as intellectual dulling, emotional lability, stupor, fearful delirium and/or multiple somatic complaints. Cerebral syphilis often responds favorably to penicillin treatment.

syphilomania *Rare.* Insanity resulting from syphilophobia.

syphilophobia Fear of syphilis.

syphilopsychosis (sif-i-lō-sī-kō′sis) Southard's term for psychosis associated with central nervous system syphilis.

syringobulbia (sir-in-gō-bul′bi-à) See *syringomyelia.*

syringomyelia (sir-in-go-mī-ē′li-à) Status dysraphicus; a chronic disease, probably due to a developmental defect, consisting of central cavitation of the spinal cord or ventricle in the medulla (syringobulbia). Symptoms begin in the second and third decades; 70 per cent of those affected are male. Enlargement of the cavity affects, in order, the following structures: the anterior commissure, the anterior horn cells, and the pyramidal tracts. Pain and temperature sensation are impaired but touch and proprioception are intact; hand and finger movements become weak and awkward, and a claw hand develops. Trophic disturbances are prominent, with thickened skin and various arthropathies (some would call this form Morvan's disease). In the bulbar form, symptoms referable to disturbances of the tenth, eighth, and fifth cranial nerves and of the medial lemniscus are seen. Affected patients usually live many years. Palliative X-ray irradiation of the affected region of the spinal cord or medulla is sometimes beneficial.

system The psychic apparatus, according to Freud, is 'a compound instrument, the component parts of which we shall call *instances,* or for the sake of clearness, *systems.* We shall then anticipate that these systems may perhaps maintain a constant spatial orientation to one another, very much as do the different and successive systems of lenses of a telescope. . . . For the sake of brevity, we shall henceforth speak of the component parts of the apparatus as "Ψ-systems." ' * (Freud, S. *The Interpretation of Dreams,* 3rd ed., tr. by Brill, A.A., Macmillan, New York, 1933)

'All our psychic activities proceed from (inner and outer) stimuli and terminate in innervations. We thus ascribe to the apparatus a sensory and a motor end; at the sensory end we find a system which receives the perceptions, and at the motor end another which opens the sluices of motility. The psychic process generally runs from the perceptive end to the motor end.' (ibid.)

Percepts leave a trace at the sensory end of the psychic apparatus; it is called a *memory-trace,* the function of which is called *memory.* There is what Freud calls the initial system which 'receives the stimuli of perception but retains nothing of them—that is, it has no memory: . . . behind it . . . lies a second system, which transforms the momentary excitation of the first into lasting traces.' The initial system is called the *P-system,* while the second is termed the *memory-system,* or *mem-system.* The latter is 'the basis of *association,'* that is, the linkage of one idea with another. (ibid.)

An element of the P-system is called a P-element and resides in consciousness; that of the mem-system is known as a mem-element. The latter is in the sphere of the unconscious; as Freud says, 'our memories, on the other hand, are unconscious in themselves; those that are most deeply impressed form no exception.' (ibid.).

There is a motor end to the psychic apparatus and 'the last of the systems at the motor and we call the *pre-conscious (Pcs.)* to denote that the exciting processes in this system can reach consciousness without any further detention. . . .' (ibid) Behind the pre-conscious system is the *unconscious (Ucs.).*

Freud adds: 'The motive-power of the dream is furnished by the *Ucs.,* and on account of this factor we shall assume the unconscious system as the starting-point for dream-formation.' (ibid.)

system, action A bodily system which

* From Ψ (*psi*), the 23rd letter of the Greek alphabet, as the initial of the word *psyche* (*psy*chic apparatus), analogously to Freud's use of the initials P., Ucs., Pcs., Cs., for Percept, Unconscious, Preconscious, Conscious, etc.

enables the organism to take action in response to a desire: a desire to keep one's feet dry will cause one to walk around and not through a puddle. The means by which this action is taken is produced by the integration of receptor, co-ordinative, effector systems into a functioning unit or action system.

The term action system was introduced by Kardiner in connection with his studies of the traumatic neuroses. Kardiner maintains that the traumatic neurosis presents a symptomatology and a psychodynamic structure which cannot be fully understood or adequately explained on the basis of instinct as an operational concept. Instead of using instinct as an operational concept in studying the traumatic neurosis, he takes as his operational concept the various action systems of the body by which instinct is put into action. The damaging of these action systems, with consequent impairment of their function, explains the traumatic neurosis and, indeed, *is* the traumatic neurosis. (Kardiner, A., and Spiegel, L. *War Stress and Neurotic Illness,* Hoeber, New York, 1947)

system, adviser A system introduced in various United States Service Units for the purpose of sustaining the 'morale' and preventing mental ailing or breakdowns through cadres of 'advisers' trained for that purpose.

'An unthoughtful, sadistic leader anywhere in the hierarchy of command can cause distress to all the men under his command; but the person with greatest influence on the emotional stability of his men is the immediate superior, the platoon leader in the army. Where the platoon leader is himself a stable person, where he knows, either with or without training, how to create good will within the group without the loss of fighting efficiency, then the neurotic level and all its accompaniments are low. The exact reverse of symptoms occurs when the platoon leader is indifferent, unthoughtful, or too egotistic to be interested in others than himself.

'A training program, termed the Adviser System, was set up at one camp to attempt to correct these defects. Platoon cadres met in groups for lectures on the "practical psychology" of the men in their units. In addition, they were made conscious of the importance of: (1) explain-

ing the thousand and one details which are accepted without question by the "old timer," but which seem meaningless to the new trainee (it is amazing how the "mind of the trainee" can be irritated by commands and demands which seem to be without reason); (2) taking a vital and personal interest in solving the emotional, domestic, and physical problems of the soldier; (3) providing the psychiatrist with an "army case history" of the soldier who is referred to the mental hygiene clinic; (4) assisting in the readjustment of the soldier as suggested by the psychiatrist through the encouragement of socialization and the proper assignment of tasks; and (5) bringing to the attention of his company commander any abuses and injustices present in the unit.

'This program was eminently successful not only in allaying psychoneurotic reactions in the unit; but the absence without leave (AWOL) decreased from 1.2 per cent in May, 1943, to 0.2 per cent in May, 1944. The program emphasized the vital importance of selecting and of training the sergeants if morale was to be high and neurotic and allied reactions low.' (Kraines, S.H. *The Therapy of the Neuroses and Psychoses,* Lea & Febiger, Philadelphia, 1948)

system, anabolic (an-à-bol'ik) In constitutional medicine two large systems are described—the anabolic and the catabolic, corresponding with the megalosplanchnic and the microsplanchnic habitus respectively. In early life connective tissue or mesenchymal is more abundant than parenchymal elements. 'Now it is certain that, as the organ gradually evolves toward the adult structure, the connective tissue, which is very abundant in early life, slowly diminishes; as De Giovanni has pointed out, the persistence in the adult organ of a great number of mesenchymal cells and a large amount of interstitial lymph is a sign of organic immaturity and of true hypoevolutism.' (Pende, N. *Constitutional Inadequacies,* tr. by Naccarati, S., Lea & Febiger, Philadelphia, 1928)

system, boarding out A system under which psychotic patients are taken care of as boarders in private homes.

system, centrencephalic (sen-tren-se-fal'-ik) Penfield's term for a hypothesized central structure of neurones in the brain skin which is conceived of as the anatomical basis for the coherent unity of mental processes. In many respects, the centrencephalic system would appear to be identical with the reticular activating system. See *formation, reticular.*

system, chronological See *complex, subject.*

system, graphogenic (graf-ō-gen'ik) See *mechanism, homogenic.*

system, graphonomic (graf-ō-nom'ik) See *mechanism, homogenic.*

system, intralaminar (in-tra-lam'in-ẽr) Morison and Dempsey's term for a diffuse, bilateral, nonspecific projection system of neurones in the thalamus. Also known as the recruiting system, the intralaminar system is associated with consciousness, sleep, and wakefulness and thus would appear to be identical with the reticular activating system in many respects. See *formation, reticular.*

system, perceptual-conscious That part of the mental apparatus which absorbs perceptions from both the external world and the interior of the mind (the id). Early in the development of the human mind, one part of it becomes the recipient of stimuli. In this part of the mind the feeling of consciousness originates and, for this reason, it is named the perceptual conscious system.

As the mind develops, its new task is to protect the organism from the stimuli which are dangerous to the organism. The mind learns to retain a true picture of the external world by its memory of the perceptions which, through reality-testing, it keeps from being contaminated by instinctual demands. With this later function, anticipation, reason, and judgment become possible and take over the control of motility or action. The part of the mental apparatus which has developed the faculties of memory, reality-testing, reason, and judgment toward the end of controlling the instincts and thus protecting the organism is called the ego. But the earliest function which is decisive for the ego must be the perception of stimuli, since without this perception none of its more complex functions can be carried out. The ego thus originates in the perceptual-conscious system, 'the most superficial portion of the mental apparatus.' (Freud, S. *New Introductory Lectures on Psychoanalysis,* Norton, New York, 1933)

system, pride Horney's term for the sum total of the neurotically (over-)valued and the neurotically (over-)hated attributes of the self.

system, psychodynamic cerebral (sī-kō-dī-nam'ik ser'e-bral) See *psychodynamics, adaptational.*

system, recruiting See *system, intralaminar.*

system, reticular (re-tik'ū-lẽr) See *formation, reticular.*

system, rotation The method some group psychotherapists employ of treating individual patients in sequence in the presence of the group.

system, sign Schilder's term for the use of language as the main tool, or instrument, of psychotherapy. Through words, the psychiatrist gains access to and unveils the patient's hidden problems and inner personality. Words in the sign system are to the psychiatrist what knives and other instruments are to the surgeon. 'The psychotherapist has no immediate access to the body of the patient and to his gratifications. The influence he has on the patient is merely due to the words he speaks.' In a broader sense, every social relation between two persons speaking to each other includes the erotic. Man needs not only actual but also future gratification, 'and humanity has elaborated a system for such gratification,' language constituting the main though by no means the only element of this system. In the relationship between the sexes, words and sentences in themselves may become signs through which the individuals obtain their social and erotic gratifications. (Schilder, P. *Psychotherapy,* Norton, New York, 1938)

system, stereogenic (ste-rē-ō-jen'ik) See *constant, central; mechanism, orthogenic.*

system, stereonomic (ster-ē-ō-nom'ik) See *constant, central; mechanism, orthogenic.*

system, villa Boarding-out system.

T

tabes (tā'bēz) (L. 'a wasting, emaciation') Tabes (tabes dorsalis, locomotor ataxia) is a chronic, progressive disease of the nervous system occurring rather late in a comparatively small percentage of individuals affected with syphilis. The main pathological process involves the posterior spinal ganglia in a mild inflammation. The roots between the ganglia and the spinal cord, and, to some extent, the meninges are also involved. There is a degeneration of the nerve fibers with a selective degeneration of the posterior columns of the cord. The cranial nerves, especially the optic and those supplying the ocular muscles, are particularly involved. The symptoms are ataxia, or muscular inco-ordination, neuralgia, anesthesia, visceral crises, lancinating pains, and muscular atrophy. Trophic disorders of the joints (arthropathies) are frequent, atrophy of the optic nerve occurs, and paralysis may be a late symptom. Mental symptoms are not usually prominent, although a severe depression may occur.

tabes, juvenile Juvenile tabes presents an essentially identical pathologic process and clinical course as in the adult. The symptoms appear from about the age of ten onward, in children who have congenital syphilis or who acquired the disease in infancy or early childhood. Ataxia is rather infrequent while optic atrophy is very common in juvenile tabes. Mental symptoms and taboparesis occur frequently. The Wasserman blood reaction is often negative. The course is much more rapid than in the adult form, and the disease terminates fatally comparatively early.

tabetic curve (ta-bet'ik) See *Lange's colloidal gold reaction.*

table, frequency The number of individuals with a given character may be arrayed in order of size with respect to the amount of the character possessed by each individual in the series. If the entire range is divided into intervals, and if to each interval is assigned the number of individuals falling within the limits of the class, the resulting distribution is called a frequency table.

AGE DISTRIBUTION OF FIRST ADMISSIONS TO NEW YORK CIVIL STATE HOSPITALS, YEAR ENDED JUNE 30, 1938

Age (Years)	Number	Per cent
Under 15	176	1.4
15–19	527	4.2
20–24	841	6.7
25–29	940	7.4
30–34	1087	8.6
35–39	1165	9.2
40–44	1119	8.9
45–49	1084	8.6
50–54	1012	8.0
55–59	870	6.9
60–64	834	6.6
65–69	884	7.0
70 and over	2091	16.5
Unascertained	5	*
Total	12,635	100.0

* Less than 0.05.

table, life A life table is an instrument for determining the number of years that any person may, on the average, be expected to live after reaching a specified age. It also enables one to determine the chance of an individual dying within any specified number of years after reaching a given age.

Example. According to the life table for continental United States, 1929 to 1931, prepared by the U.S. Bureau of the Census, the expectation of life at birth for white males was 59.12 years. Again, according to this life table, of 100,000 males born alive, 81,457 will reach age 40. Therefore 18,543 will die before reaching age 40, and the chance of dying before reaching age 40 is 185.43 per 1,000. Those who reach age 40 will live, on the average 29.22 years, or they will die at an average age of 69.22 years.

table, statistical A summary of numerical data in accordance with logical criteria, showing the manner in which the variables included in the table are distributed with respect to their relative frequencies.

taboo, tabu Freud says: 'For us the meaning of taboo branches off into two opposite directions. On the one hand it means to us, sacred, consecrated: but on the other hand it means uncanny, dangerous, forbidden and unclean. The opposite for taboo is designated in Polynesian by the word *noa* and signifies something ordinary and generally accessible. Thus something like the concept of reserve inheres in taboo; taboo expresses itself essentially in prohibitions and restrictions. Our combination of "hold dread" would often express the meaning of taboo.' (Freud, S. *The Basic Writings of Sigmund Freud,* tr. by Brill, A.A., Random House, New York, 1938)

taboparesis (tā-bō-par′ē-sis) A disease of the nervous system which combines the features of general paresis and tabes dorsalis. The mental and physical symptoms of general paresis are present together with spinal cord changes producing absent knee or ankle jerks, the Romberg sign, and bladder disturbances. This picture is not an uncommon one, especially in the terminal stages of paresis, when optic atrophy is also likely to set in.

tachy- (tak-ē-) Combining form meaning fast, quick, speedy, from Gr. *tachýs,* quick, swift, fleet. Oppos. of *brady-*.

tachycardia, orthostatic (tak-i-kär′di-à, or-thō-stat′ik) Rapidity of pulse rate beyond the normal range occurring when one changes from the reclining to the standing position; a symptom frequently observed among psychiatric patients.

tachyglossa (-glos′à) See *tachylogia.*

tachyglossal Pertaining to or characterized by tachyglossa, or rapidity of speech.

tachylalia (-lā′li-à) See *tachylogia; cluttering.*

tachylogia (-lō′ji-à) Rapid and voluble speech; it may occur in a number of psychiatric conditions. It reaches its highest form of expression in the manic phase of manic-depressive psychosis, in which an unusually great number of words is spoken over a given period of time. It is as though the patient were under the compulsion to speak out the tremendous quantity of ideas possessed by him.

tachyphagia (-fāj′i-à) Food-grabbing; extreme rapidity of eating. Tachyphagia is commonly seen in regressed, deteriorated schizophrenics, and often such patients will grab any object, edible or not, put it into the mouth, and swallow it.

tachyphemia (-fē′mi-à) See *tachylogia.*

tachyphrasia (-frā′zhi-à) See *tachylogia.*

tachypnea, tachypnoea (tak-ip′nē-à) See *polypnoea.*

tachypragia (tak-i-prā′ji-à) A word not commonly used in psychiatry. It is employed by Pende to denote 'the great swiftness of all psychic reactions.' He uses the term also to mean rapid functional reactions, physical or psychical. Exaggerated psychosomatic activity associated with hyperthyroidism is a form of tachypragia.

tachytrophism (-trō′fiz′m) Rapid or increased metabolism. It is believed that individuals with the asthenic or microsplanchnic type of body build show tachytrophism, owing to the dominance of catabolic over anabolic processes. The dominance is due in turn to the imbalance between the infantile megalosplanchnic system and the relatively mature microsplanchnic, the former serving anabolic functions, the latter catabolic. According to this doctrine the schizophrenic patient with an asthenic habitus should exhibit increased metabolism. Pende says: 'tachytrophism characterizes the microsplanchnic.'

t(a)eniophobia (tē-ni-ō-fō′bi-à) Fear of tapeworms.

taint In genetics, this term denotes the genotypical affection of an individual by a morbid factor inherited from, and manifested by, his ancestors, whether or not this factor is exhibited by the individual himself.

taint-carrier In a family survey, this genetic term is limited to the individuals who carry a particular genetic factor in their genotypes, but do not manifest it phenotypically. See *trait-carrier.*

talion (tal′i-on) In psychoanalytical literature this term has the same connotation as in the biblical quotation 'an eye for an eye, a tooth for a tooth,' and indicates retribution.

'In the case of the eye we customarily translate the obscure psychical processes implicit in the repression of scoptophilia and in the outbreak of psychogenic visual disturbance as if an accusing voice had uplifted itself within the person concerned, saying: "Because you have chosen to use your organ of sight for evil indulgence of the senses, it serves you quite right if you can see nothing at all now," thus giving its sanction to the outcome of the process. There is here, we perceive the idea of the *talion*. . . .' (Freud, S. *Collected Papers,* vol. 2, tr. by Riviere, J., Leonard and Virginia Woolf and The Institute of Psychoanalysis, London, 1924–25)

talion dread See *dread, talion.*

taming of affect See *suppression of affect.*

tantrum A child's dramatic outburst of crying, kicking, screaming, etc. in response to frustration. Such temper-tantrums are natural to the child of two or three and are an expression of aggression, anger, rage, and defiance. The child works himself rapidly, or gradually, into a rage— yells out, stamps his feet, throws his arms about, rolls on the floor, strikes everyone, throws every object within reach against the walls, curses, bites, or even bangs his head against the wall. The tantrum thus assumes uncontrolled and sweeping proportions in contrast to normal expressions of anger and rage.

Tantrums are seen almost routinely in the children of overindulgent, oversolicitous, and overprotective parents. Though originating in physical discomforts which increase the child's irritability, tantrums either are motivated by an attempt to obtain gratifications and dominate a family which allows itself to be controlled by these outbursts, or are a result of imitation of a parent or some other member of the household.

Treatment includes: (1) creation of an optimal environment which will afford conventional outlets for the expression of rage on the part of both parents and child; (2) correction of overindulgence, oversolicitousness, and overprotectiveness, when these are present; (3) attention to the acute or chronic discomforts, such as fatigue and hunger, which appear to precipitate the tantrums; (4) proper recreational and school adjustments; (5) correction of any existing jealousies within the family.

The tantrum should be treated calmly and without alarm. The child should be offered a change of scene or activity to allow him to drop the conflict without feeling complete defeat or loss of face. Under no conditions should there be any giving-in to the tantrum; the best procedure is to leave the child alone until he is calm—if tantrums gain too much for the child, they can readily become a recurrent behavior pattern.

taphephobia (taf-ē-fō′bi-à) Fear of being buried (alive).

taphophilia Taphophilia is the morbid attraction for graves and cemeteries. A patient spent all his spare time either in cemeteries or in thoughts connected with them. Though he was a highly intelligent person, he was emotionally very immature, having never resolved his early childhood relationships with his parents. He was vividly anal-erotic, expressing among other things a strong coprophagic tendency. Another patient often carried out his impulse to defecate on graves, though, as he maintained, a grave was sacred to him. He endowed graves with unlimited magic power, to which he added his own power (feces). Still another patient saved most of his excrement, burying it from time to time in a neighboring cemetery.

Tapia's syndrome (Antonio Garcia Tapia, Spanish otolaryngologist, 1875–   ) A bulbar syndrome due to involvement of the vagus and hypoglossal nerves, with homolateral paralysis and atrophy of the tongue, and homolateral paralysis of the pharynx and larynx.

tarantism (tar′an-tiz′m) 'An epidemic dancing mania prevalent in Italy in the sixteenth and seventeenth centuries, originating in fear of the bite of the tarantula, as a remedy for which the dance was adopted.' (*A Dictionary of Medicine,* edited by Quain, R., D. Appleton, New York, 1899)

taraxein (tar-ak′sān) See *ceruloplasmin.*

target multiplicity See *multiplicity, target.*

target-organ See *syndrome, general adaptation.*

Tartarism Mongolian idiocy.

TAT Thematic apperception test. See *test, thematic apperception.*

Tay-Sachs' disease (Warren Tay, English physician, 1843–1927; and Bernard Sachs, American neurologist, 1858–1944) *Amaurotic family idiocy* (q.v.).

technique In occupational therapy, the method and process involved in the execution of the handicrafts or arts.

technique, play A psychotherapeutic method devised by Melanie Klein for special use in the treatment of children. By allowing the child to play with almost anything he wants, the therapist is, through this play, able to analyze and clarify the child's emotional problem. This technique is, in effect, a very useful substitute for the 'free-association' method, in view of the child's usual lack of verbal self-expression. Adult patients will, sooner or later, translate into words not only their problems but also the actions which may take place during the analysis. With children such verbalizations are next to impossible and the play technique is of paramount importance. 'Paper dolls, rag dolls, dolls which can be taken apart, wagons, tin toys of all kinds can be used. Little blocks of wood or stone are very often useful. The child should have a choice between many toys, but the situation generally becomes obscured if the variety of toys is too great. It is usually better to use toys which do not move by themselves but which have to be moved by the child. Frequently the child accompanies his play with short remarks which elucidate the situation. Sooner or later one will have to interpret to the child what is going on. One may participate in the play and accompany one's actions with appropriate gestures. If the child is not very young it will usually be difficult to bring it to an insight into the situation without words.' (Schilder, P. *Psychotherapy*, Norton, New York, 1938)

techniques, psychodrama See *psychodrama*.

tegmentum (teg-men′tum) See *midbrain*.

tele (tel′ē) (Gr. *tēle*, 'at a distance, far away, far off') 'A feeling process projected into space and time in which one, two, or more persons may participate is called a tele. It is an experience of some real factor in the other person and not a subjective fiction. It grows out of person-to-person and person-to-object contacts from the birth level on and gradually develops the sense for inter-personal relationships. The tele process is the chief factor in determining the position of an individual in the group.

'Positive tele occurs in any relationship between two or more persons which is produced by the affinity between some real factor in one person and some real factor in another person; negative tele, in any relationship between two or more persons involving repulsion based on some real factor in one person and some real factor in another person. If a person is attracted towards a certain person, and if this person is far from him in another group, the moving of this person towards him produces an experience which is therapeutic tele.

'The proof that a factor, tele, exists and operates within the social structure is demonstrated by the statistical and mathematical calculation of social configurations. This has been accomplished by comparing sociometric findings with a common reference base ascertained by chance calculation of choices. The Chi-Square Test was applied in comparing how much the computed chance values and the experimental chance values differ.

'The probability of mutual structures in actual configurations has been found to be 213 per cent greater than in mathematical and chance findings as well. This is an illustration of the validity of tele as an objective factor.' (Moreno, J.L. *Sociometry 1*, 351, 1938)

telemnemonike (tel-em-nē-mon′i-kē) Acquiring consciousness of matters held in the memory of another person.

telencephalon (tel-en-sef′à-lon) That part of the *forebrain* (q.v.) or prosencephalon which forms the cerebral cortex, the striate bodies, the rhinencephalon, the lateral ventricles, and the anterior portion of the 3rd ventricle.

teleological (tē-lē-ō-loj′i-kal) This term is used by Adler to denote that the greatest stress is placed by him on the *goal*. The present activity of the individual is a preparation for his final state, for what he is going to be, 'like a drama which was conceived and produced for the sake of its final scene.' (Mairet, P. *ABC of Adler's Psychology*, Kegan Paul, Trench, Trubner, London, 1928)

teleology (tē-lē-ol′ō-jē) The belief that natural processes are purposefully directed toward some end or goal. In psychiatry, the term is particularly used in reference to the psychologies of Jung and of Adler. Adler, for example, considers the present activity of the individual as a preparation for his final state, for what he is going to be. Jung's analytical psychology is also teleological. Jung considers the mind as something much more than the result of past experiences; '. . . it is Becoming as well as Has Been, and therefore any analysis of it must include reference to its aims and to that which it is trying to realize within itself. In this connection the dream must therefore be regarded as partly determined by the future.' (Nicole, J. *Psychopathology,* Ballière, Tindall & Cox, London, 1948) Jung treats the symbols from the collective unconscious '. . . not only reductively as an expression of the past of the race, but synthetically also, as a sign that the unconscious is trying to exert a directive influence upon the individual's life-line. These symbols should be interpreted teleologically, as indicative of fundamental strivings that are aiming at guiding the personality along certain lines, certain necessary paths of development and fulfilment. It is only by thus giving these symbols a "final" or purposive value as well as a "causal" one, that we can adjust the unconscious to the conscious, the collective to the individual, the non-rational to the rational, without either principle doing violence to the other. This means that the physician's explanations must, of necessity, become educational and morally conditioned, thus performing a task that psycho-analysts refuse to undertake.' (ibid.)

teleophrenia (tē-lē-ō-frē'ni-à) Term coined by M. Nippe (*München. med. Wochenschr. 74,* 143, 1927) for a morbid mental condition that stands between traumatic neurosis and malingering. From Nippe's description it appears that teleophrenia closely resembles, if it actually is not, the compensation-neurosis described by most investigators.

telepathic (tel-e-path'ik) Pertaining to telepathy or characterized or communicated by thought-transference.

telepathy (te-lep'à-thē) 'The direct communication of one mind with another otherwise than in ordinary and recognized ways.' (The Century Dictionary) The phenomenon is frequently reported by psychiatric patients, particularly those expressing a paranoid reaction. It is commonplace for the patient with the paranoid form of schizophrenia to believe that others, who may be miles away, not only read his thoughts, but control them in their entirety. The patient is certain that everyone can and does read his mind.

The phenomenon is also known as *thought-transference* and *mind-reading.*

Freud states very definitely: 'You will learn nothing from this paper of mine about the enigma of telepathy.' At the conclusion of the paper he stressed his 'strict impartiality' as to the reality of

telepathy. 'I have every reason to be so, for I have no opinion; I know nothing about it.' (Freud, S. *Collected Papers,* vol. 4, tr. by Riviere, J., Leonard and Virginia Woolf and The Institute of Psychoanalysis, London, 1924–25)

In the *Psychopathology of Everyday Life,* Freud maintained that 'we must . . . at least touch upon the question whether real roots of superstition should be altogether denied, whether there are really no omens, prophetic dreams, telepathic experiences, manifestations of supernatural forces and the like. I am now far from willing to repudiate without anything further all these phenomena. . . .' (Freud, S. *The Basic Writings of Sigmund Freud,* tr. by Brill, A.A., Random House, New York, 1938)

'In view of other evidence for the reality of telepathy, the direct communication of mind with mind without the use of sense-perception, the least extravagant hypothesis for the interpretation of the facts is the hypothesis that such subconscious or secondary personalities have wide-reaching powers of telepathic reception.' (McDougall, W. *Outline of Abnormal Psychology,* Scribner's, New York, 1926)

telesthesia (tel-es-thē'zhi-à) Telepathy.

telophase (tel'ō-fāz) In genetics, the final phase or stage of mitosis.

temperament In psychoanalysis temperament is the individual's constitutional tendency to react to his environment in a certain way. Some people are more placid than others, some more vigorous, some more high-strung; it is likely that such differences are innate and recognizable from the moment of birth. Temperament is not identical with character, though often confused with it, especially in popular language. Temperament is probably instrumental in determining the particular type of character structure developed by a specific individual in that it limits the potentialities for character development: it is unlikely that a constitutionally phlegmatic individual would develop an anxious, rigid, and compulsive character structure. Character, on the other hand, is something in addition to temperament, as a component within the framework of the possibilities encompassed by the given temperament.

temperament, manic Kraepelin's designation for what is today known as one of the phases of cyclothymia. 'The intellectual endowment of the patients is for the most part mediocre, sometimes even fairly good, in isolated cases excellent. They acquire, however, as a rule, only scanty, and, in particular, very imperfect and unequal knowledge, because they show no perseverance in learning, do not like exerting themselves, are extraordinarily distractible, and seek to escape in every way from the constraint of a systematic mental training, and in place of that they pursue all possible side-occupations in variegated alternation.' (Kraepelin, E. *Manic-Depressive Insanity and Paranoia,* tr. by Barclay, R.M., Livingstone, Edinburgh, 1921) He adds that the mood is 'permanently exalted, careless, confident' and that conduct is unsteady and restless.

temper-tantrums One of the most common habit disorders of children, which consists principally in screaming and kicking. A study of the personalities of children with temper-tantrums shows that the outbursts of temper are almost never the only expression of emotional immaturity and instability. Temper-tantrums are usually associated with feeding problems, disobedience, nightmares, night terrors, enuresis, stuttering, nailbiting, thumbsucking, and tics. See *tantrum.*

temporal lobe seizure Psychomotor epilepsy. See *epilepsy.*

temporal summation See *summation.*

tendency, anagogic (an-a-goj'ik) See *tendency, katagogic.*

tendency, final This term signifies the ultimate goal or aim of the neurosis. Adler was the first to point out 'the presence of a final tendency in the structure of every neurosis.' In this respect he was guided by both Janet's theory of the *idée fixe* and Wernicke's concept of 'overcharged idea.' See *idea, overcharged.*

'The neurotic goals are not sheer strivings for power and recognition: they betoken a secret tendency toward future triumphs expressed in many forms that might even be antagonistic to each other. Nevertheless, it may be stated that every neurosis has a central idea around which the various *lay motives* group themselves.' The task of the analyst is to uncover as early as possible this central idea (the final tendency and ultimate goal of the neurosis) if success is to be expected in

treatment. (Stekel, W. *Compulsion and Doubt,* Liveright, New York, 1949)

tendency, goal The term for a concept of Jungian psychology according to which the process of individuation (self-realization through Jungian psychoanalysis) seems autonomously directed toward a goal. As the analysis penetrates deeper into the collective unconscious, concomitantly making conscious more and more material from this area, 'consciousness actively participates, experiencing every step of the process and surmising at least its meaning, then the next image manifests itself upon the higher plane already gained thereby, and so arises a *goal-tendency.*' (Jung, C.G. *Two Essays on Analytical Psychology,* tr. by Baynes, H.G. and C.F., Baillière, London, 1928) This goal-tendency is evident whenever a definite problem is made conscious, is overcome, and, finally, is integrated.

tendency, katagogic (kat-à-goj'ik) Stekel uses this term for the 'downward-leading' restrictive psychic impulses that strive to prevent the individual from achieving his positive and constructive aim in life. In fact, the katagogic tendency constitutes an inhibitory mechanism in opposition to what Stekel calls *anagogic tendency,* or 'upward-leading' impulses which are of a constructive nature. (Stekel, W. *The Interpretation of Dreams,* Liveright, New York, 1943)

tendency (of action) In objective psychobiology this expression designates the inclinations associated with action. 'One should always study the general behavior of a person while talking to him. Much can be learned from his way of entering the room, shaking hands, talking, and from his facial expression, gestures and posture.' . . . 'emotions are the regulative functions of our personality and are therefore closely related to the behavior of the person in action.' (Diethelm, O. *Treatment in Psychiatry,* Macmillan, New York, 1936)

tendency, subliminal (sub-lim'in-al) 'There is yet another theory of suggestion based upon the notion of impulses rooted in the hypertrophy of tendencies. I refer to that of F.W.H. Myers. . . . We may speak of it as the theory of *subliminal tendencies*—tendencies below the threshold of the individual consciousness.

'Substantially these authors [Myers,

Bramwell] accept the view of suggestion put forward by myself in the years 1886 to 1889, and agree with me in regarding this phenomenon as the development of an inferior tendency emancipated from the control of reflective and personal tendencies, its development in the form of an impulse.' (Janet, P. *Psychological Healing,* vols. 1–2, tr. by Paul, E. and C., Macmillan, New York, 1925)

tenesmus penile (tē-nez'mus pē'nīl) Magnus Hirschfeld uses this term synonymously with priapism.

tenesmus penis (te-nes'moos pā'nēs) (L. 'straining of the penis') Priapism.

tension, instinctual This term denotes the psychic and somatic manifestations of the need to gratify a primal trend or urge. According to Freud, instincts represent the biological needs of the body. The mind acts through the psyche, in order to secure specific forms of motor discharge for the relief of tension accruing to the ungratified instincts. See *instinct.*

tension, mental The emotional charge with which components of the psyche are infused is called mental tension. The term *charge* is used here as it is in the field of electricity. When, as in certain senile states, the psyche is relatively void of activity or energy or charge, one speaks of low mental tension. The contrary state obtains, for example, in the manic phase of manic-depressive psychosis, in which condition psychical components are heavily charged with emotions, that is, there is high mental tension. See *cathexis.* Synonymous with *psychentonia.*

tension, need A tension that develops within the organism in connection with various 'needs' essential for survival, and demands contact with the outer world for its relief. 'Being born may be said to have already interfered with the equilibrium of the intra-uterine state, because stimuli are now registered upon the organism from within (hunger) and without (cold). To relieve these *need tensions* the infant must direct itself to the outer world, or show signs of the unpleasant effects created by these tensions.' (Kardiner, A., and Spiegel, H. *War Stress and Neurotic Illness,* Hoeber, New York, 1947)

tentigo venerea (ten-tē'gō ve-ne're-à) (L. 'venereal, sexual lust') Nymphomania.

tentigo veretri (ve-rā'trē) (L. 'tension or lust of the private parts') Satyriasis.

tentorium cerebelli (ten-tō-rē-oom kā-rā-bel'ē) See *meninges.*

TEPP See *psychotomimetic.*

teratophobia (ter-à-tō-fō'bi-à) Fear of bearing a monster.

terror, night or sleep Pavor nocturnus; a disorder allied to nightmare, occurring in children. The child awakes screaming with fright, the alarm persisting for a time during a state of semiconsciousness.

test, ACE The American Council on Education intelligence test, designed for use with secondary school and college students.

test, adrenalin-Mecholyl (a-dren'a-lin-mek'ō-lil) Funkenstein test; first described by Funkenstein, Greenblatt, and Solomon in 1952 as a test of prognostic significance in relation to electroshock treatment. The test consists of the administration, on two successive days and under comparable basal conditions, of intravenous epinephrine hydrochloride and intramuscular Mecholyl chloride. The blood pressure response to each drug is then recorded. Response to Mecholyl appears to be the more significant of the two measures, and it has been observed that patients with a hypotensive response: (1) are benefited by EST; (2) show a high rate of improvement when psychotherapy is the sole method of treatment; (3) have good abstraction ability and good personality organization, and (4) appear clinically to maintain an appropriate and adequate level of affect. In general, patients with a hypertensive response to Mecholyl are not benefited by EST, show a relatively lower improvement rate with psychotherapy, have poor abstraction and inadequate or inappropriate affect, and give other evidence of personality disorganization.

test, Akerfeldt See *ceruloplasmin.*

test, analogies A test of ability to comprehend relationships, usually by asking the subject to name the fourth term which bears the same relation to the third as the second does to the first. Example: ship is to water as automobile is to what?

Test, Army General Classification See *AGCT.*

test, Arthur Point Scale A nonverbal, performance measure of intellectual ability, consisting of 10 subtests which are mainly of the form-board variety. The test is most reliable within the 7–13 years age-range and is of particular value when the subject's verbal capacity is compromised by foreign language handicap, speech or hearing defect, or personal and cultural factors.

test, Bender Visual-Motor Gestalt A projective technique consisting of nine geometrical figures that are copied by the subject; devised by Lauretta Bender and first described by her in 1938. Its chief applications are to determine retardation, loss of function, and organic brain defects in children and adults, and in the study of personality deviations which show regressive phenomena. It is of limited usefulness in the study of psychoneuroses and psychosomatic disorders.

test, beta A set of mental tests used in the U.S. Army in 1917–18, designed for illiterates. Instructions are given in signs and the material is pictorial in character, in contrast to alpha tests, which are carried out verbally.

test, block design A performance test in which the subject tries to match standard designs using colored blocks; used as a measure of intelligence and as an indicator of deterioration in brain damage and in the schizophrenics.

test, chi-square (kī-) A statistical test, developed originally by Karl Pearson, which measures the significance of differences occurring between groups. In a group of 500 cases of lobar pneumonia treated with penicillin, for example, the overall 'cure' rate was 94 per cent. But not all cases were treated with the same batch of penicillin. 100 cases were treated with batch A penicillin and 98 per cent were cured; 100 cases were treated with batch B and 89 per cent were cured; 100 cases with batch C and 95 per cent were cured; 100 cases with batch D and 92 per cent were cured; and 100 cases with batch E and 96 per cent were cured. In this imaginary example, the chi-square test could be applied to ascertain whether the different cure rates in different groups are due only to chance or whether, all other relevant factors being equal, the different results are due to differing effectiveness of the individual batches of penicillin.

test, Cornell Word Form (CWF) A modification of the word-association technique devised to distinguish 'normals' from subjects with neuropsychiatric and psychosomatic disorders in a way not apparent to the subject. The test is used primarily in industrial psychology. It consists of a list of stimulus words, each of which is followed by two response words. The subject is asked to encircle whichever of the two words seems to him to be most related to the stimulus word; e.g. mother—mine, woman.

test, draw-a-person A method of personality analysis based upon the interpretation of drawings of the human figure. Although figure drawings had been used by many workers in the field, it was Karen Machover who in 1949 outlined a system of interpretation which was correlated with clinical diagnostic categories.

test, drawing-of-a-man See *test, Goodenough.*

test, face-hand A test of diffuse cerebral dysfunction in children devised by Bender. The child, whose eyes are closed, is touched simultaneously on the cheek and the dorsum of the hand; retesting is done with the eyes open. Results are considered positive if the child fails consistently to identify both stimuli within 10 trials. By the age of seven, normal children respond with a negative test. Positive results are seen not only in clear-cut cases of cerebral dysfunction but also in schizophrenic children.

test, Funkenstein See *test, adrenalin-Mecholyl.*

test, Gesell developmental 'The Gesell Schedules consist of a series of 27 age-level recorded observations and reactions to standardized situations from birth through the first five years of life. At each age level an inventory of activities is divided into four categories of behavior: (1) Motor; (2) Adaptive; (3) Language; and (4) Personal-Social. Each of these categories of behavior is evaluated by observing the infant or child in a number of standardized situations.' (Masserman, J.H. *The Practice of Dynamic Psychiatry,* Saunders, Philadelphia, 1955)

test, good and evil Weihofen says that the 'concept of "good and evil" seems to be the first expression of what later came to be known as the right and wrong test. In many of the cases decided in the first half of the nineteenth century, "good and evil" and "right and wrong" seem to be used synonymously.' (Weihofen, H. *Insanity as a Defense in Criminal Law,* Commonwealth Fund, Oxford University Press, New York, 1933)

test, Goodenough A test of a child's intellectual level of development based upon the subject's drawing of a human figure. The test was introduced in 1926 by Florence Goodenough in her monograph 'The Measurement of Intelligence by Drawings.' She standardized children's drawing of a man and thereby produced a simple and satisfactory test of intelligence.

test, heel-to-knee A test for ataxia; the patient in a recumbent position, with the eyes open or closed, is requested to raise the foot high, touch the knee with the opposite heel and carry the heel along the shin.

test, Holmgren (Alarik Fritniof Holmgren, Swedish physiologist, 1831–97) A test for color blindness which requires the subject to match skeins of different-colored yarn with standard skeins.

test, House-Tree-Person (HTP) A type of projective test in which the subject is asked to draw a house, a tree, and a person.

testing, reality See *reality-testing.*

test, Janet's (Pierre Marie Felix Janet, French physician, 1859–1947) A test for the determination of tactile sensibility; the patient answers 'yes' or 'no' when touched by the examiner's finger.

test, Kent EGY A series of 10 questions used for a quick estimate of intelligence.

test, Knox cube A performance test, of particular value when the subject suffers from a language handicap or barrier, in which the subject taps a series of four cubes in various prescribed sequences.

tests, Kohnstamm The Kohnstamm maneuver is often used to demonstrate suggestibility to a subject being prepared for hypnotic trance induction. It is a normal neurophysiologic reaction, elicited by having the subject press his extended arm as strenuously as possible against a wall for approximately two minutes, after which the arm will rise automatically with or without a suggestion to that effect.

test, Kohs block-design An intelligence test in which the subject copies a design using small, multicolored cubes.

test, Lowenfeld See *test, mosaic.*

test, Machover See *test, draw-a-person.*

test, mosaic A projective technique, introduced by Margaret Lowenfeld and further developed by Fredric Wertham, which employs a set of 300 colored pieces (black, blue, red, green, yellow, and off-white) in six shapes (squares, diamonds, oblongs, and 3 different-sized triangles). The subject is presented with the test objects on a tray and is asked to make anything he wants on the board. The designs made by adults and children have been correlated with diagnostic categories, and individual designs can be interpreted on the basis of these correlations.

test, myokinetic psychodiagnosis (mī-ō-kin-et'ik sī-kō-dī-ag-nō'sis) A test devised by Mira which consists of drawings of patterns with both the right and the left hands. The left hand drawings are believed to reveal genotypic reactions and the right hand drawings are said to express more superficial phenotypic reactions. Comparison of the drawings is made to diagnose various conditions and character traits.

test-person The individual who is examined by the association method.

test, PMA A test of seven traits believed by Thurstone and Thurstone to account for most of the variance in primary mental abilities (PMA). These traits are: V (verbal comprehension), W (word fluency), N (number), S (space), M (associative memory), P (perceptual speed), and R (reasoning) or I (induction).

test, population 'The population test is a modification of the sociometric test. It is applied to people who anticipate moving into a new community. It is also applied to an already existing community which is in a state of disintegration.

'In the population test, heads of families anticipating settling in a new community are called to a meeting in which they express whom they wish as neighbors in the new settlement. On the basis of their choices, a psychogeographical map is drawn and the assignment of homes is made on the basis of their sociometric positions.

'In a community which has been functioning for some time, various changes may take place. Sometimes these changes are difficult to explain. Numerous people may move away for no apparent reason and frictions may develop among the groups remaining in the community. The population test is able to detect the underlying spontaneous structure of the community in repeated tests at various intervals and thus point out the causes of disintegration. The criteria used for the test may be established on the basis of visiting, borrowing, or exchanging work relations.' (Moreno, J.L. *Who Shall Survive?* Nervous & Mental Disease Publishing Company, Washington, D.C., 1934)

test, progressive matrices An intelligence test in which the subject is asked to choose, from several alternatives, the one part which will complete the abstract design presented to him. The test is made up of 60 such designs.

test, projective A type of psychologic test in which the test material presented to the subject is such that any response will necessarily be determined by his own prevailing mood or underlying psychopathology. See *method, projective.*

test, psychopenetration (sī-kō-pen-ē-trā′-shun) A psychodynamic test devised by Wilcox, who uses it in conjunction with carbon dioxide coma to serve as a guide for therapeutic procedures in different types of cases. It sorts reactions into five general classes, according to the degree of emotional flexibility or rigidity. The test consists of five questions, especially worded to elicit evidence of the degree of unconscious resistance to the concepts of attention, sex, killing, showing all feeling, and deceiving.

'Class i (flexibility plus mild CO_2 reaction) calls for electroconvulsive therapy in the presence of depression. Otherwise, Class i is the essentially normal pattern. Class ii (flexibility plus tension CO_2 reactions) yields remarkably well to carbon dioxide comas and intensive psychotherapy. Improvement coincides with a shift to Class i. Class iii (rigidity plus mild CO_2 reaction) in the presence of paranoid symptoms calls for subconvulsive electrocoma treatments. Improvement coincides with the development of flexibility and ultimately a Class i reaction. Class iv (rigidity plus tension CO_2 reactions) is a mixed group which requires trials of various types of shock-therapy to find the most effective one. Improvement is likely to be slow and the patient may follow a varying course of reactions until Class i pattern is achieved. Class v (rigidity plus

paradoxical CO_2 reaction) is the profound catatonic and requires electroconvulsive therapy, spaced by periodic psychodynamic tests. As soon as the CO_2 reaction reverses, considerable gains occur by adding CO_2 comas to the treatment. Patients who have previously been considered to be schizophrenic, but who clearly react as Class ii have quite different psychodynamic mechanisms than other schizophrenics.' (Spiegel, E.A. *Progress in Neurology and Psychiatry,* vol. 4, Grune and Stratton, New York, 1949, p. 500)

test, right and wrong See *irresponsibility; rule, M'Naghten.*

test, Rorschach (Hermann Rorschach, Swiss psychiatrist, 1884–1922) A psychological test consisting of ten inkblots of varying designs and colors which are shown to the subject one at a time with the request to interpret them. Its purpose is to furnish a description of the dynamic forces of personality through an analysis of the formal aspects of the subject's interpretations. The test yields information as to the intellectual and emotional processes, the degree of personality integration, variability in mental functioning, and the degree to which the subject responds to environmental influences and to his inner promptings. The test not only is used to obtain a picture of the subject's personality, but also serves as an aid in problems of differential psychiatric diagnosis and prognosis.

tests, alpha A series of mental tests, first used in the United States military service (1917) to determine the relative mental ability of recruits. There are eight different types of test: for directions, arithmetical ability, practical judgment, synonyms and antonyms, correct arrangement of sentences, completion of series of digits, analogies, and information. The tests are designed particularly for group application and for rapid mechanical scoring.

tests, army mental Tests devised during World War I to determine the intellectual status of recruits examined for the United States Army.

tests, Binet-Simon (bē-nā′ sē-mawN′) (Alfred Binet, French psychologist, 1857–1911, and Th. Simon.) Tests of intellectual capacity, which is expressed as the Intelligence Quotient or I.Q., introduced in France in 1905 as a result of studies made to determine whether children could be educated as the new laws required. The Stanford revision of the tests for use with American children was made in 1916, although they had already been introduced into the United States by Goddard in 1910.

test, sociometric (sō-si-ō-met′rik) 'The sociometric test is an instrument with which to measure the amount of the organization shown by social groups. It requires an individual to choose associates for any group of which he is or might become a member. The test reveals that the underlying attraction-repulsion pattern of a group differs widely from its visible structure and that groups tested upon the basis of different criteria, tend toward diversity of structures. These structures have been revealed when the criteria of the test have been applied to home groups, work groups, and school groups.

The test is constructed in such a manner that it is in itself a motive, an incentive, or a purpose, primarily for the subject rather than for the tester. It is part of the procedure to put some of the choices of the subject into operation. The test can be repeated at any time without significant loss of interest to the subject.' (Moreno, J.L. *Who Shall Survive?* Nervous & Mental Disease Publishing Company, Washington, D.C., 1934)

tests, sorting A method of psychological testing in which the subject is required to place objects into groups on the basis of similarity or some other abstract relationship. Such sorting or Zuordnung tests are particularly associated with the names of Kurt Goldstein, Vigotsky, Hanfmann, and Kasanin. Patients with cortical lesions, particularly, show impariment of abstract behavior as measured by these tests. Schizophrenics, too, do poorly on these tests; but performance is more varied than in ordinary brain damage cases, for the schizophrenic tends to project himself into the test objects and animate and embellish them.

test, spontaneity 'The spontaneity test proceeds by throwing the subject into standard life situations in which he improvises freely while acting opposite members of the group to whom he has been found emotionally related as revealed by the sociometric test, either through attraction or repulsion. The situations may express such emotions like anger, fear,

sympathy, dominance or any other emotions. They may express roles such as father, mother, employer, or any other roles.

'The spontaneity test can be considered an intensification of the sociometric test, which does not reveal any factor beyond the attraction-repulsion pattern. The spontaneity test gives an additional insight into inter-personal relationships. In the course of the situations activated it reveals the specific emotions binding persons together, the disturbances which they may have in the course of spontaneous performance, the range of words spoken and gestures shown during the acts, and the duration of the acts themselves.' (Moreno, J.L. *Who Shall Survive?* Nervous & Mental Disease Publishing Company, Washington, D.C., 1934; also Franz, J.G. *Sociometry 2,* No. 4)

test, Stanford-Binet 'The revised Stanford-Binet Intelligence Scale is the test most frequently used in the individual examination of children. It consists of 120 items, plus several alternative tests that are applicable to the age range between two years and adulthood. The tests have a variety of activities of graded difficulty, both verbal and performance, designed to tap a variety of intellectual functions such as memory, free association, orientation in time, language comprehension, knowledge of common objects, comparison of concepts, perception of contradictions, understanding of abstract terms, the ability to meet novel situations and the use of practical judgment. In addition to many other varieties of function, there are also tests of visual-motor coordination.' (Masserman, J.H. *The Practice of Dynamic Psychiatry,* Saunders, Philadelphia, 1955) The score is expressed in months of mental age, which figure is divided by the chronologic age and then multiplied by 100 to give the Intelligence Quotient.

test, Szondi A projective test, developed by Szondi in Switzerland in the 1940's, which consists of six sets of pictures, each set containing eight photographs. These eight photographs are of eight different types of mental patient—homosexual, sadist, epileptic, hysteric, catatonic schizophrenic, paranoid schizophrenic, manic-depressive depressed, manic-depressive manic. The subject chooses from each set the two pictures he likes most and the two he dislikes most. The eight different types of mental patient are presumed to be extreme pathological representatives of the eight basic emotional needs. The test is interpreted in terms of the degree of tension, and the subject's attitude to this tension, in each of these eight need-systems. The need-systems are as follows: the need for tender, feminine love ('h' factor); the need for aggression and masculinity ('s' factor); the mode of dealing with crude, aggressive emotions ('e' factor); the need to exhibit emotions ('hy' factor); narcissistic ego-needs ('k' factor); the expansive tendencies of the ego ('p' factor); the need for acquiring and mastering objects ('d' factor); and the need to cling to objects for enjoyment ('m' factor). Although the Szondi test can be used clinically, as a projective technique, without reference to the viewpoint which led to its development, the basis of the test is Szondi's theory of *genotropism* (q.v.).

test, thematic apperception (T.A.T.) A projective technique, originally described by Morgan and Murray in 1935, which focuses primarily on the dynamics of interpersonal relationships. In its present form (the third set to be used since 1935), it consists of a series of 31 pictures which depict a number of social situations and interpersonal relations. In clinical practice, ten or twelve of the pictures are usually selected by the examiner on the basis of which of the total 31 are most likely to elicit information on the subject's problems. The selected pictures are then presented to the subject, who is asked to tell a story about what is going on in each picture. The stories are interpreted in terms of the subject's relationship to authority figures, to contemporaries of both sexes, and in terms of the compromises between and the needs of the id, the ego, and the superego. There are various methods of interpreting results; the one advocated by Murray is the need-press method (see *method, need-press*). Bellak recommends interpretation in terms of the following 14 categories: main theme, main hero, attitudes to parental figures, figures introduced, objects introduced, objects omitted, attribution of blame, significant conflicts, punishment for crime, attitude to hero, signs of inhibition (in aggression, sex, etc.), outcome, pattern of need gratification, and plot.

It is to be noted that the T.A.T. is only incidentally a diagnostic tool and is not primarily designed for nosologic classification.

test, T.P.I. Treponema Pallidum Immobilization test for syphilis. This test, developed ca. 1954, depends on antibody which develops as early as the reagin detected by serologic tests but is much more specific, dependable and persistent. It is of particular value in differentiating false serologic positives (which are often seen in the collagen diseases) from true positives due to latent syphilis.

test, Wechsler-Bellevue An intelligence test, the most widely used test for the average adult, consisting of five verbal tests, five performance tests, and an additional vocabulary test. The 11 subtests are as follows: general information, general comprehension, arithmetic, digit span, similarities, vocabulary, picture arrangement, picture completion, block design, object assembly, and digit symbol. The subtests are scored on the basis of speed and accuracy, and results can be translated into standard scores which give the verbal I.Q., the performance I.Q., and the full-scale I.Q.

tetanization (tet-à-ni-zā'shun) This term is not in use in current psychiatry. It means the fixation of attention.

'The spirit of exaltation, the tetanization of the attention, and the resulting psychic analgesia explain the deeds of many self-torturers, not only among those who are clearly insane, but in certain borderline cases—for instance, those of fanatics and many so-called martyrs.' (Paton, S. *Psychiatry,* Lippincott, Philadelphia and London, 1905)

tetraethylpyrophosphate (te-trà-e-thil-pī-rō-fos'fāt) See *psychotomimetic.*

tetraethylthiuram disulfide (te-trà-e-thil-thī'ū-ram dī-sul'fīd) See *Antabuse.*

tetrahydrocannabinol (te-tra-hī-drō-kan-nab'in-ol) See *psychotomimetic.*

tetraplegia (tet-rà-plē'ji-à) Quadriplegia; paralysis of the four extremities.

tetrasomy (tet'rà-sō-mē) The 'fourfoldness' in Jung's system of psychology. See *quaternity.*

thaassophobia (thà-as-ō-fō'bi-à) Fear of sitting.

thalamotomy (thal-à-mot'ō-mē) A psychosurgical procedure which produces a lesion in the thalamus by means of thermocoagulation. A stereotaxic apparatus is employed to position a wire or cannula into the desired subcortical area. Such a method results in minimal injury to superimposed cortex or white matter, and is a much less drastic procedure than are other methods, e.g. frontal lobectomy. The thalamotomy operation was devised by Spiegel and his coworkers, whose early reports indicate that small lesions of the dorsomedial nucleus of the thalamus (medial thalamotomy) relieve anxiety, emotional reactivity, and allied symptoms in psychoses and obsessive-compulsive states. This technique is obviously applicable to the production of lesions elsewhere in the brain.

thalamus (thal'à-mus) An ovoid-shaped constellation of nuclei lying between the mesencephalon and corpora striata, forming the lateral wall of the 3rd ventricle, and completely covered by the cerebral hemisphere. The prominent posterior portion is the pulvinar, lateral to which is the lateral geniculate body. The medial surface of the thalamus is connected to the thalamus of the opposite side by the massa intermedia.

Anatomically, six major nuclear masses are recognized (Walker's terminology): midline, anterior, medial, lateral, ventral, and posterior nuclei. The posterior nuclei include the pulvinar and the medial and lateral geniculate bodies.

The thalamus has somatic, special sense, and associative sensory functions. The ventral nuclei are concerned with somatic sensory functions, the lateroventral portion with unconscious proprioception, the posteroventral portion with conscious exteroception and proprioception, the posteroventral portion with conscious exteroception and proprioception, the lateral geniculate body with vision, the medial geniculate body with audition (? and equilibrium), and the pulvinar with auditory and visual association.

Thalamic lesions are commonly followed by various paresthesiae and hyperesthesiae which are believed to be due to release from intradiencephalic and corticothalamic projections. The 'thalamic syndrome' consists of a raising of the threshold (i.e. diminished sensitivity) to pinprick, heat and cold, but when sensation is felt it is disagreeable and unpleasant (thalamic hyperpathia).

thalassophobia (thà-las-ō-fō'bi-à) Fear of the sea.

thanatomania (than-à-tō-mā'ni-à) Suicidal mania.

thanatophobia Fear of death.

Thanatos According to Freud there are two sets of instincts. He terms one the life instinct or Eros, the other the death instinct or Thanatos. 'For the sake of clearness I will repeat in a sentence the three stages in the development of Freud's ideas concerning the duality of instincts. The first was the contrast between sexual and ego instincts; the second the contrast between object-love or allo-erotic libido, and self-love, narcissistic libido; and the third is the contrast between life and death instincts, between Eros and Thanatos.' (Jones, E. *Papers on Psycho-Analysis,* 4th ed., Wood, Baltimore, 1938) See *instinct, death.*

thanatotic (than-a-tot'ik) Pertaining to or manifesting the death instinct Thanatos, as described by psychoanalysis.

theater, therapeutic 'The therapeutic theatre is a stage setting so constructed that normal subjects and mental patients can live through and project, in an experimental situation, their own problems and actual lives untrammeled by the frozen patterns of daily living, or the boundaries and resistances of normal existence. Thus, it brings the subject into a distance from his own life and milieu which he rarely attains in his own life. The therapeutic theatre is an objective setting in which the subject and patient can act free from the anxieties and pressures of the outside world. In order to accomplish this, the total situation of the patient in the outside world has to be duplicated on a spontaneous level in the therapeutic theatre, and even more than this, the invisible roles and invisible inter-personal relations he may have experienced must find a visible expression. This means that certain functions—a stage, lights, recording system, assistants, and psychiatrist or director—have to be introduced into its operation.' (Moreno, J.L. *Sociometry 1,* 16, 1937)

thelygonia (thē-li-gō'ni-à) 1. Procreation of female offspring. 2. *Obs.* Nymphomania.

theme, mythological Jung says that 'the collective unconscious—so far as we can venture a judgment upon it—seems to consist of something of the nature of mythological themes or images. For this reason the myths of peoples are the real exponents of the collective unconscious. The whole of mythology could be taken as a kind of projection of the collective unconscious.' (Jung, C.G. *Contributions to Analytical Psychology,* tr. by Baynes, H.G. and C.F., Kegan Paul, Trench, Trubner, London, 1928)

theomania (thē-ō-mā′ni-à) Delusion that one is God.

theophobia Fear of God.

theory, Cannon's See *Cannon hypothalamic theory of emotion.*

theory, catastrophe Ferenczi says: 'the sadistic impulses of neurotics are frequently based on coitus anxiety. Many neurotics unconsciously regard coitus as an activity which, either directly or subsequently, is calculated to injure life or limb, and in particular to damage the genital organ, i.e., an act in which are combined gratification and severe anxiety.' The catastrophe theory holds that the act of sexual intercourse is destructive to the penis. Ferenczi adds that 'in the normal coitus of individuals who are not neurotic, the inner tension seeking for discharge finally overcomes anxiety, although, as suggested in my ontogenetic and phylogenetic "catastrophe"-theory of coitus, some traces of anxiety may still persist.' (Ferenczi, S. *Further Contributions to the Theory and Technique of Psycho-Analysis,* tr. by Suttie, J., Leonard and Virginia Woolf and The Institute of Psychoanalysis, London, 1926)

theory, immanence The organism consists of a number of parts or organs with specific functions, which lead beyond the organ itself. For instance, the main function of the lungs is to provide oxygen, yet the lungs provide oxygen not only for their own tissues, but also for the tissues of other organs. Organ A works for organs A, B, C, and D. Organ B, in turn, maintains itself and keeps in good functional condition organs A, C, and D, etc. This functional process, therefore, takes place within a closed circle. Within the circle the function of each organ can be singled out by what it accomplishes for the rest of the organism. This is called the imma-nence hypothesis or *closed circle* hypothesis of life. According to such a view, the life process would have the pattern of a logical vicious cycle. The part processes have the function of sustaining life; and life is an aggregation of these part processes. This theory is the opposite of *holism* (q.v.). (Angyal, A. *Foundations for a Science of Personality,* The Commonwealth Fund, Oxford University Press, New York, 1941)

theory, James-Lange-Sutherland 'The bodily changes follow directly the perception of the exciting fact, and our feeling of the same changes as they occur is the emotion. . . . The elements . . . of physiological processes, which comprise the emotion . . . are all organic changes, and each of them is the reflex effect of the exciting object.' (C.G. Lange and W. James. *The Emotions,* Williams and Wilkins, Baltimore, 1922) This theory admitted of no special brain centers for emotion and has been largely replaced by Papez' modification of the Cannon-Bard hypothalamic theory of emotion.

theory, libido (li-bēd′ō) Technically, the psychoanalytic hypothesis concerning the development and vicissitudes of the sexual drive or instinct. Often, however, libido theory is used to refer to all of the psychoanalytic hypotheses about the instincts in man. The confusion arises from the fact that until 1920 Freud did not fully develop his dual-instinct theory; before that time, then, all instinctual manifestations were considered to be a part of the sexual drive. Nowadays, however, the existence of two drives is assumed: sexual (libido) and aggressive.

therapeiology (ther-à-pā-ol′ō-jē) *Obs.* Therapeutics.

therapeutic (ther-a-pū′tik) Pertaining to or consisting of medical treatment; healing, curative.

therapy (ther′à-pē) Treatment of disease; therapeutics.

therapy, active The psychoanalytical method in which the psychiatrist does not confine himself to the interpretation of psychic material, but goes further to force the patient to actions that are hindered by his neurosis. The patient has to be forced precisely into the situations he fears, in order to accustom him to these situations and, consequently to enable him to overcome his fear. According to psychoanalytical theory, such actions bring forward and make available for interpretation the psychic material which otherwise might remain hidden. 'By the repetition of the act which he fears the patient will gain a better insight into his situation which, until then, he considered dangerous.' Through this forced action the patient is taught that there are no insurmountable difficulties in the situation. It is very important that the psychiatrist find out just what actions he can demand of a patient, in order to avoid asking too much and thereby throwing the individual into a panic. In cases of simple anxiety-neurosis, like that of a 'patient who does not dare to be far away from his home, he is ordered, at first, to walk two or three blocks.' After doing this three or four times, he is ordered to walk four or five blocks, and in this manner the therapy proceeds progressively. The only thing that should be asked of the patient is action; he should never be asked to exercise will-power, or suppress his thoughts: 'Such demands are useless and increase the sense of failure in the patient.' Very often it is difficult to find actions that are appropriate to the symptoms of the patient. According to Schilder, the principle of active therapy is 'probably also valid when thoughts which seem to be unacceptable to the patient are formulated again and again'; the mere formulation of words seems to have an effect similar to the repetition of the act. (Schilder, P. *Psychotherapy,* Norton, New York, 1938)

therapy, activity group In psychiatric practice, a special technique of applying psychotherapy through group activity. 'So that these [very shy] children might not feel threatened, a program of picnics and trips was arranged for them, and after some months of such therapy it was found that not only did they evidence gain in their social behavior, but that they had made general improvement in their personalities. From this inauspicious practice grew Slavson's activity group therapy.' (Klapman, J.W. *Group Psychotherapy,* Grune and Stratton, New York, 1946)

therapy, adjuvant (aj'oo-vant) Subsidiary therapy or curative means in the treatment of the psychoneuroses, in addition to psychotherapy, which they aid or assist. These adjuvant therapies consist primarily of drugs, suggestion, and hypnosis. They

are rarely of permanent therapeutic value per se, since they do not go to the root of the trouble; they do not treat the cause of the illness, but some one symptom or symptoms of it.

therapy, analytical (an-à-lit'i-kal) From the standpoint of Jung (analytical psychology), the expression *analytical therapy* has distinctive meaning. According to Jung the contents of consciousness are antithetic to those of the unconscious. One compensates for the other. 'In the normal condition the compensation is unconscious, i.e., it performs an unconscious regulation of conscious activity. In the neurotic state the unconscious appears in such strong contrast to the conscious that compensation is disturbed. The aim of analytical therapy, therefore, is to make the unconscious contents conscious in order that compensation may be established.' (Jung, C.G. *Psychological Types,* tr. by Baynes, H.G., Harcourt, Brace, New York and London, 1923) See *constructive; reductive.*

therapy, assignment 'Assignment therapy is the placement of the individual into a group in accord with his sociometric position in the community. It tries to give the individual the best opportunity for adjustment in the group and for the ascendance to such a position in it which expresses his spontaneous abilities. Such placements take into consideration the total picture of the group as well as its sexual, racial, and leadership cleavages.' (Moreno, J.L. *Who Shall Survive?* Nervous & Mental Disease Publishing Company, Washington, D.C., 1934)

therapy, atropine coma (a'trō-pēn) ACT; the use of atropine sulphate to induce coma in the treatment of psychoses, first reported by G.R. Forrer in 1950.
Greatest benefit has been reported in tense, anxious, and agitated psychotics.

therapy, attitude Originally, a process of treating children by working with the disturbed attitudes of their parents. (Levy, David. *American Journal of Orthopsychiatry 7,* 103–113, 1937) Nowadays, a type of re-educative psychotherapy which focuses on the current attitudes of the patient, their distortions, their origins, and their present purpose. In this type of therapy, the patient is helped to adopt attitudes that make for harmonious relationships as substitutes for his maladaptive attitudes.

therapy, brief stimulus A type of electroconvulsive therapy in which the current is modified so that the average electrical energy needed to produce a seizure is much less than with the usual method. It is claimed that BST gives as satisfactory clinical results as classical ECT, with the added advantage of reducing or even eliminating confusion. A disadvantage of BST is that patients are more fearful than with the classical method; this can be overcome by using pre-treatment barbiturates.

therapy, carbon dioxide inhalation A form of somatic treatment introduced by von Meduna (who also introduced Metrazol convulsive treatment for schizophrenia). In CO_2 inhalation therapy, the patient breathes from a cylinder containing a mixture of 30 per cent CO_2 and 70 per cent O_2 to the point of unconsciousness. Treatments are given two or three times a week, sometimes to as many as 100 treatments. The method is of limited usefulness in the treatment of various psychoneuroses, and many workers feel that it may even retard or prevent recovery. Those who find it of some value feel that it is best suited to traumatic hysteria with dissociation, to conversion symptoms of recent origin, and to anxiety-hysteria.

therapy, child-guidance The treatment of emotional problems of children by the simultaneous therapy of the child and its parents, especially the mother.

therapy, client-centered Non-directive therapy; a type of therapeutic counseling associated with the name of Carl Rogers. Client-centered therapy is predicated on the belief that the patient possesses inherent potentialities for growth which need only to be released by the therapist. The patient is responsible for his own destiny and has the right of choice in the solution of his problems, and instead of imposing values on the patient the therapist must promote the free expression of feelings in the counseling relationship.

therapy, dilution 'He [the physician] should be able to indicate to the patient that one need not feel guilty about certain thoughts or impulses. He should be able to acquaint the patient with the fact that an enormous number of human beings have similar ideas and feelings [universalizing the guilt-feelings]. . . This may be called a "dilution therapy," in that the patient is able to dilute the concentration of his own guilt feelings by the addition of the knowledge of their frequency or universality.' (Levine, M. *Psychotherapy in Medical Practice,* Macmillan, New York, 1943)

therapy, directed group See *psychotherapy, group.*

therapy, diversional In occupational therapy those simple occupations are regarded as diversional which are given primarily for the amusement and distraction of the patient from himself, 'in which simple processes are used to occupy the fingers and divert the mind of the patient from his or her condition, surroundings, etc. Here it is largely a question of morale.' (Slagle, E.C. and Robeson, H.A. *Syllabus for Training of Nurses in Occupational Therapy,* State Hospitals Press, Utica, N.Y., 1933)

therapy, electric convulsion A form of somatic treatment for certain psychiatric conditions in which electrical current is applied to the brain through two electrodes placed on the temporal areas of the skull. Current is applied through a specially constructed machine, whose main features are a stop watch for time regulation to fractions of a second and a voltmeter which regulates the voltage to be applied. The desired generalized convulsions is ordinarily obtained with voltage varying between 70 and 130 volts applied for 0.1 to 0.5 seconds. The convulsion usually occurs immediately with an initial tonic phase lasting about 10 seconds. The tonic phase slowly goes over into the clonic phase, which fades out after a total of 30 or 40 seconds for the whole seizure. The convulsion is accompanied by apnea. The seizure is followed by coma which lasts from 5 to 30 or more minutes.

Complications are rare, the most frequent one being bone fractures due to muscular contraction. Intravenous muscle relaxants, such as succinylcholine, are often used to prevent this complication. Respiratory and cardiovascular complications may occur; neurological complications are extremely rare. The probability of fatal incidents does not exceed 0.06 per cent of cases.

Electric convulsive therapy, or E.C.T.,

is indicated in mania, depressions, and certain cases of schizophrenia. Results are unsatisfactory in the psychoneuroses, except in psychoneurotic depression. All types of depression react favorably to E.C.T. after some four treatments. E.C.T. gives an 80 to 100 per cent remission rate in the depressive phase of manic-depressive psychosis, in involutional melancholia, and in agitated depressions, but it does not ward off episodic recurrences. The manic phase must usually be treated more intensively, with as many as two or three treatments a day. With such treatment the remission rate approaches that in the depressed phase. The paranoid type of involutional psychosis usually requires twenty treatments, in contrast to the ordinary maximum of ten treatments in the aforementioned groups, but, even so, the remission rate is less than 50 per cent. Schizophrenics also require a minimum of twenty treatments. About 65 per cent of schizophrenic cases of less than six months' duration respond favorably, some 40 per cent among those ill from six months to two years, and less than 10 per cent of those ill more than two years. In all cases, temporary remissions may be prolonged with E.C.T. maintenance therapy at weekly, fortnightly, even monthly intervals. (Kalinowsky, L.B., and Hoch, P.H. *Shock Treatments,* Grune and Stratton, New York, 1950)

Electric convulsive therapy is often used in combination with insulin therapy, particularly in schizophrenia. In these cases, E.C.T. is likely to relieve the anxiety and apprehension components, while insulin helps to clear the underlying thought disorder. Electric convulsive therapy does not afford insight to the patient; hence, in addition to somatic therapy, psychotherapy is usually indicated in order to bring more lasting benefit.

therapy, expressive This term denotes a method of treatment in which the therapist's dominant aim is to encourage and help the patient to bring out, verbalize, act out, or emotionally express all ideas and feelings so that both the patient and the therapist come to know the dynamic emotional roots of the patient's symptoms and illness. Through encouragement and by bringing about a reversal of the *covering up* (or normal) defensive mechanism, expressive therapy endeavors to *uncover* the roots of mental and emotional illness.

As epitomized in psychoanalysis, the main purpose of expressive therapy is, through a reversal of the repressive defensive mechanisms, to shift the material from the unconscious realm into the realm of conscious thought.

On the other hand, *suppressive therapy,* which is the opposite of expressive therapy, tends to cover up, to keep down, and strengthen the repressive, defensive forces of the personality. As such, suppressive therapy tries to build up the forces of concealment of the self toward hidden portions of itself, while expressive therapy brings about painful but valuable self-revelation. Suppressive therapy tends to maintain and continue the individual's comfortable and peaceful illusion of himself, while expressive therapy becomes painfully disillusioning and thus aims in the direction of self-realization and reality.

Psychoanalysis is summarized in expressive therapy. Other expressive therapies are analytically oriented psychotherapy, hypnoanalysis, catharsis, psychiatric counseling, and group psychotherapy. (Weiss, E., and English, O.S. *Psychosomatic Medicine,* 2nd ed., Saunders, Philadelphia and London, 1949)

therapy, indirect method of A form of therapy used principally in child psychiatry; it stresses 'the environmental manipulation . . . (in) dealing with personality and behavior problems.' (Lowrey, G. 'Trends in Therapy,' *American Journal of Orthopsychiatry IX,* p. 669–706, 1939)

therapy, inter-personal From the standpoint of psychodramatics, 'inter-personal therapy is a technique which is applied in such problems and mental disorders in which the treatment interrelates dynamically all the persons involved. An illustration of a situation demanding this approach is a "triangular neurosis," i.e., an inter-personal neurosis affecting three persons, for example, a husband, wife, and another individual.

'Inter-personal therapy is carried out in alternating sessions with each of the persons involved until the psychiatrist, the auxiliary ego, has returned to the subject with whom he began. The cycle can be repeated as often as necessary until catharsis is reached.' (Moreno, J.L. *Sociometry 1, 3,* 1937)

therapy, mass A psychotherapeutic term that embraces various group techniques, particularly the didactic, recreational, and class methods used for large groups.

therapy, non-directive See *therapy, client-centered.*

therapy, occupational The American Occupational Therapy Association defined its functions in *Syllabus for Training of Nurses in Occupational Therapy* (Slagle, E.C. and Robeson, H.) as follows:

1. Occupational therapy is a method of treatment for the sick or injured by means of purposeful occupation.
2. The goals are to arouse interest, courage and confidence; to exercise mind and body in healthy activity; to overcome disability; and to reestablish capacity for industrial and social usefulness.
3. In applying occupational therapy, system and precision are as important as in other forms of treatment.
4. The treatment should be prescribed and administered under constant medical advice and supervision and correlated with the other forms of treatment the patient is receiving.
5. The treatment should in each case be specifically directed to the individual patient's need.
6. Though some patients do best alone, employment in groups is usually advisable, because it provides exercise in social adaptation and the stimulating influence of example and comment.
7. The occupation selected should be within the patient's estimated interests and capability.
8. As the patient's strength and capability increase, the type and extent of occupation should be regulated and graded accordingly.
9. The only reliable measure of the treatment is the effect on the patient.
10. Inferior workmanship, or employment in an occupation which would be trivial for the healthy, may be attended with the greatest benefit to the sick or injured, but standards worthy of entirely normal people must be maintained for proper mental stimulation.
11. The production of well-made, useful and attractive articles or the accomplishment of useful tasks, requires healthy exercise of mind and body, gives the greatest satisfaction, and thus produces the most beneficial effects.
12. Novelty, variety, individuality, and utility of the product enhances the value of an occupation as a treatment measure.
13. Quality, quantity, salability of the products may prove beneficial by satisfying and stimulating the patient, but should never be permitted to obscure the main purpose.
14. Good craftsmanship and ability to instruct are essential qualifications in the occupational therapist; understanding, sincere interest in the patient, and an optimistic, cheerful outlook and manner are equally essential.
15. Physical exercises, games and music are useful forms of occupational therapy, and fall under two broad heads: (a) Gymnastics and calisthenics that are given for their value in a patient's physical re-education, or in habit training in mental hospitals; (b) recreation and play activities, such as music, games, folk dancing, etc., which are provided because of their general and social value for the patients.

therapy, old-age See *geriatrics.*

therapy, physical Physical therapy or physiotherapy is a branch of physical medicine that makes use of physical and other effective properties of light, heat, cold, water, electricity, mechanical agents, and kinesitherapy (massage, manipulation, therapeutic exercise, mechanical devices).

therapy, play In child psychiatry, play therapy is a method of treatment which, in general, corresponds to the method of psychoanalysis in adult psychiatry, the difference being that the child expresses himself and reveals unconscious material to the therapist by means of play rather than by verbalization of thoughts, as the adult does in psychoanalysis.

The play of children, an essential part of their life, is self-expressive in its nature. If a playroom containing all manner of toys and games is set up for the child, much can be learned about the child by observing what game he chooses to play and the manner in which he plays it. For example, during a session in the play-therapy room, a nine-year-old boy took chalk of various colors and drew on the blackboard a charming picture of a house in the countryside. When the drawing had been finished the therapist warmly complimented the boy on his work, and then asked him to make up a story about the people living in that house. It was known that he was a child from a broken, poverty-stricken home in a tenement section of the city; he would not obey his mother, and allegedly had pushed his baby sister from a fire escape to her death. In play therapy he had created what he lacked, an attractive home in the country. In telling the story of the people who lived in it, his feelings about his own home and his own family were drawn out. The therapist was able to help him face his insecurity, anxiety, and hostility and to learn better ways of dealing with them. Before this release through play therapy, the boy had been uncommunicative and inaccessible in several interviews with the therapist.

therapy, reconstructive See *psychotherapy.*

therapy, recreation See *recreation.*

therapy, recreational See *recreation.*

therapy, re-educative See *psychotherapy.*

therapy, regressive electro-shock A form of electroconvulsive therapy in which several daily grand mal convulsions are produced for a number of days until the patient is out of contact and incontinent of urine and feces. In one study, four treatments were given each day for seven days; at the end of this time, in addition to the above symptoms, patients were underactive, did not talk spontaneously, lost their appetite and had to be spoon-fed, and movements were uncertain, slow and clumsy. These symptoms last for one or two weeks; recovery is gradual.

Regressive EST is ordinarily used only when the more usual methods fail and prognosis is poor, as in the schizophrenias.

therapy, relationship A term commonly used by child psychiatrists in referring to the therapy which emerges out of the totality of the relationship between patient and therapist during the entire course of treatment. Although Allen is a pioneer in relationship therapy with children, he considers the term misleading. In this connection, Kanner (*Child Psychiatry,* Thomas, Springfield, Ill., 1948) quotes Allen as follows: 'It [relationship therapy] seems to imply a special brand of psychological therapy. All therapy involves a relationship between patient and therapist.' However, 'here the therapeutic relationship is conceived as an immediate

experience. The therapist begins where the patient is and seeks to help him draw on his own capacities toward a more creative acceptance and use of the self he has. While maintaining an interest in understanding what has been wrong, the therapeutic focus is on what the individual can begin to do about what was and, more important, still is wrong. Therapy emerges, then, from an experience in living, not in isolation but within a relationship with another from whom the patient can eventually differentiate himself as he comes to perceive and accept his own self as separate and distinct.'

therapy, release See *release.*

therapy, shock A general term in psychiatry indicating the use of various somatic treatments which produce a 'shock' to the central nervous system, thus favorably influencing the course of a mental disease. The shock therapies include electroshock (EST)—also called electroconvulsive therapy (ECT)—insulin coma therapy, ambulatory insulin treatment (also called sub-shock or sub-coma insulin therapy), Metrazol convulsive treatment, brief stimulus electrotherapy, electrostimulation, and electronarcosis.

therapy, situational A term introduced by S.R. Slavson, in connection with his activity group psychotherapy, in which the social relationship and the physical environment themselves (i.e. the situation) have a therapeutic effect.

therapy, sleep-electroshock Electroshock treatment preceded by the administration of sufficient sedative or hypnotic drug to produce sleep. The method is of particular value in patients who develop a fear of electric shock and are unwilling to continue receiving such therapy. Pentothal sodium is commonly employed, administered intravenously as a 2.5 per cent solution. The electrodes are applied after sleep is induced. Many psychiatrists apply the current as soon as the patient spontaneously moves a limb during the waking process. The same amount of current is given as without the sleep-inducing drug. Other psychiatrists apply the current at a deeper stage of narcosis, as judged by the absence of spontaneous movements and the presence of a corneal reflex. With the latter method a nonconvulsive or minor reaction is obtained, but the clinical effects as measured by the maintenance of the improved state are equally satisfactory.

therapy, supportive See *psychotherapy.*

therapy, suppressive See *therapy, expressive.*

therapy, will A form of psychotherapy associated with the name of Otto Rank and based upon his belief that birth trauma (the separation of the child from the mother at the moment of birth) is the central element in neurosis. The trauma of birth is believed to lead to two sets of strivings: (1) to return to the womb or (2) to re-enact separation and achieve independence. In will-therapy, separation reactions are studied as well as the struggle of will manifested in the patient's desire to continue therapy (and dependence) or to discontinue it (and become independent). The patient is actively encouraged to assert himself so as to develop and strengthen his will.

thermanesthesia, thermoanesthesia (thẽr-man-es-thē'zhi-à, thẽr-mō-an-es-thē'-zhi-à) Loss of the ability to distinguish between heat and cold; loss of the temperature sense; insensibility to heat or to temperature changes.

thermo- (thẽr'mō-) combining form meaning heat from Gr. *thermós,* hot.

thermohyperesthesia (thẽr-mō-hī-pẽr-es-thē'zhi-à) Extreme sensitiveness to heat stimuli.

thermohypesthesia (-hip-es-thē'zhi-à) Diminished sensibility to heat stimuli.

thermoneurosis (-nū-rō'sis) An elevation of the temperature of the body due to neurosis as seen sometimes in hysteria.

theta rhythm or wave See *electroencephalogram.*

thinking, abstract See *thinking, physiognomonic.*

thinking, archaic-paralogical (är-kā'ik, par-à-loj'i-kal) A psychiatric and psychological term introduced by Domarus (1923, 1927, 1929). In an effort to clarify our understanding of the specific qualities of schizophrenic thinking, Domarus classified thinking into: '(1) *prearchaic;* (2) *archaic-paralogical;* and (3) *paralogicallogical.* The latter two he considered to be typical of primitive savages, and common in schizophrenia, and the first as typical of man's anthropoid progenitors and of schizophrenic stupor.' In 1940, Osborne

recommended changing the name of schizophrenia to palaeophrenia to emphasize the importance of regression to primitive subrational forms of thinking in the schizophrenic disorders.

Primitive thinking, primordial thinking, anthropoid thinking are all synonyms for archaic-paralogical thinking. They are all characterized by impairment or deficiency of abstraction and generalization, with a tendency toward 'concrete' rather than 'abstract' thinking. (Hunt, J.McV. *Personality and the Behavior Disorders,* vol. 2, Ronald Press, New York, 1944)

thinking-aside A disorder of associations seen in schizophrenic patients in which the patient loses himself in insignificant side association with the result that no unitary train of thought develops. Because of the paucity of genuinely casual links in such conversation or writing, thinking-aside would be considered a type of asyndesis.

thinking, associative Verbal catharsis that deals with immediate problems of patients in their everyday life rather than with traumatic problems originating in infancy. The latter sort of catharsis occurs through 'free-association.' Free association is regressive in its nature, which is not the case with associative thinking. Associative thinking is lateral in direction while free-association is vertical. (Slavson, S.R. *Analytic Group Psychotherapy,* Columbia University Press, New York, 1950, p. 189) See *presentation.*

thinking, autistic (aw-tis'tik) See *autism.*

thinking, categorical See *thinking, physiognomonic.*

thinking-compulsion See *brooding.*

thinking, concrete See *thinking, physiognomonic.*

thinking, concretistic (kon-krē-tis'tik) See *concretism.*

thinking, directed See *intellect.*

thinking-disorder See *association, disturbances of.*

thinking, double An infrequently used term with unclear definition; some authorities use the term synonymously with *thought-hearing.*

thinking, fragmentation of A disturbance in association, pathognomonic of schizophrenia, in which even such basic concepts as 'father' and 'mother' become vague and obscure and the thinking processes become so confused that they cannot result in a complete idea or action, but merely in vague movements. Bleuler calls this a 'primary symptom' of schizophrenia and believes that it is due to associations no longer following the logical pathways indicated by past experience. Instead, associations easily take new and seemingly illogical pathways, and thinking becomes bizarre. Thus two ideas, fortuitously encountered, are combined into one thought. Associations lack the concept of purpose. When the symptom is of mild degree, it may be noticed only that the patient gives generalized rather than precise answers. Thus one patient, asked to give the location of London, said 'Europe' rather than 'England.' (Bleuler, E. *Dementia Praecox or the Group of Schizophrenias,* International Universities Press, New York, 1950)

thinking, physiognomonic (fiz-i-og-nō-mon'ik) According to Kasanin, this is the first stage in the development of thought in the child. In this stage, the child animates objects and projects his ego into them, as when he plays with a stick and calls it a horse. Piaget calls this 'syncretic thinking.'

The second stage is concrete thinking, characterized by literalness and lack of generalizations. In this stage, for example, the word 'table' refers not to tables in general but to the particular table in the subject's house.

The third stage is abstract or categoried thinking, characterized by use of abstractions and generalizations. This type of thinking appears relatively late, usually after adolescence and probably only after some degree of education.

thinking, prearchaic See *thinking, archaic-paralogical.*

thinking, preconscious One of the terms used by Fenichel to describe the preverbal, prelogical, pictorial phantasy thinking which precedes the development of logical thinking in small children.

This preconscious thinking is not in accordance with reality. All of its features are primitive and archaic. First, since it is ruled by the emotions and strives for the discharge of tensions, it is full of wishful or fear-laden misconceptions. Second, it is carried out through concrete pictorial images. Third, it is a magical type of thinking. 'The object and the idea of the object, the object and a picture or model of the object, the object and a part of the object are equated: similarities are not distinguished from identities; ego and nonego are not yet separated. What happens to objects might (by identification) be experienced as happening to the ego, and what happens to the ego causes the same thing to happen to the object . . .' Last, the thinking is symbolic and thus vague, for the world is experienced and apperceived in symbolic forms. Stimuli that provoke the same emotional reactions are looked upon as identical. Thus if penis and snake provoke the same emotions, they are apprehended by a common conception: they are one and the same thing. Although illogical and ineffective, this preconscious phantasy thinking is an attempt to master reality. It does postpone immediate discharge reactions and attempts to anticipate reality and bring about a more adequate discharge of tensions.

With the acquisition of words and the development of the faculty of speech, thinking becomes logical, and organized. Words can be linked to ideas. This is the decisive step in the final differentiation of conscious and unconscious and in the development of reality-testing. Now there can be precise anticipation of action through thinking, and instinctual excitations as well as the external world can be handled in a better way.

Preconscious thinking, however, recurs in the adult in several different ways. Before acquiring verbal formulation, all thoughts run through initial phases which resemble preconscious thinking. In dreams and in fatigue, words are retranslated into pictures. Conscious ideas may be symbols hiding objectionable unconscious ideas, and in dreams symbols appear not only in order to distort, but also as a characteristic of, archaic pictorial thinking visualizing abstract thoughts. In this way the fact that the symbol and the symbolized were once the same thing is utilized. Preconscious thinking may also appear as a substitute for unpleasant reality or a reality that cannot be influenced. This occurs, for example, in the magical daydreaming phantasies of the hysterical patient. In the compulsion-neurotic the magic power of concepts can be observed. Finally, psychotic thinking is identical with the preconscious thinking of small children, described above. (Fenichel, O.

The Psychoanalytic Theory of Neurosis, Norton, New York, 1945)

thinking, syncretic (sin-kre'tik) See *thinking, physiognomonic.*

thinking, undirected See *intellect.*

third nervous system A system differentiated by Burrow on the basis of its specialization of function, not on the basis of anatomical demarcation. It involves the neural processes that govern man's symbolic interchange, and through its misuse is considered responsible for man's disordered behavior.

thlasis depressio (thlá'sis dā-pres'sē-ō) *Obs.* Melancholia.

Thom, Douglas Armour (1887–) (thōm) American psychiatrist; child psychiatry.

Thomism The philosophicotheological system of Thomas Aquinas. From the standpoint of psychiatry Thomism is a conception of the world based upon the principle of a powerful father whose commands are natural law. Because this system is a representative product of the particular sociological culture in which it is rooted, it is of interest to students of cultural psychology and especially to those concerned with the psychoanalytic study of the races, societies, and cultures of man. This also applies, of course, to any and all other systems or 'isms' considered representative products of a determining culture.

'*Thomism* is an ideological system with the unrecognized premise that "father is always right" or "it is right because father said so." It is the ideological system which brooks no change and no investigation; and if it does (as it did even in the case of St. Thomas), scientific investigation is used only to prove again that "father was right." Such an ideological system cannot be proven either right or wrong. Its tenure depends entirely on its ability to serve as a vehicle to express ideas not incompatible with the needs of the individual. The failure of *Thomism* came when this obedience principle became an obstacle and the ideologies of the Reformation sought expression for the new investigative spirit which had already validated itself in practice. The old obedience dogma was not in harmony with it.' (Kardiner, A. *The Psychological Frontiers of Society,* Columbia University Press, New York, 1945)

thought, archaic Psychiatric literature emphasizes the great importance of archaic thought in psychiatric patients. For example, the schizophrenic patient may regress almost entirely to the level of primitive mentality.

'When we examine the process we shall find, as in fact we do also with much of the content, that schizophrenic thinking shows startling analogies to the thinking of primitive man. In other words it is *archaic* in character. A reasonably adequate discussion of schizophrenic thinking would require that it be correlated with the principal historic features of the development of thought wherein it would be shown that it throws back to historically earlier ways of thinking in which feeling, perception and concreteness dominate, while reasoning, differentiation, and abstraction are little in evidence.' (White, W.A. *Outlines of Psychiatry,* 12th ed., Nervous & Mental Disease Publishing Company, Washington, D.C., 1929)

thought, audible A type of auditory hallucination in which the voice is projected into the patient himself, as though he could hear his own thoughts. These hallucinations with almost no sensory components are commonly designated as inner voices. Baillarger referred to them as psychic hallucinations. These are hallucinations of conception rather than of perception. Patients may use the term 'soundless voices' to refer to essentially the same phenomenon.

thought-blocking See *blocking.*

thought, constraint See *constraint of thought.*

thought-deprivation *Blocking* (q.v.).

thought-derailment See *derailment, thought.*

thought-disorder See *associations, disturbances of.*

thought-disorder, primary Kasanin uses the term primary thought-disorder to refer to cases of schizophrenia in which there is striking involvement of intellectual functions with marked incoherence and irrelevance, tendency to neologisms, 'word-salads,' and peculiar syntactical speech formation.

thought-echoing Hearing one's own thoughts expressed in whispered or unbearably loud tones; *écho des pensées* (q.v.).

thought, emotional See *psychodynamics, adaptational.*

thought-hearing Some patients, notably those with schizophrenia, maintain that they hear their own thoughts; they may also believe that their thoughts are heard by others, too.

thought, identity of See *process, primary psychic.*

thought, imageless A thought completely devoid of optic pictures or representations. In the process of thinking we are, in a way, concerned with pictures in the optic sphere. These pictures or images may come and go, they may be complete or incomplete, may have color or be devoid of it, may be bidimensional or tridimensional, or they may be completely absent when we have imageless thought. (Schilder, P. *Mind, Perception and Thought,* Columbia University Press, New York, 1942)

thought, inelasticity of A term sometimes used to describe the reduction of the normal flow of thought, often observed in people of old age, when thoughts become more rigid, more static than in the years of youth. One may say of this type of patients that 'they get very set in their ways.' (Sladen, F.J., ed., *Psychiatry and the War.* Thomas, Springfield, Ill., 1943)

thought, latent See *cerebration, unconscious.*

thought, multifocal Arieti's term for *asyndesis* (q v.) and similar associational disturbances which he explains as being due to the fact that the patient's thought simultaneously focuses on many different planes and on different meanings with their different objective situations.

thought-nexus The union or linkage of thoughts. 'In obedience to the pain-principle, therefore, the first psi- (Ψ) system is quite incapable of introducing anything unpleasant into the thought-nexus. The system cannot do anything but wish.' (Freud, S. *The Interpretation of Dreams,* 3rd ed., tr. by Brill, A.A., Macmillan, New York, 1933)

thought-omnipotence See *magic.*

thought-pressure This expression means that, as patients describe it, they have ideas that are forced into their mind. The patients assume little or no responsibility for developing the thoughts. This is particularly true in patients with schizophre-

nia, who may ascribe all their mental processes to the alleged pressure brought upon them by others.

The same phenomenon of thought-pressure may also appear in manic-depressive disorders, as well as in certain psychoneurotic states. In these diagnostic groups no external pressure is alleged; rather, the patients assert that the irresistible force arises within their own minds.

The condition is also known as pressure of ideas.

thought, reactive See *reinforcement, reactive.*

thought, re-enforced See *thought, supervalent.*

thought-rehearsal See *rehearsal, obsessional.*

thought, supervalent (sū-pẽr-vā'lent) Freud says that 'a normal train of thought, however intense it may be, can eventually be disposed of.' But among certain patients a train of thought is constantly with the patient and no amount of conscious reasoning can dispel it. 'A train of thought such as this may be described as exaggerated, or better *re-enforced,* or "supervalent" in Wernicke's sense of the word. It shows its pathological character, in spite of its apparently reasonable content, by the single peculiarity that no amount of conscious and voluntary effort of thought on the patient's part is able to dissipate or remove it.' (Freud, S. *Collected Papers,* vol. 3, tr. by Strachey, A. and J., Leonard and Virginia Woolf, Hogarth Press, London, 1925)

thought-transference See *telepathy.*

thought, unemotional See *psychodynamics, adaptational.*

thought-wit See *wit, thought.*

three-cornered therapy See *psychotherapy, multiple.*

threshold, sedation The amount of sodium amytal required, by intravenous injection, to produce slurring of speech and a concomitant inflection point in the 15–30 c.p.s. amplitude curve of the electroencephalogram. The EEG change occurs within 80 seconds of the time when slur is noted. Shagass has used this test to differentiate between psychotic and neurotic depressions; according to him, thresholds are low in psychotic depressions and high in neurotic depressions.

thrombosis, cerebral (throm-bō′sis, cer′e-bral) See *accident, cerebrovascular.*

thrust From the psychoanalytic point of view 'the life of each instinct' is split up 'into a series of "thrusts," distinct from one another in the time of their occurrence but each homogeneous within its own period, whose relation to one another is comparable to that of successive eruptions of lava. We can then perhaps picture to ourselves that the earliest and most primitive instinct-eruption persists in an unchanged form and undergoes no development at all. The next "thrust" would then from the outset have undergone a change of form, being turned, for instance, from active to passive, and it would then, with this new characteristic, be superimposed upon the earlier layer, and so on.' (Freud, S. *Collected Papers,* vol. 4, tr. by Riviere, J., Leonard and Virginia Woolf and The Institute of Psychoanalysis, London, 1924–25)

thumb-sucking See *sucking, thumb.*

thymergasia (thīm-ĕr-gas′i-à) Adolf Meyer's term for the psychiatric syndromes commonly known as affective psychoses or reaction-types. For example, the manic-depressive psychosis is a form of thymergasia.

-thymia (-thī′mi-à, -thim′i-à) Combining form meaning state of mind and will, from Gr. *thymós,* soul, spirit, mind, temper.

thymo- (thī′mō-) Combining form meaning soul, spirit, temper, from Gr. *thymós,* soul, spirit, mind, temper.

thymopathic (thī-mō-path′ik) E. Bleuler uses this term with the meaning 'affectively disturbed.' The premorbid personality of the manic-depressive is characterized by lack of emotional poise, distractibility, feelings of inadequacy and frustration, irascibility, and periods of sadness. These personality characteristics are present from an early age and are presumed to be evidence of inherited predisposition. Such patients constitute the thymopathic type of personality.

thymopathy (thī-mop′à-thē) A general term for morbidity of the affects.

thymopsyche (thī-mō-sī′kē) See *noöpsyche.*

thyroidism (thī′roid-iz’m) Excessive functioning of the thyroid gland.

tic Any brief, recurrent, inappropriate, irresistible movement involving a relatively small segment of the body; also known as habit spasm or habit contraction. While tics are frequently psychogenic, they are seen also in cases of chronic encephalitis, most commonly in association with disorders of respiration (e.g. yawning, sniffing, spasmodic cough, spitting). Other tics may be seen in the encephalitides, chiefly torticollis and complex co-ordinated rhythmical movements involving the jaw, lips, tongue, and palate.

When the tic is believed to have psychogenic relationship, it is often called habit tic. Tics comprise habitual repetitions, such as grimacing, blinking, shrugging the shoulders, wry-neck, various movements of the head, etc.

Some use the expression local tic, when the movement is limited to some local region, e.g. the eye.

Mimic tic relates to involuntary twitching of the facial muscles.

Psychic tic is one that is induced by some unconscious process or impulse.

The French speak of *tic de pensée,* meaning the involuntary habit of giving expression to any idea that happens to be present in the mind.

Abraham considered the tic a conversion symptom at the anal-sadistic level, and most psychoanalytic writers have emphasized the well-defined anal character and, in addition, the markedly narcissistic makeup of the tiqueur.

'The repressed situations, whose motor intentions return in tic, are highly emotional ones representing again either instinctual temptations or punishments for warded-off impulses. In tics, a movement that was once the concomitant sign of an affect (sexual excitement, rage, anxiety, grief, triumph, embarrassment) has become an equivalent of this affect, and appears instead of the warded-off affect.

'This may occur in different ways: (1) The tic represents a part of the original affective syndrome, whose mental significance remains unconscious. (2) The tic represents a movement whose unconscious meaning is a defense against the intended affect. (3) The tic does not directly represent affect or defense against affect but, rather, other movements or motor impulses that once occurred during a repressed emotional excitement, either in the patient or in another person with whom the patient has made a hysterical identification.' (O. Fenichel. *The Psychoanalytic Theory of Neurosis,* Norton, New York, 1945)

tic, attitude 'The authors [Meige and Feindel] state that there are also attitude-tics, that are no longer the lightning-like clonic convulsions but tonic rigidity in particular attitudes of the head or a limb. There is no doubt that these cases are transitional between cataclonic and catatonic innervation. These phenomena (tonic or attitude-tic) approximate nearer to the catatonic attitudes, the pathogenesis of which shows many points of contact with that of attitude-tic.' (Ferenczi, S. *Further Contributions to the Theory and Technique of Psycho-Analysis,* tr. by Suttie, J., Leonard and Virginia Woolf and The Institute of Psychoanalysis, London, 1926) Ferenczi holds that torticollis is an example of an attitude-tic.

tic convulsif (tēk' kôN-vül-sēf') (F. 'convulsive tic') Same as *tic.*

tic douloureux (tēk' dōō-lōō-rẽ') (F. 'painful tic; facial neuralgia') A chronic trigeminal neuralgia characterized by excruciating paroxysmal pain of short duration, flushing of the face, watering eyes, and rhinorrhea. The condition may affect either the second or the third division of the fifth cranial nerve, or both. The first division is rarely affected. The intermissions between paroxysms vary from weeks to as long as a year. With each succeeding attack seizures become more frequent and more severe. Many cases exhibit dolorogenetic or trigger zones on the face or mucous membranes, stimulation of which will evoke attacks. Tic douloureux is usually unilateral, is more common in adults over 40, and is more frequent among females. The cause is unknown, although the disease may be associated with dental or sinus pathology. There is probably some hereditary factor. Treatment is directed first toward remedying possible local causes. Trichlorethylene inhalations and alcohol injections into the peripheral branches of the nerve may be helpful, but the treatment of choice is retrogasserian neurectomy of the sensory root. Hyndman considers the cerebellar exposure superior to the subtemporal, even though the former requires greater care because of the risk of injury to the facial nerve. Partial section is adequate and does not give the widespread loss in sensation seen with total section. Tic douloureux is also known as trifacial neuralgia, prosopalgia, Fothergill's neuralgia, and chronic paroxysmal trigeminal neuralgia.

tic non-douloureux (nôN-dōō-lōō-rẽ') (F. 'non-painful tic') Charcot's term for a hysterical disorder of the face, usually unilateral, characterized by paroxysmal twitching of the facial muscles and anesthesia of the skin on the affected side of the face.

tic, psychic (sī'kik) A gesture of ejaculation made under the influence of an irresistible morbid impulse.

Tilney, Frederick (1876–1938), American neurologist; comparative anatomy.

time-agnosia (-ag-nō'si-à) A condition in which the meaning of time is not comprehended, even though the patient may speak of time. There is disorientation in immediate time, the patient is unable to estimate short time-intervals, and long intervals of time are frequently shortened. Thus, one patient with time-agnosia stated that World War I had ended four years before, whereas actually it had ended ten years earlier. Patients with time-agnosia are able to relate events of the distant past and their interconnection with location, but cannot give the element of time of the event or time relations. Accompanying the time-agnosia, and probably a result of it, is an indifference to the past and future and a lack of concern about the condition itself. Time-agnosia follows trauma, such as head injury, especially of the temporal area, cerebrovascular accident, and alcoholic coma.

The trauma usually results in a mentally confused state of short duration. Then the patient regains orientation in space, but remains disoriented in time for the immediate present as well as for past events, to a varying degree. Time-agnosia often disappears gradually, depending on the extent and degree of permanency of the original lesion.

Davidson has described a syndrome of time-agnosia which includes post-traumatic muscular hypertonicity, vascular eye-ground changes (congested discs), and diminution of the acuity of sensibility in a generalized way. The prepsychotic personality of such patients includes a certain simplicity of make-up and a weakness of the sexual impulse. They have ordinarily led a colorless, drifting life wherein time has had no particular meaning to them. (Davidson, G.M. 'A Syndrome of Time-agnosia,' *Journal of Nervous and Mental Disease 94,* 337, 1941)

time, reaction See *reaction-time.*

tiqueur (tē-kēr′) One who suffers from a tic.

tocomania (tō-kō-mā′ni-à) Puerperal mania.

togetherness Ackerman's term for the earliest stage in personality development, when the infant is in a state of primary psychic union with the mother, with little or no recognition of the self.

tolerance See *addiction.*

tolerance, frustration The maximal point of tolerance of frustration at which the defenses of an individual give way to the conflict and resentment that frustration sets up in him.

Tom o'Bedlam See *Abram.*

tomomania (tō-mō-mā′ni-à) A morbid desire to be operated upon.

-tonia (-tō′ni-à) Combining form meaning (presence of) tonus or tension, from Gr. *tónos,* stretching, tension, tone.

tonicity State or condition of tone or tension, mental or physical. See *tension, mental.*

tonitrophobia (ton-it-rō-fō′bi-à) Fear of thunder; astrapophobia.

tonogenic (ton-ō-jen′ik) Giving rise to increased tension or tonus.

tonogeny (tō-noj′ē-nē) Tonogeny refers to any factor giving rise to increased tension or tonus. The vagus nerve is regarded as the tone-giving nerve of the stomach and intestines. The psyche may be the origin of tone-producing stimuli; for example, anxiety may be expressed in part through increased tension or tenseness. Extreme states of tension of long duration are common in the catatonic form of schizophrenia.

tonus (tō′nus) Tonicity.

TOP The term TOP area refers to the association areas of the temporal, occipital, and parietal lobes of the cerebral hemisphere. The functions of the TOP area are imperfectly understood but presumably many of the highest psychic functions are dependent upon intactness of these regions. The TOP area and the prefrontal area are the last to develop phylogenetically.

topalgia (tō-pal′ji-à) Pain localized to one spot; the presence of a painful point or spot; a symptom occurring in hysteria or neurasthenia.

topectomy (tō-pek′tō-mē) A surgical operation for the excision (removal) of certain selected areas of the cerebral cortex (brain surface). The operation is performed as a therapeutic measure in certain cases of mental illness and hence is of great importance in psychiatry.

Brain surgery as a therapeutic modality in psychiatric conditions came into prominence during World War II. 'At the time of the entry of the United States into World War II relatively few laymen had heard of lobotomy or leucotomy, as the then current "psychosurgical" operations were called, and these operations gave little indication of changing psychiatric treatment and management markedly for a long while. to come.

'With the discharge of the first of what evidently was soon to become a large number of psychiatrically disabled veterans, the public became actively concerned about their rapid rehabilitation. By August 26, 1943, many relatives and guardians of patients who had failed to improve with shock therapy began to demand more rapid and drastic treatment and on this day the Veterans Administration found it advisable to issue a communication concerning "prefrontal lobotomy."' (Mettler, F.A. *Selective Partial Ablation of the Frontal Cortex,* Hoeber, New York, 1949)

At this time and for several years thereafter prefrontal lobotomy or leucotomy were the psychosurgical procedures commonly employed. But for a number of reasons these operations proved unsatisfactory and by 1947 they were being supplanted by a new type of operation worked out by the Columbia-Greystone group and named by them topectomy.

Essentially, the various operations prior to topectomy consisted in rendering nonfunctional certain areas of the cortex by severing (from *beneath* the cortex) the fibres communicating with these areas. In the topectomy procedure the approach is from *above,* i.e. the areas *themselves* are removed following direct surgical exposure of the brain surface.

The subcortical approach had many disadvantages. Because there was no exposure—the leukotome, or cutting instrument, simply being introduced into the white matter of the brain through a small burr hole drilled through the skull in the temporal area—the operator could not see exactly what he was doing and was forced to manipulate the leukotome 'blindly.' As a result it sometimes happened that more fibres than intended were cut, involving cortical areas which were to have remained intact. It was extremely difficult to be selective. Moreover, variations in anatomical structure sometimes resulted in the unwitting severance of important blood vessels and in unwanted interference with other structures. The supracortical, visual approach (topectomy) obviates these disadvantages.

The various psychosurgical procedures have a common rationale. In mental health there exists a sound balance between ideas and emotions—or, to put it more technically, between the prefrontal cerebral cortex (controlling ideas) and the thalamus (controlling emotions). In mental illness this balance between ideas and emotions is upset. If the fibres connecting the thalamus with the prefrontal cortex are severed, the thalamus can no longer charge a patient's ideas with disturbing, symptom-producing emotions.

'The following types of cases show the most favorable results: (1) Schizophrenic patients who, in spite of every kind of shock treatment, continue to manifest violent behavior, suicidal tendencies, homicidal tendencies, and destructiveness. . . (2) refractory obsessive-compulsive psychoneurotics who remain uninfluenced by prolonged psycho-analysis, direct interview psychotherapy, and electroshock treatment. . . (3) involutional melancholia which has failed to respond to shock therapy. . . (4) manic-depressive psychosis, with either a chronic depressed state or a chronic mania. . . (5) chronic depressions of old age, in patients over sixty who have failed to improve after electroshock treatment.' (Polatin, P. *How Psychiatry Helps,* Harper, New York, 1949)

topical flight Cameron's term for *flight of ideas* (q.v.).

topography, mental The mapping out of psychic structures is called mental topography or topographical psychology. It is a static representation of the components of the psyche, denoting their location. For example, the superego in the adult psyche is located in the realm of the unconscious; Jung's archetypes occupy one of the deeper layers of the unconscious.

'By accepting the existence of these (two or three) [i.e. conscious, preconscious, unconscious] mental symptoms, psychoanalysis has departed a step further from the descriptive psychology of consciousness and has taken to itself a new problem and a new content. Up till now, it differed from academic (descriptive) psychology mainly by reason of its dynamic conception of mental processes; now we have to add that it professes to consider mental topography also, and to indicate in respect of any given mental operation within what system or between what systems it runs its course. This attempt, too, has won it the name of "depth-psychology." ' (Freud, S. *Collected Papers,* vol. 4, tr. by Riviere, J., Leonard and Virginia Woolf and The Institute of Psychoanalysis, London, 1924–25)

When mapped out at any given time, mental topography has a static appearance, but the map often changes radically from its former aspect. It differs also from the standpoint of nosology. For example, the mental topography of the manic-depressive psychosis differs appreciably from that of hysteria. Many clinical diagnostic groups have their characteristic 'map.'

toponeurosis (top-ō-nū-rō′sis) A localized neurosis.

topophobia A general term meaning fear of place. For each individual the nature of the place is specific, although the word has come to be used as a synonym of agyiophobia, or fear of streets.

Ferenczi said that 'this combination of disturbance of gait with tremor is absent in the ordinary astasia-abasia with which we are acquainted in peace time practice, where topophobic manifestations are occasioned simply by conditions of weakness, by feelings of giddiness, etc.' (Ferenczi, S. *Further Contributions to the Theory and Technique of Psycho-Analysis,* tr. by Suttie, J.I., Leonard and Virginia Woolf and The Institute of Psychoanalysis, London, 1926)

torpedoing During the first World War 'treatment by torpedoing' was in vogue in certain military sections, for example, at Tours. It was used in a variety of neurotic conditions, particularly in those that were presumably of an hysterical character. It consisted in the application of intense electrical currents to the bodily region involved.

torpillage (tor-pē-yàzh′) (F. 'act of torpedoing') A form of treating cases of hysteria, particularly in wartime, by applying faradic currents to a shocking degree of pain—thus 'fighting fire with fire,' as it were.

'What it really consists in is giving authority to a medical officer to inflict pain on a patient up to the point at which the patient yields up his neurosis. Its unquestioned effectiveness . . . makes plain that under circumstances a military neurosis disappears under punishment.' (Bailey, P. 'War Neuroses, Shell Shock and Nervousness in Soldiers,' *Journal of the American Medical Association 71*, 2148, 1918)

torpor (tor′pĕr) (L. 'numbness, stupefaction') When consciousness is so disordered that only very strong stimuli produce a reaction, the condition is known as *torpor*.

torsion dystonia See *dystonia, torsion.*

torsion-spasm A constant and irregular twisting and turning of the body, especially of the pelvis and neck muscles, with bizarre posturing of the body and limbs.

torticollis (tor-ti-kol′is) Wry neck. Torticollis is characterized by spasmodic contractions of the muscles of the neck, particularly those supplied by the spinal accessory nerve; the head is usually drawn to one side and rotated so that the chin points to the opposite side.

The origin of the condition is undetermined. Psychiatrists are interested, because it appears that there may be some psychogenic factors connected with it. For example, Ferenczi says that torticollis is an attitude-tic and relates it to unconscious components.

torticollis, mental Spasmodic contraction of the muscles of the neck, psychically determined.

'total-push' treatment of schizophrenia A method of treatment suggested by Myerson in which he emphasizes physiotherapy, irradiation, exercise and games, diets, praise, blame, reward, punishment, regard for clothing and personal care. (Myerson, A. 'Theory and Principles of "Total-Push" Method in the Treatment of Chronic Schizophrenia,' *American Journal of Psychiatry 95*, 1197–1204, 1939)

totem The term *totem* was introduced

into psychiatry by Freud, who extensively discusses the concept from the psychoanalytic point of view. Freud credits J. Long with having learned of the name totem or totam from the North American Indians in 1791. Frazer (*The Golden Bough*) describes the concept at great length, emphasizing that 'the totem bond is stronger than the bond of blood or family in the modern sense.'

As a rule a totem is 'an animal, either edible or harmless, or dangerous and feared; more rarely the totem is a plant or a force of nature (rain, water) which stands in a peculiar relation to the whole clan. The totem is first of all the tribal ancestor of the clan, as well as its tutelary spirit and protector; it sends oracles and, though otherwise dangerous, the totem knows and spares its children. The members of a totem are therefore under a sacred obligation not to kill (destroy) their totem, to abstain from eating its meat or from any other enjoyment of it.' (Freud, S. *The Basic Writings of Sigmund Freud,* tr. by Brill, A.A., Random House, New York, 1938)

The concept possesses considerable significance in psychoanalysis from many points of view, chief of which is the savage's dread of incest.

totemism Totemism is the selection of animals, plants, and inanimate objects as representatives for the (primitive) individual and tribes.

Freud says that he divides 'the accepted theories of the derivation of totemism into three groups, (a) nominalistic, (b) sociological, (c) psychological.'

Nominalistic totemism refers to that form of totemism which differentiates tribes by names. Freud, quoting from E. Durkheim, says that, as regards sociological totemism, 'the totem is the visible representative of the social religion of these [i.e. Australian] races. It embodies the community, which is the real object of veneration.' Psychological totemism, according to Frazer, was based upon the belief in an 'outward soul.' The totem was meant to represent a safe place of refuge where the soul is deposited in order to avoid the dangers which threaten it. (Freud, S. *The Basic Writings of Sigmund Freud,* tr. by Brill, A.A., Random House, New York, 1938)

touching A disturbance in association, peculiar to schizophrenia, in which the only recognizable association to external stimuli consists of feeling with the hands the contours of objects within reach. This process is similar to 'naming' except that a different motor activity is involved. See *naming*.

tower-head *Oxycephaly* (q.v.).

toxicomania (tok-si-kō-mā′ni-à) A craving for poison.

toxicophobia Fear of poison.

toxiphobia *Obs.* Toxicophobia.

toxiphrenia Schizophrenia associated with toxic, delirious reaction. (Lewis, N.D.C.)

T.P.I. Treponema Pallidum Immobilization. See *test, T.P.I.*

trace, memory In his paper on *The Defense Neuro-Psychoses,* Freud mentions certain instances of intentional forgetting which subsequently was associated with the development of a neurotic condition. The memory of the experience that was painful was not fully repressed. 'The task which the ego undertakes in defense—of treating the unbearable idea as "non arrivée"—is absolutely insoluble; both the memory-trace and the affect attached to the idea are there once and for all, and it is no longer possible to extirpate them.' (Freud, S. *Collected Papers,* vol. 1, tr. by Riviere, J., Leonard and Virginia Woolf and The Institute of Psychoanalysis, London, 1924–25) See *system; engram*.

tract, pyramidal 'The pyramidal tracts are the means by which the nervous impulses which excite voluntary movements pass from the cerebral cortex to the lower motor neurones which arise in the brainstem and spinal cord. The pyramidal fibres or upper motor neurones are the axones of cells of the precentral convolution. Electrical excitation of these cells causes movements of the opposite side of the body. The movements thus excited are not simply contractions of isolated muscles, but always involve groups of muscles contracting harmoniously, so that an orderly movement results. The upper motor neurones therefore are organized in terms of movements, in contrast to the lower motor neurones, which are distributed to groups of muscle-fibres in individual muscles.' (Brain, W.R. *Diseases of the Nervous System,* Oxford University Press, London, 1951)

training, habit The acquisition (by the young child) of specific behavior patterns mainly related to the functions of eating, elimination, sleep, and dress. To the behaviorist, training is in the nature of conditioning. To the psychoanalyst, habit and habit training have a different meaning: 'A particular habit is for the child a defence against a particular unconscious fantasy or wish. His clinging to habit may be one of his main defences against the anxiety connected with aggressive impulses and fantasies in general.' (Isaacs, S. 'Habit,' Chapter V of *On the Bringing Up of Children,* ed. by J. Rickman, Kegan Paul, Trench, Trubner, London, 1936)

training, spontaneity 'Just as the spontaneity test is an intensification of the sociometric test, so the spontaneity training process is an intensification of the assignment technique. New situations and new roles demand from some individuals spontaneous elements which are lacking. It is through graduated training of the personality in constructed situations and roles that such individuals learn how to act on the spur of the moment and how to integrate these roles into their personality without loss of spontaneity.' (Moreno, J.L. and Jennings, H. *Sociometric Review,* 1936, 17)

trait In genetics, this means the characteristic symptomatology of a certain hereditary factor as it appears in the phenotypes of individuals who have inherited the predisposition to the given attribute.

trait-carrier In genetic family studies this means a tainted family member actually exhibiting the hereditary character under observation. These *trait-carriers* are distinguished from the *taint-carriers*.

traits, feminine, in male According to Adler, the following are feminine traits which the male neurotic perceives in himself either consciously or unconsciously: passive attitude, obedience, softness, cowardice, memory of defeat, ignorance, lack of capacity, and tenderness. The individual attempts to overcome these characteristics by developing hatred, defiance, cruelty, and egoism.

traits, neurotic (nū-rot′ik) See *behavior disorders*.

trance 1. hypnotism; 2. catalepsy; 3. ecstasy.

trance-coma The deep sleep following deep hypnotism.

trance, ecstatic See *ecstasy.*

tranquilizer Ataractic; the term tranquilizer or tranquilizing drug is currently used to refer to a group of phrenotropic compounds whose effects are exerted primarily at a subcortical level so that consciousness is not interfered with, in contrast to hypnotic and sedative drugs, which also have a calming effect. Four classes of tranquilizing drugs are generally recognized: (1) phenothiazine derivatives (chlorpromazine, promazine, proclorperazine, perphenazine, etc.), (2) Rauwolfia derivatives (reserpine, rescinnamine, deserpidine), (3) substituted propanediols (meprobamate, phenaglycodol, etc.), and (4) diphenylmethane derivatives (azacyclonol, benactyzine, etc.). Classes (1) and (2) are sometimes called *major tranquilizers* or *neuroleptica;* their principal effect is on psychomotor activity, especially when this is increased. Classes (3) and (4) are sometimes called *minor tranquilizers* or *psycholeptica* (q.v.); their principal effect is on the psyche to reduce anxiety.

Tranquilizer was used also by Dr. Benjamin Rush to refer to an invention of his designed to reduce blood flow to the head of the mental patient. It consisted of a chair to which the patient was strapped hand and foot so that he could not move.

transfer In connection with institutional statistics, a transfer is a shift from one institution directly to another institution of the same class.

Example: During the year ended June 30, 1939, 14,704 patients were removed from the books of the New York civil State hospitals. Of this total, 1,203 were transferred to other hospitals for the treatment of mental disorders in New York State.

transference In psychoanalytic therapy, the phenomenon of projection of feelings, thoughts, and wishes onto the analyst, who has come to represent an object from the patient's past. The analyst is reacted to as though he were someone from the patient's past; such reactions, while they may have been appropriate to the conditions that prevailed in the patient's previous life, are inappropriate and anachronistic when applied to an object (the analyst) in the present.

'During psychoanalytic treatment, the repressed unconscious material is revived, and since this material contains many infantile elements, the infantile strivings are reactivated and seek gratification in the transference. As the most important relationship of the child is that with his parents, the relationship between patient and analyst established in the transference becomes analogous to, or, at times, even similar to the patient's relationship with his parents in childhood. The patient endows the analyst with the same magic powers and omniscience which, in childhood, he attributed to his parents. The traits of submissiveness and rebellion, in transference, likewise reflect the attitude of the child to his parents. The patient behaves irrationally in the psychoanalytic situation; it often takes a long time to make him see the irrationality of his behavior, which is deeply rooted in his unconscious infantile life.' (Nunberg, H. *Principles of Psychoanalysis,* International Universities Press, New York, 1955)

Transference may be positive, as when the patient unrealistically overvalues or loves the analyst; or it may be negative, as when the patient dislikes or hates the analyst without due cause in reality.

It is to be noted that the term transference does not refer to reactions of the patient to the analyst that are based on reality factors in the therapeutic relationship; thus a patient may be angry with his therapist if the latter misses an appointment, but to call such a reaction a manifestation of transference is incorrect. It should also be recognized that transference can exist outside the analytic situation in relation to other people in the individual's environment.

E. Krapf (*Psychoanalytic Quarterly 26:* 519–26, 1957) considers positive transference to be predominantly libidinal, negative transference as predominantly aggressive. He notes that there is a third type of transference, the transference of anxiety which always serves as a defense, while libidinal and aggressive transference are defensive in many instances but not in all. 'Thus we may list five types of transference: 1, libidinal; 2, aggressive; 3, libidinal-defensive; 4, aggressive-defensive; and 5, anxious-defensive.'

Jung stresses the question of transference, which he calls psychological rapport. He calls it 'the intensified tie to the physician which is a compensation symptom for the defective relationship to present reality.' He holds that 'the phenomenon of transference is inevitable in every fundamental analysis. . . . The patient must find a relationship to an object in the living present, for without it he can never adequately fulfill the demands that adaptation makes upon him.' (Jung, C.G. *Contributions to Analytical Psychology*, tr. by Baynes, H.G. and C.F., Kegan Paul, Trench, Trubner, London, 1928)

transference, identification A term employed by S.R. Slavson to establish a differentiation from *libidinal* transference and *sibling* transference which occur in analytic group psychotherapy. It refers to the attitude and relations derived from identifying with other members of a therapy group of the desire to emulate or be like them. See *transference, libidinal; transference, sibling.*

transference, libidinal (li-bid'i-nal) The transference derived from and charged with libidinal and other drives that the patient had felt toward his parents and now is re-directing upon the therapist. See *transference, identification; transference, sibling.*

transference-love Love expressed by a patient for a psychoanalyst as a manifestation of the transference situation. 'Among the situations to which the transference gives rise, one is very sharply outlined, and I will select this, partly because it occurs so often and is so important in reality and partly because of its theoretical interest. The case I mean is that in which a woman or girl patient shows by unmistakable allusions or openly avows that she has fallen in love, like any other mortal woman, with the physician who is analyzing her.' (Freud, S. *Collected Papers*, vol. 2, tr. by Riviere, J., Leonard and Virginia Woolf and The Institute of Psychoanalysis, London, 1924–25)

transference, negative See *transference-resistance.*

transference-neurosis See *neurosis, transference.*

transference, positive See *transference.*

transference-resistance Transference may be positive (libidinal). It is so when the patient harmoniously transfers repressed material upon the physician. The material, however, may be rejected by the ego or

superego, that is, there is resistance offered to the appearance of the material in consciousness, as a consequence of which it may be held in the unconscious; the patient gives an indirect clue by remaining silent on the topic in question. Or the material may be projected upon the physician, then appearing as something undesirable allegedly possessed by the physician. The repressed material may return to consciousness in one of the many known forms, but it is only when it constitutes a conflict between the patient and the physician that it is known as transference-resistance. The resistance gives rise to negative transference, an animosity or opposition to the physician.

transference, sibling This term denotes attitudes and feelings similar to those a patient has heretofore entertained toward the siblings of the family and now has toward other members of the group.

transformation See *affect, transformation of in dreams.*

transformation, affective Storch writes: 'There is a psychological law of "affective transformation," which says that emotionally toned and affectively emphasized values constantly strive to increase their dimensions. . . . This inclination to transformation on the part of the affects seems to play a very important role in primitive man. In drawings by children and primitives, the parts which are affectively toned are much enlarged.' (Storch, A. *The Primitive Archaic Forms in Schizophrenia*, tr. by Willard, C., Nervous and Mental Disease Publishing Company, New York and Washington, 1924) Affective transformation may be observed in all forms of psychiatric conditions; it is particularly noticeable in schizophrenia.

transformation of affect See *affect, transformation of.*

transfusion, exchange Total replacement of blood by transfusion. See *icterus gravis neonatorum.*

transient situational personality disorders This term in the 1952 revision of psychiatric nomenclature refers to reactions of acute symptom-formation to an overwhelming situation. Recession of symptoms occurs when the stress stimulus diminishes or disappears; persistence of symptoms indicates a more severe underlying disturbance. This group includes: (1) transient situational personality disturbance; (2) gross stress reaction; (3) adult situational reaction; (4) adjustment reaction of infancy; (5) adjustment reaction of childhood, including habit disturbance, conduct disturbance and neurotic traits; (6) adjustment reaction of adolescence; and (7) adjustment reaction of late life.

transitivism (tran'si-ti-viz'm) One of the accessory or secondary changes in the person of the schizophrenic, consisting of detachment of a part of the personality from the patient with subsequent displacement of this part onto another person. In such cases, whatever the patient hallucinates or does is believed to be an experience of that other person.

transitivity (trans-si-tiv'i-tē) Transitivity, meaning the character of passing over into something, is a term applied principally to patients with schizophrenia. 'Transitivistic manifestations are nowhere so frequent as in schizophrenia. Very commonly, patients are convinced that those about them also hear their voices, sometimes even that they undergo the physical persecutions with them. A patient has holes in her hands and maintains that the nurse also has holes in her hands.' (Bleuler, E. *Textbook of Psychiatry,* tr. by Brill, A.A. Macmillan, New York, 1930)

transmissible That which can be transmitted; formerly used synonymously with *inheritable.*

transmission Practically synonymous with *inheritance* (q.v.).

transposition of affect See *affect, transposition of.*

trans-sexualism Overwhelming desire for conversion of sex; seen in some transvestites and in some schizophrenics.

transvaluation Freud uses Nietzsche's phrase 'transvaluation of all values' to refer to the displacement and evaluation of affect. For example, while discussing dreams, Freud calls attention to the frequent lack of harmony between the affect and the ideas associated with it. It is often found that an idea may occupy a foremost position, yet it is relatively without affect; likewise, an intense affect may be cathected with an idea that seems to be the least important part of a dream.

Transvaluation is a very common phenomenon of the psyche. It is evident in normal and abnormal states. It stands out vividly in schizophrenia.

It often happens that, in dreams, for instance, the value placed upon certain elements is out of all proportion to the real value of the element. As Freud says, the intensity of the elements in the dream may have nothing to do with that of the dream-material. 'The very element of the dream which is transient and hazy, and screened by more vigorous images, is often discovered to be the one and only direct derivative of the topic that completely dominates the dream-thoughts.' (Freud, S. *The Interpretation of Dreams,* 3rd ed, tr. by Brill, A.A., Macmillan, New York, 1933)

transvestitism (trans-ves'ti-tiz'm) The morbid impulse to dress in the clothing of members of the opposite sex. A male patient, strongly homosexual, was completely dressed in delicate effeminate clothing underneath his masculine outer garments. The impulse is widespread.

'Among the transvestites (personifiers) we find the most pronounced examples of masked homosexuality and stressed bisexuality.' (Stekel, W. *Bi-Sexual Love,* tr. by van Teslaar, J.S., Badger, Boston, 1922)

trauma (traw'mȧ) The term *trauma* means the same in psychiatry as it means in general medicine, namely, an injury, something hurtful. In psychoanalysis, any stimulation of such intensity that it cannot be mastered or adequately discharged is traumatic.

'Freud with Breuer, published his viewpoint in 1895. Briefly, hysteria, for instance, is due to psychic trauma. Painful ideas, usually with sexual content and which for the particular individual are unacceptable to the conscious mind are not given an emotional outlet, but are relegated or forced or repressed into the subconscious mind and become buried complexes.' (Strecker, E.A. and Ebaugh, F.G. *Practical Clinical Psychiatry,* 4th ed., Blakiston, Philadelphia, 1935)

'Trauma may produce mental symptoms in one of two ways. Either it causes structural injury to the brain, or it causes emotional disturbances which in one form or another are prolonged for some time. . . . In the second [instance] the result is usually a psychoneurosis.' (Henderson, D.K. and Gillespie, R.D. *A*

Text-Book of Psychiatry, 4th ed., Oxford University Press, London, 1936)

trauma, birth The trauma of birth is a topic extensively considered in psychiatry, particularly by psychoanalysts. The concept is described comprehensively by Otto Rank, who maintains that the circumstances of birth are deeply imprinted upon the psyche of the infant and often reappear in symbolic form in psychiatric patients.

It is said that intra-uterine existence is blissful, that it is free from all conflicts of a psychical nature. The act of being born is believed to mark a radical upheaval from both the psychical and physical points of view; it produces a psychic shock of great consequence, a trauma with which the individual is never reconciled. Rank holds that certain individuals are always attempting to reconstruct the conditions of intra-uterine existence. In its most vivid and literal form intra-uterine life is reproduced by the patient showing the catatonic form of schizophrenia.

Freud says: 'The act of birth, moreover, is the first experience attended by anxiety, and is thus the source and model of the affect of anxiety.' (Freud, S. *The Basic Writings of Sigmund Freud,* tr. by Brill, A.A., Random House, New York, 1938) He believes that Rank overestimates the importance of birth upon the psyche of the infant. Freud says that 'we certainly may not presuppose that the fetus has any kind of knowledge that it is in danger of annihilation'; the fetus can only sense 'a wholesale disturbance in the economy of its narcistic libido.'

As an example of the symbolic representation of the birth act Rank refers to the phobia concerning animals entering and leaving holes.

Ferenczi states: 'The more I observe, the more I realize that none of the developments and changes which life brings finds the individual so well prepared as for birth.' (*Further Contributions to the Theory and Technique of Psycho-Analysis,* tr. by Suttie, J., Leonard and Virginia Woolf and The Institute of Psychoanalysis, London, 1926). He believes that birth is an agreeable and triumphant transition for the infant. What Rank calls birth phantasies Ferenczi says are coital phantasies.

Referring to the analysis of a dream,

Jones says: 'Emergence, after great difficulty, from a dark chamber containing water, is a very usual way for unconscious thoughts about the birth act to be expressed. . . . In mythology the situation is often reversed by the hero being placed in an enclosing chamber and put *into,* or *onto,* water, such as with Moses in the bulrushes, Noah in the Ark, and so on. . . .' (Jones, E. *Papers on Psycho-Analysis,* 4th ed., Wood, Baltimore, 1938)

trauma, infantile The occurrence in infancy or childhood of a situation in which the psyche is bombarded by stimulation of such intensity that it can not be mastered or discharged. In such situations, anxiety develops automatically.

trauma, primal The original, supremely important, and most painful situation to which the individual has been exposed early in life. Such a basic situation is necessarily of paramount importance and very often constitutes the nucleus of the neurosis.

trauma, puberty This term applies to the painful, disagreeable, or unacceptable experiences that occur during the individual's period of puberty. According to Stekel, such traumatic experiences during puberty are as important for the development of neurosis as the traumas suffered in childhood (see *trauma, infantile*), especially among girls, whose unpleasant sexual experiences can have fateful effects in their later lives. (Stekel, W. *The Interpretation of Dreams,* Liveright, New York, 1943) See *defloration; trauma, primal.*

traumasthenia (traw-mas-thē′ni-à) Nervous exhaustion following an injury; railway-spine; traumatic neurasthenia.

traumata, life (traw′mà-tà) This is an expression used by Bleuler to denote the injurious character (from the patient's standpoint) of 'life experiences.' Certain individuals, notably those with a schizoid personality, withdraw more or less completely from the environment. Life-experiences may become life-traumata hurtful to the patient.

traumatic defect state (traw-ma′tik) See *psychosis, traumatic.*

traumatic neurosis See *neurosis, traumatic.*

traumatization (traw-ma-ti-zā′shun) See *libido, traumatization of the.*

traumatophilia (traw-ma-tō-fil′i-à) The

term literally means the love of injury or to be injured. The unconscious impulse, reenforced by some measure of conscious participation, to sustain injury is not at all uncommon among psychiatric patients.

Speaking of *Two Types of War Neuroses,* Ferenczi says: 'It is probable that consciousness generally shuts itself off automatically at first from such too-powerful stimuli. We may take it for granted that after a trauma a certain discrepancy exists between consciousness that has been relatively protected from the shock and the rest of the neuro-psychic apparatus. An equalization is here only possible when consciousness, too, becomes aware of the source of pain; this is then achieved by a certain "traumatophilic" attitude—the hyperaesthesia of the senses which in small doses gradually allows just so much anxious expectation and shock to reach consciousness as was spared to it at the time of the shock.' (Ferenczi, S. *Further Contributions to the Theory and Technique of Psycho-Analysis,* tr. by Suttie, J.I., Leonard and Virginia Woolf and The Institute of Psychoanalysis, London, 1926)

traumatophobia Fear of injury.

treatment Any measure designed to ameliorate or cure an abnormal or undesirable condition.

For specific treatments, see also listings under *therapy.*

treatment, ambulatory A patient is called ambulatory when out of bed and free to walk about. Ambulatory treatment comprises such measures as may be carried out while the patient is up and about.

treatment, ambulatory insulin 'A modification of the insulin coma treatment has been devised by Polatin and Spotnitz, for the purpose of relieving severe anxiety and tension states as well as the physical effects which may result from mental symptoms, such as loss of appetite and marked weight loss. These symptoms may occur in schizophrenia, in a patient whose head has suffered a severe blow, with resulting unconsciousness (postconcussional states), and in cases of hysterical vomiting or nervous dyspepsia as well as other psychoneuroses. The treatment is called "ambulatory," because the patients may walk about during the treatment period. They are not in a coma, as during the insulin shock treatment.

'In ambulatory insulin treatment the object is to induce, not coma, but hypoglycemia, which manifests itself by weakness, excessive perspiration and some drowsiness. The treatment consists of injecting intramuscularly relatively small doses of insulin, until the desired effect of hypoglycemia is reached. . . . Three hours after the injection of insulin, the hypoglycemia is, in all cases, terminated by a full meal rich in sugar and starches, which the patient can eat unassisted, since he is fully conscious. This treatment is given once daily, six days a week, usually for a course of one hundred treatments.' (Polatin, P., and Philtine, E. *How Psychiatry Helps,* Harper, New York, 1949) Also called *sub-shock* or *sub-coma insulin treatment.*

treatment, continuous sleep A symptomatic method of treatment in which the patient is sedated with any of a variety of drugs; the aim of treatment is to provide 20 hours of sleep per day, for periods up to 3 weeks in more agitated patients. Klaesi, in 1922, introduced continuous sleep treatment with barbiturates. The method has been superseded in large part by insulin coma, ambulatory insulin, electroconvulsive therapy, and treatment with the tranquilizing drugs; its chief uses at the present time are in manic excitements, agitated depressions, and acute anxiety neuroses.

treatment, insulin A form of treatment introduced into psychiatry by Sakel and used in certain psychiatric conditions. It consists in the production of coma, with or without convulsions, through the intramuscular administration of insulin.

treatment, malarial A form of treatment introduced by Wagner-Jauregg for syphilis of the central nervous system, especially general paralysis; blood containing tertian or quartan malaria parasites is injected into the patient, as a result of which he develops malarial fever.

treatment, Metrazol A form of treatment, introduced by von Meduna in 1934 in certain psychiatric conditions. It consists in the production of coma with or without convulsions, through the intravenous administration of Metrazol (cardiazol).

treatment, milieu (mēl-yü′) Treatment effected through the medium of the patient's surroundings and immediate environment, and specifically through the medium of the psychiatric hospital. See *community, therapeutic.*

treatment, prolonged sleep A treatment of certain types of mental patients by means of prolonged sleep, induced as a rule by chemicals such as somnifen or cloetta mixture. See *treatment, continuous sleep.*

treatment, psychiatric social 'Social treatment in psychiatric social work, as in other forms of social work, means the supervision of the patient in the community in such a way as to bring about a better social adjustment for him. In some cases all that is possible may be the modification of the environment so that a fairly satisfactory social adaptation may be made for him in spite of his mental handicap. Wherever the outlook for improvement is at all favorable, however, the aim of both the social and psychiatric treatment is to bring about a change in the attitude of the patient himself, to replace undesirable mental habits by wholesome ones, to modify his conduct by a training of his emotions, and to give him insight into his difficulties, so that he may eventually overcome his disabilities and be able to make a satisfactory adjustment in any environment.' ('Vocational Aspects of Psychiatric Social Work,' *Mental Hygiene,* 1925) See *personal approach.*

treatment, psycho-prophylactic (sĭ-kō-prō-fi-lak'tik, -prof-i-) Mental hygiene.

treatment, shock A form of treating certain psychotic conditions by inducing coma (with or without convulsions) usually by chemical means, such as Metrazol, insulin, camphor, etc.

treatment, sub-coma insulin See *treatment, ambulatory insulin.*

treble safeguard, principle of See *principle, treble safeguard.*

tremophobia (trē-mō-fō'bi-à) Fear of trembling.

tremor Shaking or trembling. A disorder of muscular tone in which the usual, normal unappreciable tonic contractions of a muscle become exaggerated to the point of awareness.

trend A term used by psychiatrists somewhat synonymously with the term 'psychological syndrome' in contrast to the expression 'organic syndrome.' It generally refers more definitely to the ideational content of the syndrome. A patient is said to have a homosexual trend, not in virtue of his actions or feelings, but in virtue of a constellation of ideas relating to homosexuality.

trend, benign Psychiatrists' term for a psychological syndrome (trend) from which the patient will recover. Expressions of homosexuality in a manic-depressive patient are said to constitute a benign trend. Delusional homosexuality in schizophrenia is a malignant trend.

trend, death See *suicide.*

trend, malignant When a mental syndrome is believed to contain components that ordinarily portend chronicity, it is said to have a malignant trend. It is further implied that deeply regressive elements are present. The syndrome showing the projection mechanism, including pronounced delusions and hallucinations, is believed to have a malignant trend.

trend, pernicious Synonymous with *trend, malignant* (q.v.).

trends, katagogic (kà-tà-goj'ik) See *ego, satanic.*

trend, statistical Uniform change in one direction as shown by statistics.

Over a long period of time natural and social phenomena tend to increase or decrease in a regular manner.

triad, anal A psychoanalytic term referring to the group of three prime or outstanding traits of the so-called anal character: (1) obstinacy; (2) parsimony; (3) pedantic orderliness. Clinical psychoanalytic observations justified the validity of the connection that had been surmised between early strong anal interests and activities in childhood and the later appearance of the three character traits above, which were grouped together and labeled by Freud as 'the anal triad.' In our everyday language the connection between miserliness and the retention of stool, both having in common the tendency to hold on to something, or holding something back, is often clearly manifested. The folk saying, 'he's so tight he couldn't pass a raspberry seed,' is an example of this symbolic and metaphorical ambiguous language. (Sterba, R. *Introduction to the Psycho-analytic Theory of the Libido,* Nervous and Mental Disease Monographs No. 68, New York, 1942) For further examples see *phase, anal second.*

triad, Charcot (Jean Martin Charcot, French neurologist, 1825–93) See *sclerosis, multiple.*

triad, oral As defined by Lewin, this refers to the desires of the infant in the early oral phase—the wish to devour, the wish to be devoured, and the wish to go to sleep.

tribade (trib'ad) A woman with an abnormally large clitoris, who plays the part of a male in homosexual practices. See *lesbianism; sapphism.*

tribute, virginal See *jus primae noctis.*

trichinophobia (trik-i-nō-fō'bi-à) Fear of trichinosis.

trichologia (tri-kō-lō'ji-à) Carphology.

trichopathophobia (-path-ō-fō'bi-à) Fear of hair.

trichophagy (tri-kof'à-jē) The tic of biting the hair.

trichophobia (tri-kō-fō'bi-à) Trichopathophobia.

trichotillomania (-til-ō-mā'ni-à) Morbid tendency to pull the hair.

trifacial neuralgia (trī-fā'shal nū-ral'ji-à) See *tic douloureux.*

trigeminal neuralgia (trī-gem'in-al) See *tic douloureux.*

trihybrid (trī-hī'brid) Hybrid that differs in three hereditary characters. See *hybrid.*

triolist (trī'ol-ist) In triangular sex-relations this term (Magnus Hirschfeld's) means one whose heterosexual partner is homosexual and, in addition, has a lover of the same sex. The origin of the term becomes more obvious when one bears in mind that commonly the conniving person's voyeur impulses are gratified by peeping at or watching the partner's intercourse with the third member of the sexual trinity.

triplet One of three children born at the same birth. See *birth, multiple.*

trisexuality (trī-sek-shoo-al'i-tē) The symbolic representation, especially in dreams, of the three currents or aspects—man, woman, and child—in which sexuality may be studied in a psychoanalytical sense. In other words, trisexuality may be considered as a kind of tripartition of the mind by which the individual may have at the same time the impulses of the three trends of sexuality. The patient will have simultaneously the desire to be a man, a woman, and a child, playing, at least symbolically, the three roles. (Stekel, W. *The Interpretation of Dreams,* Liveright, New York, 1943)

triskaidekaphobia (tris-kī'de-kà-fō'bi-à) Morbid fear of (the number) thirteen. Thirteen at table is viewed by many as an ill omen, and one more person is usually invited to join in the meal. The thirteenth day of the month is looked upon with dismay by those swayed by the superstition and, if it falls on a Friday, with double dismay—for Friday, long referred to as 'hangman's day,' was the usual day for hanging a criminal in the England of old. To prevent the possible loss of such fearsome clients (who would not live in a house No. 13) many office buildings in New York, and particularly hotels, have no thirteenth floor or rooms No. 13, or multifigured numbers ending with 13. Apparently the 'baker's dozen' (adding one roll for good measure, to avoid the severe penalties for short-counting) is an exception to this common fear of thirteen.

tristemania (trēst-ē-mā'ni-à) *Obs.* Melancholia.

tristitia (trē-stē'tē-à) *Obs.* Melancholy.

tromomania (trom-ō-mā'ni-à) Delirium tremens.

trophodermatoneurosis (trof-ō-der-mà-tō-nū-rō'sis) *Acrodynia* (q.v.).

trophoneurosis (trof-ō-nū-rō'sis) A nutritive disturbance, organically determined. It is believed that each organ of the body is supplied with nerves whose functions are definitely identified with nutrition or trophism. When such nerves are disordered, nutrition of the organ suffers.

-trophy (-tro-fē) Combining for meaning nourishment, feeding, from Gr. *trophê,* nourishment, food, from *tréphein,* to breed, rear, maintain, feed.

-tropy (-trō-pē) Combining form meaning turning, from Gr. *tropê,* turn(ing), *trépein,* to turn.

truth-serum See *narcotherapy.*

TTR Type Token ratio. See *ratio, Type Token.*

tubectomy (tū-bek'tō-mē) See *salpingectomy.*

tube, neural See *cephalogenesis.*

tuberculomania (tū-bēr-kū-lō-mā'ni-à) An

unfounded but unalterable conviction that one is suffering from tuberculosis; phthisiomania.

tuberculophobia Fear of tuberculosis or of associating in any way with a sufferer from that disease; phthisiophobia.

Tuke, Daniel Hack (1827–1895) British psychiatrist, editor of *Dictionary of Psychological Medicine.*

tumescence (tū-mes'ens) Swelling state. From the sexual point of view this refers to the swelling of genital tissues associated with sexual excitement.

'The justification for using the term "tumescence," which I here propose, is to be found in the fact that vascular congestion, more especially of the parts related to generation, is an essential preliminary to acute sexual desire.' (Ellis, H. *Studies in the Psychology of Sex,* vol. 3, Davis, Philadelphia, 1903)

tumor, brain See *tumor, intracranial.*

tumor, intracranial Any localized intracranial lesion, whether of neoplastic or of chronic inflammatory origin, which by occupying space within the skull tends to cause a rise in intracranial pressure. According to W.R. Brain (*Diseases of the Nervous System,* 4th ed., Oxford University Press, London, 1951): 'Over 1 per cent. of all deaths are due to intracranial tumours which form about 17 per cent. of all malignant neoplasms in man.' Symptoms of intracranial tumors are of two types: general symptoms, due to increased intracranial pressure, and focal symptoms, due to the local effects of the growth. The general symptoms of increased intracranial pressure include the classical triad of headache, papilledema, and vomiting. Other general symptoms are: epileptiform convulsions, aphasia, vertigo, disturbances of pulse-rate and blood pressure, and mental symptoms such as coma, confusion, disorientation, and progressive dementia.

tumultus sermonis (too-mool'toos ser-mō'nēs) (L. 'confusion, disorder of speech') Tumultuous speech.

turbid Muddled, mentally confused.

'Naturally we often observe very mild twilight states and deliria, in which the thought process is only more or less unclear. These mild forms together with deliria and twilight states may provisionally be called *turbid states.*' (Bleuler, E. *Text-*

book of Psychiatry, tr. by Brill, A.A., Macmillan, New York, 1930)

Turkish-bath method See *method, Turkish-bath.*

turrecephaly (tur-re-sef'à-lē) *Oxycephaly* (q.v.).

twilight-state Absence, a transitory disturbance of consciousness during which many acts, sometimes very complicated, may be performed without the individual's conscious volition and without retaining any remembrance of them.

Responsive as a rule only to some given complex, the individual acts in accordance with the demands of the complex, the rest of the personality being subordinated to or, as a rule, more or less completely submerged during the period of the twilight-state. For example, an epileptic patient, entirely unmindful of his natural surroundings, believed that he was walking around in Heaven; during the phase he was utterly unable to recall any part of his real life.

'During this period, if they [i.e. such patients] can be observed, they usually strike one as being abnormal; at times, however, they can use correctly ordinary means of intercourse, can associate with fellow travelers, and can even visit relatives, without betraying their condition.' (Bleuler, E. *Textbook of Psychiatry,* tr. by Brill, A.A., Macmillan, New York, 1930) See *fugue.*

twilight-state, alcoholic A type of pathological drunkenness, characterized by 'sudden excitations or twilight states set free by alcohol, usually with a mistaking of the situation, often also with illusions and hallucinations, and excessive affects, mostly of anxiety and rage. In individual cases the entire morbid process can transpire in hardly a minute, but it usually lasts longer, up to several hours.' (Bleuler, E. *Textbook of Psychiatry,* tr. by Brill, A.A., Macmillan, New York, 1930)

twilight-state, clear See *equivalent, epileptic.*

twilight-state, post-epileptic Sometimes after an epileptic attack, a so-called twilight state exists for a variable period of time. During the twilight state the patient may carry out acts for which he is later amnesic.

twin One of two individuals born from a

female that ordinarly brings forth only one offspring at a time.

In human beings there are two distinct types of twins, the *monozygotic* or *identical* twins, developed from a single egg, and the *dizygotic* or *fraternal* twins, developed from two eggs. Dizygotic twins are held to be as separate in their origin and biological development as are siblings in general. Monozygotic twins are like the right and the left halves of *one* individual; accordingly, they not only have the same genotypical structure, but also exhibit frequently the phenomenon of *reversed asymmetry* (mirror-imaging) in handedness, hair whorl, dentition, palm patterns, and other asymmetrical characters, i.e. characters which are asymmetrical in one person. The presence of mirror-imaging is confirmatory evidence of monozygosity, but its absence does not refute it.

Of the two methods used for diagnosing twins with respect to their zygotic origin, the *similarity* method is now generally preferred to the *fetal-membrane* method, since it has been discovered that one-egg twins not infrequently have separate chorions and even separate placentae.

Twin studies are of great scientific significance in human genetics, because they throw light upon many fundamental aspects of the *nature-nurture* problem as well as of the *developmental* mechanism of the human organism throughout its life from the fertilization of the ovum to death. For these purposes a twin survey is usually based upon the particular technique of comparing the likenesses or differences between identical twins with the likenesses and differences between fraternal twins.

twinned Born as a twin.

twinning The attribute of producing or state of being twins.

twins, Siamese (Chinese twins (Eng and Chang, born in Siam, 1811, died in North Carolina, 1874) whose bodies were joined by a band extending from umbilicus to the xiphoid cartilage)

Among various kinds of freak-twins, the variety of *Siamese twins* is characterized by an incomplete separation of the halves of the originally single embryo, from which the given set of monozygotic twins is developed. The division may be almost complete, so that the remaining link between the twins can be severed by opera-

tion, or it may be so incomplete as to result in twins with one body and two heads, or with one body and four legs and arms. See *birth, multiple.*

twin-study See *method, twin-study.*

type See *type, constitutional.*

type, adenoid (ad'ē-noid) In constitutional medicine, a type in which the hypertrophy of the pharyngeal tonsil is believed to be a sign of a serious general constitutional anomaly. The more marked cases of this type are said to be frequently associated with such degenerative states as oxycephaly, deaf-mutism, cretinism, status thymicus, facial asymmetry and so forth. (Pende, N. *Constitutional Inadequacies,* tr. by Naccarati, S., Lea & Febiger, Philadelphia, 1928)

type, apoplectic (a-pō-plek'tik) See *habitus apoplecticus.*

type, asthenic (as-then'ik) Within the system of constitutional types described by Kretschmer, this term designates the type characterized by the general impression of a deficiency in volume combined with an average unlessened length, so that the individual appears taller than he really is (see *type, constitutional*).

The head of the asthenic rises like a bud upon a lean, long neck. In profile, the curve of the head is interrupted by sharp irregularities. The nose is a prominent feature and juts out from the long face, thus throwing back the forehead and chin. The line connecting the upper forehead, tip of nose, and chin tends to be angular on account of this disproportion between the long, sharp nose and the small mandible. In frontal outline the face is of short egg form. The middle face is long in proportion to the rest and the upper lip is short. The primary hair is strongly developed and has a tendency to grow down the neck and into the face, producing a fur cap appearance. When baldness occurs, it has an irregular outline.

The *chest* of the asthenic is long, narrow, and flat. The upper ribs fall inward and the xiphoid angle is acute. The prominence given to the clavicle is accentuated by the stooping attitude characteristic of the asthenic. The cavity of the abdomen is poorly developed, while the limbs appear long and thin, with lean muscles. The hips in the male are usually wider than the chest measurement, accentuating the waist. The skin tends to be pale, dry, cold, with scant subjacent fat.

As a *psychological* type, the asthenics are thought to be basically *schizothymic* (q.v.), thus constituting the bulk of the schizothymic group, although the athletic and dysplastic types also contribute to it. According to Kretschmer's theories, the asthenics may fall into any one of the three divisions accepted by him: namely, the *healthy* schizothymes (polite, sensitive types, world-hostile idealists, cold-hearted egoists); the *schizoids* (the predominantly hyperesthetic temperaments including the cold, aristocratic types and pathetic idealists as well as the predominantly insensitive temperaments including despotic or passionate types and unsteady loafers); and the *schizophrenics* (q.v.).

When no attention is paid to particular modifications, it is appropriate to say that the *asthenic type* thus described corresponds fairly closely to the following types in other systems: the *habitus phthisicus* of Hippocrates, the *sensory, pneumatic, chlorotic, phthisic* and *lymphatic* constitutions of Carus, the *hypoplastic* type with a disposition to tuberculosis of Rokitansky-Benecke, the *first combination* of De Giovanni, the *macroskelic* type of Manouvrier, the *microsplanchnic* type of Viola, the *hypovegetative (dolichomorphic)* biotype of Pende, part of the *hypotonic* group of Tandler, the *asthenic habitus* of Bauer and Mills, the *narrow-chested* type of Brugsch, the *slender* biotype of Davenport and Aschner, the *linear* type of Stockard, the *T type* of Jaensch, the *regressive* type of Lewis, the *ectomorphic* type of Sheldon, the *sthenoplastic* type of Bounak, and the *hyperontomorphic* type of Beau.

type, athletic Robust, strong, vigorous. Whether this term is used as a more general expression of constitutional medicine or in particular reference to the system of constitutional types as described by Kretschmer, it means as in everyday usage, possessing a well-developed muscular system with resultant physical activity and prowess. Kretschmer's *atheltic type* is characterized by a strong development of the locomotor apparatus, so that the bones and muscles stand out in plastic relief. The head shares in the overdevelopment of the skeleton, as is usually demonstrated by prognathous jaws and a marked occipital protuberance. A line

connecting the upper forehead, tip of nose and chin forms a gentle curve. The frontal facial outline is steep egg-shaped. The head hair is abundant and tends to grow in a peak in the center of the forehead, receding in a bay-like manner on either side toward the temples.

The neck is strong and the shoulders are large. The trunk tapers down from the broad shoulder girdle, so that the trunk outline from the front appears inverted trapezoid. The limbs are relatively long, the hands and feet are large and the fingers are often blunt, thick and acromegaloid in character. The skin is thick, of good turgor, moderately tinted, and medium as to sweat secretion.

As a psychological type, the athletics, too, are assumed by Kretschmer to be basically *schizothymic,* like the asthenics and the majority of the dysplastics. According to his theories, they constitute a considerable proportion of the total group of schizothymes, although a decidedly smaller one than do the asthenics, and they may also fall into any one of his three divisions of the schizothymic group, that is, the healthy schizothymes, the schizoids, and the schizophrenics (see *type, asthenic*).

The athletic type thus described corresponds approximately to the following types in other systems: the *muscular* type of Rostan, the *second (plethoric) combination* of De Giovanni, the *normosplanchnic* type of Viola, the *hypertonic* type of Tandler, the *sthenic* type of Mills, the *medium* biotype of Davenport, the *normal* type of Aschner, the *mesoskelic* type of Manouvrier, the *eumorphic* type of Pende, part of the *hypercompensatory* type of Lewis, and the *mesomorphic* type of Sheldon.

type, attitudinal One or the other of two types of introvert and extravert attitudes toward the world and oneself, in the Jungian system of psychology.

'The introvert turns in upon himself, is absorbed in his inner world, while the extravert turns outward to the world, and is much more concerned with what goes on there than with his own private experiences. Both of these types he [Jung] subdivides into thinking, feeling, intuition, and sensation types. That is, there may be a thinking introvert, a thinking extravert, a feeling introvert or extravert and so on.' (Thompson, C. *Psychoanaly-*

sis: Evolution and Development, Hermitage House, New York, 1950) Introversion and extraversion are *attitudinal types;* thinking, feeling, intuition, and sensation are *functional types.* Jung believes that—probably by constitutional determination—every individual is a combination of one or the other *attitudinal type plus one functional type of the four.* 'Whereas the functional type describes the way in which the empirical material is specifically grasped and formed, the attitudinal type introversion-extraversion characterizes the general psychological orientation, i.e. the direction of that general psychological energy which Jung conceives the libido to be. . . The functional type to which he belongs would be in itself an index to a man's psychological character. It alone, however, would not suffice. In addition, his general psychological attitude, i.e. his way of reacting to what meets him from without or within, must be determined. Jung distinguishes two such attitudes: extraversion and introversion. They represent orientations that essentially condition all psychic processes—the reaction habitus, namely, through which one's way of behaving, of subjectively experiencing, and even of compensating through the unconscious is given.' (Jacobi, J. *The Psychology of C.G. Jung,* Kegan Paul, Trench, Trubner, London, 1942)

type, B See *imagery, eidetic.*

type, belief The expression is not commonly used in psychiatry. Ferenczi holds that there are two fundamental types of personality, from the standpoint of belief. There are those who have a tendency to 'blind beliefs'; they accept statements without any question. He believes the tendency is derived at the time when the child is disillusioned about his own omnipotence and as a consequence he projects omnipotence upon others, originally upon his parents, later upon anyone in authority. There is the second type, constituting 'blind disbelief'; is said also to stem from associations with the parents. It is a phase of disillusionment in the power of the parents or other superior individuals.

type, broad See *type, pyknic.*

type, cerebral In the system of constitutional types described by Rostan and Sigaud, this type is distinguished from the muscular, digestive, and *respiratory* types (qq.v.) by a predominance of the brain and nervous system over the other body systems. See *type, asthenic.*

type, choleric (kol'ĕr-ik) In constitutional medicine, this is one of the four classical temperamental and constitutional types of antiquity. Galen attributed the irritability of this type to the predominance of the yellow bile over the other three humors (or fluids) of the human organism. See *type, pyknic.*

type, constitutional In its original and more restricted connotation, this term refers to the constellations of traits, morphological, physiological, and psychological, that are assumed to be associated with tendencies to certain diseases, physical and mental. However, it is not infrequently used in a wider sense to include types of body and mind, even where no relation to any particular tendency to disease is postulated.

The first typological system was developed by Hippocrates, who described a tendency to apoplexy, the *habitus apoplecticus* (q.v.), in persons of thickset, rounded appearance, and a tendency to pulmonary tuberculosis, the *habitus phthisicus* (q.v.), in persons of slender, angular appearance. This dichotomizing system was extended by Galen to four human types which were related to the four fluids or humors assumed to form the basis of the body. The *sanguine* type was thought to owe his enthusiasm to the 'strength of the blood,' the *melancholic* type was said to be sad because of the overproduction of the 'black bile,' the *choleric* type was irritable owing to the predominance of the 'yellow bile,' and the *phlegmatic* type was apathetic because of the predominance of the 'phlegm.' These four classical humors lived on as the explanation of temperamental and constitutional types for centuries, until Harvey's discovery of the circulation of the blood had the twofold effect of focusing attention on the blood as the important humor, and of emphasizing the role of the blood vessels. It was Haller who demonstrated the loose connection between the blood and the temperaments, and thereby paved the way for the modern typologists to describe their types in terms of anatomical systems instead of humors.

The discovery of the internal secretions and their effect on the morphology of body and mind led in all countries to a new humoral doctrine and, thus, to a classification of types on the basis of altered secretion of one of these glands. The prefixes hyper-, hypo-, and dys- were employed to indicate oversecretion, undersecretion, or qualitatively altered secretion. The main typological systems developed on the basis of these concepts were those of the modern French, Italian, German, and American typologists.

The ordinary system of the *French* school has consisted, from the time of Rostan (1828), of the *digestive, respiratory, cerebral,* and *muscular* types (qq.v.). Other types accepted by Rostan's successors are the *reproductive* and the *atonic* types, corresponding to the old hypergenital and lymphatic types, and also the *round* and the *flat* types, explained by MacAuliffe in terms of colloidal chemistry.

The system of the *Italian* school dates from the work of De Giovanni (about 1890), who formulated the *law of deformation* (q.v.) and described three types of body build: the *first combination* or phthisic type, the *second combination* or plethoric type, and the *third combination.* Other tritypal classifications are based either on the form of the viscera, distinguishing *microsplanchnic, megalosplanchnic,* and *normosplanchnic* types (Viola), or on the total external characteristics, distinguishing *dolichomorphic, brachymorphic,* and *eumorphic* types. Pende modified this system by distinguishing a *hypervegetative* and a *hypovegetative* biotype, in addition to a number of *dysplastic* types.

The typological work of the modern *German* school was initiated by the phrenologist Gall at the end of the 18th century and continued by Beneke (*asthenic* or *hypoplastic* type, *apoplectic* or *hyperplastic* type, *normal* type); Carus (*athletic, phlegmatic, phthisic, cerebral, sterile* constitutions); Bauer (*status degenerativus, arthritic habitus, asthenic type*); and by E.R. and W. Jaensch (*integrated* and *disintegrated* types). In the field of psychiatry, the typological system of Kretschmer has certainly become the most influential one (*pyknic, asthenic, athletic,* and *dysplastic* types on the physical side; *cyclothymic* and *schizothymic* temperaments).

In the modern *American* school, the most systematic and effective work has been done by Draper (*panels of personality*), Davenport (*fleshy, slender,* and *medium* biotypes), Stockard (*lateral* and *linear* types), Lewis (*regressive, hypercompensatory,* and *normally compensating* types), and Sheldon (*ectomorphic, mesomorphic,* and *endomorphic* types).

Well-known *English* typologists are E. Miller, Spearman, and Cohen, and in the modern *Dutch* school Heymans and Wiersma are the outstanding workers.

type, degenerative See *status degenerativus.*

type, delicate See *type, cerebral.*

type, digestive In the system of constitutional types described by Rostan and Sigaud, this term is distinguished from the *muscular, respiratory,* and *cerebral* (qq.v.) types by a predominance of the alimentary system of the body over the others systems. Persons of this type correspond to Kretschmer's *pyknic* (q.v.) type.

type, disintegrated In the system of constitutional types described by E.R. and W. Jaensch, this term refers to individuals with a *distintegrated* psychological state, which is indicated by the *T type* of *eidetic imagery* (q.v.) and is further associated with particular physiological, biochemical, and clinical characteristics.

type, dysplastic (dis-plas′tik) In Kretschmer's system of constitutional types this term refers to a group of cases which, although they may differ considerably among themselves, are equally characterized by a form of physique which varies markedly from the average form of one of the main types called *asthenic, pyknic,* and *athletic* (qq.v.). Most of these dysplastic individuals are said to fall either into the category of elongated *eunuchoidism* with tower skull and, in the female, with masculinism, or into the groups of polyglandular *fat abnormalities* and *infantilism;* while their psychological make-up is held by Kretschmer to be basically *schizothymic* (q.v.).

The anomalies of the dysplastic type seem to be comparable to the *sterile, atrophic constitutions* described by Carus and to Bauer's *status degenerativus* (q.v.).

type, eidetic (ī-det′ik) Constitutional type characterized by a particular kind of *eidetic imagery* (q.v.) and by associated differences in other psychological qualities as well as in certain physiological, biochemical, and clinical features. There are two *eidetic* types, the *integrated* and the *disintegrated* (qq.v.).

type, extraverted When 'the state of extraversion becomes habitual,' Jung speaks of the individual as possessing the extraverted type of personality. When introversion is habitual, the personality is of the introverted type.

'A type is a specimen, or example, which reproduces in a characteristic way the character of a species or general class. In the narrower meaning used in this particular work, a type is a characteristic model of a general attitude (see *type, general attitude*) occurring in many individual forms.

'Thus in both *general attitude* groups (the *extravert* and *introvert*) individuals with regard to *function* (i.e., reaction to a stimulus or event) may be either (1) *rational* (a) thinking, (b) feeling, or (2) *irrational* (c) intuitive, or (d) sensational. (Jung, C.G. *Psychological Types,* tr. by Baynes, H.G. Harcourt, Brace, New York and London, 1923) See *type, functional; extraversion.*

type, feeling The second of the four functional types of personality described by Jung. With his first (*thinking* type) it constitutes the *rational* class of *functional* types.

'When the total attitude of the individual is orientated by the function of feeling, we speak of a *feeling-type.*' (Jung, C.G. *Psychological Types,* tr. by Baynes, H.G., Harcourt, Brace, New York and London, 1923)

type, flaccid See *atonic.*

type, flat MacAuliffe's name for one of his two fundamental constitutional types evolved from considerations of colloidal chemistry. The *flat* type is believed to result from a slight craving of the tissues for water and is characterized by little surface tension, rapid metabolic processes, quick general reactions, economical energy expenditure and, on the psychological side, by an inherent general sobriety. It is distinguished from the *round* (q.v.) type by its marked cellular irritability and should not be confused with the type of a merely thin person.

type, fleshy See *type, pyknic.*

type, function This is a term used by Jung in analytical psychology. He first postulates two *general attitude* types—the introverted and extraverted. 'But, in addition, I shall also try to give a certain

characterization of those special types whose particularity is due to the fact that his most differentiated function plays the principal role in an individual's adaptation or orientation to life. The former I would term *general attitude types,* since they are distinguished by the direction of general interest or libido movement, while the latter I would call *function-types.*' (Jung, C.G. *Psychological Types,* tr. by Baynes, H.G., Harcourt, Brace, New York and London, 1923)

type, functional This is an expression used by Jung (analytical psychology) to designate personality types from the standpoint of function. He postulates four functional classes, viz., thinking, feeling, intuitive, and sensational. 'In so far as such an attitude is *habitual,* thus lending a certain stamp to the character of the individual, I speak of a psychological type. These types, which are based upon the root-functions and which one can term thinking, the feeling, the intuitive, and the sensational types, may be divided into two classes according to the quality of the respective basic function: viz., the *rational* and the *irrational.* The thinking and feeling types belong to the former. The intuitive and sensational to the latter. . . .' (Jung, C.G. *Psychological Types,* tr. by Baynes, H.G., Harcourt, Brace, New York and London, 1923)

But since *functioning* presupposes a static state or general attitude as the basis for the functioning, any one of the four functional types may occur in either of the two *general attitude* groups—the *extravert* or the *introvert;* i.e. there are: A. (1) thinking, (2) feeling, (3) intuitive, (4) sensational *extraverts,* and B. (1) thinking, (2) feeling, (3) intuitive, (4) sensational *introverts,* or *eight* varieties of psychological types in all. See *type, function.*

type, general attitude Jung's expression for the total mental cast or psychic make-up which (statically) determines a person's general attitude independently of or in advance of the external stimulus. This conception aggregates all human beings into two groups of *extraverts* and *introverts* (qq.v.).

With regard to the individual's reacting (dynamically) to a life-stimulus, Jung classifies all mankind into *functional types* (see *type, functional*), also in two classes: (1) *rational* and (2) *irrational.*

type, heavy See *diathesis, arthritic.*

type, hyperaffective (hī-pēr-a-fek'tiv) In the system of constitutional types described by Pende, this term refers to a psychological type characterized by an abundance of emotional reactivity and roughly corresponding to the *cyclothymic* type.

type, hypercompensatory (hī-pēr-kom-pen'sà-tō-rē) In the system of constitutional types described by Lewis, this term denotes the type which on the physical side is characterized by *hyperplasia* of blood and lymph vessels, intestines, and ductless glands, and on the psychological side is inclined to *hypercompensatory* reactions taking the form of manic-depressive psychosis or paranoid reactions.

type, hypergenital (hī-pēr-jen'i-tal) In constitutional medicine, a type distinguished by Pende as a sub-group of the *dolichomorphic* type and, in general, corresponding roughly to the *reproductive* type of Rostan.

The male type is said to be characterized not only by an exaggerated and premature development of primary, secondary, and tertiary sexual characteristics, but also by a dolichomorphic form of trunk with a noticeable excess of thorax over abdomen, relative shortness of the extremities, large skull and heart, marked development of the skeletal muscles, and definite parasympathicotonia, and, on the psychological side, by a calm, stable, and energetic character and a strong development of artistic impulses.

In addition to an exuberant and premature development of the sexual system, especially of the pelvis, the female type is characterized by early menarche, a tendency to leucorrhoea in the intermenstrual periods, exaggerated local sensitiveness of the genital organs and breasts, megalosplanchnic proportions, great fecundity, and a stature which is somewhat below the average. 'When hypergenitalism is secondary or is combined with anomalies of the other endocrine glands, we observe as a rule marked dissociations in the sexual development or a tendency to assume the characteristics of the opposite sex. Thus, women with hyperpituitary or hyperadrenal constitutions may present masculine characteristics, homosexual inclinations and an exaggerated libido.' (Pende, N. *Constitutional Inadequacies,* tr. by Naccarati, S., Lea & Febiger, Philadelphia, 1928)

type, hypertonic (hī-pēr-ton'ik) In the system of constitutional types described by Pende this term is used in connection with the *hypersthenic* type to designate a subgroup of both the *megalosplanchnic hypervegetative* constitution, where it stands in contrast to the *atonic* and *flaccid* subgroup, and of the *microsplanchnic hypovegetative* constitution where it stands in contrast to the *atonic* and *hyposthenic* sub-group.

According to the concepts of Pende, the first variety of the *hypertonic type* includes 'those who have, superimposed upon their general megalosplanchnic bodily style, characteristics of hyperevolutism of the heart and arteries, or of the striated muscular system, the psyche or the sexual apparatus; they also show quite an active metabolism and no tendency to lymphatic stasis.'

In the microsplanchnic hypovegetative constitutions the hypersthenic and hypertonic category is designed to cover a variety not conforming to the larger atonic and hyposthenic sub-group of the microsplanchnic type. 'From the point of view of behavior of the skeletal muscular system, to which there corresponds a parallelism of the circulatory energy and also a richness of hemoglobin and abundance of red cells in the blood, we are obliged to divide the microsplanchnic constitution into two main groups, that of the hypersthenic or hypertonic on the one hand, and that of hyposthenic or atonic on the other, as we have already done in the case of the megalosplanchnic constitution. We find that the bones in normal dolichomorphics, who do not show marked stigmata of hypoevolutism or hypogenitalism, are normally developed and normally resistant. In our hyperthyroid and hyperpituitary variety, the skeleton may be robust and the long bones long and at the same time thick. Although the bellies of the skeletal muscles may be long and slender, they do not in most cases present that flaccidity and weakness that are regarded as characteristic of the phthisic constitution. If there are asthenics who deserve to be so called from their poor skeletal muscles, there are others among them who have muscular strength and remarkable resistance to such an extent that they have come out victorious in wrestling championships.' (Pende, N. *Constitutional Inadequacies,* tr. by Naccarati, S., Lea & Febiger, Philadelphia, 1928)

The term hypertonic is also used in the constitutional system of Tandler to indicate a type characterized by a high degree of tonus of the voluntary muscles. This corresponds roughly to Kretschmer's *athletic* type.

type, hypervegetative (hī-pĕr-vej'e-tā-tiv) According to Viola's constitutional concepts developed by Pende, this term implies that the vegetative system located in the trunk predominates over the animal system—comprising the muscular, nervous, and skeletal systems—in forming contact with the external world.

The hypervegetative biotype is contrasted with the hypovegetative biotype and corresponds exactly to the megalosplanchnic and brachymorphic types, and approximately to the equivalents of the pyknic type.

type, hypoaffective (hī-pō-a-fek'tiv) In Pende's system of constitutional types, this is a psychological type which in contrast to the *hyperaffective* type is characterized by a deficiency in emotional reactivity, corresponding roughly to the *schizothymic* type.

type, hypogenital (hī-pō-jen'i-tal) A particular constitutional type which has been shown by Pende to be frequently associated with *microsplanchnic* proportions.

The *primary* hypogenital type is usually called *eunuchoid* and is characterized by exaggerated length of the lower extremities, a relatively hypoplastic state of trunk and head, and a deficient development of the genital organs and sexual characteristics. Various recent observations have suggested that this eunuchoid condition is inheritable as a sex-linked genetic factor. It seems to occur in women, too, although in a milder and less recognizable form.

In addition to the complete form of primary hypogenitalism, there is an attenuated type distinguished by Pende as 'hypogenital temperament.' (Pende, N. *Constitutional Inadequacies,* tr. by Naccarati, S., Lea & Febiger, Philadelphia, 1928)

type, integrated In their system of constitutional types E.R. and W. Jaensch denote by this term the individuals with an *integrated* psychological state, of which the *B type* of *eidetic imagery* (q.v.) is but an indicator, and which is further associated with particular physiological, biochemical, and clinical characteristics.

type, introverted See *type, extraverted; extraversion.*

type, intuitive (in-tū'i-tiv) The third of Jung's four functional types of personality. With his fourth (*sensational* type) it constitutes the *irrational* class of *functional types.*

One who 'adapts himself by means of unconscious indications, which he receives through an especially fine and sharpened perception and interpretation of faintly conscious stimuli. How such a function appears is naturally hard to describe, on account of its irrational, and, so to speak, unconscious character.' The intuitive type 'raises unconscious perception to the level of a differentiated function, by which he also becomes adapted to the world.' (Jung, C.G. *Psychological Types,* tr. by Baynes, H.G., Harcourt, Brace, New York and London, 1923)

type, irrational See *type, rational.*

type, lateral See *type, pyknic.*

type, linear See *type, asthenic.*

type, lymphatic (lim-fa'tik) In the system of Carus, this corresponds to the asthenic type (Kretschmer) and the habitus phthisicus (Hippocrates). See *type, asthenic.*

type, medium See *type, athletic.*

type, megalosplanchnic (me-gal-ō-splangk'nik) In Viola's system, this corresponds to *type, pyknik* (q.v.).

type, microsplanchnic (mī-krō-splangk'-nik) In Viola's system, this corresponds to *type, asthenic* (q.v.).

type, muscular This type was first described in 1828 by Rostan of the French school. In contradistinction to the *digestive, respiratory,* and *cerebral* (qq.v.) this type is characterized by the predominance of the muscular and locomotor system over the other systems of the body and corresponds to Kretschmer's *athletic* (q.v.) type.

type, normal See *type, athletic.*

type, normally compensating In the system of constitutional types described by Lewis, this type is intermediate between his *hypercompensatory* and *regressive* types (qq.v.) and is characterized by an average intermediate degree of development of the viscera and, on the psychological side, by its capacity for compensatory reactions that are moderate and reversible and, therefore, usually of a temporary nature.

type, normosplanchnic (nor-mō-splangk'-nik) In Viola's system, this corresponds to *type, athletic* (q.v.).

type, organic reaction See *syndrome, organic.*

type, phlegmatic One of the four classical temperamental and constitutional types of antiquity. Galen attributed the torpor and apathy of this type to the predominance of the *phlegma* (mucus secreted in the air passages of the throat) over the other three humors (fluids) of the human body (see *type, pyknic*).

type, phthisic See *habitus phthisicus.*

type, plethoric (ple-thor'ik) See *type, pyknic; type, athletic.*

type, pneumatic See *type, asthenic.*

type, pyknic In Kretschmer's system of constitutional types (q.v.) this is the type characterized by roundness of contour, amplitude of body cavities, and a plentiful endowment of fat.

The *head* of a pyknic is usually circular and smooth in profile, without any sharply prominent parts. The frontal facial outline is pentagonal or shield-shaped. The face is definitely broad and fleshy, particularly the nose. The neck is short and thick, with the head set a little forward on smoothly rounded shoulders. The line from the tip of the chin to the suprasternal notch is characteristic: inasmuch as it tends to be a smoothly sloping or even a straight line, but not an angle. The hair line borders the forehead in a regular, unindented curve. There is a tendency to baldness, the areas of which are regular in outline and have a smooth shiny surface.

The typically pyknic *trunk* is thickset and barrel-shaped, with the chest broadening to the lower part of the body. The abdomen is protruding and the xiphoid angle is wide. The limbs are well developed in thickness rather than in length, and the lower extremities, while not actually short, tend to appear short relative to the rest of the body because of their massiveness. The feet are broad, and well-covered, while the hands are square or broad, with podgy, fusiform fingers. The skin is warm and moist, with a well-developed fatty layer beneath it.

The *psychological* type of a pyknic is held by Kretschmer to be basically *cyclothymic* (q.v.). According to him, the pyknics may fall into any one of the three divisions of the *cyclothymes* as distinguished by Kretschmer: (1) the *healthy* cyclothymes (the gay chatterbox, the quiet humorist, the silent good-tempered man, the happy enjoyer of life, the energetic practical man); (2) the *cycloids* (the cheery hypomanic type, the quiet contented type, the melancholic type); and (3) the *manic-depressives.*

The *pyknic type* corresponds approximately to the following types in other leading systems: the *habitus apoplecticus* of Hippocrates, the *abdominal* and *digestive* types of the French school, the *phlegmatic, boeotic, plethoric venous, choleric* constitutions of Carus, the *hyperplastic* type with a disposition to carcinoma of Rokitansky-Beneke, the *third combination* of De Giovanni, the *brachyskelic* (*mikroskelic*) type of Manouvrier, the *megalosplanchnic* of Viola, the *hypervegetative* (*brachymorphic*) biotype of Pende, the *arthritic habitus* of Bauer, part of the *hypotonic* group of Tandler, the *hypersthenic* type of Mills, the *widechested* type of Brugsch, the *fleshy* type of Davenport, the *mesontomorph* of Beau, the *lateral* type of Stockard, the *broad* type of Aschner, the *B type* of Jaensch, the *euryplastic* type of Bounak, the *endomorphic* type of Sheldon, and part of the *hypercompensatory* type of Lewis.

type, rational According to Jung there are four basic psychological types of individuals, viz., the thinking, feeling, intuitive, and sensational, which form two groups: the first two he calls *rational* types 'because they are characterized by the supremacy of the reasoning and the judging functions. It is a general distinguishing mark of both types that their life is, to a large extent, subordinated to reasoning judgment.' The second two (intuitive, sensational) are termed *irrational* 'because their commissions and omissions are based not upon reasoned judgment but upon the absolute intensity of perception. Their perception is concerned with simple happenings, where no selection has been exercised by the judgment.'

(Jung, C.G. *Psychological Types,* tr. by Baynes, H.G., Harcourt, Brace, New York and London, 1923)

type, reaction See *reaction-type.*

type, regressive In the system of constitutional types described by Lewis, this type is characterized on the physical side by *hypoplasia* of blood and lymph vessels, intestines and ductless glands and by its tendency to *tuberculosis.* Since on the psychological side this type is distinguished by its disposition to *schizophrenia,* the most severe of all regressive changes, persons of this type are comparable to the *asthenic* type in Kretschmer's system and its equivalents in other systems.

type, reproductive In Rostan's system of constitutional types this type was characterized by a predominance of the reproductive system over the other systems of the body. Although no major type of other systems is based on the degree of development of the reproductive system, this type of Rostan is comparable to the *hypergenital* type which is a sub-group of the *dolichomorphic* type (q.v.) in the system of Pende, and may best be contrasted with the sterile *'atrophic'* constitution in the system of Carus.

type, respiratory In the system of Rostan and Sigaud, this type is distinguished from the *muscular, digestive,* and *cerebral* types by a predominance of the circulatory and respiratory systems over the others. Many typologists classify such persons in the *asthenic* type, although they seem to be at the pole opposite to the asthenic with his flat underdeveloped chest, hypoplastic blood vessels, and poorly expanding lungs. See *type, asthenic.*

type, reversal Abraham and Jones use this expression for individuals who have a tendency to act in a way contrary to normal. They may express contrary opinions, though they know them to be illogical; they may dress 'out of style'; they may enumerate irrelevant items, etc.

type, round This term denotes one of the two fundamental constitutional types evolved by MacAuliffe from considerations of colloidal chemistry (MacAuliffe: *Human Life*). In contradistinction to the *flat type* (q.v.), this type is characterized by an extremely *hydrophilic* tendency of the colloidal cells, great surface tension, increased osmotic pressure, and a consid-

erable expenditure of energy with a corresponding dynamic sweep.

type, sanguine According to old constitutional medicine, this refers to one of the four classical temperamental and constitutional types distinguished by Galen. He attributed the good humor and enthusiasm of this type to the predominance of the blood over the other three humors (or fluids) of the human organism.

type, Séglas (sā-glà′) (Jules Séglas, French physician, 1856–1939) The so-called psychomotor type of paranoia.

type, sensational The last of Jung's four functional types of personality. With his third (*intuitive* type) it constitutes the *irrational* class of functional types.

'Sensation, or sensing, is that psychological function which transmits a physical stimulus to perception. It is, therefore, identical with perception. . . . Primarily sensation is a *sense-perception,* i.e. perception transmitted *via* the sense organs and "bodily senses" (kinaesthetic, vasomotor, sensation, etc.).' (Jung, C.G. *Psychological Types,* tr. by Baynes, H.G., Harcourt, Brace, New York and London, 1923) Sensation 'always predominates over thinking and feeling, though not necessarily over intuition.' It is a conscious function, 'conscious perception,' as Jung says.

The sensational type of individual shows 'little tendency either for reflection or commanding purpose. To sense the object, to have and if possible to enjoy sensations, is his constant motive. He is by no means unlovable; on the contrary, he frequently has a charming and lively capacity for enjoyment; he is sometimes a jolly fellow and often a refined aesthete.' (ibid.)

type, sensory See *type, asthenic.*

type, slender See *type, asthenic.*

type, social 'The role which a person assumes and to which he is assigned by society.' (Burgess, E.W., in Shaw, C.R. *The Jack-Roller,* University of Chicago Press, Chicago, 1930)

'The social type is the psychological parallel of the biological type. By a social type we mean a constellation of attitudes forming a personality pattern, not inherited but growing out of a social situation.' (Zorbaugh, H.W. 'The Dweller in Furnished Rooms: An Urban Type,' in *The Urban Community,* edited by Burgess, E.W., University of Chicago Press, Chicago, 1926)

'The sociologist in transforming the unique or individual experience into a representative or typical one, arrives at the social type, which consists of a set of attitudes on the part of the person toward himself and the group, and a corresponding set of attitudes of the group toward him, which all together determine the role of the person in his social milieu. The extent to which social types may be depicted depends upon the definiteness of the organization of the attitudes and their characteristic cohesion about a core of significant social traits. The range of the personality types in a given social group is indicative of the culture of that group.' (Wirth, L. 'Some Jewish Types of Personality,' in *The Urban Community,* edited by Burgess, E.W., University of Chicago Press, Chicago, 1926)

types, personality See *personality types.*

type, sthenic (sthen'ik) In constitutional medicine, this corresponds to Kretschmer's athletic type and its equivalents in other systems. See *type, athletic.*

In general psychology, the term sthenic indicates strength and vigor in different fields of emotional reactivity and adaptability. In accordance with this concept, the psycho-pathological behavior of the sthenic type has been described by Kretschmer as inclined to delusional reactions of a predominantly aggressive nature (paranoia, querulous ideas of reference), in contrast to the introspective tendency of paranoid or hypochondriac reactions in sensitive types.

type, T See *imagery, eidetic.*

type, Tartar Mongolian idiocy.

type, 'the exceptions' A character type first described by Freud; such persons, because of early frustrations, arrogate

unto themselves the right to demand life-long reimbursement from fate. This behavior is intensified if they are required to contradict a deep inner doubt as to their right to compensation.

type, thinking The first of the four functional types of personality described by Jung. With Jung's second (*feeling* type) it constitutes the *rational* class of *functional* types.

'It is a fact of experience that all the basic psychological functions seldom or never have the same strength or grade of development in one and the same individual. As a rule, one or another function predominates, in both strength and development. When *supremacy* among the psychological functions is given to thinking, i.e., when the life of an individual is mainly ruled by reflective thinking so that every important action proceeds from intellectually considered motives, or when there is at least a tendency to conform to such motives, we may fairly call this a *thinking type.* Such a type can be either introverted or extraverted.' (Jung, C.G. *Psychological Types,* tr. by Baynes, H.G., Harcourt, Brace, New York and London, 1923)

Type Token ratio See *ratio, Type Token.*

type, vital See *biotype.*

type, wide-chested See *type, pyknic.*

typhlomegaly (tĭf-lō-meg'à-lē) An unusually large size of the caecum. In Pende's system of constitutional types, this condition is frequently characteristic of the *ptotic habitus.*

typholexia, congenital (tĭf-ō-lek'si-à) A term used by Variot and Lecomte (1906) to refer to a type of *reading disability* (q.v.).

typical Pertaining to, or serving as, a type.

typology (tĭ-pol'ō-jē) Study of *types.*

U

Ucs. abbreviation for *unconscious*.

ultrasonic irradiation See *irradiation, ultrasonic*.

ululation (ūl-ū-lā′shun, ul-ū-) The inarticulate crying of hysterical or psychotic persons.

unambivalence, unambivalency (un-am-biv′ā-lens, -len-sē) Unambivalence implies the fusion of instincts. According to psychoanalysts, during the stages of pregenital development the instincts act independently of one another; love is not influenced by hate; nor is the reverse the case. The separation of the instincts is characteristic when they are in the sphere of the unconscious. Later, particularly at the initial stage of genitality, the instincts begin to fuse. When, finally, as in adult life, they are harmoniously combined, they are said to be in a state of unambivalence. When initiative is combined with love, culminating in action favorable to all concerned, the instincts are in a condition of unambivalence.

uncinate seizure (un′si-nāt) See *fit, uncinate*.

unconscious The expression *unconscious* may be used as a noun or an adjective. In psychiatry it is used with two different and separate meanings. The first meaning has to do with the absence of participation of the conscious ego or the so-called perceptive-self. When the conscious part of the mind is not functioning, the individual is said to be unconscious. Unconsciousness is usually associated with absence of orientation and perception, particularly in its extreme expression.

The second meaning of *unconscious* (used as a noun) refers to a division of the psyche. One then speaks of *the unconscious* or of *unconsciousness*. In general it may be stated that all psychic material not in the immediate field of awareness is in the unconscious. When it is near enough to the former to be more or less easily accessible to it, it is said to be in the foreconscious or preconscious.

'The oldest and best meaning of the word "unconscious" is the descriptive one; we call "unconscious" any mental process the existence of which we are obliged to assume—because, for instance, we infer it in some way from its effects—but of which we are not directly aware. . . . If we want to be more accurate, we should modify the statement by saying that we call a process "unconscious" when we have to assume that it was active *at a certain time*, although *at that time* we knew nothing about it.' (Freud, S. *New Introductory Lectures on Psycho-Analysis*, tr. by Sprott, W.J.H., Norton, New York, 1933)

'The neurotic psyche, in order to be able to attempt the attainment of its overstrained goal, must have to resort to artifices and stratagems. One of these artifices is to transfer the goal or the substituted goal into the realm of the unconscious.' (Adler, A. *Problems of Neurosis*, Cosmopolitan Book Corporation, New York, 1930)

'Modern psychopathology has in its possession a wealth of observations regarding mental activities that are entirely analogous to conscious functions, and yet are unconscious. One can perceive, think, feel, remember, decide, and act, unconsciously. . . . How this is possible can best be seen if one imagines the mental functions and contents as resembling a night landscape over which the beam of a searchlight is playing. Whatever appears in this light of perception is conscious; what lies in the darkness beyond is unconscious, although none the less living and effective.' (Jung, C.G. *Contributions to Analytical Psychology*, tr. by Baynes, H.G. and C.F., Kegan Paul, Trench, Trubner, London, 1928)

'An appropriate and descriptive term to characterize that which is devoid of the attributes of consciousness.' '. . . unfortunately, however, the term has been also employed to characterize another and distinct class of facts, namely *Co-* [*or Sub-*] *conscious Ideas*. . . . It is sufficient to say here, that as conceived of, and as we have seen, there are very *definite states of coconsciousness—a coexisting dissociated consciousness or coconsciousness of which the personal consciousness is not aware*, i.e., of which it is "unconscious." Hence they have been called "unconscious ideas." . . . But this is plainly using the term in a different sense—using it as a synonym for the longer phrase, "ideas we are unaware of," and not as a characterization of that which is physiological and non-psychological.' (Prince, M. *The Unconscious*, Macmillan, New York, 1916)

' "Unconscious ideas" in this sense (the equivalent of coconscious ideas) would include conscious states that we are not aware of simply because not in the focus of attention but in the fringe of the content of consciousness. The term would also include pathologically split-off and independently acting coconscious ideas or systems of ideas such as occur in hysteria, reaching their apogee in coconscious personalities and in automatic writings.' (ibid.)

Prince further states that 'the unconscious is the great storehouse of neurograms which are the physiological records of our mental lives.' Abbreviated as *Ucs.*

unconscious, absolute Synonymous with collective unconscious. See *collective*.

unconscious, ambiguity of the In consonance with the splitting of their personality many schizophrenic patients manifest an ambiguous attitude in their productions, and especially in their drawings. For instance, a schizophrenic will picture himself as a god and, at the same time, the opposite—a devil or a self-mocking spirit—may also be portrayed to indicate a contradictory attitude toward his conception. (Baynes, H.G. *Mythology of the Soul*, Williams and Wilkins, Baltimore, 1940)

unconscious, collective See *collective*.

unconscious, impersonal Collective unconscious. See *collective*.

unconsciousness See *unconscious*.

unconscious, personal See *collective*.

unconscious, proper Latent ideas, according to Freud, may occupy the realm of the preconscious or of the unconscious. He adds that 'we reserve the term *unconscious* (proper) for the latter type [i.e. latent ideas which do not penetrate into consciousness] which we came to study in the neuroses.' (Freud, S. *Collected Papers*, vol. 4, tr. by Riviere, J., Leonard and Virginia Woolf and The Institute of Psychoanalysis, London, 1924–25)

unconscious, super-personal Synonymous with collective unconscious. See *collective*.

undercutting, cortical See *lobotomy, prefrontal*.

undo Psychoanalytically, to undo is unconsciously to wipe out painful experiences, to disregard them or treat them as if they had never occurred. See *undoing*.

undoing One of the unconscious defense-mechanisms, consisting of a positive action which, actually or magically, is the opposite of something against which the ego must defend itself. Expiatory acts, counter-compulsions, and some forms of compulsive ceremonials and counting compulsions are among the more frequent expressions of undoing, which is characteristic of the obsessive-compulsive psychoneurosis.

union, mystic 'We have described how the unity of instinct is lost in schizophrenics and how this loss is revealed in the consciousness of the patients in manifold sexual transformations. But in some cases, on the other hand, new unities may be formed—combinations in certain directions of the instincts and tendencies present; the "destruction" is compensated for by a "construction" (the expression *construction* is sometimes used spontaneously by the patients themselves). Instead of receiving the transformation passively, the patient makes an attempt to build up a self in keeping with his strivings in the direction of self-assertion and self-exaltation, and his desire to extend his power. The thing aimed at by the patient in reconstructing his ego is mainly the attainment of greatness and likeness to God, in short, unity with the cosmos.' (Storch, A. *The Primitive Archaic Forms in Schizophrenia*, tr. by Willard, C. Nervous and Mental Disease Publishing Company, New York and Washington, 1924)

unit-character A single-gene trait transmitted independently of other unit-characters, such as pigmentation vs. albinism.

universalization (ū-ni-vĕr-sal-i-zā'shun) The security and support which patients receive from one another in analytic psychotherapy, by virtue of the well-nigh universal problems, attitudes, feelings, and urges they all have in common. As a result of this universalization, their feelings of guilt and anxiety are reduced.

Unlust (un-lust', G. oon'loost) A German psychoanalytic term synonymous with the English terms 'ego pain,' 'unpleasure,' or 'anxiety,' of which 'unpleasure,' literally the reverse or opposite of pleasure, was made up as a direct replica of the German 'Unlust.'

Unpleasure, or Unlust, refers to the sensation of mild discomfort or frustration-tension that is felt in consciousness (by the ego) when instinctual trends, seeking gratification, are totally or partly opposed or blocked by the ego. This feeling of discomfort stands in marked contrast to the expected feeling of pleasurable relief from tension that usually results from the instinct's arousal following full gratification of the instinct.

The feeling of pain, unpleasure, frustration, tension, or discomfort is frequently mixed with, or associated with, anxiety. Unlust, or unpleasure, represents ego-suffering as an antithesis to pleasurable instinct satisfaction. It is this state of affairs that embodies the catalogue of all neurotic symptoms. (Sterba, R. *Introduction to the Psycho-analytic Theory of the Libido,* Nervous and Mental Disease Monographs No. 68, New York, 1942)

unpleasure See *Unlust.*

unresolved This is a term applied by Freud to psychological states resulting when the normal phases of development have not been worked through, but where arrest occurs at some particular point producing a 'complex,' which with the associated affect causes a conflict.

For example, one speaks of an *unresolved* Oedipus complex.

unveiling A term used by Fritz Wittels to denote the uncovering or revelation of psychic components.

uranism (ū′rå-niz′m) This is a term used by Karl Heinrich Ulrichs in 1862 for homosexuality; the female homosexual he called *Urninde,* the male *Urning.*

The corresponding term for heterosexuality is *dionism* (from Dione, mother of Venus Pandemos).

Neither term is used often.

uranomania *Obs.* The delusion, expressed by certain patients, that they are of divine or celestial origin.

uranophobia Fear of heaven.

Ur-defenses Masserman's term for what he considers the three fundamental psychologic maneuvers of man—the delusion of invulnerability and immortality, the delusion of the omnipotent servant (in the form of some abstract being or gnostic principle or system), and the conviction of man's kindness to man.

urethra (ū-rē′thra) The urethra, the canal leading from the urinary bladder to the outside of the body by way of the penis, gains importance in psychiatry because of the stress laid upon it by psychoanalysis. The urethra is regarded as an erogenous zone. Thus, psychoanalysts speak of urethral erotism and sadism.

'There were also indications present of *"urethral erotism."* As a child he often vied with other boys to see which could squirt his water highest in the air. As quite a little boy he had more than once let it fall into his mouth (Sadger's secondary auto-erotism).' (Jones, E. *Papers on Psycho-Analysis,* 4th ed., Wood, Baltimore, 1938)

urethral Pertaining to the urethra: the term acquires special significance in psychiatry through the formulations of Freud with regard to the relationship of psychic energy to the urethral zone.

urinam feminae dilectae in os proprium immitere [L.] The phrase refers to a practice not uncommon among sexual perverts, namely, to drink the contents of the urinary bladder directly from a beloved woman. Quoted from Stekel.

Urninde (oor-nin′dẽ) *Obs.* Female homosexualist.

Urning (oor′ning) *Obs.* Male homosexualist.

Urningism Uranism.

urolagnia (ū-rō-lag′ni-à) Pleasure connected with urine. For example, some patients drink their own urine; some individuals gain gratification in watching others urinate.

urophilia (ū-rō-fil′i-à) A pathologic love for, or interest in, urine; a synonym of *urolagnia* (q.v.).

urorrhea Enuresis.

user A slang expression to describe a morphine or heroin addict who takes small doses daily for years to keep himself comfortable. See *hog.*

utero-mania *Obs.* Insanity associated with uterine disorder.

uvula (ū′vū-là) See *cerebellum.*

uxoricide (uks-or′i-sīd) Killing of a wife by her husband.

V

vaccine, Salk See *poliomyelitis.*

vaccinophobia (vak-si-nō-fō'bi-à) A morbid fear or dread of being vaccinated.

vaginismus (vaj-i-niz'mus) Vaginismus is a painful spasm of the vagina. It generally takes place at some time during coitus or it may have its onset during the stage of preparation for the sexual act. There may be an organic factor associated in a causal way with vaginismus, though the etiology is often psychic.

Typical cases develop spasms which make insertion of the penis impossible, and such spasms are responsible for the rare cases of penis captivus. Vaginismus usually represents inhibition of sexual excitement along with positive action to ensure maintenance of inhibition; in addition, it may be a conversion symptom expressing a wish to break off the penis and keep it.

vaginismus, psychic Painful spasm of the vagina preventing coitus; caused by repugnance to the sexual act.

vagotonia (vā-gō-tō'ni-à) Vagotonia, or excessive excitability of the vagus nerve, is said to be not uncommon in patients with schizophrenia, in whom it appears sometimes as a general condition, but more frequently as a local one.

'Under the conception of vagotonia we include all those constitutional conditions in which, in addition to the manifestations of a functionally increased vagus tonus and increased irritability in this anatomical system, there also exists a condition of increased sensitiveness to pilocarpin. In the light of the previously described antagonism between the two parts of the vegetative nervous system, we may add as a further earmark of the vagotonic disposition a relative decrease of reactivity to sympathetic stimuli.' (Eppinger, H. and Hess, L. *Vagotonia*, 2nd ed., tr. by Kraus, W.M. and Jelliffe, S.E., Nervous and Mental Disease Publishing Company, New York, 1917)

validation, consensual See *distortion, parataxic.*

validity The degree to which a test measures what it is supposed to measure; a valid intelligence test, for example, is truly a measure of general intelligence and not a test of rote memory. The degree of validity of a test depends upon the magnitude of the errors present in the measures obtained from it. Some indication of the validity of a given test is gained from a study of the correlations between scores on the given test and scores from other tests designed to measure the same factor.

value, utility and/or pleasure Since the human infant at birth is ill equipped for survival, there begins at once the long, gradual, infinitely complex process of learning to live in the outer world. The organism must become acquainted with itself and the environment and must acquire techniques of exploiting both in its own best interests. It must learn to adapt.

Kardiner says: 'Active mastery [i.e. a technique of adaptation] means the capacity to exploit the utility (or pleasure) value of objects in the outer world for one's own ends. In the development of this technique motility and manipulation play a decisive role. Both of these add much to adaptation possibilities, but they also increase the complicity of the outer world; they alter the meaning of objects in the outer world, their utility and pleasure possibilities . . . From the very first experiences at the breast, the infant can have severe frustrations, and at this time the utility value of the mouth as a feeding executive and the pleasure value of sucking are intimately fused. These two functions of the mouth, the utility and pleasure value, mutually influence each other. If the pleasure value of the mouth is predominant it is likely to lead to strong attachment to the mother, which is likely to exert a retarding influence on the development of adaptation to the outer world. Disappointments in these encounters with the outer world are likely to increase not only the pleasure value of the mouth but the ego attitude of dependency, an attitude which strongly influences the reactions to discipline later instituted. This in turn diminishes the self-confidence of the individual and lessens his enterprise.' (Kardiner, A. *War Stress and Neurotic Illness,* Hoeber, New York, 1947)

Everything exploitable, objects as well as the manipulative, integrative techniques themselves, is assessed in terms of utility value, pleasure value, or both.

vampirism, parasitic Baynes uses the expression parasitic vampirism in a special sense, namely, that in a psychoneurotic patient compulsive mechanisms are present which are constantly driving the person. These drives have a demonic appetite —the more they have the more they demand. They know no reasonable bounds. Baynes believes that the neurotic symptoms, such as phobias, obsessions, and aggressions, are similar to a devouring monster which overpowers and possesses the patient in the manner of a bloodthirsty vampire. (Baynes, H.G. *Mythology of the Soul,* Williams and Wilkins, Baltimore, 1940)

vandalism, sexual An inordinate impulse to destroy the sexual zones represented in pictures, statuary, etc.

vapores uterini (và-pō'res oo-te-rē'nē) (L. 'uterine vapors') It was an ancient belief that vapors, originating in the uterus, passed into the brain, thus producing mental disorders.

vapors *Obs.* Hysteria; hypochondriasis.

variant, epileptic There are many clinical phenomena of the so-called epilepsies. Among them are the varieties listed by S.A. Kinnier Wilson in the *Journal of Neurology and Psychopathology,* January 1928.

I. Motor Variants:
  1. Myoclonic or regional epilepsy
  2. Epilepsia partialis continua
  3. Tonic epilepsy
  4. Co-ordinated epilepsy
  5. Inhibitory or akinetic epilepsy
II. Sensory Variants:
  1. Reflex epilepsy
  2. Sensory epilepsy
  3. Affective epilepsy
III. Psychical Variants.
IV. Visceral Variants.

variation This genetic term has a specific and distinctive meaning. It applies to the varying phenotypical expressivity of hereditary characters and its meaning is determined by the fundamental biological principle that the individual manifestations of any genetic factor are *modifiable.* Since in a species originating through sexual reproduction no real hereditary homogeneity among its various individuals can be expected, the offspring of higher organisms are never exactly like the parents, but vary to a certain extent, each organism inheriting the entire characteristic modifiability of its kinship.

According to genetic theories, there are three possible mechanisms which can cause an organism to become different from its parents: *modification, combination,* and *mutation* (qq.v.).

The items in any frequency distribution differ from each other with respect to the amount of a given character which they all possess (e.g. height), and any frequency distribution may differ in a similar way from another frequency distribution describing the same character. Such differences constitute the phenomenon of variation.

vasectomy (vas-ek'tō-mē) A surgical and eugenic term; the *sterilizing* operation on men, of cutting and tying off the seminal ducts (vasa deferentia). Usually no unfavorable effect on the secondary sexual characters follows vasectomy, in contrast with the *castrating* operation of removing the testicles. See *sterilization.*

vasovagal attack of Gowers Gowers described a syndrome which he considered to be a *vasovagal attack,* and although it resembles closely that observed in anxiety hysteria, Gowers felt that this attack was not hysterical in nature. It is characterized by nausea and belching, precordial discomfort, respiratory difficulty, anxiety of impending death, and mild mental upset. The attack may last from a few minutes to an hour.

vecordia (vē-kor'di-à) *Obs.* Any mental affection.

vegetative nervous system See *autonomic nervous system.*

ventricle puncture See *puncture, ventricle.*

ventriculogram (ven-trik'ū-lō-gram) An X-ray of the skull following replacement of cerebrospinal fluid by air by means of ventricular puncture. This drains the ventricular system but not the subarachnoid spaces and cisterns; the procedure is used when an expanding intracranial lesion is suspected, since ventriculography is considered safer than encephalography in such cases.

ventriculography (ven-trik-ū-log'rà-fē) Radiography of the brain-cavity. A means of determining the presence of structural changes in the intracranial contents, which are visualized by the X-ray, after the direct injection of air into the lateral ventricles.

Veraguth, fold of (Otto Veraguth, German neurologist, 1870–1940) Contraction upward and backward of the inner third of the upper lid, this changing the arch of the upper lid into an angle. Veraguth described this change as a characteristic sign of the depressed type of manic-depressive psychosis.

verbalization In psychiatry, the state of being verbose or diffuse, commonly encountered in extreme degree in patients with the manic form of manic-depressive psychosis. In a more general sense, verbalization refers to the expression in words of thoughts, wishes, phantasies, or other psychic material which had previously been on a non-verbal level because of suppression or repression. 'Verbalize' is often used in a pseudo-erudite way when 'talk about' is meant.

verbigerate (vĕr-bij'ĕr-āt) To repeat the same word, phrase, or sentence over and over again.

verbigeration A manifestation of stereotypy, consisting of the morbid repetition of words, phrases, or sentences. A patient with the catatonic form of schizophrenia kept repeating 'muscle, muscle, muscle,' in reply to all forms of questioning.
'When language becomes stereotyped it is called *verbigeration.*' (Bleuler, E. *Textbook of Psychiatry,* tr. by Brill, A.A., Macmillan, New York, 1930)

verbigeration, hallucinatory 'Many patients hear perpetually, in endless repetition or with slight changes, the same meaningless sentences, so that there is a kind of hallucinatory *verbigeration.*' (Kraepelin, E. *Dementia Praecox and Paraphrenia,* tr. by Barclay, R.M., Livingstone, Edinburgh, 1919)

verbochromia (vĕr-bō-krō'mi-à) 'With some people certain words are accompanied by a sense of colour, varying with different words (verbochromia).' (Stoddart, W.H.B. *Mind and Its Disorders,* 5th ed., Lewis, London, 1926)

verbose Overproductive in speech.

vermis (ver'mis) See *cerebellum.*

vertigo (vĕr'ti-gō, L. ver-tē'gō) (L. 'a whirling (of the head), dizziness') Dizziness. This may be organically or psychically determined. It is a frequent phenomenon in psychiatric patients, appearing as a rule as a defense against unacceptable or painful ideas.

vesania (vē-sā'ni-à) (L. 'madness') Insanity. Vesania is an old term, as well as an old concept, that meant insanity in general. It was used by Sauvages in his *Nosologia Methodica,* of 1763. The group termed *vesania* embraced psychiatric disorders not known to be associated with any organic disease or disorder.

vesania anomala (à-nō'mà-là) (L. 'irregular insanity') *Obs.* Mania transitoria.

vesania typica circularis (tē'pē-kà kĕr-koo-lä'rēs) (L. 'typical circular insanity') In 1882 Kahlbaum used the term *cyclothymia* to designate the milder, recoverable forms of manic-depressive psychosis, and the expression *vesania typica circularis* for the chronic forms.

vestibular nerve (ves-tib'ū-lĕr) See *nerve, acoustic.*

vice allemand (vēs' àl'mäN) (F. 'German vice') A term used by Hirschfeld synonymously with homosexuality. In the 18th century the French called homosexuality 'the German vice'; at an earlier period Europeans referred to homosexuality as 'the Oriental disease.' It seems that every nation disowns responsibility for originating homosexuality, and would like to shift it upon another's shoulders. But, as a matter of fact, homosexuality is recorded in classical literature.

vicissitudes, instinctual See *libido, plasticity of.*

vigilambulism (vij-il-am'bū-liz'm) A condition of unconsciousness regarding one's surroundings, with automatism, resembling somnambulism, but occurring in the waking state.

vigilance The general alerting function or sentinel activity of the nervous system; in conditioned reflex experiments, each positive or negative conditioned stimulus causes a sharp spike of sudden alertness, termed stimulus-vigilance. Stimulus-vigilance is considered to be an emergency-reaction to a stress stimulus in a stressful situation. 'When an animal undergoing a regimen of difficult conditioning succumbs to an experimental neurosis we may suppose that its final traumatic reaction to the repeated stress situations of the conditioning laboratory was due to a gradual heightening of the vigilance level from day to day in consequence of the summation of the after-effects of stimulus-vigilance enduring for days, weeks, or months. Finally, an end point or breaking point is reached beyond which the animal's management of its emergency function becomes faulty as indicated by its neurotic manifestations. The intensity of the vigilance level of the day depends then not only upon the total stimulus load, i.e., upon the number, intensity, duration, and temporal spacing of the specific vigilance reactions aroused by the positive and negative conditioned stimuli of the experimental day, but also upon the lingering traces of stimulus-vigilance from previous conditioning sessions.' (S.H. Liddell, in *The Biology of Mental Health and Disease,* Hoeber, New York, 1952)

In 19th century writings, vigilance was equivalent to insomnia, agrypnia.

vigility of attention See *attention, vigility of.*

villa-system See *system, villa.*

viraginity (vir-à-jin′i-tē) The adoption by women of male characteristics. It is an expression of homosexuality.

virium lapsus (vē′rē-oom làp′soos) (L. 'decay of energy') *Obs.* Lypothymia.

visceral epilepsy See *epilepsy, visceral.*

viscerotonia (vis-er-ō-tō′ni-à) A personality type described by Sheldon which is correlated with the endomorph body type and which shows a love of food, comfort, and conviviality and a tendency to general relaxation.

viscosity of libido See *libido, viscosity of.*

vision See *lobe, occipital.*

visionism (vizh′un-iz'm) Voyeurism.

visions, hypnagogic (hip-nà-goj′ik) The optic perceptions present in a state midway between sleep and waking. They are literally a phase of dream phenomena. In the hypnoidal state the individual is still conscious of his surroundings, but his mind is poorly concentrated, the cortical functions being largely inhibited. The hypnagogic visions appear in a state intermediate between perceiving and phantasying. In the hypnagogic vision, however, there seems to exist two distinct interlinked attitudes, and it has not yet been determined whether this is representation or perception. Schilder thinks 'the difficulty in discussing these issues as to whether perception and representation

are fundamentally different or similar to each other arises from the fact that isolation of psychic elements like perception and representation is artificial.' (Schilder, P. *Mind, Perception and Thought,* Columbia University Press, New York, 1942)

vision, tubular (tū′bū-lẽr) See *field defect.*

visual field See *field defect.*

visual-spatial agnosia See *agnosia, visual-spatial.*

vita sexualis (vē′tà sek-soo-ä′lẽs) (L. 'sexual life') Krafft-Ebing often uses this Latin term for sexual life.

Vogt, Oskar (1870–   ) (fôKt) German neuropathologist.

Vogt-Spielmeyer's disease See *amaurotic family idiocy; Spielmeyer-Vogt's disease.*

voice, soundless See *thought, audible.*

volition, derailment of See *derailment (of volition).*

volubility (vol-ū-bil′i-tē) Overproductivity in speech.

vomiting, cyclic A disorder of children which is characterized by attacks of vomiting. The attacks begin suddenly, last several days, cease abruptly, and then recur in intervals or cycles of several weeks or months. Because of this cyclic feature of the attacks, the disorder is also known as *recurrent vomiting.* All evidence thus far adduced indicates that the condition betokens an emotional imbalance, and, accordingly, Smith writes: '. . . the attacks are precipitated by all sorts of exciting factors. The child who is subject to the attacks is usually a nervous, highstrung individual and comes from a family which is often of the same sort.' (Smith, C.H. 'Recurrent Vomiting in Children,' *Journal of Pediatrics 10,* 719–42, 1937)

vomiting, nervous A psychiatric term for functional vomiting of psychogenic emotional or neurotic origin, occurring most frequently in young women between the ages of 20 and 40. It usually expresses, in organ-language, symbolically and physically, the desire to reject a hated idea, or person, concerning whom there exist conscious and unconscious conflicts of an emotional nature; this is the only way out of the conflict left to these patients, because, in consciousness, they cannot stand their hostility and yet cannot express it verbally.

E. Weiss and O.S. English report the following case: 'A young white woman, with markedly repressed sexuality, developed frequent vomiting attacks after a marriage to which she had consented, in the main, because of her mother's urging. Her passive and dependent nature did not allow her to express hostility openly but instead her unconscious mental forces caused her to vomit as though to say: "I cannot stomach this situation." ' (*Psychosomatic Medicine,* 2nd ed., Saunders, Philadelphia and London, 1949)

von Graefe's sign (Albrecht von Graefe, German ophthalmologist, 1828–70) Lag of the upper lid in following the downward movement of the eye, due to retraction of the upper lid such as occurs in exophthalmic goiter and in lesions in the upper part of the midbrain.

von Recklinghausen's disease (Friedrich Daniel von Recklinghausen, German pathologist, 1833–1910) *Neurofibromatosis* (q.v.).

voyeur (vwà-yĕr') (F. 'onlooker, spectator, sexual pervert') Peeping Tom. One who obtains sexual gratification by looking at the genitals of another. The individual is also known as a scopophiliac.

voyeurism 'Peeping.' Sexual pleasure obtained by looking at the genitals of another.

'Sublimation of the looking impulse can be brought about if the interest is turned from the genitals to the form of the body. This, Freud thinks, normally occurs as an intermediary sexual aim and makes possible the directing of a certain amount of the libido in artistic channels.' (Healy, W., Bronner, A.F., and Bowers, A.M. *The Structure and Meaning of Psychoanalysis,* Knopf, New York, 1930)

vulvismus (vul-viz'mus) Vaginismus.

W

Wagner von Jauregg, Julius (1857–1940) (väg'nĕr fôn you'reg) Austrian psychiatrist and neurologist; fever treatment of general paresis.

WAIS Wechsler Adult Intelligence Scale.

Wallenberg's syndrome (Adolf Wallenberg, German physician, 1862–   ) The symptoms following occlusion of the posterior inferior cerebellar artery (which is known as 'the artery of thrombosis'): ipsilateral facial analgesia, ipsilateral Horner's syndrome, ipsilateral ataxia, and contralateral analgesia.

wanderlust Wanderlust or the morbid impulse to roam or wander about achieves distinction in many psychiatric conditions, among which may be mentioned the idiopathic form of epilepsy, the nosologic condition known as psychopathic personality, and schizophrenia. The impulse to wander drives the individual to aimless travels, for he knows only that he must keep searching for something; he never knows why he travels; nor when he arrives at a destination does he seek any objective there; in fact, there is no destination, for whatever the destination may be, it is always beyond his reach. The impulse is believed to be associated with the Oedipus situation in the sense that the wanderer is incessantly seeking to establish affiliation with one or both parents as he had experienced it, or longed to experience it, when he was a young child.

ward, psychopathic A ward in a general hospital for the reception and temporary treatment of the insane.

ward-work In occupational therapy this term often denotes activities which are conducted on the ward for those patients who are not able to leave the ward.

warming-up 'Spontaneous states are brought into existence by various starters. The subject puts his body and mind into motion, using body attitudes and mental images which lead him toward attainment of that state. This is called the warming up process. The warming up process can be stimulated by bodily starters (a complex physical process in which muscular contractions play a leading role), by mental starters (feelings and images in the subject which are often suggested by an-

other person), and by psychochemical starters (artificial stimulation through coffee, for example).

'Through the warming up process numerous roles are brought into expression which an individual rarely or never experiences in the daily routine of living. A warming up process which covers a small range of the personality can be absorbed and for the time being undone by a warming up process with a wider range. This fact has become the basis for a therapeutic technique. For example, involuntary contractions of the face have been overcome by a subject when he warmed up to the role of an aggressor, during which time the muscles which were needed for the production of the symptom were included and submerged in the activity of a wider range of action.' (Moreno, J.L. *Sociometry 1*, 66, 1937)

war-neurosis See *shell-shock*.

Watson, John Broadus (1878–1958) American psychologist; behaviorism.

waxy flexibility Same as *cerea flexibilitas*. See *catalepsy*.

weak-mindedness, hallucinatory *Obs.* By this expression, Kraepelin denoted one of the terminal states of schizophrenia.

weaned, mentally The term used by Lindberg to denote one of the prominent features of psycho-infantilism, namely, the failure to achieve emotional independence of the parents or parent-surrogates. Lindberg writes: 'A number of adults, however, continue to show signs of the uncertainty and helplessness which characterizes the socially immature child. These people have not reached the mental maturity normal for their age. They still feel the need of guidance and authority, of care and attention even in the simplest situations. Fundamentally, they have not advanced beyond the stage of domestic (within the home) socialization. It is this property of never being really "mentally weaned" of helplessness and uncertainty when confronted with large and small problems which is found in everyone designated as psycho-infantile.' (Lindberg, B.J. *Psycho-Infantilism*, Ejnar Munksgaard, Copenhagen, 1950) See *psycho-infantilism*.

Weber's syndrome (Sir Herman Weber, English physician, 1823–1918) Pedunculopontile syndrome; see *hemiplegia alternans.*

Weltmerism (After Sidney A. Weltmer, founder of the method and the Weltmer Institute at Nevada, Mo.) A system of therapeutics based on suggestion.

Wernicke, Carl (1848–1905) (vâr′ni-kē) German neurologist; aphasia.

Wernicke's encephalopathy (en-sef-a-lop′-à-thē) Polio-encephalitis hemorrhagica superior, described by Wernicke in 1881; this is a very severe disorder consisting of degeneration of nervous tissue especially marked in the midbrain. The syndrome occurs in a small percentage of chronic alcoholics and is probably due to a combination of nutritional deficiencies, especially a vitamin B deficiency. Onset is insidious, with vomiting, oculomotor palsies, ptosis, pupillary changes (such as Argyll-Robertson pupil), ataxia, insomnia, and a mental state consisting of an acute hallucinatory picture similar to delirium tremens except that there is no tremor and the delirium is dreamy and confused. Impaired consciousness may progress to stupor. The encephalopathy may terminate fatally, or there may be progression to a Korsakoff syndrome. Thiamine chloride has been used successfully to reverse the ophthalmoplegia and has sometimes been of help in the mental state.

Westphal's sign See *sign, Westphal.*

Westphal-Strümpell's pseudosclerosis See *degeneration, hepatolenticular.*

wet-dream Popular term for seminal ejaculation during sleep.

Weygandt, Wilhelm (1870–1939) (vī′-gänt) German psychiatrist.

whipping See *flagellation.*

White, William A. (1870–1937) American psychiatrist.

Wihtiko psychosis (wi[h]′ti-kō) A psychosis found in certain primitive people (Ojibwa or Chippewa, Eastern Cree) characterized by a morbid craving for human flesh and by a delusion of transformation into a Wihtiko, a supernatural being feared by this tribe.

Wilbur, Hervey Backus (1820–1883) American pioneer educator in the field of mental deficiency.

will, criminal According to Abrahamsen, there is no such scientific entity as a 'criminal will.' He doubts that individuals exist who perpetrate criminal acts without having experienced some kind of inner conflict more or less connected with some development of hate in childhood, resulting in feelings of guilt and anxiety or in a self-punishing mechanism. When a man kills a person it is not too far-fetched to say that he killed him a long time before actually committing the homicide. (Abrahamsen, D. *Crime and the Human Mind,* Columbia University Press, New York, 1944)

will, disturbances of the One of Bleuler's fundamental symptoms of the schizophrenias. Usually, the disturbance is in the direction of deficiency (hypobulia, hypoboulia) or lack (abulia, aboulia); such patients appear lazy, negligent of their duties, purposeless, and goalless, with no aims, ambitions, or desires. *Platonization* (q.v.) is often seen and patients appear apathetic toward their environment and disinterested in the reality about them. At other times, because they have no real goals, they appear flighty, capricious, and undependable, adopting momentarily any goal which is thrust upon them. Or they may appear stubborn, robot-like, and wedded in a perseverative way to a particular activity which they cling to rather than have to make any decision or move toward purposeful change.

A few patients are hyperbulic and show a bizarre or inappropriate application and assiduity to unimportant and trivial occupations; these are the faddists, the shifters, the individuals who are forever brewing storms in teapots.

will therapy See *therapy, will.*

will-to-be-above Adler borrowed this term from Nietzsche to indicate the tendency of the neurotic female to identify herself with the male.

It 'is produced by her manly guiding idea . . . every gesture then says, "I will be above, I will be a man, because I am afraid as a woman of being oppressed and misused." ' (Adler, A. *The Neurotic Constitution,* tr. by Glueck, B. and Lind, J.E., Moffat, Yard, New York, 1917)

will-to-be-up Adler borrowed this term from Nietzsche to denote the neurotic individual's striving toward masculine aggression.

will-to-power This term, borrowed by Adler from Nietzsche, denotes the strivings of the neurotic individual toward masculinity, in order to escape the feeling of uncertainty and inferiority which connotes femininity.

Wilmanns, Karl (1873–   ) (vil′mäns) German psychiatrist.

Wilson's disease (Samuel A.K. Wilson, English neurologist, 1878–1936) See *degeneration, hepatolenticular*.

Wimmer, August (1872–1937) (vim′ĕr) Danish psychiatrist.

windigo See *Wihtiko*.

WISC Wechsler Intelligence Scale for Children.

wish In psychiatry the term *wish*, from a psychodynamic point of view, is today associated pre-eminently with psychoanalysis. It is not always to be defined in its lay sense as desire or want, unless one includes in the definition the forces in the unconscious that strive for externalization. To Freud the expression *wish* is as much a factor of the unconscious as it is of consciousness, but because the unconscious longs to release impulses that consciousness often opposes, a new meaning must be given to wish.

A wish is an impulse, a purpose, a desire, a tendency, an urge, a striving. Holt defines it as 'a course of action which some mechanism of the body is set to carry out, whether it actually does so or does not.' (Holt, E.B. *The Freudian Wish and Its Place in Ethics,* Holt, New York, 1915)

'The kernel of the system Ucs. [unconscious] consists of instinct-presentations whose aim is to discharge their cathexis; that is to say, they are wish-impulses.' (Freud, S. *Collected Papers,* vol. 4, tr. by Riviere, J., Leonard and Virginia Woolf and The Institute of Psychoanalysis, London, 1924–25)

In the first place, 'the unconscious, then, consists of repressed mental material. A second characteristic of it is its *dynamic* nature. The unconscious is not a depository for passive material, but a region where the most active functioning goes on. Unconscious processes are typically conative in kind, and may thus be conveniently, and not inaccurately, described as *wishes*. These wishes are constantly striving for gratification, imaginary or real, and it is to this active striving that

the external of the unconscious is to be ascribed.' (Jones, E. *Papers on Psycho-Analysis,* 4th ed., Wood, Baltimore, 1938)

wish, child-penis The wish for a child with which, in her psychosexual development, the little girl replaces her wish for a penis. In the phallic stage of a woman's psychosexual development, the little girl obtains pleasurable sensations from her clitoris, which is the dominant erotogenic zone. As the psychosexual development proceeds, however, and the change to full womanhood occurs, 'the clitoris must give up to the vagina its sensitivity, and with it, its importance, either wholly or in part.' Moreover the little girl must change her love-object from the mother to the father. It is at this period in the development of the girl that the child-penis-wish emerges.

The little girl's first love-object is the mother, since it was she who provided the first satisfactions of life, nourishment, warmth, etc. The little girl's libidinal impulses to her first object, her mother, are manifold and express themselves through oral, anal, and phallic wishes, both active and passive. They are also completely ambivalent, being both tender and hostile. The phallic wishes are expressed by 'the desire to get the mother with child as well as the corresponding one, to have a child by the mother.' The mother contributed to these wishes in reality, since she aroused 'pleasurable sensations in the child's genitals in the ordinary course of attending to its bodily needs.' As the child develops, her strong attachment to her mother is replaced by an attachment to her father. This takes place in an atmosphere of hatred for the mother. Although there are many obvious sources for this hatred of the mother—the unavoidable necessity in the child's development of frustrating its insatiable desire for the breast; the birth of a sibling which deprives the little girl of the mother's exclusive attention; the frustration (with threat and disapproval from the mother) of the child's masturbatory activities, which the mother herself had unwittingly stimulated; the other necessary restrictions associated with education; and finally the strong ambivalence of the child's impulses toward her mother—Freud feels that in the girl's turning from her mother to her father the main and specific factor is her penis-envy, her wish for a penis. For when the girl first notices that the boy has something she has not—his male genitals —she feels at a great disadvantage. Now the little girl no longer enjoys her phallic sexuality. Her self-love is wounded 'by the unfavourable comparison with the boy who is so much better equipped.' and therefore she 'gives up the masturbatory satisfaction which she obtained from her clitoris . . . and . . . repudiates her love towards her mother.'

Having given up her love for her mother, who, too, is found to be castrated and, therefore, cannot satisfy her daughter's desire for a penis or the sexual phantasies associated with her masturbation, the little girl turns her love toward her father. She has not, however, relinquished her wish for a penis, which, in effect, her mother has refused her, and which she now expects from her father. Also, her passive instinctual impulses have gained the upper hand, since a certain amount of activity was surrendered along with the clitoric masturbation. Thus, the symbolic equation, child = penis, can come into effect and the wish for a penis is replaced by the wish for a child. The girl's strongest wish now is for a child by her father. 'With the transference of the child-penis-wish onto her father, the girl enters into the situation of the Oedipus complex.'

At an earlier age, before the development of her penis-envy, the little girl had expressed a wish for a child by playing with dolls. This wish for a child, however, was an expression of her active identification with her mother: she could do to the doll all that her mother used to do with her. It was not, however, associated with a wish for a penis. 'Only with the onset of the desire for a penis does the doll-child become a child by the father.' (Freud, S. *New Introductory Lectures on Psychoanalysis,* Norton, New York, 1933)

wish-dream, masochistic A dream which has to do with injury to the dreamer himself. 'From this last dream he awakens with the most unpleasant feelings; and yet it is a masochistic wish dream, which might be translated: It would serve me right if my brother were to make that sale against my interests. It would be my punishment for all the torments he has suffered at my hands.' '. . . even dreams with a painful content are to be analyzed as wish-fulfillments.' (Freud, S. *The Basic Writings of Sigmund Freud,* tr. by Brill,

A.A., Random House, New York, 1938). See *dream, punishment.*

wish-fulfillment As the term implies, this is the consummation of a desire or wish. The term is of greatest importance in psychoanalysis, where it constitutes one of the most common phenomena of the psyche. The term *wish,* however, in psychoanalysis has a wide meaning (see *wish*).

'I received the impression that my book *The Interpretation of Dreams* created more "confusion" than "enlightenment" among my colleagues, and I know that the wider reading circles have contented themselves to reduce the contents of the book to a catchword, "wish-fulfillment"—a term easily remembered and easily abused.' (Freud, S. *The Basic Writings of Sigmund Freud,* tr. by Brill, A.A., Random House, New York, 1938)

In Burrow's phylobiology this term is organismically broadened to emphasize that this mechanism is a false motivation prevalent throughout so-called normal processes and is not by any means limited to the neurotic individual. The phenomenon of wish-fulfillment is a social reaction. It affects man as a species and is fundamentally traceable to disordered physiological tensions that are definitely phyletic. (Burrow, T. *The Biology of Human Conflict,* Macmillan, New York, 1937)

wish-fulfillment, asymptotic Gratification of an impulse or desire in a substitute or 'almost but not quite' way. 'His (i.e. Schreber's) ego found compensation in his megalo-mania, while his feminine wish-phantasy gained its ascendancy and became acceptable. The struggle and the illness could cease. The patient's sense of reality, however, which had in the meantime become stronger, compelled him to postpone the solution from the present to the remote future, and to content himself with what might be described as an asymptotic wish-fulfilment.' (Freud, S. *Collected Papers,* vol. 3, tr. by Strachey, A. and J., Leonard and Virginia Woolf and the Hogarth Press, London, 1925)

wish, id A psychoanalytic term referring specifically to instinctual urges having their source in the realm of the repressed, unconscious, primitive, and infantile regions of the personality (psyche or mind).

Id wishes, or instinctual urges, emanating from the unconscious are thought of in conflict with, and in juxtaposition to, wishes having their origin in the ego, on the one hand, and in the conscience, or superego, on the other. Wishes having their origin in the ego make for reality adjustment and control; while those having their origin in the conscience, or superego, make for the attainment of 'goodness' and 'approval.'

Id wishes are characterized by a driving urgency representative of their infantile and primordial biologic nature. They are mainly of a crudely aggressive and erotic nature. E.F. Sharpe (*Collected Papers on Psycho-analysis,* Hogarth Press and The Institute of Psychoanalysis, London, 1950) states: 'The ferocity of the super-ego means also the ferocity of the id-wishes, and a belief in their omnipotent power.'

wish-impulse With this term Freud indicates that each impulse which induces a phantasy, dream, specific act, or symptom is a 'wish' whose gratification would be pleasurable.

'In general, we can rest assured that every *wish-impulse* which creates a dream today will reappear in other dreams as long as it has not been understood and withdrawn from the control of the unconscious.' (Freud, S. *Collected Papers,* vol. 2, tr. by Riviere, J., Leonard and Virginia Woolf and The Institute of Psychoanalysis, London, 1924–25)

wish, libido An unconscious craving for gratification of the instinctual impulses (see *libido*).

wish, penis See *penis-envy; wish, child-penis.*

wish-psychosis, hallucinatory See *psychosis, hallucinatory wish.*

wishes, fundamental The fundamental wishes of the person are a classification of the vast variety of desires 'which can be satisfied only by his incorporation in a society.' (Thomas, W.I. and Znaniecki, F. *The Polish Peasant in Europe and America,* Knopf, New York, 1927)

The concrete wishes of persons 'all fall under one or more of four types or patterns: (1) the desire for new experience; (2) the desire for security; (3) the desire for response; and (4) the desire for recognition.' (Park, R.E. and Miller, H.A. *Old World Traits Transplanted,* Harper, New York, 1921)

'The organization of society has always a double character: it makes possible the gratification of the individual's wishes, and even the multiplication of them, but at the same time it requires that his wishes shall be gratified only in *usual* ways, that their expression shall be so regulated as not to interfere with the expression of the wishes of others.' (ibid.)

wit Wit engages the attention of psychiatrists because of the fundamental principles associated with it, rather than because of any importance attached to it from a psychiatric point of view. The background of wit is fundamentally the same as the background of many other psychic phenomena, but wit is usually not a manifestation of morbidity, any more than are slips of the tongue or pen. There are no nosological disorders, nor syndromes, in which wit occupies the position of abnormality in the general sense of that term. To be sure, wit appears in certain clinical conditions, but its import to the total clinical picture is usually inconsiderable. In short, wit is a psychological rather than a psychiatric issue. Freud wonders just why he has treated the topic so exhaustively when he says: 'Some may inquire whether the subject of wit is worthy of such effort.' It is, he adds, because 'there is an intimate connection between all psychic occurrences' and also because wit is so universal.

Freud regards wit 'as the most social of all those psychic functions whose aim is to gain pleasure. It often requires three persons, and the psychic process which it incites requires the participation of at least one other person. It must, therefore, bind itself to the condition of intelligibleness; it may employ distortion made practicable in the unconscious through condensation and displacement, to no greater extent than can be deciphered by the intelligence of the third person.'

Freud defines wit as 'a developed play' which 'seeks to draw a small amount of pleasure from the free and unencumbered activities of our psychic apparatus, and later to seize this pleasure as an incidental gain.'

The pleasure of wit originates 'from an *economy of expenditure in inhibition;* comic arises from an *economy of expenditure in thought;* while humor originates from an *economy of expenditure in feeling.*' (*The Basic Writings of Sigmund Freud,* tr. by Brill, A.A., Random House, New York, 1938)

wit, abstract See *wit, tendency.*

wit, actuality in One of the characteristics of wit is what Freud calls the 'factor of *actuality* (dealing with actual persons, things, or events), which in many witticisms provides a prolific source of pleasure and explains several peculiarities in the life history of wit.' (Freud, S. *The Basic Writings of Sigmund Freud,* tr. by Brill, A.A., Random House, New York, 1938)

wit, allusion in Wit is often expressed through allusions, which Freud calls 'representation through "relationships and associations." '

'*Every fathom a queen,*' which is a modification of the familiar Shakespearean quotation, '*Every inch a king,*' and served as an allusion to a prominent woman who was unusually big physically. (Freud, S. *The Basic Writings of Sigmund Freud,* tr. by Brill, A.A., Random House, New York, 1938)

Freud says that *omission* is also a form of allusion. 'Once more we encounter the two Jews in front of the bathing establishment. "*Another year has passed by already,*" says one with a sigh.' (ibid.)

wit, blasphemous See *wit, critical.*

wit, characterization Freud uses the expression *characterization-wit,* when the witticism serves, among other things, to emphasize certain traits of the principal character in the witticism. He cites the story of the Jewish marriage broker who 'assured the suitor that the father of the girl was no longer living. After the engagement had been announced, the news leaked out that the father was still living and serving a sentence in prison. The suitor reproached the agent for deceiving him. "Well," said the latter, "what did I tell you? Do you call that living?" ' Freud adds that 'one might say that this joke is a "characterization-wit." It endeavors to illustrate by example the marriage agent's characteristic admixture of mendacious impudence and repartee.' (Freud, S. *The Basic Writings of Sigmund Freud,* tr. by Brill, A.A., Random House, New York, 1938)

wit, comparison in Freud expresses some doubt about jocularity in *comparison-wit.*

He cites the following from the writings of Lichtenberg: 'It is almost impossible to carry the torch of truth through a crowd without singeing somebody's beard.' (Freud, S. *The Basic Writings of Sigmund*

Freud, tr. by Brill, A.A., Random House, New York, 1938)

wit, condensation *Condensation* (q.v.) is particularly common in wit. Freud refers to the word *famillionaire,* a whimsical condensation of *famili[ar + milli]onaire* in the quoted passage: 'Rothschild treated me in a very famillionaire way,' which means: 'Rothschild treated me quite familiarly, i.e., as well as a millionaire can do that sort of thing.' (Freud, S. *The Basic Writings of Sigmund Freud,* tr. by Brill, A.A., Random House, New York, 1938)

wit, critical Certain witticisms are critical and blasphemous. Freud cites the story about Heine, who '*when the kindly priest commended him to God's mercy and inspired him with the hope that God would forgive him his sins,*' replied that God certainly would forgive him, for 'that is what he is here for, and for no other purpose have I engaged him.' (Freud, S. *The Basic Writings of Sigmund Freud,* tr. by Brill, A.A., Random House, New York, 1938)

wit, cynical There is a form of wit called tendency-wit by Freud. 'The first use of wit, which goes beyond the mere production of pleasure, points to the road ahead of us. Wit is now recognized as a powerful psychic factor whose weight can decide the issue if it falls into this or that side of the scale. The great tendencies and impulses of our psychic life enlist its service for their own purposes.' He goes on to say that 'where wit is in the service of the cynical and skeptical tendency, it shatters the respect for institutions and truths in which the hearer had believed, first by strengthening the argument, and secondly by resorting to a new method of attack. Where the argument seeks to draw the hearer's reason to its side, wit strives to push aside this reason.' (Freud, S. *The Basic Writings of Sigmund Freud,* tr. by Brill, A.A., Random House, New York, 1938)

wit, displacement When an object or a person in a joke is displaced by another, Freud speaks of *displacement-wit.*

'A beggar implored the help of a wealthy baron for a trip to Ostend, where he asserted the physicians had ordered him to take sea baths for his health. "Very well, I shall assist you," said the rich baron, "but is it absolutely necessary for you to go to Ostend, which is the most expensive of all watering-places?" "Sir," was the reproving reply, "nothing is too expensive for my health." ' (Freud, S. *The Basic Writings of Sigmund Freud,* tr. by Brill, A.A., Random House, New York, 1938)

wit, double meaning in According to Freud, 'If we delve more deeply into the variety of "manifold application" of the same word, we suddenly notice that we are confronted with forms of "double meaning" or "plays on words" which have been known a long time and which are universally acknowledged as belonging to the technique of wit.' Freud cites as an example from Shakespeare: 'Discharge thyself of our company, Pistol.' (Freud, S. *The Basic Writings of Sigmund Freud,* tr. by Brill, A.A., Random House, New York, 1938)

wit, doubt in Freud states that 'in a series of other comparisons, one is tempted to ascribe an indisputably existing witty expression to another factor which again in itself has nothing to do with the nature of the comparison.' He cites an example from Lichtenberg: 'It is a pity that one cannot see the *learned bowels* of the writers, in order to find out what they have eaten.' (Freud, S. *The Basic Writings of Sigmund Freud,* tr. by Brill, A.A., Random House, New York, 1938)

wit, ellipsis A form of wit the humor of which is dependent on omitted connections. For example, in the question: 'Do you think ignorance is bliss?' and the answer: 'Well, you seem to be happy,' at least one thought, the intermediate link: ['You are ignorant—and'] 'well, you seem to be happy' is left out between the question and the answer. (Brill, A.A. *Basic Principles of Psychoanalysis,* Doubleday, New York, 1949)

wit, exaggeration in 'There are other ways to regain the feeling of nonsense in order to derive pleasure from it; *caricature, exaggeration, parody,* and *travesty* utilize the same and thus produce "comical nonsense." ' (Freud, S. *The Basic Writings of Sigmund Freud,* tr. by Brill, A.A., Random House, New York, 1938)

wit, exhibition See *wit, obscene.*

wit, harmless See *wit, tendency.*

withdrawal The act of retracting, retiring, retreating, or going away from. With-

drawal is used in psychiatry to refer to (1) voluntary removal of the penis from the vagina in coitus interruptus and (2) the turning away from objective, external reality that is seen so often as an expression of schizophrenic autism. In this second sense, withdrawal refers to the patient's retreat from society and interpersonal relationships into a world of his own. External stimuli are reduced, and if internal stimuli predominate one speaks of preoccupation which may progress to stupor or even to coma. The withdrawn person appears aloof, detached, disinterested, removed, and apart; he has difficulty in spontaneously initiating or planning with other people. He is unable to mingle freely and communication with others is an effort. He cannot share his experiences with others and even in a group appears to work independently rather than co-operatively. In its more extreme forms, withdrawal appears to be a regressive phenomenon in which the individual relinquishes his higher symbolic and social functions and falls back to the infantile level of shutting off the perceptive system in order to avoid the anxiety aroused by interpersonal relationships.

wit, indirect See *wit, allusion in.*

wit, invectives in 'By belittling and humbling our enemy, by scorning and ridiculing him, we directly obtain the pleasure of his defeat by the laughter of the third person, the inactive spectator.' (Freud, S. *The Basic Writings of Sigmund Freud,* tr. by Brill, A.A., Random House, New York, 1938)

wit, manifold application in See *wit, double meaning in.*

wit, naïve Freud says that 'the species of the comic that is most closely allied to wit is the *naïve.*

'Another little girl of four years heard her parents refer to a Jewish acquaintance as a Hebrew, and on later hearing the latter's wife referred to as Mrs. X, she corrected her mother, saying, "No, that is not her name; if her husband is a Hebrew she is a Shebrew." ' (Freud, S. *The Basic Writings of Sigmund Freud,* tr. by Brill, A.A., Random House, New York, 1938)

wit, nonsense in It is said by Freud that 'sense lurks in . . . witty nonsense and that this sense in nonsense transforms nonsense into wit.' (Freud, S. *The Basic*

Writings of Sigmund Freud, tr. by Brill, A.A., Random House, New York, 1938)

'Never to be born would be best for mortal man.' 'But,' added the sages of the Fliegende Blätter, 'hardly one man in a hundred thousand has this luck.' (ibid.)

wit, obscene 'Whenever wit is not a means to its end, i.e., harmless, it puts itself in the service of but two tendencies which may themselves be united under one viewpoint; it is either *hostile* wit serving as an aggression, satire, or defense, or it is *obscene* wit serving as a sexual exhibition.' (Freud, S. *The Basic Writings of Sigmund Freud,* tr. by Brill, A.A., Random House, New York, 1938)

wit, omission in See *wit, allusion in.*

wit, outdoing This is a form of wit, according to Freud, in which 'a contradiction takes the place of an exaggerated confirmation.'

'A Jew noticed remnants of food on the beard of another. "I can tell you what you ate yesterday," he remarked. "Well, let's hear it," said the other. "Beans," said the first one. "You are wrong," responded the other. "I had beans the day before yesterday." ' (Freud, S. *The Basic Writings of Sigmund Freud,* tr. by Brill, A.A., Random House, New York, 1938)

wit, parody in See *wit, exaggeration in.*

wit, recognition in Wit frequently exhibits what Freud calls *recognition,* that is, 'the discovery of the familiar where one expects to find something new instead. To discover the familiar is pleasurable and it is not difficult to recognize such pleasure as economy-pleasure and to refer it to the economy of psychic expenditure.' (Freud, S. *The Basic Writings of Sigmund Freud,* tr. by Brill, A.A., Random House, New York, 1938)

wit, satire in 'Concerning a satirical comedy Heine remarked: "This satire would not have been so biting had the author of it had more to bite." ' (Freud, S. *The Basic Writings of Sigmund Freud,* tr. by Brill, A.A., Random House, New York, 1938)

wit, sophism in 'The suitor objects, because the bride has a short leg and therefore limps. The agent contradicts him. "You are wrong," he says. "Suppose you marry a woman whose legs are sound and straight. What do you gain by it? You are not sure from day to day that

she will not fall down, break a leg, and then be lame for the rest of her life. Just consider the pain, the excitement, and the doctor's bill. But if you marry this one, nothing can happen. Here you have a finished job." ' (Freud, S. *The Basic Writings of Sigmund Freud,* tr. by Brill, A.A., Random House, New York, 1938)

wit, tendency Freud says that there are two major classifications of witty productions. 'Word- and thought-wit on the one hand, and abstract- and tendency-wit on the other hand, bear no relation of dependence to each other; they are two entirely independent classifications of witty productions.' (Freud, S. *The Basic Writings of Sigmund Freud,* tr. by Brill, A.A., Random House, New York, 1938)

When 'wit is wit for its own sake and serves no other particular purpose,' it is called *abstract* or *harmless wit.* Freud cites an example from Lichtenberg: *'They sent a small octavo to the University of Göttingen; and received back in body and soul a quarto'* (a fourth-form boy). (ibid.)

Wit may serve some purpose; it may have deep meaning; it may be tendential; when such is the case, Freud speaks of *tendency-wit.* 'It makes possible the gratification of a craving (lewd or hostile) despite a hindrance which stands in the way; it eludes the hindrance and so derives pleasure from a source that has been inaccessible on account of the hindrance.' (ibid.)

wit, thought Often it is not the word, but the thought in a witticism that bears significance. Freud speaks of such a form as *thought-wit,* which like *word-wit* may be *abstract* or *tendential.*

witticism, self-critical Freud says that 'a particularly favorable case for tendency-wit results if the intended criticism of the inner resistance is directed against one's own interest, or more carefully expressed, against a person in whom one takes an interest, that is, a composite personality such as one's own people.

'Another story relates *how on the steps of a rich man's house a schnorrer (an habitual beggar) met one of his own kind. The latter counseled him to depart, saying, "Do not go up today, the Baron is out of sorts and refuses to give any one more than a dollar." "I will go up anyway," replied the first. "Why in the world should I make him the present of a dol-*

lar? Is he making me any presents?" '
(Freud, S. *The Basic Writings of Sigmund Freud,* tr. by Brill, A.A., Random House, New York, 1938)

wit, travesty in See *wit, exaggeration in.*

wit, unification in Unification in wit 'is analogous to condensation by compression into similar words.' Freud cites an example from Lichtenberg: 'January is the month in which one extends good wishes to his friends, and the rest are months in which the good wishes are not fulfilled.' (Freud, S. *The Basic Writings of Sigmund Freud,* tr. by Brill, A.A., Random House, New York, 1938)

wit, word When the strength of wit lies in the word, Freud calls it *word-wit.* He cites the following example: 'Having been forsaken by *Dame Luck,* he degenerated into a *Lame Duck.*' (Freud, S. *The Basic Writings of Sigmund Freud,* tr. by Brill, A.A., Random House, New York, 1938)

wit-work In the expression *wit-work* Freud uses the component element work in the same sense as he does in *dream-work,* namely, to denote the psychic processes operating in each case.

'But the processes which led to the same results—condensation, displacement, and indirect expression—we learned to know as peculiarities of dream-work.' (Freud, S. *The Basic Writings of Sigmund Freud,* tr. by Brill, A.A., Random House, New York, 1938)

Witzelsucht (vit'sel-zookt) Facetiousness; seen in lesions of the frontal lobe. See *lobe, frontal.*

Wolf-Man This refers to the patient reported on by Freud in his 1918 paper, 'From the History of an Infantile Neurosis.' The patient is so called because of a dream he had had at the age of four concerning six or seven white wolves sitting on a tree in front of the dreamer's window; he woke in terror, evidently of being eaten by the wolves. The interpretation of the dream extended over several years. Although the Wolf-Man responded well to psychoanalytic therapy, he suffered several relapses during which he showed increasingly severe paranoid symptoms.

Wollenberg, Robert (1862–   ) (vôl'en-bĕrk) German neurologist and psychiatrist.

womb, father's This expression describes the displacement of the affection usually set apart for the mother and the placing of it on the person of the father. In this psychic maneuver the hate for the father gives way, on the son's part, to a new affection, which is none other than that previously centered in the mother: the father becomes, so to speak, 'maternalized' and is invested with a womb.

womb-phantasy See *phantasy, womb.*

women with penis See *penis, women with.*

word-blindness Kussmaul's term (1877) for a type of *reading disability* (q.v.).

word-cathexis See *cathexis.*

word-deafness Auditory aphasia. See *aphasia, auditory.*

word-dumbness See *aphasia, motor.*

word-salad This is the type of speech, heard most frequently in advanced states of schizophrenia, characterized by a mixture of phrases that are meaningless to the listener and, as a rule, also to the patient producing them. A word-salad is a group of neologisms. They are meaningless until the patient discusses the neologisms at length, thus revealing their underlying significance. It is, so to speak, a coded language, not unlike dreams in principle; the patient holds the table to the code and only he can provide meanings to the otherwise meaningless dialect.

words, microcosm of (mī'krō-koz'm) A phrase used by Fenichel to characterize the function of words. Basically, 'words and worded concepts are shadows of things, constructed for the purpose of bringing order through trial acting into the chaos of real things.' Thus, words create a replica of the real world, a 'model world' or microcosm. 'The macrocosm of real things outside is reflected in the microcosm of things representative within.' The normal individual uses this microcosm of words for calculating and acting out in advance, before real action is taken. To him, then, words will have the characteristics of the things that they represent, but they will not have the reality or 'seriousness' which the things have. The normal person has mastered the words and, by using his words, will master the real things.

This mastery of the real world through words is markedly disturbed in the compulsion-neurotic. Being afraid of emotions, he is afraid of the things that cause emotions. He therefore retreats from the macrocosm of things to the microcosm of words. He tries to repeat the process by which as an infant he learned to use words to master frightening aspects of the real world. However, 'under the pressure of his warded-off impulses' words have now acquired 'that emotional value which things have for other persons.' They have regained the magical quality they first had in infancy, when there was no clear differentiation between the microcosm and the macrocosm. That is, the words themselves now have the values and meanings they express. Unconsciously, words and thoughts are believed to have real effects. Therefore, the compulsion-neurotic handles words and thoughts very cautiously. This is the origin of compulsive thinking. (Fenichel, O. *The Psychoanalytic Theory of Neurosis,* Norton, New York, 1945)

work, case See *case-work.*

work-cure Treatment by occupation.

worker, after-care Social worker.

work, group See *group-work.*

working-over In psychoanalysis, an internal process of rearranging, adjusting, reconstituting, and remolding the excitations produced in the psyche and thereupon being able to direct them into other channels in order to prevent their harmful effect because of the impossibility or undesirability of discharging them outward.

'We have recognized our mental apparatus above all as a device for mastering excitations which would otherwise be felt as unpleasant or would have pathogenic effects. The "working-over" of stimuli in the mind accomplishes wonders for the internal discharge of excitations which are incapable of direct discharge outwards, or for which such a discharge is, for the moment, undesirable.' (Freud, S.

Collected Papers, vol. 4, tr. by Riviere, J., Leonard and Virginia Woolf and The Institute of Psychoanalysis, London, 1924–25) For example, anxiety of the neuroses may be ameliorated by 'working-over' into conversion, reaction-formation, or defense-formation (phobia).

working-through This psychoanalytic concept appears to be synonymous with *working-over.*

'One must allow the patient time to get to know this resistance of which he is ignorant, to "work-through" it, to overcome it, by continuing the work according to the analytic rule in defiance of it.' (Freud, S., *Collected Papers,* vol. 2, tr. by Riviere, J., Leonard and Virginia Woolf and The Institute of Psychoanalysis, London, 1924–25)

According to H. Nunberg (*Principles of Psychoanalysis,* International Universities Press, New York, 1955) the term working-through applies to all those processes which lead to the recapture of infantile, repressed unconscious material and to its conversion into conscious thoughts, ideas, wishes, and strivings.

work, social See *social work.*

writing, automatic The writing done by an individual, without conscious volition, while in hypnotic trance. 'Automatic writing is a splendid means of gaining access to unconscious material that lies beyond the grasp of conscious recall. The portion of the cerebrum that controls the automatic writing seems to have access to material unavailable to centers that control speech. Consequently hypnotic verbalization of feelings and impulses may not yield information as vital as that brought up through automatic writing.' (Wolberg, L.R. *Hypnoanalysis,* Grune and Stratton, New York, 1945)

writing, mirror See *strephosymbolia.*

wryneck See *torticollis.*

X

xanthomatosis (zan-thō-ma-tō′sis) Schüller-Christian-Hand's syndrome; diabetic exophthalmic dysostosis. A rare disturbance of lipoid metabolism in which tissues are infiltrated by xanthomatous masses rich in cholesterol, this leading to diabetes insipidus, exophthalmos, and progressive erosion of the bones. Infiltration of the reticulo-endothelial cells with the lipoid material results in the characteristic foam-cell. Retardation of growth and mental development occurs in about half of the cases. The disorder begins in childhood; males are three times as frequently affected as females.

xenoglossia (zen-ō-glos′i-à) Speaking in a strange or foreign language; the word usually implies distaste for or aversion to such a speech.

xenophobia Fear of strangers.

Y

yen sleep See *sleep, yen.*

ylophobia (ī-lō-fō′bi-à) Less correctly for *hylophobia.* Fear of the forest.

Z

zelophobia (zel-ō-fō′bi-à) Fear of jealousy.

zelotypia (-tip′i-à) Excessive zeal, carried to the verge of insanity, in the advocacy of any cause.

zoanthropy (zō-an′thrō-pē) Lycanthropia.

zoara (zō-ä′rà) *Obs.* Insomnia.

zone, erogenous (ē-roj′ē-nus) An organ or organic system invested with the erotic or libidinal instinctual quality is called an erogenous zone. Of the many erogenous zones three gain special consideration: the oral, the anal, and the genital.

zone, hypnogenic (hip-nō-jen′ik) Hypnogenic spot.

zone, hysterogenic (his-tĕr-ō-jen′ik) Any area of the body which gives rise to a hysterical reaction when stimulated.
'Or, when a young girl reproaches herself most bitterly for allowing a boy secretly to caress her hand, and from that moment is the victim of neurosis, you can of course explain it by pronouncing her to be an abnormal, eccentric, hypersensitive person; but you will take a different view when analysis shows that the touch reminded her of a similar one felt in very early youth, which was part of a less harmless story, so that really the reproaches belong to that former occasion. Finally, the problem of hysterogenic areas is another of the same kind; if you touch one particular spot, you do something you did not intend: i.e., you wake a memory which may bring on an hysterical attack. . . .' (Freud, S. *Collected Papers,* vol. 1, tr. by Riviere, J., Leonard and Virginia Woolf and The Institute of Psychoanalysis, London, 1924–25)

zone, primacy A psychoanalytic term denoting the most important zone in the hierarchy of certain specific erogenous (erotogenic) zones in their relationship to others. In the developing child, some erotic zones, such as the mouth, the anus, and the genital area, are the sources of particularly intense sexual pleasure urges. Later, as the child develops, these acquire a special significance, because they begin to play a specifically more powerful role. These more prominent erotogenic zones (or areas) of the body, which are the site and source of pleasure-affording stimulation to the child, tend to marshal and dominate the pleasurable instinct excitation from *other* bodily areas. In this fashion, instinct gratification can be displaced from the less powerful or less important erotogenic zones onto the more

[787]

important zones, and vicarious, displaced, augmented gratification can thus be obtained through the discharge of instinctual tensions at the single dominant zone. These dominating erotogenic areas, by means of which more subordinated areas may find instinctual discharge through displacement, have been called 'primacy zones' and the fashion in which the weaker or residual instinct sources are subordinated to the primacy zone has been termed 'libido organization.'

In the development of the libido, one primacy zone tends to succeed another in a typical and characteristic chronological order: (1) the oral; (2) the anal; (3) the phallic; (4) the genital. (Sterba, R. *Introduction to the Psycho-analytic Theory of the Libido,* Nervous and Mental Disease Monographs No. 68, New York, 1942)

zone, ultra-marginal 'Some of these marginal elements [see *fringe*] may be so distinctly within the field of awareness that we are conscious of them, but dimly so. Others, in particular cases at least, may be so far outside and hidden in the twilight obscurity that the subject is not even dimly aware of them. In more technical parlance, we may say, they are so far dissociated that they belong to *an ultra-marginal zone and are really subconscious.*' (Prince, M. *The Unconscious,* Macmillan, New York, 1916)

zoö- (zō'ō-) Combining form meaning animal, from Gr. *zōion,* living being, animal.

zoöerasty (zō-ō'ĕr-as-tē) Krafft-Ebing's term for sexual intercourse with an animal. It is usually considered to be synonymous with *sodomy;* many psychiatrists prefer zoöerasty, since etymologically it has a more definite meaning than sodomy.

zoölagnia (zō-ō-lag'ni-à) Sexual attraction toward animals.

zoöphilia Zoöphilia, usually accompanied by the adjective *erotica,* is a term coined by Krafft-Ebing to denote sexual excitement caused by the stroking and fondling of animals. It does not refer to sexual intercourse with animals, for which act Krafft-Ebing reserves the expression *zoöerasty.*

zoöphilism, erotic (zō-of'i-liz'm) Erotic impulse to pat or stroke animals for sexual pleasure.

zoöphobia (zō-ō-fō'bi-à) Fear of animals.

zoöpsia (zō-op'si-à) Act of 'seeing' insects. E. Tanzi says: 'The patients remain immobile, and appear to be lost in prayer or adoration, enraptured by some ecstasy of love, listening to some far-off voice, threatening with closed fists and angry looks, or closely examining the ground, which they think is swarming with insects (zoöpsia).' (Tanzi, E. *A Text-Book of Mental Diseases,* tr. by Robertson, W.F. and Mackenzie, T.C., Rebman, New York, 1909)

zoösadism (zō-ō-sad'iz'm) The act of injuring animals for the morbid (as a rule, ultimately sexual) pleasure derived from it.

Zuordnungs (tsoo-ord'nungs) Sorting tests. See *tests, sorting.*

Zwischenstufe (tsvish'en-shtoo-fĕ) Intermediary stage. Magnus Hirschfeld's term for an 'in-between' or homosexualist.

zygote (zī'gōt, zig'ōt) The biological term *zygote* signifies primarily a fertilized egg produced by the union of two cells to form one single cell in sexual reproduction. By an extension of meaning, however, the organisms themselves which develop from fertilized eggs are also called zygotes, in order to distinguish them from their germ cells, which are called *gametes.*

Zygotes are *diploid* with respect to their chromosomes and have two genes of each pair, while gametes are *haploid* and have only one gene of each pair. (Shull, F. *Heredity,* 3rd ed., McGraw-Hill, New York and London, 1938)

zygotic (zī-got'ik) Pertaining to a zygote. Referring either to a single cell produced by the union of two cells in reproduction or to the individual developing from such a fertilized egg.